The Elements

Name	Symbol	Atomic Number	Relative Atomic Mass
Actinium	Ac	89	227.028
Aluminum	Al	13	26.9815
Americium	Am	95	(243)
Antimony	Sb	51	121.760
Argon	Ar	18	39.948
Arsenic	As	33	74.9216
Astatine	At	85	(210)
Barium	Ba	56	137.327
Berkelium	Bk	97	(247)
Beryllium	Be	4	9.01218
Bismuth	Bi	83	208.980
Bohrium	Bh	107	(262)
Boron	B	5	10.811
Bromine	Br	35	79.904
Cadmium	Cd	48	112.411
Calcium	Ca	20	40.078
Californium	Cf	98	(251)
Carbon	C	6	12.0107
Cerium	Ce	58	140.115
Cesium	Cs	55	132.905
Chlorine	Cl	17	35.453
Chromium	Cr	24	51.9961
Cobalt	Co	27	58.9332
Copper	Cu	29	63.546
Curium	Cm	96	(247)
Darmstadtium	Ds	110	(271)
Dubnium	Db	105	(262)
Dysprosium	Dy	66	162.50
Einsteinium	Es	99	(252)
Erbium	Er	68	167.26
Europium	Eu	63	151.965
Fermium	Fm	100	(257)
Fluorine	F	9	18.9984
Francium	Fr	87	(223)
Gadolinium	Gd	64	157.25
Gallium	Ga	31	69.723
Germanium	Ge	32	72.64
Gold	Au	79	196.967
Hafnium	Hf	72	178.49
Hassium	Hs	108	(265)
Helium	He	2	4.00260
Holmium	Ho	67	164.930
Hydrogen	H	1	1.00794
Indium	In	49	114.818
Iodine	I	53	126.904
Iridium	Ir	77	192.217
Iron	Fe	26	55.845
Krypton	Kr	36	83.798
Lanthanum	La	57	138.905
Lawrencium	Lr	103	(260)
Lead	Pb	82	207.2
Lithium	Li	3	6.941
Lutetium	Lu	71	174.967
Magnesium	Mg	12	24.3050
Manganese	Mn	25	54.9380
Meitnerium	Mt	109	(266)
Mendelevium	Md	101	(258)
Mercury	Hg	80	200.59
Molybdenum	Mo	42	95.94
Neodymium	Nd	60	144.24
Neon	Ne	10	20.1797
Neptunium	Np	93	237.048
Nickel	Ni	28	58.6934
Niobium	Nb	41	92.9064
Nitrogen	N	7	14.0067
Nobelium	No	102	(259)
Osmium	Os	76	190.23
Oxygen	O	8	15.9994
Palladium	Pd	46	106.42
Phosphorus	P	15	30.9738
Platinum	Pt	78	195.084
Plutonium	Pu	94	(244)
Polonium	Po	84	(209)
Potassium	K	19	39.0983
Praseodymium	Pr	59	140.908
Promethium	Pm	61	(145)
Protactinium	Pa	91	231.036
Radium	Ra	88	(226)
Radon	Rn	86	(222)
Rhenium	Re	75	186.207
Rhodium	Rh	45	102.906
Roentgenium	Rg	111	(272)
Rubidium	Rb	37	85.4678
Ruthenium	Ru	44	101.07
Rutherfordium	Rf	104	(261)
Samarium	Sm	62	150.36
Scandium	Sc	21	44.9559
Seaborgium	Sg	106	(263)
Selenium	Se	34	78.96
Silicon	Si	14	28.0855
Silver	Ag	47	107.868
Sodium	Na	11	22.9898
Strontium	Sr	38	87.62
Sulfur	S	16	32.065
Tantalum	Ta	73	180.948
Technetium	Tc	43	(98)
Tellurium	Te	52	127.60
Terbium	Tb	65	158.925
Thallium	Tl	81	204.383
Thorium	Th	90	232.038
Thulium	Tm	69	168.934
Tin	Sn	50	118.710
Titanium	Ti	22	47.867
Tungsten	W	74	183.84
Uranium	U	92	238.029
Vanadium	V	23	50.9415
Xenon	Xe	54	131.293
Ytterbium	Yb	70	173.04
Yttrium	Y	39	88.9059
Zinc	Zn	30	65.409
Zirconium	Zr	40	91.224

Atomic masses in this table are relative to carbon-12 and are the values recommended by the International Union of Pure and Applied Chemistry (IUPAC) (22 June 2007). For certain radioactive elements the numbers listed (in parentheses) are the mass numbers of the most stable isotopes.

GENERAL CHEMISTRY

Second Custom Edition for the University of British Columbia

Taken from:

General Chemistry: Principles and Modern Applications, Tenth Edition
by Ralph H. Petrucci, F. Geoffrey Herring, Jeffry D. Madura, and Carey Bissonnette

Organic Chemistry, Sixth Edition
by Paula Yurkanis Bruice

Learning Solutions

New York Boston San Francisco
London Toronto Sydney Tokyo Singapore Madrid
Mexico City Munich Paris Cape Town Hong Kong Montreal

Cover Art: Courtesy of Photodisc/Getty Images.

Taken from:

General Chemistry: Principles and Modern Applications, Tenth Edition
by Ralph H. Petrucci, F. Geoffrey Herring, Jeffry D. Madura, and Carey Bissonnette
Copyright © 2011 by Pearson Canada Inc.
Published by Prentice Hall
Toronto, Ontario

Organic Chemistry, Sixth Edition
by Paula Yurkanis Bruice
Copyright © 2011, 2007, 2004 by Pearson Education, Inc.
Published by Prentice Hall
Upper Saddle River, New Jersey 07458

All rights reserved. No part of this book may be reproduced, in any form or by any means, without permission in writing from the publisher.

This special edition published in cooperation with Pearson Learning Solutions.

All trademarks, service marks, registered trademarks, and registered service marks are the property of their respective owners and are used herein for identification purposes only.

Pearson Learning Solutions, 501 Boylston Street, Suite 900, Boston, MA 02116
A Pearson Education Company
www.pearsoned.com

Printed in Canada

1 2 3 4 5 6 7 8 9 10 VOYA 16 15 14 13 12 11

000200010270643741

BK

ISBN 10: 0-558-95275-5
ISBN 13: 978-0-558-95275-4

Contents

Taken from *General Chemistry: Principles and Modern Applications,* Tenth Edition by Ralph H. Petrucci, F. Geoffrey Herring, Jeffry D. Madura, and Carey Bissonnette.

Taken from *Organic Chemistry*, Sixth Edition by Paula Yurkanis Bruice.

APPENDICES

1

Introduction to Reactions in Aqueous Solutions

CONTENTS

When clear, colorless aqueous solutions of cobalt(II) chloride and sodium hydroxide are mixed, a blue cloud of solid cobalt(II) hydroxide is formed. Such precipitation reactions are one of the three types of reactions considered in this chapter.

Most reactions in the general chemistry laboratory are carried out in aqueous solutions—solutions for which water is the solvent. Aqueous solutions provide a convenient way of bringing together accurately measured amounts of reactants, and, not surprisingly, aqueous solutions feature prominently in many methods of chemical analysis. In this chapter, we will explore three different classes of reactions that occur in aqueous solutions—precipitation, acid–base, and oxidation–reduction reactions—with the goal of understanding the nature of the substances involved, the changes that occur in these substances, and the way each reaction can be used in the laboratory for analyzing samples.

Precipitation, the formation of a solid when solutions are mixed, is probably the most common evidence of a chemical reaction that general chemistry students see. A practical application of precipitation is in determining the presence of certain ions in solution. If, for example, we are uncertain whether the clear, colorless liquid in an unlabeled bottle is a barium nitrate or a barium chloride solution, we can easily find out by adding a few drops of silver nitrate solution to a small sample of the liquid. If a white solid forms, the sample is a barium chloride solution; if nothing happens, it is barium nitrate. The Ag^+ from the silver nitrate and the Cl^- from the barium chloride combine to produce an insoluble precipitate of AgCl(s). Precipitation reactions are the first reaction type we will study in this chapter. $Mg(OH)_2(s)$ is insoluble in water but soluble in hydrochloric acid, HCl(aq), as a result of an acid–base reaction. This is the reaction by which milk of magnesia neutralizes excess stomach acid. Magnesium hydroxide is a base, and acid–base reactions are the second class of reactions presented in this chapter. The third class of reactions is oxidation–reduction reactions, which are found in all aspects of life, from reactions in organisms to processes for manufacturing chemicals, to such practical matters as bleaching fabrics, purifying water, and destroying toxic chemicals.

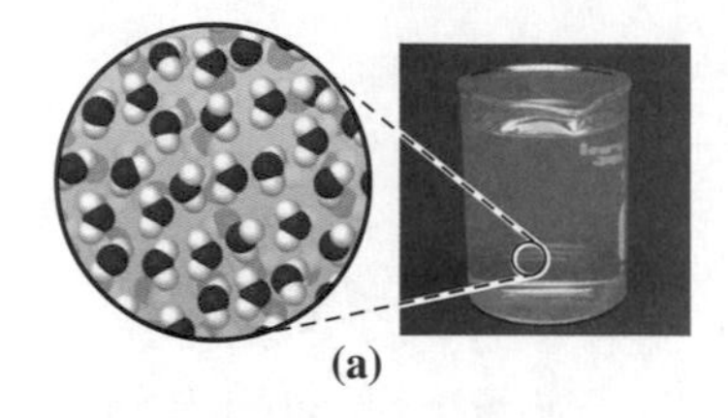
(a)

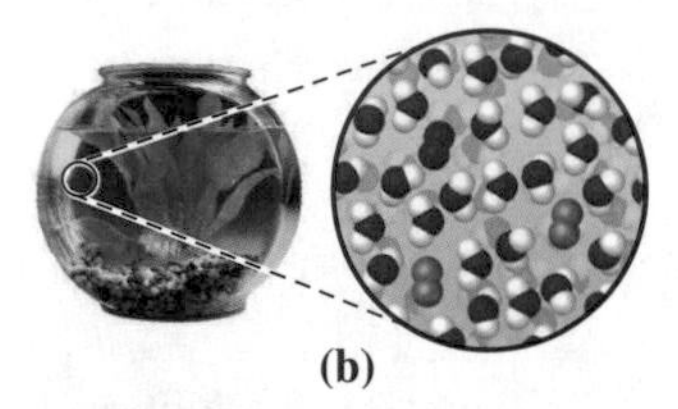
(b)

▲ FIGURE 1-1
Molecular view of water and an aqueous solution of air
(a) Water molecules (red and white) are in close proximity in liquid water. **(b)** Dissolved oxygen (red) and nitrogen (blue) molecules are far apart, separated by water molecules.

1-1 The Nature of Aqueous Solutions

Let's try to form a mental image of a solution at the molecular level. The solvent molecules, which are rather tightly packed, greatly outnumber all other molecules. Water is the solvent in an aqueous solution, and our mental image of water might look something like Figure 1-1(a). Solute particles—molecules or ions—are present in much smaller number and are randomly distributed among the solvent molecules. Our mental image of an aqueous solution of air might look something like Figure 1-1(b).

Because we will encounter aqueous solutions of ions throughout this chapter, it is useful to examine the nature of such solutions in a bit more detail. An important characteristic of an aqueous solution of ions is that it will conduct electricity, provided the concentration of ions is not too low. An aqueous solution of ions conducts electricity because the ions move essentially independently of each other, each one carrying a certain quantity of charge. (In a metallic conductor, such as copper or tungsten, electrons carry the charge.) The manner in which ions conduct electric current is suggested by Figure 1-2.

Whether or not an aqueous solution is a conductor of electricity depends on the nature of the solute(s). Pure water contains so few ions that it does not conduct electric current. However, some solutes produce ions in solution, thereby making the solution an electrical conductor. Solutes that provide ions when dissolved in water are called **electrolytes**. Solutes that that do not provide ions in water are called **nonelectrolytes**. All electrolytes provide ions in water but not all electrolytes are equal in their tendencies for providing ions. A **strong electrolyte** is a substance that is essentially *completely ionized* in aqueous solution. Stated another way, a strong electrolyte has a strong (or

▶ If a solute is *completely ionized*, then essentially all the dissolved solute exists as ions. If a solute is *partially ionized*, then only some (not all) of the solute molecules have been converted into ions.

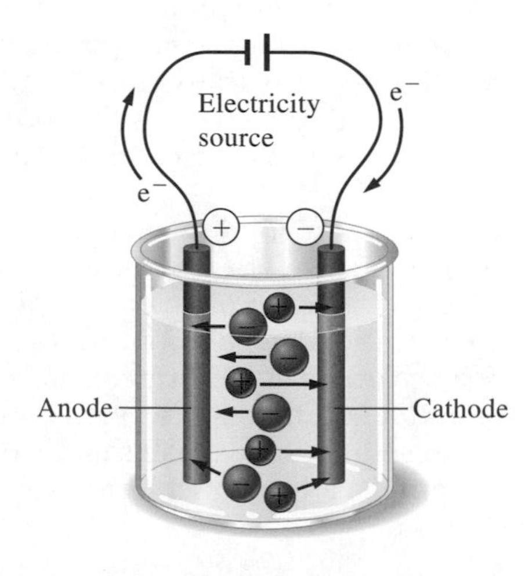

▶ FIGURE 1-2
Conduction of electricity through a solution
Two graphite rods called electrodes are placed in a solution. The external source of electricity pulls electrons from one rod and forces them onto the other, creating a positive charge on one electrode and a negative charge on the other (right). In the solution, positive ions (cations) are attracted to the negative electrode, the *cathode*; negative ions (anions) are attracted to the positive electrode, the *anode*. Thus, electric charge is carried through the solution by the migration of ions. Other important aspects of electrical conductivity are discussed in Chapter 7.

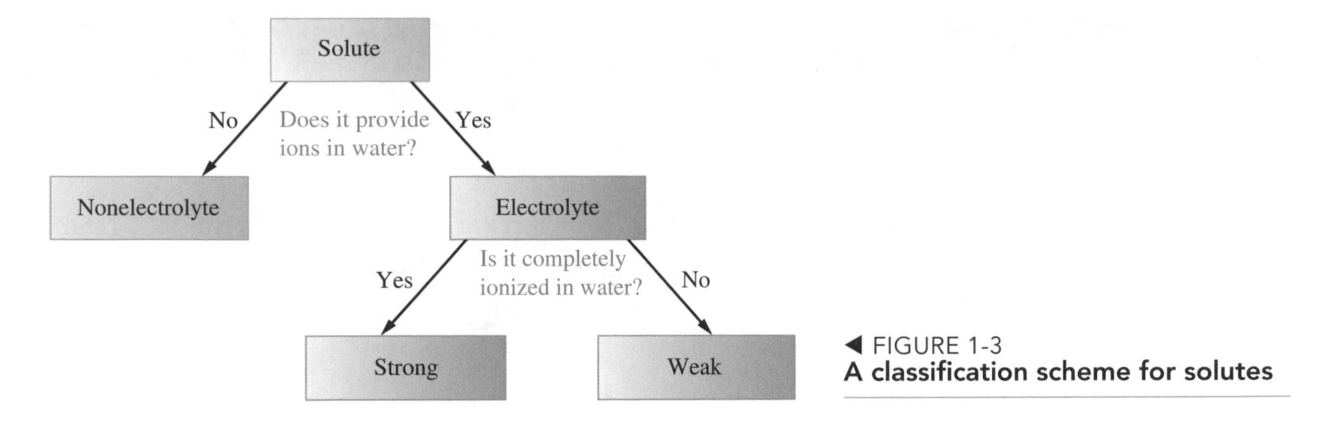

◀ FIGURE 1-3
A classification scheme for solutes

high) tendency for providing ions. A **weak electrolyte** is a substance that is only *partially ionized* in aqueous solution. A weak electrolyte has a weak (or small) tendency for providing ions. One scheme for classifying solutes is summarized in Figure 1-3.

With the apparatus depicted in Figure 1-4, we can detect the presence of ions in an aqueous solution by measuring how well the solution conducts electricity. We can make one of three possible observations:

- *The lamp fails to light up* (Fig. 1-4a). Conclusion: no ions are present (or if some are present, their concentration is extremely low). The solution is either a solution of a nonelectrolyte or a very dilute solution of an electrolyte. Methanol, CH_3OH, is an example of a solute that does not provide ions in water; methanol is a *nonelectrolyte*. The microscopic view in Figure 1-4(a) is for an aqueous solution of methanol, and in this view we see that none of the CH_3OH molecules are ionized in water.
- *The lamp lights up brightly* (Fig. 1-4b). Conclusion: the concentration of ions in solution is high. The solute is a *strong electrolyte*. Magnesium chloride, $MgCl_2$, is an ionic compound that is completely ionized in water. The microscopic view in Figure 1-4(b) shows that an aqueous solution of $MgCl_2$ consists of Mg^{2+} and Cl^- ions in the solvent.
- *The lamp lights up only dimly* (Fig. 1-4c). Conclusion: ions are present in solution but the concentration of ions is low. The solution could be a solution of a weak electrolyte, such as acetic acid (CH_3COOH), or it could be a dilute—but not too dilute—solution of a strong electrolyte. The microscopic view in Figure 1-4(c) is for an aqueous solution of CH_3COOH and it shows that, in water, only some of the CH_3COOH molecules are ionized. An aqueous solution of CH_3COOH is only a weak conductor of electricity.

KEEP IN MIND

that the electrical conductivity of a solution depends on two factors: (1) the total concentration of the electrolyte, and (2) the extent to which the electrolyte dissociates into ions. For example, a 0.001 M HCl(aq) solution will conduct electricity, but a 1×10^{-6} M HCl(aq) solution will not, even though every HCl molecule dissociates into H^+ and Cl^- ions in both solutions.

The following generalization is helpful when deciding whether a particular solute in an aqueous solution is most likely to be a nonelectrolyte, a strong electrolyte, or a weak electrolyte.

- Essentially all soluble ionic compounds and only a relatively few molecular compounds are strong electrolytes.
- Most molecular compounds are either nonelectrolytes or weak electrolytes.

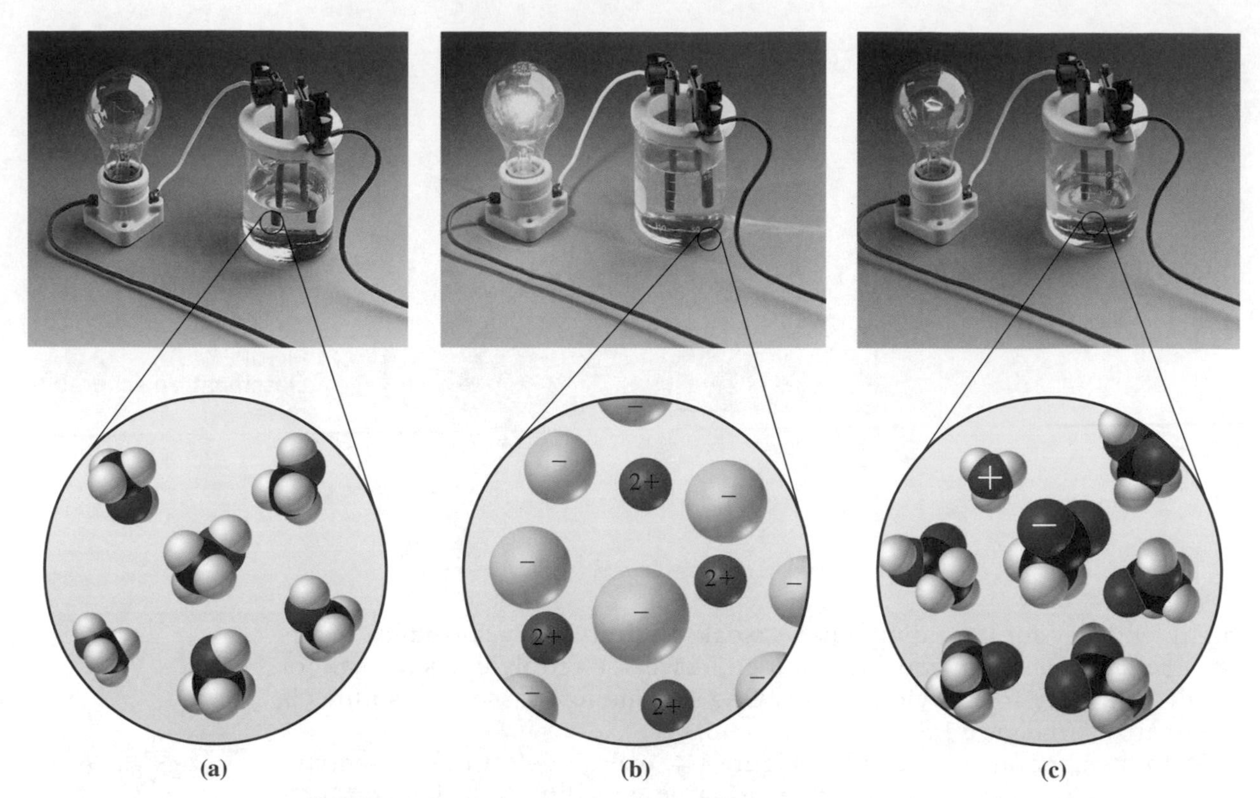

▲ FIGURE 1-4
Three types of electrolytes
In **(a)**, there are no ions present to speak of—only molecules. Methanol (methyl alcohol), CH_3OH, is a *nonelectrolyte* in aqueous solutions. In **(b)**, the solute is present almost entirely as individual ions. $MgCl_2$ is a *strong electrolyte* in aqueous solutions. In **(c)**, although most of the solute is present as molecules, a small fraction of the molecules ionize. CH_3COOH is a *weak electrolyte* in aqueous solution. The CH_3COOH molecules that ionize produce acetate ions CH_3COO^- and H^+ ions, and the H^+ ions attach themselves to water molecules to form hydronium ions, H_3O^+.

KEEP IN MIND

that the solvent molecules are densely packed. In such diagrams as Figure 1-4, we will often show the solvent as a uniformly colored background and depict only the solute particles.

Now let us consider how best to represent these three types of substances in chemical equations. For water-soluble $MgCl_2$, an ionic compound, we can write

$$MgCl_2(aq) \longrightarrow Mg^{2+}(aq) + 2\,Cl^-(aq)$$

This equation means that, in the presence of water, formula units of $MgCl_2$ are dissociated into the separate ions. The best representation of $MgCl_2(aq)$, then, is $Mg^{2+}(aq) + 2\,Cl^-(aq)$.

Hydrogen chloride, HCl, is an example of a molecular compound that is a strong electrolyte. When HCl dissolves in water, the following reaction occurs:

$$HCl(aq) \longrightarrow H^+(aq) + Cl^-(aq)$$

The best representation of hydrochloric acid, HCl(aq), is $H^+(aq) + Cl^-(aq)$.

The hydrogen cation H^+ is an interesting and important species that has been the subject of intensive research. The ion H^+—a bare proton—is a small particle that interacts with the water molecules surrounding it. The simple hydrogen ion, H^+, does not exist in aqueous solutions. Its actual form is as *hydronium ion*, H_3O^+, in which an H^+ ion is attached to an H_2O molecule. The hydronium ion, in turn, interacts with the water molecules surrounding it to

▶ The International Union of Pure and Applied Chemistry (IUPAC) has recommended that the H_3O^+, ion be referred to as the *oxonium* ion. However, this recommendation has not yet been universally adopted by chemists.

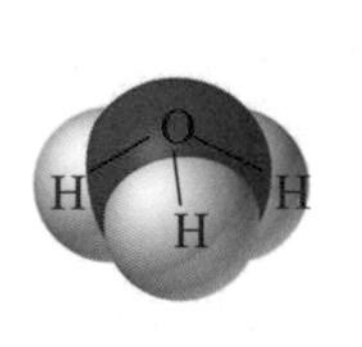

Hydronium ion
H_3O^+

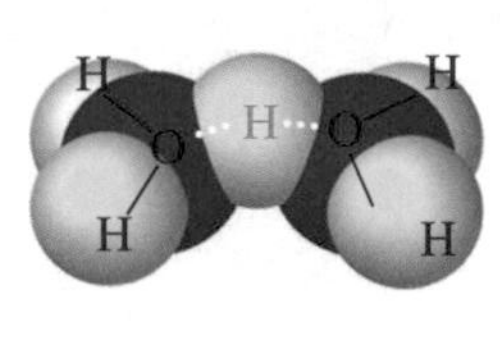

A hydrated proton
$H_5O_2^+$

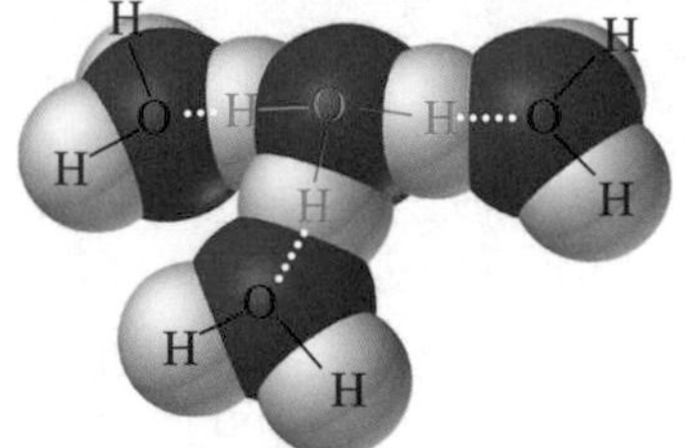

A hydrated proton
$H_9O_4^+$

◀ FIGURE 1-5
The hydrated proton
The hydronium ion, H_3O^+, interacts with other water molecules through electrostatic attractions.

form additional species, such as $H_5O_2^+$, $H_7O_3^+$, $H_9O_4^+$ (shown in Figure 1-5) and many others. These interactions are called *hydration*, and the hydrated proton is represented as $H^+(aq)$, a shorthand notation. The interaction of the proton with a single water molecule is emphasized by using $H_3O^+(aq)$. The basis for these interactions will be discussed in Chapter 3 and employed extensively in Chapter 8.

For a solution of a weak electrolyte, the reaction that produces ions does not go to completion. In such solutions, only a fraction of the solute molecules in solution are ionized. Equations for solutions of this type are written with double arrows, as shown below.

$$CH_3COOH(aq) \rightleftharpoons H^+(aq) + CH_3COO^-(aq)$$

The double arrows indicate that the process is *reversible*—that is, while some CH_3COOH (acetic acid) molecules ionize, some H^+ and CH_3COO^- ions in solution recombine to form new CH_3COOH molecules. However, the relative proportions of ionized and nonionized (molecular) acid remain fixed. The predominant species is the molecule CH_3COOH, and the solution is best represented by $CH_3COOH(aq)$, *not* $H^+(aq) + CH_3COO^-(aq)$. If we could tag a particular CH_3COO group and watch it over time, we would sometimes see it as the ion CH_3COO^-, but most of the time it would be in a molecule, CH_3COOH.

KEEP IN MIND

that there are different ways to write the formulas for acetic acid. The molecular formula, $C_2H_4O_2$, makes no distinction between the types of H atoms; $HC_2H_3O_2$ emphasizes that there is only one ionizable H atom; and CH_3COOH and CH_3CO_2H emphasize that the ionizable H atom is part of the carboxyl group.

For a nonelectrolyte, we simply write the molecular formula. Thus, for a solution of methanol in water, we would write $CH_3OH(aq)$.

With this new information about the nature of aqueous solutions, we can introduce a useful notation for solution concentrations. In a solution that is 0.0050 M $MgCl_2$, we assume that the $MgCl_2$ is completely dissociated into ions. Because there are two Cl^- ions for every Mg^{2+} ion, the solution is 0.0050 M Mg^{2+} but 0.0100 M Cl^-. Better still, let us introduce a special symbol for the concentration of a species in solution—the bracket symbol [ ]. The statement $[Mg^{2+}] = 0.0050$ M means that the concentration of the species within the brackets—that is, Mg^{2+}—is 0.0050 mol/L. Thus,

$$\textit{in 0.0050 M MgCl}_2\text{:}\quad [Mg^{2+}] = 0.0050\text{ M}; [Cl^-] = 0.0100\text{ M}; [MgCl_2] = 0\text{ M}$$

Although we do not usually write expressions like $[MgCl_2] = 0$, it is done here to emphasize that there is essentially no undissociated $MgCl_2$ in the solution.*

Example 1-1 shows how to calculate the concentrations of ions in a strong electrolyte solution.

*To say that a strong electrolyte is completely dissociated into individual ions in aqueous solution is a good approximation but somewhat of an oversimplification. Some of the cations and anions in solution may become associated into units called *ion pairs*. Generally, though, at the low solution concentrations we will be using, assuming complete dissociation will not seriously affect our results.

EXAMPLE 1-1 Calculating Ion Concentrations in a Solution of a Strong Electrolyte

What are the aluminum and sulfate ion concentrations in 0.0165 M $Al_2(SO_4)_3$?

Analyze

The solute is a strong electrolyte. Thus, it dissociates completely in water. First, we write a balanced chemical equation for the dissociation of $Al_2(SO_4)_3(aq)$, and then set up stoichiometric factors to relate Al^{3+} and SO_4^{2-} to the molarity of $Al_2(SO_4)_3$.

Solve

The dissociation of $Al_2(SO_4)_3$ is represented by the equation below.

$$Al_2(SO_4)_3(s) \xrightarrow{H_2O} 2\,Al^{3+}(aq) + 3\,SO_4^{2-}(aq)$$

The stoichiometric factors, shown in blue in the following equations, are derived from the fact that 1 mol $Al_2(SO_4)_3$ produces 2 mol Al^{3+} and 3 mol SO_4^{2-}.

$$[Al^{3+}] = \frac{0.0165\ \text{mol}\ Al_2(SO_4)_3}{1\ \text{L}} \times \frac{2\ \text{mol}\ Al^{3+}}{1\ \text{mol}\ Al_2(SO_4)_3} = \frac{0.0330\ \text{mol}\ Al^{3+}}{1\ \text{L}}$$
$$= 0.0330\ \text{M}$$

$$[SO_4^{2-}] = \frac{0.0165\ \text{mol}\ Al_2(SO_4)_3}{1\ \text{L}} \times \frac{3\ \text{mol}\ SO_4^{2-}}{1\ \text{mol}\ Al_2(SO_4)_3} = \frac{0.0495\ \text{mol}\ SO_4^{2-}}{1\ \text{L}}$$
$$= 0.0495\ \text{M}$$

Assess

For a strong electrolyte, the concentrations of the ions will always be integer multiples of the electrolyte molarity. For example, in 0.0165 M $MgCl_2$, we have $[Mg^{2+}] = 1 \times 0.0165$ M and $[Cl^-] = 2 \times 0.0165$ M.

PRACTICE EXAMPLE A: The chief ions in seawater are Na^+, Mg^{2+}, and Cl^-. Seawater is approximately 0.438 M NaCl and 0.0512 M $MgCl_2$. What is the molarity of Cl^-—that is, the total $[Cl^-]$—in seawater?

PRACTICE EXAMPLE B: A water treatment plant adds fluoride ion to the water to the extent of 1.5 mg F^-/L.

(a) What is the molarity of fluoride ion in this water?

(b) If the fluoride ion in the water is supplied by calcium fluoride, what mass of calcium fluoride is present in 1.00×10^6 L of this water?

1-1 CONCEPT ASSESSMENT

(1) Which solution is the best electrical conductor? **(a)** 0.50 M CH_3COCH_3; **(b)** 0.50 M CH_3CH_2OH; **(c)** 1.00 M $CH_2OHCHOHCH_2OH$; **(d)** 0.050 M CH_3COOH; **(e)** 0.025 M $RbNO_3$.

(2) Which solution has the highest total molarity of ions? **(a)** 0.008 M $Ba(OH)_2$; **(b)** 0.010 M KI; **(c)** 0.011 M CH_3COOH; **(d)** 0.030 M $HOCH_2CH_2OH$; **(e)** 0.004 M $Al_2(SO_4)_3$?

1-2 Precipitation Reactions

Some metal salts, such as NaCl, are quite soluble in water, while others, such as AgCl, are not very soluble at all. In fact, so little AgCl dissolves in water that this compound is generally considered to be *insoluble*. Precipitation reactions occur when certain cations and anions combine to produce an insoluble ionic solid called a **precipitate**. One laboratory use of precipitation reactions is in identifying the ions present in a solution, as shown in Figure 1-6. In industry, precipitation reactions are used to manufacture numerous chemicals. In the extraction of magnesium metal from seawater, for instance, the first step is to precipitate Mg^{2+} as $Mg(OH)_2(s)$. In this section, the objective is to represent precipitation reactions by chemical equations and to apply some simple rules for predicting precipitation reactions.

▲ FIGURE 1-6
Qualitative test for Cl^- in tap water
The test involves the addition of a few drops of $AgNO_3(aq)$ to tap water. The formation of a precipitate of $AgCl(s)$ confirms the presence of Cl^-.

Net Ionic Equations

The reaction of silver nitrate and sodium iodide in an aqueous solution yields sodium nitrate in solution and a pale yellow or cream-colored precipitate of silver iodide, as shown in Figure 1-7. Applying the principles of equation writing, we can write

$$AgNO_3(aq) + NaI(aq) \longrightarrow AgI(s) + NaNO_3(aq) \quad \textbf{(1.1)}$$

You might note a contradiction, however, between equation (1.1) and something we learned earlier in this chapter. In their aqueous solutions, the soluble ionic compounds $AgNO_3$, NaI, and $NaNO_3$—all *strong* electrolytes—should be represented by their separate ions.

$$Ag^+(aq) + NO_3^-(aq) + Na^+(aq) + I^-(aq) \longrightarrow$$
$$AgI(s) + Na^+(aq) + NO_3^-(aq) \quad \textbf{(1.2)}$$

We might say that equation (1.1) is the "whole formula" form of the equation, whereas equation (1.2) is the "ionic" form. Notice also that in equation (1.2) $Na^+(aq)$ and $NO_3^-(aq)$ appear on both sides of the equation. These ions are not reactants; they go through the reaction unchanged. We call them **spectator ions**. If we eliminate the spectator ions, all that remains is the net ionic equation:

$$Ag^+(aq) + I^-(aq) \longrightarrow AgI(s) \quad \textbf{(1.3)}$$

A **net ionic equation** is an equation that includes only the actual participants in a reaction, with each participant denoted by the symbol or formula that best represents it. Symbols are written for individual ions, such as $Ag^+(aq)$, and whole formulas are written for insoluble solids, such as AgI(s). Because net ionic equations include electrically charged species—ions—a net ionic equation must be balanced both for the numbers of atoms of all types and for electric charge. The same net electric charge must appear on both sides of the equation. Throughout the remainder of this chapter, we will represent most chemical reactions in aqueous solution by net ionic equations.

KEEP IN MIND

that although the insoluble solid consists of ions, we don't represent ionic charges in the whole formula. That is, we write AgI(s), not $Ag^+I^-(s)$.

Predicting Precipitation Reactions

Suppose we are asked whether precipitation occurs when the following aqueous solutions are mixed.

$$AgNO_3(aq) + KBr(aq) \longrightarrow ? \quad \textbf{(1.4)}$$

(a)

(b)

(c)

◄ FIGURE 1-7
A precipitate of silver iodide
When an aqueous solution of $AgNO_3$ **(a)** is added to one of NaI **(b)**, insoluble pale yellow or cream-colored AgI(s) precipitates from solution **(c)**.

A good way to begin is to rewrite expression (1.4) in the ionic form.

$$Ag^+(aq) + NO_3^-(aq) + K^+(aq) + Br^-(aq) \longrightarrow ? \qquad (1.5)$$

There are only two possibilities. Either some cation–anion combination leads to an insoluble solid—a precipitate—or no such combination is possible, and there is no reaction at all.

To predict what will happen without doing experiments, we need some information about which sorts of ionic compounds are water soluble and which are water insoluble. We expect the insoluble ones to form when the appropriate ions are mixed in solution. We don't have all-encompassing rules for predicting solubilities, but a few guidelines work for the majority of common ionic solutes. A concise form of these guidelines is presented in Table 1.1.

▶ In principle, all ionic compounds dissolve in water to some extent, though this may be very slight. For practical purposes, we consider a compound to be insoluble if the maximum amount that can dissolve is less than about 0.01 mol/L.

TABLE 1.1 Solubility Guidelines for Common Ionic Solids

Follow the lower-numbered guideline when two guidelines are in conflict. This leads to the correct prediction in most cases.

1. Salts of group 1 cations (with some exceptions for Li^+) and the NH_4^+ cation are soluble.
2. Nitrates, acetates, and perchlorates are soluble.
3. Salts of silver, lead, and mercury(I) are insoluble.
4. Chlorides, bromides, and iodides are soluble.
5. Carbonates, phosphates, sulfides, oxides, and hydroxides are insoluble (sulfides of group 2 cations and hydroxides of Ca^{2+}, Sr^{2+}, and Ba^{2+} are slightly soluble).
6. Sulfates are soluble except for those of calcium, strontium, and barium.

KEEP IN MIND

that when two ionic compounds form a solid precipitate, they do so by exchanging ions. In the formation of AgBr from KBr and $AgNO_3$, the following exchange takes place.

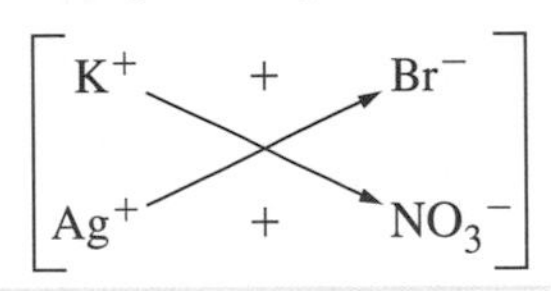

The guidelines from Table 1.1 are applied in the order listed, with the lower-numbered guideline taking precedence in cases of a conflict. According to these guidelines, AgBr(s) is insoluble in water (because rule 3 takes precedence over rule 4) and should precipitate, whereas $KNO_3(s)$ is soluble (because of rule 1). Written as an ionic equation, expression (1.5) becomes

$$Ag^+(aq) + NO_3^-(aq) + K^+(aq) + Br^-(aq) \longrightarrow AgBr(s) + K^+(aq) + NO_3^-(aq)$$

For the net ionic equation, we have

$$Ag^+(aq) + Br^-(aq) \longrightarrow AgBr(s) \qquad (1.6)$$

The three predictions concerning precipitation reactions made in Example 1-2 are verified in Figure 1-8.

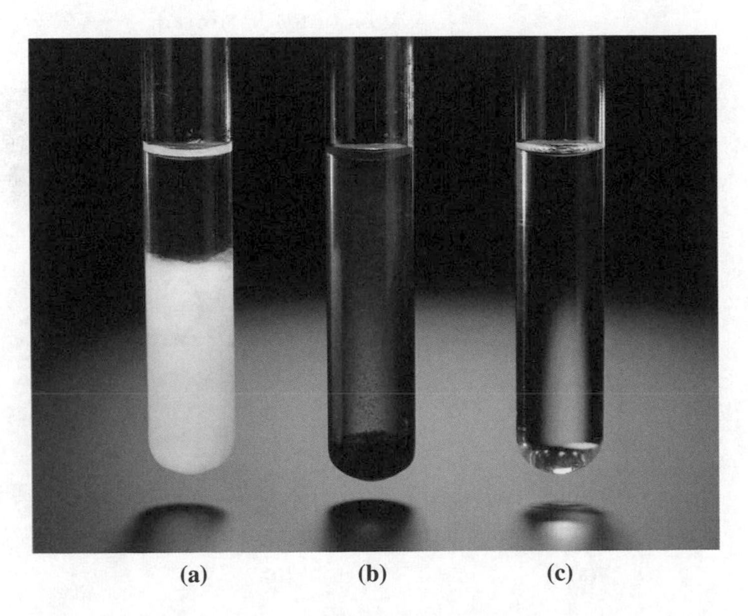

▶ FIGURE 1-8
Verifying the predictions made in Example 1-2
(a) When NaOH(aq) is added to $MgCl_2(aq)$, a white precipitate of $Mg(OH)_2(s)$ forms. **(b)** When colorless BaS(aq) is added to blue $CuSO_4(aq)$, a dark precipitate forms. The precipitate is a mixture of white $BaSO_4(s)$ and black CuS(s); a slight excess of $CuSO_4$ remains in solution. **(c)** No reaction occurs when colorless $(NH_4)_2SO_4(aq)$ is added to colorless $ZnCl_2(aq)$.

EXAMPLE 1-2 Using Solubility Guidelines to Predict Precipitation Reactions

Predict whether a reaction will occur in each of the following cases. If so, write a net ionic equation for the reaction.

(a) $NaOH(aq) + MgCl_2(aq) \longrightarrow ?$
(b) $BaS(aq) + CuSO_4(aq) \longrightarrow ?$
(c) $(NH_4)_2SO_4(aq) + ZnCl_2(aq) \longrightarrow ?$

Analyze

All the compounds shown in **(a)**, **(b)**, and **(c)** are soluble and they provide ions in solution. By using the solubility guidelines in Table 1.1, determine whether the positive ions from one compound combine with the negative ions of the other to form soluble or insoluble compounds. If only soluble compounds are formed, then all ions remain in solution (no reaction). If an insoluble compound is formed, then the insoluble compound precipitates from the solution. The net ionic equation for the precipitation reaction is obtained by eliminating the spectator ions from the full ionic equation.

Solve

For each of **(a)**, **(b)** and **(c)**, apply the strategy described above.

(a) In aqueous solution, we get Na^+ and OH^- from NaOH and Mg^{2+} and Cl^- from $MgCl_2$. The combination of Na^+ and Cl^- gives NaCl, a soluble compound; thus, the Na^+ and Cl^- ions remain in solution. However, the Mg^{2+} and OH^- ions combine to produce $Mg(OH)_2$, an insoluble compound. The full, ionic equation is

$$2\,Na^+(aq) + 2\,OH^-(aq) + Mg^{2+}(aq) + 2\,Cl^-(aq) \longrightarrow Mg(OH)_2(s) + 2\,Na^+(aq) + 2\,Cl^-(aq)$$

With the elimination of spectator ions, we obtain

$$2\,OH^-(aq) + Mg^{2+}(aq) \longrightarrow Mg(OH)_2(s)$$

(b) In aqueous solution, we get Ba^{2+} and S^{2-} from BaS and Cu^{2+} and SO_4^{2-} from $CuSO_4$. The Ba^{2+} and SO_4^{2-} ions combine to form $BaSO_4$, an insoluble compound, and the Cu^{2+} and S^{2-} ions combine to form CuS, also an insoluble compound. The full ionic equation is

$$Ba^{2+}(aq) + S^{2-}(aq) + Cu^{2+}(aq) + SO_4^{2-}(aq) \longrightarrow BaSO_4(s) + CuS(s)$$

The equation above is also the net ionic equation because there are no spectator ions.

(c) We get $NH_4^+, SO_4^{2-}, Zn^{2+}$, and Cl^- ions in solution. Because all possible combinations of positive and negative ions lead to water soluble compounds, all of the ions remain in solution. No reaction occurs.

Na^+ + OH^- — $Mg(OH)_2$ is insoluble.
Mg^{2+} + $2\,Cl^-$ — NaCl is soluble.

Assess

Problems of this type can also be solved by using a diagrammatic approach which is illustrated for part **(a)**.

As you gain experience, you should be able to go directly to a net ionic equation without first having to write an ionic equation that includes spectator ions.

PRACTICE EXAMPLE A: Indicate whether a precipitate forms by completing each equation as a net ionic equation. If no reaction occurs, so state.

(a) $AlCl_3(aq) + KOH(aq) \longrightarrow ?$
(b) $K_2SO_4(aq) + FeBr_3(aq) \longrightarrow ?$
(c) $CaI_2(aq) + Pb(NO_3)_2(aq) \longrightarrow ?$

PRACTICE EXAMPLE B: Indicate through a net ionic equation whether a precipitate forms when the following compounds in aqueous solution are mixed. If no reaction occurs, so state.

(a) sodium phosphate + aluminum chloride $\longrightarrow$?
(b) aluminum sulfate + barium chloride $\longrightarrow$?
(c) ammonium carbonate + lead nitrate $\longrightarrow$?

1-2 CONCEPT ASSESSMENT

Apply the solubility guidelines in Table 1.1 to predict whether each of the following solids is water soluble or insoluble. For which are the solubility guidelines inconclusive? **(a)** $Al_2(SO_4)_3$; **(b)** $Cr(OH)_3$; **(c)** K_3PO_4; **(d)** Li_2CO_3; **(e)** ZnS; **(f)** $Mg(MnO_4)_2$; **(g)** $AgClO_4$; **(h)** $CaSO_4$; **(i)** PbO.

1-1 ARE YOU WONDERING...

Whether an insoluble ionic compound, such as AgCl, is a strong electrolyte or a weak electrolyte?

Silver chloride, AgCl, is an ionic compound. When AgCl dissolves in water, it is 100% dissociated into Ag^+ and Cl^- ions; there are no AgCl ion pairs. If we focus only on the degree of dissociation, then AgCl, like HCl, is a strong electrolyte.

At one time, a strong electrolyte was defined in more practical terms as a substance that when dissolved in water, gives a solution that is a good conductor of electricity. Because AgCl has very low solubility in water, approximately 1×10^{-5} moles per liter, a solution of AgCl is not a good conductor of electricity.

Today, most chemists would argue that AgCl is a strong electrolyte (because it is 100% dissociated in aqueous solution) but some may argue that it is a weak electrolyte (because an aqueous solution of AgCl is not a good conductor of electricity).

Does it matter that chemists may not totally agree on whether AgCl should be called a strong electrolyte or a weak electrolyte? Not at all, because all chemists agree on the following facts: (1) AgCl is essentially 100% dissociated in water; (2) only a small amount of AgCl can be dissolved in water; and (3) an aqueous solution of AgCl is not a good conductor of electricity.

1-3 Acid–Base Reactions

Ideas about acids and bases (or alkalis) date back to ancient times. The word *acid* is derived from the Latin *acidus* (sour). *Alkali* (base) comes from the Arabic *al-qali*, referring to the ashes of certain plants from which alkaline substances can be extracted. The acid–base concept is a major theme in the history of chemistry. In this section, we emphasize the view proposed by Svante Arrhenius in 1884 but also introduce a more modern theory proposed in 1923 by Thomas Lowry and by Johannes Brønsted.

Acids

From a practical standpoint, acids can be identified by their sour taste, their ability to react with a variety of metals and carbonate minerals, and the effect they have on the colors of substances called *acid–base indicators*. Methyl red is an acid–base indicator that appears red in acidic environments and yellow otherwise (see Figure 1-9). From a chemist's point of view, however, an **acid** can be defined as a substance that provides hydrogen ions (H^+) in aqueous solution. This definition was first proposed by Svante Arrhenius in 1884.

KEEP IN MIND

that $H^+(aq)$ actually represents a hydrated proton, that is, a proton attached to one H_2O molecule, as in H_3O^+, or to several H_2O molecules, as in $H_9O_4^+$.

Different acids exhibit different tendencies for producing H^+ ions in aqueous solution. **Strong acids** have a strong tendency for producing H^+ ions. Strong acids are molecular compounds that are almost completely ionized into $H^+(aq)$ and accompanying anions when in aqueous solution. Hydrogen chloride, HCl, and nitric acid, HNO_3, are examples of strong acids. When HCl dissolves in water, complete ionization into $H^+(aq)$ and $Cl^-(aq)$ occurs:

$$HCl(aq) \longrightarrow H^+(aq) + Cl^-(aq) \quad (1.7)$$

◀ FIGURE 1-9
An acid, a base, and an acid–base indicator
The acidic nature of lemon juice is shown by the red color of the acid–base indicator *methyl red.* The basic nature of soap is indicated by the change in color of the indicator from red to yellow.

When HNO_3 dissolves in water, complete ionization into $H^+(aq)$ and $NO_3^-(aq)$ occurs. There are so few common strong acids that they make only a short list. The list of common strong acids is given in Table 1.2. It is imperative that you memorize this list.

Weak acids are molecular compounds that have a weak tendency for producing H^+ ions; weak acids are incompletely ionized in aqueous solution. The vast majority of acids are weak acids. The ionization of a weak acid is best described in terms of a reversible reaction that does not go to completion. As described on page 5, the ionization reaction for acetic acid, CH_3COOH, is

$$CH_3COOH(aq) \rightleftharpoons H^+(aq) + CH_3COO^-(aq) \quad \textbf{(1.8)}$$

Equation (1.8) has the following interpretation: in aqueous solution, only some of the CH_3COOH molecules are converted into H^+ and CH_3COO^- ions. The fraction of molecules that ionize can be calculated, but the calculation is not simple. We will defer such calculations until Chapter 8.

Equations (1.7) and (1.8) are based on the Arrhenius theory of acids and bases, and these equations might lead you to think that acids simply fall apart into H^+ ions and the accompanying anions when they are dissolved in water. However, plenty of experimental evidence proves that this is not the case. In 1923, Johannes Brønsted in Denmark and Thomas Lowry in Great Britain independently proposed that the key process responsible for the properties of acids (and bases) was the transfer of an H^+ ion (a proton) from one substance to another. For example, when acids dissolve in water, H^+ ions are transferred from acid molecules to water molecules, as shown below for HCl and CH_3COOH.

$$HCl(aq) + H_2O(l) \longrightarrow H_3O^+(aq) + Cl^-(aq) \quad \textbf{(1.9)}$$

$$CH_3COOH(aq) + H_2O(l) \rightleftharpoons H_3O^+(aq) + CH_3COO^-(aq) \quad \textbf{(1.10)}$$

In equations (1.9) and (1.10), the acid molecules are acting as proton donors and the water molecules are acting as proton acceptors. According to the Brønsted-Lowry theory, an acid is a **proton donor**.

It is partly a matter of preference whether we include water as a reactant in the equation for the reaction that occurs when an acid is dissolved in water. Some chemists prefer to write the reaction without water as a reactant, as we did in equations (1.7) and (1.8), to eliminate the clutter of "extra" water molecules. If that is also your preference, then you must remember that the H^+ ion is not a free proton in solution but rather is firmly bound to a water molecule and exists as an H_3O^+ ion. The H_3O^+ ion is even further hydrated (see Figure 1-5). Many chemists prefer to include H_2O as a reactant, as we did in equations (1.9) and (1.10), to emphasize that the reactions actually involve the transfer of protons from acid molecules to water molecules.

TABLE 1.2 Common Strong Acids and Strong Bases

Acids	Bases
HCl	LiOH
HBr	NaOH
HI	KOH
$HClO_4$	RbOH
HNO_3	CsOH
H_2SO_4[a]	$Ca(OH)_2$
	$Sr(OH)_2$
	$Ba(OH)_2$

[a] H_2SO_4 ionizes in two distinct steps. It is a strong acid only in its first ionization step (see Section 8-6).

KEEP IN MIND

that a hydrogen atom consists of one proton and one electron. Therefore, a hydrogen ion, H^+, is simply a proton.

Bases

From a practical standpoint, we can identify bases through their bitter taste, slippery feel, and effect on the colors of acid–base indicators (Fig. 1-9). The Arrhenius definition of a **base** is a substance that produces hydroxide ions (OH^-) in aqueous solution. Consider a soluble ionic hydroxide, such as NaOH. In the solid state, this compound consists of Na^+ and OH^- ions. When the solid dissolves in water, the ions dissociate.

$$NaOH(aq) \longrightarrow Na^+(aq) + OH^-(aq)$$

The equation above indicates that NaOH(aq) is best represented as $Na^+(aq)$ plus $OH^-(aq)$.

A base that dissociates completely, or very nearly so, in aqueous solution is a **strong base**. As is true of strong acids, the number of common strong bases is small (see Table 1.2). They are primarily the hydroxides of group 1 and some group 2 metals. Memorize the list.

Certain substances produce OH^- ions by reacting with water, not just by dissolving in it. Such substances, for example, ammonia, are also bases.

$$NH_3(aq) + H_2O(l) \rightleftharpoons NH_4^+(aq) + OH^-(aq) \quad \textbf{(1.11)}$$

KEEP IN MIND

that $NH_4^+(aq)$ is formed by the transfer of a proton from an H_2O to a NH_3 molecule, and NH_4^+ interacts with water in much the same way as the hydronium ion does. A ball-and-stick model of the ammonium ion is shown below.

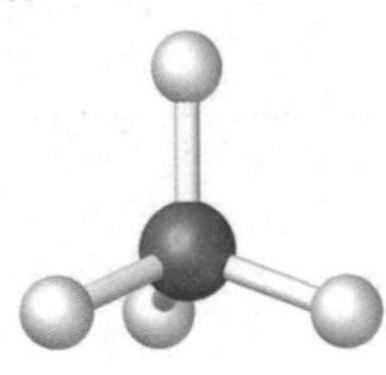

Ammonium ion

NH_3 is a weak electrolyte; its reaction with water does not go to completion. A base that is incompletely ionized in aqueous solution is a **weak base**. Most basic substances are weak bases.

We can also examine equation (1.11) in terms of the Brønsted-Lowry theory, which focuses on the transfer of protons from one substance to another. According to this theory, a base is a **proton acceptor**. In equation (1.11), NH_3 behaves as a proton acceptor (a Brønsted-Lowry base) and H_2O behaves as a proton donor (a Brønsted-Lowry acid).

Acidic and Basic Solutions

We have seen that when dissolved in water, an acid produces H^+ ions and a base produces OH^- ions. However, experiment shows small numbers of H^+ and OH^- ions are present even in pure water. In pure water, the following reaction occurs to a limited extent, hence the use of a double arrow ($\rightleftharpoons$) rather than a single arrow ($\longrightarrow$).

$$H_2O(l) \rightleftharpoons H^+(aq) + OH^-(aq)$$

Careful measurements show that $[H^+]_{water} = [OH^-]_{water} = 1.0 \times 10^{-7}$ M at 25 °C. (The subscripts on the square brackets are there to emphasize that the values given for $[H^+]$ and $[OH^-]$ are for pure water only.) Because an acid produces H^+ ions in solution, we expect that a solution of acid at 25 °C will have $[H^+] > 1.0 \times 10^{-7}$ M. Such a solution is said to be *acidic*. An acidic solution has a greater concentration of H^+ ions than does pure water. A base produces OH^- ions, and so a solution of base will have $[OH^-] > 1.0 \times 10^{-7}$ M at 25 °C. Such a solution is said to be *basic*. These ideas are summarized below.

An *acidic* solution has $[H^+] > [H^+]_{water}$.
A *basic* solution has $[OH^-] > [OH^-]_{water}$.

The statements above can be expressed another way. An acidic solution has an excess of H^+ ions (compared with pure water), and a basic solution has an excess of OH^- ions. We will use these ideas in Section 1-5 and encounter them again in Chapter 8.

Neutralization

Perhaps the most significant property of acids and bases is the ability of each to cancel or neutralize the properties of the other. In a **neutralization reaction**, an acid and a base react to form water and an aqueous solution of an ionic compound called a **salt**. Thus, in molecular form,

$$\begin{array}{ccccccc} HCl(aq) & + & NaOH(aq) & \longrightarrow & NaCl(aq) & + & H_2O(l) \\ \text{(acid)} & + & \text{(base)} & \longrightarrow & \text{(salt)} & + & \text{(water)} \end{array}$$

Switching to the ionic form we write,

$$\underbrace{H^+(aq) + Cl^-(aq)}_{\text{(acid)}} + \underbrace{Na^+(aq) + OH^-(aq)}_{\text{(base)}} \longrightarrow \underbrace{Na^+(aq) + Cl^-(aq)}_{\text{salt}} + \underbrace{H_2O(l)}_{\text{water}}$$

When the spectator ions are eliminated, the net ionic equation shows the essential nature of the neutralization of a strong acid by a strong base: H^+ ions from the acid and OH^- ions from the base combine to form water.

$$H^+(aq) + OH^-(aq) \longrightarrow H_2O(l)$$

In a neutralization involving the weak base $NH_3(aq)$, we can think of H^+ from an acid combining directly with NH_3 molecules to form NH_4^+. The neutralization can be represented by an ionic equation, for example,

$$\underbrace{H^+(aq) + Cl^-(aq)}_{\text{(acid)}} + \underbrace{NH_3(aq)}_{\text{(base)}} \longrightarrow \underbrace{NH_4^+(aq) + Cl^-(aq)}_{\text{(salt)}}$$

or by a net ionic equation

$$H^+(aq) + NH_3(aq) \longrightarrow NH_4^+(aq)$$

All the neutralization reactions given above involve a strong acid or a strong base and all of them go essentially to completion, that is, until the limiting reagent is used up. Thus, we use a single arrow ($\longrightarrow$) rather than a double arrow ($\rightleftharpoons$) in the equations for these reactions.

◀ The formula of $NH_3(aq)$ is sometimes written as NH_4OH (ammonium hydroxide) and its ionization represented as

$$NH_4OH(aq) \rightleftharpoons NH_4^+(aq) + OH^-(aq)$$

There is no hard evidence for the existence of NH_4OH, however, that is, in the sense of a discrete substance comprising NH_4^+ and OH^- ions. We will use only the formula $NH_3(aq)$.

Recognizing Acids and Bases

Acids contain *ionizable* hydrogen atoms, which are generally identified by the way in which the formula of an acid is written. Ionizable H atoms are separated from other H atoms in the formula either by writing them first in the molecular formula or by indicating where they are found in the molecule. Thus, there are two ways that we can show that one H atom in the acetic acid molecule is ionizable and the other three H atoms are not.

$$\underbrace{HC_2H_3O_2 \text{ or } CH_3COOH}_{\text{acetic acid}}$$

In contrast to acetic acid, methane has four H atoms, but they are not ionizable. CH_4 is neither an acid nor a base.

A substance whose formula indicates a combination of OH^- ions with cations is generally a strong base (for example, NaOH). To identify a weak base, we usually need a chemical equation for the ionization reaction, as in equation (1.11). The main weak base we will work with at present is NH_3. Note that ethanol, CH_3CH_2OH, is not a base. The OH group is not present as OH^-, both in pure ethanol and in its aqueous solutions.

More Acid–Base Reactions

$Mg(OH)_2$ is a base because it contains OH^-, but this compound is quite insoluble in water. Its finely divided solid particles form a suspension in water that is the familiar milk of magnesia, used as an antacid. In this suspension, $Mg(OH)_2(s)$ does dissolve very slightly, producing some OH^- in solution. If an acid is added, H^+ from the acid combines with this OH^- to form water—neutralization occurs. More $Mg(OH)_2(s)$ dissolves to produce more OH^- in solution, which is neutralized by more H^+, and so on. In this way, the neutralization reaction results in the dissolving of otherwise insoluble $Mg(OH)_2(s)$. The net ionic equation for the reaction of $Mg(OH)_2(s)$ with a strong acid is

$$Mg(OH)_2(s) + 2\,H^+(aq) \longrightarrow Mg^{2+}(aq) + 2\,H_2O(l) \quad \textbf{(1.12)}$$

▲ FIGURE 1-10
Damage caused by acid rain
This marble statue has been eroded by acid rain. Marble consists primarily of $CaCO_3$. Acids react with and dissolve marble through the reaction described in equation (1.14).

$Mg(OH)_2(s)$ also reacts with a weak acid, such as acetic acid. In the net ionic equation, acetic acid is written in its molecular form. But remember that some H^+ and CH_3COO^- ions are always present in an acetic acid solution. The H^+ ions react with OH^- ions, as in reaction (1.12), followed by further ionization of CH_3COOH, more neutralization, and so on. If enough acetic acid is present, the $Mg(OH)_2$ will dissolve completely. The equation for the reaction is given below.

$$Mg(OH)_2(s) + 2\,CH_3COOH(aq) \longrightarrow Mg^{2+}(aq) + 2\,CH_3COO^-(aq) + 2\,H_2O(l) \quad \textbf{(1.13)}$$

Calcium carbonate, which is present in limestone and marble, is another water-insoluble solid that is soluble in strong and weak acids. Here the solid produces a low concentration of CO_3^{2-} ions, which combine with H^+ to form the weak acid H_2CO_3. This causes more of the solid to dissolve, and so on. Carbonic acid, H_2CO_3, is a very unstable substance that decomposes into H_2O and $CO_2(g)$. The net ionic equation for the reaction of $CaCO_3$ with an acid is given below.

$$CaCO_3(s) + 2\,H^+(aq) \longrightarrow Ca^{2+}(aq) + H_2O(l) + CO_2(g) \quad \textbf{(1.14)}$$

Thus, a gas is given off when $CaCO_3(s)$ reacts with an acid and dissolves. The reaction represented by equation (1.14) is responsible for the erosion of marble statues by acid rain, such as the one shown in Figure 1-10. Equation (1.14) also shows that $CaCO_3(s)$ has the ability to neutralize acids. Not surprisingly, calcium carbonate, like magnesium hydroxide, is used as an antacid.

The Arrhenius definition recognizes only OH^- as a base, but when we reconsider acids and bases in more detail in Chapter 8, we will see that modern theories identify CO_3^{2-} and many other anions, including OH^-, as bases. Table 1.3 lists several common anions and one cation that produce gases in acid–base reactions.

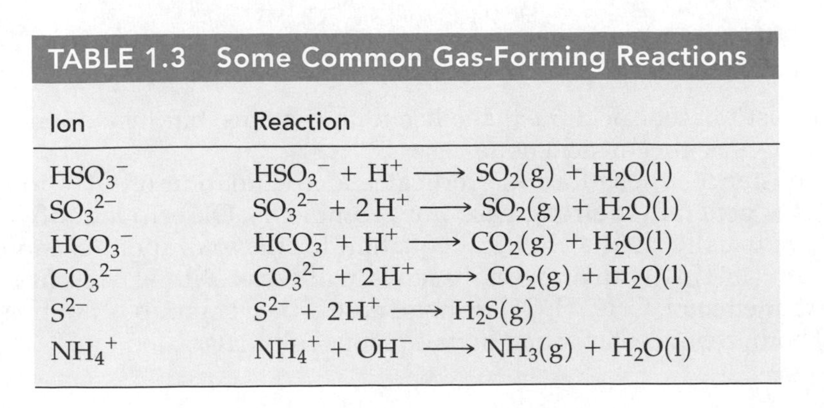

TABLE 1.3 Some Common Gas-Forming Reactions

Ion	Reaction
HSO_3^-	$HSO_3^- + H^+ \longrightarrow SO_2(g) + H_2O(l)$
SO_3^{2-}	$SO_3^{2-} + 2\,H^+ \longrightarrow SO_2(g) + H_2O(l)$
HCO_3^-	$HCO_3^- + H^+ \longrightarrow CO_2(g) + H_2O(l)$
CO_3^{2-}	$CO_3^{2-} + 2\,H^+ \longrightarrow CO_2(g) + H_2O(l)$
S^{2-}	$S^{2-} + 2\,H^+ \longrightarrow H_2S(g)$
NH_4^+	$NH_4^+ + OH^- \longrightarrow NH_3(g) + H_2O(l)$

EXAMPLE 1-3 Writing Equations for Acid–Base Reactions

Write a net ionic equation to represent the reaction of **(a)** aqueous strontium hydroxide with nitric acid; **(b)** solid aluminum hydroxide with hydrochloric acid.

Analyze

The reactions are neutralization reactions, which means they are of the general form acid + base $\longrightarrow$ salt + water. We can start with the whole formula equation, switch to the ionic equation, and then delete the spectator ions to arrive at the net ionic equation.

Solve

(a) $2\,HNO_3(aq) + Sr(OH)_2(aq) \longrightarrow Sr(NO_3)_2(aq) + 2\,H_2O(l)$

Ionic form:

$$2\,H^+(aq) + 2\,NO_3^-(aq) + Sr^{2+}(aq) + 2\,OH^-(aq) \longrightarrow Sr^{2+}(aq) + 2\,NO_3^-(aq) + 2\,H_2O(l)$$

Net ionic equation: Delete the spectator ions (Sr^{2+} and NO_3^-).

$$2\,H^+(aq) + 2\,OH^-(aq) \longrightarrow 2\,H_2O(l)$$

or, more simply,

$$H^+(aq) + OH^-(aq) \longrightarrow H_2O(l)$$

(b) $Al(OH)_3(s) + 3\,HCl(aq) \longrightarrow AlCl_3(aq) + 3\,H_2O(l)$

Ionic form:

$$Al(OH)_3(s) + 3\,H^+(aq) + 3\,Cl^-(aq) \longrightarrow Al^{3+}(aq) + 3\,Cl^-(aq) + 3\,H_2O(l)$$

Net ionic equation: Delete the spectator ion (Cl^-).

$$Al(OH)_3(s) + 3\,H^+(aq) \longrightarrow Al^{3+}(aq) + 3\,H_2O(l)$$

Assess

In part **(a)**, the net ionic equation is $H^+(aq) + OH^-(aq) \rightarrow H_2O(l)$, as is always the case when the neutralization reaction involves a soluble strong acid and a soluble strong base. In part **(b)**, the base was not soluble; thus, the net ionic equation includes a solid.

PRACTICE EXAMPLE A: Write a net ionic equation to represent the reaction of aqueous ammonia with propionic acid, CH_3CH_2COOH. Assume that the neutralization reaction goes to completion. What is the formula and name of the salt that results from this neutralization?

PRACTICE EXAMPLE B: Calcium carbonate is a major constituent of the hard water deposits found in teakettles and automatic coffeemakers. Vinegar, which is essentially a dilute aqueous solution of acetic acid, is commonly used to remove such deposits. Write a net ionic equation for the reaction that occurs. Assume that the neutralization reaction goes to completion.

1-3 CONCEPT ASSESSMENT

You are given the four solids, K_2CO_3, CaO, $ZnSO_4$, and $BaCO_3$, and three solvents, $H_2O(l)$, $HCl(aq)$, and $H_2SO_4(aq)$. You are asked to prepare four solutions, each containing one of the four cations, that is, one with $K^+(aq)$, one with $Ca^{2+}(aq)$, and so on. Using water as your *first* choice, what solvent would you use to prepare each solution? Explain your choices.

1-4 Oxidation–Reduction Reactions: Some General Principles

Practical applications of oxidation–reduction reactions can be traced back thousands of years to the period in human culture when metal tools were first made. The metal needed to make tools was obtained by heating copper or iron ores, such as cuprite (Cu_2O) or hematite (Fe_2O_3), in the presence of carbon. Since

◀ An ore is a mineral from which a metal can be extracted. Many metal ores are oxides and the metals are obtained from their oxides by the removal of oxygen.

that time, iron has become the most widely used of all metals and it is produced in essentially the same way: by heating Fe_2O_3 in the presence of carbon in a blast furnace. A simplified chemical equation for the reaction is given below.

▶ In a blast furnace, carbon from the coke is converted to CO, which then reacts with Fe_2O_3.

$$Fe_2O_3(s) + 3\,CO(g) \xrightarrow{\Delta} 2\,Fe(l) + 3\,CO_2(g) \quad \textbf{(1.15)}$$

In this reaction, we can think of the CO(g) as taking O atoms away from Fe_2O_3 to produce $CO_2(g)$ and the free element iron. A commonly used term to describe a reaction in which a substance gains O atoms is *oxidation*, and a reaction in which a substance loses O atoms is *reduction*. In reaction (1.15), CO(g) is oxidized and $Fe_2O_3(s)$ is reduced. Oxidation and reduction must always occur together, and such a reaction is called an **oxidation–reduction**, or **redox, reaction**. The oxygen in Fe_2O_3 can also be removed by igniting a finely divided mixture of Fe_2O_3 and Al. The reaction produces a spectacular display, shown in Figure 1-11, and releases a tremendous amount of heat, which causes the iron to melt. Mixtures of finely divided Fe_2O_3 and Al are used by railway workers to produce liquid iron for welding together iron railway tracks.

▶ Because it is easier to say, the term *redox* is often used instead of oxidation–reduction.

Definitions of oxidation and reduction based solely on the transfer of O atoms are too restrictive. By using broader definitions, many reactions in aqueous solution can be described as oxidation–reduction reactions, even when no oxygen is involved.

▲ FIGURE 1-11
Thermite reaction
Iron atoms of iron(III) oxide give up O atoms to Al atoms, producing Al_2O_3.
$Fe_2O_3(s) + 2\,Al(s) \longrightarrow Al_2O_3(s) + 2\,Fe(l)$

Oxidation State Changes

Suppose we rewrite equation (1.15) and indicate the oxidation states (O.S.) of the elements on both sides of the equation.

$$\overset{+3\,-2}{Fe_2O_3} + 3\,\overset{+2\,-2}{CO} \longrightarrow 2\,\overset{0}{Fe} + 3\,\overset{+4\,-2}{CO_2}$$

The O.S. of oxygen is −2 everywhere it appears in this equation. That of iron (shown in red) changes. It *decreases* from +3 in Fe_2O_3 to 0 in the free element, Fe. The O.S. of carbon (shown in blue) also changes. It *increases* from +2 in CO to +4 in CO_2. In terms of oxidation state changes, in an oxidation process, the O.S. of some element increases; in a reduction process, the O.S. of some element decreases.

Even though we assess oxidation state changes by element, oxidation and reduction involve the entire species in which the element is found. Thus, for the reaction above, the whole compound Fe_2O_3 is reduced, not just the Fe atoms; and CO is oxidized, not just the C atom.

EXAMPLE 1-4 Identifying Oxidation–Reduction Reactions

Indicate whether each of the following is an oxidation–reduction reaction.

(a) $MnO_2(s) + 4\,H^+(aq) + 2\,Cl^-(aq) \longrightarrow Mn^{2+}(aq) + 2\,H_2O(l) + Cl_2(g)$

(b) $H_2PO_4^-(aq) + OH^-(aq) \longrightarrow HPO_4^{2-}(aq) + H_2O(l)$

Analyze

In each case, indicate the oxidation states of the elements on both sides of the equation, and look for changes.

Solve

(a) The O.S. of Mn decreases from +4 in MnO_2 to +2 in Mn^{2+}. MnO_2 is reduced to Mn^{2+}. The O.S. of O remains at −2 throughout the reaction, and that of H, at +1. The O.S. of Cl increases from −1 in Cl^- to 0 in Cl_2. Cl^- is oxidized to Cl_2. The reaction is an oxidation–reduction reaction.

(b) The O.S. of H is +1 on both sides of the equation. Oxygen remains at O.S. −2 throughout. The O.S. of phosphorus is +5 in $H_2PO_4^-$ and also +5 in HPO_4^{2-}. There are no changes in O.S. This is not an oxidation–reduction reaction. (It is, in fact, an acid–base reaction.)

Assess

Because many redox reactions involve H^+, OH^-, or insoluble ionic compounds, it is easy to confuse a redox reaction with an acid–base or a precipitation reaction. It is important that you remember the defining features of each type of reaction. Precipitation reactions involve the combination of ions in solution to produce an insoluble precipitate, acid–base reactions involve proton (H^+) transfer, and redox reactions involve electron transfer and changes in oxidation states.

PRACTICE EXAMPLE A: Identify whether each of the following is an oxidation–reduction reaction.

(a) $(NH_4)_2SO_4(aq) + Ba(NO_3)_2(aq) \longrightarrow BaSO_4(s) + 2\,NH_4NO_3(aq)$

(b) $2\,Pb(NO_3)_2(s) \longrightarrow 2\,PbO(s) + 4\,NO_2(g) + O_2(g)$

PRACTICE EXAMPLE B: Identify the species that is oxidized and the species that is reduced in the reaction below.

$$5\,VO^{2+}(aq) + MnO_4^-(aq) + H_2O(l) \longrightarrow 5\,VO_2^+(aq) + Mn^{2+}(aq) + 2\,H^+(aq)$$

Oxidation and Reduction Half-Reactions

The reaction illustrated in Figure 1-12 is an oxidation–reduction reaction. The chemical equation for the reaction is given below.

$$Zn(s) + Cu^{2+}(aq) \longrightarrow Zn^{2+}(aq) + Cu(s)$$

We can show that the reaction is an oxidation–reduction reaction by evaluating changes in oxidation state, but there is another especially useful way to establish this. Think of the reaction as involving two **half-reactions** occurring at the same time—an oxidation and a reduction. The overall reaction is the

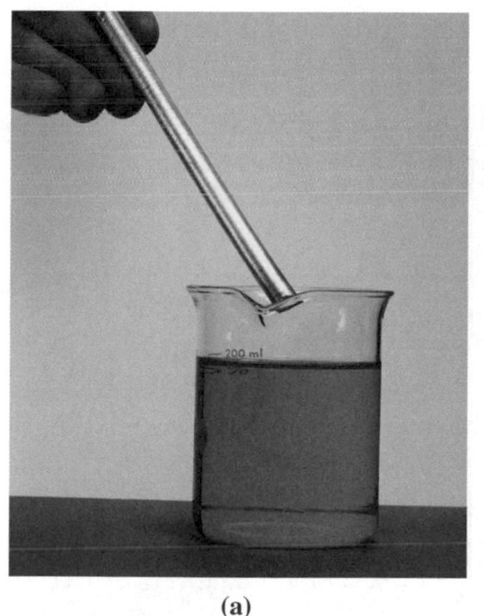

(a)

(b)

(c)

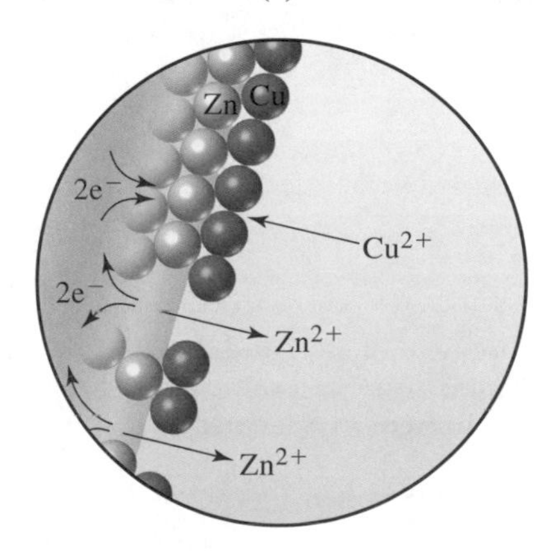

▲ FIGURE 1-12
An oxidation–reduction reaction
(a) A zinc rod above an aqueous solution of copper(II) sulfate. **(b)** Following immersion of the Zn rod in the $CuSO_4(aq)$ for several hours, the blue color of $Cu^{2+}(aq)$ disappears and a deposit of copper forms on the rod. In the microscopic view on the left, the gray spheres represent Zn atoms and the red spheres represent Cu atoms. In the reaction, Zn atoms lose electrons to the metal surface and enter the solution as Zn^{2+} ions. Cu^{2+} ions from the solution pick up electrons and deposit on the metal surface as atoms of solid copper. **(c)** The pitted zinc rod (providing evidence that zinc was consumed in a chemical reaction) and the collected copper metal.

sum of the two half-reactions. We can represent the half-reactions by half-equations and the overall reaction by an overall equation.

Oxidation:	$Zn(s) \longrightarrow Zn^{2+}(aq) + 2\,e^-$	**(1.16)**
Reduction:	$Cu^{2+}(aq) + 2\,e^- \longrightarrow Cu(s)$	**(1.17)**
Overall:	$Zn(s) + Cu^{2+}(aq) \longrightarrow Zn^{2+}(aq) + Cu(s)$	**(1.18)**

In half-reaction (1.16), Zn is oxidized—its oxidation state increases from 0 to +2. This change corresponds to a loss of two electrons by each zinc atom. In half-reaction (1.17), Cu^{2+} is reduced—its oxidation state decreases from +2 to 0. This change corresponds to the gain of two electrons by each Cu^{2+} ion. To summarize,

- **Oxidation** is a process in which the O.S. of some element *increases* as electrons are lost. Electrons appear on the *right* side of a half-equation.
- **Reduction** is a process in which the O.S. of some element *decreases* as electrons are gained. Electrons appear on the *left* side of a half-equation.
- Oxidation and reduction half-reactions must always occur together, and the total number of electrons associated with the oxidation must *equal* the total number associated with the reduction.

Redox reactions are similar to acid–base reactions in that both types of reactions involve the transfer of small, fundamental particles; protons are transferred in acid–base reactions and electrons are transferred in redox reactions. However, acid-base reactions are easily identified because the hydrogen atoms and protons (H^+) are shown explicitly in the balanced chemical equation. Redox reactions are much more difficult to identify because the electrons are "hidden." When we write out the half-equations for the oxidation and reduction processes, the electrons are shown explicitly and the key feature of a redox reaction, electron transfer, is emphasized.

Figure 1-13 and Example 1-5 suggest some fundamental questions about oxidation–reduction. For example,

- Why does Fe react with HCl(aq), displacing $H_2(g)$, whereas Cu does not?
- Why does Fe form Fe^{2+} and not Fe^{3+} in this reaction?

EXAMPLE 1-5 Representing an Oxidation–Reduction Reaction Through Half-Equations and an Overall Equation

Write equations for the oxidation and reduction processes that occur and the overall equation for the reaction of iron with hydrochloric acid solution to produce $H_2(g)$ and Fe^{2+}. The reaction is shown in Figure 1-13.

Analyze

The reactants are Fe(s) and HCl(aq), and the products are $H_2(g)$ and $FeCl_2(aq)$, a soluble ionic compound. In the reaction, the oxidation state of iron changes from 0 in Fe to +2 in $FeCl_2$, and the oxidation state of hydrogen changes from +1 in HCl to 0 in H_2. Thus, iron is oxidized and hydrogen is reduced.

Solve

The balanced chemical equations are as follows.

Oxidation:	$Fe(s) \longrightarrow Fe^{2+}(aq) + 2\,e^-$
Reduction:	$2\,H^+(aq) + 2\,e^- \longrightarrow H_2(g)$
Overall:	$Fe(s) + 2\,H^+(aq) \longrightarrow Fe^{2+}(aq) + H_2(g)$

Assess

This example illustrates that iron dissolves in acid solution. Iron is a major component of steel and the reaction in this example contributes to the corrosion of steel that is exposed to air and moisture. For example, H^+ ions from acid rain cause Fe atoms in steel to become oxidized to Fe^{2+} ions. The oxidation of iron creates small pits in the steel surface and leads to corrosion.

▲ FIGURE 1-13
Displacement of H^+ (aq) by iron—Example 1-5 illustrated
(a) An iron nail is wrapped in a piece of copper screen. **(b)** The nail and screen are placed in HCl(aq). Hydrogen gas is evolved as the nail reacts. **(c)** The nail reacts completely and produces Fe^{2+}(aq), but the copper does not react.

PRACTICE EXAMPLE A: Represent the reaction of aluminum with hydrochloric acid to produce $AlCl_3(aq)$ and $H_2(g)$ by oxidation and reduction half-equations and an overall equation.

PRACTICE EXAMPLE B: Represent the reaction of chlorine gas with aqueous sodium bromide to produce liquid bromine and aqueous sodium chloride by oxidation and reduction half-equations and an overall equation.

Even now, you can probably see that the answers to these questions lie in the relative abilities of Fe and Cu atoms to give up electrons—to become oxidized. Fe gives up electrons more easily than does Cu; also, Fe is more readily oxidized to Fe^{2+} than it is to Fe^{3+}. We can give more complete answers after we develop specific criteria describing electron loss and gain. For now, the information in Table 1.4 should be helpful. The table lists some common metals that react with acids to displace $H_2(g)$ and a few that do not. As noted in the table, most of the group 1 and 2 metals are so reactive that they will react with cold water to produce $H_2(g)$ and a solution of the metal hydroxide.

TABLE 1.4 Behavior of Some Common Metals with Nonoxidizing Acids[a]

React to Produce $H_2(g)$	Do Not React
Alkali metals (group 1)[b] Alkaline earth metals (group 2)[b] Al, Zn, Fe, Sn, Pb	Cu, Ag, Au, Hg

[a]A nonoxidizing acid (for example, HCl, HBr, HI) is one in which the only possible reduction half-reaction is the reduction of H^+ to H_2.
[b]With the exception of Be and Mg, all group 1 and group 2 metals also react with cold water to produce $H_2(g)$; the metal hydroxide is the other product.

1-4 CONCEPT ASSESSMENT

Disregarding the fact that the equations below are not balanced, is it likely that either represents a reaction that could possibly occur? Explain.

(a) $MnO_4^-(aq) + Cr_2O_7^{2-}(aq) + H^+(aq) \longrightarrow MnO_2(s) + Cr^{3+}(aq) + H_2O(l)$

(b) $Cl_2(g) + OH^-(aq) \longrightarrow Cl^-(aq) + ClO_3^-(aq) + H_2O(l)$

1-5 Balancing Oxidation–Reduction Equations

▶ *Half-reaction* or *half-equation*, which is it? *Reaction* refers to the actual process. An *equation* is a notation we write out to indicate the formulas of the reactants and products, and their mole relationships. Many chemists refer to what we balance here as half-reactions but half-equation is more proper.

In a chemical reaction, atoms are neither created nor lost; they are simply rearranged. In a redox reaction, we have additional considerations. Electrons are transferred from one substance to another and so we must keep track of electrons and the charge that these electrons carry. Therefore, in balancing the chemical equation for a redox reaction, we focus equally on three factors: (1) the number of atoms of each type, (2) the number of electrons transferred, and (3) the total charges on reactants and products. We should point out, however, that if we balance the equation with respect to the number of atoms and the number of electrons transferred, then the equation is automatically balanced with respect to the total charges.

Because it is very challenging to deal with all three of these factors simultaneously, only a small proportion of oxidation–reduction equations can be balanced by simple inspection. To make this point clear, consider the following reactions, each of which appears to be balanced. The reactions are balanced with respect to the number of atoms of each type and the total charges on reactants and products, but not with respect to the number of electrons transferred.

▶ For brevity, the physical forms of reactants and products are not included in these equations. For all ions, as well as H_2O_2, the physical form is "(aq)." Of course, the physical forms of oxygen and water are O_2(g) and H_2O(l).

$$2\,MnO_4^- + H_2O_2 + 6\,H^+ \longrightarrow 2\,Mn^{2+} + 3\,O_2 + 4\,H_2O \quad \textbf{(1.19)}$$

$$2\,MnO_4^- + 3\,H_2O_2 + 6\,H^+ \longrightarrow 2\,Mn^{2+} + 4\,O_2 + 6\,H_2O \quad \textbf{(1.20)}$$

$$2\,MnO_4^- + 5\,H_2O_2 + 6\,H^+ \longrightarrow 2\,Mn^{2+} + 5\,O_2 + 8\,H_2O \quad \textbf{(1.21)}$$

$$2\,MnO_4^- + 7\,H_2O_2 + 6\,H^+ \longrightarrow 2\,Mn^{2+} + 6\,O_2 + 10\,H_2O \quad \textbf{(1.22)}$$

These are just a few of the "balanced" chemical equations we can write for the reaction. However, only one, equation (1.21), is properly balanced because it is the only one that is balanced with respect to the number of electrons transferred.

To balance the chemical equation for a redox reaction, we need to make use of a systematic approach that considers each of the relevant factors in turn. Although several methods are available, we emphasize one that focuses first on balancing separate half-equations and then on combining the two half-equations to obtain the overall chemical equation. The method is summarized below. An alternative method is described in Exercise 98.

The Half-Equation Method

The basic steps in this method of balancing a redox equation are as follows:

- Write and balance separate half-equations for oxidation and reduction.
- Adjust coefficients in the two half-equations so that the same number of electrons appear in each half-equation.
- Add together the two half-equations (canceling out electrons) to obtain the balanced overall equation.

TABLE 1.5 Balancing Equations for Redox Reactions in Acidic Aqueous Solutions by the Half-Equation Method: A Summary

- Write the equations for the oxidation and reduction half-reactions.
- In each half-equation
  (1) Balance atoms of all the elements except H and O
  (2) Balance oxygen by using H_2O
  (3) Balance hydrogen by using H^+
  (4) Balance charge by using electrons
- If necessary, equalize the number of electrons in the oxidation and reduction half-equations by multiplying one or both half-equations by appropriate integers.
- Add the half-equations, then cancel species common to both sides of the overall equation.
- Check that both numbers of atoms and charges balance.

This first step in this method actually involves several steps. A detailed description of the method is given in Table 1.5. The method is appropriate for reactions that occur in an acidic solution. Because an acidic solution contains an excess of H^+ ions, the method uses H^+ ions in balancing the half-equations.

EXAMPLE 1-6 Balancing the Equation for a Redox Reaction in an Acidic Solution

The reaction described by expression (1.23) below is used to determine the sulfite ion concentration present in wastewater from a papermaking plant. Use the half-equation method to obtain a balanced equation for this reaction in an acidic solution.

$$SO_3^{2-}(aq) + MnO_4^-(aq) \longrightarrow SO_4^{2-}(aq) + Mn^{2+}(aq) \quad \textbf{(1.23)}$$

Analyze

The reaction occurs in acidic aqueous solution. We can use the method summarized in Table 1.5 to balance it.

Solve

The O.S. of sulfur increases from +4 in SO_3^{2-} to +6 in SO_4^{2-}. The O.S. of Mn decreases from +7 in MnO_4^- to +2 in Mn^{2+}. Thus, SO_3^{2-} is oxidized and MnO_4^- is reduced.

Step 1. *Write skeleton half-equations based on the species undergoing oxidation and reduction.* The half-equations are

$$SO_3^{2-}(aq) \longrightarrow SO_4^{2-}(aq)$$
$$MnO_4^-(aq) \longrightarrow Mn^{2+}(aq)$$

Step 2. *Balance each half-equation for numbers of atoms, in this order:*

- atoms other than H and O
- O atoms, by adding H_2O with the appropriate coefficient
- H atoms, by adding H^+ with the appropriate coefficient

The other atoms (S and Mn) are already balanced in the half-equations. To balance O atoms, we add one H_2O molecule to the left side of the first half-equation and four to the right side of the second.

$$SO_3^{2-}(aq) + H_2O(l) \longrightarrow SO_4^{2-}(aq)$$
$$MnO_4^-(aq) \longrightarrow Mn^{2+}(aq) + 4\,H_2O(l)$$

To balance H atoms, we add two H^+ ions to the right side of the first half-equation and eight to the left side of the second.

$$SO_3^{2-}(aq) + H_2O(l) \longrightarrow SO_4^{2-}(aq) + 2\,H^+(aq)$$
$$MnO_4^-(aq) + 8\,H^+(aq) \longrightarrow Mn^{2+}(aq) + 4\,H_2O(l)$$

(continued)

Step 3. *Balance each half-equation for electric charge.* Add the number of electrons necessary to get the same electric charge on both sides of each half-equation. By doing this, you will see that the half-equation in which electrons appear on the right side is the *oxidation half-equation*. The other half-equation, with electrons on the left side, is the *reduction half-equation.*

Oxidation: $SO_3^{2-}(aq) + H_2O(l) \longrightarrow SO_4^{2-}(aq) + 2\,H^+(aq) + 2\,e^-$
(net charge on each side, −2)

Reduction: $MnO_4^-(aq) + 8\,H^+(aq) + 5\,e^- \longrightarrow Mn^{2+}(aq) + 4\,H_2O(l)$
(net charge on each side, +2)

Step 4. *Obtain the overall redox equation by combining the half-equations.* Multiply the oxidation half-equation by 5 and the reduction half-equation by 2. This results in 10 e⁻ on each side of the overall equation. These terms cancel out. *Electrons must not appear in the final equation.*

Overall:

$$5\,SO_3^{2-}(aq) + 5\,H_2O(l) \longrightarrow 5\,SO_4^{2-}(aq) + 10\,H^+(aq) + \cancel{10\,e^-}$$
$$2\,MnO_4^-(aq) + 16\,H^+(aq) + \cancel{10\,e^-} \longrightarrow 2\,Mn^{2+}(aq) + 8\,H_2O(l)$$
$$5\,SO_3^{2-}(aq) + 2\,MnO_4^-(aq) + 5\,H_2O(l) + 16\,H^+(aq) \longrightarrow 5\,SO_4^{2-}(aq) + 2\,Mn^{2+}(aq) + 8\,H_2O(l) + 10\,H^+(aq)$$

Step 5. *Simplify.* The overall equation should not contain the same species on both sides. Subtract 5 H_2O from each side of the equation in step 4. This leaves 3 H_2O on the right. Also subtract 10 H^+ from each side, leaving 6 H^+ on the left.

$$5\,SO_3^{2-}(aq) + 2\,MnO_4^-(aq) + 6\,H^+(aq) \longrightarrow 5\,SO_4^{2-}(aq) + 2\,Mn^{2+}(aq) + 3\,H_2O(l)$$

Step 6. *Verify.* Check the overall equation to ensure that it is balanced both for numbers of atoms and electric charge. For example, show that in the balanced equation from step 5, the net charge on each side of the equation is −6: (5 × 2−) + (2 × 1−) + (6 × 1+) = (5 × 2−) + (2 × 2+) = −6.

Assess

The final check completed in step 6 gives us confidence that our result is correct. This is an important step; always take the time to complete it. It is also worth pointing out that, in this example, there was only one atom per formula that was oxidized or reduced. (Refer to the skeleton half-equations given in step 1.) Many students have difficulty balancing half-equations in which more than one atom per formula is oxidized or reduced, as is the case when $Cr_2O_7^{2-}$ is reduced to Cr^{3+}. Had we used $Cr_2O_7^{2-}$ instead of MnO_4^- in equation (1.23), the balanced chemical equation for the reaction would have been $3\,SO_3^{2-} + Cr_2O_7^{2-} + 8\,H^+ \rightarrow 3\,SO_4^{2-} + 2\,Cr^{3+} + 4\,H_2O$.

PRACTICE EXAMPLE A: Balance the equation for this reaction in acidic solution.

$$Fe^{2+}(aq) + MnO_4^-(aq) \longrightarrow Fe^{3+}(aq) + Mn^{2+}(aq)$$

PRACTICE EXAMPLE B: Balance the equation for this reaction in acidic solution.

$$UO^{2+}(aq) + Cr_2O_7^{2-}(aq) \longrightarrow UO_2^{2+}(aq) + Cr^{3+}(aq)$$

Balancing Redox Equations in a Basic Solution

To balance equations for redox reactions in a basic solution, a step or two must be added to the procedure used in Example 1-6. The problem is that in basic solution, OH^-, not H^+, must appear in the final balanced equation. (Recall that, in basic solutions, OH^- ions are present in excess.) Because both OH^- and H_2O contain H and O atoms, at times it is hard to decide on which side of the half-equations to put each one. One simple approach is to treat the reaction as though it were occurring in an acidic solution, and balance it as in Example 1-6. Then, add to each side of the overall redox equation a number of OH^- ions equal to the number of H^+ ions. Where H^+ and OH^- appear on the same side of the equation, combine them to produce H_2O molecules. If H_2O now appears on both sides of the equation, subtract the same number of H_2O molecules from each side, leaving a remainder of H_2O on just one side. This method is illustrated in Example 1-7. For ready reference, the procedure is summarized in Table 1.6.

EXAMPLE 1-7 Balancing the Equation for a Redox Reaction in Basic Solution

Balance the equation for the reaction in which cyanide ion is oxidized to cyanate ion by permanganate ion in a basic solution, and the permanganate is itself reduced to $MnO_2(s)$.

$$MnO_4^-(aq) + CN^-(aq) \longrightarrow MnO_2(s) + OCN^-(aq) \quad \textbf{(1.24)}$$

Analyze

The reaction occurs in basic solution. We can balance it by using the method described in Table 1.6 on the next page. The half-reactions and the overall reaction are initially treated as though they were occurring in an acidic solution and, finally, the overall equation is adjusted to a basic solution.

Solve

Step 1. *Write half-equations for the oxidation and reduction half-reactions, and balance them for Mn, C, and N atoms.*

$$MnO_4^-(aq) \longrightarrow MnO_2(s)$$
$$CN^-(aq) \longrightarrow OCN^-(aq)$$

Step 2. *Balance the half-equations for O and H atoms. Add H_2O and/or H^+ as required.* In the MnO_4^- half-equation, there are four O's on the left and two on the right. Adding 2 H_2O balances the O's on the right. Since there are now four H's on the right, it is necessary to add 4 H^+ on the left side to balance them. In the CN^- half-equation, there is one O on the right but none on the left, so H_2O must be added to the left side and 2 H^+ to the right.

$$MnO_4^-(aq) + 4\,H^+(aq) \longrightarrow MnO_2(s) + 2\,H_2O(l)$$
$$CN^-(aq) + H_2O(l) \longrightarrow OCN^-(aq) + 2\,H^+(aq)$$

Step 3. *Balance the half-equations for electric charge by adding the appropriate numbers of electrons.*

Reduction: $MnO_4^-(aq) + 4\,H^+(aq) + 3\,e^- \longrightarrow MnO_2(s) + 2\,H_2O(l)$

Oxidation: $CN^-(aq) + H_2O(l) \longrightarrow OCN^-(aq) + 2\,H^+(aq) + 2\,e^-$

Step 4. *Combine the half-equations to obtain an overall redox equation.* Multiply the reduction half-equation by two and the oxidation half-equation by three to obtain the common multiple $6\,e^-$ in each half-equation. Make the appropriate cancellations of H^+ and H_2O.

$$2\,MnO_4^-(aq) + 8\,H^+(aq) + \cancel{6e^-} \longrightarrow 2\,MnO_2(s) + 4\,H_2O(l)$$
$$3\,CN^-(aq) + 3\,H_2O(l) \longrightarrow 3\,OCN^-(aq) + 6\,H^+(aq) + \cancel{6e^-}$$

Overall: $2\,MnO_4^-(aq) + 3\,CN^-(aq) + 2\,H^+(aq) \longrightarrow 2\,MnO_2(s) + 3\,OCN^-(aq) + H_2O(l)$

Step 5. *Change from an acidic to a basic medium by adding $2\,OH^-$ to both sides of the overall equation; combine $2\,H^+$ and $2\,OH^-$ to form $2\,H_2O$, and simplify.*

$$2\,MnO_4^-(aq) + 3\,CN^-(aq) + 2\,H^+(aq) + 2\,OH^-(aq) \longrightarrow 2\,MnO_2(s) + 3\,OCN^-(aq) + H_2O(l) + 2\,OH^-(aq)$$

$$2\,MnO_4^-(aq) + 3\,CN^-(aq) + 2\,H_2O(l) \longrightarrow 2\,MnO_2(s) + 3\,OCN^-(aq) + H_2O(l) + 2\,OH^-(aq)$$

Subtract one H_2O molecule from each side to obtain the overall balanced redox equation for reaction (1.24).

$$2\,MnO_4^-(aq) + 3\,CN^-(aq) + H_2O(l) \longrightarrow 2\,MnO_2(s) + 3\,OCN^-(aq) + 2\,OH^-(aq)$$

Step 6. *Verify.* Check the final overall equation to ensure that it is balanced both for number of atoms and for electric charge. For example, show that in the balanced equation from step 5, the net charge on each side of the equation is -5.

Assess

We can use the rules for assigning oxidation states to deduce that manganese is reduced from +7 in MnO_4^- to +4 in MnO_2. We conclude that the other substance, CN^-, is oxidized. (The rules do not allow us to assign oxidation states to C and N in CN^- or CNO^-.) Even though we cannot identify the oxidation states of C or N, we could still balance the equation for the reaction. That is one advantage of the methods we presented in Tables 1-5 and 1-6.

(continued)

PRACTICE EXAMPLE A: Balance the equation for this reaction in basic solution.

$$S(s) + OCl^-(aq) \longrightarrow SO_3^{2-}(aq) + Cl^-(aq)$$

PRACTICE EXAMPLE B: Balance the equation for this reaction in basic solution.

$$MnO_4^-(aq) + SO_3^{2-}(aq) \longrightarrow MnO_2(s) + SO_4^{2-}(aq)$$

▶ As an alternative method for half-equations in basic solutions, add *two* OH^- for every O required to the O-deficient side, and add *one* H_2O to the other side (the net effect is adding one O to the O-deficient side). Then add *one* H_2O for every H required to the H-deficient side, and add *one* OH^- to the other side (the net effect is adding one H to the H-deficient side).

TABLE 1.6 Balancing Equations for Redox Reactions in Basic Aqueous Solutions by the Half-Equation Method: A Summary

- Balance the equation as if the reaction were occurring in acidic medium by using the method for acidic aqueous solutions summarized in Table 1-5.
- Add a number of OH^- ions equal to the number of H^+ ions to both sides of the overall equation.
- On the side of the overall equation containing both H^+ and OH^- ions, combine them to form H_2O molecules. If H_2O molecules now appear on both sides of the overall equation, cancel the same number from each side, leaving a remainder of H_2O on just one side.
- Check that both numbers of atoms and charges balance.

Disproportionation Reactions

In some oxidation–reduction reactions, called **disproportionation reactions**, the same substance is both oxidized and reduced. An example is the decomposition of hydrogen peroxide, H_2O_2, into H_2O and O_2:

$$2\,H_2O_2(aq) \longrightarrow 2\,H_2O(l) + O_2(g) \qquad \textbf{(1.25)}$$

In reaction (1.25), the oxidation state of oxygen changes from -1 in H_2O_2 to -2 in H_2O (a reduction) and to 0 in $O_2(g)$ (an oxidation). H_2O_2 is both oxidized and reduced. Reaction (1.25) produces $O_2(g)$, which bubbles out of the solution. (See Figure 1-14.)

Another example is the disproportionation of $S_2O_3^{2-}$ in acid solution:

$$S_2O_3^{2-}(aq) + 2\,H^+(aq) \longrightarrow S(s) + SO_2(g) + H_2O(l) \qquad \textbf{(1.26)}$$

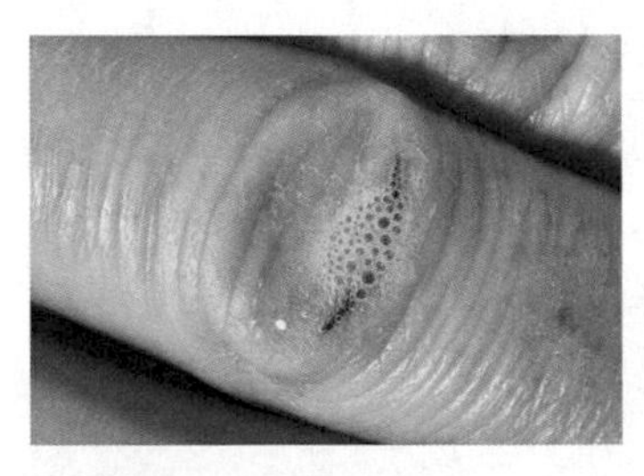

▲ FIGURE 1-14
Antiseptic action of hydrogen peroxide solution
Dilute aqueous solutions of hydrogen peroxide (usually 3% hydrogen peroxide by mass) were once commonly used to clean minor cuts and scrapes. A solution of hydrogen peroxide bubbles when poured over a cut because of the production of gaseous oxygen.

The oxidation states of S are +2 in $S_2O_3^{2-}$, 0 in S, and +4 in SO_2. Thus, $S_2O_3^{2-}$ is simultaneously oxidized and reduced. Solutions of sodium thiosulfate ($Na_2S_2O_3$) are often used in the laboratory in redox reactions, and stock solutions of $Na_2S_2O_3$ sometimes develop small deposits of sulfur, a pale yellow solid, over time.

The same substance appears on the left side in each half-equation for a disproportionation reaction. The balanced half-equations and overall equation for reaction (1.26) are given below.

Oxidation: $S_2O_3^{2-}(aq) + H_2O(l) \longrightarrow 2\,SO_2(g) + 2\,H^+(aq) + \cancel{4e^-}$

Reduction: $S_2O_3^{2-}(aq) + 6\,H^+(aq) + \cancel{4e^-} \longrightarrow 2\,S(s) + 3\,H_2O(l)$

$2\,S_2O_3^{2-}(aq) + 4\,H^+(aq) \longrightarrow 2\,S(s) + 2\,SO_2(g) + 2\,H_2O(l)$

Overall: $S_2O_3^{2-}(aq) + 2\,H^+(aq) \longrightarrow S(s) + SO_2(g) + H_2O(l)$

1-5 CONCEPT ASSESSMENT

Is it possible for two different reactants in a redox reaction to yield a single product? Explain.

1-2 ARE YOU WONDERING...

How to balance the equation for a redox reaction that occurs in a medium other than an aqueous solution?

An example of such a reaction is the oxidation of $NH_3(g)$ to $NO(g)$, the first step in the commercial production of nitric acid.

$$NH_3(g) + O_2(g) \longrightarrow NO(g) + H_2O(g)$$

Some people prefer a method called the *oxidation-state change method (see below)* for reactions of this type, but the half-equation method works just as well. All that is needed is to treat the reaction as if it were occurring in an aqueous acidic solution; H^+ should appear as both a reactant and a product and cancel out in the overall equation, as seen below.

Oxidation: $4\{NH_3 + H_2O \longrightarrow NO + 5\,H^+ + 5\,e^-\}$

Reduction: $5\{O_2 + 4\,H^+ + 4\,e^- \longrightarrow 2\,H_2O\}$

Overall: $4\,NH_3 + 5\,O_2 \longrightarrow 4\,NO + 6\,H_2O$

Oxidation-state change method

In this method, changes in oxidation states are identified. That of nitrogen increases from -3 in NH_3 to $+2$ in NO, corresponding to a "loss" of five electrons per N atom. That of oxygen decreases from 0 in O_2 to -2 in NO and H_2O, corresponding to a "gain" of two electrons per O atom. The proportion of N to O atoms must be 2 N (loss of 10 e^-) to 5 O (gain of 10 e^-).

$$2\,NH_3 + \frac{5}{2}O_2 \longrightarrow 2\,NO + 3\,H_2O \quad \text{or} \quad 4\,NH_3 + 5\,O_2 \longrightarrow 4\,NO + 6\,H_2O$$

1-6 Oxidizing and Reducing Agents

Chemists frequently use the terms *oxidizing agent* and *reducing agent* to describe certain of the reactants in redox reactions, as in statements like "fluorine gas is a powerful oxidizing agent," or "calcium metal is a good reducing agent." Let us briefly consider the meaning of these terms.

In a redox reaction, the substance that makes it possible for some other substance to be oxidized is called the **oxidizing agent**, or **oxidant**. In doing so, the oxidizing agent is itself reduced. Similarly, the substance that causes some other substance to be reduced is called the **reducing agent**, or **reductant**. In the reaction, the reducing agent is itself oxidized. Or, stated in other ways,

An oxidizing agent (oxidant)

- causes another substance to be oxidized
- contains an element whose oxidation state *decreases* in a redox reaction
- *gains* electrons (electrons are found on the left side of its half-equation)
- is reduced

A reducing agent (reductant)

- causes another substance to be reduced
- contains an element whose oxidation state *increases* in a redox reaction
- *loses* electrons (electrons are found on the right side of its half-equation)
- is oxidized

In general, a substance with an element in one of its highest possible oxidation states is an oxidizing agent. If the element is in one of its lowest possible oxidation states, the substance is a reducing agent.

Species	O.S.
NO_3^-	+5
N_2O_4	+4
NO_2^-	+3
NO	+2
N_2O	+1
N_2	0
NH_2OH	−1
N_2H_4	−2
NH_3	−3

This species cannot be oxidized further. (NO_3^-)

This species cannot be reduced further. (NH_3)

▶ FIGURE 1-15
Oxidation states of nitrogen: Identifying oxidizing and reducing agents
In NO_3^- and N_2O_4, nitrogen is in one of its highest possible oxidation states (O.S). These species are usually oxidizing agents in redox reactions. In N_2H_4 and NH_3, nitrogen is in one of its lowest oxidation states. These species are usually reducing agents.

Figure 1-15 shows the range of oxidation states of nitrogen and the species to which they correspond. The oxidation state of the nitrogen in dinitrogen tetroxide (N_2O_4) is nearly the maximum value attainable, and hence N_2O_4 is generally an oxidizing agent. Conversely, the nitrogen atom in hydrazine (N_2H_4) is in nearly the lowest oxidation state, and hence hydrazine is generally a reducing agent. When these two liquid compounds are mixed, a vigorous reaction takes place:

$$N_2O_4(l) + 2\,N_2H_4(l) \longrightarrow 3\,N_2(g) + 4\,H_2O(g)$$

In this reaction, N_2O_4 is the oxidizing agent and N_2H_4 is the reducing agent. This reaction releases so much energy that it is used in some rocket propulsion systems.

Certain substances in which the oxidation state of an element is between its highest and lowest possible values may act as oxidizing agents in some instances and reducing agents in others. For example, in the reaction of hydrazine with hydrogen to produce ammonia, hydrazine acts as an oxidizing agent.

$$N_2H_4(l) + H_2(g) \longrightarrow 2\,NH_3(g)$$

Permanganate ion, MnO_4^-, is a versatile oxidizing agent that has many uses in the chemical laboratory. In the next section, we describe its use in the quantitative analysis of iron—that is, the determination of the exact (quantitative) amount of iron in an iron-containing material. Ozone, $O_3(g)$, a triatomic form of oxygen, is an oxidizing agent used in water purification, as in the oxidation of the organic compound phenol, C_6H_5OH.

$$C_6H_5OH(aq) + 14\,O_3(g) \longrightarrow 6\,CO_2(g) + 3\,H_2O(l) + 14\,O_2(g)$$

▲ FIGURE 1-16
Bleaching action of NaOCl(aq)
A red cloth becomes white when immersed in NaOCl(aq), which oxidizes the red pigment to colorless products.

Aqueous sodium hypochlorite, NaOCl(aq), is a powerful oxidizing agent. It is the active ingredient in many liquid chlorine bleaches. The bleaching action of NaOCl(aq) is associated with the reduction of the OCl^- ion to Cl^-; the electrons required for the reduction come from colored compounds in stains. The bleaching action of NaOCl(aq) is demonstrated in Figure 1-16.

Thiosulfate ion, $S_2O_3^{2-}$, is an important reducing agent. One of its industrial uses is as an antichlor to destroy residual chlorine from the bleaching of fibers.

$$S_2O_3^{2-}(aq) + 4\,Cl_2(aq) + 5\,H_2O(l) \longrightarrow 2\,HSO_4^-(aq) + 8\,H^+(aq) + 8\,Cl^-(aq)$$

Oxidizing and reducing agents also play important roles in biological systems—in photosynthesis (using solar energy to synthesize glucose), metabolism (oxidizing glucose), and the transport of oxygen.

EXAMPLE 1-8 Identifying Oxidizing and Reducing Agents

Hydrogen peroxide, H_2O_2, is a versatile chemical. Its uses include bleaching wood pulp and fabrics and substituting for chlorine in water purification. One reason for its versatility is that it can be either an oxidizing or a reducing agent. For the following reactions, identify whether hydrogen peroxide is an oxidizing or reducing agent.

(a) $H_2O_2(aq) + 2\,Fe^{2+}(aq) + 2\,H^+(aq) \longrightarrow 2\,H_2O(l) + 2\,Fe^{3+}(aq)$
(b) $5\,H_2O_2(aq) + 2\,MnO_4^-(aq) + 6\,H^+(aq) \longrightarrow 8\,H_2O(l) + 2\,Mn^{2+}(aq) + 5\,O_2(g)$

Analyze

Before we can identify the oxidizing and reducing agents, we must first assign oxidation states, and then identify which substance is being oxidized and which substance is being reduced. The oxidizing agent causes another substance to be oxidized. The reducing agent causes another substance to be reduced.

Solve

(a) Fe^{2+} is oxidized to Fe^{3+} and because H_2O_2 makes this possible, it is an oxidizing agent. Viewed another way, we see that the oxidation state of oxygen in H_2O_2 is -1. In H_2O, it is -2. Hydrogen peroxide is reduced and thereby acts as an oxidizing agent.

(b) MnO_4^- is reduced to Mn^{2+}, and H_2O_2 makes this possible. In this situation, hydrogen peroxide is a reducing agent. Or, the oxidation state of oxygen increases from -1 in H_2O_2 to 0 in O_2. Hydrogen peroxide is oxidized and thereby acts as a reducing agent.

Assess

The versatility of H_2O_2 lies in its ability to act as an oxidizing agent and a reducing agent. When H_2O_2 acts as an oxidizing agent, it is reduced to H_2O, in an acidic solution, as was the case in part **(a)**, or to OH^- in basic solution. When it acts as a reducing agent, it is oxidized to $O_2(g)$, as was the case in part **(b)**.

PRACTICE EXAMPLE A: Is $H_2(g)$ an oxidizing or reducing agent in this reaction? Explain.

$$2\,NO_2(g) + 7\,H_2(g) \longrightarrow 2\,NH_3(g) + 4\,H_2O(g)$$

PRACTICE EXAMPLE B: Identify the oxidizing agent and the reducing agent in the reaction.

$$4\,Au(s) + 8\,CN^-(aq) + O_2(g) + 2\,H_2O(l) \longrightarrow 4[Au(CN)_2]^-(aq) + 4\,OH^-(aq)$$

1-6 CONCEPT ASSESSMENT

A newspaper account of an accidental spill of hydrochloric acid in an area where sodium hydroxide solution was also stored spoke of the potential hazardous release of chlorine gas if the two solutions should come into contact. Was this an accurate accounting of the hazard involved? Explain.

1-7 Stoichiometry of Reactions in Aqueous Solutions: Titrations

If our objective is to obtain the maximum yield of a product at the lowest cost, we would generally choose the most expensive reactant as the limiting reactant and use excess amounts of the other reactants. This is the case in most precipitation reactions. In some instances, as in determining the concentration of a solution, we may not be interested in the products of a reaction but only in the relationship between two reactants. Then we have to carry out the reaction in such a way that neither reactant is in excess. A method that has long been used for doing this is known as *titration*. The glassware typically used in a titration is shown in Figure 1-17.

A solution of one reactant is placed in a small beaker or flask. Another reactant, also in solution and commonly referred to as titrant, is in a *buret*, a long,

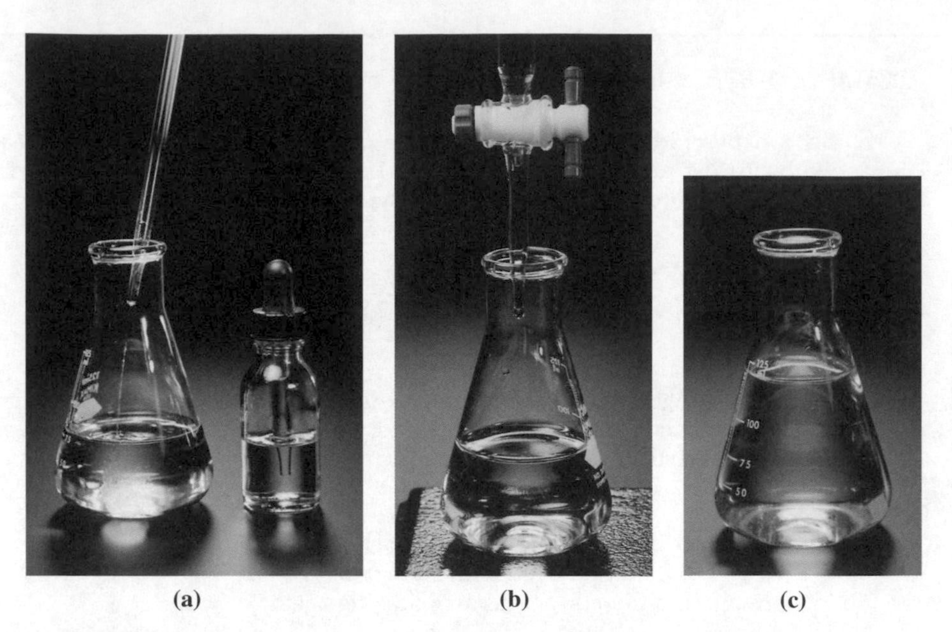

(a) (b) (c)

▲ FIGURE 1-17
An acid–base titration—Example 1-9 illustrated
(a) A 5.00 mL sample of vinegar, a small quantity of water, and a few drops of phenolphthalein indicator are added to a flask. **(b)** 0.1000 M NaOH from a previously filled buret is slowly added. **(c)** As long as the acid is in excess, the solution in the flask remains colorless. When the acid has been neutralized, an additional drop of NaOH(aq) causes the solution to become slightly basic. The phenolphthalein indicator turns a light pink. The first lasting appearance of the pink color is taken to be the equivalence point of the titration.

graduated tube equipped with a stopcock valve. The second solution is slowly added to the first by manipulating the stopcock. **Titration** is a reaction carried out by the carefully controlled addition of one solution to another. The trick is to stop the titration at the point where both reactants have reacted completely, a condition called the **equivalence point** of the titration. Key to every titration is that at the equivalence point, the two reactants have combined in stoichiometric proportions; both have been consumed, and neither remains in excess.

▶ The key to a successful acid–base titration is in selecting the right indicator. We learn how to do this when we consider theoretical aspects of titration in Chapter 9.

In modern chemical laboratories, appropriate measuring instruments are used to signal when the equivalence point is reached. Still widely used, though, is a technique in which a very small quantity of a substance added to the reaction mixture changes color at or very near the equivalence point. Such substances are called **indicators**. Figure 1-17 illustrates the neutralization of an acid by a base by the titration technique. Calculations that use titration data are illustrated in Example 1-9.

Suppose we need a $KMnO_4$(aq) solution of exactly known molarity, close to 0.020 M. We cannot prepare this solution by weighing out the required amount of $KMnO_4$(s) and dissolving it in water. The solid is not pure, and its actual purity (that is, the mass percent $KMnO_4$) is *not known*. Conversely, we can obtain iron wire in essentially pure form and allow the wire to react with an acid to yield Fe^{2+}(aq). Fe^{2+}(aq) is oxidized to Fe^{3+}(aq) by $KMnO_4$(aq) in an acidic solution. By determining the volume of $KMnO_4$(aq) required to oxidize a known quantity of Fe^{2+}(aq), we can calculate the exact molarity of the $KMnO_4$(aq). This procedure, which determines the exact molarity of a solution, is called **standardization of a solution**. It is illustrated in Example 1-10 and Figure 1-18.

▶ *Standardize* means determine the concentration of a solution, usually to three or four significant figures. It is not so important that the concentration be a round number (as 0.1000 vs. 0.1035 M), but rather that the concentration be accurately known.

EXAMPLE 1-9 Using Titration Data to Establish the Concentrations of Acids and Bases

Vinegar is a dilute aqueous solution of acetic acid produced by the bacterial fermentation of apple cider, wine, or other carbohydrate material. The legal minimum acetic acid content of vinegar is 4% by mass. A 5.00 mL sample of a particular vinegar is titrated with 38.08 mL of 0.1000 M NaOH. Does this sample exceed the minimum limit? (Vinegar has a density of about 1.01 g/mL.)

Analyze

Acetic acid, CH_3COOH, is a weak acid and NaOH is a strong base. The reaction between CH_3COOH and NaOH is an acid–base neutralization reaction. We start by writing a balanced chemical equation for the reaction. We must convert mL NaOH to CH_3COOH. The necessary conversions are as follows:

$$\text{mL NaOH} \longrightarrow \text{L NaOH} \longrightarrow \text{mol NaOH} \longrightarrow \text{mol } CH_3COOH \longrightarrow \text{g } CH_3COOH$$

Solve

The balanced chemical equation for the reaction is given below.

$$CH_3COOH(aq) + NaOH(aq) \longrightarrow NaCH_3COO(aq) + H_2O(l)$$

$$?\text{ g } HC_2H_3O_2 = 38.08\text{ mL} \times \frac{1\text{ L}}{1000\text{ mL}} \times \frac{0.1000\text{ mol NaOH}}{1\text{ L}}$$

$$\times \frac{1\text{ mol } CH_3COOH}{1\text{ mol NaOH}} \times \frac{60.05\text{ g } CH_3COOH}{1\text{ mol } CH_3COOH}$$

$$= 0.2287\text{ g } CH_3COOH$$

This mass of CH_3COOH is found in 5.00 mL of vinegar of density 1.01 g/mL. The percent mass of CH_3COOH is

$$\%\ CH_3COOH = \frac{0.2287\text{ g } CH_3COOH}{5.00\text{ mL vinegar}} \times \frac{1\text{ mL vinegar}}{1.01\text{ g vinegar}} \times 100\%$$

$$= 4.53\%\ CH_3COOH$$

The vinegar sample exceeds the legal minimum limit but only slightly. There is also a standard for the maximum amount of acetic acid allowed in vinegar. A vinegar producer might use this titration technique to ensure that the vinegar stays between these limits.

Assess

Such problems as this one involve many steps or conversions. Try to break the problem into simpler ones involving fewer steps or conversions. It may also help to remember that solving a stoichiometry problem involves three steps: (1) converting to moles, (2) converting between moles, and (3) converting from moles. Use molarities and molar masses to carry out volume–mole conversions and gram–mole conversions, respectively, and stoichiometric factors to carry out mole–mole conversions. The stoichiometric factors are constructed from a balanced chemical equation.

PRACTICE EXAMPLE A: A particular solution of NaOH is supposed to be approximately 0.100 M. To determine the exact molarity of the NaOH(aq), a 0.5000 g sample of $KHC_8H_4O_4$ is dissolved in water and titrated with 24.03 mL of the NaOH(aq). What is the actual molarity of the NaOH(aq)?

$$HC_8H_4O_4^-(aq) + OH^-(aq) \longrightarrow C_8H_4O_4^{2-}(aq) + H_2O(l)$$

PRACTICE EXAMPLE B: A 0.235 g sample of a solid that is 92.5% NaOH and 7.5% $Ca(OH)_2$, by mass, requires 45.6 mL of a HCl(aq) solution for its titration. What is the molarity of the HCl(aq)?

1-7 CONCEPT ASSESSMENT

A 10.00 mL sample of 0.311 M KOH is added to 31.10 mL of 0.100 M HCl. Is the resulting mixture acidic, basic, or exactly neutral? Explain.

(a) (b) (c)

▲ FIGURE 1-18
Standardizing a solution of an oxidizing agent through a redox titration—Example 1-10 illustrated
(a) The solution contains a known amount of Fe^{2+}, and the buret is filled with the intensely colored $KMnO_4(aq)$ to be standardized. **(b)** As it is added to the strongly acidic solution of $Fe^{2+}(aq)$, the $KMnO_4(aq)$ is immediately decolorized as a result of reaction (1.27). **(c)** When all the Fe^{2+} has been oxidized to Fe^{3+}, additional $KMnO_4(aq)$ has nothing left to oxidize and the solution turns a distinctive pink. Even a fraction of a drop of the $KMnO_4(aq)$ beyond the equivalence point is sufficient to cause this pink coloration.

EXAMPLE 1-10 Standardizing a Solution for Use in Redox Titrations

A piece of iron wire weighing 0.1568 g is converted to $Fe^{2+}(aq)$ and requires 26.24 mL of a $KMnO_4(aq)$ solution for its titration. What is the molarity of the $KMnO_4(aq)$?

$$5\,Fe^{2+}(aq) + MnO_4^-(aq) + 8\,H^+(aq) \longrightarrow 5\,Fe^{3+}(aq) + Mn^{2+}(aq) + 4\,H_2O(l) \qquad (1.27)$$

Analyze

The key to a titration calculation is that the amounts of two reactants consumed in the titration are stoichiometrically equivalent—neither reactant is in excess. We are given an amount of Fe (0.156 g) and must determine the number of moles of $KMnO_4$ in the 26.24 mL sample. The following conversions are required:

$$\text{g Fe} \longrightarrow \text{mol Fe} \longrightarrow \text{mol Fe}^{2+} \longrightarrow \text{mol MnO}_4^- \longrightarrow \text{mol KMnO}_4$$

The third conversion, from mol Fe^{2+} to mol MnO_4^-, requires a stoichiometric factor constructed from the coefficients in equation (1.27).

Solve

First, determine the amount (in moles) of $KMnO_4$ consumed in the titration.

$$? \text{ mol KMnO}_4 = 0.1568 \text{ g Fe} \times \frac{1 \text{ mol Fe}}{55.847 \text{ g Fe}} \times \frac{1 \text{ mol Fe}^{2+}}{1 \text{ mol Fe}} \times \frac{1 \text{ mol MnO}_4^-}{5 \text{ mol Fe}^{2+}} \times \frac{1 \text{ mol KMnO}_4}{1 \text{ mol MnO}_4^-}$$
$$= 5.615 \times 10^{-4} \text{ mol KMnO}_4$$

The volume of solution containing the 5.615×10^{-4} mol $KMnO_4$ is 26.24 mL = 0.02624 L, which means that

$$\text{concn } KMnO_4 = \frac{5.615 \times 10^{-4} \text{ mol } KMnO_4}{0.02624 \text{ L}} = 0.02140 \text{ M } KMnO_4$$

Assess

For practical applications, such as for titrations, we use solutions with molarities that are neither very large nor very small. Typically, the molarities lie in the range 0.001 M to 0.1 M. If you calculate a molarity that is significantly larger than 0.1 M, or significantly smaller than 0.001 M, then you must carefully check your calculation for possible errors.

PRACTICE EXAMPLE A: A 0.376 g sample of an iron ore is dissolved in acid, and the iron reduced to $Fe^{2+}(aq)$ and then titrated with 41.25 mL of 0.02140 M $KMnO_4$. Determine the mass percent Fe in the iron ore. [*Hint:* Use equation (1.27).]

PRACTICE EXAMPLE B: Another substance that may be used to standardize $KMnO_4(aq)$ is sodium oxalate. If 0.2482 g $Na_2C_2O_4$ is dissolved in water and titrated with 23.68 mL $KMnO_4$, what is the molarity of the $KMnO_4(aq)$?

$$MnO_4^-(aq) + C_2O_4^{2-}(aq) + H^+(aq) \longrightarrow Mn^{2+}(aq) + H_2O(l) + CO_2(g) \quad \text{(not balanced)}$$

Summary

1-1 The Nature of Aqueous Solutions—Solutes in aqueous solution are characterized as **nonelectrolytes**, which do not produce ions, or **electrolytes**, which produce ions. **Weak electrolytes** dissociate to a limited extent, and **strong electrolytes** dissociate almost completely into ions. In addition to the molarity based on the solute as a whole, a solution's concentration can be stated in terms of the molarities of the individual solute species present—molecules and ions. Calculating ion concentrations in a strong electrolyte solution is easily done.

1-2 Precipitation Reactions—Some reactions in aqueous solution involve the combination of ions to yield a water-insoluble solid—a **precipitate**. Precipitation reactions are generally represented by **net ionic equations**, a form in which only the reacting ions and solid precipitates are shown, and **spectator ions** are deleted. Precipitation reactions usually can be predicted by using a few simple solubility guidelines (Table 1.1).

1-3 Acid–Base Reactions—According to the Arrhenius theory, a substance that ionizes to produce H^+ ions in aqueous solution is an **acid**. It is a **strong acid** (Table 1.2) if the ionization goes essentially to completion and a **weak acid** if the ionization is limited. Similarly, a **base** produces OH^- ions in aqueous solution and is either a **strong base** (Table 1.2) or a **weak base**, depending on the extent of the ionization. According to the Brønsted-Lowry theory, in an acid–base reaction, protons are transferred from the acid (the **proton donor**) to the base (the **proton acceptor**). In a typical acid–base, or **neutralization, reaction**, H^+ ions from the acid and OH^- ions from the base combine to form HOH (water). The other product of the reaction is an ionic compound, a **salt**. Some reactions in which gases are evolved can also be treated as acid–base reactions (Table 1.3).

1-4 Oxidation–Reduction Reactions: Some General Principles—In an **oxidation–reduction (redox) reaction** certain atoms undergo an increase in oxidation state, a process called **oxidation**. Other atoms undergo a decrease in oxidation state, or **reduction**. Another useful view of redox reactions is as the combination of separate **half-reactions** for the oxidation and the reduction.

1-5 Balancing Oxidation–Reduction Equations—An effective way to balance a redox equation is to break down the reaction into separate half-reactions, write and balance half-equations for these half-reactions, and recombine the balanced half-equations into an overall balanced equation (Table 1.5). A slight variation of this method is used for a reaction that occurs in a basic aqueous solution (Table 1.6). A redox reaction in which the same substance is both oxidized and reduced is called a **disproportionation reaction**.

1-6 Oxidizing and Reducing Agents—The **oxidizing agent (oxidant)** is the key reactant in an oxidation half-reaction and is *reduced* in the redox reaction. The **reducing agent (reductant)** is the key reactant in a reduction half-reaction and is *oxidized* in the redox reaction. Some substances act only as oxidizing agents; others, only as reducing agents. Many can act as either, depending on the reaction (Fig. 1-15).

1-7 Stoichiometry of Reactions in Aqueous Solutions: Titrations—A common laboratory technique applicable to precipitation, acid–base, and redox reactions is **titration**. The key point in a titration is the **equivalence point**, which is assessed with the aid of an **indicator**. Titration data can be used to establish a solution's molarity, called **standardization of a solution**, or to provide other information about the compositions of samples being analyzed.

Integrative Example

Sodium dithionite, $Na_2S_2O_4$, is an important reducing agent. One interesting use is the reduction of chromate ion to insoluble chromium(III) hydroxide by dithionite ion, $S_2O_4^{2-}$, in basic solution. Sulfite ion is another product. The chromate ion may be present in wastewater from a chromium-plating plant, for example. What mass of $Na_2S_2O_4$ is consumed in a reaction with 100.0 L of wastewater having $[CrO_4^{2-}] = 0.0148$ M?

◀ White solid sodium dithionite, $Na_2S_2O_4$, is added to a yellow solution of potassium chromate, $K_2CrO_4(aq)$ (left). A product of the reaction is gray-green chromium(III) hydroxide, $Cr(OH)_3(s)$ (right).

Analyze

The phrase "reduction of chromate" tells us that the reaction between CrO_4^{2-} and $S_2O_4^{2-}$ is a redox reaction. We must obtain a balanced chemical equation for the reaction by using the method summarized in Table 1.6, and then convert 100.0 L of wastewater into grams of $Na_2S_2O_4$. The necessary conversions are as follows:

$$100.0\text{ L wastewater} \longrightarrow \text{mol } CrO_4^{2-} \longrightarrow \text{mol } S_2O_4^{2-} \longrightarrow \text{mol } Na_2S_2O_4 \longrightarrow \text{g } Na_2S_2O_4$$

Solve

1. *Write an ionic expression representing the reaction.*

$$CrO_4^{2-}(aq) + S_2O_4^{2-}(aq) + OH^-(aq) \longrightarrow Cr(OH)_3(s) + SO_3^{2-}(aq)$$

2. *Balance the redox equation.* Begin by writing skeleton half-equations.

$$CrO_4^{2-} \longrightarrow Cr(OH)_3$$
$$S_2O_4^{2-} \longrightarrow SO_3^{2-}$$

Balance the half-equations for Cr, S, O, and H atoms as if the half-reactions occur in acidic solution.

$$CrO_4^{2-} + 5\,H^+ \longrightarrow Cr(OH)_3 + H_2O$$
$$S_2O_4^{2-} + 2\,H_2O \longrightarrow 2\,SO_3^{2-} + 4\,H^+$$

Balance the half-equations for charge, and label them as oxidation and reduction.

Oxidation: $S_2O_4^{2-} + 2\,H_2O \longrightarrow 2\,SO_3^{2-} + 4\,H^+ + 2\,e^-$

Reduction: $CrO_4^{2-} + 5\,H^+ + 3\,e^- \longrightarrow Cr(OH)_3 + H_2O$

Combine the half-equations into an overall equation.

$$3 \times [S_2O_4^{2-} + 2\,H_2O \longrightarrow 2\,SO_3^{2-} + 4\,H^+ + 2\,e^-]$$
$$2 \times [CrO_4^{2-} + 5\,H^+ + 3\,e^- \longrightarrow Cr(OH)_3 + H_2O]$$
$$3\,S_2O_4^{2-} + 2\,CrO_4^{2-} + 4\,H_2O \longrightarrow 6\,SO_3^{2-} + 2\,Cr(OH)_3 + 2\,H^+$$

3. *Change the conditions to basic solution.* Add 2 OH^- to each side of the equation for acidic solution, and combine 2 H^+ and 2 OH^- to form 2 H_2O on the right.

$$3\,S_2O_4^{2-} + 2\,CrO_4^{2-} + 4\,H_2O + 2\,OH^- \longrightarrow 6\,SO_3^{2-} + 2\,Cr(OH)_3 + 2\,H_2O$$

Subtract 2 H_2O from each side of the equation to obtain the final balanced equation.

$$3\,S_2O_4^{2-}(aq) + 2\,CrO_4^{2-}(aq) + 2\,H_2O(l) + 2\,OH^-(aq) \longrightarrow 6\,SO_3^{2-}(aq) + 2\,Cr(OH)_3(s)$$

4. *Complete the stoichiometric calculation.* The conversion pathway is
100.0 L waste water $\longrightarrow$ mol CrO_4^{2-} $\longrightarrow$
mol $S_2O_4^{2-}$ $\longrightarrow$ mol $Na_2S_2O_4$ $\longrightarrow$ g $Na_2S_2O_4$.

$$? \text{ g } Na_2S_2O_4 = 100.0 \text{ L} \times \frac{0.0148 \text{ mol } CrO_4^{2-}}{1 \text{ L}} \times \frac{3 \text{ mol } S_2O_4^{2-}}{2 \text{ mol } CrO_4^{2-}} \times \frac{1 \text{ mol } Na_2S_2O_4}{1 \text{ mol } S_2O_4^{2-}} \times \frac{174.1 \text{ g } Na_2S_2O_4}{1 \text{ mol } Na_2S_2O_4} = 387 \text{ g } Na_2S_2O_4$$

Assess

In solving this problem the major effort was to balance a redox equation for a reaction under basic conditions. This allowed us to find the molar relationship between dithionite and chromate ions. The remainder of the problem was a stoichiometry calculation for a reaction in solution. A quick check of the final result involves (1) ensuring that the redox equation is balanced, and (2) noting that the number of moles of CrO_4^{2-} is about 1.5 (i.e., 100×0.0148), that the number of moles of $S_2O_4^{2-}$ is about 2.25 (i.e., $1.5 \times 3/2$), and that the mass of $Na_2S_2O_4$ is somewhat more than 350 (i.e., 2.25×175).

PRACTICE EXAMPLE A: The amount of potassium chlorate, $KClO_3$, in a 0.1432 g sample was determined as follows. The sample was dissolved in 50.00 mL of 0.09101 M $Fe(NO_3)_2$ and the solution was acidified. The excess Fe^{2+} was back-titrated with 12.59 mL of 0.08362 M $Ce(NO_3)_4$ solution. What is the percentage by mass of $KClO_3$ in the sample? Chemical equations for the reactions involved are as follows:
$ClO_3^-(aq) + Fe^{2+}(aq) \rightarrow Cl^-(aq) + Fe^{3+}(aq)$ (not balanced) and $Fe^{2+}(aq) + Ce^{4+}(aq) \rightarrow Fe^{3+}(aq) + Ce^{3+}(aq)$.

PRACTICE EXAMPLE B: The amount of arsenic, As, in a 7.25 g sample was determined by converting all the arsenic in the sample to arsenous acid (H_3AsO_3), and then titrating H_3AsO_3 with 23.77 mL of 0.02144 M $KMnO_4$. What is the percentage by mass of As in the sample? The unbalanced chemical equation for the titration reaction is
$H_3AsO_3(aq) + MnO_4^-(aq) \rightarrow H_3AsO_4(aq) + Mn^{2+}(aq)$.

Exercises

Strong Electrolytes, Weak Electrolytes, and Nonelectrolytes

1. Using information from this chapter, indicate whether each of the following substances in aqueous solution is a nonelectrolyte, weak electrolyte, or strong electrolyte. **(a)** HC_6H_5O; **(b)** Li_2SO_4; **(c)** MgI_2; **(d)** $(CH_3CH_2)_2O$; **(e)** $Sr(OH)_2$.
2. Select the **(a)** best and **(b)** poorest electrical conductors from the following solutions, and explain the reason for your choices: 0.10 M NH_3; 0.10 M NaCl; 0.10 M CH_3COOH (acetic acid); 0.10 M CH_3CH_2OH (ethanol).
3. What response would you expect in the apparatus of Figure 1-4 if the solution tested were 1.0 M HCl? What response would you expect if the solution were both 1.0 M HCl and 1.0 M CH_3COOH?
4. $NH_3(aq)$ conducts electric current only weakly. The same is true for $CH_3COOH(aq)$. When these solutions are mixed, however, the resulting solution is a good conductor. How do you explain this?
5. Sketches **(a–c)** are molecular views of the solute in an aqueous solution. For each of the sketches, indicate whether the solute is a strong, weak, or nonelectrolyte; and which of these substances it is: sodium chloride, propionic acid, hypochlorous acid, ammonia, barium bromide, ammonium chloride, methanol.

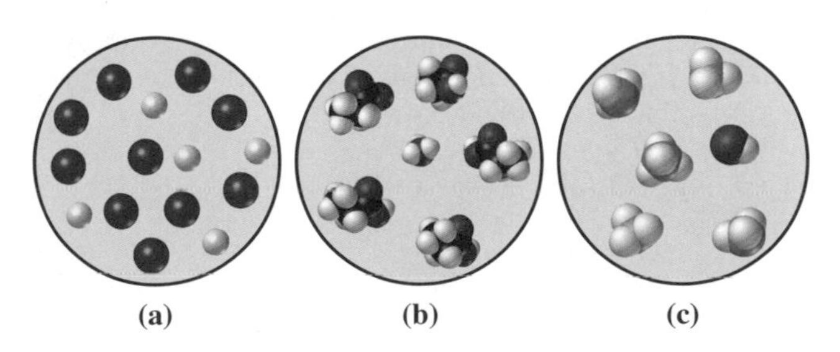

6. After identifying the three substances represented by the sketches in Exercise 5, sketch molecular views of aqueous solutions of the remaining four substances listed.

Ion Concentrations

7. Determine the concentration of the ion indicated in each solution. **(a)** $[K^+]$ in 0.238 M KNO_3; **(b)** $[NO_3^-]$ in 0.167 M $Ca(NO_3)_2$; **(c)** $[Al^{3+}]$ in 0.083 M $Al_2(SO_4)_3$; **(d)** $[Na^+]$ in 0.209 M Na_3PO_4.
8. Which solution has the greatest $[SO_4^{2-}]$: **(a)** 0.075 M H_2SO_4; **(b)** 0.22 M $MgSO_4$; **(c)** 0.15 M Na_2SO_4; **(d)** 0.080 M $Al_2(SO_4)_3$; **(e)** 0.20 M $CuSO_4$?
9. A solution is prepared by dissolving 0.132 g $Ba(OH)_2 \cdot 8\,H_2O$ in 275 mL of water solution. What is $[OH^-]$ in this solution?
10. A solution is 0.126 M KCl and 0.148 M $MgCl_2$. What are $[K^+]$, $[Mg^{2+}]$, and $[Cl^-]$ in this solution?
11. Express the following data for cations in solution as molarities. **(a)** 14.2 mg Ca^{2+}/L; **(b)** 32.8 mg K^+/100 mL; **(c)** 225 μg Zn^{2+}/mL.
12. What molarity of NaF(aq) corresponds to a fluoride ion content of 0.9 mg F^-/L, the federal government's recommended limit for fluoride ion in drinking water?
13. Which of the following aqueous solutions has the highest concentration of K^+? **(a)** 0.0850 M K_2SO_4; **(b)** a solution containing 1.25 g KBr/100 mL; **(c)** a solution having 8.1 mg K^+/mL.
14. Which aqueous solution has the greatest $[H^+]$: **(a)** 0.011 M CH_3COOH; **(b)** 0.010 M HCl; **(c)** 0.010 M H_2SO_4; **(d)** 1.00 M NH_3? Explain your choice.
15. How many milligrams of MgI_2 must be added to 250.0 mL of 0.0876 M KI to produce a solution with $[I^-] = 0.1000$ M?
16. If 25.0 mL H_2O evaporates from 1.00 L of a solution containing 12.0 mg K_2SO_4/mL, what is $[K^+]$ in the solution that remains?
17. Assuming the volumes are additive, what is the $[Cl^-]$ in a solution obtained by mixing 225 mL of 0.625 M KCl and 615 mL of 0.385 M $MgCl_2$?
18. Assuming the volumes are additive, what is the $[NO_3^-]$ in a solution obtained by mixing 275 mL of 0.283 M KNO_3, 328 mL of 0.421 M $Mg(NO_3)_2$, and 784 mL of H_2O?

Predicting Precipitation Reactions

19. Complete each of the following as a net ionic equation, indicating whether a precipitate forms. If no reaction occurs, so state.
    (a) $Na^+ + Br^- + Pb^{2+} + 2\,NO_3^- \longrightarrow$
    (b) $Mg^{2+} + 2\,Cl^- + Cu^{2+} + SO_4^{2-} \longrightarrow$
    (c) $Fe^{3+} + 3\,NO_3^- + Na^+ + OH^- \longrightarrow$
20. Complete each of the following as a net ionic equation. If no reaction occurs, so state.
    (a) $Ca^{2+} + 2\,I^- + 2\,Na^+ + CO_3^{2-} \longrightarrow$
    (b) $Ba^{2+} + S^{2-} + 2\,Na^+ + SO_4^{2-} \longrightarrow$
    (c) $2\,K^+ + S^{2-} + Ca^{2+} + 2\,Cl^- \longrightarrow$
21. Predict in each case whether a reaction is likely to occur. If so, write a net ionic equation.
    (a) $HI(aq) + Zn(NO_3)_2(aq) \longrightarrow$
    (b) $CuSO_4(aq) + Na_2CO_3(aq) \longrightarrow$
    (c) $Cu(NO_3)_2(aq) + Na_3PO_4(aq) \longrightarrow$
22. Predict in each case whether a reaction is likely to occur. If so, write a net ionic equation.
    (a) $AgNO_3(aq) + CuCl_2(aq) \longrightarrow$
    (b) $Na_2S(aq) + FeCl_2(aq) \longrightarrow$
    (c) $Na_2CO_3(aq) + AgNO_3(aq) \longrightarrow$
23. What reagent solution might you use to separate the cations in the following mixtures, that is, with one ion appearing in solution and the other in a precipitate? [*Hint:* Refer to Table 1.1, and consider water also to be a reagent.]
    (a) $BaCl_2(s)$ and $MgCl_2(s)$
    (b) $MgCO_3(s)$ and $Na_2CO_3(s)$
    (c) $AgNO_3(s)$ and $Cu(NO_3)_2(s)$
24. What reagent solution might you use to separate the cations in each of the following mixtures? [*Hint:* Refer to Exercise 23.]
    (a) $PbSO_4(s)$ and $Cu(NO_3)_2(s)$
    (b) $Mg(OH)_2(s)$ and $BaSO_4(s)$
    (c) $PbCO_3(s)$ and $CaCO_3(s)$
25. You are provided with NaOH(aq), $K_2SO_4(aq)$, $Mg(NO_3)_2(aq)$, $BaCl_2(aq)$, NaCl(aq), $Sr(NO_3)_2(aq)$, $AgNO_3(aq)$, and $BaSO_4(s)$. Write net ionic equations to show how you would use one or more of those reagents to obtain **(a)** $SrSO_4(s)$; **(b)** $Mg(OH)_2(s)$; **(c)** KCl(aq).
26. Write net ionic equations to show how you would use one or more of the reagents in Exercise 25 to obtain **(a)** $BaSO_4(s)$; **(b)** AgCl(s); **(c)** $KNO_3(aq)$.

Acid–Base Reactions

27. Complete each of the following as a *net ionic equation*. If no reaction occurs, so state.
    (a) $Ba^{2+} + 2\,OH^- + CH_3COOH \longrightarrow$
    (b) $H^+ + Cl^- + CH_3CH_2COOH \longrightarrow$
    (c) $FeS(s) + H^+ + I^- \longrightarrow$
    (d) $K^+ + HCO_3^- + H^+ + NO_3^- \longrightarrow$
    (e) $Mg(s) + H^+ \longrightarrow$
28. Every antacid contains one or more ingredients capable of reacting with excess stomach acid (HCl). The essential neutralization products are CO_2 and/or H_2O. Write net ionic equations to represent the neutralizing action of the following popular antacids.
    (a) Alka-Seltzer (sodium bicarbonate)
    (b) Tums (calcium carbonate)
    (c) milk of magnesia (magnesium hydroxide)
    (d) Maalox (magnesium hydroxide, aluminum hydroxide)
    (e) Rolaids $[NaAl(OH)_2CO_3]$

29. In this chapter, we described an acid as a substance capable of producing H^+ and a salt as the ionic compound formed by the neutralization of an acid by a base. Write ionic equations to show that sodium hydrogen sulfate has the characteristics of both a salt and an acid (sometimes called an *acid salt*).
30. A neutralization reaction between an acid and a base is a common method of preparing useful salts. Give net ionic equations showing how the following salts could be prepared in this way: **(a)** $(NH_4)_2HPO_4$; **(b)** NH_4NO_3; and **(c)** $(NH_4)_2SO_4$.
31. Which solutions would you use to precipitate Mg^{2+} from an aqueous solution of $MgCl_2$? Explain your choice. **(a)** $KNO_3(aq)$; **(b)** $NH_3(aq)$; **(c)** $H_2SO_4(aq)$; **(d)** $HC_2H_3O_2(aq)$.
32. Determine which of the following react(s) with HCl(aq) to produce a gas, and write a net ionic equation(s) for the reaction(s). **(a)** Na_2SO_4; **(b)** $KHSO_3$; **(c)** $Zn(OH)_2$; **(d)** $CaCl_2$.

Oxidation–Reduction (Redox) Equations

33. Assign oxidation states to the elements involved in the following reactions. Indicate which are redox reactions and which are not.
    (a) $MgCO_3(s) + 2\,H^+(aq) \longrightarrow Mg^{2+}(aq) + H_2O(l) + CO_2(g)$
    (b) $Cl_2(aq) + 2\,Br^-(aq) \longrightarrow 2\,Cl^-(aq) + Br_2(aq)$
    (c) $Ag(s) + 2\,H^+(aq) + NO_3^-(aq) \longrightarrow Ag^+(aq) + H_2O(l) + NO_2(g)$
    (d) $2\,Ag^+(aq) + CrO_4^{2-}(aq) \longrightarrow Ag_2CrO_4(s)$
34. Explain why these reactions cannot occur as written.
    (a) $Fe^{3+}(aq) + MnO_4^-(aq) + H^+(aq) \longrightarrow Mn^{2+}(aq) \mid Fe^{2+}(aq) \mid H_2O(l)$
    (b) $H_2O_2(aq) + Cl_2(aq) \longrightarrow ClO^-(aq) + O_2(g) + H^+(aq)$
35. Complete and balance these half-equations.
    (a) $SO_3^{2-} \longrightarrow S_2O_3^{2-}$ (acidic solution)
    (b) $HNO_3 \longrightarrow N_2O(g)$ (acidic solution)
    (c) $Al(s) \longrightarrow Al(OH)_4^-$ (basic solution)
    Indicate whether oxidation or reduction is involved.
36. Complete and balance these half-equations.
    (a) $C_2O_4^{2-} \longrightarrow CO_2$ (acidic solution)
    (b) $Cr_2O_7^{2-} \longrightarrow Cr^{3+}$ (acidic solution)
    (c) $MnO_4^- \longrightarrow MnO_2$ (basic solution)
    Indicate whether oxidation or reduction is involved.
37. Balance these equations for redox reactions occurring in acidic solution.
    (a) $MnO_4^- + I^- \longrightarrow Mn^{2+} + I_2(s)$
    (b) $BrO_3^- + N_2H_4 \longrightarrow Br^- + N_2$
    (c) $VO_4^{3-} + Fe^{2+} \longrightarrow VO^{2+} + Fe^{3+}$
    (d) $UO^{2+} + NO_3^- \longrightarrow UO_2^{2+} + NO(g)$
38. Balance these equations for redox reactions occurring in acidic solution.
    (a) $P_4(s) + NO_3^- \longrightarrow H_2PO_4^- + NO(g)$
    (b) $S_2O_3^{2-} + MnO_4^- \longrightarrow SO_4^{2-} + Mn^{2+}$
    (c) $HS^- + HSO_3^- \longrightarrow S_2O_3^{2-}$
    (d) $Fe^{3+} + NH_3OH^+ \longrightarrow Fe^{2+} + N_2O(g)$
39. Balance these equations for redox reactions in basic solution.
    (a) $MnO_2(s) + ClO_3^- \longrightarrow MnO_4^- + Cl^-$
    (b) $Fe(OH)_3(s) + OCl^- \longrightarrow FeO_4^{2-} + Cl^-$
    (c) $ClO_2 \longrightarrow ClO_3^- + Cl^-$
    (d) $Ag(s) + CrO_4^{2-} \longrightarrow Ag^+ + Cr(OH)_3(s)$
40. Balance these equations for redox reactions occurring in basic solution.
    (a) $CrO_4^{2-} + S_2O_4^{2-} \longrightarrow Cr(OH)_3(s) + SO_3^{2-}$
    (b) $[Fe(CN)_6]^{3-} + N_2H_4 \longrightarrow [Fe(CN)_6]^{4-} + N_2(g)$
    (c) $Fe(OH)_2(s) + O_2(g) \longrightarrow Fe(OH)_3(s)$
    (d) $CH_3CH_2OH + MnO_4^- \longrightarrow CH_3COO^- + MnO_2(s)$
41. Balance these equations for disproportionation reactions.
    (a) $Cl_2(g) \longrightarrow Cl^- + ClO_3^-$ (basic solution)
    (b) $S_2O_4^{2-} \longrightarrow S_2O_3^{2-} + HSO_3^-$ (acidic solution)
42. Balance these equations for disproportionation reactions.
    (a) $MnO_4^{2-} \longrightarrow MnO_2(s) + MnO_4^-$ (basic solution)
    (b) $P_4(s) \longrightarrow H_2PO_2^- + PH_3(g)$ (basic solution)
    (c) $S_8(s) \longrightarrow S^{2-} + S_2O_3^{2-}$ (basic solution)
    (d) $As_2S_3 + H_2O_2 \longrightarrow AsO_4^{3-} + SO_4^{2-}$
43. Write a balanced equation for these redox reactions.
    (a) The oxidation of nitrite ion to nitrate ion by permanganate ion, MnO_4^-, in acidic solution (MnO_4^- ion is reduced to Mn^{2+}).
    (b) The reaction of manganese(II) ion and permanganate ion in basic solution to form solid manganese dioxide.
    (c) The oxidation of ethanol by dichromate ion in acidic solution, producing chromium(III) ion, acetaldehyde (CH_3CHO), and water as products.
44. Write a balanced equation for the redox reactions.
    (a) The reaction of aluminum metal with hydroiodic acid.
    (b) The reduction of vanadyl ion (VO^{2+}) to vanadic ion (V^{3+}) in acidic solution with zinc metal as the reducing agent.
    (c) The oxidation of methanol by chlorate ion in acidic solution, producing carbon dioxide gas, water, and chlorine dioxide gas as products.
45. The following reactions do not occur in aqueous solutions. Balance their equations by the half-equation method, as suggested in Are You Wondering 1-2.
    (a) $CH_4(g) + NO(g) \longrightarrow CO_2(g) + N_2(g) + H_2O(g)$
    (b) $H_2S(g) + SO_2(g) \longrightarrow S_8(s) + H_2O(g)$
    (c) $Cl_2O(g) + NH_3(g) \longrightarrow N_2(g) + NH_4Cl(s) + H_2O(l)$
46. The following reactions do not occur in aqueous solutions. Balance their equations by the half-equation method, as suggested in Are You Wondering 1-2.
    (a) $CH_4(g) + NH_3(g) + O_2(g) \longrightarrow HCN(g) + H_2O(g)$
    (b) $NO(g) + H_2(g) \longrightarrow NH_3(g) + H_2O(g)$
    (c) $Fe(s) + H_2O(l) + O_2(g) \longrightarrow Fe(OH)_3(s)$

Oxidizing and Reducing Agents

47. What are the oxidizing and reducing agents in the following redox reactions?

(a) $5\,SO_3^{2-} + 2\,MnO_4^- + 6\,H^+ \longrightarrow 5\,SO_4^{2-} + 2\,Mn^{2+} + 3\,H_2O$

(b) $2\,NO_2(g) + 7\,H_2(g) \longrightarrow 2\,NH_3(g) + 4\,H_2O(g)$

(c) $2\,[Fe(CN)_6]^{4-} + H_2O_2 + 2\,H^+ \longrightarrow 2\,[Fe(CN)_6]^{3-} + 2\,H_2O$

48. Thiosulfate ion, $S_2O_3^{2-}$, is a reducing agent that can be oxidized to different products, depending on the strength of the oxidizing agent and other conditions. By adding H^+, H_2O, and/or OH^- as necessary, write redox equations to show the oxidation of $S_2O_3^{2-}$ to

(a) $S_4O_6^{2-}$ by I_2 (iodide ion is another product)

(b) HSO_4^- by Cl_2 (chloride ion is another product)

(c) SO_4^{2-} by OCl^- in basic solution (chloride ion is another product)

Neutralization and Acid–Base Titrations

49. What volume of 0.0962 M NaOH is required to exactly neutralize 10.00 mL of 0.128 M HCl?

50. The exact neutralization of 10.00 mL of 0.1012 M $H_2SO_4(aq)$ requires 23.31 mL of NaOH. What must be the molarity of the NaOH(aq)?

$$H_2SO_4(aq) + 2\,NaOH(aq) \longrightarrow Na_2SO_4(aq) + 2\,H_2O(l)$$

51. How many milliliters of 2.155 M KOH are required to titrate 25.00 mL of 0.3057 M CH_3CH_2COOH (propionic acid)?

52. How many milliliters of 0.0844 M $Ba(OH)_2$ are required to titrate 50.00 mL of 0.0526 M HNO_3?

53. An NaOH(aq) solution cannot be made up to an exact concentration simply by weighing out the required mass of NaOH, because the NaOH is not pure. Also, water vapor condenses on the solid as it is being weighed. The solution must be standardized by titration. For this purpose, a 25.00 mL sample of an NaOH(aq) solution requires 28.34 mL of 0.1085 M HCl. What is the molarity of the NaOH(aq)?

$$HCl(aq) + NaOH(aq) \longrightarrow NaCl(aq) + H_2O(l)$$

54. Household ammonia, used as a window cleaner and for other cleaning purposes, is $NH_3(aq)$. The NH_3 present in a 5.00 mL sample is neutralized by 28.72 mL of 1.021 M HCl. The net ionic equation for the neutralization is

$$NH_3(aq) + H^+(aq) \longrightarrow NH_4^+(aq)$$

What is the molarity of NH_3 in the sample?

55. We want to determine the acetylsalicylic acid content of a series of aspirin tablets by titration with NaOH(aq). Each of the tablets is expected to contain about 0.32 g of $HC_9H_7O_4$. What molarity of NaOH(aq) should we use for titration volumes of about 23 mL? (This procedure ensures good precision and allows the titration of two samples with the contents of a 50 mL buret.)

$$HC_9H_7O_4(aq) + OH^-(aq) \longrightarrow C_9H_7O_4^-(aq) + H_2O(l)$$

56. For use in titrations, we want to prepare 20 L of HCl(aq) with a concentration known to four significant figures. This is a two-step procedure beginning with the preparation of a solution of about 0.10 M HCl. A sample of this dilute HCl(aq) is titrated with a NaOH(aq) solution of known concentration.

(a) How many milliliters of concentrated HCl(aq) (d = 1.19 g/mL; 38% HCl, by mass) must be diluted with water to 20.0 L to prepare 0.10 M HCl?

(b) A 25.00 mL sample of the approximately 0.10 M HCl prepared in part (a) requires 20.93 mL of 0.1186 M NaOH for its titration. What is the molarity of the HCl(aq)?

(c) Why is a titration necessary? That is, why not prepare a standard solution of 0.1000 M HCl simply by an appropriate dilution of the concentrated HCl(aq)?

57. A 25.00 mL sample of 0.132 M HNO_3 is mixed with 10.00 mL of 0.318 M KOH. Is the resulting solution acidic, basic, or exactly neutralized?

58. A 7.55 g sample of $Na_2CO_3(s)$ is added to 125 mL of a vinegar that is 0.762 M CH_3COOH. Will the resulting solution still be acidic? Explain.

59. Refer to Example 1-9. Suppose the analysis of all vinegar samples uses 5.00 mL of the vinegar and 0.1000 M NaOH for the titration. What volume of the 0.1000 M NaOH would represent the legal minimum 4.0%, by mass, acetic acid content of the vinegar? That is, calculate the volume of 0.1000 M NaOH so that if a titration requires more than this volume, the legal minimum limit is met (less than this volume, and the limit is not met).

60. The electrolyte in a lead storage battery must have a concentration between 4.8 and 5.3 M H_2SO_4 if the battery is to be most effective. A 5.00 mL sample of a battery acid requires 49.74 mL of 0.935 M NaOH for its complete reaction (neutralization). Does the concentration of the battery acid fall within the desired range? [*Hint:* Keep in mind that the H_2SO_4 produces two H^+ ions per formula unit.]

61. Which of the following points in a titration is represented by the molecular view shown in the sketch?

(a) 20% of the necessary titrant added in the titration of $NH_4Cl(aq)$ with HCl(aq)

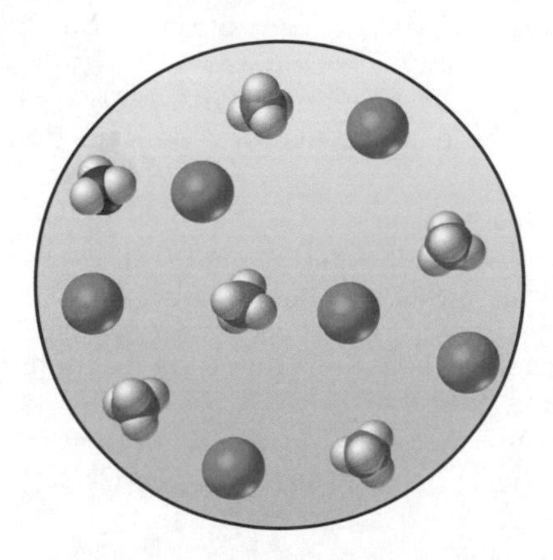

(b) 20% of the necessary titrant added in the titration of $NH_3(aq)$ with $HCl(aq)$
(c) the equivalence point in the titration of $NH_3(aq)$ with $HCl(aq)$
(d) 120% of the necessary titrant added in the titration of $NH_3(aq)$ with $HCl(aq)$

62. Using the sketch in Exercise 61 as a guide, sketch the molecular view of a solution in which
(a) $HCl(aq)$ is titrated to the equivalence point with $KOH(aq)$
(b) $CH_3COOH(aq)$ is titrated halfway to the equivalence point with $NaOH(aq)$.

Stoichiometry of Oxidation–Reduction Reactions

63. A $KMnO_4(aq)$ solution is to be standardized by titration against $As_2O_3(s)$. A 0.1078 g sample of As_2O_3 requires 22.15 mL of the $KMnO_4(aq)$ for its titration. What is the molarity of the $KMnO_4(aq)$?

$$5\,As_2O_3 + 4\,MnO_4^- + 9\,H_2O + 12\,H^+ \longrightarrow 10\,H_3AsO_4 + 4\,Mn^{2+}$$

64. Refer to Example 1-6. Assume that the only reducing agent present in a particular wastewater is SO_3^{2-}. If a 25.00 mL sample of this wastewater requires 31.46 mL of 0.02237 M $KMnO_4$ for its titration, what is the molarity of SO_3^{2-} in the wastewater?

65. An iron ore sample weighing 0.9132 g is dissolved in $HCl(aq)$, and the iron is obtained as $Fe^{2+}(aq)$. This solution is then titrated with 28.72 mL of 0.05051 M $K_2Cr_2O_7$. What is the mass percent Fe in the ore sample?

$$6\,Fe^{2+} + 14\,H^+ + Cr_2O_7^{2-} \longrightarrow 6\,Fe^{3+} + 2\,Cr^{3+} + 7\,H_2O$$

66. The concentration of $Mn^{2+}(aq)$ can be determined by titration with $MnO_4^-(aq)$ in basic solution. A 25.00 mL sample of $Mn^{2+}(aq)$ requires 37.21 mL of 0.04162 M $KMnO_4$ for its titration. What is $[Mn^{2+}]$ in the sample?

$$Mn^{2+} + MnO_4^- \longrightarrow MnO_2(s) \quad \text{(not balanced)}$$

67. The titration of 5.00 mL of a saturated solution of sodium oxalate, $Na_2C_2O_4$, at 25 °C requires 25.8 mL of 0.02140 M $KMnO_4$ in acidic solution. What mass of $Na_2C_2O_4$ in grams would be present in 1.00 L of this saturated solution?

$$C_2O_4^{2-} + MnO_4^- \longrightarrow Mn^{2+} + CO_2(g) \quad \text{(not balanced)}$$

68. Refer to the Integrative Example. In the treatment of 1.00×10^2 L of a wastewater solution that is 0.0126 M CrO_4^{2-}, how many grams of **(a)** $Cr(OH)_3(s)$ would precipitate; **(b)** $Na_2S_2O_4$ would be consumed?

Integrative and Advanced Exercises

69. Write net ionic equations for the reactions depicted in photo **(a)** sodium metal reacts with water to produce hydrogen; photo **(b)** an excess of aqueous iron(III) chloride is added to the solution in **(a)**; and photo **(c)** the precipitate from **(b)** is collected and treated with an excess of $HCl(aq)$.

(a) (b) (c)

70. Following are some laboratory methods occasionally used for the preparation of small quantities of chemicals. Write a balanced equation for each.
(a) preparation of $H_2S(g)$: $HCl(aq)$ is heated with $FeS(s)$
(b) preparation of $Cl_2(g)$: $HCl(aq)$ is heated with $MnO_2(s)$; $MnCl_2(aq)$ and $H_2O(l)$ are other products
(c) preparation of N_2: Br_2 and NH_3 react in aqueous solution; NH_4Br is another product
(d) preparation of chlorous acid: an aqueous suspension of solid barium chlorite is treated with dilute $H_2SO_4(aq)$

71. When concentrated $CaCl_2(aq)$ is added to $Na_2HPO_4(aq)$, a white precipitate forms that is 38.7% Ca by mass. Write a net ionic equation representing the probable reaction that occurs.

72. You have a solution that is 0.0250 M $Ba(OH)_2$ and the following pieces of equipment: 1.00, 5.00, 10.00, 25.00, and 50.00 mL pipets and 100.0, 250.0, 500.0, and 1000.0 mL volumetric flasks. Describe how you would use this equipment to produce a solution in which $[OH^-]$ is 0.0100 M.

73. Sodium hydroxide used to make standard $NaOH(aq)$ solutions for acid–base titrations is invariably contaminated with some sodium carbonate. **(a)** Explain why, except in the most precise work, the presence of this sodium carbonate generally does not seriously affect the results obtained, for example, when $NaOH(aq)$ is used to titrate $HCl(aq)$. **(b)** Conversely, show that if Na_2CO_3 comprises more than 1% to 2% of the solute in $NaOH(aq)$, the titration results are affected.

74. A 110.520 g sample of mineral water is analyzed for its magnesium content. The Mg^{2+} in the sample is first precipitated as $MgNH_4PO_4$, and this precipitate is then converted to $Mg_2P_2O_7$, which is found to weigh 0.0549 g. Express the quantity of magnesium in the sample in parts per million (that is, in grams of Mg per million grams of H_2O).

75. What volume of 0.248 M $CaCl_2$ must be added to 335 mL of 0.186 M KCl to produce a solution with a concentration of 0.250 M Cl^-? Assume that the solution volumes are additive.

76. An unknown white solid consists of two compounds, each containing a different cation. As suggested in the illustration, the unknown is partially soluble in water. The solution is treated with NaOH(aq) and yields a white precipitate. The part of the original solid that is insoluble in water dissolves in HCl(aq) with the evolution of a gas. The resulting solution is then treated with $(NH_4)_2SO_4$(aq) and yields a white precipitate. **(a)** Is it possible that any of the cations Mg^{2+}, Cu^{2+}, Ba^{2+}, Na^+, or NH_4^+ were present in the original unknown? Explain your reasoning. **(b)** What compounds could be in the unknown mixture (that is, what anions might be present)?

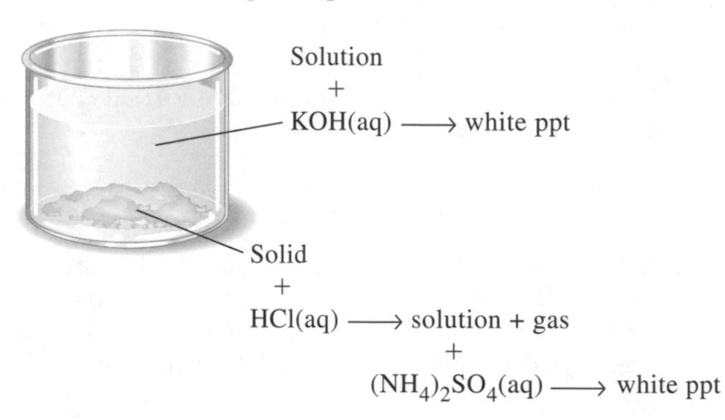

77. Balance these equations for reactions in acidic solution.
(a) $IBr + BrO_3^- + H^+ \longrightarrow IO_3^- + Br^- + H_2O$
(b) $C_2H_5NO_3 + Sn \longrightarrow NH_2OH + CH_3CH_2OH + Sn^{2+}$
(c) $As_2S_3 + NO_3^- \longrightarrow H_3AsO_4 + S + NO$
(d) $H_5IO_6 + I_2 \longrightarrow IO_3^- + H^+ + H_2O$
(e) $S_2F_2 + H_2O \longrightarrow S_8 + H_2S_4O_6 + HF$

78. Balance these equations for reactions in basic solution.
(a) $Fe_2S_3 + H_2O + O_2 \longrightarrow Fe(OH)_3 + S$
(b) $O_2^- + H_2O \longrightarrow OH^- + O_2$
(c) $CrI_3 + H_2O_2 \longrightarrow CrO_4^{2-} + IO_4^-$
(d) $Ag + CN^- + O_2 + OH^- \longrightarrow [Ag(CN)_2]^- + H_2O$
(e) $B_2Cl_4 + OH^- \longrightarrow BO_2^- + Cl^- + H_2O + H_2$

79. A method of producing phosphine, PH_3, from elemental phosphorus, P_4, involves heating the P_4 with H_2O. An additional product is phosphoric acid, H_3PO_4. Write a balanced equation for this reaction.

80. Iron (Fe) is obtained from rock that is extracted from open pit mines and then crushed. The process used to obtain the pure metal from the crushed rock produces solid waste, called *tailings*, which are stored in disposal areas near the mines. The tailings pose a serious environmental risk because they contain sulfides, such as pyrite (FeS_2), which oxidize in air to produce metal ions and H^+ ions that can enter into surface water or ground water. The oxidation of FeS_2 to Fe^{3+} is described by the unbalanced chemical equation below.

$$FeS_2(s) + O_2(g) + H_2O(l) \longrightarrow Fe^{3+}(aq) + SO_4^{2-}(aq) + H^+(aq) \quad \text{(not balanced)}$$

Thus, the oxidation of pyrite produces Fe^{3+} and H^+ ions that can leach into surface or ground water. The leaching of H^+ ions causes the water to become very acidic. To prevent acidification of nearby ground or surface water, limestone ($CaCO_3$) is added to the tailings to neutralize the H^+ ions:

$$CaCO_3(s) + 2\,H^+(aq) \longrightarrow Ca^{2+}(aq) + H_2O(l) + CO_2(g)$$

(a) Balance the equation above for the reaction of FeS_2 and O_2. [*Hint:* Start with the half-equations $FeS_2(s) \longrightarrow Fe^{3+}(aq) + SO_4^{2-}(aq)$ and $O_2(g) \longrightarrow H_2O(l)$.]
(b) What is the minimum amount of $CaCO_3$(s) required, per kilogram of tailings, to prevent contamination if the tailings contain 3% S by mass? Assume that all the sulfur in the tailings is in the form FeS_2.

81. A sample of battery acid is to be analyzed for its sulfuric acid content. A 1.00 mL sample weighs 1.239 g. This 1.00 mL sample is diluted to 250.0 mL, and 10.00 mL of this diluted acid requires 32.44 mL of 0.00498 M $Ba(OH)_2$ for its titration. What is the mass percent of H_2SO_4 in the battery acid? (Assume that complete ionization and neutralization of the H_2SO_4 occurs.)

82. A piece of marble (assume it is pure $CaCO_3$) reacts with 2.00 L of 2.52 M HCl. After dissolution of the marble, a 10.00 mL sample of the resulting solution is withdrawn, added to some water, and titrated with 24.87 mL of 0.9987 M NaOH. What must have been the mass of the piece of marble? Comment on the precision of this method; that is, how many significant figures are justified in the result?

83. The reaction below can be used as a laboratory method of preparing small quantities of Cl_2(g). If a 62.6 g sample that is 98.5% $K_2Cr_2O_7$ by mass is allowed to react with 325 mL of HCl(aq) with a density of 1.15 g/mL and 30.1% HCl by mass, how many grams of Cl_2(g) are produced?

$$Cr_2O_7^{2-} + H^+ + Cl^- \longrightarrow Cr^{3+} + H_2O + Cl_2(g) \quad \text{(not balanced)}$$

84. Refer to Example 1-10. Suppose that the $KMnO_4$(aq) were standardized by reaction with As_2O_3 instead of iron wire. If a 0.1304 g sample that is 99.96% As_2O_3 by mass had been used in the titration, how many milliliters of the $KMnO_4$(aq) would have been required?

$$As_2O_3 + MnO_4^- + H^+ + H_2O \longrightarrow H_3AsO_4 + Mn^{2+} \quad \text{(not balanced)}$$

85. A new method under development for water treatment uses chlorine dioxide rather than chlorine. One method of producing ClO_2 involves passing Cl_2(g) into a concentrated solution of sodium chlorite. Cl_2(g) and sodium chlorite are the sole reactants, and NaCl(aq) and ClO_2(g) are the sole products. If the reaction has a 97% yield, what mass of ClO_2 is produced per gallon of 2.0 M $NaClO_2$(aq) treated in this way?

86. The active component in one type of calcium dietary supplement is calcium carbonate. A 1.2450 g tablet of the supplement is added to 50.00 mL of 0.5000 M HCl and allowed to react. After completion of the reaction, the excess HCl(aq) requires 40.20 mL of 0.2184 M NaOH for its titration to the equivalence point. What is the calcium content of the tablet, expressed in milligrams of Ca^{2+}?

87. A 0.4324 g sample of a potassium hydroxide–lithium hydroxide mixture requires 28.28 mL of 0.3520 M HCl for its titration to the equivalence point. What is the mass percent lithium hydroxide in this mixture?

88. Chile saltpeter is a natural source of $NaNO_3$; it also contains $NaIO_3$. The $NaIO_3$ can be used as a source of iodine. Iodine is produced from sodium iodate in a two-step process occurring under acidic conditions:

$$IO_3^-(aq) + HSO_3^-(aq) \longrightarrow I^-(aq) + SO_4^{2-}(aq) \quad \text{(not balanced)}$$

$$I^-(aq) + IO_3^-(aq) \longrightarrow I_2(s) + H_2O(l) \quad \text{(not balanced)}$$

In the illustration, a 5.00 L sample of a $NaIO_3(aq)$ solution containing 5.80 g $NaIO_3$/L is treated with the stoichiometric quantity of $NaHSO_3$ (no excess of either reactant). Then, a further quantity of the initial $NaIO_3(aq)$ is added to the reaction mixture to bring about the second reaction. **(a)** How many grams of $NaHSO_3$ are required in the first step? **(b)** What additional volume of the starting solution must be added in the second step?

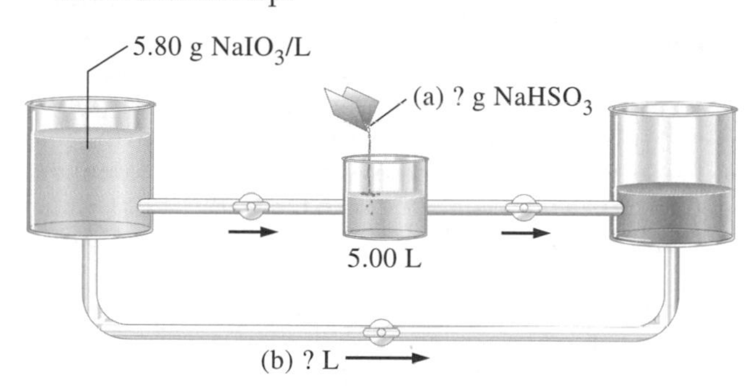

89. The active ingredients in a particular antacid tablet are aluminum hydroxide, $Al(OH)_3$, and magnesium hydroxide, $Mg(OH)_2$. A 5.00×10^2 mg sample of the active ingredients was dissolved in 50.0 mL of 0.500 M HCl. The resulting solution, which was still acidic, required 16.5 mL of 0.377 M NaOH for neutralization. What are the mass percentages of $Al(OH)_3$ and $Mg(OH)_2$ in the sample?

90. A compound contains only Fe and O. A 0.2729 g sample of the compound was dissolved in 50 mL of concentrated acid solution, reducing all the iron to Fe^{2+} ions. The resulting solution was diluted to 100 mL and then titrated with a 0.01621 M $KMnO_4$ solution. The unbalanced chemical equation for reaction between Fe^{2+} and MnO_4^- is given below.

$$MnO_4^-(aq) + Fe^{2+}(aq) \longrightarrow Mn^{2+}(aq) + Fe^{3+}(aq) \quad \text{(not balanced)}$$

The titration required 42.17 mL of the $KMnO_4$ solution to reach the pink endpoint. What is the empirical formula of the compound?

91. Warfarin, $C_{19}H_{16}O_4$, is the active ingredient used in some anticoagulant medications. The amount of warfarin in a particular sample was determined as follows. A 13.96 g sample was first treated with an alkaline I_2 solution to convert $C_{19}H_{16}O_4$ to CHI_3. This treatment gives one mole of CHI_3 for every mole of $C_{19}H_{16}O_4$ that was initially present in the sample. The iodine in CHI_3 is then precipitated as AgI(s) by treatment with excess $AgNO_3(aq)$:

$$CHI_3(aq) + 3\,AgNO_3(aq) + H_2O(l) \longrightarrow 3\,AgI(s) + 3\,HNO_3(aq) + CO(g)$$

If 0.1386 g solid AgI were obtained, then what is the percentage by mass of warfarin in the sample analyzed?

92. Copper refining traditionally involves "roasting" insoluble sulfide ores (CuS) with oxygen. Unfortunately, the process produces large quantities of $SO_2(g)$, which is a major contributor to pollution and acid rain. An alternative process involves treating the sulfide ore with $HNO_3(aq)$, which dissolves the CuS without generating any SO_2. The unbalanced chemical equation for the reaction is given below.

$$CuS(s) + NO_3^-(aq) \longrightarrow Cu^{2+}(aq) + NO(g) + HSO_4^-(aq) \quad \text{(not balanced)}$$

What volume of concentrated nitric acid solution is required per kilogram of CuS? Assume that the concentrated nitric acid solution is 70% HNO_3 by mass and has a density of 1.40 g/mL.

93. Phosphorus is essential for plant growth, but an excess of phosphorus can be catastrophic in aqueous ecosystems. Too much phosphorus can cause algae to grow at an explosive rate and this robs the rest of the ecosystem of oxygen. Effluent from sewage treatment plants must be treated before it can be released into lakes or streams because the effluent contains significant amounts of $H_2PO_4^-$ and HPO_4^{2-}. (Detergents are a major contributor to phosphorus levels in domestic sewage because many detergents contain Na_2HPO_4.) A simple way to remove $H_2PO_4^-$ and HPO_4^{2-} from the effluent is to treat it with lime, CaO, which produces Ca^{2+} and OH^- ions in water. The OH^- ions convert $H_2PO_4^-$ and HPO_4^{2-} ions into PO_4^{3-} ions and, finally, Ca^{2+}, OH^-, and PO_4^{3-} ions combine to form a precipitate of $Ca_5(PO_4)_3OH(s)$.
(a) Write balanced chemical equations for the four reactions described above.
[*Hint*: The reactants are CaO and H_2O; $H_2PO_4^-$ and OH^-; HPO_4^{2-} and OH^-; Ca^{2+}, PO_4^{3-}, and OH^-.]
(b) How many kilograms of lime are required to remove the phosphorus from a 1.00×10^4 L holding tank filled with contaminated water, if the water contains 10.0 mg of phosphorus per liter?

Feature Problems

94. Sodium cyclopentadienide, NaC_5H_5, is a common reducing agent in the chemical laboratory, but there is a problem in using it: NaC_5H_5 is contaminated with tetrahydrofuran (THF), C_4H_8O, a solvent used in its preparation. The THF is present as $NaC_5H_5 \cdot (THF)_x$, and it is generally necessary to know exactly how much of this $NaC_5H_5 \cdot (THF)_x$ is present. This is accomplished by allowing a small amount of the $NaC_5H_5 \cdot (THF)_x$ to react with water,

$$NaC_5H_5 \cdot (C_4H_8O)_x + H_2O \longrightarrow NaOH(aq) + C_5H_5{-}H + x\,C_4H_8O$$

followed by titration of the NaOH(aq) with a standard acid. From the sample data tabulated below, determine the value of x in the formula $NaC_5H_5 \cdot (THF)_x$.

	Trial 1	Trial 2
Mass of $NaC_5H_5 \cdot (THF)_x$	0.242 g	0.199 g
Volume of 0.1001 M HCl required to titrate NaOH(aq)	14.92 mL	11.99 mL

95. Manganese is derived from pyrolusite ore, an impure manganese dioxide. In the procedure used to analyze a pyrolusite ore for its MnO_2 content, a 0.533 g sample is treated with 1.651 g oxalic acid ($H_2C_2O_4 \cdot 2\,H_2O$) in an acidic medium. Following this reaction, the excess oxalic acid is titrated with 0.1000 M $KMnO_4$, 30.06 mL being required. What is the mass percent MnO_2 in the ore?

$$H_2C_2O_4 + MnO_2 + H^+ \longrightarrow Mn^{2+} + H_2O + CO_2 \quad \text{(not balanced)}$$

$$H_2C_2O_4 + MnO_4^- + H^+ \longrightarrow Mn^{2+} + H_2O + CO_2 \quad \text{(not balanced)}$$

96. The Kjeldahl method is used in agricultural chemistry to determine the percent protein in natural products. The method is based on converting all the protein nitrogen to ammonia and then determining the amount of ammonia by titration. The percent nitrogen in the sample under analysis can be calculated from the quantity of ammonia produced. Interestingly, the majority of protein molecules in living matter contain just about 16% nitrogen.

A 1.250 g sample of meat is heated with concentrated sulfuric acid and a catalyst to convert all the nitrogen in the meat to $(NH_4)_2SO_4$. Then excess NaOH(aq) is added to the mixture, which is heated to expel $NH_3(g)$. All the nitrogen from the sample is found in the $NH_3(g)$, which is then absorbed in and neutralized by 50.00 mL of dilute $H_2SO_4(aq)$. The excess $H_2SO_4(aq)$ requires 32.24 mL of 0.4498 M NaOH for its titration. A separate 25.00 mL sample of the dilute $H_2SO_4(aq)$ requires 22.24 mL of 0.4498 M NaOH for its titration. What is the percent protein in the meat?

97. Blood alcohol content (BAC) is often reported in weight–volume percent (w/v%). For example, a BAC of 0.10% corresponds to 0.10 g CH_3CH_2OH per 100 mL of blood. Estimates of BAC can be obtained from breath samples by using a number of commercially available instruments, including the Breathalyzer for which a patent was issued to R. F. Borkenstein in 1958. The chemistry behind the Breathalyzer is described by the oxidation–reduction reaction below, which occurs in acidic solution:

$$\underset{\text{ethyl alcohol}}{CH_3CH_2OH(g)} + \underset{\text{(yellow-orange)}}{Cr_2O_7^{2-}(aq)} \longrightarrow CH_3COOH(aq) + \underset{\text{(green)}}{Cr^{3+}(aq)} \quad \text{(not balanced)}$$

A Breathalyzer instrument contains two ampules, each of which contains 0.75 mg $K_2Cr_2O_7$ dissolved in 3 mL of 9 mol/L $H_2SO_4(aq)$. One of the ampules is used as reference. When a person exhales into the tube of the Breathalyzer, the breath is directed into one of the ampules, and ethyl alcohol in the breath converts $Cr_2O_7^{2-}$ into Cr^{3+}. The instrument compares the colors of the solutions in the two ampules to determine the breath alcohol content (BrAC), and then converts this into an estimate of BAC. The conversion of BrAC into BAC rests on the assumption that 2100 mL of air exhaled from the lungs contains the same amount of alcohol as 1 mL of blood. With the theory and assumptions described in this problem, calculate the molarity of $K_2Cr_2O_7$ in the ampules before and after a breath test in which a person with a BAC of 0.05% exhales 0.500 L of his breath into a Breathalyzer instrument.

98. In this problem, we describe an alternative method for balancing equations for oxidation-reduction reactions. The method is similar to the method given previously in Tables 1.5 and 1.6, but it places more emphasis on the assignment of oxidation states. (The method summarized in Tables 1.5 and 1.6 does not require you to assign oxidation states.) An emphasis on oxidation states is warranted because oxidation states are useful not only for keeping track of electrons but also for predicting chemical properties. The method is summarized in the table below.

A Method for Balancing Equations for Oxidation–Reduction Reactions That Occur in an Acidic or a Basic Aqueous Solution

1. Assign oxidation states to each element in the reaction and identify the species being oxidized and reduced.
2. Write separate, unbalanced equations for the oxidation and reduction half-reactions.
3. Balance the separate half-equations, in this order:
   - first with respect to the element being oxidized or reduced
   - then by adding electrons to one side or the other to account for the number of electrons produced (oxidation) or consumed (reduction)
4. Combine the half-reactions algebraically so that the total number of electrons cancels out.
5. Balance the net charge by either adding OH^- (for basic solutions) or H^+ (for acidic solutions).
6. Balance the O and H atoms by adding H_2O.
7. Check that the final equation is balanced with respect to each type of atom and with respect to charge.

The method offers a couple of advantages. First, the method applies to both acidic and basic environments because we balance charges by using either H^+ (for acidic environments) or OH^- (for basic environments). Second, the method is somewhat more efficient than the method we described previously because, in the method described here, we balance only once for charge and only once for hydrogen and oxygen. In the other method, we focus on the half-equations separately and must balance twice for charge and twice for hydrogen and oxygen.

Use the alternative method described above to balance the following oxidation-reduction equations.

(a) $Cr_2O_7^{2-}(aq) + Cl^-(aq) \longrightarrow Cr^{3+}(aq) + Cl_2(g)$ (acidic solution)

(b) $C_2O_4^{2-}(aq) + MnO_4^-(aq) \longrightarrow CO_3^{2-}(aq) + MnO_2(s)$ (basic solution)

Self-Assessment Exercises

99. In your own words, define or explain the terms or symbols **(a)** $\rightleftharpoons$ **(b)** [ ]; **(c)** spectator ion; **(d)** weak acid.

100. Briefly describe **(a)** half-equation method of balancing redox equations; **(b)** disproportionation reaction; **(c)** titration; **(d)** standardization of a solution.

101. Explain the important distinctions between **(a)** a strong electrolyte and strong acid; **(b)** an oxidizing agent and reducing agent; **(c)** precipitation reactions and neutralization reactions; **(d)** half-reaction and overall reaction.

102. The number of moles of hydroxide ion in 0.300 L of 0.0050 M $Ba(OH)_2$ is **(a)** 0.0015; **(b)** 0.0030; **(c)** 0.0050; **(d)** 0.010.

103. The highest $[H^+]$ will be found in an aqueous solution that is **(a)** 0.10 M HCl; **(b)** 0.10 M NH_3; **(c)** 0.15 M CH_3COOH; **(d)** 0.10 M H_2SO_4.

104. To precipitate Zn^{2+} from $Zn(NO_3)_2(aq)$, add **(a)** NH_4Cl; **(b)** $MgBr_2$; **(c)** K_2CO_3; **(d)** $(NH_4)_2SO_4$.

105. When treated with dilute HCl(aq), the solid that reacts to produce a gas is **(a)** $BaSO_3$; **(b)** ZnO; **(c)** NaBr; **(d)** Na_2SO_4.

106. What is the net ionic equation for the reaction that occurs when an aqueous solution of KI is added to an aqueous solution of $Pb(NO_3)_2$?

107. When aqueous sodium carbonate, Na_2CO_3, is treated with dilute hydrochloric acid, HCl, the products are sodium chloride, water, and carbon dioxide gas. What is the net ionic equation for this reaction?

108. Describe the synthesis of each of the following ionic compounds, starting from solutions of sodium and nitrate salts. Then write the net ionic equation for each synthesis.
(a) $Zn_3(PO_4)_2$;
(b) $Cu(OH)_2$;
(c) $NiCO_3$.

109. Consider the following redox reaction:

$$4\,NO(g) + 3\,O_2(g) + 2\,H_2O(l) \longrightarrow 4\,NO_3^-(aq) + 4\,H^+(aq)$$

(a) Which species is oxidized?
(b) Which species is reduced?
(c) Which species is the oxidizing agent?
(d) Which species is the reducing agent?
(e) Which species gains electrons?
(f) Which species loses electrons?

110. In the equation

$$?\,Fe^{2+}(aq) + O_2(g) + 4\,H^+(aq) \longrightarrow\ ?\,Fe^{3+}(aq) + 2\,H_2O(l)$$

the missing coefficients **(a)** are each 2; **(b)** are each 4; **(c)** can have any values as long as they are the same; **(d)** must be determined by experiment.

111. What is the simplest ratio $a{:}b$ when the equation below is properly balanced?

$$a\,ClO^-(aq) + b\,I_2(aq) \xrightarrow[\text{solution}]{\text{acidic}} c\,Cl^-(aq) + d\,IO_3^-(aq)$$

(a) 2:5; **(b)** 5:2; **(c)** 1:5; **(d)** 5:1; **(e)** 2:3.

112. In the half-reaction in which NpO_2^+ is converted to Np^{4+}, the number of electrons appearing in the half-equation is **(a)** 1; **(b)** 2; **(c)** 3; **(d)** 4.

113. Classify each of the following statements as true or false.
(a) Barium chloride, $BaCl_2$, is a weak electrolyte in aqueous solution.
(b) In the reaction $H^-(aq) + H_2O(l) \rightarrow H_2(g) + OH^-(aq)$, water acts as both an acid and an oxidizing agent.
(c) A precipitate forms when aqueous sodium carbonate, $Na_2CO_3(aq)$, is treated with excess aqueous hydrochloric acid, HCl(aq).
(d) Hydrofluoric acid, HF, is a strong acid in water.
(e) Compared with a 0.010 M solution of $NaNO_3$, a 0.010 M solution of $Mg(NO_3)_2$ is a better conductor of electricity.

114. Which of the following reactions are oxidation–reduction reactions?
(a) $H_2CO_3(aq) \longrightarrow H_2O(l) + CO_2(g)$
(b) $2\,Li(s) + 2\,H_2O(l) \longrightarrow 2\,LiOH(aq) + H_2(g)$
(c) $4\,Ag(s) + PtCl_4(aq) \longrightarrow 4\,AgCl(s) + Pt(s)$
(d) $2\,HClO_4(aq) + Ca(OH)_2(aq) \longrightarrow 2\,H_2O(l) + Ca(ClO_4)_2(aq)$

115. Similar to Figure 1-4(c), but using the formulas HAc, Ac^-, and H_3O^+, give a more accurate representation of $CH_3COOH(aq)$ in which ionization is 5% complete.

2

Gases

CONTENTS

Hot-air balloons have intrigued people from the time the simple gas laws fundamental to their operation came to be understood more than 200 years ago.

You shouldn't overinflate a bicycle tire, or discard an aerosol can in an incinerator, or search for a gas leak with an open flame. In each case there is a danger of explosion. These and many other observations concerning gases can be explained by concepts considered in this chapter. The behaviors of the bicycle tire and the aerosol can are based on relationships among pressure, temperature, volume, and amount of gas. Other examples of the behavior of gases can be seen in a balloon filled with helium or hot air rising in air and carbon dioxide gas vaporizing from a block of dry ice and sinking to the floor. An understanding of the lifting power of lighter-than-air balloons comes in large part from knowledge of gas densities and their dependence on molar mass, temperature, and pressure. Predicting how far and how fast gas molecules migrate through air requires knowing something about the phenomenon of diffusion.

For a quantitative description of the behavior of gases, we will employ some simple gas laws and a more general expression called the *ideal gas equation*. These laws will be explained by the kinetic-molecular theory of gases. The topics covered in this chapter extend the discussion of reaction stoichiometry from the previous chapter and lay some groundwork for use

◀ FIGURE 2-1
The gaseous states of three halogens (group 17)
The greenish yellow gas is $Cl_2(g)$; the brownish red gas is $Br_2(g)$ above a small pool of liquid bromine; the violet gas is $I_2(g)$ in contact with grayish-black solid iodine. Most other common gases, such as H_2, O_2, N_2, CO, and CO_2, are colorless.

in Chapter 4 on thermochemistry. The relationships between gases and the other states of matter—liquids and solids—are discussed in Chapter 3.

2-1 Properties of Gases: Gas Pressure

Some characteristics of gases are familiar to everyone. Gases expand to fill their containers and assume the shapes of their containers. They diffuse into one another and mix in all proportions. We cannot see individual particles of a gas, although we can see the bulk gas if it is colored (Fig. 2-1). Some gases, such as hydrogen and methane, are combustible; whereas others, such as helium and neon, are chemically unreactive.

Four properties determine the physical behavior of a gas: the amount of the gas (in moles) and the volume, temperature, and pressure of the gas. If we know any three of these, we can usually calculate the value of the remaining one by using a mathematical equation called an *equation of state* (such as the ideal gas equation, given on page 54). To some extent we have already discussed the properties of amount, volume, and temperature, but we need to consider the idea of pressure.

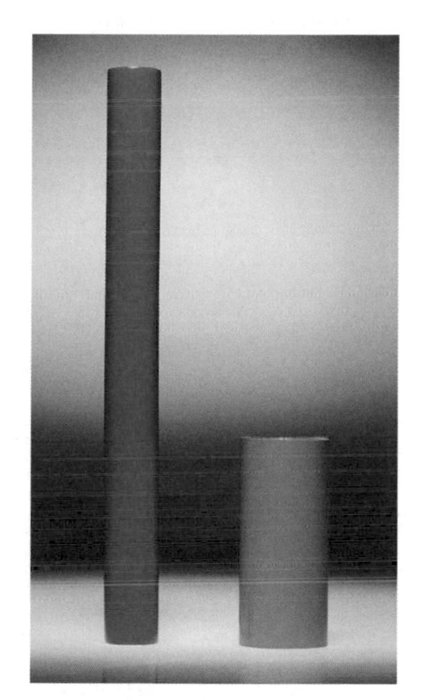

▲ FIGURE 2-2
Illustrating the pressure exerted by a solid
The two cylinders have the same mass and exert the same force on the supporting surface ($F = g \times m$). The tall, thin one has a smaller area of contact, however, and exerts a greater pressure ($P = F/A$).

The Concept of Pressure

A balloon expands when it is inflated with air, but what keeps the balloon in its distended shape? A plausible hypothesis is that molecules of a gas are in constant motion, frequently colliding with one another and with the walls of their container. In their collisions, the gas molecules exert a force on the container walls. This force keeps the balloon distended. It is not easy, however, to measure the total force exerted by a gas. Instead of focusing on this total force, we consider instead the gas pressure. **Pressure** is defined as a force per unit area, that is, a force divided by the area over which the force is distributed. Figure 2-2 illustrates the idea of pressure exerted by a solid.

In SI, the unit of force is a *newton* (N), which is the force, F, required to produce an acceleration of one meter per second per second ($1\ \text{m s}^{-2}$) in a one-kilogram mass (1 kg), that is, $1\ \text{N} = 1\ \text{kg m s}^{-2}$. The corresponding force per unit area—pressure—is expressed in the unit N/m^2. A pressure of one newton per square meter is defined as one **pascal (Pa)**. Thus, a pressure in pascals is

$$P\,(\text{Pa}) = \frac{F\,(\text{N})}{A\,(\text{m}^2)} \tag{2.1}$$

A pascal is a rather small pressure unit, so the **kilopascal (kPa)** is more commonly used. The pascal honors Blaise Pascal (1623–1662), who studied pressure and its transmission through fluids—the basis of modern hydraulics.

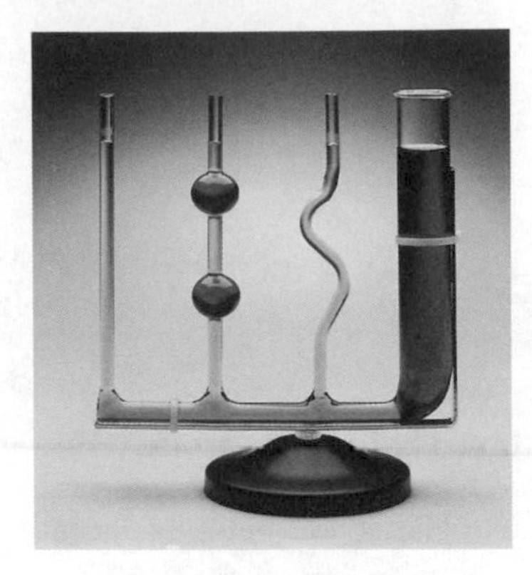

▲ FIGURE 2-3
The concept of liquid pressure
All the interconnected vessels fill to the same height. As a result, the liquid pressures are the same despite the different shapes and volumes of the containers.

Liquid Pressure

Because it is difficult to measure the total force exerted by gas molecules, it is also difficult to apply equation (2.1) to gases. The pressure of a gas is usually measured indirectly, by comparing it with a liquid pressure. Figure 2-3 illustrates the concept of liquid pressure and suggests that the pressure of a liquid depends only on the height of the liquid column and the density of the liquid. To confirm this statement, consider a liquid with density d, contained in a cylinder with cross-sectional area A, filled to a height h.

Now recall that (1) weight is a force, and weight (W) and mass (m) are proportional: $W = g \times m$. (2) The mass of a liquid is the product of its volume and density: $m = V \times d$. (3) The volume of a cylinder is the product of its height and cross-sectional area: $V = h \times A$. We use these facts to derive the equation:

$$P = \frac{F}{A} = \frac{W}{A} = \frac{g \times m}{A} = \frac{g \times V \times d}{A} = \frac{g \times h \times \cancel{A} \times d}{\cancel{A}} = g \times h \times d \qquad (2.2)$$

Thus, because g is a constant, *liquid pressure is directly proportional to the liquid density and the height of the liquid column.*

Barometric Pressure

In 1643, Evangelista Torricelli constructed the device pictured in Figure 2-4 to measure the pressure exerted by the atmosphere. This device is called a **barometer**.

If a glass tube that is open at both ends stands upright in a container of mercury (Fig. 2-4a), the mercury levels inside and outside the tube are the same. To create the situation in Figure 2-4(b), we seal one end of a long glass tube, completely fill the tube with Hg(l), cover the open end, and invert the tube into a container of Hg(l). Then we reopen the end that is submerged in the mercury. The mercury level in the tube falls to a certain height and stays there. Something keeps the mercury at a greater height inside the tube than outside. Some tried to ascribe this phenomenon to forces within the tube, but Torricelli understood that the forces involved originated outside the tube.

In the open-end tube (Fig. 2-4a), the atmosphere exerts the same pressure on the surface of the mercury both inside and outside the tube, and the liquid levels are equal. Inside the closed-end tube (Fig. 2-4b), there is no air above the mercury (only a trace of mercury vapor). The atmosphere exerts a force on the surface of the mercury in the outside container. This force is transmitted through the liquid, holding up the mercury column within the tube. The column exerts a downward pressure that depends on its height and the density of Hg(l). When the pressure at the bottom of the mercury column is equal to the pressure of the atmosphere, the column height is maintained.

The height of mercury in a barometer provides a measure of **barometric pressure.** Barometric pressures may be expressed in a unit called **millimeter of mercury (mmHg),** defined as the pressure exerted by a column of mercury that is exactly 1 mm in height when the density of mercury is equal to $13.5951\ g/cm^3$(0 °C) and the acceleration due to gravity, g, is equal to $9.80655\ m/s^2$. Notice that this unit of pressure assumes specific values for the density of mercury and the acceleration due to gravity. This is because the density of Hg(l) depends on temperature and g depends on the specific location on Earth. Typically, the pressure exerted by the atmosphere can support a column of mercury that is about 760 mm high and thus, atmospheric pressure is typically about 760 mmHg. Let's use equation (2.2) to calculate the pressure exerted by a column of mercury that is exactly 760 mm high when the density of mercury is $d = 13.5951\ g/cm^3 = 1.35951 \times 10^4\ kg/m^3$ and $g = 9.80655\ m/s^2$.

▶ In this calculation, we have written the units of d and g in the form $kg\ m^{-3}$ and $m\ s^{-2}$, respectively, rather than as kg/m^3 and m/s^2. You must become equally comfortable with using either negative exponents or a slash (/) when working with derived units. For example, the unit $kg\ m^{-1}\ s^{-2}$ may also be written as $kg/(m\ s^2)$.

$$P = (9.80665\ m\ s^{-2})(0.760000\ m)(1.35951\ 10^4\ kg\ m^{-3})$$
$$= 1.01325\ 10^5\ kg\ m^{-1}\ s^{-2}$$

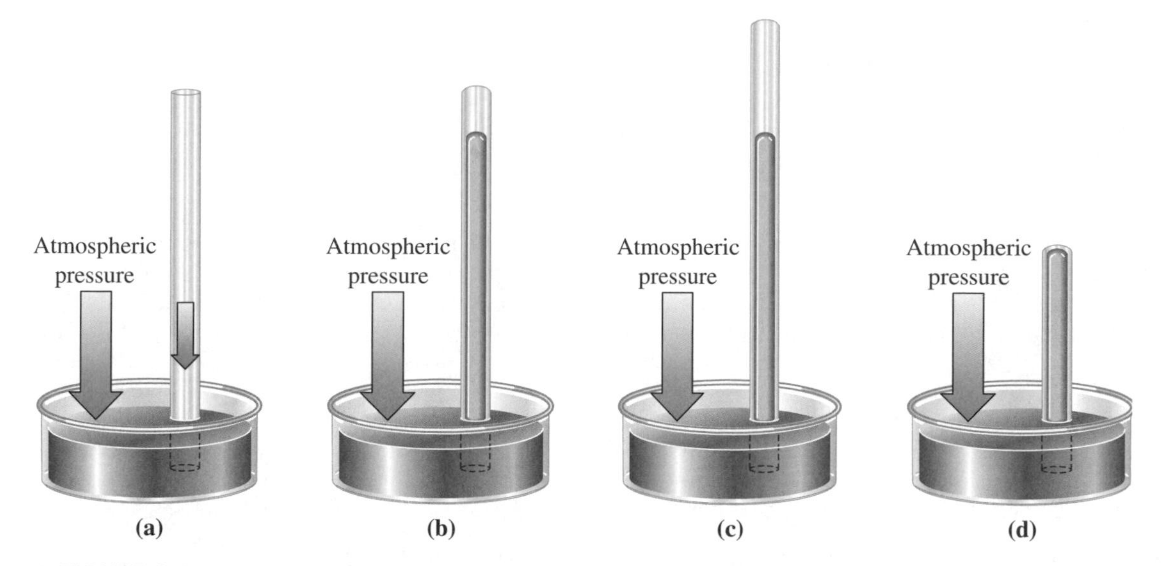

▲ FIGURE 2-4
Measurement of atmospheric pressure with a mercury barometer
Arrows represent the pressure exerted by the atmosphere. **(a)** The liquid mercury levels are equal inside and outside the open-end tube. **(b)** A column of mercury 760 mm high is maintained in the closed-end tube, regardless of the overall height of the tube **(c)** as long as it exceeds 760 mm. **(d)** A column of mercury fills a closed-end tube that is shorter than 760 mm. In the closed-end tubes in (b) and (c), the region above the mercury column is devoid of air and contains only a trace of mercury vapor.

The unit that arises in this calculation, $kg\ m^{-1}\ s^{-2}$, is the SI unit for pressure and, as mentioned earlier, is called the pascal (Pa). A pressure of exactly 101,325 Pa or 101.325 kPa, has special significance because in the SI system of units, **one standard atmosphere (atm)** is defined to be exactly equal to 101,325 Pa, or 101.325 kPa. Another pressure unit that is sometimes encountered is a unit called a **torr** and denoted by the symbol **Torr**. This unit honors Torricelli and is defined as exactly 1/760 of a standard atmosphere. The following expression shows the relationships among these units.

$$1\ \text{atm} = 760\ \text{Torr} \approx 760\ \text{mmHg} \qquad \textbf{(2.3)}$$

As indicated above, the units torr and millimeters of mercury are not strictly equal. This is because 760 Torr is *exactly* equal to 101,325 Pa but 760 mmHg is only *approximately* equal to 101,325 Pa (that is, to about six or seven significant figures). The difference between a torr and a millimeter of mercury is too small to worry about, except in highly accurate work. Thus, in this text, we will use the pressure units of Torr and mmHg interchangeably.

Mercury is a relatively rare, expensive, and poisonous liquid. Why use it rather than water in a barometer? As we will see in Example 2-1, the extreme height required for a water barometer is a distinct disadvantage. Whereas atmospheric pressure can be measured with a mercury barometer less than 1 m high, a water barometer would have to be as tall as a three-storey building.

When you use a drinking straw, you reduce the air pressure above the liquid inside the straw by inhaling. Atmospheric pressure on the liquid outside the straw then pushes the liquid up the straw and into your mouth. An old-fashioned hand suction pump for pumping water (once common in rural areas) works by the same principle. The result of Example 2-1 indicates, however, that even if all the

EXAMPLE 2-1 Comparing Liquid Pressures

What is the height of a column of water that exerts the same pressure as a column of mercury 76.0 cm (760 mm) high?

Analyze

Equation (2.2) shows that, for a given liquid pressure, the column height is inversely proportional to the liquid density. The lower the liquid density, the greater the height of the liquid column. Mercury is 13.6 times as dense as water ($13.6\ g/cm^3$ versus $1.00\ g/cm^3$). If columns of water and mercury exert the same pressure, then the column of water is 13.6 times as high as the column of mercury.

Solve

Although we have already reasoned out the answer, we can arrive at the same conclusion by applying equation (2.2) twice, and then setting the two pressures equal to each other. Equation (2.2) can be used to describe the pressure of the mercury column of known height and the pressure of the water column of unknown height. Then we can set the two pressures equal to each other.

$$\text{pressure of Hg column} = g \times h_{Hg} \times d_{Hg} = g \times 76.0\ \text{cm} \times 13.6\ \text{g/cm}^3$$

$$\text{pressure of H}_2\text{O column} = g \times h_{H_2O} \times d_{H_2O} = g \times h_{H_2O} \times 1.00\ \text{g/cm}^3$$

$$g \times h_{H_2O} \times 1.00\ \text{g/cm}^3 = g \times 76.0\ \text{cm} \times 13.6\ \text{g/cm}^3$$

$$h_{H_2O} = 76.0\ \text{cm} \times \frac{13.6\ \text{g/cm}^3}{1.00\ \text{g/cm}^3} = 1.03 \times 10^3\ \text{cm} = 10.3\ \text{m}$$

Assess

We can think about equation (2.2) in another way. For a column of liquid of fixed height, the greater the density of the liquid, the greater the pressure exerted by the liquid column. A column of mercury that is 760 mm high will exert a pressure 13.6 times as great as a column of water that is 760 mm high.

PRACTICE EXAMPLE A: A barometer is filled with diethylene glycol ($d = 1.118\ g/cm^3$). The liquid height is found to be 9.25 m. What is the barometric (atmospheric) pressure expressed in millimeters of mercury?

PRACTICE EXAMPLE B: A barometer is filled with triethylene glycol. The liquid height is found to be 9.14 m when the atmospheric pressure is 757 mmHg. What is the density of triethylene glycol?

2-1 CONCEPT ASSESSMENT

Explain how the action of a water siphon is related to that of a suction pump.

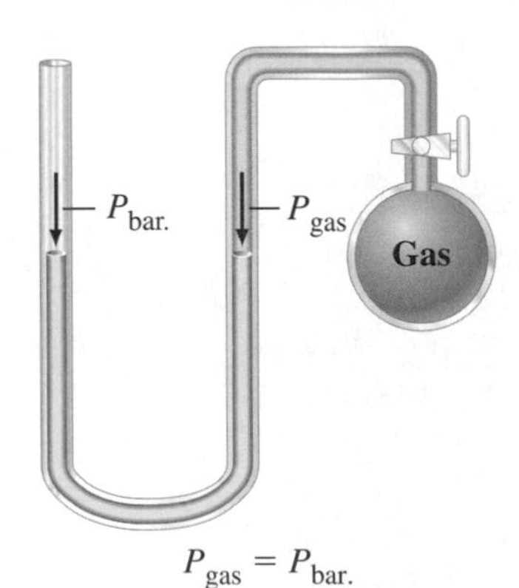

(a) The gas pressure is equal to the barometric pressure.

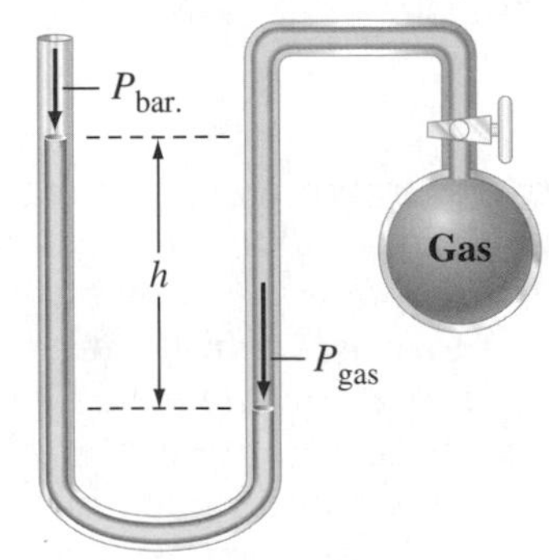

(b) The gas pressure is greater than the barometric pressure.

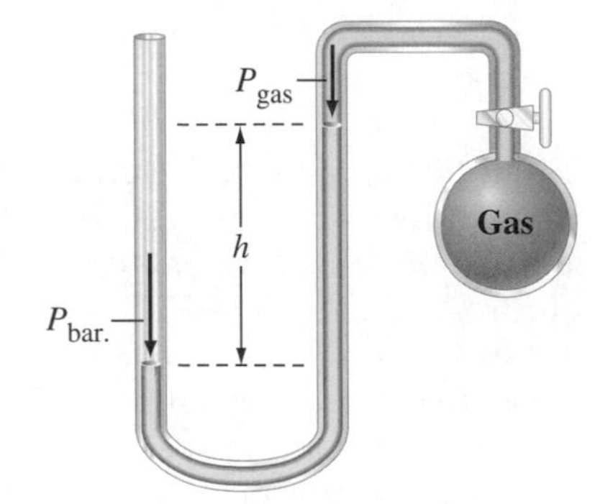

(c) The gas pressure is less than the barometric pressure.

▲ FIGURE 2-5
Measurement of gas pressure with an open-end manometer
The possible relationships between barometric pressure and a gas pressure under measurement are pictured here and described in Example 2–2. If P_{gas} and $P_{bar.}$ are expressed in mmHg, then ΔP is numerically equal to the height h expressed in millimeters.

EXAMPLE 2-2 Using a Manometer to Measure Gas Pressure

When the manometer in Figure 2-5(c) is filled with liquid mercury ($d = 13.6\ g/cm^3$), the barometric pressure is 748.2 mmHg, and the difference in mercury levels is 8.6 mmHg. What is the gas pressure P_{gas}?

Analyze

We must first establish which is greater: the barometric pressure or the gas pressure. In Figure 2-5(c), the barometric pressure forces liquid mercury down the tube toward the gas sample. The barometric pressure is greater than the gas pressure. Thus, $\Delta P = P_{gas} - P_{bar.} < 0$.

Solve

The gas pressure is less than the barometric pressure. Therefore, we subtract 8.6 mmHg from the barometric pressure to obtain the gas pressure.

$$P_{gas} = P_{bar.} + \Delta P = 748.2\ \text{mmHg} - 8.6\ \text{mmHg} = 739.6\ \text{mmHg}$$

Assess

Because all pressures are expressed in millimeters of mercury, the pressure difference (ΔP) is numerically equal to the difference in mercury levels. Thus, the density of mercury does not enter into the calculation.

PRACTICE EXAMPLE A: Suppose that the mercury level in Example 2-2 is 7.8 mm higher in the arm open to the atmosphere than in the closed arm. What would be the value of P_{gas}?

PRACTICE EXAMPLE B: Suppose $P_{bar.}$ and P_{gas} are those described in Example 2-2, but the manometer is filled with liquid glycerol ($d = 1.26\ g/cm^3$) instead of mercury. What would be the difference in the two levels of the liquid?

air could be removed from inside a pipe, atmospheric pressure outside the pipe could not raise water to a height of more than about 10 m. Thus, a suction pump works only for shallow wells. To pump water from a deep well, a mechanical pump is required. The mechanical pump pushes the water upward by using a force that is greater than the force of the atmosphere pushing the water down.

Manometers

Although a mercury barometer is indispensable for measuring the pressure of the atmosphere, it is rarely used alone to measure other gas pressures. The difficulty with a barometer is in placing it inside the container of gas whose pressure is to be measured. However, the pressure of the gas to be measured can be compared with barometric pressure by using a **manometer**. Figure 2-5 illustrates the principle of an open-end manometer. When the gas pressure being measured and the prevailing atmospheric (barometric) pressure are equal, the heights of the mercury columns in the two arms of the manometer are equal. A difference in height of the two arms signifies a difference between the gas pressure and barometric pressure.

Units of Pressure: A Summary

Table 2.1 lists several different units used to express pressure. The units shown in red are used frequently by chemists, even though they are not part of the SI system. The atmosphere is a useful unit because volumes of gases are often measured at the prevailing atmospheric pressure. Typically, the atmospheric pressure is close to 1 atm, or 760 Torr. The units shown in blue are those preferred in the SI system.

The units shown in black in Table 2.1 are based on the unit **bar**. One bar is 100 times as large as a kilopascal. Atmospheric pressure is typically close to 1 bar. The unit *millibar* is commonly used by meteorologists.

Although we can generally choose freely among the pressure units in Table 2.1 when doing calculations involving gases, we will encounter situations that require SI units. This is the case in Example 2-3.

TABLE 2.1 Some Common Pressure Units

Atmosphere	atm	
Millimeter of mercury	mmHg	1 atm ≃ 760 mmHg
Torr	Torr	= 760 Torr
Pascal	Pa	= 101,325 Pa
Kilopascal	kPa	= 101.325 kPa
Bar	bar	= 1.01325 bar
Millibar	mbar	= 1013.25 mbar

EXAMPLE 2-3 Using SI Units of Pressure

The 1.000 kg red cylinder in Figure 2-2 has a diameter of 4.10 cm. What pressure, expressed in Torr, does this cylinder exert on the surface beneath it?

Analyze

We must apply equation (2.2). It is best to use SI units and obtain a pressure in SI units (Pa), and then convert the pressure to the required units (Torr).

Solve

Expression (2.1) defines pressure as force divided by area.

$$P = \frac{F}{A}$$

The force exerted by the cylinder is its weight.

$$F = W = m \times g$$

The mass is 1.000 kg, and g (the acceleration due to gravity) is 9.81 m s^{-2}. The product of these two terms is the force in newtons.

$$F = m \times g = 1.000\ \text{kg} \times 9.81\ \text{m s}^{-2} = 9.81\ \text{N}$$

The force is exerted on the area of contact between the cylinder and the underlying surface. This circular area is calculated by using the radius of the cylinder—one-half the 4.10 cm diameter, expressed in meters.

$$A = \text{p}r^2 = 3.1416 \times \left(2.05\ \text{cm} \times \frac{1\ \text{m}}{100\ \text{cm}}\right)^2 = 1.32 \times 10^{-3}\ \text{m}^2$$

The force divided by the area (in square meters) gives the pressure in pascals.

$$P = \frac{F}{A} = \frac{9.81\ \text{N}}{1.32 \times 10^{-3}\ \text{m}^2} = 7.43 \times 10^3\ \text{Pa}$$

The relationship between the units Torr and pascal (Table 2.1) is used for the final conversion.

$$P = 7.43 \times 10^3\ \text{Pa} \times \frac{760\ \text{Torr}}{101{,}325\ \text{Pa}} = 55.7\ \text{Torr}$$

Assess

It's difficult to tell at a glance whether this is a reasonable result. To check our result, let us focus instead on a cylindrical column of mercury that is 55.7 mm high and has a diameter of 4.10 cm. This column of mercury also exerts a pressure of 55.7 mmHg = 55.7 Torr. The volume of mercury in this column is $V = \text{p}r^2 h = \text{p} \times (2.05\ \text{cm})^2 \times 5.57\ \text{cm} = 73.5\ \text{cm}^3$. The density of mercury is about 13.6 g/cm^3 (page 44) and thus, the mass of the mercury column is $73.5\ \text{cm}^3 \times 13.6\ \text{g/cm}^3 = 1.00 \times 10^3\ \text{g} = 1.00\ \text{kg}$. This is exactly the mass of the steel cylinder.

PRACTICE EXAMPLE A: The 1.000 kg green cylinder in Figure 2-2 has a diameter of 2.60 cm. What pressure, expressed in Torr, does this cylinder exert on the surface beneath it?

PRACTICE EXAMPLE B: We want to increase the pressure exerted by the 1.000 kg red cylinder in Example 2-3 to 100.0 mb by placing a weight on top of it. What must be the mass of this weight? Must the added weight have the same cross-sectional area as the cylinder? Explain.

2-2 The Simple Gas Laws

In this section, we consider relationships involving the pressure, volume, temperature, and amount of a gas. Specifically, we will see how one variable depends on another, as the remaining two are held fixed. Collectively, these relationships are referred to as the simple gas laws. You can use these laws in problem solving, but

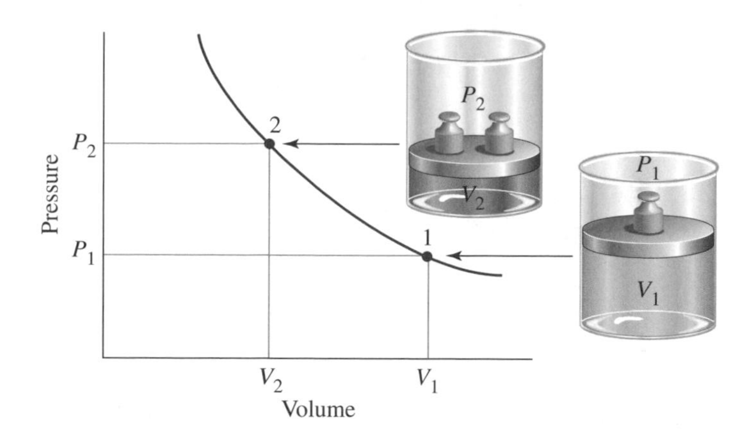

◀ FIGURE 2-6
Relationship between gas volume and pressure—Boyle's law
When the temperature and amount of gas are held constant, gas volume is inversely proportional to the pressure: A doubling of the pressure causes the volume to decrease to one-half its original value.

you will probably prefer the equation developed in the next section—the ideal gas equation. You may find that the greatest use of the simple gas laws is in solidifying your qualitative understanding of the behavior of gases.

Boyle's Law

In 1662, working with air, Robert Boyle discovered the first of the simple gas laws, now known as **Boyle's law**.

> For a fixed amount of gas at a constant temperature, the gas volume is inversely proportional to the gas pressure. **(2.4)**

Consider the gas in Figure 2-6. It is confined in a cylinder closed off by a freely moving "weightless" piston. The pressure of the gas depends on the total weight placed on top of the piston. This weight (a force) divided by the area of the piston yields the gas pressure. If the weight on the piston is doubled, the pressure doubles and the gas volume decreases to one-half its original value. If the pressure of the gas is tripled, the volume decreases to one-third. Conversely, if the pressure is reduced by one-half, the gas volume doubles, and so on. Mathematically, the inverse relationship between gas pressure and volume is expressed as

$$P \propto \frac{1}{V} \quad \text{or} \quad PV = a \text{ (a constant)} \qquad \textbf{(2.5)}$$

When the proportionality sign ($\propto$) is replaced with an equal sign and a proportionality constant, the product of the pressure and volume of a fixed amount of gas at a given temperature is seen to be a constant (a). The value of a depends on the amount of gas and the temperature. The graph in Figure 2-6 is that of $PV = a$. It is called a hyperbola.

The equation $PV = a$ can be used to derive another equation that is useful for situations in which a gas undergoes a change at constant temperature. If we write equation (2.5) for the initial state (i) and for the final state (f), we get $P_i V_i = a$ and $P_f V_f = a$. Because both PV products are equal to the same value of a, we obtain the result

$$P_i V_i = P_f V_f \qquad (n \text{ constant}, T \text{ constant})$$

The equation above is often used to relate pressure and volume changes.

2-2 CONCEPT ASSESSMENT

A 50.0 L cylinder contains nitrogen gas at a pressure of 21.5 atm. The contents of the cylinder are emptied into an evacuated tank of unknown volume. If the final pressure in the tank is 1.55 atm, then what is the volume of the tank? **(a)** $(21.5/1.55) \times 50.0$ L; **(b)** $(1.55/21.5) \times 50.0$ L; **(c)** $21.5/(1.55 \times 50)$ L; **(d)** $1.55/(21.5 \times 50)$ L.

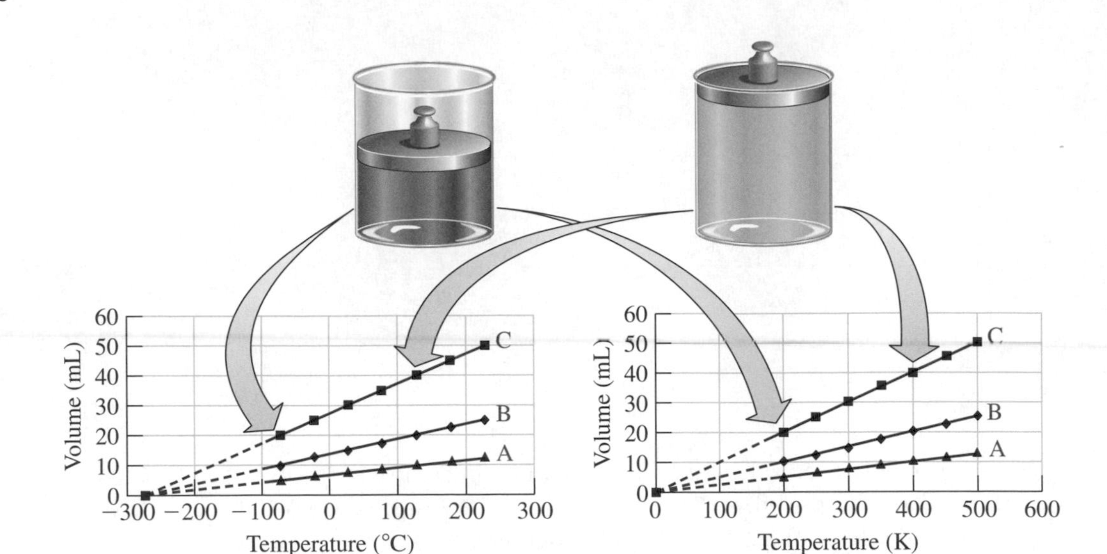

▲ FIGURE 2-7
Gas volume as a function of temperature
Volume is plotted against temperature on two different scales—Celsius and Kelvin. The volumes of three different gases (A, B, and C) are measured at 1 atm and 500 K. As the temperature is lowered, the volume decreases as predicted by Charles's law. Thus, at 250 K (−23 °C), for example, the volume of gas C has become 25 mL, one-half of the original 50 mL. Although the relationship between volume and temperature is linear for both the Celsius and Kelvin temperature scales, the volume is directly proportional only to the absolute temperature. That is, the volume must be zero at a temperature of zero. Only the Kelvin scale meets this requirement.

▶ It is probably fair to say that the absolute zero of temperature was "discovered" by noting that a plot of V (or P) vs. T for any gas extrapolates to −273 °C.

Charles's Law

The relationship between the volume of a gas and temperature was discovered by the French physicists Jacques Charles in 1787 and, independently, by Joseph Louis Gay-Lussac, who published it in 1802.

Figure 2-7 pictures a fixed amount of gas confined in a cylinder. The pressure is held constant at 1 atm while the temperature is varied. The volume of gas increases as the temperature is raised and decreases as the temperature is lowered. The relationship is linear. Figure 2-7 shows the linear dependence of volume on temperature for three gases at three different initial conditions. One point in common to the three lines is their intersection with the temperature axis. Although they differ at every other temperature, the gas volumes all reach a value of zero at the same temperature. The temperature at which the volume of a hypothetical* gas becomes zero is the absolute zero of temperature: −273.15 °C on the Celsius scale or 0 K on the **absolute**, or **Kelvin**, scale. The relationship between the Kelvin temperature, T, and the Celsius temperature, t, is shown below in equation (2.6).

▶ When converting from °C to K, apply the addition and subtraction significant figure rule: the two-significant-figure 25 °C, when added to 273.15, becomes the three-significant-figure 298 K. Similarly, 25.0 °C becomes 298.2 K (that is, $25.0 + 273.15 = 298.15$, which rounds to 298.2).

$$T(\text{K}) = t(^\circ\text{C}) + 273.15 \tag{2.6}$$

The graph on the right hand side of Figure 2-7 shows that, from a volume of zero at 0 K, the gas volume is directly proportional to the Kelvin temperature. The statement of **Charles's law** given below in (2.7) summarizes the relationship between volume and temperature.

▶ Charles's ideas about the effect of temperature on the volume of a gas were probably influenced by his passion for hot-air balloons, a popular craze of the late eighteenth century.

> The volume of a fixed amount of gas at constant pressure is directly proportional to the Kelvin (absolute) temperature. **(2.7)**

*All gases condense to liquids or solids before the temperature approaches absolute zero. Also, when we speak of the volume of a gas, we mean the free volume among the gas molecules, not the volume of the molecules themselves. Thus, the gas we refer to here is *hypothetical*. It is a gas whose molecules have mass but no volume and that does not condense to a liquid or solid.

In mathematical terms, Charles's law is

$$V \propto T \qquad \text{or} \qquad V = bT \text{ (where } b \text{ is a constant)} \qquad \textbf{(2.8)}$$

The value of the constant b depends on the amount of gas and the pressure. It does *not* depend on the identity of the gas.

From either expression (2.7) or (2.8), we see that doubling the Kelvin temperature of a gas causes its volume to double. Reducing the Kelvin temperature by one-half (say, from 300 to 150 K) causes the volume to decrease to one-half, and so on.

Equation (2.8) can be used to derive an equation that is useful for situations in which a gas undergoes a change at constant pressure. If we apply equation (2.8) twice, once for the initial state (i) and once for the final state (f), we get $(V_i/T_i) = b$ and $(V_f/T_f) = b$. Because both (V/T) quotients are equal to the same value of b, we obtain the result

$$\frac{V_i}{T_i} = \frac{V_f}{T_f} \qquad (n \text{ constant}, P \text{ constant})$$

The equation above is often used to relate volume and temperature changes.

▲ Charles experimented with the first hydrogen-filled balloons, much like the one shown here, though smaller. He also invented most of the features of modern ballooning, including the suspended basket and the valve to release gas.

2-3 CONCEPT ASSESSMENT

A balloon is inflated to a volume of 2.50 L inside a house that is kept at 24 °C. Then it is taken outside on a very cold winter day. If the temperature outside is −25 °C, what will be the volume of the balloon when it is taken outside? Assume that the quantity of air in the balloon and its pressure both remain constant. **(a)** (248/297) × 2.50 L; **(b)** (297/248) × 2.50 L; **(c)** 248/(297 × 2.50) L; **(d)** 297/(248 × 2.50) L.

2-4 CONCEPT ASSESSMENT

Doubling a gas temperature from 100 K to 200 K causes a gas volume to double. Would you expect a similar doubling of the gas volume when a gas is heated from 100 °C to 200 °C? Explain.

Standard Conditions of Temperature and Pressure

Because gas properties depend on temperature and pressure, it is useful to have a set of standard conditions of temperature and pressure that can be used for comparing different gases. The standard temperature for gases is taken to be 0 °C = 273.15 K and standard pressure, 1 bar = 100 kPa = 10^5 Pa. **Standard conditions of temperature and pressure** are usually abbreviated as **STP**. It is important to emphasize that STP was defined differently in the past, and some texts and chemists still use the old definition. The old definition, which was based on a standard pressure of 1 atm, is discouraged. In this text, we use the definition recommended by the International Union of Pure and Applied Chemistry (IUPAC):

◄ Although IUPAC has recommended that one *bar* should replace the *atmosphere* as the standard state condition for gas law and thermodynamic data, use of the atmosphere persists.

Standard Temperature and Pressure (STP): 0 °C and 1 bar = 10^5 Pa

Avogadro's Law

In 1808, Gay-Lussac reported that gases react by volumes in the ratio of small whole numbers. One proposed explanation was that equal volumes of gases at the same temperature and pressure contain equal numbers of atoms. Dalton did not agree with this proposition, however. If Gay-Lussac's proposition

2 vol. H_2 + 1 vol. O_2 → 2 vol. H_2O

▲ FIGURE 2-8
Formation of water—actual observation and Avogadro's hypothesis
In the reaction $2\,H_2(g) + 1\,O_2(g) \longrightarrow 2\,H_2O(g)$, only one-half as many O_2 molecules are required as are H_2 molecules. If equal volumes of gases contain equal numbers of molecules, this means the volume of $O_2(g)$ is one-half that of $H_2(g)$. The combining ratio by volume is 2:1:2.

were true, then the reaction of hydrogen and oxygen to form water would be $H(g) + O(g) \longrightarrow HO(g)$, with combining volumes of 1:1:1, rather than the 2:1:2 that was observed.

▶ Avogadro's hypothesis and statements derived from it apply only to gases. There is no similar relationship for liquids or solids.

In 1811, Amedeo Avogadro resolved this dilemma by proposing not only the "equal volumes–equal numbers" hypothesis, but also that molecules of a gas may break up into half-molecules when they react. Using modern terminology, we would say that O_2 molecules split into atoms, which then combine with molecules of H_2 to form H_2O molecules. In this way, the volume of oxygen needed is only one-half that of hydrogen. Avogadro's reasoning is outlined in Figure 2-8.

Avogadro's equal volumes–equal numbers hypothesis can be stated in either of two ways.

1. Equal volumes of different gases compared at the same temperature and pressure contain equal numbers of molecules.
2. Equal numbers of molecules of different gases compared at the same temperature and pressure occupy equal volumes.

▲ **Amedeo Avogadro (1776–1856)—a scientist ahead of his time**
Avogadro's hypothesis and its ramifications were not understood by his contemporaries but were effectively communicated by Stanislao Cannizzaro (1826–1910) about 50 years later.

A relationship that follows from *Avogadro's hypothesis*, often called **Avogadro's law**, is as follows.

At a fixed temperature and pressure, the volume of a gas is directly proportional to the amount of gas. **(2.9)**

If the number of moles of gas (n) is doubled, the volume doubles, and so on. A mathematical statement of this fact is

$$V \propto n \quad \text{and} \quad V = c \times n$$

The constant c, which is equal to V/n, is the volume per mole of gas, a quantity we call the molar volume. Molar volumes of gases vary with temperature and pressure but experiment reveals that, for given values of T and P, the molar volumes of all gases are approximately equal. The data in Table 2.2 show that the molar volume of a gas is approximately 22.414 L at 0 °C and 1 atm and 22.711 L at STP. The following statement summarizes these observations.

$$1 \text{ mol gas} = 22.414 \text{ L (at 0 °C, 1 atm)} = 22.711 \text{ L (at STP)} \qquad \textbf{(2.10)}$$

▶ In general, relating the amount of gas and its volume is best done with the ideal gas equation (Section 2-3).

Figure 2-9 should help you to visualize 22.414 L of a gas.

TABLE 2.2 Densities and Molar Volumes of Various Gases

Gas	Molar Mass, $g\,mol^{-1}$	Density (at STP), $g\,L^{-1}$	Molar Volume,[a] $L\,mol^{-1}$	
			(at STP)	(at 0°C, 1 atm)
H_2	2.01588	8.87104×10^{-2}	22.724	22.427
He	4.00260	0.17615	22.722	22.425
Ideal gas	–	–	22.711	22.414
N_2	28.0134	1.23404	22.701	22.404
CO	28.0101	1.23375	22.696	22.399
O_2	31.9988	1.41034	22.689	22.392
CH_4	16.0425	0.70808	22.656	22.360
NF_3	71.0019	3.14234	22.595	22.300
CO_2	44.0095	1.95096	22.558	22.263
N_2O	44.0128	1.95201	22.550	22.255
C_2H_6	30.0690	1.33740	22.483	22.189
NH_3	17.0352	0.76139	22.374	22.081
SF_6	146.0554	6.52800	22.374	22.081
C_3H_8	44.0956	1.98318	22.235	21.944
SO_2	64.064	2.89190	22.153	21.863

Source: The densities are from the National Institute of Standards and Technology (NIST) *Chemistry WebBook*, available online at http://webbook.nist.gov/chemistry/.

[a]The molar volume is equal to the molar mass divided by the density. The molar volume at 0 °C and 1 atm is obtained by dividing the molar volume at STP by 1.01325.

2-5 CONCEPT ASSESSMENT

Without doing an actual calculation, determine which of the following expressions equals the final volume of gas if 20.0 g O_2 is added to 40.0 g O_2 at 0 °C and 1 atm, the temperature is changed to 30 °C, and the pressure to 825 Torr.

(a) $\left(\frac{40.0}{20.0} \times \frac{1}{32.00} \times 22.4 \times \frac{760}{825} \times \frac{303}{273}\right)$ L

(b) $\left(\frac{20.0}{40.0} \times \frac{1}{32.00} \times 22.4 \times \frac{825}{760} \times \frac{273}{303}\right)$ L

(c) $\left(60.0 \times \frac{1}{32.00} \times 22.4 \times \frac{825}{760} \times \frac{303}{273}\right)$ L

(d) $\left(\frac{3}{2} \times 40.0 \times \frac{1}{32.00} \times 22.4 \times \frac{760}{825} \times \frac{303}{273}\right)$ L

(e) $\left(\frac{2}{3} \times 60.0 \times \frac{1}{32.00} \times 22.4 \times \frac{760}{825} \times \frac{303}{273}\right)$ L

◀ FIGURE 2-9
Molar volume of a gas visualized
The wooden cube is 28.2 cm on edge and has approximately the same volume as one mole of gas at 1 atm and 0 °C: 22.414 L. By contrast, the volume of the basketball is 7.5 L; the soccer ball, 6.0 L; and the football, 4.4 L.

▶ The ideal gas equation will probably not be supplied on exams and should be memorized. Values of R given here, however, will be available. There is really only one R but like many properties and constants, its value can be expressed in a variety of units.

2-3 Combining the Gas Laws: The Ideal Gas Equation and the General Gas Equation

Each of the three simple gas laws describes the effect that changes in one variable have on the gas volume when the other two variables are held constant.

1. Boyle's law describes the effect of pressure, $V \propto 1/P$.
2. Charles's law describes the effect of temperature, $V \propto T$.
3. Avogadro's law describes the effect of the amount of gas, $V \propto n$.

These three laws can be combined into a single equation—the **ideal gas equation**—that includes all four gas variables: volume, pressure, temperature, and amount of gas.

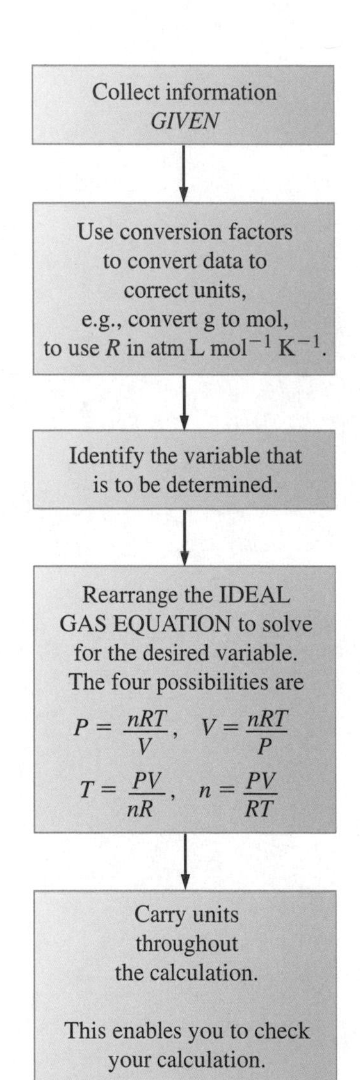

Collect information
GIVEN
Use conversion factors to convert data to correct units, e.g., convert g to mol, to use R in atm L mol^{-1} K^{-1}.
Identify the variable that is to be determined.
Rearrange the IDEAL GAS EQUATION to solve for the desired variable. The four possibilities are
$P = \frac{nRT}{V}$, $V = \frac{nRT}{P}$
$T = \frac{PV}{nR}$, $n = \frac{PV}{RT}$
Carry units throughout the calculation.
This enables you to check your calculation.

▲ **Applying the ideal gas equation**

The Ideal Gas Equation

In accord with the three simple gas laws, the volume of a gas is *directly* proportional to the amount of gas, *directly* proportional to the Kelvin temperature, and *inversely* proportional to pressure. That is,

$$V \propto \frac{nT}{P} \quad \text{and} \quad V = \frac{RnT}{P}$$

$$PV = nRT \tag{2.11}$$

A gas whose behavior conforms to the ideal gas equation is called an **ideal**, or **perfect, gas**. Before we can apply equation (2.11), we need a value for the constant R, called the **gas constant**. One way to obtain this is to substitute into equation (2.11) the molar volume of an ideal gas at 0 °C and 1 atm. However, the value of R will then depend on which units are used to express pressure and volume. With a molar volume of 22.4140 L and pressure in atmospheres,

$$R = \frac{PV}{nT} = \frac{1\ \text{atm} \times 22.4140\ \text{L}}{1\ \text{mol} \times 273.15\ \text{K}} = 0.082057\ \text{atm L mol}^{-1}\ \text{K}^{-1}$$

Using the SI units of m^3 for volume and Pa for pressure gives

$$R = \frac{PV}{nT} = \frac{101{,}325\ \text{Pa} \times 2.24140 \times 10^{-2}\ \text{m}^3}{1\ \text{mol} \times 273.15\ \text{K}} = 8.3145\ \text{Pa m}^3\ \text{mol}^{-1}\ \text{K}^{-1}$$

The units Pa m^3 mol^{-1} K^{-1} also have another significance. The pascal has units kg m^{-1} s^{-2}, so the units m^3 Pa become kg m^2 s^{-2}, which is the SI unit of energy—the joule. Thus R also has the value

$$R = 8.3145\ \text{J mol}^{-1}\ \text{K}^{-1}$$

We will use this value of R when we consider the energy involved in gas expansion and compression.

Common values of the gas constant are listed in Table 2.3, and you will have a chance to use all of them in the Practice Examples and end-of-chapter exercises in this chapter. A general strategy for applying the ideal gas equation is illustrated in the diagram in the margin.

TABLE 2.3 Five Common Values of R

0.082057 atm L mol^{-1} K^{-1}
0.083145 bar L K^{-1} mol^{-1}
8.3145 kPa L K^{-1} mol^{-1}
8.3145 Pa m^3 mol^{-1} K^{-1}
8.3145 J mol^{-1} K^{-1}

The General Gas Equation

In Examples 2-4 and 2-5, the ideal gas equation is applied to a single set of conditions (P, V, n, and T). Sometimes a gas is described under two different

EXAMPLE 2-4 Calculating a Gas Volume with the Ideal Gas Equation

What is the volume occupied by 13.7 g $Cl_2(g)$ at 45 °C and 745 mmHg?

Analyze

This is a relatively straightforward application of the ideal gas equation. We are given an amount of gas (in grams), a pressure (in mmHg), and a temperature (in °C). Before using the ideal gas equation, we must express the amount in moles, the pressure in atmospheres, and the temperature in Kelvin. Include units throughout the calculation to ensure that the final result has acceptable units.

Solve

$$P = 745\ \text{mmHg} \times \frac{1\ \text{atm}}{760\ \text{mmHg}} = 0.980\ \text{atm}$$

$$V = ?$$

$$n = 13.7\ \text{g Cl}_2 \times \frac{1\ \text{mol Cl}_2}{70.91\ \text{g Cl}_2} = 0.193\ \text{mol Cl}_2$$

$$R = 0.08206\ \text{atm L mol}^{-1}\,\text{K}^{-1}$$

$$T = 45\ °\text{C} + 273 = 318\ \text{K}$$

Divide both sides of the ideal gas equation by P to solve for V.

$$\frac{PV}{P} = \frac{nRT}{P} \quad \text{and} \quad V = \frac{nRT}{P}$$

$$V = \frac{nRT}{P} = \frac{0.193\ \cancel{\text{mol}} \times 0.08206\ \cancel{\text{atm}}\ \text{L}\ \cancel{\text{mol}^{-1}}\ \cancel{\text{K}^{-1}} \times 318\ \cancel{\text{K}}}{0.980\ \cancel{\text{atm}}} = 5.14\ \text{L}$$

Assess

A useful check of the calculated result is to make certain the units cancel properly. In the setup above, all units cancel except for L, a unit of volume. Keep in mind that when canceling units, such a unit as mol^{-1} is the same as 1/mol. Thus, $\text{mol} \times \text{mol}^{-1} = 1$ and $\text{K} \times \text{K}^{-1} = 1$.

PRACTICE EXAMPLE A: What is the volume occupied by 20.2 g $NH_3(g)$ at −25°C and 752 mmHg?

PRACTICE EXAMPLE B: At what temperature will a 13.7 g Cl_2 sample exert a pressure of 0.993 bar when confined in a 7.50 L container?

EXAMPLE 2-5 Calculating a Gas Pressure with the Ideal Gas Equation

What is the pressure, in kilopascals, exerted by 1.00×10^{20} molecules of N_2 in a 305 mL flask at 175°C?

Analyze

We are given an amount of gas (in molecules), a volume (in mL), and a temperature (in °C). Before using these quantities in the ideal gas equation, we must express the amount in moles, the volume in liters, and the temperature in Kelvin. Include units throughout the calculation to ensure that the final result has acceptable units.

Solve

Because we seek a pressure in kilopascals, let us use the form of the ideal gas equation having

$$R = 8.3145\ \text{Pa m}^3\ \text{mol}^{-1}\,\text{K}^{-1}$$

The first step is to convert from molecules to moles of a gas, n.

$$n = 1.00 \times 10^{20}\ \text{molecules N}_2 \times \frac{1\ \text{mol N}_2}{6.022 \times 10^{23}\ \text{molecules N}_2}$$

$$= 0.000166\ \text{mol N}_2$$

(continued)

Convert from milliliters to liters and then to cubic meters.

$$V = 305\,\text{mL} \times \frac{1\,\text{L}}{1000\,\text{mL}} \times \frac{1\,\text{m}^3}{1000\,\text{L}} = 3.05 \times 10^{-4}\,\text{m}^3$$

Express gas temperature on the Kelvin scale.

$$T = 175°\text{C} + 273 = 448\,\text{K}$$

Rearrange the ideal gas equation to the form $P = nRT/V$, and substitute the above data.

$$P = \frac{nRT}{V} = \frac{0.000166\,\text{mol} \times 8.3145\,\text{Pa m}^3\,\text{mol}^{-1}\,\text{K}^{-1} \times 448\,\text{K}}{3.05 \times 10^{-4}\,\text{m}^3}$$
$$= 2.03 \times 10^3\,\text{Pa}$$

Finally, convert the pressure to the unit kilopascal.

$$P = 2.03 \times 10^3\,\text{Pa} \times \frac{1\,\text{kPa}}{1000\,\text{Pa}} = 2.03\,\text{kPa}$$

Assess

Again, we see from the cancellation of units above that only the desired unit—a pressure unit—remains.

PRACTICE EXAMPLE A: How many moles of He(g) are in a 5.00 L storage tank filled with helium at 10.5 atm pressure at 30.0 °C?

PRACTICE EXAMPLE B: How many molecules of $N_2(g)$ remain in an ultrahigh vacuum chamber of $3.45\,\text{m}^3$ volume when the pressure is reduced to 6.67×10^{-7} Pa at 25 °C?

sets of conditions. Here, the ideal gas equation must be applied twice—to an initial condition and a final condition. That is,

Initial condition (i)	*Final condition* (f)
$P_iV_i = n_iRT_i$	$P_fV_f = n_fRT_f$
$R = \dfrac{P_iV_i}{n_iT_i}$	$R = \dfrac{P_fV_f}{n_fT_f}$

The above expressions are equal to each other because each is equal to R.

$$\frac{P_iV_i}{n_iT_i} = \frac{P_fV_f}{n_fT_f} \qquad \textbf{(2.12)}$$

Expression (2.12) is called the **general gas equation**. It is often applied in cases in which one or two of the gas properties are held constant, and the equation can be simplified by eliminating these constants. For example, if a constant mass of gas is subject to changes in temperature, pressure, and volume, n_i and n_f cancel because they are equal (constant moles); thus we have

$$\frac{P_iV_i}{T_i} = \frac{P_fV_f}{T_f} \quad (n\text{ constant})$$

This equation is sometimes referred to as the *combined gas law*. In Example 2-6, both volume and mass are constant, and this establishes the simple relationship between gas pressure and temperature known as *Amontons's law*: The pressure of a fixed amount of gas confined to a fixed volume is directly proportional to the Kelvin temperature.

Using the Gas Laws

When confronted with a problem involving gases, students sometimes wonder which gas equation to use. Gas law problems can often be thought of in more than one way. When a problem involves a comparison of two gases or two states (initial and final) of a single gas, use the general gas equation (2.12) after eliminating any term (n, P, T, V) that remains constant. Otherwise, use the ideal gas equation (2.11).

EXAMPLE 2-6 Applying the General Gas Equation

The situation pictured in Figure 2-10(a) is changed to that in Figure 2-10(b). What is the gas pressure in Figure 2-10(b)?

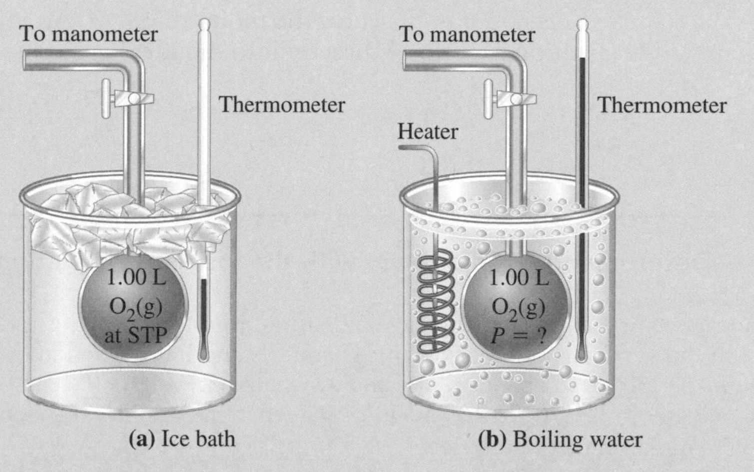

▲ FIGURE 2-10
Pressure of a gas as a function of temperature—Example 2-6 visualized
The amount of gas and volume are held constant. **(a)** 1.00 L $O_2(g)$ at STP; **(b)** 1.00 L $O_2(g)$ at 100 °C.

Analyze

Identify the quantities in the general gas equation that remain constant. Cancel out these quantities and solve the equation that remains.

Solve

In this case, the amount of O_2 is constant ($n_i = n_f$) and the volume is constant ($V_i = V_f$).

$$\frac{P_i V_i}{n_i T_i} = \frac{P_f V_f}{n_f T_f} \quad \text{and} \quad \frac{P_i}{T_i} = \frac{P_f}{T_f} \quad \text{and} \quad P_f = P_i \times \frac{T_f}{T_i}$$

Since $P_i = 1.00$ bar, $T_i = 273$ K, and $T_f = 373$ K, then

$$P_f = 1.00\ \text{bar} \times \frac{373\ \text{K}}{273\ \text{K}} = 1.37\ \text{bar}$$

Assess

We can base our check on a qualitative, intuitive understanding of what happens when a gas is heated in a closed container. Its pressure increases (possibly to the extent that the container bursts). If, by error, we had used the ratio of temperatures 273 K/373 K, the final pressure would have been less than 1.00 bar—an impossible result.

PRACTICE EXAMPLE A: A 1.00 mL sample of $N_2(g)$ at 36.2 °C and 2.14 atm is heated to 37.8 °C, and the pressure changed to 1.02 atm. What volume does the gas occupy at this final temperature and pressure?

PRACTICE EXAMPLE B: Suppose that in Figure 2-10 we want the pressure to remain at 1.00 bar when the $O_2(g)$ is heated to 100 °C. What mass of $O_2(g)$ must we release from the flask?

2-4 Applications of the Ideal Gas Equation

Although the ideal gas equation can always be used as it was presented in equation (2.11), it is useful to recast it into slightly different forms for some applications. We will consider two such applications in this section: determination of molar masses and gas densities.

Molar Mass Determination

If we know the volume of a gas at a fixed temperature and pressure, we can solve the ideal gas equation for the amount of the gas in moles. Because the number of moles of gas (n) is equal to the mass (m) of gas divided by the molar mass (M), if we know the mass and number of moles of gas, we can solve the expression $n = m/M$ for the molar mass, M. An alternative is to make the substitution $n = m/M$ directly into the ideal gas equation.

$$PV = \frac{mRT}{M} \tag{2.13}$$

EXAMPLE 2-7 Determining a Molar Mass with the Ideal Gas Equation

Propylene is an important commercial chemical (about ninth in the amount produced among manufactured chemicals) used in the synthesis of other organic chemicals and in production of plastics (polypropylene). A glass vessel weighs 40.1305 g when clean, dry, and evacuated; it weighs 138.2410 g when filled with water at 25.0 °C (density of water = 0.9970 g/mL) and 40.2959 g when filled with propylene gas at 740.3 mmHg and 24.0 °C. What is the molar mass of propylene?

Analyze

We are given a pressure (in mmHg), a temperature (in °C), and information that will enable us to determine the amount of gas (in grams) and the volume of the vessel. If we express these quantities in Kelvin, atmospheres, moles, and liters, respectively, then we can use equation (2.13), with $R = 0.08206 \text{ atm L K}^{-1} \text{ mol}^{-1}$, to calculate the molar mass of the gas.

Solve

First determine the mass of water required to fill the vessel.

$$\text{mass of water to fill vessel} = 138.2410 \text{ g} - 40.1305 \text{ g} = 98.1105 \text{ g}$$

Use the density of water in a conversion factor to obtain the volume of water (and hence, the volume of the glass vessel).

$$\text{volume of water (volume of vessel)} = 98.1105 \text{ g } H_2O \times \frac{1 \text{ mL } H_2O}{0.9970 \text{ g } H_2O} = 98.41 \text{ mL} = 0.09841 \text{ L}$$

The mass of the gas is the difference between the weight of the vessel filled with propylene gas and the weight of the empty vessel.

$$\text{mass of gas} = 40.2959 \text{ g} - 40.1305 \text{ g} = 0.1654 \text{ g}$$

The values of temperature and pressure are given.

$$T = 24.0 \text{ °C} + 273.15 = 297.2 \text{ K}$$

$$P = 740.3 \text{ mmHg} \times \frac{1 \text{ atm}}{760 \text{ mmHg}} = 0.9741 \text{ atm}$$

Substitute data into the rearranged version of equation (2.13).

$$M = \frac{mRT}{PV} = \frac{0.1654 \text{ g} \times 0.08206 \text{ atm L mol}^{-1} \text{ K}^{-1} \times 297.2 \text{ K}}{0.9741 \text{ atm} \times 0.09841 \text{ L}} = 42.08 \text{ g mol}^{-1}$$

Assess

Cancellations leave the units g and mol^{-1}. The unit g mol^{-1} or g/mol is that for molar mass, the quantity we are seeking. We can use another approach to solving this problem. We can substitute the pressure (0.9741 atm), temperature (297.2 K), and volume (0.09841 L) into the ideal gas equation to calculate the number of moles in the gas sample (0.003931 mol). Because the sample contains 0.003931 mol and has a mass of 0.125 g, the molar mass is 0.165 g/0.003931 mol = 42.0 g mol^{-1}. The advantage of this alternative approach is that it makes use of only the ideal gas equation; you do not have to memorize or derive equation (2.13) for the cases when you might need it.

PRACTICE EXAMPLE A: The same glass vessel used in Example 2-7 is filled with an unknown gas at 772 mmHg and 22.4 °C. The gas-filled vessel weighs 40.4868 g. What is the molar mass of the gas?

PRACTICE EXAMPLE B: A 1.27 g sample of an oxide of nitrogen, believed to be either NO or N_2O, occupies a volume of 1.07 L at 25 °C and 737 mmHg. Which oxide is it?

Equation (2.13) is used to determine a molar mass in Example 2-7, but note that the equation can also be used when the molar mass of a gas is known and the mass of a particular sample of the gas is sought.

Suppose that we want to determine the formula of an unknown hydrocarbon. With combustion analysis we can establish the mass percent composition, and from this, we can determine the empirical formula. The method of Example 2-7 gives us a molar mass, in g mol^{-1}, which is numerically equal to the molecular mass, in u. This is all the information we need to establish the true molecular formula of the hydrocarbon (see Exercise 84).

Gas Densities

To determine the density of a gas, we can start with the density equation, $d = m/V$. Then we can express the mass of gas as the product of the number of moles of gas and the molar mass: $m = n \times M$. This leads to

$$d = \frac{m}{V} = \frac{n \times M}{V} = \frac{n}{V} \times M$$

Now, with the ideal gas equation, we can replace n/V by its equivalent, P/RT, to obtain

$$d = \frac{m}{V} = \frac{MP}{RT} \qquad \textbf{(2.14)}$$

The density of a gas at STP can easily be calculated by dividing its molar mass by the molar volume (22.7 L/mol). For $O_2(g)$ at STP, for example, the density is 32.0 g/22.7 L = 1.41 g/L. Equation (2.14) can be used for other conditions of temperature and pressure.

KEEP IN MIND

that gas densities are typically much smaller than those of liquids and solids. Gas densities are usually expressed in grams per *liter* rather than grams per *milliliter*.

EXAMPLE 2-8 Using the Ideal Gas Equation to Calculate a Gas Density

What is the density of oxygen gas (O_2) at 298 K and 0.987 atm?

Analyze

The gas is identified, and therefore the molar mass can be calculated. We are given a temperature in Kelvin and a pressure in atmospheres, so we can use equation (2.14) directly with $R = 0.08206$ atm L K^{-1} mol^{-1}.

Solve

The molar mass of O_2 is 32.0 g mol^{-1}. Now, use equation (2.14).

$$d = \frac{m}{V} = \frac{MP}{RT} = \frac{32.00 \text{ g mol}^{-1} \times 0.987 \text{ atm}}{0.08206 \text{ atm L mol}^{-1} \text{ K}^{-1} \times 298 \text{ K}} = 1.29 \text{ g/L}$$

Assess

We can solve this problem in another way. To calculate the density of a gas at a certain temperature and pressure, use a 1.00 L sample of the gas. The mass of a 1.00 L sample is equal to the density in grams per liter. To calculate the mass of a 1.00 L sample, first use the ideal gas equation to calculate the number of moles in the sample, and then convert the amount in moles to an amount in grams by using the molar mass as a conversion factor. In the present case, the amount of $O_2(g)$ in a 1.00 L sample at 0.987 atm and 298 K is 0.0404 mol O_2, or 1.29 g O_2. Because a 1.00 L sample of O_2 at this temperature and pressure has a mass of 1.29 g, the density is 1.29 g/L.

PRACTICE EXAMPLE A: What is the density of helium gas at 298 K and 0.987 atm? Based on your answer, explain why we can say that helium is "lighter than air."

PRACTICE EXAMPLE B: The density of a sample of gas is 1.00 g/L at 745 mmHg and 109 °C. What is the molar mass of the gas?

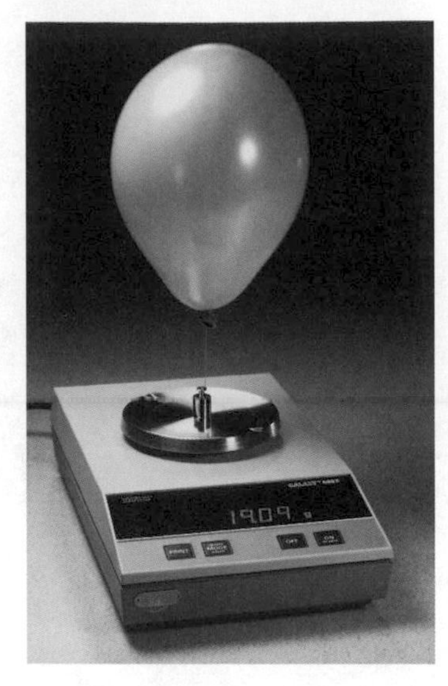

▲ FIGURE 2-11
The helium-filled balloon exerts a lifting force on the 20.00 g weight, so that the balloon and the weight together weigh only 19.09 g.

The density of gases differs from that of solids and liquids in two important ways.

1. Gas densities depend strongly on pressure and temperature, increasing as the gas pressure increases and decreasing as the temperature increases. Densities of liquids and solids also depend somewhat on temperature, but they depend far less on pressure.
2. The density of a gas is directly proportional to its molar mass. No simple relationship exists between density and molar mass for liquids and solids.

An important application of gas densities is in establishing conditions for lighter-than-air balloons. A gas-filled balloon will rise in the atmosphere only if the density of the gas is less than that of the surrounding air. Because gas densities are directly proportional to molar masses, the lower the molar mass of the gas, the greater its lifting power. The lowest molar mass is that of hydrogen, but hydrogen is flammable and forms explosive mixtures with air. The explosion of the dirigible *Hindenburg* in 1937 spelled the end to transoceanic travel by hydrogen-filled airships. Now, airships, such as the Goodyear blimps, use helium, which has a molar mass only twice that of hydrogen (Fig. 2-11) but is inert. Hydrogen is still used for weather and other observational balloons.

Another alternative is to fill a balloon with *hot* air. Equation (2.14) indicates that the density of a gas is *inversely* proportional to temperature. Hot air is less dense than cold air. However, because the density of air decreases rapidly with altitude, there is a limit to how high a hot-air balloon or any gas-filled balloon can rise.

2-5 Gases in Chemical Reactions

Reactions involving gases as reactants or products (or both) are no strangers to us. We now have a new tool to apply to reaction stoichiometry calculations: the ideal gas equation. Specifically, we can now handle information about gases in terms of volumes, temperatures, and pressures, as well as by mass and amount in moles. A practical application is the nitrogen-forming reaction in an automobile air-bag safety system, which utilizes the rapid decomposition of sodium azide.

$$2\,NaN_3(s) \xrightarrow{\Delta} 2\,Na(l) + 3\,N_2(g)$$

The essential components of the system are an ignition device and a pellet containing sodium azide and appropriate additives. When activated, the system inflates an air bag in 20 to 60 ms and converts Na(l) to a harmless solid residue.

For reactions involving gases, we can (1) use stoichiometric factors to relate the amount of a gas to amounts of other reactants or products, and (2) use the ideal gas equation to relate the amount of gas to volume, temperature, and pressure. In Example 2-9, we use this approach to determine the volume of $N_2(g)$ produced in a typical air-bag system.

Law of Combining Volumes

If the reactants and products involved in a stoichiometric calculation are gases, sometimes we can use a particularly simple approach. Consider this reaction.

$$2\,NO(g) + O_2(g) \longrightarrow 2\,NO_2(g)$$
$$2\,mol\,NO(g) + 1\,mol\,O_2(g) \longrightarrow 2\,mol\,NO_2(g)$$

EXAMPLE 2-9 Using the Ideal Gas Equation in Reaction Stoichiometry Calculations

What volume of N_2, measured at 735 mmHg and 26 °C, is produced when 75.0 g NaN_3 is decomposed?

$$2\,NaN_3(s) \xrightarrow{\Delta} 2\,Na(l) + 3\,N_2(g)$$

Analyze

The following conversions are required.

$$g\,NaN_3 \longrightarrow mol\,NaN_3 \longrightarrow mol\,N_2 \longrightarrow L\,N_2$$

The molar mass of NaN_3 is used for the first conversion. The second conversion makes use of a stoichiometric factor constructed from the coefficients of the chemical equation. The ideal gas equation is used to complete the final conversion.

Solve

$$?\,mol\,N_2 = 75.0\,g\,NaN_3 \times \frac{1\,mol\,NaN_3}{65.01\,g\,NaN_3} \times \frac{3\,mol\,N_2}{2\,mol\,NaN_3} = 1.73\,mol\,N_2$$

$$P = 735\,mmHg \times \frac{1\,atm}{760\,mmHg} = 0.967\,atm$$

$$V = ?$$

$$n = 1.73\,mol$$

$$R = 0.08206\,atm\,L\,mol^{-1}\,K^{-1}$$

$$T = 26\,°C + 273 = 299\,K$$

$$V = \frac{nRT}{P} = \frac{1.73\,mol \times 0.08206\,atm\,L\,mol^{-1}\,K^{-1} \times 299\,K}{0.967\,atm} = 43.9\,L$$

Assess

75.0 g NaN_3 is slightly more than one mole ($M \approx 65$ g/mol). From this amount of NaN_3 we should expect a little more than 1.5 mol $N_2(g)$. At 0 °C and 1 atm, 1.5 mol $N_2(g)$ would occupy a volume of $1.5 \times 22.4 = 33.6$ L. Because the temperature is higher than 0 °C and the pressure is lower than 1 atm, the sample should have a volume somewhat greater than 33.6 L.

PRACTICE EXAMPLE A: How many grams of NaN_3 are needed to produce 20.0 L of $N_2(g)$ at 30.0 °C and 776 mmHg?

PRACTICE EXAMPLE B: How many grams of Na(l) are produced per liter of $N_2(g)$ formed in the decomposition of sodium azide if the gas is collected at 25 °C and 1.0 bar?

Suppose the gases are compared at the same T and P. Under these conditions, one mole of gas occupies a particular volume, call it V liters; two moles of gas occupy $2V$ liters; and so on.

$$2\,V\,L\,NO(g) + V\,L\,O_2(g) \longrightarrow 2\,V\,L\,NO_2(g)$$

If we divide each coefficient by V, we get the following result:

$$2\,L\,NO(g) + 1\,L\,O_2(g) \longrightarrow 2\,L\,NO_2(g)$$

Thus, the volume ratio of the gases consumed and produced in a chemical is the same as the mole ratio, provided the volumes are all measured at the same temperature and pressure.

What we have just done is to develop, in modern terms, **Gay-Lussac's law of combining volumes**. We previewed this law on page 201 by suggesting that the volumes of gases involved in a reaction are in the ratio of small whole numbers. The small whole numbers are simply the stoichiometric coefficients in the balanced equation. We apply this law in Example 2-10.

EXAMPLE 2-10 Applying the Law of Combining Volumes

Zinc blende, ZnS, is the most important zinc ore. Roasting (strong heating) of ZnS in oxygen is the first step in the commercial production of zinc.

$$2\,ZnS(s) + 3\,O_2(g) \xrightarrow{\Delta} 2\,ZnO(s) + 2\,SO_2(g)$$

What volume of $SO_2(g)$ can be obtained from 1.00 L $O_2(g)$ and excess ZnS(s)? Both gases are measured at 25 °C and 745 mmHg.

Analyze

The reactant and product being compared are both gases, and both are at the same temperature and pressure. Therefore, we can use the law of combining volumes and treat the coefficients in the balanced chemical equation as if they had units of liters.

Solve

The stoichiometric factor (shown below in blue) converts from L $O_2(g)$ to L $SO_2(g)$.

$$?\,L\,SO_2(g) = 1.00\,L\,O_2(g) \times \frac{2\,L\,SO_2(g)}{3\,L\,O_2(g)} = 0.667\,L\,SO_2(g)$$

Assess

Some students would solve this problem by using the following sequence of conversions: L $O_2 \longrightarrow$ mol $O_2 \longrightarrow$ mol $SO_2 \longrightarrow$ L SO_2. This approach is acceptable but not as simple as the approach we used.

PRACTICE EXAMPLE A: The first step in making nitric acid is to convert ammonia to nitrogen monoxide. This is done under conditions of high temperature and in the presence of a platinum catalyst. What volume of $O_2(g)$ is consumed per liter of NO(g) formed?

$$4\,NH_3(g) + 5\,O_2(g) \xrightarrow[850\,°C]{Pt} 4\,NO(g) + 6\,H_2O(g)$$

PRACTICE EXAMPLE B: If all gases are measured at the same temperature and pressure, what volume of $NH_3(g)$ is produced when 225 L $H_2(g)$ are consumed in the reaction $N_2(g) + H_2(g) \longrightarrow NH_3(g)$ (not balanced)?

2-6 CONCEPT ASSESSMENT

Would the answer in Example 2-10 be greater than, less than, or equal to 0.677 L if (a) both gases were measured at STP; (b) if the O_2 were measured at STP and the SO_2 were measured at 25 °C and 745 mmHg?

2-6 Mixtures of Gases

The simple gas laws, such as Boyle's and Charles's laws, were based on the behavior of air—a mixture of gases. So, the simple gas laws and the ideal gas equation apply to a *mixture* of nonreactive gases as well as to individual gases. Where possible, the simplest approach to working with gaseous mixtures is just to use for the value of n the *total* number of moles of the gaseous mixture (n_{tot}).

As a specific example, consider a mixture of gases in a vessel of fixed volume V at temperature T. The total pressure of the mixture is determined by the total number of moles:

$$P_{tot} = \frac{n_{tot}RT}{V} \quad (T \text{ constant}, V \text{ constant}) \qquad \textbf{(2.15)}$$

For fixed values of T and P, the total volume of a mixture of gases is also determined by the total number of moles:

$$V_{tot} = \frac{n_{tot}RT}{P} \quad (T \text{ constant}, P \text{ constant})$$

EXAMPLE 2-11 Applying the Ideal Gas Equation to a Mixture of Gases

What is the pressure, in bar, exerted by a mixture of 1.0 g H_2 and 5.00 g He when the mixture is confined to a volume of 5.0 L at 20 °C?

Analyze

For fixed T and V, the total pressure of a mixture of gases is determined by the total number of moles of gas: $P_{tot} = n_{tot}RT/V$.

Solve

$$n_{tot} = \left(1.0\,g\,H_2 \times \frac{1\,mol\,H_2}{2.02\,g\,H_2}\right) + \left(5.00\,g\,He \times \frac{1\,mol\,He}{4.003\,g\,He}\right)$$

$$= 0.50\,mol\,H_2 + 1.25\,mol\,He = 1.75\,mol\,gas$$

$$P = \frac{1.75\,mol \times 0.0831\,bar\,L\,mol^{-1}\,K^{-1} \times 293\,K}{5.0\,L} = 8.5\,bar$$

Assess

It is also possible to solve this problem by starting from equation (2.12). Because 1 mol of ideal gas occupies 22.7 L at 0 °C and 1 bar, the pressure exerted by 1.75 mol of gas in a 5.0 L vessel at 293 K is $(1.75\,mol/1.00\,mol) \times (293\,K/273\,K) \times (22.7\,L/5.0\,L) \times 1.0\,bar = 8.5\,bar$.

PRACTICE EXAMPLE A: What will be the total gas pressure if 12.5 g Ne is added to the mixture of gases described in Example 2-11 and the temperature is then raised to 55 °C? [*Hint:* What is the new number of moles of gas? What effect does raising the temperature have on the pressure of a gas at constant volume?]

PRACTICE EXAMPLE B: 2.0 L of $O_2(g)$ and 8.0 L of $N_2(g)$, each at 0.00 °C and 1.00 atm, are mixed together. The nonreactive gaseous mixture is compressed to occupy 2.0 L at 298 K. What is the pressure exerted by this mixture?

John Dalton made an important contribution to the study of gaseous mixtures. He proposed that in a mixture, each gas expands to fill the container and exerts the same pressure (called its **partial pressure**) that it would if it were alone in the container. **Dalton's law of partial pressures** states that the total pressure of a mixture of gases is the sum of the partial pressures of the components of the mixture, as shown in Figure 2-12. For a mixture of gases, A, B, and so on,

$$P_{tot} = P_A + P_B + \cdots \qquad \textbf{(2.16)}$$

KEEP IN MIND

that when this expression is used, $V_A = V_B = \cdots = V_{tot}$

In a gaseous mixture of n_A moles of A, n_B moles of B, and so on, the volume each gas would individually occupy at a pressure equal to P_{tot} is

$$V_A = n_ART/P_{tot}\,;\, V_B = n_BRT/P_{tot}\,;\, \cdots$$

The total volume of the gaseous mixture is

$$V_{tot} = V_A + V_B \cdots$$

and the commonly used expression *percent by volume* is

$$\text{volume \% A} = \frac{V_A}{V_{tot}} \times 100\%;\ \text{Volume \% B} = \frac{V_B}{V_{tot}} \times 100\%;\ \cdots$$

KEEP IN MIND

that when using this expression, $P_A = P_B = \cdots = P_{tot}$

We can derive a particularly useful expression from the following ratios,

$$\frac{P_A}{P_{tot}} = \frac{n_A(\cancel{RT/V_{tot}})}{n_{tot}(\cancel{RT/V_{tot}})} = \frac{n_A}{n_{tot}} \quad \text{and} \quad \frac{V_A}{V_{tot}} = \frac{n_A(\cancel{RT/P_{tot}})}{n_{tot}(\cancel{RT/P_{tot}})} = \frac{n_A}{n_{tot}}$$

which means that

$$\frac{n_A}{n_{tot}} = \frac{P_A}{P_{tot}} = \frac{V_A}{V_{tot}} = x_A \qquad \textbf{(2.17)}$$

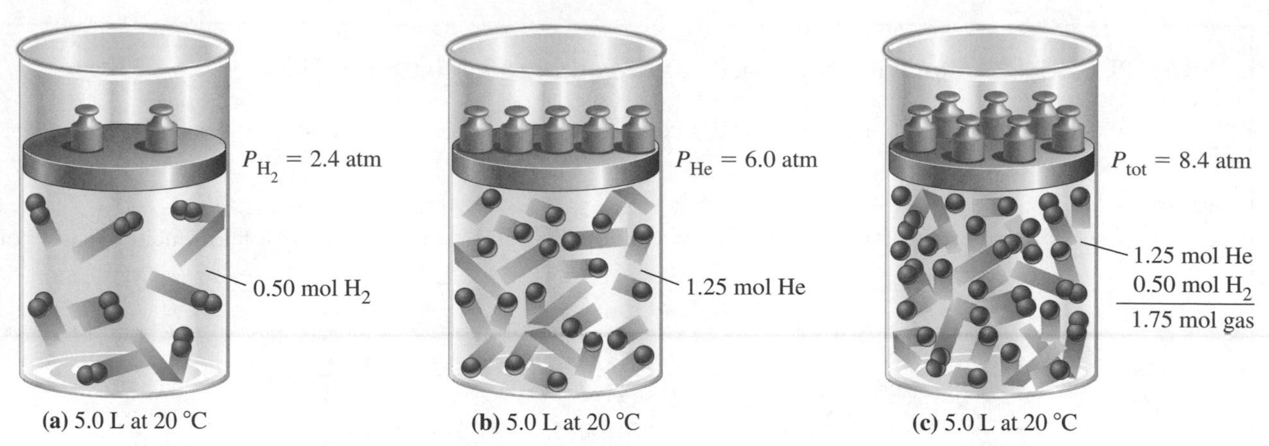

▲ FIGURE 2-12
Dalton's law of partial pressures illustrated
The pressure of each gas is proportional to the number of moles of gas. The total pressure is the sum of the partial pressures of the individual gases.

The term n_A/n_{tot} is given a special name, the mole fraction of A, x_A. The **mole fraction** of a component in a mixture is the fraction of all the molecules in the mixture contributed by that component. The sum of all the mole fractions in a mixture is one.

As illustrated in Example 2-12, we can often think about mixtures of gases in more than one way.

EXAMPLE 2-12 Calculating the Partial Pressures in a Gaseous Mixture

What are the partial pressures of H_2 and He in the gaseous mixture described in Example 2-11?

Analyze

The ideal gas equation can be applied to each gas individually to obtain the partial pressure of each gas.

Solve

One approach involves a direct application of Dalton's law in which we calculate the pressure that each gas would exert if it were alone in the container.

$$P_{H_2} = \frac{n_{H_2} \times RT}{V} = \frac{0.50\ \text{mol} \times 0.0821\ \text{atm L mol}^{-1}\ \text{K}^{-1} \times 293\ \text{K}}{5.0\ \text{L}} = 2.4\ \text{atm}$$

$$P_{He} = \frac{n_{He} \times RT}{V} = \frac{1.25\ \text{mol} \times 0.0821\ \text{atm L mol}^{-1}\ \text{K}^{-1} \times 293\ \text{K}}{5.0\ \text{L}} = 6.0\ \text{atm}$$

Expression (2.17) gives us a simpler way to answer the question because we already know the number of moles of each gas and the total pressure from Example 2-11 ($P_{tot} = 8.4$ atm).

$$P_{H_2} = \frac{n_{H_2}}{n_{tot}} \times P_{tot} = \frac{0.50}{1.75} \times 8.4\ \text{atm} = 2.4\ \text{atm}$$

$$P_{He} = \frac{n_{He}}{n_{tot}} \times P_{tot} = \frac{1.25}{1.75} \times 8.4\ \text{atm} = 6.0\ \text{atm}$$

Assess

An effective way of checking an answer is to obtain the same answer when the problem is done in different ways, as was the case here.

PRACTICE EXAMPLE A: A mixture of 0.197 mol $CO_2(g)$ and 0.00278 mol $H_2O(g)$ is held at 30.0 °C and 2.50 atm. What is the partial pressure of each gas?

PRACTICE EXAMPLE B: The percent composition of air by volume is 78.08% N_2, 20.95% O_2, 0.93% Ar, and 0.036% CO_2. What are the partial pressures of these four gases in a sample of air at a barometric pressure of 748 mmHg?

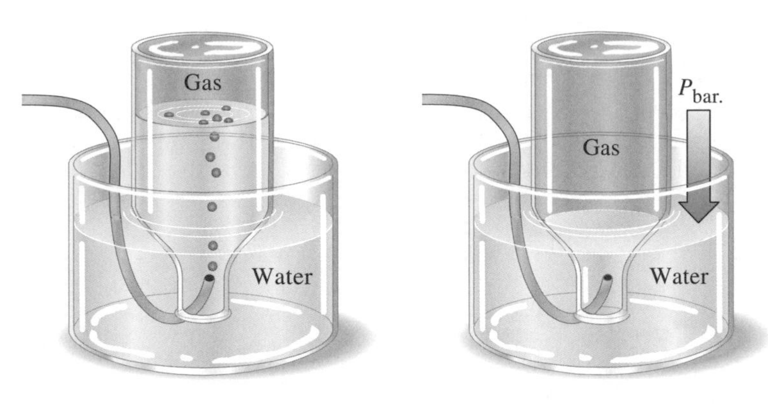

▲ FIGURE 2-13
Collecting a gas over water
The bottle is filled with water and its open end is held below the water level in the container. Gas from a gas-generating apparatus is directed into the bottle. As gas accumulates in the bottle, water is displaced from the bottle into the container. To make the total gas pressure in the bottle equal to barometric pressure, the position of the bottle must be adjusted so that the water levels inside and outside the bottle are the same.

2-7 CONCEPT ASSESSMENT

Without doing a detailed calculation, state the outcome(s) you would expect in Figure 2-12(c) if an additional 0.50 mol H_2 were added to the cylinder in Figure 2-12(a): **(a)** the mole fraction of H_2 would double; **(b)** the partial pressure of He would remain the same; **(c)** the mole fraction of He would remain the same; **(d)** the total gas pressure would increase by 50%; **(e)** the total mass of gas would increase by 1.0 g.

The device pictured in Figure 2-13, a *pneumatic trough*, played a crucial role in isolating gases in the early days of chemistry. The method works, of course, only for gases that are insoluble in and do not react with the liquid being displaced. Many important gases meet these criteria. For example, H_2, O_2, and N_2 are all essentially insoluble in and unreactive with water.

◀ Some early experimenters used mercury in the pneumatic trough so as to be able to collect gases soluble in water.

A gas collected in a pneumatic trough filled with water is said to be *collected over water* and is "wet." It is a mixture of two gases—the desired gas and water vapor. The gas being collected expands to fill the container and exerts its partial pressure, P_{gas}. Water vapor, formed by the evaporation of liquid water, also fills the container and exerts a partial pressure, P_{H_2O}. The pressure of the water vapor depends only on the temperature of the water, as shown in Table 2.4.

According to Dalton's law, the total pressure of the wet gas is the sum of the two partial pressures. The total pressure can be made equal to the prevailing pressure of the atmosphere (barometric pressure) by adjusting the position of the bottle; thus we can write

$$P_{tot} = P_{bar.} = P_{gas} + P_{H_2O} \quad \text{or} \quad P_{gas} = P_{bar.} - P_{H_2O}$$

Once P_{gas} has been established, it can be used in stoichiometric calculations as illustrated in Example 2-13.

TABLE 2.4 Vapor Pressure of Water at Various Temperatures

Temperature, °C	Vapor Pressure, mmHg
15.0	12.79
17.0	14.53
19.0	16.48
21.0	18.65
23.0	21.07
25.0	23.76
30.0	31.82
50.0	92.51

EXAMPLE 2-13 Collecting a Gas over a Liquid (Water)

In the following reaction, 81.2 mL of $O_2(g)$ is collected over water at 23 °C and barometric pressure 751 mmHg. What mass of $Ag_2O(s)$ decomposed? (The vapor pressure of water at 23 °C is 21.1 mmHg.)

$$2\,Ag_2O(s) \longrightarrow 4\,Ag(s) + O_2(g)$$

(continued)

Analyze

The key concept is that the gas collected is wet, that is, a *mixture* of $O_2(g)$ and water vapor. Use $P_{bar.} = P_{O_2} + P_{H_2O}$ to calculate P_{O_2}, and then use the ideal gas equation to calculate the number of moles of O_2. The following conversions are used to complete the calculation: mol $O_2 \longrightarrow$ mol $Ag_2O \longrightarrow$ g Ag_2O.

Solve

$$P_{O_2} = P_{bar.} - P_{H_2O} = 751\ \text{mmHg} - 21.1\ \text{mmHg} = 730\ \text{mmHg}$$

$$P_{O_2} = 730\ \text{mmHg} \times \frac{1\ \text{atm}}{760\ \text{mmHg}} = 0.961\ \text{atm}$$

$$V = 81.2\ \text{mL} = 0.0812\ \text{L}$$

$$n = ?$$

$$R = 0.08206\ \text{atm L mol}^{-1}\ \text{K}^{-1}$$

$$T = 23\ °\text{C} + 273 = 296\ \text{K}$$

$$n = \frac{PV}{RT} = \frac{0.961\ \text{atm} \times 0.0812\ \text{L}}{0.08206\ \text{atm L mol}^{-1}\ \text{K}^{-1} \times 296\ \text{K}} = 0.00321\ \text{mol}$$

From the chemical equation we obtain a factor to convert from moles of O_2 to moles of Ag_2O. The molar mass of Ag_2O provides the final factor.

$$?\ \text{g}\ Ag_2O = 0.00321\ \text{mol}\ O_2 \times \frac{2\ \text{mol}\ Ag_2O}{1\ \text{mol}\ O_2} \times \frac{231.7\ \text{g}\ Ag_2O}{1\ \text{mol}\ Ag_2O} = 1.49\ \text{g}\ Ag_2O$$

Assess

The determination of the number of moles of O_2 in the sample is the key calculation. We can quickly estimate the number of moles of O_2 in the sample by using the fact that for typical conditions ($T \approx 298$ K, $P \approx 760$ mmHg), the molar volume of an ideal gas is about 24 L. The number of moles of gas (mostly O_2) in the sample is approximately 0.08 L/24 L $\approx$ 0.003 mol. This estimate is quite close to the value calculated above.

PRACTICE EXAMPLE A: The reaction of aluminum with hydrochloric acid produces hydrogen gas. The balanced chemical equation for the reaction is given below.

$$2\ \text{Al(s)} + 6\ \text{HCl(aq)} \longrightarrow 2\ \text{AlCl}_3\text{(aq)} + 3\ \text{H}_2\text{(g)}$$

If 35.5 mL of $H_2(g)$ is collected over water at 26 °C and a barometric pressure of 755 mmHg, how many moles of HCl must have been consumed? (The vapor pressure of water at 26 °C is 25.2 mmHg.)

PRACTICE EXAMPLE B: An 8.07 g sample of impure Ag_2O decomposes into solid silver and $O_2(g)$. If 395 mL $O_2(g)$ is collected over water at 25 °C and 749.2 mmHg barometric pressure, then what is the percent by mass of Ag_2O in the sample? The vapor pressure of water at 25 °C is 23.8 mmHg. What is the volume of gas collected?

Integrative Example

Combustion of 1.110 g of a gaseous hydrocarbon yields 3.613 g CO_2 and 1.109 g H_2O, and no other products. A 0.288 g sample of the hydrocarbon occupies a volume of 131 mL at 24.8 °C and 753 mmHg. Write a plausible structural formula for a hydrocarbon corresponding to these data.

Analyze

Use the $P - V - T$ data in equation (2.13) for the 0.288 g sample to determine the molar mass and molecular mass of the hydrocarbon. By comparing the empirical formula mass and the molecular mass, establish the molecular formula. Now write a structural formula consistent with the molecular formula.

Solve

Calculate the number of moles of C and H in the 1.110 g sample of hydrocarbon based on the masses of CO_2 and H_2O obtained in its combustion.

$$? \text{ mol C} = 3.613 \text{ g CO}_2 \times \frac{1 \text{ mol CO}_2}{44.01 \text{ g CO}_2} \times \frac{1 \text{ mol C}}{1 \text{ mol CO}_2} = 0.08209 \text{ mol C}$$

$$? \text{ mol H} = 1.109 \text{ g H}_2\text{O} \times \frac{1 \text{ mol H}_2\text{O}}{18.02 \text{ g H}_2\text{O}} \times \frac{2 \text{ mol H}}{1 \text{ mol H}_2\text{O}} = 0.1231 \text{ mol H}$$

Use these numbers of moles as the provisional subscripts in the formula.

$$C_{0.08209}H_{0.1231}$$

Divide each provisional subscript by the smaller of the two to obtain the empirical formula.

$$C_{\frac{0.08209}{0.08209}}H_{\frac{0.1231}{0.08209}}$$

$$CH_{1.500} = C_2H_3$$

To determine the molar mass, use a modified form of equation (2.13).

$$M = \frac{mRT}{PV} = \frac{0.288 \text{ g} \times 0.08206 \text{ atm L K}^{-1} \text{mol}^{-1} \times (24.8 + 273.2) \text{ K}}{(753 \text{ mmHg} \times 1 \text{ atm}/760 \text{ mmHg}) \times 0.131 \text{ L}}$$

$$= 54.3 \text{ g mol}^{-1}$$

The empirical formula mass is

$$\left(2 \text{ C atoms} \times \frac{12.0 \text{ u}}{1 \text{ C atom}}\right) + \left(3 \text{ H atoms} \times \frac{1.01 \text{ u}}{1 \text{ H atom}}\right) = 27.0 \text{ u}$$

The molar mass based on the empirical formula, 27.0 g mol^{-1}, is almost exactly one-half the observed molar mass of 54.3 g mol^{-1}. The molecular formula of the hydrocarbon is

$$C_{2\times2}H_{2\times3} = C_4H_6$$

The four-carbon alkane is butane, C_4H_{10}. Removal of 4 H atoms to obtain the formula C_4H_6 is achieved by inserting two C-to-C double bonds.

$$H_2C{=}CH \quad CH{=}CH_2 \quad \text{or} \quad H_2C{=}C{=}CH{-}CH_3$$

Two other possibilities involve the presence of a C-to-C triple bond.

$$H_3C{-}C{\equiv}C{-}CH_3 \quad \text{or} \quad H_3C{-}CH_2{-}C{\equiv}CH$$

Assess

The combination of combustion data and gas-law data yields a molecular formula with certainty. However, because of isomerism the exact structural formula cannot be pinpointed. All that we can say is that the hydrocarbon might have any one of the four structures shown, but it might be still another structure, for example, based on a ring of C atoms rather than a straight chain.

PRACTICE EXAMPLE A: When a 0.5120 g sample of a gaseous hydrocarbon was burned in excess oxygen, 1.687 g CO_2 and 0.4605 g H_2O were obtained. The density of the compound, in its vapor form, is 1.637 g/L at 25 °C and 101.3 kPa. Determine the molecular formula of the hydrocarbon, and draw a plausible structural formula for the molecule.

PRACTICE EXAMPLE B: An organic compound contains only C, H, N, and O. When the compound is burned in oxygen, with appropriate catalysts, nitrogen gas (N_2), carbon dioxide (CO_2), and water vapor (H_2O) are produced. A 0.1023 g sample of the compound yielded 151.2 mg CO_2, 69.62 mg H_2O, and 9.62 mL of $N_2(g)$ at 0.00 °C and 1.00 atm. The density of the compound, in its vapor form, was found to be 3.57 g L^{-1} at 127 °C and 748 mmHg. What is the molecular formula of the compound?

Exercises

Pressure and Its Measurement

1. Convert each pressure to an equivalent pressure in atmospheres. **(a)** 736 mmHg; **(b)** 0.776 bar; **(c)** 892 Torr; **(d)** 225 kPa.
2. Calculate the height of a mercury column required to produce a pressure **(a)** of 0.984 atm; **(b)** of 928 Torr; **(c)** equal to that of a column of water 142 ft high.
3. Calculate the height of a column of liquid benzene ($d = 0.879\ g/cm^3$), in meters, required to exert a pressure of 0.970 atm.
4. Calculate the height of a column of liquid glycerol ($d = 1.26\ g/cm^3$), in meters, required to exert the same pressure as 3.02 m of $CCl_4(l)$ ($d = 1.59\ g/cm^3$).
5. What is the pressure (in mmHg) of the gas inside the apparatus below if $P_{bar.} = 740\ mmHg$, $h_1 = 30\ mm$ and $h_2 = 50\ mm$?

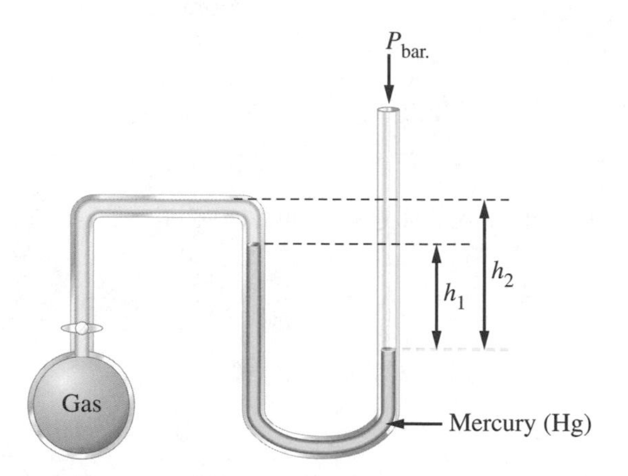

6. What is the pressure (in mmHg) of the gas inside the apparatus below if $P_{bar.} = 740\ mmHg$, $h_1 = 30\ mm$ and $h_2 = 40\ mm$?

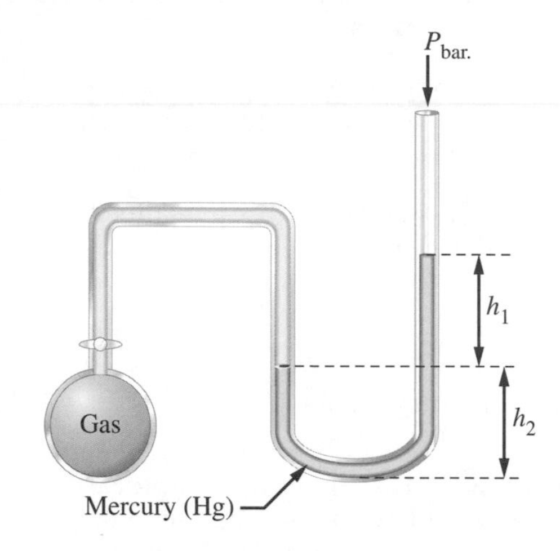

7. At times, a pressure is stated in units of *mass* per unit area rather than *force* per unit area. Express $P = 1\ atm$ in the unit kg/cm^2.
   [*Hint:* How is a mass in kilograms related to a force?]
8. Express $P = 1\ atm$ in pounds per square inch (psi).
   [*Hint:* Refer to Exercise 7.]

The Simple Gas Laws

9. A sample of $O_2(g)$ has a volume of 26.7 L at 762 Torr. What is the new volume if, with the temperature and amount of gas held constant, the pressure is **(a)** lowered to 385 Torr; **(b)** increased to 3.68 atm?
10. An 886 mL sample of Ne(g) is at 752 mmHg and 26 °C. What will be the new volume if, with the pressure and amount of gas held constant, the temperature is **(a)** increased to 98 °C; **(b)** lowered to −20 °C?
11. If 3.0 L of oxygen gas at 177 °C is cooled at constant pressure until the volume becomes 1.50 L, then what is the final temperature?
12. We want to change the volume of a fixed amount of gas from 725 mL to 2.25 L while holding the temperature constant. To what value must we change the pressure if the initial pressure is 105 kPa?
13. A 35.8 L cylinder of Ar(g) is connected to an evacuated 1875 L tank. If the temperature is held constant and the final pressure is 721 mmHg, what must have been the original gas pressure in the cylinder, in atmospheres?
14. A sample of $N_2(g)$ occupies a volume of 42.0 mL under the existing barometric pressure. Increasing the pressure by 85 mmHg reduces the volume to 37.7 mL. What is the prevailing barometric pressure, in millimeters of mercury?
15. A weather balloon filled with He gas has a volume of $2.00 \times 10^3\ m^3$ at ground level, where the atmospheric pressure is 1.000 atm and the temperature 27 °C. After the balloon rises high above Earth to a point where the atmospheric pressure is 0.340 atm, its volume increases to $5.00 \times 10^3\ m^3$. What is the temperature of the atmosphere at this altitude?
16. The photographs show the contraction of an argon-filled balloon when it is cooled by liquid nitrogen. To what approximate fraction of its original volume will the balloon shrink when it is cooled from a room temperature of 22 °C to a final temperature of about −22 °C?

17. What is the mass of argon gas in a 75.0 mL volume at STP?
18. What volume of gaseous chlorine at STP would you need to obtain a 250.0 g sample of gas?
19. A 27.6 mL sample of $PH_3(g)$ (used in the manufacture of flame-retardant chemicals) is obtained at STP.
 (a) What is the mass of this gas, in milligrams?
 (b) How many molecules of PH_3 are present?
20. A 5.0×10^{17} atom sample of radon gas is obtained.
 (a) What is the mass of this sample, in micrograms?
 (b) What is the volume of this sample at STP, in microliters?
21. You purchase a bag of potato chips at an ocean beach to take on a picnic in the mountains. At the picnic, you notice that the bag has become inflated, almost to the point of bursting. Use your knowledge of gas behavior to explain this phenomenon.
22. Scuba divers know that they must not ascend quickly from deep underwater because of a condition known as the *bends*. Another concern is that they must constantly exhale during their ascent to prevent damage to the lungs and blood vessels. Describe what would happen to the lungs of a diver who inhaled compressed air at a depth of 30 m and held her breath while rising to the surface.

General Gas Equation

23. A sample of gas has a volume of 4.25 L at 25.6 °C and 748 mmHg. What will be the volume of this gas at 26.8 °C and 742 mmHg?
24. A 10.0 g sample of a gas has a volume of 5.25 L at 25 °C and 762 mmHg. If 2.5 g of the same gas is added to this *constant* 5.25 L volume and the temperature raised to 62 °C, what is the new gas pressure?
25. A constant-volume vessel contains 12.5 g of a gas at 21 °C. If the pressure of the gas is to remain constant as the temperature is raised to 210 °C, how many grams of gas must be released?
26. A 34.0 L cylinder contains 305 g $O_2(g)$ at 22 °C. How many grams of $O_2(g)$ must be released to reduce the pressure in the cylinder to 1.15 atm if the temperature remains constant?

Ideal Gas Equation

27. What is the volume, in milliliters, occupied by 89.2 g $CO_2(g)$ at 37 °C and 737 mmHg?
28. A 12.8 L cylinder contains 35.8 g O_2 at 46 °C. What is the pressure of this gas, in atmospheres?
29. Kr(g) in a 18.5 L cylinder exerts a pressure of 11.2 atm at 28.2 °C. How many grams of gas are present?
30. A 72.8 L constant-volume cylinder containing 7.41 g He is heated until the pressure reaches 3.50 atm. What is the final temperature in degrees Celsius?
31. A laboratory high vacuum system is capable of evacuating a vessel to the point that the amount of gas remaining is 5.0×10^9 molecules per cubic meter. What is the residual pressure in pascals?
32. What is the pressure, in pascals, exerted by 1242 g CO(g) when confined at −25 °C to a cylindrical tank 25.0 cm in diameter and 1.75 m high?
33. What is the molar volume of an ideal gas at **(a)** 25 °C and 1.00 atm; **(b)** 100 °C and 748 Torr?
34. At what temperature is the molar volume of an ideal gas equal to 22.4 L, if the pressure of the gas is 2.5 atm?

Determining Molar Mass

35. A 0.418 g sample of gas has a volume of 115 mL at 66.3 °C and 743 mmHg. What is the molar mass of this gas?
36. What is the molar mass of a gas found to have a density of 0.841 g/L at 415 K and 725 Torr?
37. What is the molecular formula of a gaseous fluoride of sulfur containing 70.4% F and having a density of approximately 4.5 g/L at 20 °C and 1 atm?
38. A 2.650 g sample of a gaseous compound occupies 428 mL at 24.3 °C and 742 mmHg. The compound consists of 15.5% C, 23.0% Cl, and 61.5% F, by mass. What is its molecular formula?
39. A gaseous hydrocarbon weighing 0.231 g occupies a volume of 102 mL at 23 °C and 749 mmHg. What is the molar mass of this compound? What conclusion can you draw about its molecular formula?
40. A 132.10 mL glass vessel weighs 56.1035 g when evacuated and 56.2445 g when filled with the gaseous hydrocarbon acetylene at 749.3 mmHg and 20.02 °C. What is the molar mass of acetylene? What conclusion can you draw about its molecular formula?

Gas Densities

41. A particular application calls for $N_2(g)$ with a density of 1.80 g/L at 32 °C. What must be the pressure of the $N_2(g)$ in millimeters of mercury? What is the molar volume under these conditions?
42. Monochloroethylene is used to make polyvinylchloride (PVC). It has a density of 2.56 g/L at 22.8 °C and 756 mmHg. What is the molar mass of monochloroethylene? What is the molar volume under these conditions?
43. In order for a gas-filled balloon to rise in air, the density of the gas in the balloon must be less than that of air.
    (a) Consider air to have a molar mass of 28.96 g/mol; determine the density of air at 25 °C and 1 atm, in g/L.
    (b) Show by calculation that a balloon filled with carbon dioxide at 25 °C and 1 atm could not be expected to rise in air at 25 °C.
44. Refer to Exercise 43, and determine the minimum temperature to which the balloon described in part **(b)** would have to be heated before it could begin to rise in air. (Ignore the mass of the balloon itself.)
45. The density of phosphorus vapor is 2.64 g/L at 310 °C and 775 mmHg. What is the molecular formula of the phosphorus under these conditions?
46. A particular gaseous hydrocarbon that is 82.7% C and 17.3% H by mass has a density of 2.33 g/L at 23 °C and 746 mmHg. What is the molecular formula of this hydrocarbon?

Gases in Chemical Reactions

47. What volume of $O_2(g)$ is consumed in the combustion of 75.6 L $C_3H_8(g)$ if both gases are measured at STP?
48. How many liters of $H_2(g)$ at STP are produced per gram of Al(s) consumed in the following reaction?

$$2\,Al(s) + 6\,HCl(aq) \longrightarrow 2\,AlCl_3(aq) + 3\,H_2(g)$$

49. A particular coal sample contains 3.28% S by mass. When the coal is burned, the sulfur is converted to $SO_2(g)$. What volume of $SO_2(g)$, measured at 23 °C and 738 mmHg, is produced by burning 1.2×10^6 kg of this coal?
50. One method of removing $CO_2(g)$ from a spacecraft is to allow the CO_2 to react with LiOH. How many liters of $CO_2(g)$ at 25.9 °C and 751 Torr can be removed per kilogram of LiOH consumed?

$$2\,LiOH(s) + CO_2(g) \longrightarrow Li_2CO_3(s) + H_2O(l)$$

51. A 3.57 g sample of a $KCl-KClO_3$ mixture is decomposed by heating and produces 119 mL $O_2(g)$, measured at 22.4 °C and 738 mmHg. What is the mass percent of $KClO_3$ in the mixture?

$$2\,KClO_3(s) \longrightarrow 2\,KCl(s) + 3\,O_2(g)$$

52. Hydrogen peroxide, H_2O_2, is used to disinfect contact lenses. How many milliliters of $O_2(g)$ at 22 °C and 752 mmHg can be liberated from 10.0 mL of an aqueous solution containing 3.00% H_2O_2 by mass? The density of the aqueous solution of H_2O_2 is 1.01 g/mL.

$$2\,H_2O_2(aq) \longrightarrow 2\,H_2O(l) + O_2(g)$$

53. Calculate the volume of $H_2(g)$, measured at 26 °C and 751 Torr, required to react with 28.5 L CO(g), measured at 0 °C and 760 Torr, in this reaction.

$$3\,CO(g) + 7\,H_2(g) \longrightarrow C_3H_8(g) + 3\,H_2O(l)$$

54. The Haber process is the principal method for fixing nitrogen (converting N_2 to nitrogen compounds).

$$N_2(g) + 3\,H_2(g) \longrightarrow 2\,NH_3(g)$$

Assume that the reactant gases are completely converted to $NH_3(g)$ and that the gases behave ideally.
(a) What volume of $NH_3(g)$ can be produced from 152 L $N_2(g)$ and 313 L of $H_2(g)$ if the gases are measured at 315 °C and 5.25 atm?
(b) What volume of $NH_3(g)$, measured at 25 °C and 727 mmHg, can be produced from 152 L $N_2(g)$ and 313 L $H_2(g)$, measured at 315°C and 5.25 atm?

Mixtures of Gases

55. What is the volume, in liters, occupied by a mixture of 15.2 g Ne(g) and 34.8 g Ar(g) at 7.15 atm pressure and 26.7 °C?
56. A balloon filled with $H_2(g)$ at 0.0 °C and 1.00 atm has a volume of 2.24 L. What is the final gas volume if 0.10 mol He(g) is added to the balloon and the temperature is then raised to 100 °C while the pressure and amount of gas are held constant?
57. A gas cylinder of 53.7 L volume contains $N_2(g)$ at a pressure of 28.2 atm and 26 °C. How many grams of Ne(g) must we add to this same cylinder to raise the total pressure to 75.0 atm?
58. A 2.35 L container of $H_2(g)$ at 762 mmHg and 24 °C is connected to a 3.17 L container of He(g) at 728 mmHg and 24 °C. After mixing, what is the total gas pressure, in millimeters of mercury, with the temperature remaining at 24 °C?
59. Which actions would you take to establish a pressure of 2.00 atm in a 2.24 L cylinder containing 1.60 g $O_2(g)$ at 0 °C? **(a)** add 1.60 g O_2; **(b)** release 0.80 g O_2; **(c)** add 2.00 g He; **(d)** add 0.60 g He.
60. A mixture of 4.0 g $H_2(g)$ and 10.0 g He(g) in a 4.3 L flask is maintained at 0 °C.
    (a) What is the total pressure in the container?
    (b) What is the partial pressure of each gas?
61. A 2.00 L container is filled with Ar(g) at 752 mmHg and 35 °C. A 0.728 g sample of C_6H_6 vapor is then added.
    (a) What is the total pressure in the container?
    (b) What is the partial pressure of Ar and of C_6H_6?

62. The chemical composition of air that is exhaled (expired) is different from ordinary air. A typical analysis of expired air at 37 °C and 1.00 atm, expressed as percent by volume, is 74.2% N_2, 15.2% O_2, 3.8% CO_2, 5.9% H_2O, and 0.9% Ar. The composition of ordinary air is given in Practice Example 2-12B.
(a) What is the ratio of the partial pressure of $CO_2(g)$ in expired air to that in ordinary air?
(b) Would you expect the density of expired air to be greater or less than that of ordinary air at the same temperature and pressure? Explain.
(c) Confirm your expectation by calculating the densities of ordinary air and expired air at 37 °C and 1.00 atm.

63. In the drawing below, 1.00 g $H_2(g)$ is maintained at 1 atm pressure in a cylinder closed off by a freely moving piston. Which sketch, (a), (b), or (c), best represents the mixture obtained when 1.00 g He(g) is added? Explain.

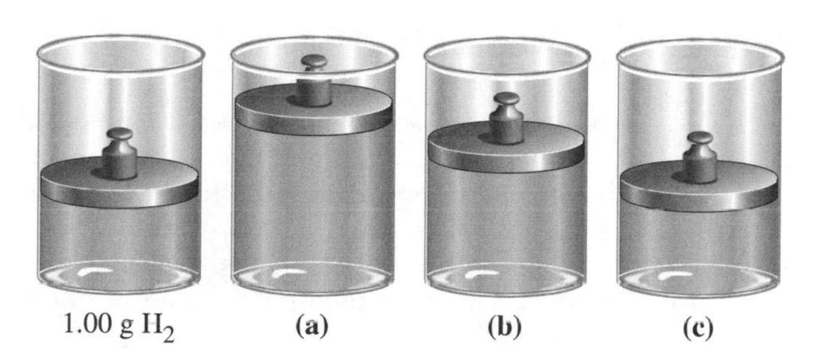

64. In the drawing above, 1.00 g $H_2(g)$ at 300 K is maintained at 1 atm pressure in a cylinder closed off by a freely moving piston. Which sketch, **(a)**, **(b)**, or **(c)**, best represents the mixture obtained when 0.50 g $H_2(g)$ is added and the temperature is reduced to 275 K? Explain your answer.

65. A 4.0 L sample of O_2 gas has a pressure of 1.0 atm. A 2.0 L sample of N_2 gas has a pressure of 2.0 atm. If these two samples are mixed and then compressed in a 2.0 L vessel, what is the final pressure of the mixture? Assume that the temperature remains unchanged.

66. The following figure shows the contents and pressures of three vessels of gas that are joined by a connecting tube.

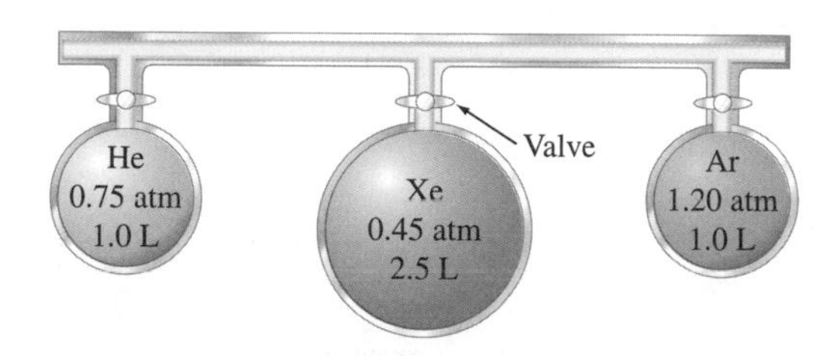

After the valves on the vessels are opened, the final pressure is measured and found to be 0.675 atm. What is the total volume of the connecting tube? Assume that the temperature remains constant.

Kinetic-Molecular Theory

67. Calculate the average kinetic energy, $\overline{e_k}$, for $O_2(g)$ at 298 K and 1.00 atm.

68. Calculate the total kinetic energy, in joules, of 155 g $N_2(g)$ at 25 °C and 1.00 atm. [*Hint*: First calculate the average kinetic energy, $\overline{e_k}$.]

Diffusion and Effusion of Gases

69. If 0.00484 mol $N_2O(g)$ effuses through an orifice in a certain period of time, how much $NO_2(g)$ would effuse in the same time under the same conditions?

70. A sample of $N_2(g)$ effuses through a tiny hole in 38 s. What must be the molar mass of a gas that requires 64 s to effuse under identical conditions?

71. What are the ratios of the diffusion rates for the pairs of gases **(a)** N_2 and O_2; **(b)** H_2O and D_2O (D = deuterium, i.e., ${}^2_1H$); **(c)** ${}^{14}CO_2$ and ${}^{12}CO_2$; **(d)** ${}^{235}UF_6$ and ${}^{238}UF_6$?

72. Which of the following visualizations best represents the distribution of O_2 and SO_2 molecules near an orifice some time after effusion occurs in the direction indicated by the arrows? The initial condition was one of equal numbers of O_2 molecules (●) and SO_2 molecules (●) on the left side of the orifice. Explain.

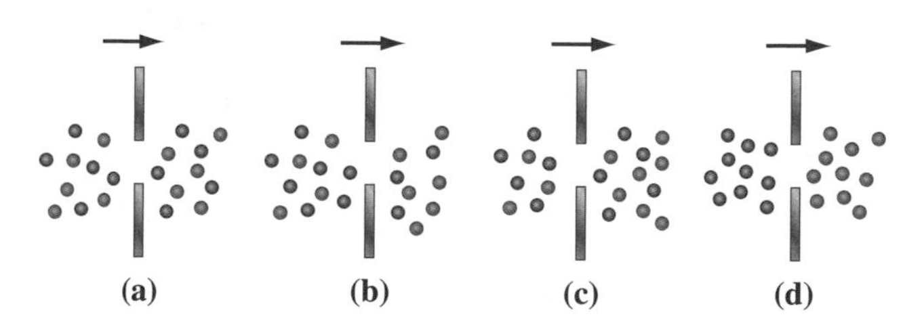

73. It takes 22 hours for a neon-filled balloon to shrink to half its original volume at STP. If the same balloon had been filled with helium, then how long would it have taken for the balloon to shrink to half its original volume at STP?

74. The molar mass of radon gas was first estimated by comparing its diffusion rate with that of mercury vapor, Hg(g). What is the molar mass of radon if mercury vapor diffuses 1.082 times as fast as radon gas? Assume that Graham's law holds for diffusion.

Nonideal Gases

75. Refer to Example 2-17. Recalculate the pressure of $Cl_2(g)$ by using both the ideal gas equation and the van der Waals equation at the temperatures **(a)** 100 °C; **(b)** 200 °C; **(c)** 400 °C. From the results, confirm the statement that a gas tends to be more ideal at high temperatures than at low temperatures.

76. Use both the ideal gas equation and the van der Waals equation to calculate the pressure exerted by 1.50 mol of $SO_2(g)$ when it is confined at 298 K to a volume of **(a)** 100.0 L, **(b)** 50.0 L, **(c)** 20.0 L, **(d)** 10.0 L. Under which of these conditions is the pressure calculated with the ideal gas equation within a few percent of that calculated with the van der Waals equation? Use values of a and b from Table 2.5.

77. Use the value of the van der Waals constant b for He(g), given in Table 2.5, to estimate the radius, r, of a single helium atom. Give your answer in picometers. [*Hint*: The volume of a sphere of radius r is $4\pi r^3/3$.]

78. **(a)** Use the value of the van der Waals constant b for $CH_4(g)$, given in Table 2.5, to estimate the radius of the CH_4 molecule. (See Exercise 77.) How does your estimate of the radius compare with the value $r = 228$ pm, obtained experimentally from an analysis of the structure of solid methane? **(b)** The density of $CH_4(g)$ is 66.02 g mL^{-1} at 100 bar and 325 K. What is the value of compressibility factor at this temperature and pressure?

Integrative and Advanced Exercises

79. Explain why it is necessary to include the density of Hg(l) and the value of the acceleration due to gravity, g, in a precise definition of a millimeter of mercury (page 44).

80. Assume the following initial conditions for the graphs labeled A, B, and C in Figure 2-7. (A) 10.0 mL at 400 K; (B) 20.0 mL at 400 K; (C) 40.0 mL at 400 K. Use Charles's law to calculate the volume of each gas at 0, −100, −200, −250, and −270 °C. Show that the volume of each gas becomes zero at −273.15 °C.

81. Consider the diagram below. The "initial" sketch illustrates, both at the macroscopic and molecular levels, an initial condition: 1 mol of a gas at 273 K and 1.00 atm. With as much detail as possible, illustrate the final condition after each of the following changes.
(a) The pressure is changed to 250 mmHg while standard temperature is maintained.
(b) The temperature is changed to 140 K while standard pressure is maintained.
(c) The pressure is changed to 0.5 atm while the temperature is changed to 550 K.
(d) An additional 0.5 mol of gas is introduced into the cylinder, the temperature is changed to 135 °C, and the pressure is changed to 2.25 atm.

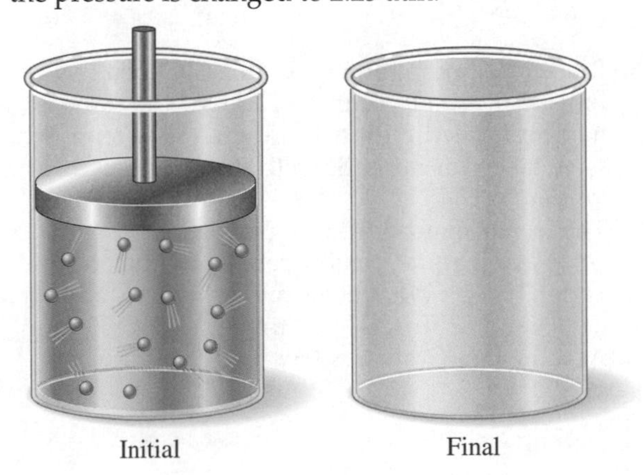

82. Two evacuated bulbs of equal volume are connected by a tube of negligible volume. One of the bulbs is placed in a constant-temperature bath at 225 K and the other bulb is placed in a constant-temperature bath at 350 K. Exactly 1 mol of an ideal gas is injected into the system. Calculate the final number of moles of gas in each bulb.

83. A compound is 85.6% carbon by mass. The rest is hydrogen. When 10.0 g of the compound is evaporated at 50.0 °C, the vapor occupies 6.30 L at 1.00 atm pressure. What is the molecular formula of the compound?

84. A 0.7178 g sample of a hydrocarbon occupies a volume of 390.7 mL at 65.0 °C and 99.2 kPa. When the sample is burned in excess oxygen, 2.4267 g CO_2 and 0.4967 g H_2O are obtained. What is the molecular formula of the hydrocarbon? Write a plausible structural formula for the molecule.

85. A 3.05 g sample of $NH_4NO_3(s)$ is introduced into an evacuated 2.18 L flask and then heated to 250 °C. What is the total gas pressure, in atmospheres, in the flask at 250 °C when the NH_4NO_3 has completely decomposed?

$$NH_4NO_3(s) \longrightarrow N_2O(g) + 2\,H_2O(g)$$

86. Ammonium nitrite, NH_4NO_2, decomposes according to the chemical equation below.

$$NH_4NO_2(s) \longrightarrow N_2(g) + 2\,H_2O(g)$$

What is the total volume of products obtained when 128 g NH_4NO_2 decomposes at 819 °C and 101 kPa?

87. A mixture of 1.00 g H_2 and 8.60 g O_2 is introduced into a 1.500 L flask at 25 °C. When the mixture is ignited, an explosive reaction occurs in which water is the only product. What is the total gas pressure when the flask is returned to 25 °C? (The vapor pressure of water at 25 °C is 23.8 mmHg.)

88. In the reaction of $CO_2(g)$ and solid sodium peroxide (Na_2O_2), solid sodium carbonate (Na_2CO_3) and oxygen gas are formed. This reaction is used in submarines and space vehicles to remove expired $CO_2(g)$ and to generate some of the $O_2(g)$ required for breathing. Assume that the volume of gases exchanged in the lungs equals 4.0 L/min, the CO_2 content of expired air is 3.8% CO_2 by volume, and the gases are at 25 °C and 735 mmHg. If the $CO_2(g)$ and $O_2(g)$ in the above reaction are measured at the same temperature and pressure, **(a)** how many milliliters of $O_2(g)$ are produced per minute and **(b)** at what rate is the $Na_2O_2(s)$ consumed, in grams per hour?

89. What is the partial pressure of $Cl_2(g)$, in millimeters of mercury, at 0.00 °C and 1.00 atm in a gaseous mixture that consists of 46.5% N_2, 12.7% Ne, and 40.8% Cl_2, by mass?

90. A gaseous mixture of He and O_2 has a density of 0.518 g/L at 25 °C and 721 mmHg. What is the mass percent He in the mixture?

91. Gas cylinder A has a volume of 48.2 L and contains $N_2(g)$ at 8.35 atm at 25 °C. Gas cylinder B, of unknown volume, contains He(g) at 9.50 atm and 25 °C. When the two cylinders are connected and the gases mixed, the pressure in each cylinder becomes 8.71 atm. What is the volume of cylinder B?

92. The accompanying sketch is that of a closed-end manometer. Describe how the gas pressure is measured. Why is a measurement of $P_{bar.}$ not necessary when using this manometer? Explain why the closed-end manometer is more suitable for measuring low pressures and the open-end manometer more suitable for measuring pressures nearer atmospheric pressure.

93. Producer gas is a type of fuel gas made by passing air or steam through a bed of hot coal or coke. A typical producer gas has the following composition in percent by volume: 8.0% CO_2, 23.2% CO, 17.7% H_2, 1.1% CH_4, and 50.0% N_2.
(a) What is the density of this gas at 23 °C and 763 mmHg, in grams per liter?
(b) What is the partial pressure of CO in this mixture at 0.00 °C and 1 atm?
(c) What volume of air, measured at 23 °C and 741 Torr, is required for the complete combustion of 1.00×10^3 L of this producer gas, also measured at 23 °C and 741 Torr?
[*Hint:* Which three of the constituent gases are combustible?]

94. The heat required to sustain animals while they hibernate comes from the biochemical combustion of fatty acids, such as arachidonic acid, $C_{20}H_{32}O_2$. What volume of air, measured at 298 K and 1.00 atm, is required to burn 2.00 kg $C_{20}H_{32}O_2$? Air is approximately 78.1% N_2 and 20.9% O_2, by volume. Other gases make up the remaining 1.0%.

95. A mixture of $H_2(g)$ and $O_2(g)$ is prepared by electrolyzing 1.32 g water, and the mixture of gases is collected over water at 30 °C and 748 mmHg. The volume of "wet" gas obtained is 2.90 L. What must be the vapor pressure of water at 30 °C?

$$2\,H_2O(l) \xrightarrow{\text{electrolysis}} 2\,H_2(g) + O_2(g)$$

96. Aluminum (Al) and iron (Fe) each react with hydrochloric acid solution (HCl) to produce a chloride salt and hydrogen gas, $H_2(g)$. A 0.1924 g sample of a mixture of Al and Fe is treated with excess HCl solution. A volume of 159 mL of H_2 gas is collected over water at 19.0 °C and 841 Torr. What is the percent (by mass) of Fe in the mixture? The vapor pressure of water at 19.0 °C is 16.5 Torr.

97. A 0.168 L sample of $O_2(g)$ is collected over water at 26 °C and a barometric pressure of 737 mmHg. In the gas that is collected, what is the percent water vapor **(a)** by volume; **(b)** by number of molecules; **(c)** by mass? (Vapor pressure of water at 26 °C = 25.2 mmHg.)

98. A breathing mixture is prepared in which He is substituted for N_2. The gas is 79% He and 21% O_2, by volume. **(a)** What is the density of this mixture in grams per liter at 25 °C and 1.00 atm? **(b)** At what pressure would the He–O_2 mixture have the same density as that of air at 25 °C and 1.00 atm? See Exercise 103 for the composition of air.

99. Chlorine dioxide, ClO_2, is sometimes used as a chlorinating agent for water treatment. It can be prepared from the reaction below:

$$Cl_2(g) + 4\,NaClO(aq) \longrightarrow 4\,NaCl(aq) + 2\,ClO_2(g)$$

In an experiment, 1.0 L $Cl_2(g)$, measured at 10.0 °C and 4.66 atm, is dissolved in 0.750 L of 2.00 M NaClO(aq). If 25.9 g of pure ClO_2 is obtained, then what is the percent yield for this experiment?

100. The amount of ozone, O_3, in a mixture of gases can be determined by passing the mixture through a solution of excess potassium iodide, KI. Ozone reacts with the iodide ion as follows:

$$O_3(g) + 3I^-(aq) + H_2O(l) \longrightarrow O_2(g) + I_3^-(aq) + 2OH^-(aq)$$

The amount of I_3^- produced is determined by titrating with thiosulfate ion, $S_2O_3^{2-}$:

$$I_3^-(aq) + 2\,S_2O_3^{2-}(aq) \longrightarrow 3I^-(aq) + S_4O_6^{2-}(aq)$$

A mixture of gases occupies a volume of 53.2 L at 18 °C and 0.993 atm. The mixture is passed slowly through a solution containing an excess of KI to ensure that all the ozone reacts. The resulting solution requires 26.2 mL of 0.1359 M $Na_2S_2O_3$ to titrate to the end point. Calculate the mole fraction of ozone in the original mixture.

101. A 0.1052 g sample of $H_2O(l)$ in an 8.050 L sample of dry air at 30.1 °C evaporates completely. To what temperature must the air be cooled to give a relative humidity of 80.0%? Vapor pressures of water: 20 °C, 17.54 mmHg; 19 °C, 16.48 mmHg; 18 °C, 15.48 mmHg; 17 °C, 14.53 mmHg; 16 °C, 13.63 mmHg; 15 °C, 12.79 mmHg. [*Hint*: Go to Focus On feature for Chapter 6 on the MasteringChemistry site, www.masteringchemistry.com, for a discussion of relative humidity.]

102. An alternative to Figure 2-6 is to plot P against $1/V$. The resulting graph is a straight line passing through the origin. Use Boyle's data from Feature Problem 125 to draw such a straight-line graph. What factors would affect the *slope* of this straight line? Explain.

103. We have noted that atmospheric pressure depends on altitude. Atmospheric pressure as a function of altitude can be calculated with an equation known as the barometric formula:

$$P = P_0 \times 10^{-Mgh/2.303RT}$$

In this equation, P and P_0 can be in any pressure units, for example, Torr. P_0 is the pressure at sea level, generally taken to be 1.00 atm or its equivalent. The units in the exponential term must be SI units, however. Use the barometric formula to

(a) estimate the barometric pressure at the top of Mt. Whitney in California (altitude: 14,494 ft; assume a temperature of 10 °C)

(b) show that barometric pressure decreases by one-thirtieth in value for every 900-ft increase in altitude

104. Consider a sample of $O_2(g)$ at 298 K and 1.0 atm. Calculate **(a)** u_{rms} and **(b)** the fraction of molecules that have speed equal to u_{rms}.

105. A nitrogen molecule (N_2) having the average kinetic energy at 300 K is released from Earth's surface to travel upward. If the molecule could move upward without colliding with other molecules, then how high would it go before coming to rest? Give your answer in kilometers. [*Hint*: When the molecule comes to rest, the potential energy of the molecule will be mgh, where m is the molecular mass in kilograms, $g = 9.81\ \text{m s}^{-2}$ is the acceleration due to gravity, and h is the height, in meters, above Earth's surface.]

106. If the van der Waals equation is solved for volume, a cubic equation is obtained.

(a) Derive the equation below by rearranging equation (2.26).

$$V^3 - n\left(\frac{RT + bP}{P}\right)V^2 + \left(\frac{n^2a}{P}\right)V - \frac{n^3ab}{P} = 0$$

(b) What is the volume, in liters, occupied by 185 g $CO_2(g)$ at a pressure of 12.5 atm and 286 K? For $CO_2(g)$, $a = 3.61\ \text{L}^2\ \text{atm mol}^{-2}$ and $b = 0.0429\ \text{L mol}^{-1}$. [*Hint*: Use the ideal gas equation to obtain an estimate of the volume. Then refine your estimate, either by trial and error, or using the method of successive approximations.]

107. According to the *CRC Handbook of Chemistry and Physics* (83rd ed.), the molar volume of $O_2(g)$ is $0.2168\ \text{L mol}^{-1}$ at 280 K and 10 MPa. (Note: $1\ \text{MPa} = 1 \times 10^6\ \text{Pa}$.)

(a) Use the van der Waals equation to calculate the pressure of one mole of $O_2(g)$ at 280 K if the volume is 0.2168 L. What is the % error in the calculated pressure? The van der Waals constants are $a = 1.382\ \text{L}^2\ \text{bar mol}^{-2}$ and $b = 0.0319\ \text{L mol}^{-1}$.

(b) Use the ideal gas equation to calculate the volume of one mole of $O_2(g)$ at 280 K and 10 MPa. What is the % error in the calculated volume?

108. A particular equation of state for $O_2(g)$ has the form

$$P\overline{V} = RT\left(1 + \frac{B}{\overline{V}} + \frac{C}{\overline{V}^2}\right)$$

where $\overline{V}$ is the molar volume, $B = -21.89\ \text{cm}^3/\text{mol}$ and $C = 1230\ \text{cm}^6/\text{mol}$.

(a) Use the equation to calculate the pressure exerted by 1 mol $O_2(g)$ confined to a volume of $500\ \text{cm}^3$ at 273 K.

109. A 0.156 g sample of a magnesium–aluminum alloy dissolves completely in an excess of HCl(aq). The liberated $H_2(g)$ is collected over water at 5 °C when the barometric pressure is 752 Torr. After the gas is collected, the water and gas gradually warm to the prevailing room temperature of 23 °C. The pressure of the collected gas is again equalized against the barometric pressure of 752 Torr, and its volume is found to be 202 mL. What is the percent composition of the magnesium–aluminum alloy? (Vapor pressure of water: 6.54 mmHg at 5 °C and 21.07 mmHg at 23 °C).

Feature Problems

110. In 1860, Stanislao Cannizzaro showed how Avogadro's hypothesis could be used to establish the atomic masses of elements in gaseous compounds. Cannizzaro took the atomic mass of hydrogen to be exactly one and assumed that hydrogen exists as H_2 molecules (molecular mass = 2). Next, he determined the volume of $H_2(g)$ at 0.00 °C and 1.00 atm that has a mass of exactly 2 g. This volume is 22.4 L. Then he assumed that 22.4 L of any other gas would have the same number of molecules as in 22.4 L of $H_2(g)$. (Here is where Avogadro's hypothesis entered in.) Finally, he reasoned that the ratio of the mass of 22.4 L of any other gas to the mass of 22.4 L of $H_2(g)$ should be the same as the ratio of their molecular masses. The sketch below illustrates Cannizzaro's reasoning in establishing the atomic weight of oxygen as 16. The gases in the table all contain the element X. Their molecular masses were determined by Cannizzaro's method. Use the percent composition data to deduce the atomic mass of X, the number of atoms of X in each of the gas molecules, and the identity of X.

Compound	Molecular Mass, u	Mass Percent X, %
Nitryl fluoride	65.01	49.4
Nitrosyl fluoride	49.01	32.7
Thionyl fluoride	86.07	18.6
Sulfuryl fluoride	102.07	31.4

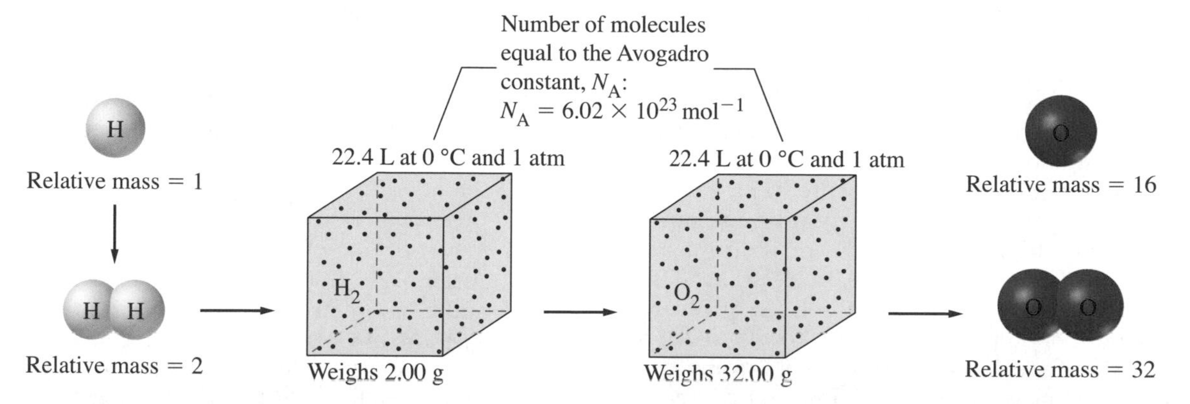

111. In research that required the careful measurement of gas densities, John Rayleigh, a physicist, found that the density of $O_2(g)$ had the same value whether the gas was obtained from air or derived from one of its compounds. The situation with $N_2(g)$ was different, however. The density of $N_2(g)$ had the same value when the $N_2(g)$ was derived from any of various compounds, but a *different* value if the $N_2(g)$ was extracted from air. In 1894, Rayleigh enlisted the aid of William Ramsay, a chemist, to solve this apparent mystery; in the course of their work they discovered the noble gases.

(a) Why do you suppose that the $N_2(g)$ extracted from liquid air did *not* have the same density as $N_2(g)$ obtained from its compounds?

(b) Which gas do you suppose had the greater density: $N_2(g)$ extracted from air or $N_2(g)$ prepared from nitrogen compounds? Explain.

(c) The way in which Ramsay proved that nitrogen gas extracted from air was itself a mixture of gases involved allowing this nitrogen to react with magnesium metal to form magnesium nitride. Explain the significance of this experiment.

(d) Calculate the *percent difference* in the densities at 0.00 °C and 1.00 atm of Rayleigh's $N_2(g)$ extracted from air and $N_2(g)$ derived from nitrogen compounds. [The volume percentages of the major components of air are 78.084% N_2, 20.946% O_2, 0.934% Ar, and 0.0379% CO_2.]

112. The equation $d/P = M/RT$, which can be derived from equation (2.14), suggests that the ratio of the density (d) to pressure (P) of a gas at constant temperature should be a constant. The gas density data at the end of this question were obtained for $O_2(g)$ at various pressures at 273.15 K.

(a) Calculate values of d/P, and with a graph or by other means determine the ideal value of the term d/P for $O_2(g)$ at 273.15 K.
[*Hint:* The ideal value is that associated with a perfect (ideal) gas.]

(b) Use the value of d/P from part **(a)** to calculate a precise value for the atomic mass of oxygen, and compare this value with that listed on the inside front cover.

P, mmHg:	760.00	570.00	380.00	190.00
d, g/L:	1.428962	1.071485	0.714154	0.356985

113. A sounding balloon is a rubber bag filled with $H_2(g)$ and carrying a set of instruments (the payload). Because this combination of bag, gas, and payload has a smaller mass than a corresponding volume of air, the balloon rises. As the balloon rises, it expands. From the table below, estimate the maximum height to which a spherical balloon can rise given the mass of balloon, 1200 g; payload, 1700 g: quantity of $H_2(g)$ in balloon, 120 ft^3 at 0.00 °C and 1.00 atm; diameter of balloon at maximum height, 25 ft. Air pressure and temperature as functions of altitude are:

Altitude, km	Pressure, mb	Temperature, K
0	1.0×10^3	288
5	5.4×10^2	256
10	2.7×10^2	223
20	5.5×10^1	217
30	1.2×10^1	230
40	2.9×10^0	250
50	8.1×10^{-1}	250
60	2.3×10^{-1}	256

Self-Assessment Exercises

114. In your own words, define or explain each term or symbol. **(a)** atm; **(b)** STP; **(c)** R; **(d)** partial pressure; **(e)** u_{rms}.

115. Briefly describe each concept or process: **(a)** absolute zero of temperature; **(b)** collection of a gas over water; **(c)** effusion of a gas; **(d)** law of combining volumes.

116. Explain the important distinctions between **(a)** barometer and manometer; **(b)** Celsius and Kelvin temperature; **(c)** ideal gas equation and general gas equation; **(d)** ideal gas and real gas.

117. Which exerts the greatest pressure, **(a)** a 75.0 cm column of Hg(l) ($d = 13.6$ g/mL); **(b)** a column of air 10 mi high; **(c)** a 5.0 m column of CCl_4(l) ($d = 1.59$ g/mL); **(d)** 10.0 g H_2(g) at STP?

118. For a fixed amount of gas at a fixed pressure, changing the temperature from 100.0 °C to 200 K causes the gas volume to **(a)** double; **(b)** increase, but not to twice its original value; **(c)** decrease; **(d)** stay the same.

119. A fragile glass vessel will break if the internal pressure equals or exceeds 2.0 bar. If the vessel is sealed at 0 °C and 1.0 bar, then at what temperature will the vessel break? Assume that the vessel does not expand when heated.

120. Which of the following choices represents the molar volume of an ideal gas at 25 °C and 1.5 atm? **(a)** $(298 \times 1.5/273) \times 22.4$ L; **(b)** 22.4 L; **(c)** $(273 \times 1.5/298) \times 22.4$ L; **(d)** $[298/(273 \times 1.5)] \times 22.4$ L; **(e)** $[273/(298 \times 1.5)] \times 22.4$ L.

121. The gas with the greatest density at STP is **(a)** N_2O; **(b)** Kr; **(c)** SO_3; **(d)** Cl_2.

122. If the Kelvin temperature of a sample of ideal gas doubles (e.g., from 200 K to 400 K), what happens to the root-mean-square speed, u_{rms}? **(a)** u_{rms} increases by a factor of $\sqrt{2}$; **(b)** u_{rms} increases by a factor of 2; **(c)** u_{rms} decreases by a factor of 2; **(d)** u_{rms} increases by a factor of 4; **(e)** u_{rms} decreases by a factor of 4.

123. Consider the statements (a) to (e) below. Assume that H_2(g) and O_2(g) behave ideally. State whether each of the following statements is true or false. For each false statement, explain how you would change it to make it a true statement.

(a) Under the same conditions of temperature and pressure, the average kinetic energy of O_2 molecules is less than that of H_2 molecules.

(b) Under the same conditions of temperature and pressure, H_2 molecules move faster, on average, than O_2 molecules.

(c) The volume of 1.00 mol of H_2(g) at 25.0 °C, 1.00 atm is 22.4 L.

(d) The volume of 2.0 g H_2(g) is equal to the volume of 32.0 g O_2(g), at the same temperature and pressure.

(e) In a mixture of H_2 and O_2 gases, with partial pressures P_{H_2} and P_{O_2}, respectively, the total pressure is the larger of P_{H_2} and P_{O_2}.

124. A sample of O_2(g) is collected over water at 23 °C and a barometric pressure of 751 Torr. The vapor pressure of water at 23 °C is 21 mmHg. The partial pressure of O_2(g) in the sample collected is **(a)** 21 mmHg; **(b)** 751 Torr; **(c)** 0.96 atm; **(d)** 1.02 atm.

125. At 0 °C and 0.500 atm, 4.48 L of gaseous NH_3 **(a)** contains 6.02×10^{22} molecules; **(b)** has a mass of 17.0 g; **(c)** contains 0.200 mol NH_3; **(d)** has a mass of 3.40 g.

126. To establish a pressure of 2.00 atm in a 2.24 L cylinder containing 1.60 g O_2(g) at 0 °C, **(a)** add 1.60 g O_2; **(b)** add 0.60 g He(g); **(c)** add 2.00 g He(g); **(d)** release 0.80 g O_2(g).

127. Carbon monoxide, CO, and hydrogen react according to the equation below.

$$3\,CO(g) + 7\,H_2(g) \longrightarrow C_3H_8(g) + 3\,H_2O(g)$$

What volume of which reactant gas remains if 12.0 L CO(g) and 25.0 L H_2(g) are allowed to react? Assume that the volumes of both gases are measured at the same temperature and pressure.

128. A mixture of 5.0×10^{-5} mol H_2(g) and 5.0×10^{-5} mol SO_2(g) is placed in a 10.0 L container at 25 °C. The container has a pinhole leak. After a period of time, the partial pressure of H_2(g) in the container **(a)** is less than that of the SO_2(g); **(b)** is equal to that of the SO_2(g); **(c)** exceeds that of the SO_2(g); **(d)** is the same as in the original mixture.

129. Under which conditions is Cl_2 most likely to behave like an ideal gas? Explain. **(a)** 100 °C and 10.0 atm;

(b) 0 °C and 0.50 atm; **(c)** 200 °C and 0.50 atm; **(d)** 400 °C and 10.0 atm.

130. Without referring to Table 2.5, state which species in each of the following pairs has the greater value for the van der Waals constant a, and which one has the greater value for the van der Waals constant b. **(a)** He or Ne; **(b)** CH_4 or C_3H_8; **(c)** H_2 or Cl_2.

131. Explain why the height of the mercury column in a barometer is independent of the diameter of the barometer tube.

132. A gaseous hydrocarbon that is 82.7% C and 17.3% H by mass has a density of 2.35 g/L at 25 °C and 752 Torr. What is the molecular formula of this hydrocarbon?

133. Draw a box to represent a sample of air containing N_2 molecules (represented as squares) and O_2 molecules (represented as circles) in their correct proportions. How many squares and circles would you need to draw to also represent the $CO_2(g)$ in air through a single mark? What else should you add to the box for this more complete representation of air?

3

Intermolecular Forces: Liquids and Solids

CONTENTS

In this scene from Antarctica, water exists in all three states of matter—solid in the ice, liquid in the sea, and gas in the atmosphere.

When we make ice cubes by placing water in a tray in a freezer, energy is removed from the water molecules, which gradually slow down. Attractive (intermolecular) forces between the molecules take over, and the water solidifies into ice. When an ice cube melts, energy from the surroundings is absorbed by the water molecules, which overcome the intermolecular forces within the ice cube and enter the liquid state. In our study of gases, we intentionally sought conditions in which the intermolecular forces were negligible. This approach allowed us to describe gases with the ideal gas equation and to explain their behavior with the kinetic-molecular theory of gases. To describe the other states of matter—liquids and solids—we must first be able to identify the various intermolecular forces and then find situations in which the intermolecular forces are significant. We then consider some interesting properties of liquids and solids related to the strengths of these forces.

▶ Two of the many natural phenomena described in this chapter include the more ordered structure of the solid compared with the liquid state and the variation of density with the state of matter.

3-1 Intermolecular Forces

In our study of gases, we noted that at high pressures and low temperatures intermolecular forces cause gas behavior to depart from ideality. When these forces are sufficiently strong, a gas condenses to a liquid. That is, the intermolecular forces keep the molecules in such close proximity that they are confined to a definite volume, as expected for the liquid state.

Intermolecular forces are important in establishing the form and behavior of matter. The origin of intermolecular forces, those interactions between molecules, arises from the permanent and momentary unequal distribution of electron density within molecules.

Van der Waals Forces

Because helium forms no stable chemical bonds, we might expect it to remain a gas right down to 0 K. Although helium remains gaseous to very low temperatures, it does condense to a liquid at 4 K and freeze to a solid (at 25 atm pressure) at 1 K. These data suggest that intermolecular forces, even though very weak, must exist among He atoms. If the temperature is sufficiently low, these forces overcome thermal agitation and cause helium to condense. In this section, we will examine the types of intermolecular forces known collectively as **van der Waals forces**. The intermolecular forces contributing to the term $a(n/V)^2$ in the van der Waals equation for nonideal gases (equation 1.26) are of this type.

Instantaneous and Induced Dipoles

In describing electronic structures, we speak of electron charge density, or the probability that an electron is in a certain region at a given time. One probability is that at some particular instant—purely by chance—electrons are concentrated in one region of an atom or a molecule. This displacement of electrons causes a normally nonpolar species to become momentarily polar. An *instantaneous dipole* is formed. That is, the molecule has an instantaneous dipole moment. After this, electrons in a neighboring atom or molecule may be displaced to also produce a dipole. This is a process of induction (Fig. 3-1), and the newly formed dipole is called an *induced dipole.*

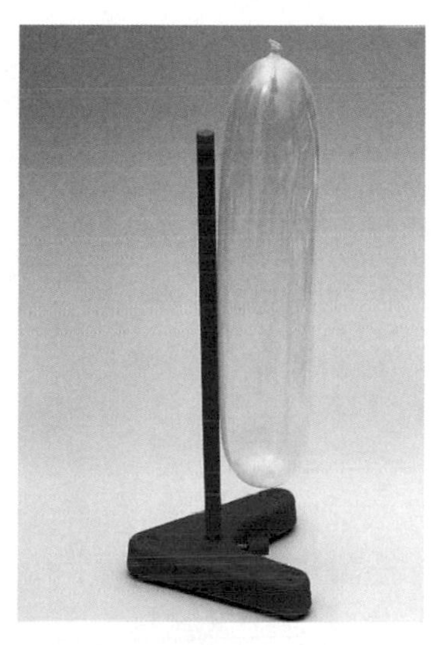

▲ FIGURE 3-1
The phenomenon of induction
The attraction of a balloon to a surface is a commonplace example of induction. The balloon is charged by rubbing, and the charged balloon induces an opposite charge on the surface.

Taken together, these two events lead to an intermolecular force of attraction (Fig. 3-2). We can call this an instantaneous dipole–induced dipole attraction, but the names more commonly used are **dispersion force** and **London force**. (In 1928, Fritz London offered a theoretical explanation of these forces.)

Polarizability is the term used to describe the relative tendency for a charge distribution to distort from its normal shape in an atom or a molecule. The greater this tendency, the more polarizable an atom or a molecule is said to be. Polarizability increases with atomic or molecular size (see the table on the next page), which is defined by the volume of the electron cloud around a substance. Also, in large molecules, some electrons, being farther from atomic nuclei, are less firmly held. These electrons are more easily displaced, and the polarizability

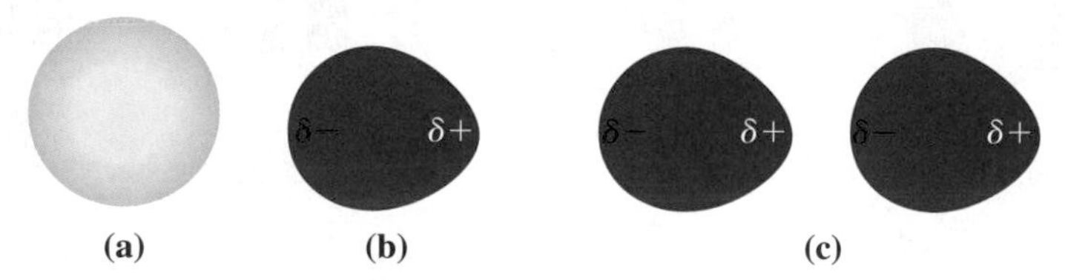

▲ FIGURE 3-2
Instantaneous and induced dipoles
(a) In the *normal condition*, a nonpolar molecule has a symmetrical charge distribution. **(b)** In the *instantaneous condition*, a displacement of the electronic charge produces an instantaneous dipole with a charge separation represented as δ+ and δ−. **(c)** In an *induced dipole*, the instantaneous dipole on the left induces a charge separation in the molecule on the right. The result is an instantaneous dipole–induced dipole attraction.

KEEP IN MIND

that a bond dipole results from the separation of centers of positive and negative charge in a covalent bond, that a resultant dipole moment, μ is a summation of bond dipoles taking into account their magnitudes and directions, and that a *polar* molecule is one that has a permanent resultant dipole moment.

Compound	Polarizability,* 10^{-25} cm^3	Molar Mass, amu	Boiling Point, K
H_2	7.90	2.0158	20.35
O_2	16.0	31.9988	90.19
N_2	17.6	28.0134	77.35
CH_4	26.0	16.04	109.15
C_2H_6	44.7	30.07	184.55
Cl_2	46.1	70.906	238.25
C_3H_8	62.9	44.11	231.05
CCl_4	105	153.81	349.95

*Sometimes polarizability is referred to as *polarizability volume.* Note that the units of polarizability given above have the units of volume. That provides a measure of the atomic or molecular volume.

of the molecule increases. Because dispersion forces become stronger (more attractive) as polarizability increases, and because polarizability generally increases with molecular mass, the melting points and boiling points of molecular substances generally increase with increasing molecular mass. For instance, helium (atomic mass, 4 u) has a boiling point of 4 K, whereas radon (atomic mass, 222 u) has a boiling point of 211 K. The melting points and boiling points of the halogens increase in a similar way in the series F_2, Cl_2, Br_2, I_2.

▶ Recall that a molecular substance is made up of molecules. The molecules interact with each other through relatively weak intermolecular forces. The atoms of a given molecule are held together by relatively strong covalent bonds.

The strength of dispersion forces also depends on *molecular shape.* Electrons in elongated molecules are more easily displaced than are those in small, compact, symmetrical molecules; the elongated molecules are more polarizable. Two substances with identical numbers and kinds of atoms but different molecular shapes (*isomers*) may have different properties. This idea is illustrated in Figure 3-3.

Dipole–Dipole Interactions

In a *polar* substance, the molecules have permanent dipole moments, so the molecules tend to line up with the positive end of one dipole directed toward the negative ends of neighboring dipoles (Fig. 3-4). This additional partial ordering of molecules can cause a substance to persist as a solid or liquid at temperatures higher than otherwise expected. Consider N_2, O_2, and NO. There are no electronegativity differences in N_2 and O_2, and both substances are nonpolar. In NO, conversely, there is an electronegativity difference, and the molecule has a slight dipole moment. Considering only dispersion forces, we would expect the boiling point of NO(l) to be intermediate to those of N_2(l) and O_2(l), but in the comparison on the next page, we see that it is not. NO(l) has the highest boiling point of the three because of its additional permanent dipole.

(a) Neopentane
bp = 9.5 °C

(b) Pentane
bp = 36.1 °C

▲ FIGURE 3-3
Molecular shapes and polarizability
The elongated pentane molecule is more polarized than is the compact neopentane molecule. Intermolecular forces are stronger in pentane than they are in neopentane. As a result, pentane boils at a higher temperature than neopentane.

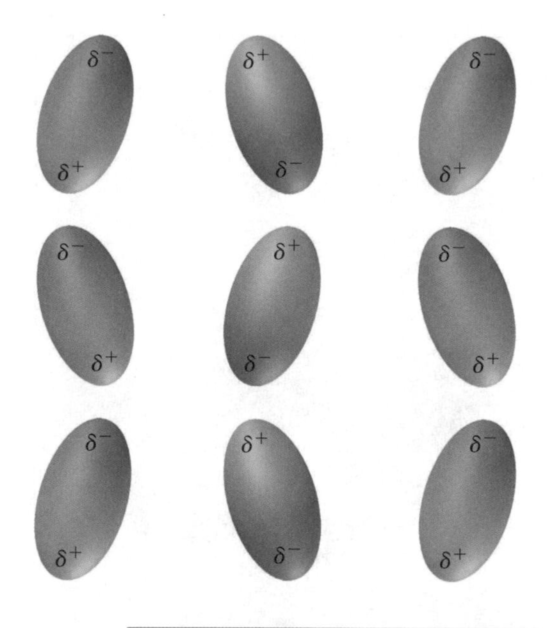

◀ FIGURE 3-4
Dipole–dipole interactions
Dipoles tend to arrange themselves with the positive end of one dipole pointed toward the negative end of a neighboring dipole. Ordinarily, thermal motion upsets this orderly array. Nevertheless, this tendency for dipoles to align themselves can affect physical properties, such as the melting points of solids and the boiling points of liquids.

N_2	NO	O_2
$\mu = 0$ (nonpolar) mol. mass = 28 u bp = 77.34 K	$\mu = 0.153$ D (polar) mol. mass = 30 u bp = 121.39 K	$\mu = 0$ (nonpolar) mol. mass = 32 u bp = 90.19 K

◀ The SI unit for dipole moment, C m, is inconvenient for expressing molecular dipole moments. The non-SI unit, debye (D), is often used. One debye is approximately 3.34×10^{-30} C m.

Hydrogen Bonding

Figure 3-5, in which the boiling points of a series of similar compounds are plotted as a function of molecular mass, demonstrates some features that we cannot explain by the types of intermolecular forces considered to this point. The hydrogen compounds (hydrides) of the group 14 elements display normal behavior; that is, the boiling points increase regularly as the molecular mass increases. But there are three striking exceptions in groups 15, 16, and 17. The boiling points of NH_3, H_2O, and HF are as high or higher than those of any other hydride in their group—not lowest, as we might expect. A special type of intermolecular force

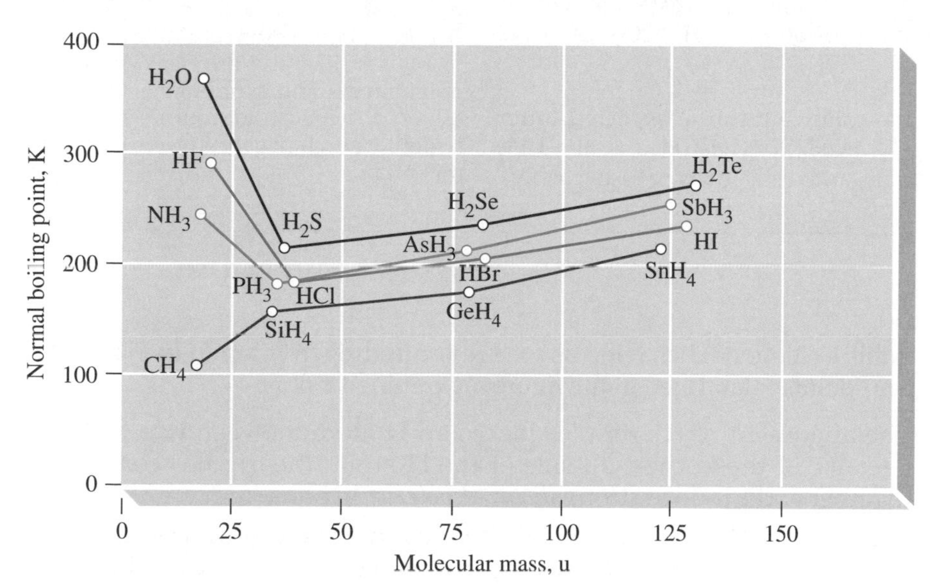

▲ FIGURE 3-5
Comparison of boiling points of some hydrides of the elements of groups 14,15,16, and 17
The values for NH_3, H_2O, and HF are unusually high compared with those of other members of their groups.

EXAMPLE 3-1 Comparing Physical Properties of Polar and Nonpolar Substances

Which would you expect to have the higher boiling point, the hydrocarbon fuel butane, C_4H_{10}, or the organic solvent acetone, $(CH_3)_2CO$?

Analyze

Ordinarily, the first clue comes in a comparison of molecular masses. However, because the two substances have the same molecular mass (58 u), we have to look elsewhere for a factor on which to base our prediction.

The next consideration is the polarity of the molecules. The electronegativity difference between C and H is so small that we generally expect hydrocarbons, such as butane, to be nonpolar. However, we notice that one of the molecules contains a carbon-oxygen bond, and thus, a strong carbon-to-oxygen dipole. At times, it is helpful to sketch the structure of a molecule to see whether symmetrical features cause bond dipoles to cancel. It is not necessary to sketch the structure of the acetone molecule to deduce that it is a polar molecule. The C=O bond dipole in acetone cannot be offset by other bond dipoles. Thus, acetone is polar.

Solve

Given two substances with the same molecular mass, one polar and one nonpolar, we expect the polar substance—acetone—to have the higher boiling point. (The measured boiling points are butane, −0.5 °C; acetone, 56.2 °C.)

Assess

In general, when comparing the properties of different substances, we must consider the various types of intermolecular forces and the factors that affect the strength of each type of force. Although it wasn't important here, the three-dimensional shape of a molecule is usually a very important consideration and it is usually necessary to sketch the molecular structure to see how molecular shape plays a role.

PRACTICE EXAMPLE A: Which of the following substances would you expect to have the highest boiling point: C_3H_8, CO_2, CH_3CN? Explain.

PRACTICE EXAMPLE B: Arrange the following in the expected order of increasing boiling point: C_8H_{18}, $CH_3CH_2CH_2CH_3$, $(CH_3)_3CH$, C_6H_5CHO (octane, butane, isobutane, and benzaldehyde respectively).

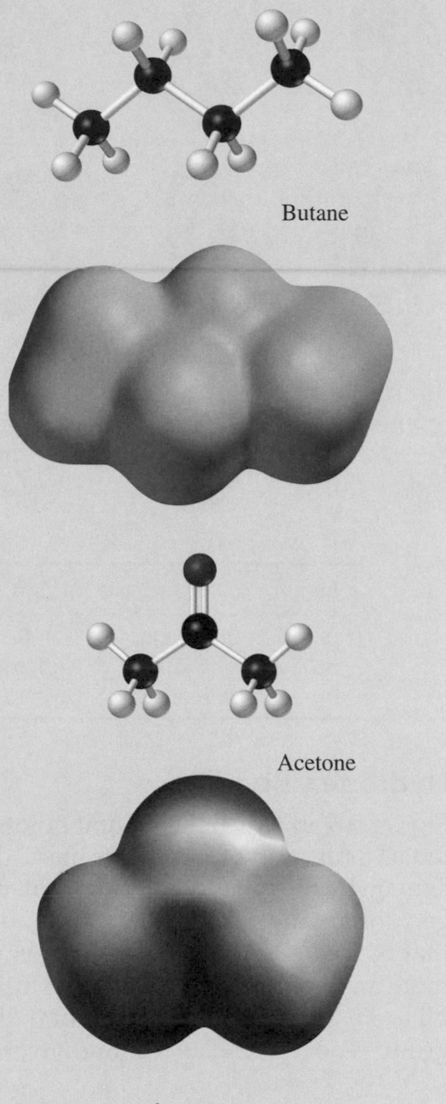

▲ **Butane and acetone**
The lower diagrams are electrostatic potential diagrams for butane and acetone. The red color indicates regions of high negative electrostatic potential.

causes this exceptional behavior, as we see for hydrogen fluoride in Figure 3-6. The main points established in the figure are outlined below.

- The alignment of HF dipoles places an H atom between two F atoms. Because of the very small size of the H atom, the dipoles come close together and produce strong *dipole–dipole* attractions.
- Although an H atom is covalently bonded to one F atom, it is also weakly bonded to the F atom of a nearby HF molecule. This occurs through a lone pair of electrons on the F atom. Each H atom acts as a bridge between two F atoms.
- The bond angle between two F atoms bridged by an H atom (that is, the angle F—HF···F) is about 180°.

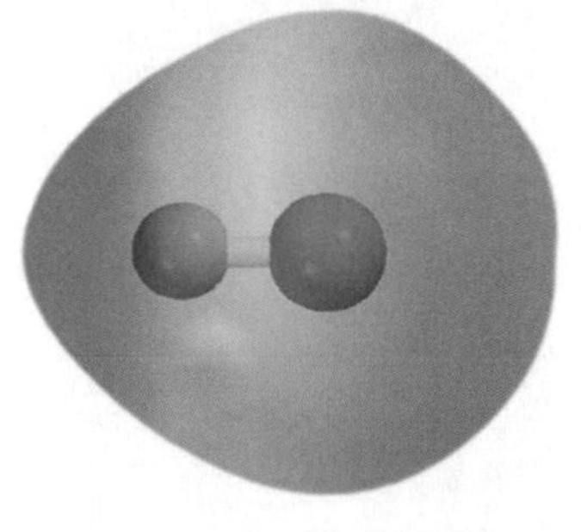

▲ **Electrostatic potential map of HF**

The type of intermolecular force just described is called a hydrogen bond, although it is simply an electrostatic attraction and not an actual chemical bond like a covalent bond. In a **hydrogen bond** an H atom is covalently bonded to a highly electronegative atom, which attracts electron density away from the H nucleus. This in turn allows the H nucleus, a proton, to be simultaneously attracted to a lone pair of electrons on a highly electronegative atom in a neighboring molecule.

Hydrogen bonds are possible only with certain hydrogen-containing compounds because all atoms other than H have inner-shell electrons to shield their nuclei from attraction by lone-pair electrons of nearby atoms. Only F, O, and N easily meet the requirements for hydrogen-bond formation. Weak hydrogen bonding is occasionally encountered between an H atom of one molecule and a Cl or S atom in a neighboring molecule. Compared with other intermolecular forces, hydrogen bonds are relatively strong, having energies of the order of 15 to 40 $kJ\ mol^{-1}$. By contrast, single covalent bonds (also known as intramolecular bonds) are much stronger still—greater than 150 $kJ\ mol^{-1}$.

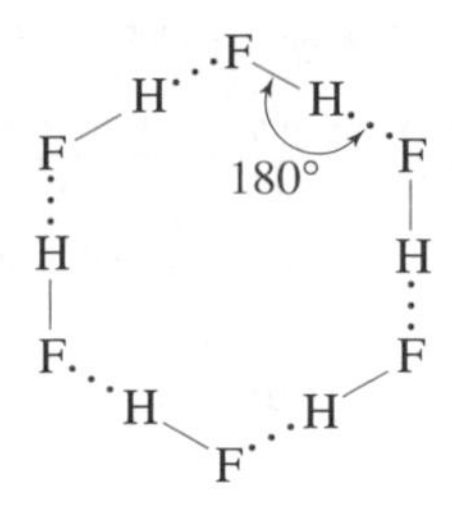

▲ FIGURE 3-6
Hydrogen bonding in gaseous hydrogen fluoride
In gaseous hydrogen fluoride, many of the HF molecules are associated into cyclic $(HF)_6$ structures of the type pictured here. Each H atom is bonded to one F atom by a single covalent bond (—) and to another F atom through a hydrogen bond (···).

Hydrogen Bonding in Water

Ordinary water is certainly the most common substance in which hydrogen bonding occurs. Figure 3-7 shows how one water molecule is held to four neighbors in a tetrahedral arrangement by hydrogen bonds. In ice, hydrogen bonds hold the water molecules in a rigid but rather open structure. As ice melts, only a fraction of the hydrogen bonds are broken. One indication of this is the relatively low heat of fusion of ice (6.01 $kJ\ mol^{-1}$). It is much less than we would expect if all the hydrogen bonds were to break during melting.

The open structure of ice shown in Figure 3-7(b) gives ice a low density. When ice melts, some of the hydrogen bonds are broken. This allows the water

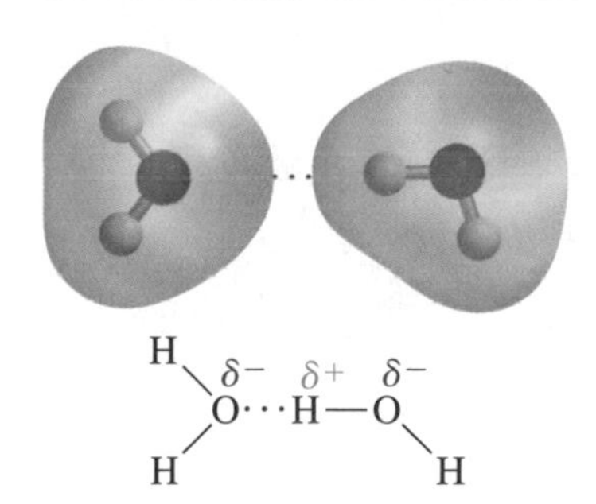

▲ **Hydrogen bonding between H_2O molecules**

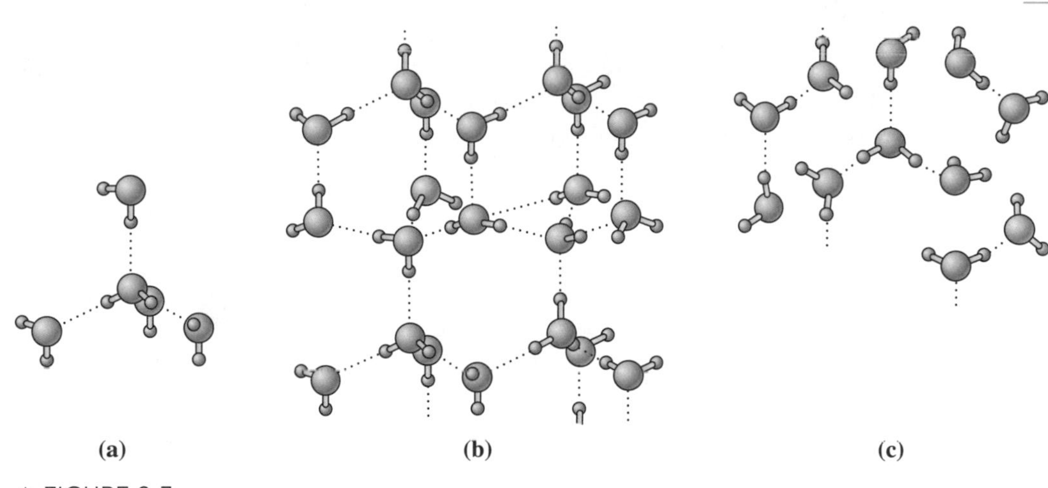

▲ FIGURE 3-7
Hydrogen bonding in water
(a) Each water molecule is linked to four others through hydrogen bonds. The arrangement is tetrahedral. Each H atom is situated along a line joining two O atoms, but closer to one O atom (100 pm) than to the other (180 pm). **(b)** For the crystal structure of ice, H atoms lie between pairs of O atoms, again closer to one O atom than to the other. (Molecules behind the plane of the page are light blue.) O atoms are arranged in bent hexagonal rings arranged in layers. This characteristic pattern is similar to the hexagonal shapes of snowflakes. **(c)** In the liquid, water molecules have hydrogen bonds to only some of their neighbours. This allows the water molecules to pack more densely in the liquid than in the solid.

▲ FIGURE 3-8
Solid and liquid densities compared
The sight of ice cubes floating on liquid water (left) is a familiar one; ice is less dense than liquid water. The more common situation, however, is that of paraffin wax (right). Solid paraffin is denser than the liquid and sinks to the bottom of the beaker.

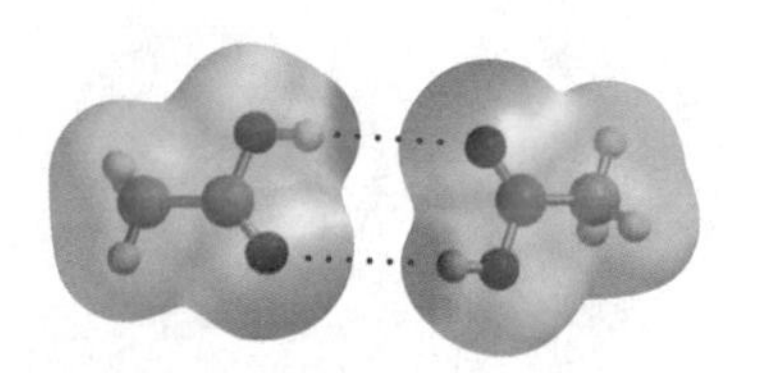

▲ FIGURE 3-9
An acetic acid dimer
Electrostatic potential maps showing hydrogen bonding.

molecules to be more compactly arranged, accounting for the increase in density when ice melts. That is, the number of H_2O molecules per unit volume is greater in the liquid than in the solid.

As liquid water is heated above the melting point, hydrogen bonds continue to break. The molecules become even more closely packed, and the density of the liquid water continues to increase. Liquid water attains its maximum density at 3.98 °C. Above this temperature, the water behaves in a "normal" fashion: Its density decreases as temperature increases. The unusual freezing-point behavior of water explains why a freshwater lake freezes from the top down. When the water temperature falls below 4 °C, the denser water sinks to the bottom of the lake and the colder surface water freezes. The ice over the top of the lake then tends to insulate the water below from further heat loss. This allows fish to survive the winter in a lake that has been frozen over. Without hydrogen bonding, all lakes would freeze from the bottom up; and fish, small bottom-feeding animals, and aquatic plants would not survive the winter. The density relationship between liquid water and ice is compared in Figure 3-8 with the more common liquid–solid density relationship.

Other Properties Affected by Hydrogen Bonding

Water is one example of a substance whose properties are affected by hydrogen bonding. There are numerous others. In acetic acid, CH_3COOH, pairs of molecules tend to join together into *dimers* (double molecules), both in the liquid and in the vapor states (Fig. 3-9). Not all the hydrogen bonds are disrupted when liquid acetic acid vaporizes, and, as a result, the heat of vaporization is abnormally low.

Certain trends in viscosity can also be explained by hydrogen bonding. In alcohols, the H atom in a —OH group in one molecule can form a hydrogen bond to the O atom in a neighboring alcohol molecule. An alcohol molecule with two —OH groups (a *diol*) has more possibilities for hydrogen-bond formation than a comparable alcohol with a single —OH group. Having stronger intermolecular forces, we expect the diol to flow more slowly, that is, to have a greater viscosity, than the simple alcohol. When still more —OH groups are present (*polyols*), we expect a further increase in viscosity. These comparisons are illustrated by the three common alcohols below. (The unit cP is a centipoise. The SI unit of viscosity is $1\ N\ s\ m^{-2} = 10\ P$. The Greek letter eta, η, is typically used as a symbol for viscosity.)

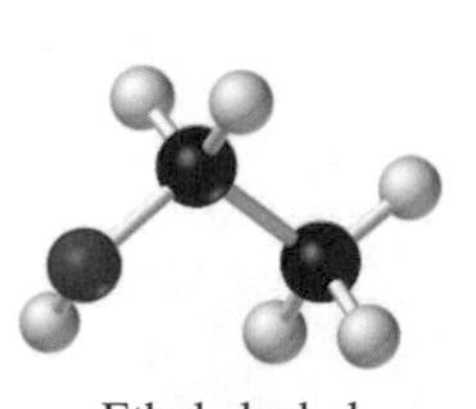

Ethyl alcohol
(ethanol)
at 20 °C: $\eta = 1.20$ cP

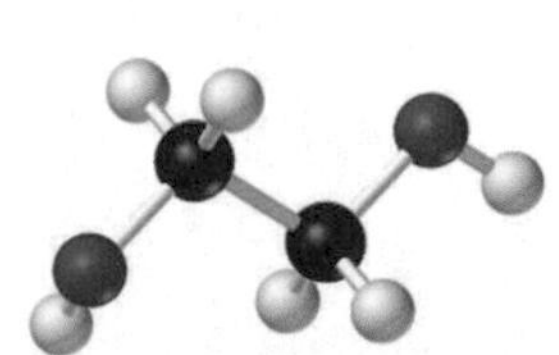

Ethylene glycol
(1,2-ethanediol)
at 20 °C: $\eta = 19.9$ cP

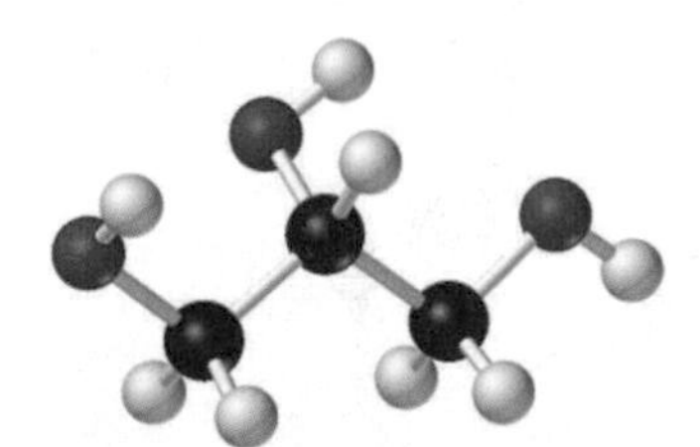

Glycerol
(1,2,3-propanetriol)
at 20 °C: $\eta = 1490$ cP

*Inter*molecular and *Intra*molecular Hydrogen Bonding

All the examples of hydrogen bonding presented to this point have involved an intermolecular force *between two molecules*, and this is called an *intermolecular hydrogen bond*. Another possibility occurs in molecules with an H atom covalently bonded to one highly electronegative atom (for example, O or N) and with another highly electronegative atom nearby in the same molecule. This type of hydrogen bonding *within a molecule* is called *intramolecular hydrogen bonding*. As shown in the molecular model of salicylic acid on the facing page, an intramolecular hydrogen bond (represented by a dotted line) joins the —OH group to the doubly bonded oxygen atom of the —COOH group on the same molecule. To underscore the importance of molecular geometry in establishing the conditions necessary for intramolecular hydrogen bonding, we need only turn to an isomer of salicylic acid called *para*-hydroxybenzoic acid. In this molecule, the H atom of the —COOH group is too close to the doubly bonded O atom of the same group to form a hydrogen bond, and the H atom of the —OH group on the opposite side of the molecule is too far away. Intramolecular hydrogen bonding does not occur in this situation.

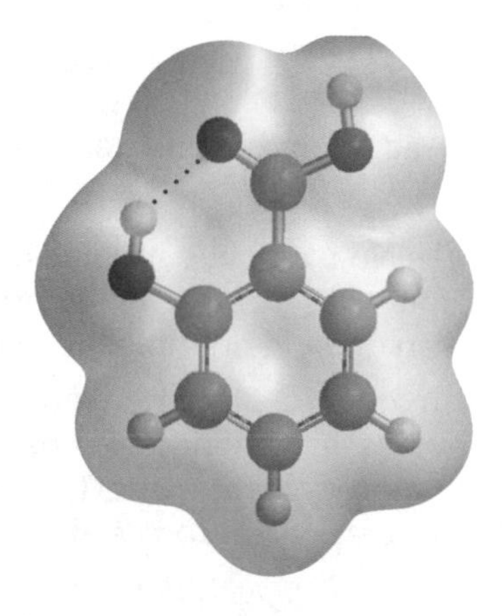

▲ Electrostatic potential map of salicylic acid showing intramolecular hydrogen bonding. The double bond character of certain bonds are not shown in the ball-and-stick model.

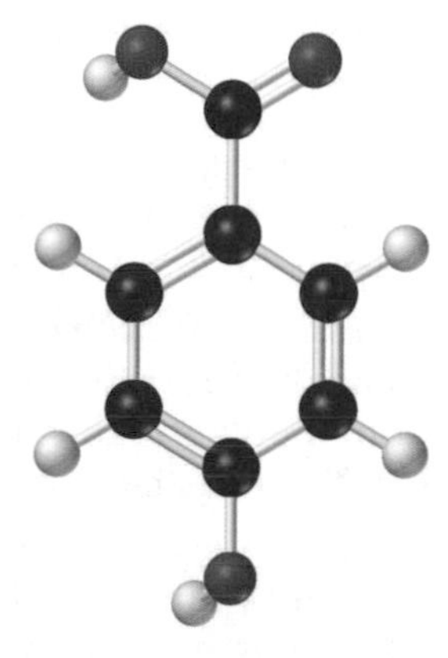

▲ There is no intramolecular hydrogen bonding in *para*-hydroxybenzoic acid.

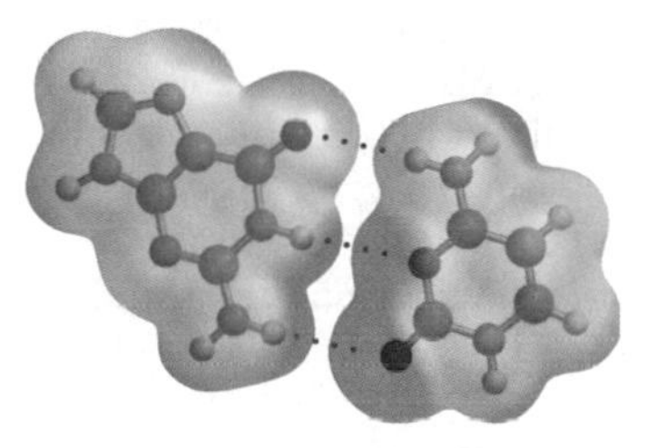

▲ Hydrogen bonding between guanine (left) and cytosine (right) in DNA

Hydrogen Bonding In Living Matter

Some chemical reactions in living matter involve complex structures, such as proteins and DNA, and in these reactions certain bonds must be easily broken and re-formed. Hydrogen bonding is the only type of bonding with energies of just the right magnitude to allow this. We will also find that both intra- and intermolecular hydrogen bonding is involved in these complex structures.

Hydrogen bonding seems to provide an answer to the puzzle of how some trees are able to grow to great heights. We learned that atmospheric pressure is capable of pushing a column of water to a maximum height of only about 10 m—other factors must be involved in transporting water to the tops of redwood trees up to 100 m tall. Hydrogen bonding seems to be a factor in transporting water in trees. Thin columns of water (in xylem, a plant tissue) extend from the roots to the leaves in the very tops of trees. In these columns, the water molecules are hydrogen-bonded to one another, with each water molecule acting like a link in a cohesive chain. When one water molecule evaporates from a leaf, another molecule in the chain moves to take its place and all the other molecules are pulled up the chain. Ultimately, a new water molecule joins the chain in the root system. In the next chapter, we will learn about another factor in transporting water in trees: osmotic pressure and its ability to force water through a membrane.

▲ Sequoia trees
The mystery of how these trees can bring water to leaves that are hundreds of feet up may be explained by hydrogen bonding.

3-1 CONCEPT ASSESSMENT

What are the types of intermolecular interactions in $CH_3CH_2NH_2(l)$, and which is the strongest?

TABLE 3.1 Intermolecular Forces and Properties of Selected Substances

	Molecular Mass, u	Dipole Moment, D	Van der Waals Forces		ΔH_{vap}, kJ mol^{-1}	Boiling Point, K
			% Dispersion	% Dipole		
F_2	38.00	0	100	0	6.86	85.01
HCl	36.46	1.08	81.4	18.6	16.15	188.11
HBr	80.92	0.82	94.5	5.5	17.61	206.43
HI	127.91	0.44	99.5	0.5	19.77	237.80

Summary of van der Waals Forces

When assessing the importance of van der Waals forces, consider the following statements.

- *Dispersion (London) forces exist between all molecules.* They involve displacements of all the electrons in molecules, and they increase in strength with increasing molecular mass. The forces also depend on molecular shapes.
- *Forces associated with permanent dipoles* involve displacements of electron pairs in bonds rather than in molecules as a whole. These forces are found only in substances with resultant dipole moments (polar molecules). Their existence *adds* to the effect of dispersion forces also present.
- *When comparing substances of roughly comparable molecular masses,* dipole forces can produce significant differences in properties such as melting point, boiling point, and enthalpy of vaporization.
- *When comparing substances of widely different molecular masses,* dispersion forces are usually more significant than dipole forces.

▶ In our discussion of London forces, we use molar mass only as a guide to the number of electrons present in a molecule; the forces holding a molecule in a liquid are not gravitational in nature.

Let's see how these statements relate to the data in Table 3.1, which includes a rough breakdown of van der Waals forces into dispersion forces and forces caused by dipoles. HCl and F_2 have comparable molecular masses, but because HCl is polar, it has a significantly larger ΔH_{vap} and a higher boiling point. Within the series HCl, HBr, and HI, molecular mass increases sharply and ΔH_{vap} and boiling points increase in the order HCl $<$ HBr $<$ HI. The more polar nature of HCl and HBr relative to HI is not sufficient to reverse the trends produced by the increasing molecular masses—dispersion forces are the predominant intermolecular forces.

3-1 ARE YOU WONDERING...

Are there other types of intermolecular forces?

There are other types of intermolecular forces in addition to London dispersion, dipole–dipole, and hydrogen bonding. Table 3.2 summarizes some of the more commonly encountered intermolecular forces, along with their typical strengths.

In Table 3.2 one of the strongest forces between ions or molecules arises from the electrostatic attraction of opposite charge (ion–ion). This type of intermolecular force is what gives rise to the high melting points of ionic solids, along with their brittle nature. In such molecules as biomolecules, interactions between different charged groups, also known as salt bridges, increase their stability.

Molecules have dipole moments because of electronegativity differences between atoms. The dipole moment in a molecule will interact with a charged ion to form an ion–dipole interaction. Ion–dipole interactions are important in understanding the dissolution of salts.

In the absence of charges and dipole moments, other higher-order moments (e.g., quadrupole moments) become dominant. An example of quadrupole–quadrupole interactions would be between two CO_2 molecules.

KEEP IN MIND

that the term *intermolecular forces* is used to classify a specific set of noncovalent interactions.

TABLE 3.2 Summary of Noncovalent Interactions

Force	Energy,[a] kJ/mol	Example	Model
Intermolecular			
London dispersion	0.05–40	$CH_4 \cdots CH_4$	
Dipole–induced dipole	2–10	$CH_3(CO)CH_3 \ldots CH_5H_{12}$	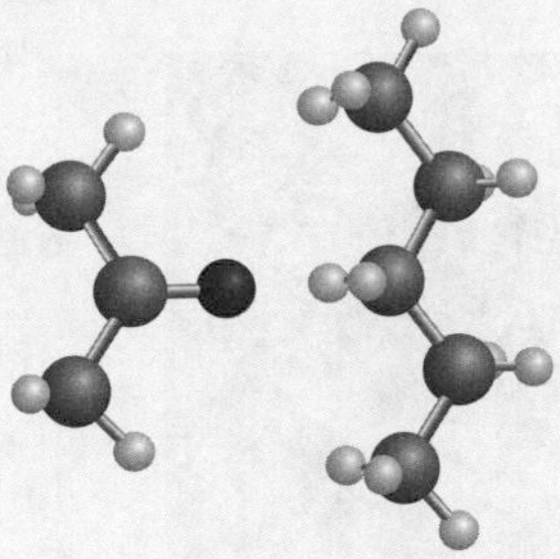
Ion–induced dipole	3–15	$Li^+ \ldots C_5H_{12}$	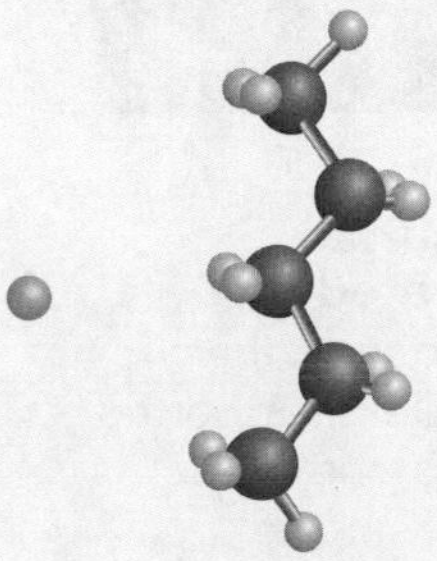
Dipole–dipole	5–25	$H_2O \ldots CO$	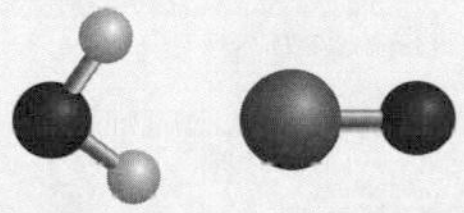
Hydrogen bond	10–40	$CH_3OH \ldots H_2O$	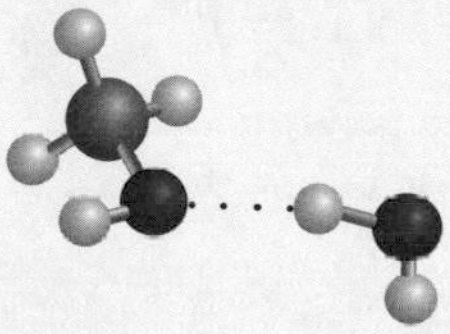
Ion–dipole	40–600	$K^+ \ldots H_2O$	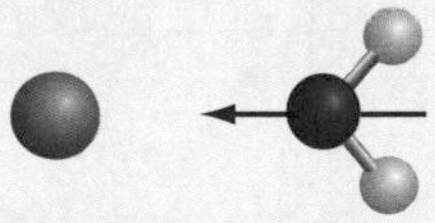
Ion–ion	400–4000	$Lys^+ \ldots Glu^-$	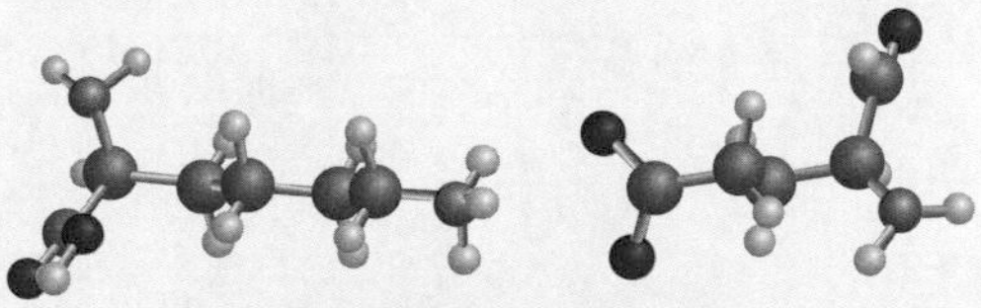
Interatomic			
London dispersion	0.05–40	Ar...Ar	
Ion–ion	400–4000	$Na^+ \ldots Cl^-$	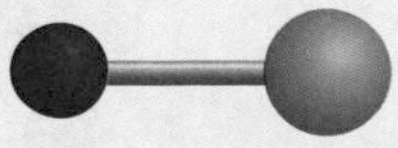
Metallic	100–1000	Ag...Ag	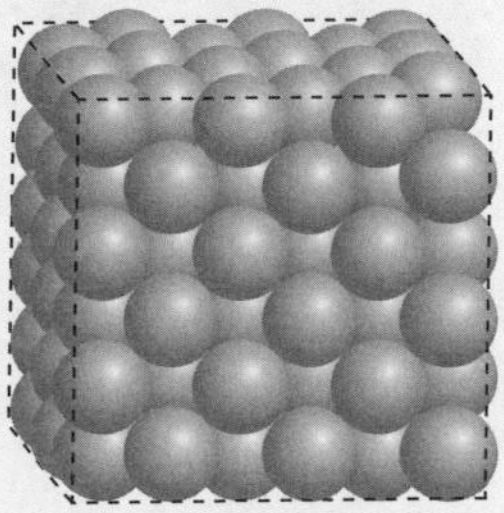

[a]These are gas phase values.

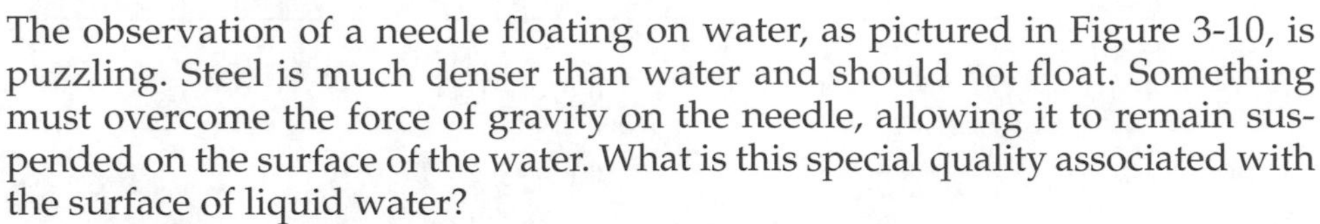

3-2 Some Properties of Liquids

Surface Tension

The observation of a needle floating on water, as pictured in Figure 3-10, is puzzling. Steel is much denser than water and should not float. Something must overcome the force of gravity on the needle, allowing it to remain suspended on the surface of the water. What is this special quality associated with the surface of liquid water?

▲ FIGURE 3-10
An effect of surface tension illustrated
Despite being denser than water, the needle is supported on the surface of the water. The property of surface tension accounts for this unexpected behaviour.

Figure 3-11 suggests an important difference in the forces experienced by molecules within the bulk of a liquid and by those at the surface. Interior molecules have more neighbors and experience more attractive intermolecular interactions than surface molecules. The increased number of attractions by neighboring molecules places an interior molecule in a more stable environment (lower energy state) than a surface molecule. Consequently, as many molecules as possible tend to enter the bulk of a liquid, while as few as possible remain at the surface. Thus, liquids tend to maintain a minimum surface area. To increase the surface area of a liquid requires that molecules be moved from the interior to the surface of a liquid, and this requires that work be done. The steel needle of Figure 3-10 remains suspended on the surface of the water because energy is required to spread the surface of the water over the top of the needle.

Surface tension is the energy, or work, required to increase the surface area of a liquid. Surface tension is often represented by the Greek letter gamma (γ) and has the units of energy per unit area, typically joules per square meter ($J\ m^{-2}$). As the temperature—and hence the intensity of molecular motion—increases, intermolecular forces become less effective. Less work is required to extend the surface of a liquid, meaning that surface tension *decreases* with *increased* temperature.

▶ The surface tension of water at 20 °C, for example, is $7.28 \times 10^{-2}\ J\ m^{-2}$, and that of mercury is more than six times as large, at $47.2 \times 10^{-2}\ J\ m^{-2}$.

When a drop of liquid spreads into a film across a surface, we say that the liquid *wets* the surface. Whether a drop of liquid wets a surface or retains its spherical shape and stands on the surface depends on the strengths of two types of intermolecular forces. The forces exerted between molecules holding them together in the drop are **cohesive forces**, and the forces between liquid molecules and the surface are **adhesive forces**. If cohesive forces are strong compared with adhesive forces, a drop maintains its shape. If adhesive forces are strong enough, the energy requirement for spreading the drop into a film is met through the work done by the collapsing drop.

Water wets many surfaces, such as glass and certain fabrics. This characteristic is essential to its use as a cleaning agent. If glass is coated with a film of oil

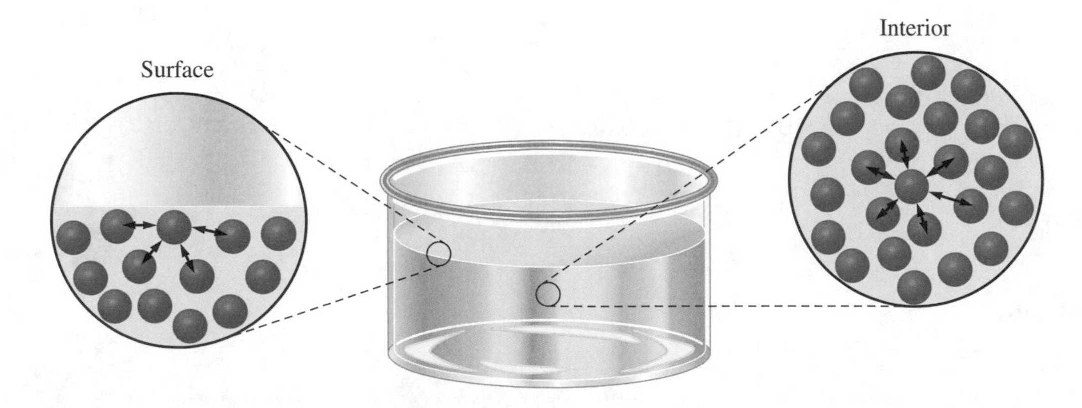

▲ FIGURE 3-11
Intermolecular forces in a liquid
Molecules at the surface are attracted only by other surface molecules and by molecules below the surface. Molecules in the interior experience forces from neighbouring molecules in all directions.

▲ FIGURE 3-12
Wetting of a surface
Water spreads into a thin film on a clean glass surface (left). If the glass is coated with oil or grease, the adhesive forces between the water and oil are not strong enough to spread the water, and droplets stand on the surface (right).

▲ FIGURE 3-13
Meniscus formation
Water wets glass (left). The meniscus is concave—the bottom of the meniscus is below the level of the water–glass contact line. Mercury does not wet glass. The meniscus is convex—the top of the meniscus is above the mercury–glass contact line.

or grease, water no longer wets the surface and water droplets stand on the glass, as shown in Figure 3-12. When we clean glassware in the laboratory, we have done a good job if water forms a uniform thin film on the glass. When we wax a car, we have done a good job if water uniformly beads up all along the surface.

Adding a detergent to water has two effects: The detergent solution dissolves grease to expose a clean surface, and the detergent lowers the surface tension of water. Lowering the surface tension means lowering the energy required to spread drops into a film. Substances that reduce the surface tension of water and allow it to spread more easily are known as *wetting agents*. They are used in applications ranging from dish washing to industrial processes.

Figure 3-13 illustrates another familiar observation. If the liquid in the glass tube is water, the water is drawn slightly up the walls of the tube by adhesive forces between water and glass. The interface between the water and the air above it, called a *meniscus*, is concave, or curved in. With liquid mercury, the meniscus is convex, or curved out. Cohesive forces in mercury, consisting of metallic bonds between Hg atoms, are strong; mercury does not wet glass. The effect of meniscus formation is greatly magnified in tubes of small diameter, called *capillary tubes*. In the *capillary action* shown in Figure 3-14, the water level inside the capillary tube is noticeably higher than outside. The soaking action of a sponge depends on the rise of water into capillaries of a fibrous material, such as cellulose. The penetration of water into soils also depends in part on capillary action. Conversely, mercury—with its strong cohesive forces and weaker adhesive forces—does not show a capillary rise. Rather, mercury in a glass capillary tube will have a lower level than the mercury outside the capillary.

▲ FIGURE 3-14
Capillary action
A thin film of water spreads up the inside walls of the capillary because of strong adhesive forces between water and glass (water wets glass). The pressure below the meniscus falls slightly. Atmospheric pressure then pushes a column of water up the tube to eliminate the pressure difference. The *smaller* the diameter of the capillary, the *higher* the liquid rises. Because its magnitude is also directly proportional to surface tension, capillary rise provides a simple experimental method of determining surface tension.

Viscosity

Another property at least partly related to intermolecular forces is **viscosity**—a liquid's resistance to flow. The stronger the intermolecular forces of attraction, the greater the viscosity. When a liquid flows, one portion of the liquid moves with respect to neighboring portions. Cohesive forces within the liquid create an internal friction, which reduces the rate of flow. In liquids of low viscosity, such as ethyl alcohol and water, the effect is weak, and they flow easily. Liquids such as honey and heavy motor oil flow much more sluggishly. We say that they are *viscous*. One method of measuring viscosity is to time the fall of a steel ball through a certain depth of liquid (Fig. 3-15). The greater the viscosity of the liquid, the longer it takes for the ball to fall. Because intermolecular forces of attraction can be offset by higher molecular kinetic energies, viscosity generally *decreases* with *increased* temperature for liquids.

◀ For liquids, viscosity decreases with increasing temperature, but for gases, the viscosity increases with increasing temperature.

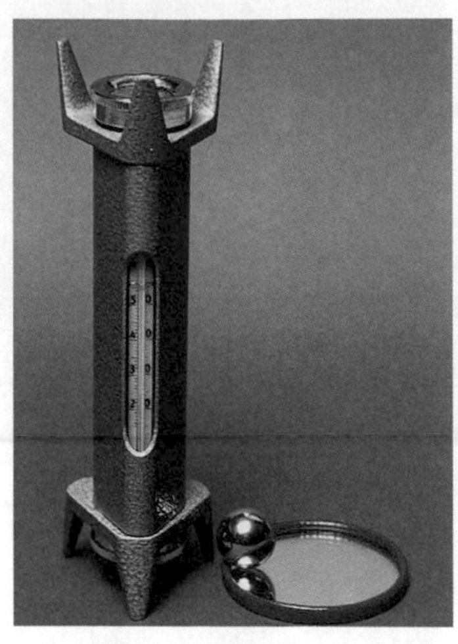

▲ FIGURE 3-15
Measuring viscocity
By measuring the velocity of a ball dropping through a liquid, a measure of the liquid viscosity can be obtained.

3-2 CONCEPT ASSESSMENT

The viscosity of automotive motor oil is designated by its SAE number, such as 40 W. When compared in a ball viscometer (Fig. 3-15), the ball drops much faster through 10 W oil than through 40 W oil. Which of these two oils provides better winter service in the Arctic region of Canada? Which is best suited for summer use in the American Southwest? Which oil has the stronger intermolecular forces of attraction?

Enthalpy of Vaporization

In our study of the kinetic-molecular theory, we saw that the speeds and kinetic energies of molecules vary over a wide range at any given temperature. Molecules having kinetic energies sufficiently above the average value are able to overcome intermolecular forces of attraction and escape from the surface of the liquid into the gaseous state. This passage of molecules from the surface of a liquid into the gaseous, or vapor, state is called **vaporization** or **evaporation**. Vaporization occurs more readily with

- *increased temperature*—more molecules have sufficient kinetic energy to overcome intermolecular forces of attraction in the liquid.
- *increased surface area* of the liquid—a greater proportion of the liquid molecules are at the surface.
- *decreased strength of intermolecular forces*—the kinetic energy needed to overcome intermolecular forces of attraction is less, and more molecules have enough energy to escape.

Because the molecules lost through evaporation are much more energetic than average, the average kinetic energy of the remaining molecules decreases. The temperature of the evaporating liquid falls. This accounts for the cooling sensation you feel when a volatile liquid, such as ethyl alcohol, evaporates on your skin.

To vaporize a liquid at constant temperature, we must replace the excess kinetic energy carried away by the vaporizing molecules by adding heat to the liquid. The *enthalpy of vaporization* is the quantity of heat that must be absorbed if a certain quantity of liquid is vaporized at a constant temperature. Stated in another way,

$$\Delta H_{\text{vaporization}} = H_{\text{vapor}} - H_{\text{liquid}}$$

Because vaporization is an *endothermic* process, $\Delta H_{\text{vaporization}}$ (or ΔH_{vap} as it is more commonly denoted) is always positive. We will generally express enthalpies of vaporizations in terms of one mole of liquid vaporized, as seen in Table 3.3. The differences in enthalpies of vaporization in Table 3.3 are the result of intermolecular forces. For example, the intermolecular forces of diethyl ether are dispersion, while those of methyl alcohol are a combination of dipole and hydrogen bonding, creating the difference in their enthalpies of vaporization. Likewise, the higher dispersion in ethyl alcohol than in methyl alcohol yields a stronger interaction between ethyl alcohol's molecules and therefore

TABLE 3.3 Some Enthalpies of Vaporization at 298 K[a]

Liquid	ΔH_{vap}, kJ mol^{-1}
Diethyl ether, $(C_2H_5)_2O$	29.1
Methyl alcohol, CH_3OH	38.0
Ethyl alcohol, CH_3CH_2OH	42.6
Water, H_2O	44.0

[a] ΔH_{vap} values are somewhat temperature-dependent (see Exercise 63).

an increase in its enthalpy of vaporization. The reason that water has a much higher enthalpy of vaporization than the alcohols is that water forms four hydrogen bonds, whereas the alcohols can form only three hydrogen bonds.

The conversion of a gas or vapor to a liquid is called **condensation**. From a thermochemical standpoint, condensation is the reverse of vaporization.

$$\Delta H_{condensation} = H_{liquid} - H_{vapor} = -\Delta H_{vap}$$

Because it is opposite in sign but equal in magnitude to ΔH_{vap}, $\Delta H_{condensation}$ (ΔH_{cond}) is always negative. Condensation is an *exothermic* process. This explains why burns produced by a given mass of steam (vaporized water) are much more severe than burns produced by the same mass of hot water. Hot water burns only by releasing heat as it cools. Steam releases a large quantity of heat when it condenses to liquid water, followed by the further release of heat as the hot water cools.

KEEP IN MIND

that absolute enthalpies, such as H_{vapor} and H_{liquid}, cannot be measured. However, because enthalpy is a function of state, the difference between the absolute enthalpies has a unique value, and it *can* be measured.

EXAMPLE 3-2 Estimating the Heat Evolved in the Condensation of Steam

A 0.750 L sample of steam obtained at the normal boiling point of water was allowed to condense on a slightly cooler surface. Estimate the quantity of heat evolved. Why is the result only an estimate?

Analyze

First, let us describe the steam sample a bit more precisely. Steam is water vapor, $H_2O(g)$; and when in equilibrium with liquid water at its normal boiling point, the steam is at 1.000 atm pressure.

Solve

We are given a volume of gas (0.750 L) at a fixed temperature (100.00 °C)and pressure (1.000 atm), and so we use the ideal gas equation to calculate the number of moles of $H_2O(g)$. That is,

$$n_{H_2O} = \frac{PV}{RT} = \frac{1.000 \text{ atm} \times 0.750 \text{ L}}{0.08206 \text{ L atm mol}^{-1} \text{ K}^{-1} \times (273.15 + 100.00) \text{ K}}$$
$$= 0.0245 \text{ mol}$$

On a molar basis, estimate the enthalpy of condensation of the $H_2O(g)$ to be the *negative* of the value of ΔH_{vap} of H_2O given in Table 3.3, that is, $-44.0 \text{ kJ mol}^{-1}$. For the 0.0245 mol sample of steam,

$$\Delta H_{cond} = 0.0245 \text{ mol} \times (-44.0 \text{ kJ mol}^{-1}) = -1.08 \text{kJ}$$

Assess

This result is only an estimate for two reasons: (1) ΔH_{cond}, like ΔH_{vap}, is temperature dependent. The value used was for 298 K, whereas it should have been for 373 K, a value that was not given. (2) The condensed liquid water was at a temperature lower than 373 K ("slightly cooler surface"). An additional small quantity of heat was liberated as the condensed steam cooled to that lower temperature.

PRACTICE EXAMPLE A: How much heat is required to vaporize a 2.35 g sample of diethyl ether at 298 K?

PRACTICE EXAMPLE B: Calculate a more accurate answer to Example 3-2 by using $\Delta H_{vap} = 40.7 \text{ kJ mol}^{-1}$ for water at 100 °C, 85.0 °C as the temperature of the surface on which the steam condenses, and $4.21 \text{ J g}^{-1} \text{ °C}^{-1}$ as the average specific heat of $H_2O(l)$ in the temperature range 85 to 100 °C.

Vapor Pressure

Water left in an open beaker evaporates completely. A different condition results if the beaker with the water is placed in a closed container. As shown in Figure 3-16, in a container with both liquid and vapor present, vaporization and condensation occur simultaneously. If sufficient liquid is present, eventually a condition is reached in which the amount of vapor remains constant. This condition is one of *dynamic equilibrium*. Dynamic equilibrium always implies that two opposing processes are occurring simultaneously and at equal rates.

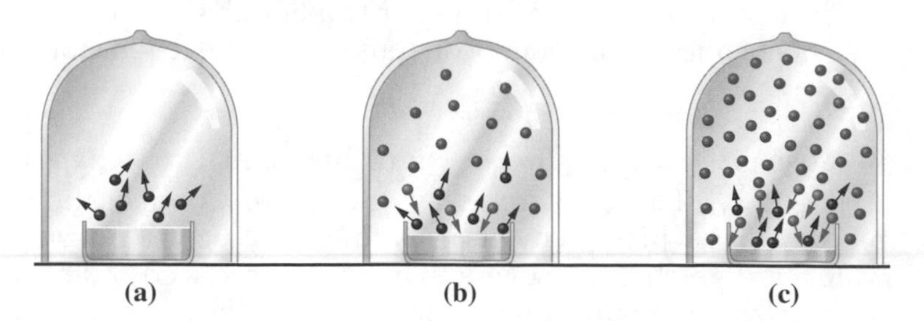

▶ FIGURE 3-16
Establishing liquid–vapor equilibrium
(a) A liquid is allowed to evaporate into a closed container. Initially, only vaporization occurs. **(b)** Condensation begins. The rate at which molecules evaporate is greater than the rate at which they condense, and the number of molecules in the vapor state continues to increase. **(c)** The rate of condensation is equal to the rate of vaporization. The number of vapor molecules remains constant over time, as does the pressure exerted by this vapor.

As a result, there is no net change with time once equilibrium has been established. A symbolic representation of the liquid–vapor equilibrium is shown below.

$$\text{liquid} \underset{\text{condensation}}{\overset{\text{vaporization}}{\rightleftharpoons}} \text{vapor}$$

▶ Gasoline is a mixture of volatile hydrocarbons and is an important precursor of smog, whether it is vaporized from oil refineries, filling-station operations, automobile gas tanks, or power lawn mowers.

The pressure exerted by a vapor in dynamic equilibrium with its liquid is called the **vapor pressure**. Liquids with high vapor pressures at room temperature are said to be *volatile,* and those with very low vapor pressures are *nonvolatile.* Whether a liquid is volatile or not is determined primarily by the strengths of its intermolecular forces—the weaker these forces, the more volatile the liquid (the higher its vapor pressure). Diethyl ether and acetone are volatile liquids; at 25 °C their vapor pressures are 534 and 231 mmHg, respectively. Water at ordinary temperatures is a moderately volatile liquid; at 25 °C, its vapor pressure is 23.8 mmHg. Mercury is essentially a nonvolatile liquid; at 25 °C, its vapor pressure is 0.0018 mmHg.

As an excellent first approximation, the vapor pressure of a liquid depends only on the particular liquid and its temperature. Vapor pressure depends on neither the amount of liquid nor the amount of vapor, as long as some of each is present at equilibrium. These statements are illustrated in Figure 3-17. A graph of vapor pressure as a function of temperature is known as a **vapor pressure curve**. Vapor pressure curves always have the appearance of those in Figure 3-18: *Vapor pressure increases with temperature.* Vapor pressures of water at different temperatures are presented in Table 3.4.

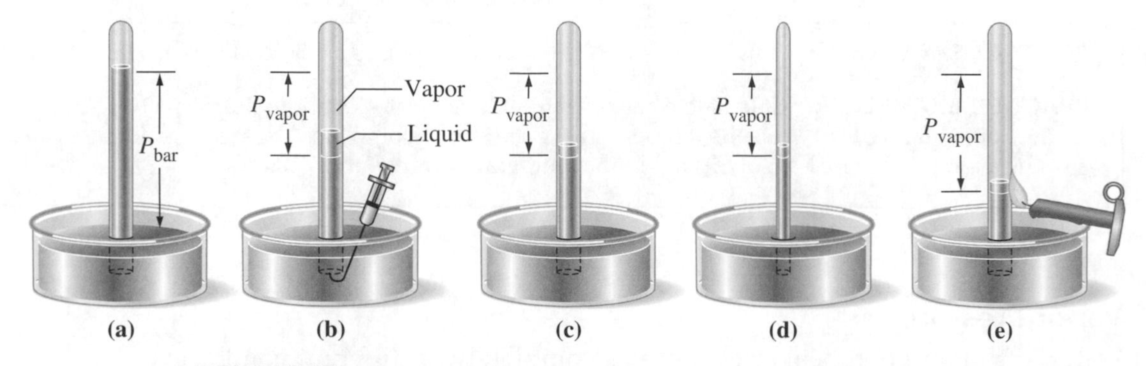

▲ FIGURE 3-17
Vapour pressure illustrated
(a) A mercury barometer. **(b)** The pressure exerted by the vapor in equilibrium with a liquid injected to the top of the mercury column depresses the mercury level. **(c)** Compared with (b), the vapor pressure is independent of the volume of liquid injected. **(d)** Compared with (c), the vapor pressure is independent of the volume of vapor present. **(e)** Vapor pressure increases with an increase in temperature.

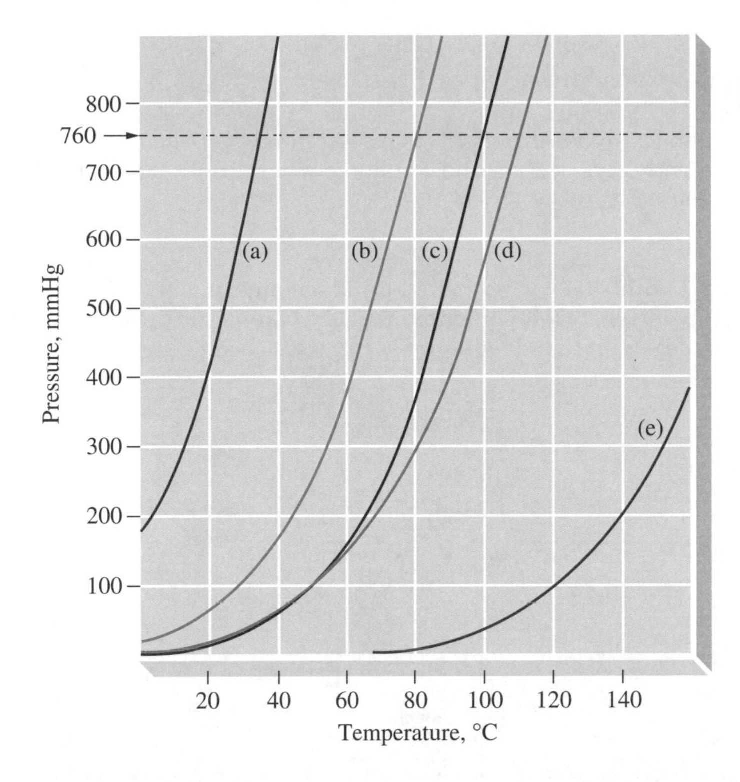

◀ FIGURE 3-18
Vapor pressure curves of several liquids
(a) Diethyl ether, $C_4H_{10}O$; **(b)** benzene, C_6H_6; **(c)** water, H_2O; **(d)** toluene, C_7H_8; **(e)** aniline, C_6H_7N. The normal boiling points are the temperatures at the intersection of the dashed line at $P = 760$ mmHg with the vapor pressure curves.

TABLE 3.4 Vapor Pressure of Water at Various Temperatures

Temperature, °C	Pressure, mmHg	Temperature, °C	Pressure, mmHg	Temperature, °C	Pressure, mmHg
0.0	4.6	29.0	30.0	93.0	588.6
10.0	9.2	30.0	31.8	94.0	610.9
20.0	17.5	40.0	55.3	95.0	633.9
21.0	18.7	50.0	92.5	96.0	657.6
22.0	19.8	60.0	149.4	97.0	682.1
23.0	21.1	70.0	233.7	98.0	707.3
24.0	22.4	80.0	355.1	99.0	733.2
25.0	23.8	90.0	525.8	100.0	760.0
26.0	25.2	91.0	546.0	110.0	1074.6
27.0	26.7	92.0	567.1	120.0	1489.1
28.0	28.3				

Measuring Vapor Pressure

Figure 3-17 suggests one method of determining vapor pressure—inject a small sample of the target liquid at the top of a mercury barometer, and measure the depression of the mercury level. The method does not give very precise results, however, and it is not useful for measuring vapor pressures that are either very low or quite high. Better results are obtained with methods in which the pressure above a liquid is continuously varied and measured, and the liquid–vapor equilibrium temperature is recorded. In short, the boiling point of the liquid changes in accordance with the change in the pressure above the liquid, and the vapor pressure curve of the liquid can be traced. The pressure measurements are made with either a closed-end or open-end manometer. A method that is useful for determining very low vapor pressures is based on the rate of effusion of a gas through a tiny orifice. In this method, equations from the kinetic-molecular theory are applied. Example 3-3 illustrates a method (called the transpiration method) in which an inert gas is saturated with the vapor under study. Then the ideal gas equation is used to calculate the vapor pressure.

EXAMPLE 3-3 Using the Ideal Gas Equation to Calculate a Vapor Pressure

A sample of 113 L of helium gas at 1360 °C and prevailing barometric pressure is passed through molten silver at the same temperature. The gas becomes saturated with silver vapor, and the liquid silver loses 0.120 g in mass. What is the vapor pressure of liquid silver at 1360 °C?

Analyze

Let's assume that after the gas has become saturated with silver vapor, its volume remains at 113 L. This assumption will be valid if the vapor pressure of the silver is quite low compared with the barometric pressure. According to Dalton's law of partial pressures we can deal with the silver vapor as if it were a single gas occupying a volume of 113 L.

Solve

The data required in the ideal gas equation are listed below.

$P = ?$ $V = 113\ \text{L}$

$R = 0.08206\ \text{L atm mol}^{-1}\ \text{K}^{-1}$ $T = 1360 + 273.15 = 1633\ \text{K}$

$$n = 0.120\ \text{g Ag} \times \frac{1\ \text{mol Ag}}{107.9\ \text{g Ag}} = 0.00111\ \text{mol Ag}$$

$$P = \frac{nRT}{V}$$

$$P = \frac{0.00111\ \text{mol} \times 0.08206\ \text{L atm mol}^{-1}\ \text{K}^{-1} \times 1633\ \text{K}}{113\ \text{L}}$$

$$= 1.32 \times 10^{-3}\ \text{atm (1.00 Torr)}$$

Assess

The assumption we made appears to be valid, because the experimental vapor pressure of liquid silver at 1360 °C is 1 mmHg or 1.32×10^{-3} atm.

PRACTICE EXAMPLE A: Equilibrium is established between liquid hexane, C_6H_{14}, and its vapor at 25.0 °C. A sample of the vapor is found to have a density of 0.701 g/L. Calculate the vapor pressure of hexane at 25.0 °C, expressed in Torr.

PRACTICE EXAMPLE B: With the help of Figure 3-18, estimate the density of the vapor in equilibrium with liquid diethyl ether at 20.0 °C.

Using Vapor Pressure Data

One use of vapor pressure data is in calculations dealing with the collection of gases over liquids, particularly water (Section 2-6). Another use, illustrated in Example 3-4, is in predicting whether a substance exists solely as a gas (vapor) or as a liquid and vapor in equilibrium.

EXAMPLE 3-4 Making Predictions with Vapor Pressure Data

As a result of a chemical reaction, 0.132 g H_2O is produced and maintained at a temperature of 50.0 °C in a closed flask of 525 mL volume. Will the water be present as liquid only, vapor only, or liquid and vapor in equilibrium (Fig. 3-19)?

Analyze

Let's consider each of the three possibilities in the order that they are given.

Solve

LIQUID ONLY

With a density of about 1 g/mL, a 0.132 g sample of H_2O has a volume of only about 0.13 mL. There is no way that the sample could completely fill a 525 mL flask. The condition of liquid only is *impossible*.

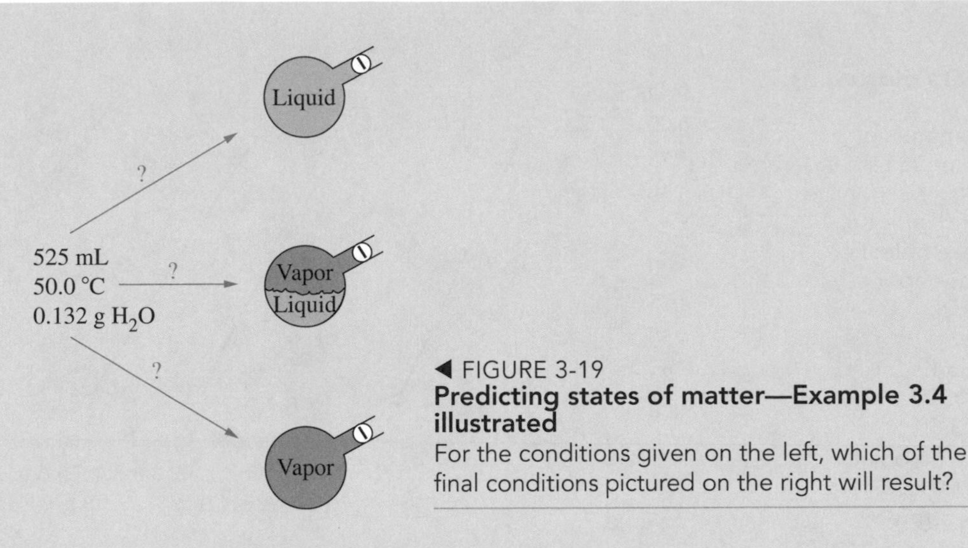

◀ FIGURE 3-19
Predicting states of matter—Example 3.4 illustrated
For the conditions given on the left, which of the final conditions pictured on the right will result?

VAPOR ONLY

The portion of the flask that is not occupied by liquid water must be filled with something (it cannot remain a vacuum). That something is water vapor. The question is, will the sample vaporize completely, leaving no liquid? Let's use the ideal gas equation to calculate the pressure that would be exerted if the entire 0.132 g H_2O were present in the gaseous state.

$$P = \frac{nRT}{V}$$

$$= \frac{0.132 \text{ g } H_2O \times \dfrac{1 \text{ mol } H_2O}{18.02 \text{ g } H_2O} \times 0.08206 \text{ L atm mol}^{-1} \text{ K}^{-1} \times 323.2 \text{ K}}{0.525 \text{ L}}$$

$$= 0.370 \text{ atm} \times \frac{760 \text{ mmHg}}{1 \text{ atm}} = 281 \text{ mmHg}$$

Now compare this calculated pressure with the vapor pressure of water at 50.0 °C (Table 3.4). The calculated pressure—281 mmHg—greatly exceeds the vapor pressure—92.5 mmHg. Water formed in the reaction as $H_2O(g)$ condenses to $H_2O(l)$ when the gas pressure reaches 92.5 mmHg, for this is the pressure at which the liquid and vapor are in equilibrium at 50.0 °C. The condition of vapor only is *impossible*.

LIQUID AND VAPOR

This is the only possibility for the final condition in the flask. Liquid water and water vapor coexist in equilibrium at 50.0 °C and 92.5 mmHg.

Assess

We found the solution to this problem through the application of the ideal gas equation and our understanding of vapor pressure. Note that in the first two steps, we considered the two extremes, with the first being just liquid water and the second all vapor.

PRACTICE EXAMPLE A: If the reaction described in this example resulted in H_2O produced and maintained at 80.0 °C, would the water be present as vapor only or as liquid and vapor in equilibrium? Explain.

PRACTICE EXAMPLE B: For the situation described in Example 3.4, what mass of water is present as liquid and what mass as vapor?

An Equation for Expressing Vapor Pressure Data

If you look for vapor pressure data on a liquid in a handbook or in data tables, you are unlikely to find graphs like Figure 3-18. Also, with the exception of a few liquids, such as water and mercury, you are unlikely to find data tables like Table 3.4. What you will find, instead, are mathematical equations relating vapor pressures and temperatures. Such equations can summarize in one line data that might otherwise take a full page. Equation (3.1) is a particularly common form of vapor pressure equation. It expresses the natural logarithm

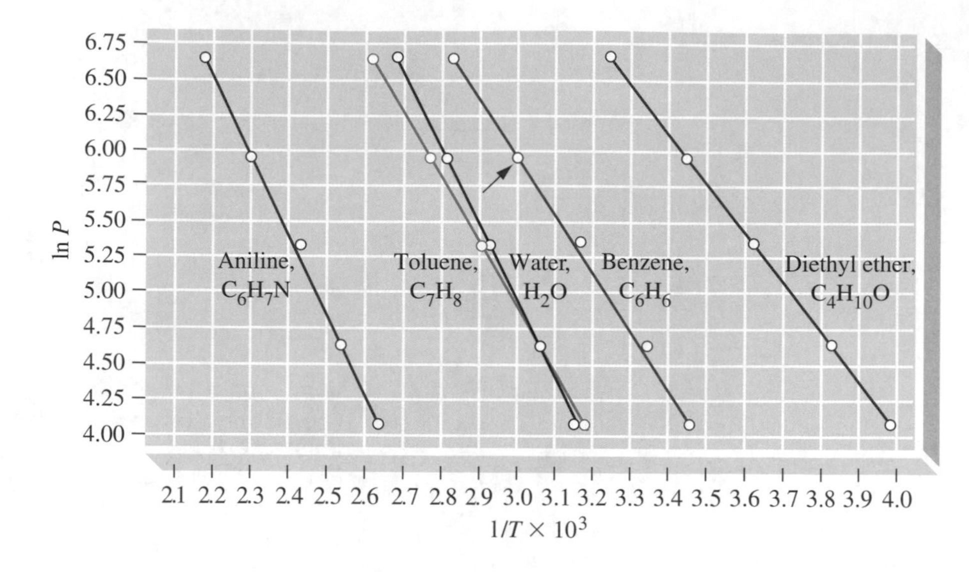

▶ FIGURE 3-20
Vapor pressure data plotted as ln P versus $1/T$
Pressures are in millimeters of mercury, and temperatures are in Kelvin. Data from Figure 3-18 have been recalculated and replotted as in the following example: For benzene at 60 °C, the vapor pressure is 400 mmHg; $\ln P = \ln 400 = 5.99$. $T = 60 + 273 = 333$ K; $1/T = 1/333 = 0.00300 = 3.00 \times 10^{-3}$; $1/T \times 10^3 = 3.00 \times 10^{-3} \times 10^3 = 3.00$. The point corresponding to (3.00, 5.99) is marked by the black arrow.

(ln) of vapor pressure as a function of the reciprocal of the Kelvin temperature $(1/T)$. The relationship is that of a straight line, and the straight-line plots for the liquids featured in Figure 3-18 are drawn in Figure 3-20.

$$\underbrace{\ln P}_{y} = \underbrace{-A}_{m}\underbrace{\left(\frac{1}{T}\right)}_{x} + \underbrace{B}_{b} \tag{3.1}$$

Equation of straight line: $y = m \times x + b$

To use equation (3.1), we need values for the two constants, A and B. The constant A is related to the enthalpy of vaporization of the liquid: $A = \Delta H_{vap}/R$, where ΔH_{vap} is expressed in the unit J mol^{-1} and the value used for R is 8.3145 J mol^{-1}K^{-1}. It is customary to eliminate B by rewriting equation (3.1) for two different temperatures, in a form called the Clausius–Clapeyron equation.

KEEP IN MIND

that the heat of vaporization in this equation cannot be ΔH°_{vap}, since in general the pressure is not 1 bar.

$$\ln\left(\frac{P_2}{P_1}\right) = -\frac{\Delta H_{vap}}{R}\left(\frac{1}{T_2} - \frac{1}{T_1}\right) \tag{3.2}$$

We apply equation (3.2) in Example 3-5.

EXAMPLE 3-5 Applying the Clausius–Clapeyron Equation

Calculate the vapor pressure of water at 35.0 °C using data from Tables 3.3 and 3.4.

Analyze

Starting with the Clausius-Clapeyron equation, we recognize that we need four pieces of data to solve for the fifth. Since we are asked to calculate a vapor pressure, we will need two temperatures, a pressure, and the enthalpy of vaporization.

Solve

Designate the unknown vapor pressure as P_1 at the temperature T_1. That is,

$$P_1 = ? \qquad T_1 = (35.0 + 273.15)\text{ K} = 308.2\text{ K}$$

For P_2 and T_2 choose known data for a temperature close to 35.0 °C, for example, 40.0 °C.

$$P_2 = 55.3\text{ mmHg} \qquad T_2 = (40.0 + 273.15)\text{ K} = 313.2\text{ K}$$

For ΔH_{vap}, let's assume that the value given in Table 3.3 applies throughout the temperature range from 30.0 °C to 40.0 °C.

$$\Delta H_{vap} = 44.0\text{ kJ mol}^{-1} \times \frac{1000\text{ J}}{1\text{ kJ}} = 44.0 \times 10^3\text{ J mol}^{-1}$$

Now substitute these values into equation (3.2) to obtain

$$\ln\left(\frac{55.3\,\text{mmHg}}{P_1}\right) = -\frac{44.0 \times 10^3\,\text{J mol}^{-1}}{8.3145\,\text{J mol}^{-1}\,\text{K}^{-1}}\left(\frac{1}{313.2} - \frac{1}{308.2}\right)\text{K}^{-1}$$
$$= -5.29 \times 10^3(0.003193 - 0.003245) = 0.28$$

Next, determine that $e^{0.28} = 1.32$. Thus,

$$\frac{55.3\,\text{mmHg}}{P_1} = e^{0.28} = 1.32$$
$$P_1 = 55.3\,\text{mmHg}/1.32 = 41.9\,\text{mmHg}$$

Assess

Here, P_1 must be *smaller than* P_2 because $T_1 < T_2$. Thus, regardless of how we write equation (3.2)—different formulations are possible—or choose (T_1, P_1) and (T_2, P_2), we are guided by the fact that vapor pressure always increases with temperature. One way to check our answer is to repeat the calculation by using this pressure as the known pressure to see whether we obtain the pressure given in the problem. We can also check this against the experimentally determined vapor pressure of water at 35.0 °C, which is 42.175 mmHg.

PRACTICE EXAMPLE A: A handbook lists the vapor pressure of methyl alcohol as 100 mmHg at 21.2 °C. What is its vapor pressure at 25.0 °C?

PRACTICE EXAMPLE B: A handbook lists the normal boiling point of isooctane, a gasoline component, as 99.2 °C and its enthalpy of vaporization (ΔH_{vap}) as 35.76 kJ mol^{-1} C_8H_{18}. Calculate the vapor pressure of isooctane at 25 °C.

Boiling and the Boiling Point

When a liquid is heated in a container *open to the atmosphere*, there is a particular temperature at which vaporization occurs throughout the liquid rather than simply at the surface. Vapor bubbles form within the bulk of the liquid, rise to the surface, and escape. The pressure exerted by escaping molecules equals that exerted by molecules of the atmosphere, and **boiling** is said to occur. During boiling, energy absorbed as heat is used only to convert molecules of liquid to vapor. The temperature remains constant until all the liquid has boiled away, as is dramatically illustrated in Figure 3-21. The temperature at which the vapor pressure of a liquid is equal to standard atmospheric pressure (1 atm = 760 mmHg) is the **normal boiling point**. In other words, the normal boiling point is the boiling point of a liquid at 1 atm pressure. The normal boiling points of several liquids can be determined from the intersection of the dashed line in Figure 3-18 with the vapor pressure curves for the liquids.

◀ When a pan of water is put on the stove to boil, small bubbles are usually observed as the water begins to warm. These are bubbles of dissolved air being expelled. Once the water boils, however, all the dissolved air is expelled and the bubbles consist only of water vapor.

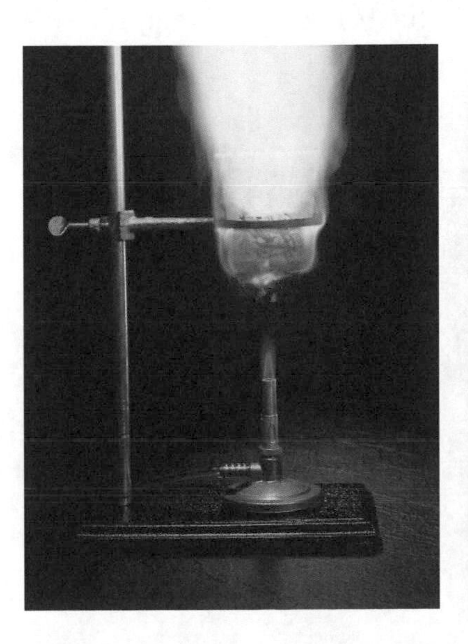

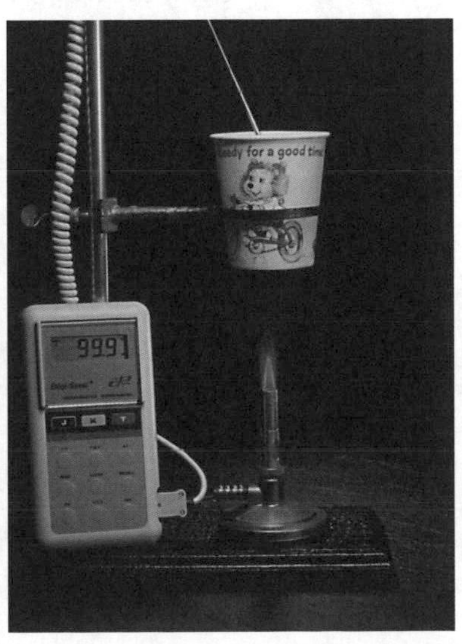

◀ FIGURE 3-21
Boiling water in a paper cup
An empty paper cup heated over a Bunsen burner quickly bursts into flame. If a paper cup is filled with water, it can be heated for an extended time as the water boils. This is possible for three reasons: (1) Because of the high heat capacity of water, heat from the burner goes primarily into heating the water, not the cup. (2) As the water boils, large quantities of heat (ΔH_{vap}) are required to convert the liquid to its vapor. (3) The temperature of the cup does not rise above the boiling point of water as long as liquid water remains. The boiling point of 99.9 °C instead of 100.0 °C suggests that the prevailing barometric pressure was slightly below 1 atm.

▶ A more extreme case is that on the summit of Mt. Everest, where a climber would barely be able to heat a cup of tea to 70 °C.

Figure 3-18 also helps us see that the boiling point of a liquid varies significantly with barometric pressure. Shift the dashed line shown at $P = 760$ mmHg to higher or lower pressures, and the new points of intersection with the vapor pressure curves come at different temperatures. Barometric pressures below 1 atm are commonly encountered at high altitudes. At an altitude of 1609 m (that of Denver, Colorado), barometric pressure is about 630 mmHg. The boiling point of water at this pressure is 95 °C(203 °F). It takes longer to cook foods under conditions of lower boiling-point temperatures. A three–minute boiled egg takes longer than three minutes to cook. We can counteract the effect of high altitudes by using a pressure cooker. In a pressure cooker, the cooking water is maintained under higher-than-atmospheric pressure and its boiling temperature increases, for example, to about 120 °C at 2 atm pressure.

▲ A liquid boils at low pressure
Water boils when its vapor pressure equals the pressure on its surface. Bubbles form throughout the liquid.

3-3 CONCEPT ASSESSMENT

Why does a three-minute boiled egg take longer than three minutes to cook in Switzerland and not on Manhattan Island in New York City?

The Critical Point

In describing boiling, we made an important qualification: Boiling occurs "in a container open to the atmosphere." If a liquid is heated in a *sealed* container, boiling does not occur. Instead, the temperature and vapor pressure rise continuously. Pressures many times atmospheric pressure may be attained. If just the right quantity of liquid is sealed in a glass tube and the tube is heated, as in Figure 3-22, the following phenomena can be observed:

- The density of the liquid decreases, that of the vapor increases, and eventually the two densities become equal.
- The surface tension of the liquid approaches zero. The interface between the liquid and vapor becomes less distinct and eventually disappears.

▶ Although the term *gas* can be used exclusively, sometimes the term *vapor* is used for the gaseous state at temperatures *below* T_c and gas at temperatures *above* T_c.

The **critical point** is the point at which these conditions are reached and the liquid and vapor become indistinguishable. The temperature at the critical point is the critical temperature, T_c, and the pressure is the critical pressure, P_c. The critical point is the highest point on a vapor pressure curve and represents the highest temperature at which the liquid can exist. Several critical temperatures and pressures are listed in Table 3.5.

A gas can be liquefied only at temperatures *below* its critical temperature, T_c. If room temperature is *below* T_c, this liquefaction can be accomplished just by applying sufficient pressure. If room temperature is *above* T_c, however, added pressure *and* a lowering of temperature to a value below T_c are required. We will comment further on the liquefaction of gases.

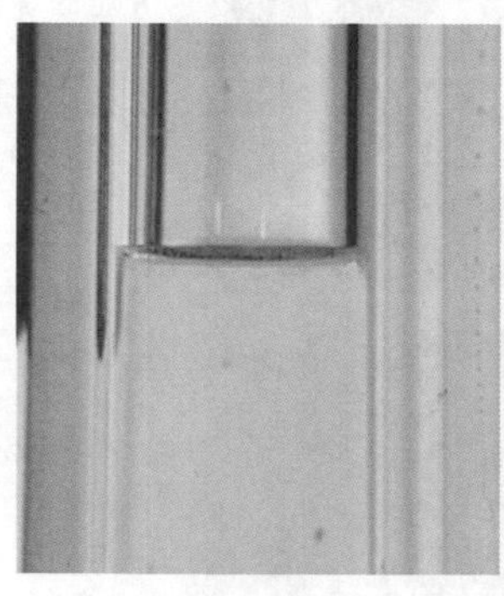

About 10 °C below T_c

About 1 °C below T_c

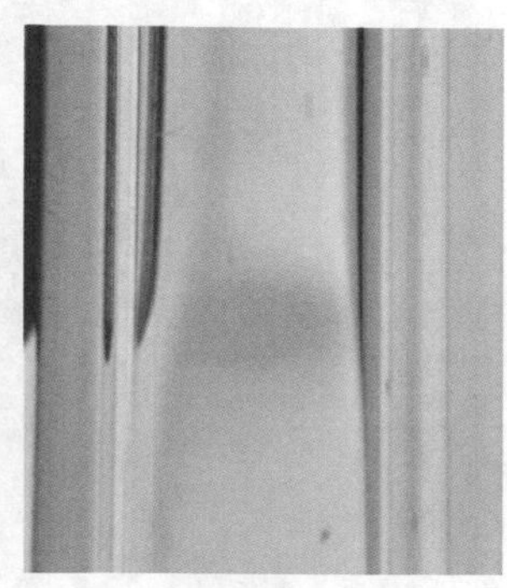

Critical temp. T_c

▶ FIGURE 3-22
Attainment of the critical point for benzene
In a sealed container, the meniscus separating a liquid from its vapor is just barely visible at the instant the critical point is reached. At the critical point—the liquid and vapor become indistinguishable.

TABLE 3.5 Some Critical Temperatures, T_c, and Critical Pressures, P_c

Substance	T_c, K	P_c, atm
"Permanent" gases[a]		
H_2	33.3	12.8
N_2	126.2	33.5
O_2	154.8	50.1
CH_4	191.1	45.8
"Nonpermanent" gases[b]		
CO_2	304.2	72.9
HCl	324.6	82.1
NH_3	405.7	112.5
SO_2	431.0	77.7
H_2O	647.3	218.3

[a]Permanent gases cannot be liquefied at 25 °C (298 K).
[b]Nonpermanent gases can be liquefied at 25 °C.

3-4 CONCEPT ASSESSMENT

Compare the critical temperatures of NH_3 and N_2 (Table 3.5). Which gas has the stronger intermolecular forces?

EXAMPLE 3-6 Relating Intermolecular Forces and Physical Properties

Arrange the following substances in the order in which you would expect their boiling points to increase: $CCl_4, Cl_2, ClNO, N_2$.

Analyze

Recall that boiling point trends are related to intermolecular forces. We should begin by identifying the types and strengths of intermolecular forces at work.

Solve

Three of the substances are nonpolar. For these, the strengths of dispersion forces, and hence the boiling points, should increase with increasing molecular mass, that is, $N_2 < Cl_2 < CCl_4$. ClNO has a molecular mass (65.5 u) comparable to that of Cl_2 (70.9 u), but the ClNO molecule is polar (bond angle $\approx 120°$). This suggests stronger intermolecular forces and a higher boiling point for ClNO than for Cl_2. We should not expect the boiling point of ClNO to be higher than that of CCl_4, however, because of the large difference in their molecular masses (65.5 u compared with 154 u). The expected order is $N_2 < Cl_2 < ClNO < CCl_4$. (The observed boiling points are 77.3, 239.1, 266.7, and 349.9 K, respectively.)

Assess

Even though one molecule (ClNO) is polar, it does not have the highest boiling point, indicating that dispersion forces can be stronger than dipole–dipole forces.

PRACTICE EXAMPLE A: Arrange the following in the expected order of increasing boiling point: Ne, He, $Cl_2, (CH_3)_2CO, O_2, O_3$.

PRACTICE EXAMPLE B: Following are some values of ΔH_{vap} for several liquids at their normal boiling points: H_2, 0.92 kJ mol^{-1}; CH_4, 8.16 kJ mol^{-1}; C_6H_6, 31.0 kJ mol^{-1}; CH_3NO_2, 34.0 kJ mol^{-1}. Explain the differences among these values.

3-5 CONCEPT ASSESSMENT

Explain why CCl_4 has a higher boiling point than CH_3Cl, despite the polarity of CH_3Cl.

3-3 Some Properties of Solids

We mentioned some properties of solids (for example, malleability, ductility) at the beginning of this text, and we will continue to consider additional properties. For now, we will comment on some properties that allow us to think of solids in relation to the other states of matter—liquids and gases.

Melting, Melting Point, and Heat of Fusion

As a crystalline solid is heated, its atoms, ions, or molecules vibrate more vigorously. Eventually a temperature is reached at which these vibrations disrupt the ordered crystalline structure. The atoms, ions, or molecules can slip past one another, and the solid loses its definite shape and is converted to a liquid. This process is called **melting**, or fusion, and the temperature at which it occurs is the **melting point**. The reverse process, the conversion of a liquid to a solid, is called **freezing**, or solidification, and the temperature at which it occurs is the **freezing point**. The melting point of a solid and the freezing point of its liquid are identical. At this temperature, solid and liquid coexist in equilibrium.

If we add heat uniformly to a solid–liquid mixture at equilibrium, the temperature remains constant while the solid melts. Only when all the solid has melted does the temperature begin to rise. Conversely, if we remove heat uniformly from a solid–liquid mixture at equilibrium, the liquid freezes at a constant temperature. The quantity of heat required to melt a solid is the *enthalpy of fusion*, ΔH_{fus}. Some typical enthalpies of fusion, expressed in kilojoules per mole, are listed in Table 3.6. Perhaps the most familiar example of a melting (and freezing) point is that of water, 0 °C. This is the temperature at which liquid and solid water, in contact with air and under standard atmospheric pressure, are in equilibrium. The enthalpy of fusion of water is 6.01 kJ mol^{-1}, which we can express as

$$H_2O(s) \longrightarrow H_2O(l) \qquad \Delta H_{fus} = +6.01 \text{ kJ mol}^{-1} \qquad (3.3)$$

Here is an easy way to determine the freezing point of a liquid. Allow the liquid to cool, and measure the liquid temperature as it falls with time. When freezing begins, the temperature *remains constant* until all the liquid has frozen. Then the temperature is again free to fall as the solid cools. If we plot temperatures against time, we get a graph known as a *cooling curve*. Figure 3-23 is a

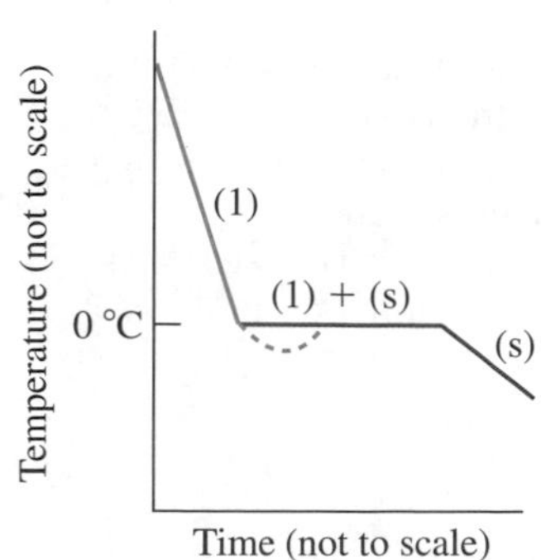

▲ FIGURE 3-23
Cooling curve for water
The broken-line portion represents the condition of supercooling that occasionally occurs.
(l) = liquid; (s) = solid.

TABLE 3.6 Some Enthalpies of Fusion

Substance	Melting Point, °C	ΔH_{fus}, kJ mol^{-1}
Mercury, Hg	−38.9	2.30
Sodium, Na	97.8	2.60
Methyl alcohol, CH_3OH	−97.7	3.21
Ethyl alcohol, CH_3CH_3COOH	−114	5.01
Water, H_2O	0.0	6.01
Benzoic acid, C_6H_5COOH	122.4	18.08
Naphthalene, $C_{10}H_8$	80.2	18.98

cooling curve for water. We can also run this process backward, that is, by starting with the solid and adding heat. Now the temperature remains constant while melting occurs. This temperature–time plot is called a *heating curve.* Generally speaking, the appearance of the heating curve is that of a cooling curve that has been flipped from left to right. A heating curve for water is sketched in Figure 3-24.

Often, an experimentally determined cooling curve does not look quite like the solid–line plot in Figure 3-23. The temperature may drop below the freezing point without any solid appearing. This condition is known as *supercooling.* For a crystalline solid to start forming from a liquid at the freezing point, the liquid must contain some small particles (for example, suspended dust particles) on which crystals can form. If a liquid contains a very limited number of particles on which crystals can grow, it may supercool for a time before freezing. When a supercooled liquid does begin to freeze, however, the temperature rises back to the normal freezing point while freezing is completed. We can always recognize supercooling through a slight dip in a cooling curve just before the horizontal portion.

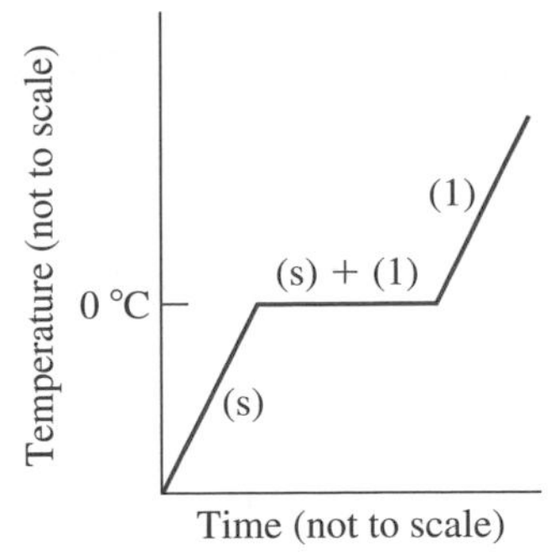

▲ FIGURE 3-24
Heating curve for water
This curve traces the changes that occur as ice is heated from below the melting point to produce liquid water somewhat above the melting point.

◀ Examples of supercooled substances are water droplets in the sky. They remain liquid at temperatures well below the freezing point. When they find a bit of dust on which they can nucleate, the droplets spontaneously turn to ice.

Sublimation

Like liquids, solids can also give off vapors, although because of the stronger intermolecular forces present, solids are generally not as volatile as liquids at a given temperature. The direct passage of molecules from the solid to the vapor state is called **sublimation**. The reverse process, the passage of molecules from the vapor to the solid state, is called **deposition**. When sublimation and deposition occur at equal rates, a dynamic equilibrium exists between a solid and its vapor. The vapor exerts a characteristic pressure called the *sublimation pressure.* A plot of sublimation pressure as a function of temperature is called a *sublimation curve.* The *enthalpy of sublimation* (ΔH_{sub}) is the quantity of heat needed to convert a solid to vapor. At the sublimation point, sublimation (solid $\longrightarrow$ vapor) is equivalent to melting (solid $\longrightarrow$ liquid) followed by vaporization (liquid $\longrightarrow$ vapor). This suggests the following relationship among ΔH_{fus}, ΔH_{vap}, and ΔH_{sub} at the melting point.

$$\Delta H_{sub} = \Delta H_{fus} + \Delta H_{vap} \qquad \textbf{(3.4)}$$

The value of ΔH_{sub} obtained with equation (3.4) can replace the enthalpy of vaporization in the Clausius–Clapeyron equation (3.2), so that sublimation pressures can be calculated as a function of temperature.

Two familiar solids with significant sublimation pressures are ice and dry ice (solid carbon dioxide). If you live in a cold climate, you are aware that snow may disappear from the ground even though the temperature may fail to rise above 0 °C. Under these conditions, the snow does not melt; it sublimes. The sublimation pressure of ice at 0 °C is 4.58 mmHg. That is, the solid ice has a vapor pressure of 4.58 mmHg at 0 °C. If the air is not already saturated with water vapor, the ice will sublime. The sublimation and deposition of iodine are pictured in Figure 3-25.

▲ FIGURE 3-25
Sublimation of iodine
Even at temperatures well below its melting point of 114 °C, solid iodine exhibits an appreciable sublimation pressure. Here, purple iodine vapor is produced at about 70 °C. Deposition of the vapor to solid iodine occurs on the colder walls of the flask.

3-6 CONCEPT ASSESSMENT

Recall the discussion of dew and frost formation. Do the surroundings absorb or lose heat when water vapor condenses to dew or frost? Is the quantity of heat per gram of $H_2O(g)$ condensed the same whether the condensate is dew or frost? Explain.

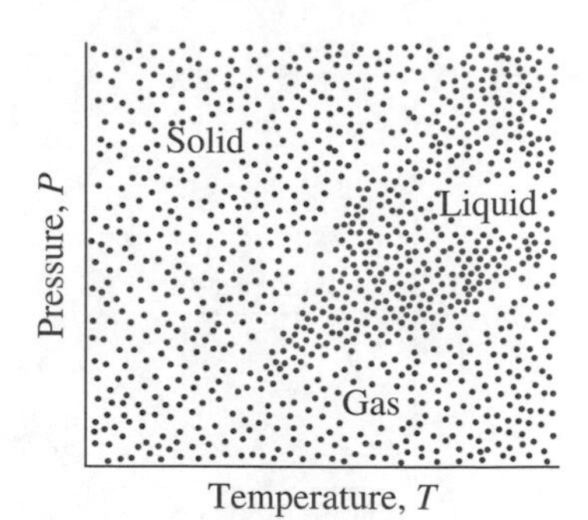

▲ FIGURE 3-26
Temperature, pressure, and states of matter
The outline of a phase diagram is suggested by the distribution of points. The red points identify the temperatures and pressures at which solid is the stable phase; the blue points identify the temperatures and pressures at which liquid is the stable phase; and the brown points represent the temperatures and pressures at which gas is the stable phase. (See also Figures 3-27 and 3-28.)

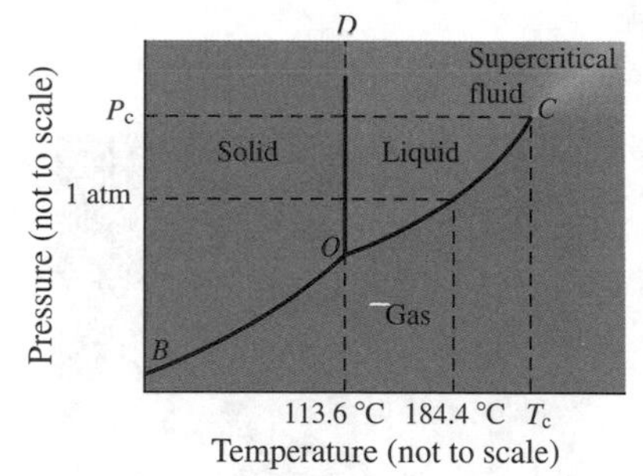

▲ FIGURE 3-27
Phase diagram for iodine
Note that the melting point and triple point temperatures for iodine are essentially the same. Generally, large pressure increases are required to produce even small changes in solid–liquid equilibrium temperatures. The pressure and temperature axes on a phase diagram are generally not drawn to scale so that the significant features of the diagram can be more readily emphasized.

3-4 Phase Diagrams

Imagine constructing a pressure–temperature graph in which each point on the graph represents a condition under which a substance might be found. At low temperatures and high pressures, such as the red points in Figure 3-26, we expect the atoms, ions, or molecules of a substance to be in a close orderly arrangement—a solid. At high temperatures and low pressures—the brown points in Figure 3-26—we expect the gaseous state; and at intermediate temperatures and pressures, we expect a liquid (blue points in Figure 3-26).

Figure 3-26 is a **phase diagram**, a graphical representation of the conditions of temperature and pressure at which solids, liquids, and gases (vapors) exist, either as single phases, or states, of matter or as two or more phases in equilibrium with one another. The different regions of the diagram correspond to single phases, or states, of matter. Straight or curved lines where single-phase regions adjoin represent two phases in equilibrium.

Iodine

One of the simplest phase diagrams is that of iodine shown in Figure 3-27. The curve *OC* is the vapor pressure curve of liquid iodine, and C is the critical point. *OB* is the sublimation curve of solid iodine. The nearly vertical line *OD* represents the effect of pressure on the melting point of iodine; it is called the *fusion curve*. The point *O* has a special significance. It defines the *unique* temperature and pressure at which the *three* states of matter, solid, liquid, and gas, coexist in equilibrium. It is called a **triple point**. For iodine, the triple point is at 113.6 °C and 91.6 mmHg. The normal melting point (113.6 °C) and the boiling point (184.4 °C) are the temperatures at which a line at $P = 1$ atm intersects the fusion and vapor pressure curves, respectively. Melting is essentially unaffected by pressure in the limited range from 91.6 mmHg to 1 atm, and the normal melting point and the triple point are at almost the same temperature.

The sublimation curve for iodine in Figure 3-27 appears to be a continuation of the vapor pressure curve, but if the data are plotted to scale, a discontinuity is seen at the triple point *O*. Moreover, this must *always* be the case. If these two curves were continuous, then the lines representing the variation of ln *P* with $1/T$ (Fig. 3-20) would have the same slope—but this is not possible. The value of ΔH_{vap} determines the slope of the vapor pressure line (recall equation 3.1), whereas ΔH_{sub} determines the slope of the sublimation line. However, these two enthalpy changes can never be the same, because $\Delta H_{sub} = \Delta H_{vap} + \Delta H_{fus}$.

The extreme range of temperatures and pressures required for the entire phase diagram precludes plotting it to scale. This is why the axes are labeled "not to scale."

Carbon Dioxide

The case of carbon dioxide, shown in Figure 3-28, differs from that of iodine in one important respect—the pressure at the triple point *O* is greater than 1 atm. A line at $P = 1$ atm intersects the *sublimation curve*, not the vapor pressure curve. If solid CO_2 is heated in an open container, it sublimes away at a constant temperature of −78.5 °C. It *does not melt* at atmospheric pressure (and so is called "dry ice"). Because it maintains a low temperature and does not produce a liquid by melting, dry ice is widely used in freezing and preserving foods.

Liquid CO_2 can be obtained at pressures above 5.1 atm and it is most frequently encountered in CO_2 fire extinguishers. All three states of matter are involved in the action of these fire extinguishers. When the liquid CO_2 is released, most of it quickly vaporizes. The heat required for this vaporization is extracted from the remaining $CO_2(l)$, which has its temperature lowered to the point that it freezes and falls as a $CO_2(s)$ "snow." In turn, the $CO_2(s)$ quickly sublimes to $CO_2(g)$. All of this helps to quench a fire by displacing the air around the fire with a "blanket" of $CO_2(g)$ and by cooling the area somewhat.

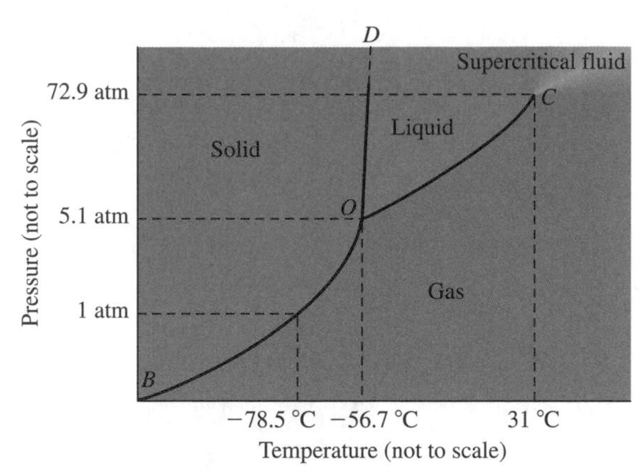

▲ FIGURE 3-28
Phase diagram for carbon dioxide
Several aspects of this diagram are described in the text. An additional feature not shown here is the curvature of the fusion curve *OD* to the right at very high pressures, ultimately reaching temperatures above the critical temperature.

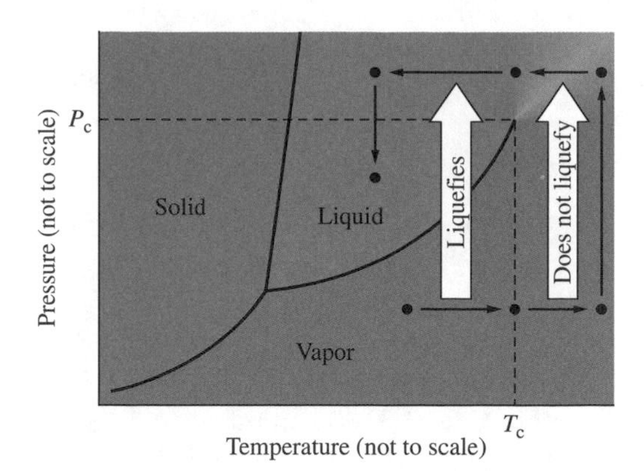

▲ FIGURE 3-29
Critical point and critical isotherm
Applying pressure to a gas at temperatures below the critical isotherm, T_c, causes a liquid to form with the appearance of a meniscus, a discontinuous phase change. Applying pressure above the critical isotherm simply increases the density of the supercritical fluid. In a path traced by the small arrows, gas changes to liquid without exhibiting a discontinuous phase transition.

Supercritical Fluids

Because the liquid and gaseous states become identical and indistinguishable at the critical point, it is difficult to know what to call the state of matter at temperatures and pressures above the critical point. For example, this state of matter has the high density of a liquid and the low viscosity of a gas. The term that is now commonly used is *supercritical fluid* (SCF). Above the critical temperature, no amount of pressure can liquefy a supercritical fluid. Consider the generic phase diagram in Figure 3-29. The path of dots starting with a vapor below the critical isotherm takes us to a low-density gas above the isotherm. When the pressure is greatly increased, we produce a supercritical fluid of much greater density. If, while the pressure exceeds the critical pressure, P_c, the temperature is reduced below the critical temperature, we obtain a liquid. Even with further reduction of pressure, the sample remains in the liquid phase. In following the path described, we have gone from a gas to a liquid without observing a liquid–gas interface. The only way to observe the liquid–vapor interface is to cross the phase boundary below the critical temperature. Note that in the present case we could observe the liquid–vapor interface by lowering the pressure on the liquid to a point on the vapor pressure curve.

Although we do not ordinarily think of liquids or solids as being soluble in gases, *volatile* liquids and solids are. The mole fraction solubility is simply the ratio of the vapor pressure (or the sublimation pressure) to the total gas pressure. And liquids and solids become much more soluble in a gas that is above its critical pressure and temperature, mostly because the density of the SCF is high and approaches that of a liquid. Molecules in supercritical fluids, being in much closer proximity than in ordinary gases, can exert strong attractive forces on the molecules of a liquid or solid solute. SCFs display solvent properties similar to ordinary liquid solvents. To vary the pressure of an SCF means to vary its density and also its solvent properties. Thus, a given SCF, such as carbon dioxide, can be made to behave like many different solvents.

▲ **Decaffeinated coffee**
"Naturally" decaffeinated coffee is made through a process that uses supercritical fluid CO_2 as a solvent to dissolve the caffeine in green coffee beans. Afterward, the beans are roasted and sold to consumers.

Until recently, the principal method of decaffeinating coffee was to extract the caffeine with a solvent, such as methylene chloride (CH_2Cl_2). This solvent is objectionable because it is hazardous in the workplace and difficult to completely remove from the coffee. Now, supercritical fluid CO_2 is used. In one process, green coffee beans are brought into contact with CO_2 at about 90 °C and 160 to 220 atm. The caffeine content of the coffee is reduced from its

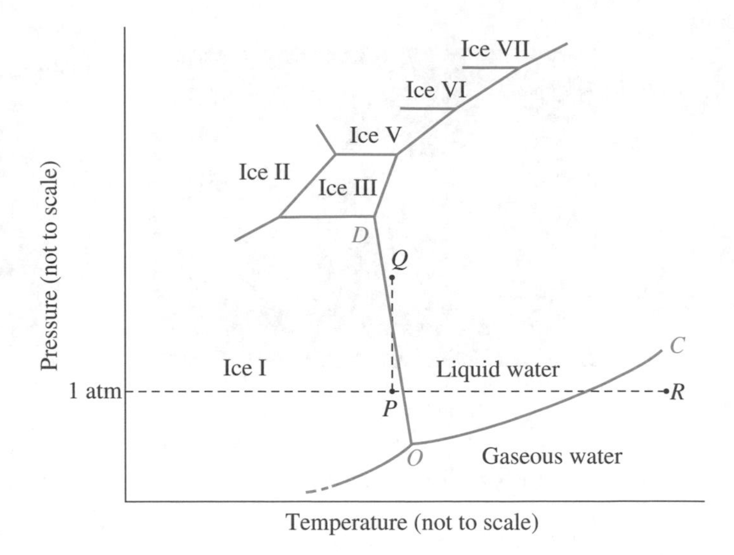

▶ FIGURE 3-30
Phase diagram for water
Point *O*, the triple point, is at 0.0098 °C and 4.58 mmHg. (The normal melting point is at exactly 0 °C and 760 mmHg.) The critical point, *C*, is at 374.1 °C and 218.2 atm. At point *D* the temperature is −22.0 °C and the pressure is 2045 atm. The negative slope of the fusion curve, *OD* (greatly exaggerated here), and the significance of the broken straight lines are discussed in the text.

normal 1% to 3% to about 0.02%. When the temperature and pressure of the CO_2 are reduced, the caffeine precipitates and the CO_2 is recycled.

Water

▶ Since the L-S line in the phase diagram of water is negative, that means that ice floats. If ice did not float, then the polar seas would fill with ice that would never melt. Most solids are more dense than their liquid state. Water is, for us, a happy exception.

The phase diagram of water (Fig. 3-30) presents several new features. One is that the fusion curve *OD* has a *negative* slope; that is, it slopes toward the pressure axis. The melting point of ice *decreases* with an increase in pressure, and this is rather unusual behavior for a solid (bismuth and antimony also behave in this way). However, because large changes in pressure are required to produce even small decreases in the melting point, we do not commonly observe this melting behavior of ice. One example that has been given comes from ice-skating. Presumably, the pressure of the skate blades melts the ice, and the skater skims along on a thin lubricating film of liquid water. This explanation is unlikely, however, because the pressure of the blades doesn't produce a significant lowering of the melting point and certainly cannot explain the ability to skate on ice at temperatures much below the freezing point. (Recent experimental evidence suggests that molecules in a very thin surface layer on ice are mobile in the same way as in liquid water, and this mobility persists even at very low temperatures.)

Another feature illustrated in the phase diagram of water is **polymorphism**, the existence of a solid substance in more than one form. Ordinary ice, called ice I, exists under ordinary pressures. The other forms exist only at high pressures. Polymorphism is more the rule than the exception among solids. Where it occurs, a phase diagram has triple points in addition to the usual solid-liquid-vapor triple point. For example at point *D* in Figure 3-30, ice I, ice III, and liquid H_2O are in equilibrium at −22.0 °C and 2045 atm. Note that the fusion curves for the forms of ice other than ice I have *positive* slopes. Thus, the triple point with ice VI, ice VII, and liquid water is at 81.6 °C and 21,700 atm.

▶ An increase in pressure to 125 atm lowers the freezing point of water by only about 1 °C.

Phases and Phase Transitions

What's the difference between a phase and a state of matter? These terms tend to be used synonymously, but there is a small distinction between them. As we have already noted, there are just *three* states of matter: solid, liquid, and gas. A *phase* is any sample of matter with definite composition and uniform properties that is distinguishable from other phases with which it is in contact. Thus, we can describe liquid water in equilibrium with its vapor as a two-phase mixture. The liquid is one phase and the gas, or vapor, is the other. In this case, the phases (liquid and gas) are the same as the states of matter present (liquid and gas).

We can describe the equilibrium mixture at the triple point *D* in Figure 3-30 as a *three-phase* mixture, even though only *two* states of matter are present (solid and liquid). Two of the phases are in the solid state—the polymorphic forms ice I and ice III. For mixtures of two or more components, different phases may exist in the liquid state as well as in the solid state. For example, most mixtures of triethylamine, $N(CH_2CH_3)_3$, and water at 25 °C separate into two physically distinct liquid phases. One is a saturated solution of triethylamine in water and the other, a saturated solution of water in triethylamine. Because the pressure–temperature diagrams we have been describing can accommodate all the phases in a system, we call them *phase* diagrams. We call the crossing of a two-phase curve in a phase diagram a *phase transition*.

Listed below are six common names assigned to phase transitions.

melting (s $\longrightarrow$ l)	freezing (l $\longrightarrow$ s)
vaporization (l $\longrightarrow$ g)	condensation (g $\longrightarrow$ l)
sublimation (s $\longrightarrow$ g)	deposition (g $\longrightarrow$ s)

Following are two useful generalizations about the changes that occur when crossing a two-phase equilibrium curve in a phase diagram.

- From lower to higher temperatures along a *constant-pressure* line (an isobar), enthalpy *increases*. (Heat is absorbed.)
- From lower to higher pressures along a *constant-temperature* line (an isotherm), volume *decreases*. (The phase at the higher pressure has the higher density.)

The second generalization helps us to understand why a fusion curve usually has a positive slope. Typical behavior is for a solid to have a greater density than the corresponding liquid. Example 3-7 illustrates how we can use a phase diagram to describe the phase transitions that a substance can undergo.

◀ Because ice I is less dense than $H_2O(l)$, the fusion curve *OD* in Figure 3-30 has a negative slope.

EXAMPLE 3-7 Interpreting a Phase Diagram

A sample of ice is maintained at 1 atm and at a temperature represented by point *P* in Figure 3-30. Describe what happens when (a) the temperature is raised, at constant pressure, to point *R*, and (b) the pressure is raised, at constant temperature, to point *Q*. The sketches Figure 3-31 suggest the conditions at points *P*, *Q*, and *R*.

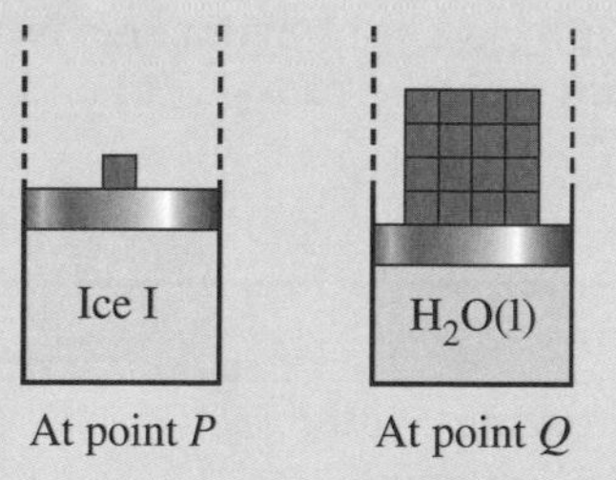

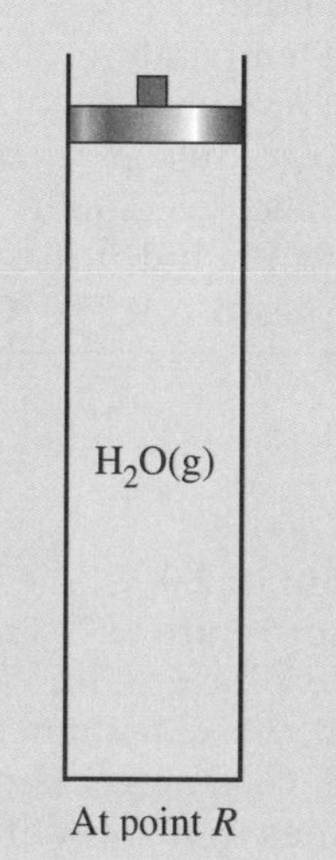

◀ FIGURE 3-31
Example 3-7 illustrated
A sample of pure water is confined in a cylinder by a freely moving piston surmounted by weights to establish the confining pressure. Sketched here are conditions at the points labeled *P*, *Q*, and *R* in Figure 3-30. The transition from point *P* to *Q* is accomplished by changing the pressure at constant temperature (isothermal). The transition from point *P* to *R* is accomplished by changing the temperature at constant pressure (isobaric).

Analyze

Recall that the lines separating the different phases represent coexistence lines. At these coexistence lines, the system is a mixture of both phases. On either side of those lines, the system is in that particular phase. Also recall that as the system moves from one phase to another at the coexistence lines, the temperature remains constant until all of one phase is converted to another.

Solve

(a) When the temperature reaches a point on the fusion curve *OD* (0 °C), ice begins to melt. The temperature remains constant as ice is converted to liquid. When melting is complete, the temperature

(continued)

again increases. No vapor appears in the cylinder until the temperature reaches 100 °C, at which point the vapor pressure is 1 atm. When all the liquid has vaporized, the temperature is again free to rise to a final value of *R*.

(b) Because solids are not very compressible, very little change occurs until the pressure reaches the point of intersection of the constant-temperature line *PQ* with the fusion curve *OD*. Here melting begins. A significant *decrease* in volume occurs (about 10%) as ice is converted to liquid water. After melting, additional pressure produces very little change because liquids are not very compressible.

Assess

Phase diagrams are very useful for understanding the conditions needed to observe the different phases of matter. We should now be able to use the phase diagram in Figure 3-30 to determine the pressure required to observe sublimation instead of melting.

PRACTICE EXAMPLE A: With as much detail as possible, describe the phase changes that would occur if a sample of water represented by point *R* in Figure 3-30 were brought first to point *P* and then to point *Q*.

PRACTICE EXAMPLE B: Draw a sketch showing the condition prevailing along the line *PR* when 1.00 mol of water has been brought to the point where exactly one-half of it has vaporized. Compare this to the condition at point *R* in Figure 3-31, assuming that this is also based on 1.00 mol of water. For example, is the volume of the system the same as that in Figure 3-31? If not, is it larger or smaller, and by how much? Assume that the temperature at point *R* is the same as the critical temperature of water and that water vapor behaves as an ideal gas.

3-7 CONCEPT ASSESSMENT

One method of restoring water-damaged books after a fire is extinguished in a library is by "freeze drying" them in evacuated chambers. Describe how this method might work.

Integrative Example

Use data from the table of physical properties of hydrazine, N_2H_4, to calculate the partial pressure of $N_2H_4(g)$ when a container filled with an equilibrium mixture of $N_2H_4(g)$ and $N_2H_4(l)$ at 25.0 °C is cooled to the temperature of an ice–water bath.

Property	Value
Freezing point	2.0 °C
Boiling point	113.5 °C
Critical temperature	380 °C
Critical pressure	145.4 atm
Enthalpy of fusion	12.66 kJ mol^{-1}
Heat capacity of liquid	98.84 J mol^{-1} $°C^{-1}$
Density of liquid at 25.0 °C	1.0036 g mL^{-1}
Vapor pressure at 25.0 °C	14.4 Torr

Analyze

At a temperature below its freezing point of 2.0 °C, the hydrazine will be present as a solid in equilibrium with its vapor. We are seeking the sublimation pressure of $N_2H_4(s)$ at the melting point of ice, 0 °C. At its freezing point of 2.0 °C, the hydrazine coexists in three phases—liquid, solid, and vapor. We must first determine the vapor pressure of hydrazine at 2.0 °C. Then we can then use the Clausius–Clapeyron equation (3.2) to calculate the vapor (sublimation) pressure at 0 °C. Our principal task will be to identify the data needed to apply the Clausius–Clapeyron equation, three times in all, as detailed in the stepwise solution to the problem.

Solve

To determine a value of ΔH_{vap}, choose the vapor pressure data at 25.0 °C for T_1 and P_1 and at the normal boiling point for T_2 and P_2 for substitution into equation (3.2).

$$\ln\frac{P_2}{P_1} = -\frac{\Delta H_{vap}}{R}\left(\frac{1}{T_2} - \frac{1}{T_1}\right)$$

$$\ln\frac{760\text{ Torr}}{14.4\text{ Torr}} = -\frac{\Delta H_{vap}}{8.3145\text{ J mol}^{-1}\text{K}^{-1}} \times \left(\frac{1}{386.7\text{ K}} - \frac{1}{298.2\text{ K}}\right) = 3.967$$

$$\Delta H_{vap} = -\frac{8.3145\text{ J mol}^{-1}\text{K}^{-1} \times 3.967}{(0.002586 - 0.003353)\text{ K}^{-1}} = 4.30 \times 10^4\text{ J mol}^{-1}$$

Return to the Clausius–Clapeyron equation (3.2) by using the value of ΔH_{vap} just obtained. Also use the same data as in the first calculation for T_1 and P_1, but now with $T_2 = 2.0 + 273.15 = 275.2\ K$ and P_2 as an unknown. Solve the equation for P_2.

$$\ln\frac{P_2}{14.4} = -\frac{4.30 \times 10^4\text{ J mol}^{-1}}{8.3145\text{ J mol}^{-1}\text{K}^{-1}} \times \left(\frac{1}{275.2\text{ K}} - \frac{1}{298.2\text{ K}}\right)$$

$$= -5.17 \times 10^3 \times (2.80 \times 10^{-4}) = -1.45$$

$$P_2/14.4 = e^{-1.45} = 0.235$$

$$P_2 = 0.235 \times 14.4 = 3.38\text{ Torr}$$

We now have the triple point data for hydrazine. The triple point temperature is 2.0 °C (275.2 K) and the triple point pressure is 3.38 Torr. In our final application of equation (3.2), we use those data as T_2 and P_2. The temperature T_1 is 0 °C (273.2 K) and the unknown sublimation pressure is P_1. The enthalpy change needed in this final calculation must be the enthalpy of sublimation, which is

$$\Delta H_{sub} = \Delta H_{fus} + \Delta H_{vap}$$

$$= \left(12.66\frac{\text{kJ}}{\text{mol}} \times \frac{1000\text{ J}}{1\text{ kJ}}\right) + 4.30 \times 10^4\text{ J mol}^{-1} = 5.57 \times 10^4\text{ J mol}^{-1}$$

Finally, we substitute these data into equation (3.2) and solve for P_1, the sublimation pressure of hydrazine at 0 °C.

$$\ln\frac{3.38\text{ Torr}}{P_1} = -\frac{5.57 \times 10^4\text{ J mol}^{-1}}{8.3145\text{ J mol}^{-1}\text{K}^{-1}} \times \left(\frac{1}{275.2} - \frac{1}{273.2}\right)\text{K}^{-1}$$

$$\ln\frac{3.38\text{ Torr}}{P_1} = -6.70 \times 10^3 \times (-2.66 \times 10^{-5}) = 0.178$$

$$\frac{3.38\text{ Torr}}{P_1} = e^{0.178} = 1.19$$

$$P_1 = \frac{3.38\text{ Torr}}{1.19} = 2.84\text{ Torr}$$

Assess

Observe that, compared with the vapor pressure at 25 °C (14.4 Torr), the calculated triple point pressure (3.38 Torr) is smaller; and the sublimation pressure at 0 °C (2.84 Torr) is smaller still. This is certainly the trend expected for the three values. In the three situations in which equation (3.2) is used, the first one is the most subject to error because the difference between T_2 and T_1 is 89 °C, while in the other two it is 23 °C and 2 °C, respectively. Both ΔH_{vap} and ΔH_{sub} are undoubtedly temperature-dependent.

PRACTICE EXAMPLE A: The normal boiling point of isooctane (a gasoline component with a high octane rating) is 99.2 °C, and its ΔH_{vap} is 35.76 kJ mol^{-1}. Because isooctane and water have nearly identical boiling points, will they have nearly equal vapor pressures at room temperature? If not, which would you expect to be more volatile? Explain.

PRACTICE EXAMPLE B: We cannot measure the second electron affinity of oxygen directly:

$$O^-(g) + e^- \longrightarrow O_2^-(g) \quad EA_2 = ?$$

The O_2^- ion can exist in the solid state, however, where the high energy requirement for its formation is offset by the large lattice energies of ionic oxides.

(a) Show that EA_2 can be calculated from the enthalpy of formation and lattice energy of MgO(s), the enthalpy of sublimation of Mg(s), the ionization energies of Mg, the bond energy of O_2, and the EA_1 for O(g).

(b) The lattice energy of MgO is -3925 kJ mol^{-1}. Combine this with other values in the text to estimate EA_2 for oxygen.

Exercises

Intermolecular Forces

1. For each of the following substances describe the importance of dispersion (London) forces, dipole–dipole interactions, and hydrogen bonding: **(a)** HCl; **(b)** Br_2; **(c)** ICl; **(d)** HF; **(e)** CH_4.
2. When another atom or group of atoms is substituted for one of the hydrogen atoms in benzene, C_6H_6, the boiling point changes. Explain the order of the following boiling points: C_6H_6, 80 °C; C_6H_5Cl, 132 °C; C_6H_5Br, 156 °C; C_6H_5OH, 182 °C.
3. Arrange the liquids represented by the following molecular models in the expected order of increasing viscosity at 25 °C.

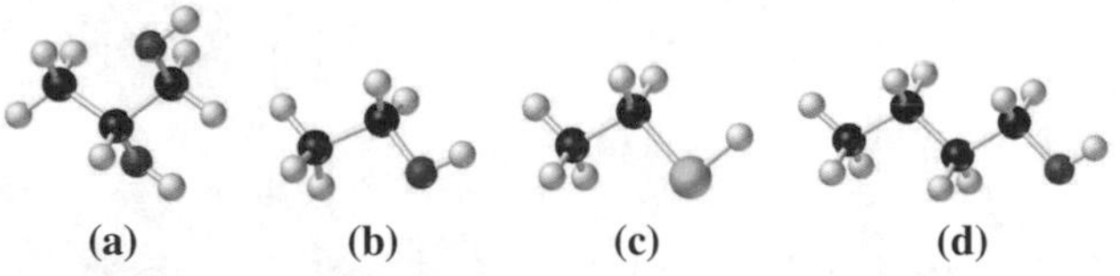

4. Arrange the liquids represented by the following molecular models in the expected order of increasing normal boiling point.

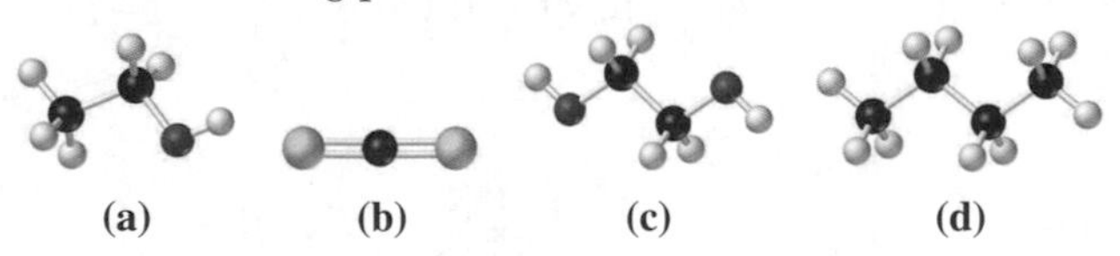

5. One of the following substances is a liquid at room temperature and the others are gaseous: CH_3OH; C_3H_8; N_2; N_2O. Which do you think is the liquid? Explain.
6. In which of the following compounds do you think that intramolecular hydrogen bonding is an important factor: **(a)** $CH_3CH_2CH_2CH_3$; **(b)** $HOOCCH_2CH_2CH_2CH_2COOH$; **(c)** CH_3COOH; **(d)** *ortho*-phthalic acid? Explain.

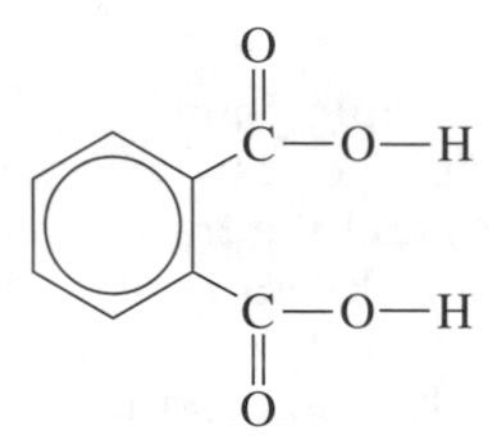

ortho-Phthalic acid

7. How many water molecules can hydrogen bond to methanol?
8. What is the maximum number of hydrogen bonds that can form between two acetic acid molecules?
9. In DNA the nucleic acid bases form hydrogen bonds between them, which are responsible for the formation of the double-stranded helix. Arrange the bases guanine and cytosine to give the maximum number of hydrogen bonds.

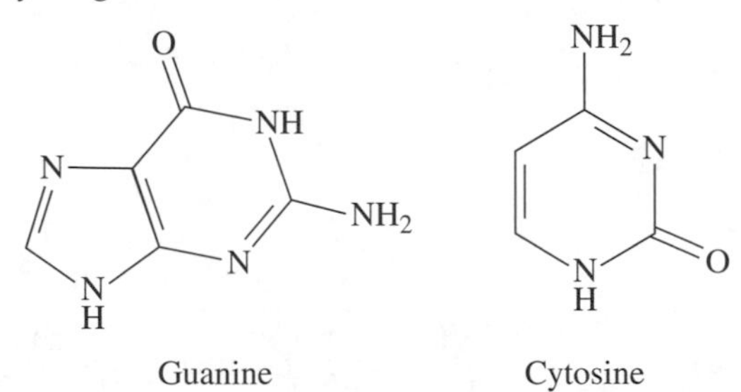

10. Water molecules will form small, stable clusters. Draw one possible water cluster by using six water molecules and maximizing the number of hydrogen bonds for each water molecule.

Surface Tension and Viscosity

11. Silicone oils, such as $H_3C[SiO(CH_3)_2]_n Si(CH_3)$, are used in water repellents for treating tents, hiking boots, and similar items. Explain how silicone oils function.
12. Surface tension, viscosity, and vapor pressure are all related to intermolecular forces. Why do surface tension and viscosity decrease with temperature, whereas vapor pressure increases with temperature?
13. Is there any scientific basis for the colloquial expression "slower than molasses in January"? Explain.
14. A television commercial claims that a product makes water "wetter." Can there be any basis to this claim? Explain.
15. Rank the following in order of increasing surface tension (at room temperature): **(a)** CH_3OH; **(b)** CCl_4; **(c)** $CH_3CH_2OCH_2CH_3$.

16. Would you predict the surface tension of t-butyl alcohol, $(CH_3)_3COH$, to be greater than or less than that of n-butyl alcohol, $CH_3CH_2CH_2CH_2OH$? Explain.
17. Butanol and pentane have approximately the same mass, however, the viscosity (at 20 °C) of butanol is $\eta = 2.948$ cP, and the viscosity of pentane is $\eta = 0.240$ cP. Explain this difference.
18. Carbon tetrachloride (CCl_4) and mercury have similar viscosities at 20 °C. Explain.

Vaporization

19. As a liquid evaporated from an open container, its temperature was observed to remain roughly constant. When the same liquid evaporated from a thermally insulated container (a vacuum bottle or Dewar flask), its temperature was observed to drop. How would you account for this difference?
20. Explain why vaporization occurs only at the surface of a liquid until the boiling point temperature is reached. That is, why does vapor not form throughout the liquid at all temperatures?
21. The enthalpy of vaporization of benzene, $C_6H_6(l)$, is 33.9 kJ mol^{-1} at 298 K. How many liters of $C_6H_6(g)$, measured at 298 K and 95.1 mmHg, are formed when 1.54 kJ of heat is absorbed by $C_6H_6(l)$ at a constant temperature of 298 K?
22. A vapor volume of 1.17 L forms when a sample of liquid acetonitrile, CH_3CN, absorbs 1.00 kJ of heat at its normal boiling point (81.6 °C and 1 atm). What is ΔH_{vap} in kilojoules per mole of CH_3CN?
23. Use data from the Integrative Example (page 107) to determine how much heat is required to convert 25.00 mL of liquid hydrazine at 25.0 °C to hydrazine vapor at its normal boiling point.
24. How much heat is required to raise the temperature of 215 g $CH_3OH(l)$ from 20.0 to 30.0 °C and then vaporize it at 30.0 °C? Use data from Table 3.3 and a molar heat capacity of $CH_3OH(l)$ of 81.1 J $mol^{-1}K^{-1}$.
25. How many liters of $CH_4(g)$, measured at 23.4 °C and 768 mmHg, must be burned to provide the heat needed to vaporize 3.78 L of water at 100 °C? $\Delta H_{combustion} = -8.90 \times 10^2$ kJ mol^{-1} CH_4. For $H_2O(l)$ at 100 °C, $d = 0.958$ g cm^{-3}, and $\Delta H_{vap} = 40.7$ kJ mol^{-1}.
26. A 50.0 g piece of iron at 152 °C is dropped into 20.0 g $H_2O(l)$ at 89 °C in an open, thermally insulated container. How much water would you expect to vaporize, assuming no water splashes out? The specific heats of iron and water are 0.45 and 4.21 J g^{-1} °C^{-1}, respectively, and $\Delta H_{vap} = 40.7$ kJ $mol^{-1}H_2O$.

Vapor Pressure and Boiling Point

27. From Figure 3-18, estimate (a) the vapor pressure of C_6H_7N at 100 °C; (b) the normal boiling point of C_7H_8.
28. Use data in Figure 3-20 to estimate **(a)** the normal boiling point of aniline; **(b)** the vapor pressure of diethyl ether at 25 °C.
29. Equilibrium is established between $Br_2(l)$ and $Br_2(g)$ at 25.0 °C. A 250.0 mL sample of the vapor weighs 0.486 g. What is the vapor pressure of bromine at 25.0 °C, in millimeters of mercury?
30. The density of acetone vapor in equilibrium with liquid acetone, $(CH_3)_2CO$, at 32 °C is 0.876 g L^{-1}. What is the vapor pressure of acetone at 32 °C, expressed in kilopascals?
31. A double boiler is used when a careful control of temperature is required in cooking. Water is boiled in an outside container to produce steam, and the steam condenses on the outside walls of an inner container in which cooking occurs. (A related laboratory device is called a steam bath.) **(a)** How is heat energy conveyed to the food to be cooked in a double boiler? **(b)** What is the maximum temperature that can be reached in the inside container?
32. One popular demonstration in chemistry labs is performed by boiling a small quantity of water in a metal can (such as a used soda can), picking up the can with tongs and quickly submerging it upside down in cold water. The can collapses with a loud and satisfying pop. Give an explanation of this crushing of the can. (Note: If you try this demonstration, do not heat the can over an open flame.)
33. Pressure cookers achieve a high cooking temperature to speed the cooking process by heating a small amount of water under a constant pressure. If the pressure is set at 2 atm, what is the boiling point of the water? Use information from Table 3.4.
34. Use data from Table 3.4 to estimate **(a)** the boiling point of water in Santa Fe, New Mexico, if the prevailing atmospheric pressure is 640 mmHg; **(b)** the prevailing atmospheric pressure at Lake Arrowhead, California, if the observed boiling point of water is 94 °C.
35. A 25.0 L volume of He(g) at 30.0 °C is passed through 6.220 g of liquid aniline ($C_6H_5NH_2$) at 30.0 °C. The liquid remaining after the experiment weighs 6.108 g. Assume that the He(g) becomes saturated with aniline vapor and that the total gas volume and temperature remain constant. What is the vapor pressure of aniline at 30.0 °C?
36. A 7.53 L sample of $N_2(g)$ at 742 mmHg and 45.0 °C is bubbled through $CCl_4(l)$ at 45.0 °C. Assuming the gas becomes saturated with $CCl_4(g)$, what is the volume of the resulting gaseous mixture, if the total pressure remains at 742 mmHg and the temperature remains at 45 °C? The vapor pressure of CCl_4 at 45 °C is 261 mmHg.
37. Some vapor pressure data for Freon-12, CCl_2F_2, once a common refrigerant, are −12.2 °C, 2.0 atm; 16.1 °C, 5.0 atm; 42.4 °C, 10.0 atm; 74.0 °C, 20.0 atm. Also, bp = −29.8 °C, $T_c = 111.5$ °C, $P_c = 39.6$ atm. Use these data to plot the vapor pressure curve of Freon-12.

What approximate pressure would be required in the compressor of a refrigeration system to convert Freon-12 vapor to liquid at 25.0 °C?

38. A 10.0 g sample of liquid water is sealed in a 1515 mL flask and allowed to come to equilibrium with its vapor at 27 °C. What is the mass of $H_2O(g)$ present when equilibrium is established? Use vapor pressure data from Table 3.4.

The Clausius–Clapeyron Equation

39. Cyclohexanol has a vapor pressure of 10.0 mmHg at 56.0 °C and 100.0 mmHg at 103.7 °C. Calculate its enthalpy of vaporization, ΔH_{vap}.

40. The vapor pressure of methyl alcohol is 40.0 mmHg at 5.0 °C. Use this value and other information from the text to estimate the normal boiling point of methyl alcohol.

41. The normal boiling point of acetone, an important laboratory and industrial solvent, is 56.2 °C and its ΔH_{vap} is 25.5 kJ mol^{-1}. At what temperature does acetone have a vapor pressure of 375 mmHg?

42. The vapor pressure of trichloromethane (chloroform) is 40.0 Torr at −7.1 °C. Its enthalpy of vaporization is 29.2 kJ mol^{-1}. Calculate its normal boiling point.

43. Benzaldehyde, C_6H_5CHO, has a normal boiling point of 179.0 °C and a critical point at 422 °C and 45.9 atm. Estimate its vapor pressure at 100.0 °C.

44. With reference to Figure 3-20, which is the more volatile liquid, benzene or toluene? At approximately what temperature does the less volatile liquid have the same vapor pressure as the more volatile one at 65 °C?

Critical Point

45. Which substances listed in Table 3.5 can exist as liquids at room temperature (about 20.0 °C)? Explain.

46. Can SO_2 be maintained as a liquid under a pressure of 100 atm at 0 °C? Can liquid methane be obtained under the same conditions?

Crystal Structures

47. Silicon tetrafluoride molecules are arranged in a body-centered cubic unit cell. How many silicon atoms are in the unit cell?

48. Two views, a top and side view, for the unit cell for rutile (TiO_2) are shown here. **(a)** How many titanium atoms (blue) are in this unit cell? **(b)** How many oxygen atoms (red) are in this unit cell?

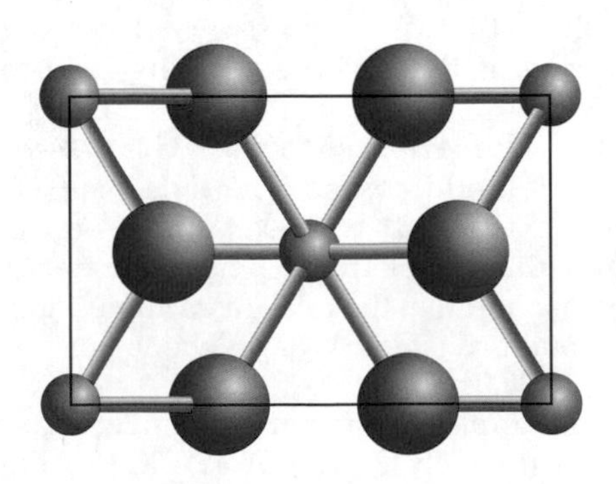

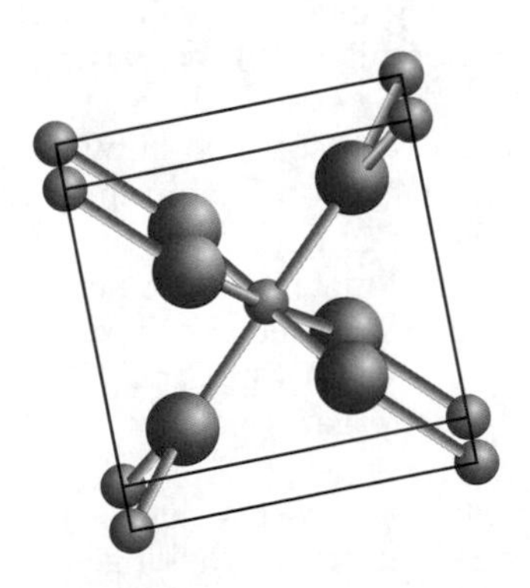

Ionic Crystal Structures

49. Show that the unit cells for CaF_2 and TiO_2 in Figure 3-50 are consistent with their formulas.

50. Using methods similar to Examples 3-10 and 3-11, calculate the density of CsCl. Use 169 pm as the radius of Cs^+.

51. The crystal structure of magnesium oxide, MgO, is of the NaCl type (Fig. 3-48). Use this fact, together with ionic radii from Figure 9-8, to establish the following.
(a) the coordination numbers of Mg^{2+} and O^{2-};
(b) the number of formula units in the unit cell;
(c) the length and volume of a unit cell;
(d) the density of MgO.

52. Potassium chloride has the same crystal structure as NaCl. Careful measurement of the internuclear distance between K^+ and Cl^- ions gave a value of 314.54 pm. The density of KCl is 1.9893 g/cm^3. Use these data to evaluate the Avogadro constant, N_A.

53. Use data from Figure 9-9 to predict the type of cubic unit cell adopted by **(a)** CaO; **(b)** CuCl; **(c)** LiO_2 (the radius of the O_2^- ion is 128 pm).

54. Use data from Figure 9-9 to predict the type of cubic unit cell adopted by **(a)** BaO; **(b)** CuI; **(c)** LiS_2. (The radii of Ba^{2+} and S_2^- ions are 135 and 198 pm, respectively.)

Lattice Energy

55. *Without doing calculations*, indicate how you would expect the lattice energies of LiCl(s), KCl(s), RbCl(s), and CsCl(s) to compare with the value of -787 kJ mol^{-1} for NaCl(s). [*Hint:* Assume that the enthalpies of sublimation of the alkali metals are comparable in value.]

56. Determine the lattice energy of KF(s) from the following data: $\Delta H_f^\circ[\text{KF(s)}] = -567.3 \text{ kJ mol}^{-1}$; enthalpy of sublimation of K(s), 89.24 kJ mol^{-1}; enthalpy of dissociation of $F_2(g)$, 159 kJ mol^{-1} F_2; I_1 for K(g), 418.9 kJ mol^{-1}; EA for F(g), -328kJ mol^{-1}.

57. Refer to Example 3-12. Together with data given there, use the data here to calculate ΔH_f° for 1 mol $MgCl_2(s)$. Explain why you would expect $MgCl_2$ to be a much more stable compound than MgCl. (Second ionization energy of Mg, $I_2 = 1451 \text{ kJ mol}^{-1}$; lattice energy of $MgCl_2(s) = -2526 \text{ kJ mol}^{-1}$ $MgCl_2$.)

58. In ionic compounds with certain metals, hydrogen exists as the hydride ion, H^-. Determine the electron affinity of hydrogen; that is, ΔH for the process $H(g) + e^- \rightarrow H^-(g)$. To do so, use data from Section 3-7; -812 kJ mol^{-1} NaH for the lattice energy of NaH(s); and -57 kJ mol^{-1} NaH for the enthalpy of formation of NaH(s).

Integrative and Advanced Exercises

59. When a wax candle is burned, the fuel consists of *gaseous* hydrocarbons appearing at the end of the candle wick. Describe the phase changes and processes by which the solid wax is ultimately consumed.

60. The normal boiling point of water is 100.00 °C and the enthalpy of vaporization at this temperature is $\Delta H_{vap} = 40.657 \text{ kJ mol}^{-1}$. What would be the boiling point of water if it were based on a pressure of 1 bar instead of the standard atm?

61. A supplier of cylinder gases warns customers to determine how much gas remains in a cylinder by weighing the cylinder and comparing this mass to the original mass of the full cylinder. In particular, the customer is told not to try to estimate the mass of gas available from the measured gas pressure. Explain the basis of this warning. Are there cases where a measurement of the gas pressure *can* be used as a measure of the remaining available gas? If so, what are they?

62. Use the following data to determine the quantity of heat needed to convert 15.0 g of solid mercury at −50.0 °C to mercury vapor at 25 °C. Specific heats: Hg(s), 24.3 $\text{J mol}^{-1}\text{K}^{-1}$; Hg(l), 28.0 $\text{J mol}^{-1}\text{K}^{-1}$. Melting point of Hg(s), −38.87 °C. Heat of fusion, 2.33 kJ mol^{-1}.

63. To vaporize 1.000 g water at 20 °C requires 2447 J of heat. At 100 °C, 10.00 kJ of heat will convert 4.430 g $H_2O(l)$ to $H_2O(g)$. Do these observations conform to your expectations? Explain.

64. Estimate how much heat is absorbed when 1.00 g of Instant Car Kooler vaporizes. Comment on the effectiveness of this spray in cooling the interior of a car. Assume the spray is 10% $C_2H_5OH(aq)$ by mass, the temperature is 55 °C, the heat capacity of air is 29 J mol^{-1} K^{-1}, and use ΔH_{vap} data from Table 3.3.

65. Because solid *p*-dichlorobenzene, $C_6H_4Cl_2$, sublimes rather easily, it has been used as a moth repellent. From the data given, estimate the sublimation pressure of $C_6H_4Cl_2(s)$ at 25 °C. For $C_6H_4Cl_2$; mp = 53.1 °C; vapor pressure of $C_6H_4Cl_2(l)$ at 54.8 °C is 10.0 mmHg; ΔH_{fus} = 17.88 kJ mol^{-1}; ΔH_{vap} = 72.22 kJ mol^{-1}.

66. A 1.05 mol sample of $H_2O(g)$ is compressed into a 2.61 L flask at 30.0 °C. Describe the point(s) in Figure 3-30 representing the final condition.

4

Thermochemistry

CONTENTS

Potassium reacts with water, liberating sufficient heat to ignite the hydrogen evolved. The transfer of heat between substances in chemical reactions is an important aspect of thermochemistry.

Natural gas consists mostly of methane, CH_4. The combustion of a hydrocarbon, such as methane, yields carbon dioxide and water as products. More important, however, is another "product" of this reaction, which we have not previously mentioned: heat. This heat can be used to produce hot water in a water heater, to heat a house, or to cook food.

Thermochemistry is the branch of chemistry concerned with the heat effects that accompany chemical reactions. To understand the relationship between heat and chemical and physical changes, we must start with some basic definitions. We will then explore the concept of heat and the methods used to measure the transfer of energy across boundaries. Another form of energy transfer is work, and, in combination with heat, we will define the first law of thermodynamics. At this point, we will establish the relationship between heats of reaction and changes in internal energy and enthalpy. We will see that the tabulation of the change in internal energy and change in enthalpy can be used to calculate, directly or indirectly, energy changes during chemical and physical changes. Finally, concepts introduced in this chapter will answer a host of practical questions, such as

◀ Thermochemistry is a subfield of a larger discipline called *thermodynamics*.

why natural gas is a better fuel than coal and why the energy value of fats is greater than that of carbohydrates and proteins.

4-1 Getting Started: Some Terminology

In this section, we introduce and define some very basic terms. Most are discussed in greater detail in later sections, and your understanding of these terms should grow as you proceed through the chapter.

Let us think of the universe as being comprised of a system and its surroundings. A **system** is the part of the universe chosen for study, and it can be as large as all the oceans on Earth or as small as the contents of a beaker. Most of the systems we will examine will be small and we will look, particularly, at the transfer of *energy* (as heat and work) and *matter* between the system and its surroundings. The **surroundings** are that part of the universe outside the system with which the system interacts. Figure 4-1 pictures three common systems: first, as we see them and, then, in an abstract form that chemists commonly use. An **open system** freely exchanges energy and matter with its surroundings (Fig. 4-1a). A **closed system** can exchange energy, but not matter, with its surroundings (Fig. 4-1b). An **isolated system** does not interact with its surroundings (approximated in Figure 4-1c).

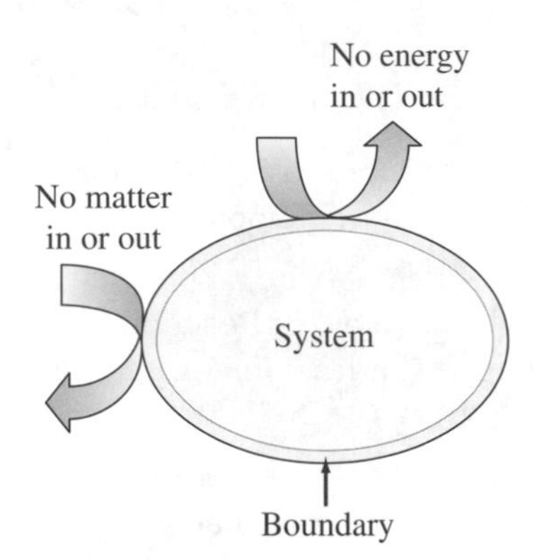

▲ **Isolated system**
Neither energy nor matter is transferred between the system and its surroundings.

The remainder of this section says more, in a general way, about energy and its relationship to work. Like many other scientific terms, *energy* is derived from Greek. It means "work within." **Energy** is the capacity to do work. **Work** is done when a force acts through a distance. Moving objects do work when they slow down or are stopped. Thus, when one billiard ball strikes another and sets it in motion, work is done. The energy of a moving object is called **kinetic energy** (the word *kinetic* means "motion" in Greek). We can see the relationship between work and energy by comparing the units for these two quantities. The kinetic energy (e_k) of an object is based on its mass (m) and

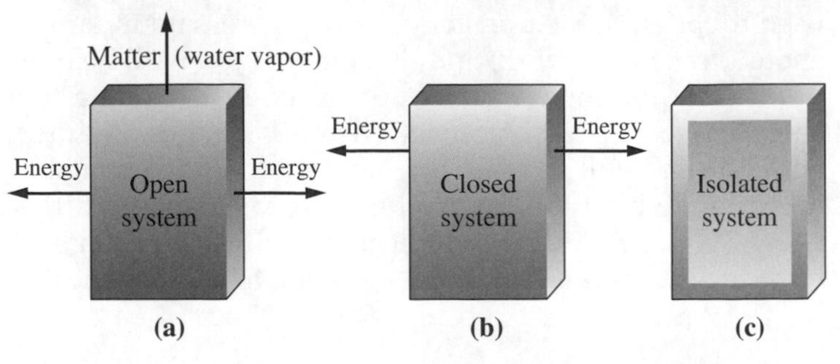

▶ FIGURE 4-1
Systems and their surroundings
(a) *Open system.* The beaker of hot coffee transfers energy to the surroundings—it loses heat as it cools. Matter is also transferred in the form of water vapor. **(b)** *Closed system.* The flask of hot coffee transfers energy (heat) to the surroundings as it cools. Because the flask is stoppered, no water vapor escapes and no matter is transferred. **(c)** *Isolated system.* Hot coffee in an insulated container approximates an isolated system. No water vapor escapes, and, for a time at least, little heat is transferred to the surroundings. (Eventually, though, the coffee in the container cools to room temperature.)

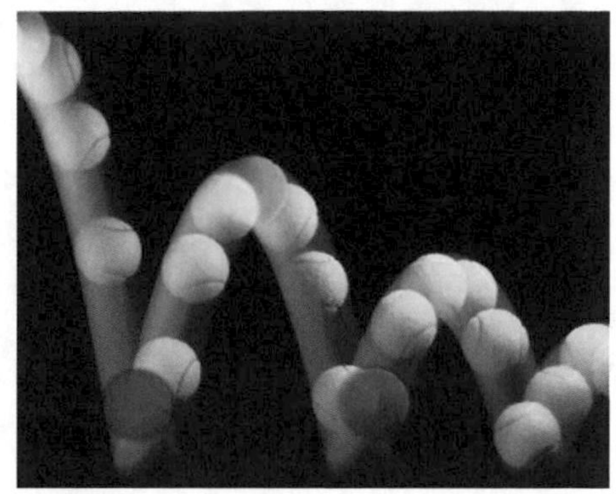

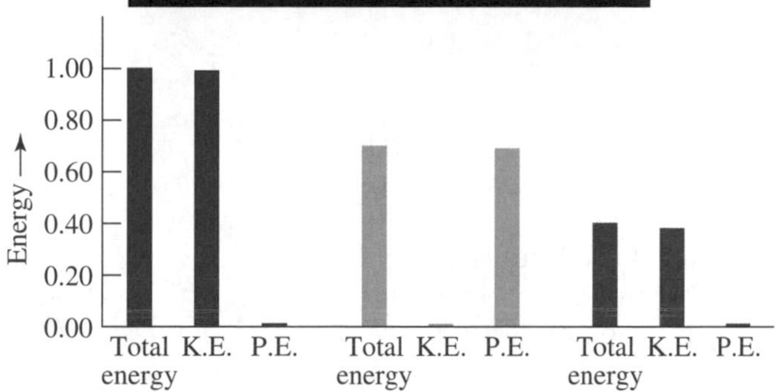

◀ FIGURE 4-2
Potential energy (P.E.) and kinetic energy (K.E.)
The energy of the bouncing tennis ball changes continuously from potential to kinetic energy and back again. The maximum potential energy is at the top of each bounce, and the maximum kinetic energy occurs at the moment of impact. The sum of P.E. and K.E. decreases with each bounce as the thermal energies of the ball and the surroundings increase. The ball soon comes to rest. The bar graph below the bouncing balls illustrates the relative contributions that the kinetic and potential energy make to the total energy for each ball position. The red bars correspond to the red ball, green bars correspond to the green ball and the blue bars correspond to the blue ball.

velocity (u) through the first equation below; work (w) is related to force [mass (m) $\times$ acceleration (a)] and distance (d) by the second equation.

$$e_k = \frac{1}{2}mu^2$$
$$w = m \times a \times d \qquad (4.1)$$

When mass, speed, acceleration, and distance are expressed in SI units, the units of both kinetic energy and work will be kg m^2 s^{-2}, which is the SI unit of energy—the *joule* (J). That is, 1 J = 1 kg m^2 s^{-2}.

The bouncing ball in Figure 4-2 suggests something about the nature of energy and work. First, to lift the ball to the starting position, we have to apply a force through a distance (to overcome the force of gravity). The work we do is "stored" in the ball as energy. This stored energy has the potential to do work when released and is therefore called potential energy. **Potential energy** is energy resulting from condition, position, or composition; it is an energy associated with forces of attraction or repulsion between objects.

◀ A unit of work, heat, and energy is the joule, but work and heat are not forms of energy but *processes* by which the energy of a system is changed.

When we release the ball, it is pulled toward Earth's center by the force of gravity—it falls. Potential energy is converted to kinetic energy during this fall. The kinetic energy reaches its maximum just as the ball strikes the surface. On its rebound, the kinetic energy of the ball decreases (the ball slows down), and its potential energy increases (the ball rises). If the collision of the ball with the surface were perfectly *elastic*, like collisions between molecules in the kinetic-molecular theory, the sum of the potential and kinetic energies of the ball would remain constant. The ball would reach the same maximum height on each rebound, and it would bounce forever. But we know this doesn't happen—the bouncing ball soon comes to rest. All the energy originally invested in the ball as potential energy (by raising it to its initial position) eventually appears as additional kinetic energy of the atoms and molecules that make up the ball, the surface, and the surrounding air. This kinetic energy associated with random molecular motion is called **thermal energy**.

In general, thermal energy is proportional to the temperature of a system, as suggested by the kinetic theory of gases. The more vigorous the motion of the molecules in the system, the hotter the sample and the greater is its thermal energy. However, the thermal energy of a system also depends on the number of particles present, so that a small sample at a high temperature (for example, a cup of coffee at 75 °C) may have less thermal energy than a larger sample at a lower temperature (for example, a swimming pool at 30 °C). Thus, temperature and thermal energy must be carefully distinguished. Equally important, we need to distinguish between energy changes produced by the action of forces through distances—*work*—and those involving the transfer of thermal energy—*heat*.

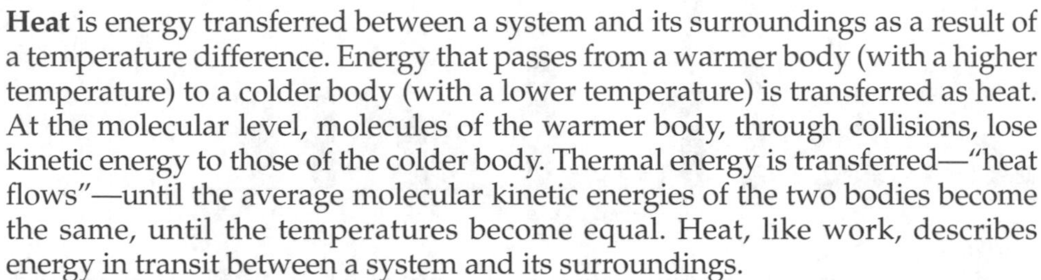

4-1 CONCEPT ASSESSMENT

Consider the following situations: a stick of dynamite exploding deep within a mountain cavern, the titration of an acid with base in a laboratory, and a cylinder of a steam engine with all of its valves closed. To what type of thermodynamic systems do these situations correspond?

4-2 Heat

▲ James Joule (1818–1889)—an amateur scientist
Joule's primary occupation was running a brewery, but he also conducted scientific research in a home laboratory. His precise measurements of quantities of heat formed the basis of the law of conservation of energy.

Heat is energy transferred between a system and its surroundings as a result of a temperature difference. Energy that passes from a warmer body (with a higher temperature) to a colder body (with a lower temperature) is transferred as heat. At the molecular level, molecules of the warmer body, through collisions, lose kinetic energy to those of the colder body. Thermal energy is transferred—"heat flows"—until the average molecular kinetic energies of the two bodies become the same, until the temperatures become equal. Heat, like work, describes energy in transit between a system and its surroundings.

Not only can heat transfer cause a change in temperature but, in some instances, it can also change a state of matter. For example, when a solid is heated, the molecules, atoms, or ions of the solid move with greater vigor and eventually break free from their neighbors by overcoming the attractive forces between them. Energy is required to overcome these attractive forces. During the process of melting, the temperature remains constant as a thermal energy transfer (heat) is used to overcome the forces holding the solid together. A process occurring at a constant temperature is said to be *isothermal*. Once a solid has melted completely, any further heat flow will raise the temperature of the resulting liquid.

Although we commonly use expressions like "heat is lost," "heat is gained," "heat flows," and "the system loses heat to the surroundings," you should not take these statements to mean that a system contains heat. It does not. The energy content of a system, as we shall see in Section 4-5, is a quantity called the *internal energy*. Heat is simply a form in which a quantity of energy may be *transferred* across a boundary between a system and its surroundings.

It is reasonable to expect that the quantity of heat, q, required to change the temperature of a substance depends on

- how much the temperature is to be changed
- the quantity of substance
- the nature of the substance (type of atoms or molecules)

Historically, the quantity of heat required to change the temperature of one gram of water by one degree Celsius has been called the **calorie** (**cal**). The calorie is a small unit of energy, and the unit *kilocalorie* (kcal) has also been widely used. The SI unit for heat is simply the basic SI energy unit, the joule (J).

$$1\ \text{cal} = 4.184\ \text{J} \qquad \textbf{(4.2)}$$

Although the joule is used almost exclusively in this text, the calorie is widely encountered in older scientific literature. In the United States, the kilocalorie is commonly used for measuring the energy content of foods.

The quantity of heat required to change the temperature of a system by one degree is called the **heat capacity** of the system. If the system is a mole of substance, the term *molar heat capacity* is applicable. If the system is one gram of substance, the applicable term is *specific heat capacity*, or more commonly, **specific heat** (sp ht).* The specific heats of substances are somewhat temperature dependent. At 25 °C, the specific heat of water is

$$\frac{4.18\ \text{J}}{\text{g}\ °\text{C}} = 4.18\ \text{J g}^{-1}\ °\text{C}^{-1} \qquad \textbf{(4.3)}$$

In Example 4-1, the objective is to calculate a quantity of heat based on the amount of a substance, the specific heat of that substance, and its temperature change.

EXAMPLE 4-1 Calculating a Quantity of Heat

How much heat is required to raise the temperature of 7.35 g of water from 21.0 to 98.0 °C? (Assume the specific heat of water is $4.18\ \text{J g}^{-1}\ °\text{C}^{-1}$ throughout this temperature range.)

Analyze

To answer this question, we begin by multiplying the specific heat capacity by the mass of water to obtain the heat capacity of the system. To find the amount of heat required to produce the desired temperature change we multiply the heat capacity by the temperature difference.

Solve

The specific heat is the heat capacity of 1.00 g water:

$$\frac{4.18\ \text{J}}{\text{g water}\ °\text{C}}$$

The heat capacity of the system (7.35 g water) is

$$7.35\ \cancel{\text{g water}} \times \frac{4.18\ \text{J}}{\cancel{\text{g water}}\ °\text{C}} = 30.7\frac{\text{J}}{°\text{C}}$$

The required temperature change in the system is

$$(98.0 - 21.0)\ °\text{C} = 77.0\ °\text{C}$$

The heat required to produce this temperature change is

$$30.7\frac{\text{J}}{\cancel{°\text{C}}} \times 77.0\ \cancel{°\text{C}} = 2.36 \times 10^3\ \text{J}$$

Assess

Remember that specific heat is a quantity that depends on the amount of material. Also note that the change in temperature is determined by subtracting the initial temperature from the final temperature. This will be important in determining the sign on the value you determine for heat, as will become apparent in the next section.

PRACTICE EXAMPLE A: How much heat, in kilojoules (kJ), is required to raise the temperature of 237 g of cold water from 4.0 to 37.0 °C (body temperature)?

PRACTICE EXAMPLE B: How much heat, in kilojoules (kJ), is required to raise the temperature of 2.50 kg Hg(l) from −20.0 to −6.0 °C? Assume a density of 13.6 g/mL and a molar heat capacity of $28.0\ \text{J mol}^{-1}\ °\text{C}^{-1}$ for Hg(l).

The line of reasoning used in Example 4-1 can be summarized in equation (4.5), which relates a quantity of heat to the mass of a substance, its specific heat, and the temperature change.

$$\text{quantity of heat} = \underbrace{\text{mass of substance} \times \text{specific heat}}_{\text{heat capacity} = C} \times \text{temperature change} \qquad \textbf{(4.4)}$$

$$q = m \times \text{specific heat} \times \Delta T = C \times \Delta T \qquad \textbf{(4.5)}$$

◀ The Greek letter delta, Δ, indicates a *change* in some quantity.

*The original meaning of specific heat was that of a *ratio*: the quantity of heat required to change the temperature of a mass of substance divided by the quantity of heat required to produce the same temperature change in the same mass of water—this definition would make specific heat dimensionless. The meaning given here is more commonly used.

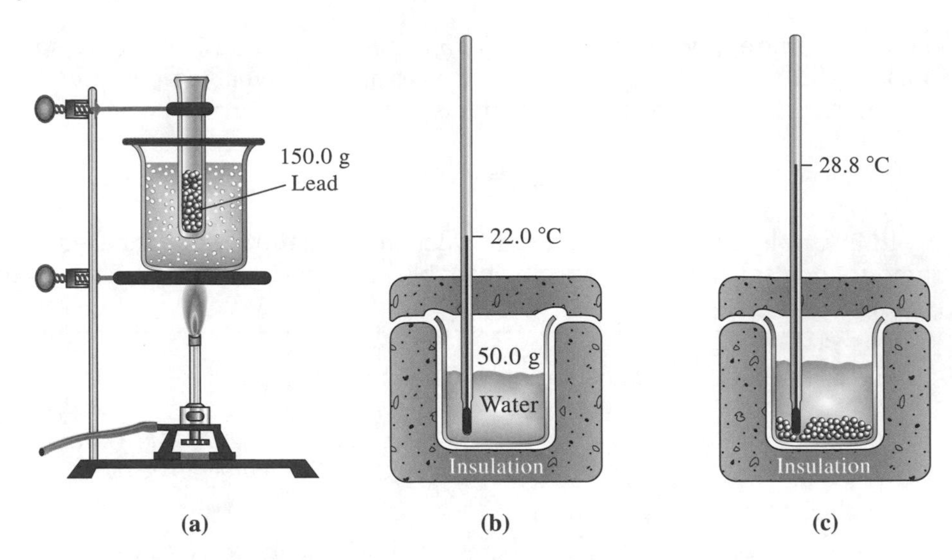

▶ FIGURE 4-3
Determining the specific heat of lead—Example 4-2 illustrated
(a) A 150.0 g sample of lead is heated to the temperature of boiling water (100.0 °C). **(b)** A 50.0 g sample of water is added to a thermally insulated beaker, and its temperature is found to be 22.0 °C. **(c)** The hot lead is dumped into the cold water, and the temperature of the final lead–water mixture is 28.8 °C.

▶ The symbol > means "greater than," and < means "less than."

In equation (4.5), the temperature change is expressed as $\Delta T = T_f - T_i$, where T_f is the final temperature and T_i is the initial temperature. When the temperature of a system increases ($T_f > T_i$), ΔT is *positive*. A positive q signifies that heat is absorbed or *gained* by the system. When the temperature of a system decreases ($T_f < T_i$), ΔT is *negative*. A negative q signifies that heat is evolved or *lost* by the system.

Another idea that enters into calculations of quantities of heat is the **law of conservation of energy**: In interactions between a system and its surroundings, the total energy remains *constant*—energy is neither created nor destroyed. Applied to the exchange of heat, this means that

$$q_{\text{system}} + q_{\text{surroundings}} = 0 \tag{4.6}$$

Thus, heat *gained* by a system is *lost* by its surroundings, and vice versa.

$$q_{\text{system}} = -q_{\text{surroundings}} \tag{4.7}$$

Experimental Determination of Specific Heats

Let us consider how the law of conservation of energy is used in the experiment outlined in Figure 4-3. The object is to determine the specific heat of lead. The transfer of energy, as heat, from the lead to the cooler water causes the temperature of the lead to decrease and that of the water to increase, until the lead and water are at the same temperature. Either the lead or the water can be considered the system. If we consider lead to be the system, we can write $q_{\text{lead}} = q_{\text{system}}$. Furthermore, if the lead and water are maintained in a thermally insulated enclosure, we can assume that $q_{\text{water}} = q_{\text{surroundings}}$. Then, applying equation (4.7), we have

$$q_{\text{lead}} = -q_{\text{water}} \tag{4.8}$$

We complete the calculation in Example 4-2.

EXAMPLE 4-2 Determining a Specific Heat from Experimental Data

Use data presented in Figure 4-3 to calculate the specific heat of lead.

Analyze

Keep in mind that if we know any four of the five quantities—q, m, specific heat, T_f, T_i—we can solve equation (4.5) for the remaining one. We know from Figure 4-3 that a known quantity of lead is heated and then dumped into a known amount of water at a known temperature, which is the initial temperature. Once the system comes to equilibrium, the water temperature is the final temperature. In this type of question, we will use equation (4.5).

Solve

First, use equation (4.5) to calculate q_{water}.

$$q_{water} = 50.0 \text{ g water} \times \frac{4.18 \text{ J}}{\text{g water °C}} \times (28.8 - 22.0) \text{ °C} = 1.4 \times 10^3 \text{ J}$$

From equation (4.8) we can write

$$q_{lead} = -q_{water} = -1.4 \times 10^3 \text{ J}$$

Now, from equation (4.5) again, we obtain

$$q_{lead} = 150.0 \text{ g lead} \times \text{specific heat of lead} \times (28.8 - 100.0) \text{ °C} = -1.4 \times 10^3 \text{ J}$$

$$\text{specific heat of lead} = \frac{-1.4 \times 10^3 \text{ J}}{150.0 \text{ g lead} \times (28.8 - 100.0) \text{ °C}} = \frac{-1.4 \times 10^3 \text{ J}}{150.0 \text{ g lead} \times -71.2 \text{ °C}} = 0.13 \text{ J g}^{-1} \text{ °C}^{-1}$$

Assess

The key concept to recognize is that energy, in the form of heat, flowed from the lead, which is our system, to the water, which is part of the surroundings. A quick way to make sure that we have done the problem correctly is to check the sign on the final answer. For specific heat, the sign should always be positive and have the units of $\text{J g}^{-1} \text{ °C}^{-1}$.

PRACTICE EXAMPLE A: When 1.00 kg lead (specific heat $= 0.13 \text{ J g}^{-1} \text{ °C}^{-1}$) at 100.0 °C is added to a quantity of water at 28.5 °C, the final temperature of the lead–water mixture is 35.2 °C. What is the mass of water present?

PRACTICE EXAMPLE B: A 100.0 g copper sample (specific heat $= 0.385 \text{ J g}^{-1} \text{ °C}^{-1}$) at 100.0 °C is added to 50.0 g water at 26.5 °C. What is the final temperature of the copper–water mixture?

4-2 CONCEPT ASSESSMENT

With a minimum of calculation, estimate the final temperature reached when 100.0 mL of water at 10.00 °C is added to 200.0 mL of water at 70.00 °C. What basic principle did you use and what assumptions did you make in arriving at this estimate?

Specific Heats of Some Substances

Table 4.1 lists specific heats of some substances. For many substances, the specific heat is less than $1 \text{ J g}^{-1} \text{ °C}^{-1}$. A few substances, $H_2O(l)$ in particular, have specific heats that are substantially larger. Can we explain why liquid water has a high specific heat? The answer is most certainly yes, but the explanation relies on concepts we have not yet discussed. The fact that water molecules form hydrogen bonds is an important part of the reason why water has a large specific heat value.

Because of their greater complexity at the molecular level, compounds generally have more ways of storing internal energy than do the elements; they tend to have higher specific heats. Water, for example, has a specific heat that is more than 30 times as great as that of lead. We need a much larger quantity of heat to change the temperature of a sample of water than of an equal mass of a metal.

An environmental consequence of the high specific heat of water is found in the effect of large lakes on local climates. Because a lake takes much longer to heat up in summer and cool down in winter than other types of terrain, lakeside communities tend to be cooler in summer and warmer in winter than communities more distant from the lake.

4-3 CONCEPT ASSESSMENT

Two objects of the same mass absorb the same amount of heat when heated in a flame, but the temperature of one object increases more than the temperature of the other. Which object has the greater specific heat?

TABLE 4.1 Some Specific Heat Values, $\text{J g}^{-1} \text{ °C}^{-1}$

Substance	Specific heat
Solids	
$Pb(s)$	0.130
$Cu(s)$	0.385
$Fe(s)$	0.449
$S_8(s)$	0.708
$P_4(s)$	0.769
$Al(s)$	0.897
$Mg(s)$	1.023
$H_2O(s)$	2.11
Liquids	
$Hg(l)$	0.140
$Br_2(l)$	0.474
$CCl_4(l)$	0.850
$CH_3COOH(l)$	2.15
$CH_3CH_2OH(l)$	2.44
$H_2O(l)$	4.18
Gases	
$CO_2(g)$	0.843
$N_2(g)$	1.040
$C_3H_8(g)$	1.67
$NH_3(g)$	2.06
$H_2O(g)$	2.08

Source: CRC Handbook of Chemistry and Physics, 90th ed., David R. Lide (ed.), Boca Raton, FL: Taylor & Francis Group, 2010.

4-3 Heats of Reaction and Calorimetry

In Section 4-1, we introduced the notion of *thermal energy*—kinetic energy associated with random molecular motion. Another type of energy that contributes to the internal energy of a system is **chemical energy**. This is energy associated with chemical bonds and intermolecular attractions. If we think of a chemical reaction as a process in which some chemical bonds are broken and others are formed, then, in general, we expect the chemical energy of a system to change as a result of a reaction. Furthermore, we might expect some of this energy change to appear as heat. A **heat of reaction**, q_{rxn}, is the quantity of heat exchanged between a system and its surroundings when a chemical reaction occurs within the system at *constant temperature*. One of the most common reactions studied is the combustion reaction. This is such a common reaction that we often refer to the *heat of combustion* when describing the heat released by a combustion reaction.

If a reaction occurs in an *isolated* system, that is, one that exchanges no matter or energy with its surroundings, the reaction produces a change in the thermal energy of the system—the temperature either increases or decreases. Imagine that the previously isolated system is allowed to interact with its surroundings. The heat of reaction is the quantity of heat exchanged between the system and its surroundings as the system is restored to its initial temperature (Fig. 4-4). In actual practice, we do not physically restore the system to its initial temperature. Instead, we calculate the quantity of heat that *would be* exchanged in this restoration. To do this, a probe (thermometer) is placed within the system to record the temperature change produced by the reaction. Then, we use the temperature change and other system data to calculate the heat of reaction that would have occurred at constant temperature.

Two widely used terms related to heats of reaction are exothermic and endothermic reactions. An **exothermic reaction** is one that produces a temperature increase in an isolated system or, in a nonisolated system, gives off heat to the surroundings. For an exothermic reaction, the heat of reaction is a negative quantity ($q_{rxn} < 0$). In an **endothermic reaction**, the corresponding situation is a temperature decrease in an isolated system or a gain of heat from the surroundings by a nonisolated system. In this case, the heat of reaction is a positive quantity ($q_{rxn} > 0$). Heats of reaction are experimentally determined in a **calorimeter**, a device for measuring quantities of heat. We will consider two types of calorimeters in this section, and we will treat both of them as *isolated* systems.

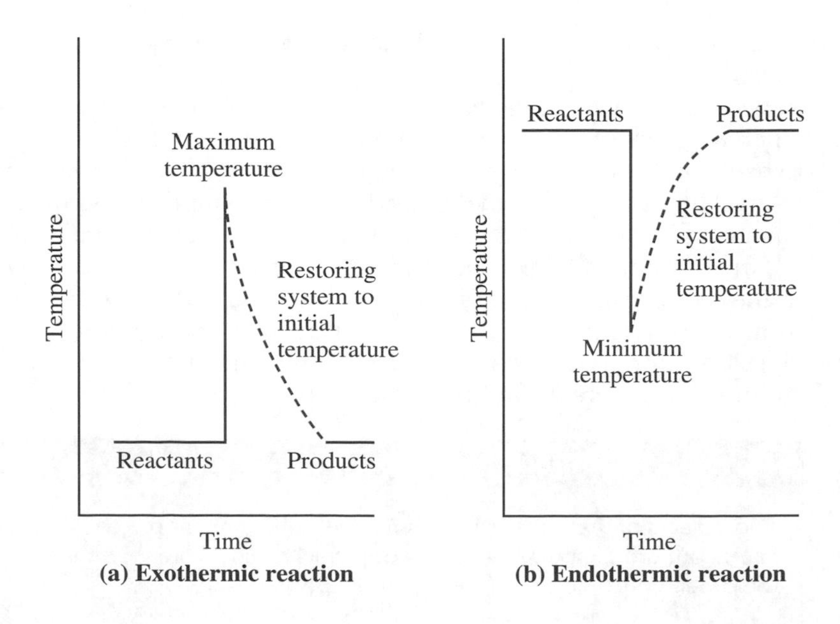

▶ FIGURE 4-4
Conceptualizing a heat of reaction at constant temperature
The solid lines indicate the initial temperature and the **(a)** maximum and **(b)** minimum temperature reached in an isolated system, in an exothermic and an endothermic reaction, respectively. The broken lines represent pathways to restoring the system to the initial temperature. The heat of reaction is the heat lost or gained by the system in this restoration.

(a)

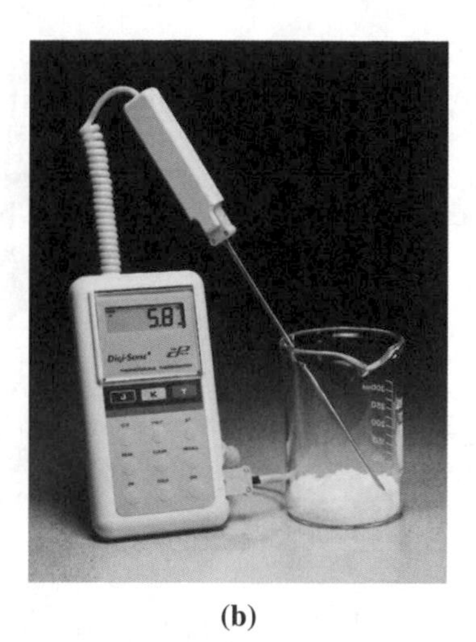

(b)

◀ **Exothermic and endothermic reactions**
(a) An exothermic reaction. Slaked lime, $Ca(OH)_2$, is produced by the action of water on quicklime, (CaO). The reactants are mixed at room temperature, but the temperature of the mixture rises to 40.5 °C.

$$CaO(s) + H_2O(l) \longrightarrow Ca(OH)_2\,(s)$$

(b) An endothermic reaction. $Ba(OH)_2 \cdot 8\,H_2O(s)$ and $NH_4Cl(s)$ are mixed at room temperature, and the temperature falls to 5.8 °C in the reaction.

$$Ba(OH)_2 \cdot 8\,H_2O(s) + 2\,NH_4Cl(s) \longrightarrow BaCl_2 \cdot 2H_2O(s) + 2\,NH_3(aq) + 8\,H_2O(l)$$

Bomb Calorimetry

Figure 4-5 shows a **bomb calorimeter**, which is ideally suited for measuring the heat evolved in a combustion reaction. The system is everything within the double-walled outer jacket of the calorimeter. This includes the bomb and its contents, the water in which the bomb is immersed, the thermometer, the stirrer, and so on. The system is *isolated* from its surroundings. When the combustion reaction occurs, chemical energy is converted to thermal energy, and the temperature of the system rises. The heat of reaction, as described earlier, is the quantity of heat that the system would have to *lose* to its surroundings to be restored to its initial temperature. This quantity of heat, in turn, is just the *negative* of the thermal energy gained by the calorimeter and its contents ($q_{calorim}$).

$$q_{rxn} = -q_{calorim}\;(\text{where } q_{calorim} = q_{bomb} + q_{water} \cdots) \qquad \textbf{(4.9)}$$

KEEP IN MIND

that the temperature of a reaction mixture usually changes during a reaction, so the mixture must be returned to the initial temperature (actually or hypothetically) before we assess how much heat is exchanged with the surroundings.

If the calorimeter is assembled in exactly the same way each time we use it—that is, use the same bomb, the same quantity of water, and so on—we can define a *heat capacity of the calorimeter*. This is the quantity of heat required to raise the temperature of the calorimeter assembly by one degree Celsius. When this heat capacity is multiplied by the observed temperature change, we get $q_{calorim}$.

◀ The heat capacity of a bomb calorimeter must be determined by experiment.

$$q_{calorim} = \text{heat capacity of calorim} \times \Delta T \qquad \textbf{(4.10)}$$

And from $q_{calorim}$, we then establish q_{rxn}, as in Example 4-3, where we determine the heat of combustion of sucrose (table sugar).

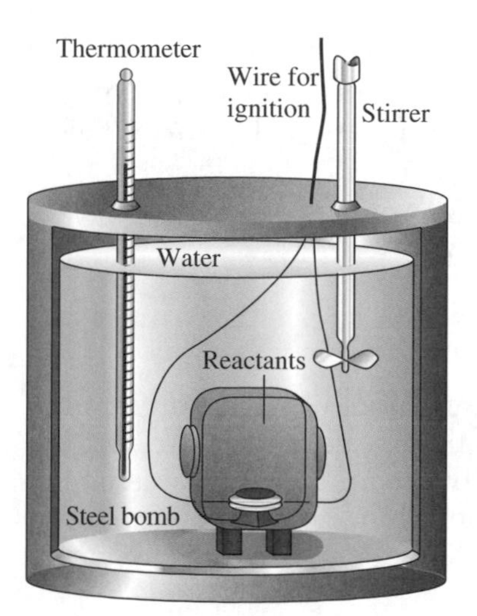

◀ FIGURE 4-5
A bomb calorimeter assembly
An iron wire is embedded in the sample in the lower half of the bomb. The bomb is assembled and filled with $O_2(g)$ at high pressure. The assembled bomb is immersed in water in the calorimeter, and the initial temperature is measured. A short pulse of electric current heats the sample, causing it to ignite. The final temperature of the calorimeter assembly is determined after the combustion. Because the bomb confines the reaction mixture to a fixed volume, the reaction is said to occur at *constant volume*.

EXAMPLE 4-3 Using Bomb Calorimetry Data to Determine a Heat of Reaction

The combustion of 1.010 g sucrose, $C_{12}H_{22}O_{11}$, in a bomb calorimeter causes the temperature to rise from 24.92 to 28.33 °C. The heat capacity of the calorimeter assembly is 4.90 kJ/°C. **(a)** What is the heat of combustion of sucrose expressed in kilojoules per mole of $C_{12}H_{22}O_{11}$? **(b)** Verify the claim of sugar producers that one teaspoon of sugar (about 4.8 g) contains only 19 Calories.

Analyze

We are given a specific heat and two temperatures, the initial and the final, which indicate that we are to use equation (4.5). In these kinds of experiments one obtains the amount of heat generated by the reaction by measuring the temperature change in the surroundings. This means that $q_{rxn} = -q_{calorim}$.

Solve

(a) Calculate $q_{calorim}$ with equation (4.10).

$$q_{calorim} = 4.90\ \text{kJ/°C} \times (28.33 - 24.92)\ \text{°C} = (4.90 \times 3.41)\ \text{kJ} = 16.7\ \text{kJ}$$

Now, using equation (4.9), we get

$$q_{rxn} = -q_{calorim} = -16.7\ \text{kJ}$$

This is the heat of combustion of the 1.010 g sample.
Per gram $C_{12}H_{22}O_{11}$:

$$q_{rxn} = \frac{-16.7\ \text{kJ}}{1.010\ \text{g}\ C_{12}H_{22}O_{11}} = -16.5\ \text{kJ/g}\ C_{12}H_{22}O_{11}$$

Per mole $C_{12}H_{22}O_{11}$:

$$q_{rxn} = \frac{-16.5\ \text{kJ}}{\text{g}\ C_{12}H_{22}O_{11}} \times \frac{342.3\ \text{g}\ C_{12}H_{22}O_{11}}{1\ \text{mol}\ C_{12}H_{22}O_{11}} = -5.65 \times 10^3\ \text{kJ/mol}\ C_{12}H_{22}O_{11}$$

(b) To determine the caloric content of sucrose, we can use the heat of combustion per gram of sucrose determined in part **(a)**, together with a factor to convert from kilojoules to kilocalories. (Because 1 cal = 4.184 J, 1 kcal = 4.184 kJ.)

$$?\ \text{kcal} = \frac{4.8\ \text{g}\ C_{12}H_{22}O_{11}}{\text{tsp}} \times \frac{-16.5\ \text{kJ}}{\text{g}\ C_{12}H_{22}O_{11}} \times \frac{1\ \text{kcal}}{4.184\ \text{kJ}} = \frac{-19\ \text{kcal}}{\text{tsp}}$$

1 food Calorie (1 Calorie with a capital C) is actually 1000 cal, or 1 kcal. Therefore, 19 kcal = 19 Calories. The claim is justified.

Assess

A combustion reaction is an exothermic reaction, which means that energy flows, in the form of heat, from the reaction system to the surroundings. Therefore, the q for a combustion reaction is negative.

PRACTICE EXAMPLE A: Vanillin is a natural constituent of vanilla. It is also manufactured for use in artificial vanilla flavoring. The combustion of 1.013 g of vanillin, $C_8H_8O_3$, in the same bomb calorimeter as in Example 4-3 causes the temperature to rise from 24.89 to 30.09 °C. What is the heat of combustion of vanillin, expressed in kilojoules per mole?

PRACTICE EXAMPLE B: The heat of combustion of benzoic acid is −26.42 kJ/g. The combustion of a 1.176 g sample of benzoic acid causes a temperature *increase* of 4.96°C in a bomb calorimeter assembly. What is the heat capacity of the assembly?

The "Coffee-Cup" Calorimeter

In the general chemistry laboratory you are much more likely to run into the simple calorimeter pictured in Figure 4-6 than a bomb calorimeter. We mix the reactants (generally in aqueous solution) in a Styrofoam cup and measure the temperature change. Styrofoam is a good heat insulator, so there is very little heat transfer between the cup and the surrounding air. We treat the system—the cup and its contents—as an *isolated* system.

As with the bomb calorimeter, the heat of reaction is defined as the quantity of heat that would be exchanged with the surroundings in restoring the calorimeter to its initial temperature. But, again, the calorimeter is not physically restored to its initial conditions. We simply take the heat of reaction to be the *negative* of the quantity of heat producing the temperature change in the calorimeter. That is, we use equation (4.9): $q_{rxn} = -q_{calorim}$.

In Example 4-4, we make certain assumptions to simplify the calculation, but for more precise measurements, these assumptions would not be made (see Exercise 25).

EXAMPLE 4-4 Determining a Heat of Reaction from Calorimetric Data

In the neutralization of a strong acid with a strong base, the essential reaction is the combination of $H^+(aq)$ and $OH^-(aq)$ to form water.

$$H^+(aq) + OH^-(aq) \longrightarrow H_2O(l)$$

Two solutions, 25.00 mL of 2.50 M HCl(aq) and 25.00 mL of 2.50 M NaOH(aq), both initially at 21.1 °C, are added to a Styrofoam-cup calorimeter and allowed to react. The temperature rises to 37.8 °C. Determine the heat of the neutralization reaction, expressed per mole of H_2O formed. Is the reaction endothermic or exothermic?

Analyze

In addition to assuming that the calorimeter is an isolated system, assume that all there is in the system to absorb heat is 50.00 mL of water. This assumption ignores the fact that 0.0625 mol each of NaCl and H_2O are formed in the reaction, that the density of the resulting NaCl(aq) is not exactly 1.00 g/mL, and that its specific heat is not exactly $4.18\ \text{J g}^{-1}\,{}^\circ\text{C}^{-1}$. Also, ignore the small heat capacity of the Styrofoam cup itself.

Because the reaction is a neutralization reaction, let us call the heat of reaction q_{neutr}. Now, according to equation (4.9), $q_{neutr} = -q_{calorim}$, and if we make the assumptions described above, we can solve the problem.

Solve

We begin with

$$q_{calorim} = 50.00\ \text{mL} \times \frac{1.00\ \text{g}}{\text{mL}} \times \frac{4.18\ \text{J}}{\text{g}\ {}^\circ\text{C}} \times (37.8 - 21.1)\ {}^\circ\text{C} = 3.5 \times 10^3\ \text{J}$$

$$q_{neutr} = -q_{calorim} = -3.5 \times 10^3\ \text{J} = -3.5\ \text{kJ}$$

In 25.00 mL of 2.50 M HCl, the amount of H^+ is

$$?\ \text{mol H}^+ = 25.00\ \text{mL} \times \frac{1\ \text{L}}{1000\ \text{mL}} \times \frac{2.50\ \text{mol}}{1\ \text{L}} \times \frac{1\ \text{mol H}^+}{1\ \text{mol HCl}} = 0.0625\ \text{mol H}^+$$

Similarly, in 25.00 mL of 2.50 M NaOH there is 0.0625 mol OH^-. Thus, the H^+ and the OH^- combine to form 0.0625 mol H_2O. (The two reactants are in *stoichiometric* proportions; neither is in excess.)

The amount of heat produced per mole of H_2O is

$$q_{neutr} = \frac{-3.5\ \text{kJ}}{0.0625\ \text{mol H}_2\text{O}} = -56\ \text{kJ/mol H}_2\text{O}$$

Assess

Because q_{neutr} is a *negative* quantity, the neutralization reaction is *exothermic*. Even though, in this example, we considered a specific reaction, the result $q_{neutr} = -56$ kJ/mol is more general. We will obtain the same value of q_{neutr} by considering any strong acid-strong base reaction because the net ionic equation is the same for all strong acid-strong base reactions.

PRACTICE EXAMPLE A: Two solutions, 100.0 mL of 1.00 M $AgNO_3$(aq) and 100.0 mL of 1.00 M NaCl(aq), both initially at 22.4 °C, are added to a Styrofoam-cup calorimeter and allowed to react. The temperature rises to 30.2 °C. Determine q_{rxn} per mole of AgCl(s) in the reaction.

$$Ag^+(aq) + Cl^-(aq) \longrightarrow AgCl(s)$$

PRACTICE EXAMPLE B: Two solutions, 100.0 mL of 1.020 M HCl and 50.0 mL of 1.988 M NaOH, both initially at 24.52 °C, are mixed in a Styrofoam-cup calorimeter. What will be the final temperature of the mixture? Make the same assumptions, and use the heat of neutralization established in Example 4-4. [*Hint:* Which is the limiting reactant?]

▲ FIGURE 4-6
A Styrofoam "coffee-cup" calorimeter
The reaction mixture is in the inner cup. The outer cup provides additional thermal insulation from the surrounding air. The cup is closed off with a cork stopper through which a thermometer and a stirrer are inserted and immersed into the reaction mixture. The reaction in the calorimeter occurs under the *constant pressure* of the atmosphere. We consider the difference between constant-volume and constant-pressure reactions in Section 4-6.

4-4 CONCEPT ASSESSMENT

How do we determine the specific heat of the bomb calorimeter or the solution calorimeter (coffee-cup calorimeter)?

4-4 Work

We have just learned that heat effects generally accompany chemical reactions. In some reactions, work is also involved—that is, the system may do work on its surroundings or vice versa. Consider the decomposition of potassium chlorate to potassium chloride and oxygen. Suppose that this decomposition is carried out in the strange vessel pictured in Figure 4-7. The walls of the container resist moving under the pressure of the expanding $O_2(g)$ except for the piston that closes off the cylindrical top of the vessel. The pressure of the $O_2(g)$ exceeds the atmospheric pressure and the piston is lifted—the system does work on the surroundings. Can you see that even if the piston were removed, work still would be done as the expanding $O_2(g)$ pushed aside other atmospheric gases? Work involved in the expansion or compression of gases is called **pressure–volume work**. Pressure–volume, or *P–V*, work is the type of work performed by explosives and by the gases formed in the combustion of gasoline in an automobile engine.

Now let us switch to a somewhat simpler situation to see how to calculate a quantity of *P–V* work.

In the hypothetical apparatus pictured in Figure 4-8(a), a weightless piston is attached to a weightless wire support, to which is attached a weightless pan. On the pan are two identical weights just sufficient to stop the gas from expanding. The gas is confined by the cylinder walls and piston, and the space above the piston is a vacuum. The cylinder is contained in a constant-temperature water bath, which keeps the temperature of the gas constant. Now imagine that one of the two weights is removed, leaving half the original mass on the pan. Let us call this remaining mass M. The gas will expand and the remaining weight will move against gravity, the situation represented by Figure 4-8(b). After the expansion, we find that the piston has risen through a vertical distance, Δh; that the volume of gas has doubled; and that the pressure of the gas has decreased.

Now let us see how pressure and volume enter into calculating how much *pressure–volume* work the expanding gas does. First we can calculate the work done by the gas in moving the weight of mass M through a displacement Δh. Recall from equation (4.1) that the work can be calculated by

$$\text{work } (w) = \text{force } (M \times g) \times \text{distance } (\Delta h) = -M \times g \times \Delta h$$

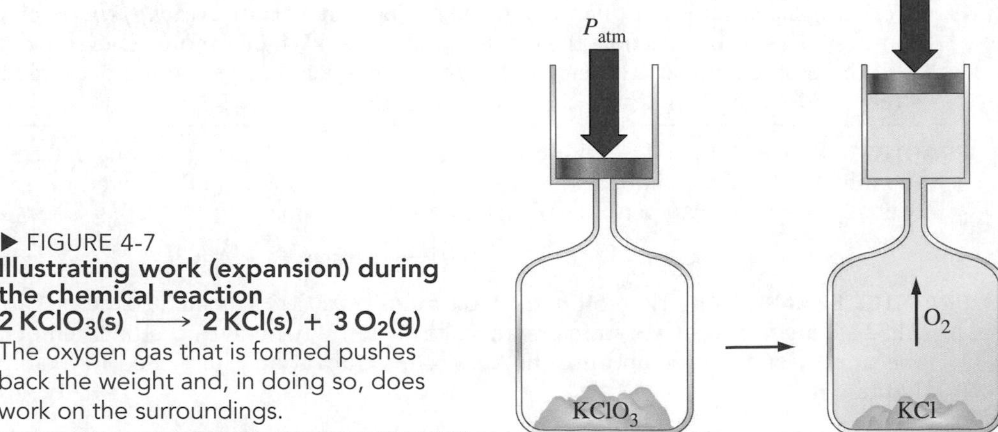

▶ FIGURE 4-7
Illustrating work (expansion) during the chemical reaction
$2\,KClO_3(s) \longrightarrow 2\,KCl(s) + 3\,O_2(g)$
The oxygen gas that is formed pushes back the weight and, in doing so, does work on the surroundings.

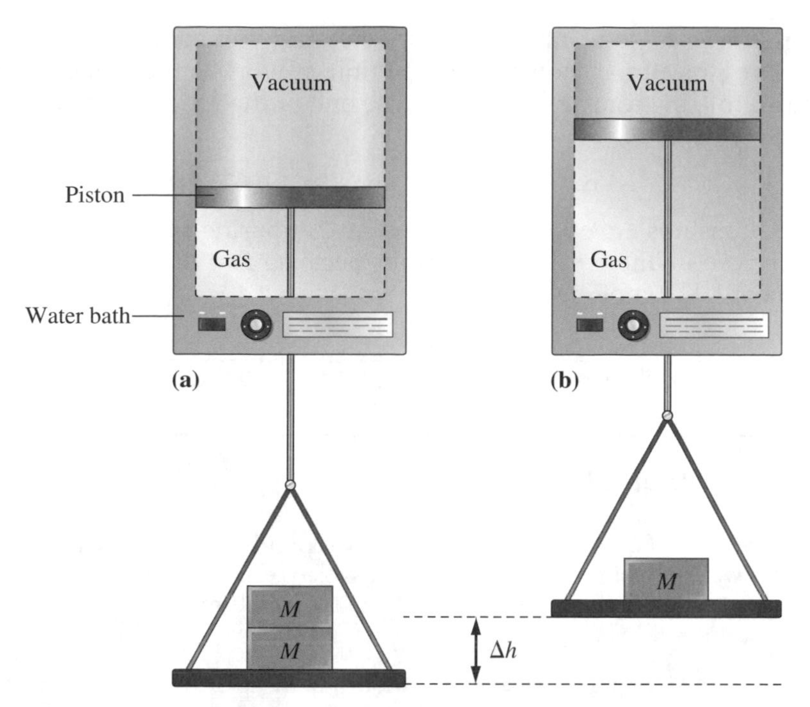

▲ FIGURE 4-8
Pressure–volume work
(a) In this hypothetical apparatus, a gas is confined by a massless piston of area A. A massless wire is attached to the piston and the gas is held back by two weights with a combined mass of $2M$ resting on the massless pan. The cylinder is immersed in a large water bath in order to keep the gas temperature constant. The initial state of the gas is $P_i = 2\,Mg/A$ with a volume V_i at temperature, T. **(b)** When the external pressure on the confined gas is suddenly lowered by removing one of the weights the gas expands, pushing the piston up by the distance, Δh. The increase in volume of the gas (ΔV) is the product of the cross-sectional area of the cylinder (A) and the distance (Δh). The final state of the gas is $P_f = Mg/A$, V_f, and T.

The magnitude of the force exerted by the weight is $M \times g$, where g is the acceleration due to gravity. The negative sign appears because the force is acting in a direction opposite to the piston's direction of motion.

Now recall equation (6.1)—pressure = force $(M \times g)$/area (A)—so that if the expression for work is multiplied by A/A we get

$$w = -\frac{M \times g}{A} \times \Delta h \times A = -P_{ext}\Delta V \quad \textbf{(4.11)}$$

The "pressure" part of the pressure–volume work is seen to be the external pressure (P_{ext}) on the gas, which in our thought experiment is equal to the weight pulling down on the piston and is given by Mg/A. Note that the product of the area (A) and height (Δh) is equal to a volume—the volume change, ΔV, produced by the expansion.

Two significant features to note in equation (4.11) are the *negative* sign and the factor P_{ext}. The negative sign is necessary to conform to sign conventions that we will introduce in the next section. When a gas expands, ΔV is positive and w is negative, signifying that energy leaves the system as work. When a gas is compressed, ΔV is negative and w is positive, signifying that energy (as work) enters the system. P_{ext} is the *external* pressure—the pressure against which a system expands or the applied pressure that compresses a system. In many instances the internal pressure in a system will be essentially equal to the external pressure, in which case the pressure in equation (4.11) is expressed simply as P.

◀ Work is negative when energy is transferred out of the system and is positive when energy is transferred into the system. This is consistent with the signs associated with the heat of a reaction (q) during endothermic and exothermic processes.

▶ The unit atm L, often written as L atm, is the liter-atmosphere. The use of this unit still persists.

If pressure is stated in bars or atmospheres and volume in liters, the unit of work is bar L or atm L. However, the SI unit of work is the joule. To convert from bar L to J, or from atm L to J, we use one of the following relationships, both of which are *exact*.

$$1 \text{ bar L} = 100 \text{ J} \qquad 1 \text{ atm L} = 101.325 \text{ J}$$

These relationships are easily established by comparing values of the gas constant, R, given in Table 6.3. For example, because $R = 8.3145 \text{ J K}^{-1} \text{ mol}^{-1} = 0.083145 \text{ bar L K}^{-1} \text{ mol}^{-1}$, we have

$$\frac{8.3145 \text{ J } \cancel{\text{K}^{-1}} \cancel{\text{mol}^{-1}}}{0.083145 \text{ bar L } \cancel{\text{K}^{-1}} \cancel{\text{mol}^{-1}}} = 100 \frac{\text{J}}{\text{bar L}}$$

EXAMPLE 4-5 Calculating Pressure–Volume Work

Suppose the gas in Figure 4-8 is 0.100 mol He at 298 K, the two weights correspond to an external pressure of 2.40 atm in Figure 4-8(a), and the single weight in Figure 4-8(b) corresponds to an external pressure of 1.20 atm. How much work, in joules, is associated with the gas expansion at constant temperature?

Analyze

We are given enough data to calculate the initial and final gas volumes (note that the identity of the gas does not enter into the calculations because we are assuming ideal gas behavior). With these volumes, we can obtain ΔV. The external pressure in the pressure–volume work is the *final* pressure: 1.20 atm. The product $-P_{ext} \times \Delta V$ must be multiplied by a factor to convert work in liter-atmospheres to work in joules.

Solve

First calculate the initial and final volumes.

$$V_{\text{initial}} = \frac{nRT}{P_i} = \frac{0.100 \text{ mol} \times 0.0821 \text{ L atm mol}^{-1} \text{K}^{-1} \times 298 \text{ K}}{2.40 \text{ atm}} = 1.02 \text{ L}$$

$$V_{\text{final}} = \frac{nRT}{P_f} = \frac{0.100 \text{ mol} \times 0.0821 \text{ L atm mol}^{-1} \text{K}^{-1} \times 298 \text{ K}}{1.20 \text{ atm}} = 2.04 \text{ L}$$

$$\Delta V = V_f - V_i = 2.04 \text{ L} - 1.02 \text{ L} = 1.02 \text{ L}$$

$$w = -P_{ext} \times \Delta V = -1.20 \text{ atm} \times 1.02 \text{ L} \times \frac{101 \text{ J}}{1 \text{ L atm}} = -1.24 \times 10^2 \text{ J}$$

Assess

The negative value signifies that the expanding gas (i.e., the system) does work on its surroundings. Keep in mind that the ideal gas equation embodies Boyle's law: The volume of a fixed amount of gas at a fixed temperature is inversely proportional to the pressure. Thus, in Example 4-5 we could simply write that

$$V_f = 1.02 \text{ L} \times \frac{2.40 \text{ atm}}{1.20 \text{ atm}}$$

$$V_f = 2.04 \text{ L}$$

PRACTICE EXAMPLE A: How much work, in joules, is involved when 0.225 mol N_2 at a constant temperature of 23 °C is allowed to expand by 1.50 L in volume against an external pressure of 0.750 atm? [*Hint:* How much of this information is required?]

PRACTICE EXAMPLE B: How much work is done, in joules, when an external pressure of 2.50 atm is applied, at a constant temperature of 20.0 °C, to 50.0 g $N_2(g)$ in a 75.0 L cylinder? The cylinder is like that shown in Figure 4-8.

4-5 CONCEPT ASSESSMENT

A gas in a 1.0 L closed cylinder has an initial pressure of 10.0 bar. It has a final pressure of 5.0 bar. The volume of the cylinder remained constant during this time. What form of energy was transferred across the boundary to cause this change? In which direction did the energy flow?

This result confirms that 1 bar L = 100 J. How do we establish that 1 atm L is exactly 101.325 J? Recall that 1 atm is exactly 1.01325 bar (see Table 2.1). Thus, 1 atm L = 1.01325 bar L = 1.01325 × 100 J = 101.325 J.

4-5 The First Law of Thermodynamics

The absorption or evolution of heat and the performance of work require changes in the energy of a system and its surroundings. When considering the energy of a system, we use the concept of internal energy and how heat and work are related to it.

Internal energy, U, is the total energy (both kinetic and potential) in a system, including *translational kinetic energy* of molecules, the energy associated with molecular rotations and vibrations, the energy stored in chemical bonds and intermolecular attractions, and the energy associated with electrons in atoms. Some of these forms of internal energy are illustrated in Figure 4-9. Internal energy also includes energy associated with the interactions of protons and neutrons in atomic nuclei, although this component is unchanged in chemical reactions. A system contains *only* internal energy. A system does not contain energy in the form of heat or work. Heat and work are the means by which a system exchanges energy with its surroundings. *Heat and work exist only during a change in the system.* The relationship between heat (q), work (w), and changes in internal energy (ΔU) is dictated by the law of conservation of energy, expressed in the form known as the **first law of thermodynamics.**

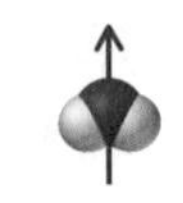
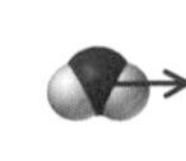

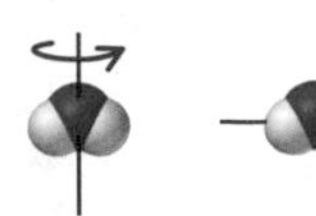

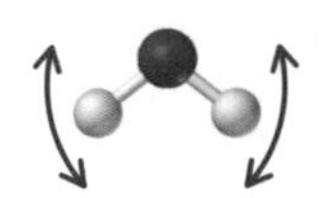

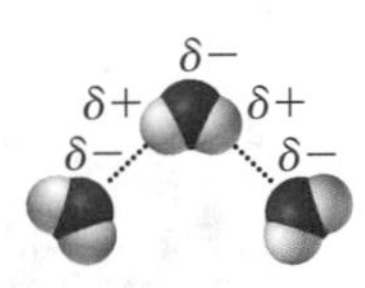

▲ FIGURE 4-9
Some contributions to the internal energy of a system
The models represent water molecules, and the arrows represent the types of motion they can undergo. In the intermolecular attractions between water molecules, the symbols $\delta+$ and $\delta-$ signify a separation of charge, producing centers of positive and negative charge that are smaller than ionic charges.

$$\Delta U = q + w \qquad (4.12)$$

An isolated system is unable to exchange either heat or work with its surroundings, so that $\Delta U_{\text{isolated system}} = 0$, and we can say

The energy of an isolated system is constant.

In using equation (4.12) we must keep these important points in mind.

- Any energy *entering* the system carries a *positive* sign. Thus, if heat is *absorbed* by the system, $q > 0$. If work is done *on* the system, $w > 0$.
- Any energy *leaving* the system carries a *negative* sign. Thus, if heat is *given off* by the system, $q < 0$. If work is done *by* the system, $w < 0$.
- In general, the internal energy of a system changes as a result of energy entering or leaving the system as heat and/or work. If, on balance, more energy enters the system than leaves, ΔU is *positive*. If more energy leaves than enters, ΔU is *negative*.
- A consequence of $\Delta U_{\text{isolated system}} = 0$ is that $\Delta U_{\text{system}} = -\Delta U_{\text{surroundings}}$; that is, energy is conserved.

These ideas are summarized in Figure 4-10 and illustrated in Example 4-6.

KEEP IN MIND

that heat is the disordered flow of energy and work is the ordered flow of energy.

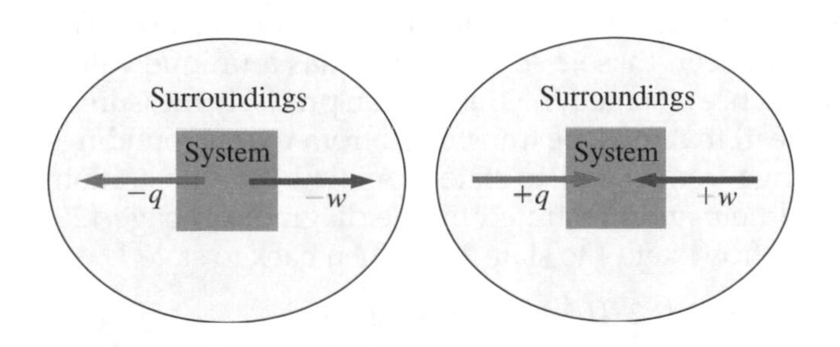

◀ FIGURE 4-10
Illustration of sign conventions used in thermodynamics
Arrows represent the direction of heat flow (⟶) and work (⟶). In the left diagram, the minus (−) signs signify energy leaving the system and entering the surroundings. In the right diagram the plus (+) signs refer to energy entering the system from the surroundings. These sign conventions are consistent with the expression $\Delta U = q + w$.

EXAMPLE 4-6 **Relating ΔU, q, and w Through the First Law of Thermodynamics**

A gas, while expanding (recall Figure 4-8), absorbs 25 J of heat and does 243 J of work. What is ΔU for the gas?

Analyze

The key to problems of this type lies in assigning the correct signs to the quantities of heat and work. Because heat is absorbed by (enters) the system, q is *positive*. Because work done *by* the system represents energy *leaving* the system, w is *negative*. You may find it useful to represent the values of q and w, with their correct signs, within parentheses. Then complete the algebra.

Solve

$$\Delta U = q + w = (+25\,\text{J}) + (-243\,\text{J}) = 25\,\text{J} - 243\,\text{J} = -218\,\text{J}$$

Assess

The negative sign for the change in internal energy, ΔU, signifies that the system, in this case the gas, has lost energy.

PRACTICE EXAMPLE A: In compressing a gas, 355 J of work is done on the system. At the same time, 185 J of heat escapes from the system. What is ΔU for the system?

PRACTICE EXAMPLE B: If the internal energy of a system *decreases* by 125 J at the same time that the system *absorbs* 54 J of heat, does the system do work or have work done on it? How much?

4-6 CONCEPT ASSESSMENT

When water is injected into a balloon filled with ammonia gas, the balloon shrinks and feels warm. What are the sources of heat and work, and what are the signs of q and w in this process?

Functions of State

To describe a system completely, we must indicate its temperature, its pressure, and the kinds and amounts of substances present. When we have done this, we have specified the *state* of the system. Any property that has a unique value for a specified state of a system is said to be a **function of state**, or a **state function**. For example, a sample of pure water at 20 °C (293.15 K) and under a pressure of 100 kPa is in a specified state. The density of water in this state is 0.99820 g/mL. We can establish that this density is a unique value—a function of state—in the following way: Obtain three different samples of water—one purified by extensive distillation of groundwater; one synthesized by burning pure $H_2(g)$ in pure $O_2(g)$; and one prepared by driving off the water of hydration from $CuSO_4 \cdot 5\,H_2O$ and condensing the gaseous water to a liquid. The densities of the three different samples for the state that we specified will all be the same: 0.99820 g/mL. Thus, the value of a function of state depends on the state of the system, and not on how that state was established.

The internal energy of a system is a function of state, although there is no simple measurement or calculation that we can use to establish its value. That is, we cannot write down a value of U for a system in the same way that we can write $d = 0.99820$ g/mL for the density of water at 20 °C. Fortunately, we don't need to know actual values of U. Consider, for example, heating 10.0 g of ice at 0 °C to a final temperature of 50 °C. The internal energy of the ice at 0 °C has one unique value, U_1, while that of the liquid water at 50 °C has another, U_2. The *difference* in internal energy between these two states also has a unique value, $\Delta U = U_2 - U_1$, and this difference *is* something that we can precisely measure. It is the quantity of energy (as heat) that must be transferred from the surroundings to the system during the change from state 1 to state 2. As a further illustration, consider the scheme outlined here and illustrated by the diagram on page 129. Imagine that a system changes from state 1 to state 2 and then back to state 1.

$$\text{State 1 } (U_1) \xrightarrow{\Delta U} \text{State 2 } (U_2) \xrightarrow{-\Delta U} \text{State 1 } (U_1)$$

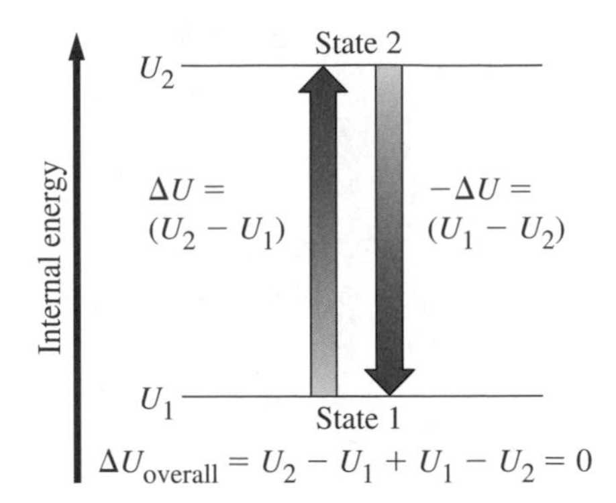

Because U has a unique value in each state, ΔU also has a unique value; it is $U_2 - U_1$. The change in internal energy when the system is returned from state 2 to state 1 is $-\Delta U = U_1 - U_2$. Thus, the *overall* change in internal energy is

$$\Delta U + (-\Delta U) = (U_2 - U_1) + (U_1 - U_2) = 0$$

This means that the internal energy returns to its initial value of U_1, which it must do, since it is a function of state. It is important to note here that when we reverse the direction of change, we change the sign of ΔU.

Path-Dependent Functions

Unlike internal energy and changes in internal energy, heat (q) and work (w) are *not* functions of state. Their values depend on the path followed when a system undergoes a change. We can see why this is so by considering again the process described by Figure 4-8 and Example 4-5. Think of the 0.100 mol of He at 298 K and under a pressure of 2.40 atm as *state 1*, and under a pressure of 1.20 atm as *state 2*. The change from state 1 to state 2 occurred in a single step. Suppose that in another instance, we allowed the expansion to occur through an intermediate stage pictured in Figure 4-11. That is, suppose the external pressure on the gas was first reduced from 2.40 atm to 1.80 atm (at which point, the gas volume would be 1.36 L). Then, in a second stage, reduced from 1.80 atm to 1.20 atm, thereby arriving at state 2.

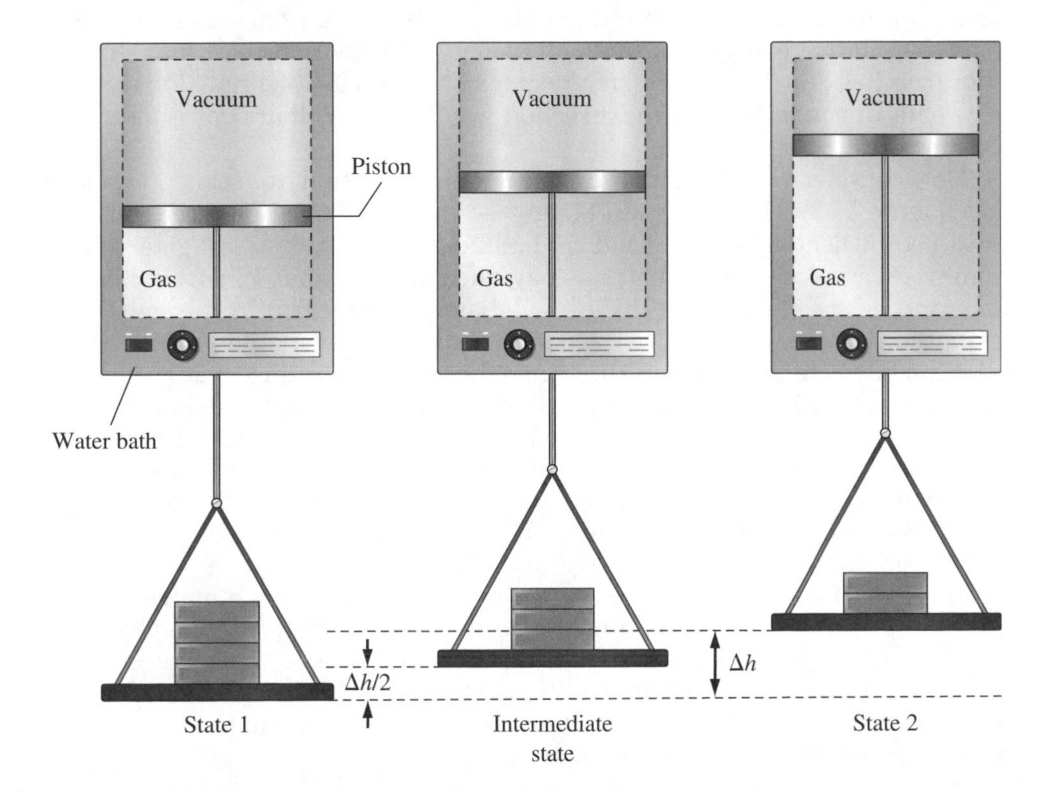

◀ FIGURE 4-11
A two-step expansion for the gas shown in Figure 4-8
In the initial state there are four weights of mass $M/2$ holding the gas back. In the intermediate state one of these weights has been removed and in the final state a second weight of mass $M/2$ has been removed. The initial and final states in this figure are the same as in Figure 4-8. This two-step expansion helps us to establish that the work of expansion depends on the path taken.

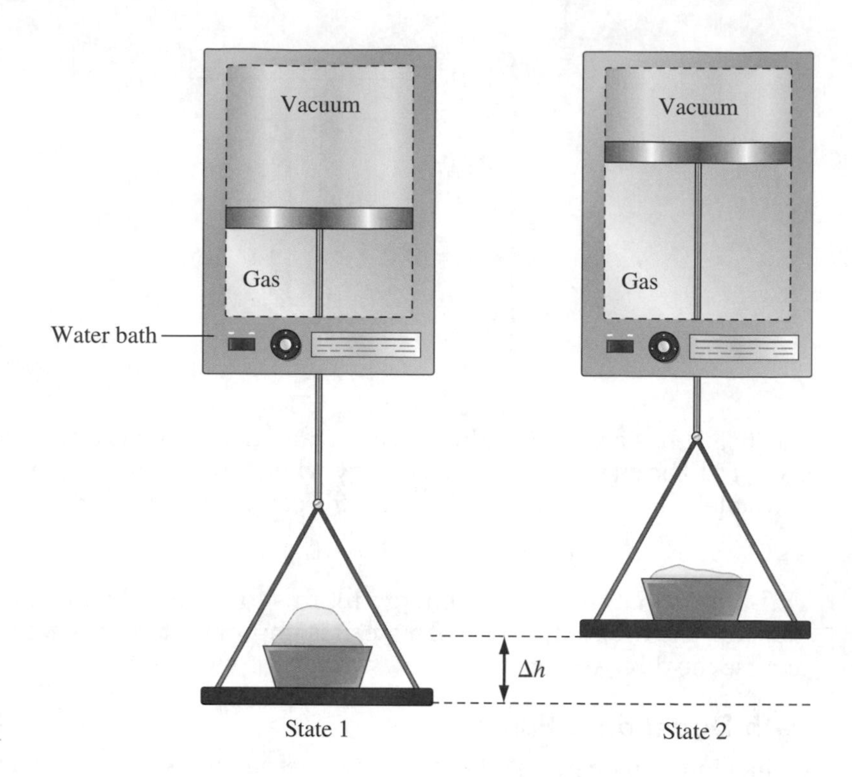

▶ FIGURE 4-12
A different method of achieving the expansion of a gas
In this expansion process, the weights in Figures 4-8 and 4-11 have been replaced by a pan containing sand, which has a mass of $2M$, equivalent to that of the weights in the initial state. In the final state the mass of the sand has been reduced to M.

We calculated the amount of work done by the gas in a single-stage expansion in Example 4-5; it was $w = -1.24 \times 10^2$ J. The amount of work done in the two-stage process is the sum of two terms: the pressure–volume work for each stage of the expansion.

$$\begin{aligned} w &= -1.80\text{ atm} \times (1.36\text{ L} - 1.02\text{ L}) - 1.20\text{ atm} \times (2.04\text{ L} - 1.36\text{ L}) \\ &= -0.61\text{ L atm} - 0.82\text{ L atm} \\ &= -1.43\text{ L atm} \times \frac{101\text{ J}}{1\text{ L atm}} = -1.44 \times 10^2\text{ J} \end{aligned}$$

KEEP IN MIND

that if w differs in the two expansion processes, q must also differ, and in such a way that $q + w = \Delta U$ has a unique value, as required by the first law of thermodynamics.

The value of ΔU is the same for the single- and two-stage expansion processes because internal energy is a function of state. However, we see that slightly more work is done in the two-stage expansion. Work is not a function of state; it is path dependent. In the next section, we will stress that heat is also path dependent.

Now consider a different way to carry out the expansion from state 1 to state 2 (see Figure 4-12). The weights in Figures 4-8 and 4-11 have now been replaced by an equivalent amount of sand so that the gas is in state 1. Imagine sand is removed very slowly from this pile—say, one grain at a time. When exactly half the sand has been removed, the gas will have reached state 2. This very slow expansion proceeds in a nearly reversible fashion. A **reversible process** is one that can be made to reverse its direction when an infinitesimal change is made in a system variable. For example, adding a grain of sand rather than removing one would reverse the expansion we are describing. However, the process is not quite reversible because grains of sand have more than an infinitesimal mass. In this approximately reversible process we have made a very large number of intermediate expansions. This process provides more work than when the gas expands directly from state 1 to state 2.

The important difference between the expansion in a finite number of steps and the reversible expansion is that the gas in the reversible process is always in equilibrium with its surroundings whereas in a stepwise process this is never the case. The stepwise processes are said to be **irreversible** because the system is not in equilibrium with the surroundings, and the process cannot be reversed by an infinitesimal change in a system variable.

In comparing the quantity of work done in the two different expansions (Figs. 4-8 and 4-11), we found them to be different, thereby proving that work is not a state function. Additionally, the quantity of work performed is greater in the two-step expansion (Fig. 4-11) than in the single-step expansion (Fig. 4-8). We leave it to the interested student to demonstrate, through Feature Problem 125, that the maximum possible work is that done in a reversible expansion (Fig. 4-12).

4-7 CONCEPT ASSESSMENT

A sample can be heated very slowly or very rapidly. The darker shading in the illustration indicates a higher temperature. Which of the two sets of diagrams do you think corresponds to reversible heating and which to spontaneous, or irreversible, heating?

◀ Although no perfectly reversible process exists, the melting and freezing of a substance at its transition temperature is an example of a process that is nearly reversible: pump in heat (melts), take out heat (freezes).

4-6 Heats of Reaction: ΔU and ΔH

Think of the reactants in a chemical reaction as the initial state of a system and the products as the final state.

$$\underset{\substack{\text{(initial state)} \\ U_i}}{\text{reactants}} \longrightarrow \underset{\substack{\text{(final state)} \\ U_f}}{\text{products}}$$

$$\Delta U = U_f - U_i$$

According to the first law of thermodynamics, we can also say that $\Delta U = q + w$. We have previously identified a heat of reaction as q_{rxn}, and so we can write

$$\Delta U = q_{rxn} + w$$

Now consider again a combustion reaction carried out in a bomb calorimeter (see Figure 4-5). The original reactants and products are confined within the bomb, and we say that the reaction occurs at *constant volume*. Because the volume is constant, $\Delta V = 0$, and no work is done. That is, $w = -P\Delta V = 0$. Denoting the heat of reaction for a constant-volume reaction as q_V, we see that $\Delta U = q_V$.

$$\Delta U = q_{rxn} + w = q_{rxn} + 0 = q_{rxn} = q_V \qquad \textbf{(4.13)}$$

The heat of reaction measured in a bomb calorimeter is equal to ΔU.

Chemical reactions are not ordinarily carried out in bomb calorimeters. The metabolism of sucrose occurs under the conditions present in the human body. The combustion of methane (natural gas) in a water heater occurs in an open flame. This question then arises: How does the heat of a reaction measured in a

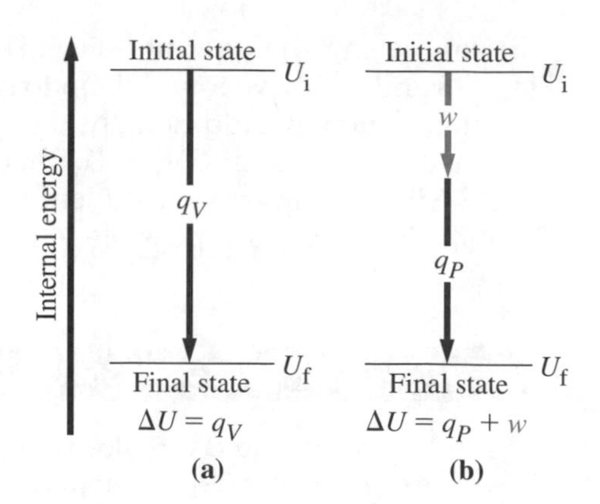

▶ FIGURE 4-13
Two different paths leading to the same internal energy change in a system
In path **(a)**, the volume of the system remains constant and no internal energy is converted into work—think of burning gasoline in a bomb calorimeter. In path **(b)**, the system does work, so some of the internal energy change is used to do work—think of burning gasoline in an automobile engine to produce heat and work.

bomb calorimeter compare with the heat of reaction if the reaction is carried out in some other way? The usual other way is in beakers, flasks, and other containers open to the atmosphere and under the *constant pressure* of the atmosphere. We live in a world of constant pressure! The neutralization reaction of Example 4-4 is typical of this more common method of conducting chemical reactions.

In many reactions carried out at constant pressure, a small amount of pressure–volume work is done as the system expands or contracts (recall Figure 4-7). In these cases, the heat of reaction, q_P, is different from q_V. We know that the change in internal energy (ΔU) for a reaction carried out between a given initial and a given final state has a unique value. Furthermore, for a reaction at constant volume, $\Delta U = q_V$. From Figure 4-13 and the first law of thermodynamics, we see that for the same reaction at constant pressure $\Delta U = q_P + w$, which means $\Delta U = q_V = q_P + w$. Thus, unless $w = 0$, q_V and q_P must be different. The fact that q_V and q_P for a reaction may differ, even though ΔU has the same value, underscores that U is a function of state and q and w are not.

The relationship between q_V and q_P can be used to devise another state function that represents the heat flow for a process at constant pressure. To do this, we begin by writing

$$q_V = q_P + w$$

Now, using $\Delta U = q_V$, $w = -P\Delta V$ and rearranging terms, we obtain

$$\Delta U = q_P - P\Delta V$$
$$q_P = \Delta U + P\Delta V$$

The quantities U, P, and V are all state functions, so it should be possible to derive the expression $\Delta U + P\Delta V$ from yet another state function. This state function, called **enthalpy, *H***, is the sum of the internal energy and the pressure–volume product of a system: $H = U + PV$. The **enthalpy change**, ΔH, for a process between initial and final states is

$$\Delta H = H_f - H_i = (U_f + P_f V_f) - (U_i + P_i V_i)$$
$$\Delta H = (U_f - U_i) + (P_f V_f - P_i V_i)$$
$$\Delta H = \Delta U + \Delta PV$$

If the process is carried out at a constant temperature and pressure ($P_i = P_f$) and with work limited to pressure–volume work, the enthalpy change is

$$\Delta H = \Delta U + P\Delta V$$

and the heat flow for the process under these conditions is

$$\Delta H = q_P \qquad \textbf{(4.14)}$$

4-8 CONCEPT ASSESSMENT

Suppose a system is subjected to the following changes: a 40 kJ quantity of heat is added and the system does 15 kJ of work; then the system is returned to its original state by cooling and compression. What is the value of ΔH?

Enthalpy (ΔH) and Internal Energy (ΔU) Changes in a Chemical Reaction

We have noted that the heat of reaction at constant pressure, ΔH, and the heat of reaction at constant volume, ΔU, are related by the expression

$$\Delta U = \Delta H - P\Delta V \tag{4.15}$$

The last term in this expression is the energy associated with the change in volume of the system under a constant external pressure. To assess just how significant pressure–volume work is, consider the following reaction, which is also illustrated in Figure 4-14.

$$2\,CO(g) + O_2(g) \longrightarrow 2\,CO_2(g)$$

If the heat of this reaction is measured under constant-pressure conditions at a constant temperature of 298 K, we get -566.0 kJ, indicating that 566.0 kJ of energy has left the system as heat: $\Delta H = -566.0$ kJ. To evaluate the pressure–volume work, we begin by writing

$$P\Delta V = P(V_f - V_i)$$

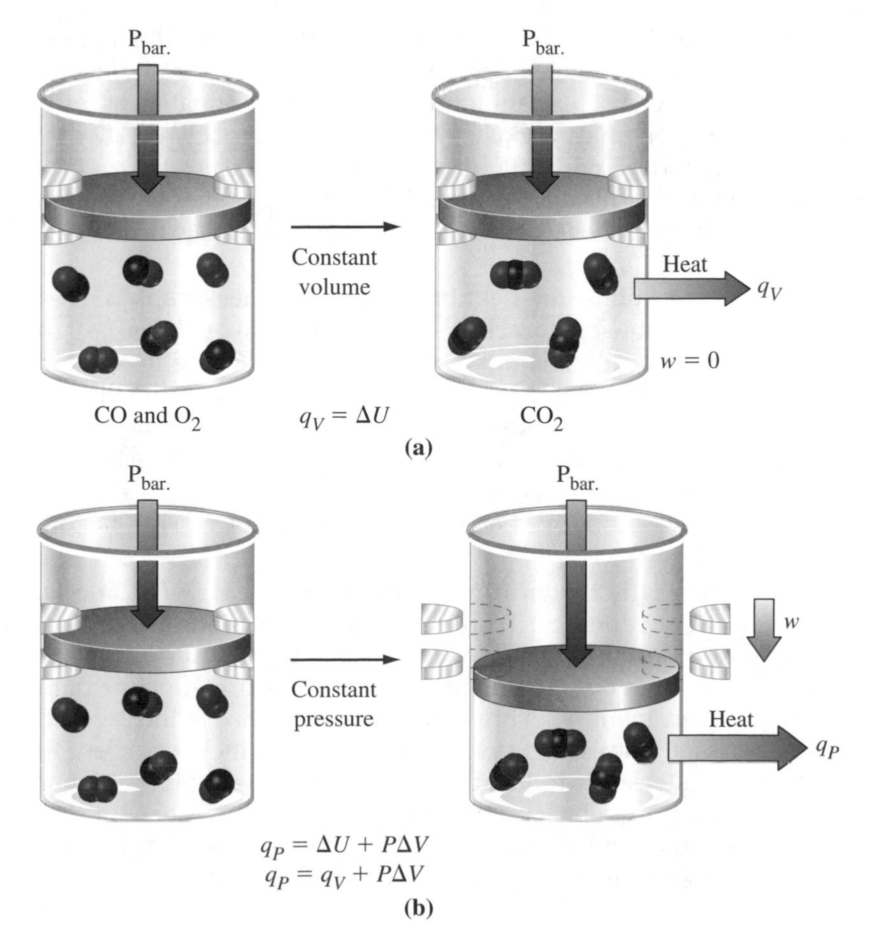

◀ FIGURE 4-14
Comparing heats of reaction at constant volume and constant pressure for the reaction $2\,CO(g) + O_2(g) \longrightarrow 2\,CO_2(g)$
(a) No work is performed at constant volume because the piston cannot move because of the stops placed through the cylinder walls; $q_V = \Delta U = -563.5$ kJ. **(b)** When the reaction is carried out at constant pressure, the stops are removed. This allows the piston to move and the surroundings do work on the system, causing it to shrink into a smaller volume. More heat is evolved than in the constant-volume reaction; $q_P = \Delta H = -566.0$ kJ.

Then we can use the ideal gas equation to write this alternative expression.

$$P\Delta V = RT(n_f - n_i)$$

Here, n_f is the number of moles of gas in the products (2 mol CO_2) and n_i is the number of moles of gas in the reactants (2 mol CO + 1 mol O_2). Thus,

$$P\Delta V = 0.0083145\ \text{kJ mol}^{-1}\ \text{K}^{-1} \times 298\ \text{K} \times [2 - (2 + 1)]\ \text{mol} = -2.5\ \text{kJ}$$

The change in internal energy is

$$\begin{aligned}\Delta U &= \Delta H - P\Delta V \\ &= -566.0\ \text{kJ} - (-2.5\ \text{kJ}) \\ &= -563.5\ \text{kJ}\end{aligned}$$

This calculation shows that the $P\Delta V$ term is quite small compared to ΔH and that ΔU and ΔH are almost the same. An additional interesting fact here is that the volume of the system decreases as a consequence of the work done on the system by the surroundings.

In the combustion of sucrose at a fixed temperature, the heat of combustion turns out to be the same, whether at constant volume (q_V) or constant pressure (q_P). Only heat is transferred between the reaction mixture and the surroundings; no pressure–volume work is done. This is because the volume of a system is almost entirely determined by the volume of gas and because 12 mol $CO_2(g)$ occupies the same volume as 12 mol $O_2(g)$. There is no change in volume in the combustion of sucrose: $q_P = q_V$. Thus, the result of Example 4-3 can be represented as

$$C_{12}H_{22}O_{11}(s) + 12\,O_2(g) \longrightarrow 12\,CO_2(g) + 11\,H_2O(l) \quad \Delta H = -5.65 \times 10^3\ \text{kJ} \qquad \textbf{(4.16)}$$

That is, 1 mol $C_{12}H_{22}O_{11}(s)$ reacts with 12 mol $O_2(g)$ to produce 12 mol $CO_2(g)$, 11 mol $H_2O(l)$, and 5.65×10^3 kJ of evolved heat. Strictly speaking, the unit for ΔH should be kilojoules per mole, meaning per mole of reaction. "One mole of reaction" relates to the amounts of reactants and products in the equation as written. Thus, reaction (4.16) involves 1 mol $C_{12}H_{22}O_{11}(s)$, 12 mol $O_2(g)$, 12 mol $CO_2(g)$, 11 mol $H_2O(l)$, and -5.65×10^3 kJ of enthalpy change *per mol reaction*. The mol^{-1} part of the unit of ΔH is often dropped, but there are times we need to carry it to achieve the proper cancellation of units. We will find this to be the case in Chapters 5 and 7.

In summary, in most reactions, the heat of reaction we measure is ΔH. In some reactions, notably combustion reactions, we measure ΔU (that is, q_V). In reaction (4.16), $\Delta U = \Delta H$, but this is not always the case. Where it is not, a value of ΔH can be obtained from ΔU by the method illustrated in the discussion of expression (4.15), but even in those cases, ΔH and ΔU will be nearly equal. In this text, all heats of reactions are treated as ΔH values unless there is an indication to the contrary.

Example 4-7 shows how enthalpy changes can provide conversion factors for problem solving.

You may be wondering why the term ΔH is used instead of ΔU, q, and w. It's mainly a matter of convenience. Think of an analogous situation from daily life—buying gasoline at a gas station. The gasoline price posted on the pump is actually the sum of a base price and various taxes that must be paid to different levels of government. This breakdown is important to the accountants who must determine how much tax is to be paid to which agencies. To the consumer, however, it's easier to be given just the total cost per gallon or liter. After all, this determines what he or she must pay. In thermochemistry, our chief interest is generally in heats of reaction, not pressure–volume work. And because most reactions are carried out under atmospheric pressure, it's

EXAMPLE 4-7 Stoichiometric Calculations Involving Quantities of Heat

How much heat is associated with the complete combustion of 1.00 kg of sucrose, $C_{12}H_{22}O_{11}$?

Analyze

Equation (4.16) represents the combustion of 1 mol of sucrose. In that reaction the amount of heat generated is given as $\Delta H = -5.65 \times 10^3$ kJ/mol. The first step is to determine the number of moles in 1.00 kg of sucrose, and then use that value with the change in enthalpy for the reaction.

Solve

Express the quantity of sucrose in moles.

$$? \text{ mol} = 1.00 \text{ kg } C_{12}H_{22}O_{11} \times \frac{1000 \text{ g } C_{12}H_{22}O_{11}}{1 \text{ kg } C_{12}H_{22}O_{11}} \times \frac{1 \text{ mol } C_{12}H_{22}O_{11}}{342.3 \text{ g } C_{12}H_{22}O_{11}} = 2.92 \text{ mol } C_{12}H_{22}O_{11}$$

Formulate a conversion factor (shown in blue) based on the information in equation (4.16)—that is, -5.65×10^3 kJ of heat is associated with the combustion of 1 mol $C_{12}H_{22}O_{11}$.

$$? \text{ kJ} = 2.92 \text{ mol } C_{12}H_{22}O_{11} \times \frac{-5.65 \times 10^3 \text{ kJ}}{1 \text{ mol } C_{12}H_{22}O_{11}} = -1.65 \times 10^4 \text{ kJ}$$

The negative sign denotes that heat is given off in the combustion.

Assess

As discussed on page 121, the heat produced by a combustion reaction is not immediately transferred to the surroundings. Use data from Table 4.1 to show that the heat released by this reaction is *more* than that required to raise the temperature of the products to 100 °C.

PRACTICE EXAMPLE A: What mass of sucrose must be burned to produce 1.00×10^3 kJ of heat?

PRACTICE EXAMPLE B: A 25.0 mL sample of 0.1045 M HCl(aq) was neutralized by NaOH(aq). Use the result of Example 4-4 to determine the heat evolved in this neutralization.

helpful to have a function of state, enthalpy, H, whose change is exactly equal to something we can measure: q_P.

Enthalpy Change (ΔH) Accompanying a Change in State of Matter

When a liquid is in contact with the atmosphere, energetic molecules at the surface of the liquid can overcome forces of attraction to their neighbors and pass into the gaseous, or vapor, state. We say that the liquid *vaporizes*. If the temperature of the liquid is to remain constant, the liquid must absorb heat from its surroundings to replace the energy carried off by the vaporizing molecules. The heat required to vaporize a fixed quantity of liquid is called the enthalpy (or heat) of vaporization. Usually the fixed quantity of liquid chosen is one mole, and we can call this quantity the *molar enthalpy of vaporization*. For example,

$$H_2O(l) \longrightarrow H_2O(g) \qquad \Delta H = 44.0 \text{ kJ at } 298 \text{ K}$$

We described the melting of a solid in a similar fashion (page 244). The energy requirement in this case is called the enthalpy (or heat) of fusion. For the melting of one mole of ice, we can write

$$H_2O(s) \longrightarrow H_2O(l) \qquad \Delta H = 6.01 \text{ kJ at } 273.15 \text{ K}$$

We can use the data represented in these equations, together with other appropriate data, to answer questions like those posed in Example 4-8 and its accompanying Practice Examples.

EXAMPLE 4-8 Enthalpy Changes Accompanying Changes in States of Matter

Calculate ΔH for the process in which 50.0 g of water is converted from liquid at 10.0 °C to vapor at 25.0 °C.

Analyze

The key to this calculation is to view the process as proceeding in two steps: first raising the temperature of liquid water from 10.0 to 25.0 °C, and then completely vaporizing the liquid at 25.0 °C. The total enthalpy change is the sum of the changes in the two steps. For a process at constant pressure, $\Delta H = q_P$, so we need to calculate the heat absorbed in each step.

Solve

HEATING WATER FROM 10.0 TO 25.0°C

This heat requirement can be determined by the method shown in Example 4-1; that is, we apply equation (4.5).

$$? \text{ kJ} = 50.0 \text{ g } H_2O \times \frac{4.18 \text{ J}}{\text{g } H_2O \text{ °C}} \times (25.0 - 10.0) \text{ °C} \times \frac{1 \text{ kJ}}{1000 \text{ J}} = 3.14 \text{ kJ}$$

VAPORIZING WATER AT 25.0°C

For this part of the calculation, the quantity of water must be expressed in moles so that we can then use the molar enthalpy of vaporization at 25 °C: 44.0 kJ/mol.

$$? \text{ kJ} = 50.0 \text{ g } H_2O \times \frac{1 \text{ mol } H_2O}{18.02 \text{ g } H_2O} \times \frac{44.0 \text{ kJ}}{1 \text{ mol } H_2O} = 122 \text{ kJ}$$

TOTAL ENTHALPY CHANGE

$$\Delta H = 3.14 \text{ kJ} + 122 \text{ kJ} = 125 \text{ kJ}$$

Assess

Note that the enthalpy change is positive, which reflects that the system (i.e., the water) gains energy. The reverse would be true for condensation of water at 25.0 °C and cooling it to 10.0 °C.

PRACTICE EXAMPLE A: What is the enthalpy change when a cube of ice 2.00 cm on edge is brought from −10.0 °C to a final temperature of 23.2 °C? For ice, use a density of 0.917 g/cm^3, a specific heat of 2.01 J g^{-1} °C^{-1}, and an enthalpy of fusion of 6.01 kJ/mol.

PRACTICE EXAMPLE B: What is the maximum mass of ice at −15.0 °C that can be completely converted to water vapor at 25.0 °C if the available heat for this transition is 5.00×10^3 kJ?

Standard States and Standard Enthalpy Changes

The measured enthalpy change for a reaction has a unique value *only* if the initial state (reactants) and final state (products) are precisely described. If we define a particular state as *standard* for the reactants and products, we can then say that the standard enthalpy change is the enthalpy change in a reaction in which the reactants and products are in their standard states. This so-called **standard enthalpy of reaction** is denoted with a degree symbol, $\Delta H°$.

The **standard state** of a solid or liquid substance is the pure element or compound at a pressure of *1 bar* (10^5 Pa)* and at the temperature of interest. For a gas, the standard state is the pure gas behaving as an (hypothetical) ideal gas at a pressure of 1 bar and the temperature of interest. Although temperature is not part of the definition of a standard state, it still must be specified in tabulated values of $\Delta H°$, because $\Delta H°$ depends on temperature. The values given in this text are all for 298.15 K (25 °C) unless otherwise stated.

*The International Union of Pure and Applied Chemistry (IUPAC) recommended that the standard-state pressure be changed from 1 atm to 1 bar about 25 years ago, but some data tables are still based on the 1 atm standard. Fortunately, the differences in values resulting from this change in standard-state pressure are very small—almost always small enough to be ignored.

In the rest of this chapter, we will mostly use standard enthalpy changes.

Enthalpy Diagrams

The negative sign of ΔH in equation (4.16) means that the enthalpy of the products is lower than that of the reactants. This *decrease* in enthalpy appears as heat evolved to the surroundings. The combustion of sucrose is an exothermic reaction. In the reaction

$$N_2(g) + O_2(g) \longrightarrow 2\,NO(g) \qquad \Delta H^\circ = 180.50\ \text{kJ} \qquad \textbf{(4.17)}$$

the products have a *higher* enthalpy than the reactants; ΔH is positive. To produce this increase in enthalpy, heat is absorbed from the surroundings. The reaction is endothermic. An **enthalpy diagram** is a diagrammatic representation of enthalpy changes in a process. Figure 4-15 shows how exothermic and endothermic reactions can be represented through such diagrams.

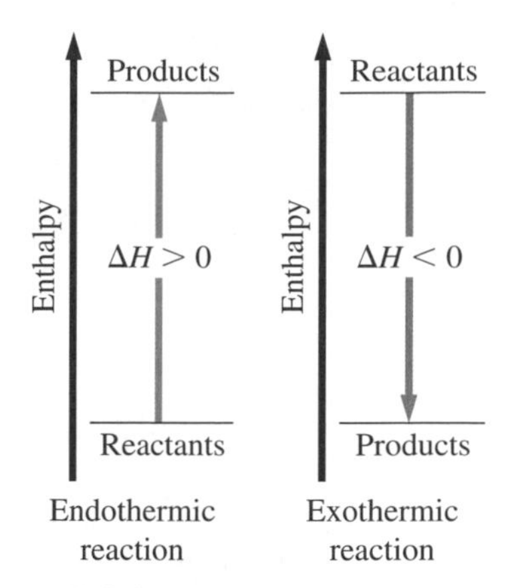

▲ FIGURE 4-15
Enthalpy diagrams
Horizontal lines represent absolute values of enthalpy. The higher a horizontal line, the greater the value of H that it represents. Vertical lines or arrows represent changes in enthalpy (ΔH). Arrows pointing up signify increases in enthalpy—endothermic reactions. Arrows pointing down signify decreases in enthalpy—exothermic reactions.

4-1 ARE YOU WONDERING...

Why ΔH depends on temperature?

The difference in ΔH for a reaction at two different temperatures is determined by the amount of heat involved in changing the reactants and products from one temperature to the other under constant pressure. These quantities of heat can be calculated with the help of equation (4.5): q_P = heat capacity $\times$ temperature change = $C_P \times \Delta T$. We write an expression of this type for each reactant and product and combine these expressions with the measured ΔH value at one temperature to obtain the value of ΔH at another. This method is illustrated in Figure 4-16 and applied in Exercise 117.

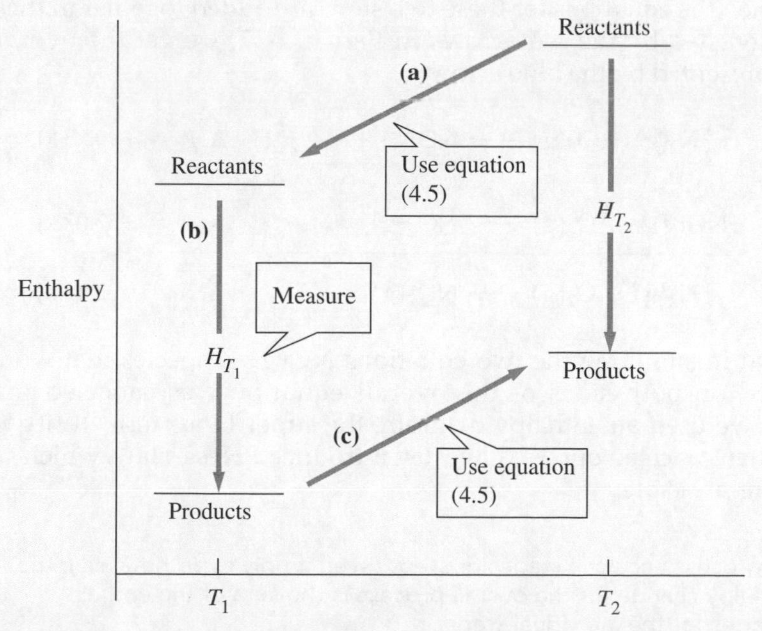

▲ FIGURE 4-16
Conceptualizing ΔH as a function of temperature
In the three-step process outlined here, **(a)** the reactants are cooled from the temperature T_2 to T_1. **(b)** The reaction is carried out at T_1, and **(c)** the products are warmed from T_1 to T_2. When the quantities of heat associated with each step are combined, the result is the same as if the reaction had been carried out at T_2, that is, ΔH_{T_2}.

4-7 Indirect Determination of ΔH: Hess's Law

One of the reasons that the enthalpy concept is so useful is that a large number of heats of reaction can be calculated from a small number of measurements. The following features of enthalpy change (ΔH) make this possible.

- **ΔH Is an Extensive Property.** Consider the standard enthalpy change in the formation of NO(g) from its elements at 25 °C.

$$N_2(g) + O_2(g) \longrightarrow 2\,NO(g) \qquad \Delta H° = 180.50\text{ kJ}$$

To express the enthalpy change in terms of *one mole* of NO(g), we divide all coefficients *and the ΔH value* by *two*.

▶ Although we have avoided fractional coefficients previously, we need them here. The coefficient of NO(g) must be one.

$$\frac{1}{2}N_2(g) + \frac{1}{2}O_2(g) \longrightarrow NO(g) \qquad \Delta H° = \frac{1}{2} \times 180.50 = 90.25\text{ kJ}$$

Enthalpy change is directly proportional to the amounts of substances in a system.

- **ΔH Changes Sign When a Process Is Reversed.** As we learned on page 129, if a process is reversed, the change in a function of state reverses sign. Thus, ΔH for the *decomposition* of one mole of NO(g) is $-\Delta H$ for the *formation* of one mole of NO(g).

$$NO(g) \longrightarrow \frac{1}{2}N_2(g) + \frac{1}{2}O_2(g) \quad \Delta H° = -90.25\text{ kJ}$$

- **Hess's Law of Constant Heat Summation.** To describe the standard enthalpy change for the formation of $NO_2(g)$ from $N_2(g)$ and $O_2(g)$,

$$\frac{1}{2}N_2(g) + O_2(g) \longrightarrow NO_2(g) \quad \Delta H° = ?$$

we can think of the reaction as proceeding in two steps: First we form NO(g) from $N_2(g)$ and $O_2(g)$, and then $NO_2(g)$ from NO(g) and $O_2(g)$. When the equations for these two steps are added together in the manner suggested by the red arrows in Figure 4-17, we get the overall result represented by the blue arrow.

$$\frac{1}{2}N_2(g) + O_2(g) \longrightarrow \cancel{NO(g)} + \cancel{\frac{1}{2}O_2(g)} \quad \Delta H° = +90.25\text{ kJ}$$

$$\cancel{NO(g)} + \cancel{\frac{1}{2}O_2(g)} \longrightarrow NO_2(g) \qquad \Delta H° = -57.07\text{ kJ}$$

$$\frac{1}{2}N_2(g) + O_2(g) \longrightarrow NO_2(g) \qquad \Delta H° = +33.18\text{ kJ}$$

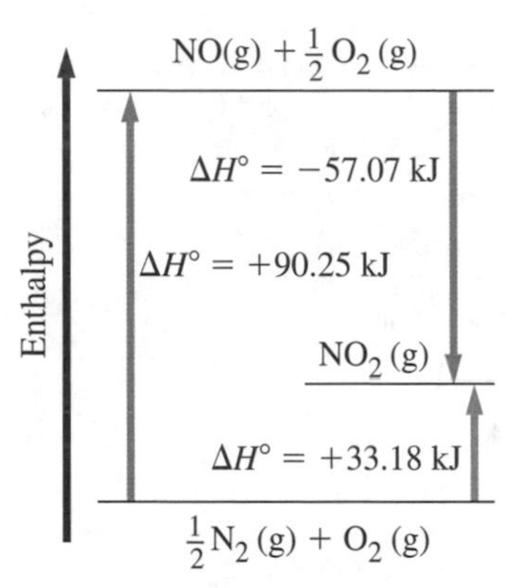

▲ FIGURE 4-17
An enthalpy diagram illustrating Hess's law
Whether the reaction occurs through a single step (blue arrow) or in two steps (red arrows), the enthalpy change is $\Delta H° = 33.18$ kJ for the overall reaction $\frac{1}{2}N_2(g) + O_2(g) \longrightarrow NO_2(g)$.

Note that in summing the two equations NO(g), a species that would have appeared on both sides of the overall equation was canceled out. Also, because we used an enthalpy diagram, the superfluous term $\frac{1}{2}O_2(g)$ entered in and then canceled out. We have just introduced **Hess's law**, which states the following principle:

> If a process occurs in stages or steps (even if only hypothetically), the enthalpy change for the overall process is the sum of the enthalpy changes for the individual steps.

KEEP IN MIND

that $\Delta H°$ is an extensive property. In a chemical equation, the stoichiometric coefficients specify the amounts involved, and the unit kJ suffices for $\Delta H°$. When $\Delta H°$ is not accompanied by an equation, the amount involved must somehow be specified, such as per mole of $C_3H_8(g)$ in the expression $\Delta H°_{comb} = -2219.9\text{ kJ/mol } C_3H_8(g)$.

Hess's law is simply a consequence of the state function property of enthalpy. Regardless of the path taken in going from the initial state to the final state, ΔH (or $\Delta H°$ if the process is carried out under standard conditions) has the same value.

Suppose we want the standard enthalpy change for the reaction

$$3\,C(\text{graphite}) + 4\,H_2(g) \longrightarrow C_3H_8(g) \qquad \Delta H° = ? \qquad (4.18)$$

How should we proceed? If we try to get graphite and hydrogen to react, a slight reaction will occur, but it will not go to completion. Furthermore, the product will not be limited to propane (C_3H_8); several other hydrocarbons will form as well. The fact is that we cannot directly measure $\Delta H°$ for reaction (4.18). Instead, we must resort to an *indirect calculation* from $\Delta H°$ values that can be established by experiment. Here is where Hess's law is of greatest value. It permits us to calculate ΔH values that we cannot measure directly. In Example 4-9,

EXAMPLE 4-9 Applying Hess's Law

Use the heat of combustion data from page 140 to determine $\Delta H°$ for reaction (4.18)

$$3\,C(\text{graphite}) + 4\,H_2(g) \longrightarrow C_3H_8(g) \qquad \Delta H° = ?$$

Analyze

To determine an enthalpy change with Hess's law, we need to combine the appropriate chemical equations. A good starting point is to write chemical equations for the given combustion reactions based on *one mole* of the indicated reactant. Recall that the products of the combustion of carbon–hydrogen–oxygen compounds are $CO_2(g)$ and $H_2O(l)$.

Solve

Begin by writing the following equations

$$\textbf{(a)}\quad C_3H_8(g) + 5\,O_2(g) \longrightarrow 3\,CO_2(g) + 4\,H_2O(l) \qquad \Delta H° = -2219.9\text{ kJ}$$

$$\textbf{(b)}\quad C(\text{graphite}) + O_2(g) \longrightarrow CO_2(g) \qquad \Delta H° = -393.5\text{ kJ}$$

$$\textbf{(c)}\quad H_2(g) + \frac{1}{2}O_2(g) \longrightarrow H_2O(l) \qquad \Delta H° = -285.8\text{ kJ}$$

Because our objective in reaction (4.18) is to *produce* $C_3H_8(g)$, the next step is to find a reaction in which $C_3H_8(g)$ is formed—the *reverse* of reaction **(a)**.

$$-(a):\ 3\,CO_2(g) + 4\,H_2O(l) \longrightarrow C_3H_8(g) + 5\,O_2(g) \qquad \Delta H° = -(-2219.9)\text{ kJ} = +2219.9\text{ kJ}$$

Now, we turn our attention to the reactants, C(graphite) and $H_2(g)$. To get the proper number of moles of each, we must multiply equation **(b)** by three and equation **(c)** by four.

$$3\times(b):\ 3\,C(\text{graphite}) + 3\,O_2(g) \longrightarrow 3\,CO_2(g) \qquad \Delta H° = 3(-393.5\text{ kJ}) = -1181\text{ kJ}$$

$$4\times(c):\ 4\,H_2(g) + 2\,O_2(g) \longrightarrow 4\,H_2O(l) \qquad \Delta H° = 4(-285.8\text{ kJ}) = -1143\text{ kJ}$$

Here is the overall change we have described: 3 mol C(graphite) and 4 mol $H_2(g)$ have been consumed, and 1 mol $C_3H_8(g)$ has been produced. This is exactly what is required in equation (4.18). We can now combine the three modified equations.

$$\begin{array}{lrcll} -(a): & \cancel{3\,CO_2(g)} + \cancel{4\,H_2O(l)} & \longrightarrow & C_3H_8(g) + \cancel{5\,O_2(g)} & \Delta H° = +2219.9\text{ kJ} \\ 3\times(b): & 3\,C(\text{graphite}) + \cancel{3\,O_2(g)} & \longrightarrow & \cancel{3\,CO_2(g)} & \Delta H° = -1181\text{ kJ} \\ 4\times(c): & 4\,H_2(g) + \cancel{2\,O_2(g)} & \longrightarrow & \cancel{4\,H_2O(l)} & \Delta H° = -1143\text{ kJ} \\ \hline & 3\,C(\text{graphite}) + 4\,H_2(g) & \longrightarrow & C_3H_8(g) & \Delta H° = -104\text{ kJ} \end{array}$$

Assess

Hess's law is a powerful technique to determine the enthalpy of reaction by using a series of unrelated reactions, along with their enthalpies of reaction. In this example, we took three unrelated combustion reactions and were able to determine the enthalpy of reaction of another reaction.

PRACTICE EXAMPLE A: The standard heat of combustion of propene, $C_3H_6(g)$, is $-2058\text{ kJ/mol }C_3H_6(g)$. Use this value and other data from this example to determine $\Delta H°$ for the hydrogenation of propene to propane.

$$CH_3CH{=}CH_2(g) + H_2(g) \longrightarrow CH_3CH_2CH_3(g) \qquad \Delta H° = ?$$

PRACTICE EXAMPLE B: From the data in Practice Example 4-9A and the following equation, determine the standard enthalpy of combustion of one mole of 2-propanol, $CH_3CH(OH)CH_3(l)$.

$$CH_3CH{=}CH_2(g) + H_2O(l) \longrightarrow CH_3CH(OH)CH_3(l) \qquad \Delta H° = -52.3\text{ kJ}$$

we use the following standard heats of combustion ΔH°_{comb} to calculate ΔH° for reaction (4.18).

$$\Delta H^\circ_{comb} \quad C_3H_8(g) = -2219.9\ \text{kJ/mol}\ C_3H_8(g)$$
$$C(\text{graphite}) = -393.5\ \text{kJ/mol}\ C(\text{graphite})$$
$$H_2(g) = -285.8\ \text{kJ/mol}\ H_2(g)$$

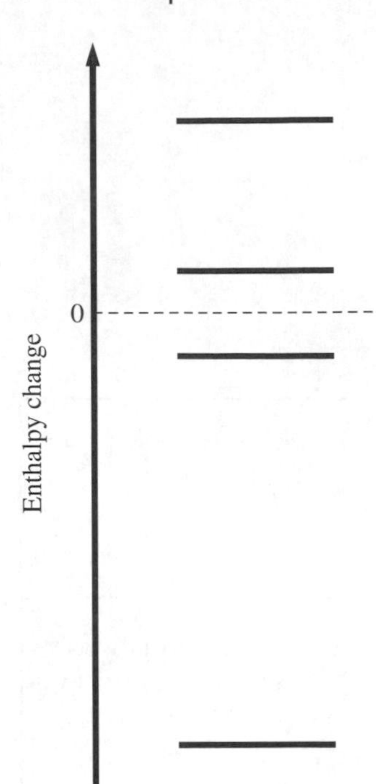

4-9 CONCEPT ASSESSMENT

The heat of reaction between carbon (graphite) and the corresponding stoichiometric amounts of hydrogen gas to form $C_2H_2(g)$, $C_2H_4(g)$, and $C_2H_6(g)$ are 226.7, 52.3 and −84.7 kJ mol^{-1}, respectively. Relate these values to the enthalpy diagram shown in the margin. Indicate on the diagram the standard enthalpy change for the reaction $C_2H_2(g) + 2\,H_2(g) \longrightarrow C_2H_6(g)$.

4-8 Standard Enthalpies of Formation

In the enthalpy diagrams we have drawn, we have not written any numerical values on the enthalpy axis. This is because we cannot determine *absolute* values of enthalpy, H. However, enthalpy *is* a function of state, so *changes* in enthalpy, ΔH, have unique values. We can deal just with these changes. Nevertheless, as with many other properties, it is still useful to have a starting point, a zero value.

Consider a map-making analogy: What do we list as the height of a mountain? Do we mean by this the vertical distance between the mountaintop and the center of Earth? Between the mountaintop and the deepest trench in the ocean? No. By agreement, we mean the vertical distance between the mountaintop and mean sea level. We *arbitrarily* assign to mean sea level an elevation of zero, and all other points on Earth are relative to this zero elevation. The elevation of Mt. Everest is +8848 m; that of Badwater, Death Valley, California, is −86 m. We do something similar with enthalpies. We relate our zero to the enthalpies of certain forms of the elements and determine the enthalpies of other substances relative to this zero.

KEEP IN MIND

that we use the expression "standard enthalpy of formation" even though what we are describing is actually a standard enthalpy *change*.

The **standard enthalpy of formation (ΔH°_f)** of a substance is the enthalpy *change* that occurs in the formation of one mole of the substance in the standard state from the *reference* forms of the elements in their standard states. The reference forms of the elements in all but a few cases are the most stable forms of the elements at one bar and the given temperature. The degree symbol denotes that the enthalpy change is a standard enthalpy change, and the subscript "f" signifies that the reaction is one in which a substance is formed from its elements. Because the formation of the most stable form of an element from itself is no change at all,

> the standard enthalpy of formation of a pure element in its reference form is 0.

Listed here are the most stable forms of several elements at 298.15 K, the temperature at which thermochemical data are commonly tabulated.

$$Na(s) \quad H_2(g) \quad N_2(g) \quad O_2(g) \quad C(\text{graphite}) \quad Br_2(l)$$

▲ Diamond and graphite.

The situation with carbon is an interesting one. In addition to graphite, carbon also exists naturally in the form of diamond. However, because there is a measurable enthalpy difference between them, they cannot both be assigned $\Delta H^\circ_f = 0$.

$$C(\text{graphite}) \longrightarrow C(\text{diamond}) \qquad \Delta H^\circ = 1.9\ \text{kJ}$$

We choose as the reference form the more stable form, the one with the lower enthalpy. Thus, we assign $\Delta H^\circ_f(\text{graphite}) = 0$, and $\Delta H^\circ_f(\text{diamond}) =$

1.9 kJ/mol. Although we can obtain bromine in either the gaseous or liquid state at 298.15 K, $Br_2(l)$ is the most stable form. $Br_2(g)$, if obtained at 298.15 K and 1 bar pressure, immediately condenses to $Br_2(l)$.

$$Br_2(l) \longrightarrow Br_2(g) \qquad \Delta H_f^\circ = 30.91\ \text{kJ}$$

The enthalpies of formation are $\Delta H_f^\circ[Br_2(l)] = 0$ and $\Delta H_f^\circ[Br_2(g)] = 30.91$ kJ/mol.

A rare case in which the reference form is not the most stable form is the element phosphorus. Although over time it converts to solid red phosphorus, solid white phosphorus has been chosen as the reference form.

$$P(s, \text{white}) \longrightarrow P(s, \text{red}) \qquad \Delta H_f^\circ = -17.6\ \text{kJ}$$

The standard enthalpies of formation are $\Delta H_f^\circ[P(s, \text{white})] = 0$ and $\Delta H_f^\circ[P(s, \text{red})] = -17.6$ kJ/mol.

Standard enthalpies of formation of some common substances are presented in Table 4.2. Figure 4-18 emphasizes that both positive and negative standard enthalpies of formation are possible. It also suggests that standard enthalpies of formation are related to molecular structure.

We will use standard enthalpies of formation in a variety of calculations. Often, the first thing we must do is write the chemical equation to which a ΔH_f° value applies, as in Example 4-10.

▲ Liquid bromine vaporizing.

TABLE 4.2 Some Standard Molar Enthalpies of Formation, ΔH_f° at 298.15 K

Substance	kJ/mol[a]	Substance	kJ/mol[a]
$CO(g)$	−110.5	$HBr(g)$	−36.40
$CO_2(g)$	−393.5	$HI(g)$	26.48
$CH_4(g)$	−74.81	$H_2O(g)$	−241.8
$C_2H_2(g)$	226.7	$H_2O(l)$	−285.8
$C_2H_4(g)$	52.26	$H_2S(g)$	−20.63
$C_2H_6(g)$	−84.68	$NH_3(g)$	−46.11
$C_3H_8(g)$	−103.8	$NO(g)$	90.25
$C_4H_{10}(g)$	−125.6	$N_2O(g)$	82.05
$CH_3OH(l)$	−238.7	$NO_2(g)$	33.18
$C_2H_5OH(l)$	−277.7	$N_2O_4(g)$	9.16
$HF(g)$	−271.1	$SO_2(g)$	−296.8
$HCl(g)$	−92.31	$SO_3(g)$	−395.7

[a]Values are for reactions in which one mole of substance is formed. Most of the data have been rounded off to four significant figures.

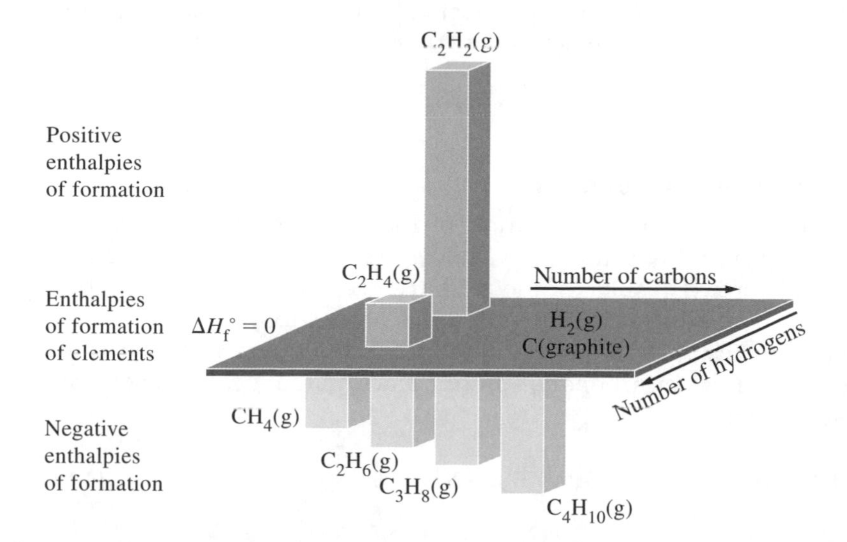

◀ FIGURE 4-18
Some standard enthalpies of formation at 298.15 K
Standard enthalpies of formation of elements are shown in the central plane, with $\Delta H_f^\circ = 0$. Substances with positive enthalpies of formation are above the plane, while those with negative enthalpies of formation are below the plane.

EXAMPLE 4-10 Relating a Standard Enthalpy of Formation to a Chemical Equation

The enthalpy of formation of formaldehyde is $\Delta H_f^\circ = -108.6$ kJ/mol HCHO(g) at 298 K. Write the chemical equation to which this value applies.

Analyze

The equation must be written for the formation of one mole of gaseous HCHO. The most stable forms of the elements at 298.15 K and 1 bar are gaseous H_2 and O_2 and solid carbon in the form of graphite (Fig. 4-19). Note that we need one fractional coefficient in this equation.

Solve

$$H_2(g) + \frac{1}{2}O_2(g) + C(\text{graphite}) \longrightarrow HCHO(g) \qquad \Delta H_f^\circ = -108.6 \text{ kJ}$$

Assess

When answering these types of problems, we must remember to use the elements in their most stable form under the given conditions. In this example, the stated conditions were 298 K and 1 bar.

PRACTICE EXAMPLE A: The standard enthalpy of formation for the amino acid leucine is -637.3 kJ/mol $C_6H_{13}O_2N(s)$. Write the chemical equation to which this value applies.

PRACTICE EXAMPLE B: How is ΔH° for the following reaction related to the standard enthalpy of formation of $NH_3(g)$ listed in Table 4.2? What is the value of $\Delta H^\circ = ?$

$$2\,NH_3(g) \longrightarrow N_2(g) + 3\,H_2(g) \qquad \Delta H^\circ = ?$$

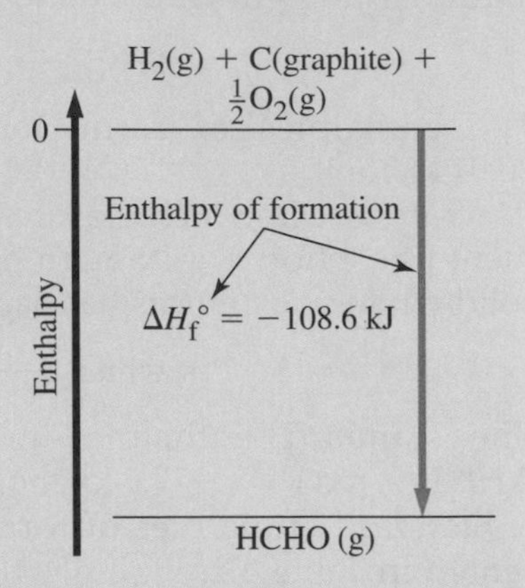

▲ FIGURE 4-19 **Standard enthalpy of formation of formaldehyde, HCHO(g)** The formation of HCHO(g) from its elements in their standard states is an exothermic reaction. The heat evolved per mole of HCHO(g) formed is the standard enthalpy (heat) of formation.

4-2 ARE YOU WONDERING...

What is the significance of the sign of a ΔH_f° value?

A compound having a positive value of ΔH_f° is formed from its elements by an endothermic reaction. If the reaction is reversed, the compound decomposes into its elements in an exothermic reaction. We say that the compound is unstable with respect to its elements. This does not mean that the compound cannot be made, but it does suggest a tendency for the compound to enter into chemical reactions yielding products with lower enthalpies of formation.

When no other criteria are available, chemists sometimes use enthalpy change as a rough indicator of the likelihood of a chemical reaction occurring—exothermic reactions generally being more likely to occur unassisted than endothermic ones. We'll present much better criteria later in the text.

Standard Enthalpies of Reaction

We have learned that if the reactants and products of a reaction are in their standard states, the enthalpy change is a *standard* enthalpy change, which we can denote as ΔH° or ΔH°_{rxn}. One of the primary uses of standard enthalpies of formation is in calculating standard enthalpies of reaction.

Let us use Hess's law to calculate the standard enthalpy of reaction for the decomposition of sodium bicarbonate, a minor reaction that occurs when baking soda is used in baking.

$$2\,NaHCO_3(s) \longrightarrow Na_2CO_3(s) + H_2O(l) + CO_2(g) \qquad \Delta H^\circ = ? \qquad \textbf{(4.19)}$$

From Hess's law, we see that the following four equations yield equation (4.19) when added together.

(a) $2\,NaHCO_3(s) \longrightarrow 2\,Na(s) + H_2(g) + 2\,C\,(graphite) + 3\,O_2(g)$
$$\Delta H^\circ = -2 \times \Delta H_f^\circ[NaHCO_3(s)]$$

(b) $2\,Na(s) + C(graphite) + \frac{3}{2}O_2(g) \longrightarrow Na_2CO_3(s)$
$$\Delta H^\circ = \Delta H_f^\circ[Na_2CO_3(s)]$$

(c) $H_2(g) + \frac{1}{2}O_2(g) \longrightarrow H_2O(l)$ $\quad \Delta H^\circ = \Delta H_f^\circ[H_2O(l)]$

(d) $C(graphite) + O_2(g) \longrightarrow CO_2(g)$ $\quad \Delta H^\circ = \Delta H_f^\circ[CO_2(g)]$

$2\,NaHCO_3(s) \longrightarrow Na_2CO_3(s) + H_2O(l) + CO_2(g)$ $\quad \Delta H^\circ = ?$

Equation (a) is the *reverse* of the equation representing the formation of two moles of $[NaHCO_3(s)]$ from its elements. This means that ΔH° for reaction (a) is the *negative* of twice $\Delta H_f^\circ[NaHCO_3(s)]$. Equations (b), (c) and (d) represent the formation of *one* mole each of $Na_2CO_3(s)$, $CO_2(g)$ and $H_2O(l)$. Thus, we can express the value of ΔH° for the decomposition reaction as

$$\Delta H^\circ = \Delta H_f^\circ[Na_2CO_3(s)] + \Delta H_f^\circ[H_2O(l)] + \Delta H_f^\circ[CO_2(g)] - 2 \times \Delta H_f^\circ[NaHCO_3(s)] \quad \textbf{(4.20)}$$

We can use the enthalpy diagram in Figure 4-20 to visualize the Hess's law procedure and to show how the state function property of enthalpy enables us to arrive at equation (4.20). Imagine the decomposition of sodium bicarbonate taking place in two steps. In the first step, suppose a vessel contains 2 mol $NaHCO_3$, which is allowed to decompose into 2 mol Na(s), 2 mol C(graphite), 1 mol $H_2(g)$, and 3 mol $O_2(g)$, as in equation (a) above. In the second step, recombine the 2 mol Na(s), 2 mol C(graphite), 1 mol $H_2(g)$, and 3 mol $O_2(g)$ to form the products according to equations (b), (c), and (d) above.

The pathway shown in Figure 4-20 *is not* how the reaction actually occurs. This does not matter, though, because enthalpy is a state function and the change of any state function is independent of the path chosen. The enthalpy change for the overall reaction is the sum of the standard enthalpy changes of the individual steps.

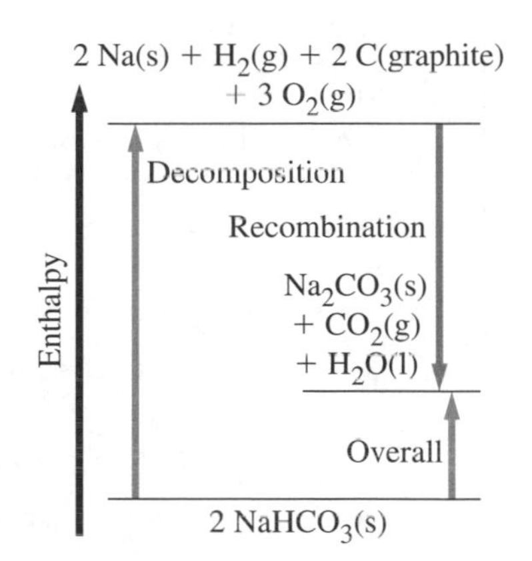

▲ FIGURE 4-20
Computing heats of reaction from standard enthalpies of formation
Enthalpy is a state function, hence ΔH° for the overall reaction $2\,NaHCO_3(s) \longrightarrow Na_2CO_3(s) + CO_2(g) + H_2O(l)$ is the sum of the enthalpy changes for the two steps shown.

$$\Delta H^\circ = \Delta H^\circ_{decomposition} + \Delta H^\circ_{recombination}$$
$$\Delta H^\circ_{decomposition} = -2 \times \Delta H_f^\circ[NaHCO_3(s)]$$
$$\Delta H^\circ_{recombination} = \Delta H_f^\circ[Na_2CO_3(s)] + \Delta H_f^\circ[H_2O(l)] + \Delta H_f^\circ[CO_2(g)]$$

so that

$$\Delta H^\circ = \Delta H_f^\circ[Na_2CO_3(s)] + \Delta H_f^\circ[H_2O(l)] + \Delta H_f^\circ[CO_2(g)] - 2 \times \Delta H_f^\circ[NaHCO_3(s)]$$

Equation (4.20) is a specific application of the following more general relationship for a standard enthalpy of reaction.

$$\Delta H^\circ = \sum v_p \Delta H_f^\circ(\text{products}) - \sum v_r \Delta H_f^\circ(\text{reactants}) \quad \textbf{(4.21)}$$

The symbol Σ (Greek, sigma) means "the sum of." The terms that are added together are the products of the standard enthalpies of formation (ΔH_f°) and their stoichiometric coefficients, v. One sum is required for the reaction products (subscript p), and another for the initial reactants (subscript r). The enthalpy change of the reaction is the sum of terms for the products *minus* the sum of terms for the reactants. Equation (4.21) avoids the manipulation of a number of chemical equations. The state function basis for equation (4.21) is shown in Figure 4-21 and is applied in Example 4-11.

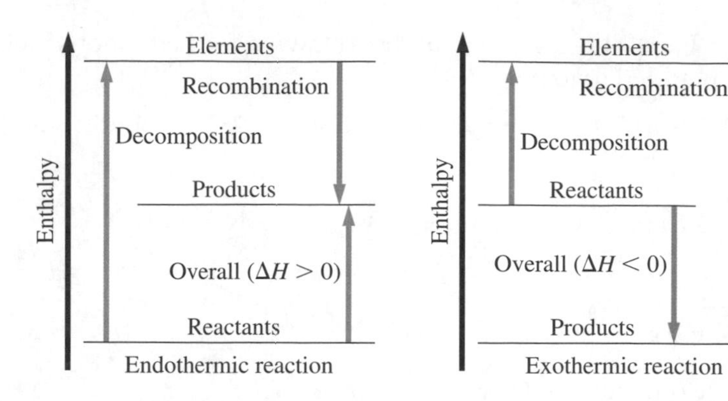

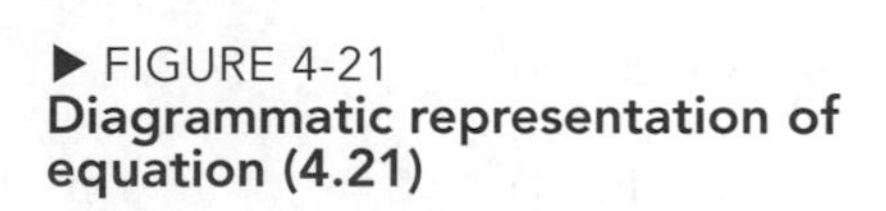
▶ FIGURE 4-21
Diagrammatic representation of equation (4.21)

EXAMPLE 4-11 Calculating $\Delta H°$ from Tabulated Values of $\Delta H_f°$

Let us apply equation (4.21) to calculate the standard enthalpy of combustion of ethane, $C_2H_6(g)$, a component of natural gas.

Analyze

This type of problem is a straightforward application of equation (4.21). Appendix A has a table of thermodynamic data which includes the standard enthalpy of formation for a number of compounds.

Solve

The reaction is

$$C_2H_6(g) + \frac{7}{2}O_2(g) \longrightarrow 2\,CO_2(g) + 3\,H_2O(l)$$

The relationship we need is equation (4.21). The data we substitute into the relationship are from Table 4.2.

$$\begin{aligned}\Delta H° &= \{2\text{ mol } CO_2 \times \Delta H_f°[CO_2(g)] + 3\text{ mol } H_2O \times \Delta H_f°[H_2O(l)]\}\\ &\quad - \{1\text{ mol } C_2H_6 \times \Delta H_f°[C_2H_6(g)] + \frac{7}{2}\text{mol } O_2 \times \Delta H_f°[O_2(g)]\}\\ &= 2\text{ mol } CO_2 \times (-393.5\text{ kJ/mol } CO_2) + 3\text{ mol } H_2O \times (-285.8\text{ kJ/mol } H_2O)\\ &\quad - 1\text{ mol } C_2H_6 \times (-84.7\text{ kJ/mol } C_2H_6) - \frac{7}{2}\text{mol } O_2 \times 0\text{ kJ/mol } O_2\\ &= -787.0\text{ kJ} - 857.4\text{ kJ} + 84.7\text{ kJ} = -1559.7\text{ kJ}\end{aligned}$$

Assess

In these types of problems, we must make sure to subtract the sum of the products' standard enthalpies of formation from the sum of the reactants' standard enthalpies of formation. We must also keep in mind that the standard enthalpy of formation of an element in its reference form is zero. Thus, we can drop the term involving $\Delta H_f°[O_2(g)]$ at any time in the calculation.

PRACTICE EXAMPLE A: Use data from Table 4.2 to calculate the standard enthalpy of combustion of ethanol, $CH_3CH_2OH(l)$, at 298.15 K.

PRACTICE EXAMPLE B: Calculate the standard enthalpy of combustion at 298.15 K *per mole* of a gaseous fuel that contains C_3H_8 and C_4H_{10} in the mole fractions 0.62 and 0.38, respectively.

A type of calculation as important as the one illustrated in Example 4-11 is the determination of an unknown $\Delta H_f°$ value from a set of known $\Delta H_f°$ values and a known standard enthalpy of reaction, $\Delta H°$. As shown in Example 4-12, the essential step is to rearrange expression (4.21) to isolate the unknown $\Delta H_f°$ on one side of the equation. Also shown is a way of organizing the data that you may find helpful.

EXAMPLE 4-12 Calculating an Unknown ΔH_f° Value

Use the data here and in Table 4.2 to calculate ΔH_f° of benzene, $C_6H_6(l)$.

$$2\,C_6H_6(l) + 15\,O_2(g) \longrightarrow 12\,CO_2(g) + 6\,H_2O(l) \qquad \Delta H^\circ = -6535\text{ kJ}$$

Analyze

We have a chemical equation and know the standard enthalpy of reaction. We are asked to determine a standard enthalpy of formation. Equation (4.21) relates a standard enthalpy of reaction to standard enthalpy of formations for reactants and products. To begin, we organize the data needed in the calculation by writing the chemical equation for the reaction with ΔH_f° data listed under the chemical formulas.

Solve

$$2\,C_6H_6(l) + 15\,O_2(g) \longrightarrow 12\,CO_2(g) + 6\,H_2O(l) \qquad \Delta H^\circ = -6535\text{ kJ}$$

	$2\,C_6H_6(l)$	$15\,O_2(g)$	$12\,CO_2(g)$	$6\,H_2O(l)$
ΔH_f°, kJ/mol	?	0	−393.5	−285.8

Now, we can substitute known data into expression (4.21) and rearrange the equation to obtain a lone term on the left: $\Delta H_f^\circ[C_6H_6(l)]$. The remainder of the problem simply involves numerical calculations.

$$\Delta H^\circ = \{12\text{ mol }CO_2 \times -(393.5\text{ kJ/mol }CO_2) + 6\text{ mol }H_2O \times (\ 285.8\text{ kJ/mol }H_2O)\}$$
$$- 2\text{ mol }C_2H_6 \times \Delta H_f^\circ[C_6H_6(l)] = -6535\text{ kJ}$$

$$\Delta H_f^\circ[C_6H_6(l)] = \frac{\{-4722\text{ kJ} - 1715\text{ kJ}\} + 6535\text{ kJ}}{2\text{ mol }C_6H_6} = 49\text{ kJ/mol }C_6H_6(l)$$

Assess

By organizing the data as shown, we were able to identify what is unknown and see how to use equation (4.21). To obtain the correct answer, we also needed to use the correct states for the compounds. In combustion reactions, the water in the product is always liquid. If we had used the standard enthalpy of formation for gaseous water, we would have obtained the wrong answer.

PRACTICE EXAMPLE A: The overall reaction that occurs in photosynthesis in plants is

$$6\,CO_2(g) + 6\,H_2O(l) \longrightarrow C_6H_{12}O_6(s) + 6\,O_2(g) \qquad \Delta H^\circ = 2803\text{ kJ}$$

Determine the standard enthalpy of formation of glucose, $C_6H_{12}O_6(s)$, at 298 K.

PRACTICE EXAMPLE B: A handbook lists the standard enthalpy of combustion of gaseous dimethyl ether at 298 K as $-31.70\text{ kJ/g}(CH_3)_2O(g)$. What is the standard molar enthalpy of formation of dimethyl ether at 298 K?

Ionic Reactions in Solutions

Many chemical reactions in aqueous solution are best thought of as reactions between ions and best represented by net ionic equations. Consider the neutralization of a strong acid by a strong base. Using a somewhat more accurate enthalpy of neutralization than we obtained in Example 4-4, we can write

$$H^+(aq) + OH^-(aq) \longrightarrow H_2O(l) \qquad \Delta H^\circ = -55.8\text{ kJ} \qquad \textbf{(4.22)}$$

We should also be able to calculate this enthalpy of neutralization by using enthalpy of formation data in expression (4.21), but this requires us to have enthalpy of formation data for individual ions. And there is a slight problem in getting these. We cannot create ions of a single type in a chemical reaction. We always produce cations and anions simultaneously, as in the reaction of sodium and chlorine to produce Na^+ and Cl^- in NaCl. We must choose a particular ion to which we assign an enthalpy of formation of *zero* in its aqueous solutions. We then compare the enthalpies of formation of other ions to this reference ion. The ion we arbitrarily choose for our zero is $H^+(aq)$. Now let us see how we can use expression (4.21) and data from equation (4.22) to determine the enthalpy of formation of $OH^-(aq)$.

$$\Delta H° = 1\,\text{mol}\,H_2O \times \Delta H_f°[H_2O(l)] - \{1\,\text{mol}\,H^+ \times \Delta H_f°[H^+(aq)] + 1\,\text{mol}\,OH^- \times \Delta H_f°[OH^-(aq)]\} = -55.8\,\text{kJ}$$

$$\Delta H_f°[OH^-(aq)] = \frac{55.8\,\text{kJ} + (1\,\text{mol}\,H_2O \times \Delta H_f°[H_2O(l)]) - (1\,\text{mol}\,H^+ \times \Delta H_f°[H^+(aq)])}{1\,\text{mol}\,OH^-}$$

$$\Delta H_f°[OH^-(aq)] = \frac{55.8\,\text{kJ} - 285.8\,\text{kJ} - 0\,\text{kJ}}{1\,\text{mol}\,OH^-} = -230.0\,\text{kJ/mol}\,OH^-$$

Table 4.3 lists data for several common ions in aqueous solution. Enthalpies of formation in solution depend on the solute concentration. These data are representative for *dilute* aqueous solutions (about 1 M), the type of solution that we normally deal with. Some of these data are used in Example 4-13.

TABLE 4.3 Some Standard Molar Enthalpies of Formation, $\Delta H_f°$ of Ions in Aqueous Solution at 298.15 K

Ion	kJ/mol	Ion	kJ/mol
H^+	0	OH^-	−230.0
Li^+	−278.5	Cl^-	−167.2
Na^+	−240.1	Br^-	−121.6
K^+	−252.4	I^-	−55.19
NH_4^+	−132.5	NO_3^-	−205.0
Ag^+	105.6	CO_3^{2-}	−677.1
Mg^{2+}	−466.9	S^{2-}	33.05
Ca^{2+}	−542.8	SO_4^{2-}	−909.3
Ba^{2+}	−537.6	$S_2O_3^{2-}$	−648.5
Cu^{2+}	64.77	PO_4^{3-}	−1277
Al^{3+}	−531		

EXAMPLE 4-13 Calculating the Enthalpy Change in an Ionic Reaction

Given that $\Delta H_f°[BaSO_4(s)] = -1473$ kJ/mol, what is the standard enthalpy change for the precipitation of barium sulfate?

Analyze

First, write the net ionic equation for the reaction and introduce the relevant data. Then make use of equation (4.21).

Solve

Start by organizing the data in a table.

	$Ba^{2+}(aq)$ +	$SO_4^{2-}(aq)$ ⟶	$BaSO_4(s)$	$\Delta H° = ?$
$\Delta H_f°$, kJ/mol	−537.6	−909.3	−1473	

Then substitute data into equation (4.21).

$$\begin{aligned}\Delta H° &= 1\,\text{mol}\,BaSO_4 \times \Delta H_f°[BaSO_4(s)] - 1\,\text{mol}\,Ba^{2+} \times \Delta H_f°[Ba^{2+}(aq)] - 1\,\text{mol}\,SO_4^{2-} \times \Delta H_f°[SO_4^{2-}(aq)]\\ &= 1\,\text{mol}\,BaSO_4 \times (-1473\,\text{kJ/mol}\,BaSO_4) - 1\,\text{mol}\,Ba^{2+} \times (-537.6\,\text{kJ/mol}\,Ba^{2+})\\ &\quad - 1\,\text{mol}\,SO_4^{2-} \times (-909.3\,\text{kJ/mol}\,SO_4^{2-})\\ &= -1473\,\text{kJ} + 537.6\,\text{kJ} + 909.3\,\text{kJ} = -26\,\text{kJ}\end{aligned}$$

Assess

The standard enthalpy of reaction determined here is the heat given off by the system (i.e., the ionic reaction).

PRACTICE EXAMPLE A: Given that $\Delta H_f°[AgI(s)] = -61.84$ kJ/mol, what is the standard enthalpy change for the precipitation of silver iodide?

PRACTICE EXAMPLE B: The standard enthalpy change for the precipitation of $Ag_2CO_3(s)$ is −39.9 kJ per mole of $Ag_2CO_3(s)$ formed. What is $\Delta H_f°[Ag_2CO_3(s)]$?

4-10 CONCEPT ASSESSMENT

Is it possible to calculate a heat of reaction at 373.15 K by using standard enthalpies of formation at 298.15 K? If so, explain how you would do this, and indicate any additional data you might need.

4-9 Fuels as Sources of Energy

One of the most important uses of thermochemical measurements and calculations is in assessing materials as energy sources. For the most part, these materials, called fuels, liberate heat through the process of combustion. We will briefly survey some common fuels, emphasizing matters that a thermochemical background helps us to understand.

Fossil Fuels

The bulk of current energy needs are met by petroleum, natural gas, and coal—so-called fossil fuels. These fuels are derived from plant and animal life of millions of years ago. The original source of the energy locked into these fuels is solar energy. In the process of *photosynthesis*, CO_2 and H_2O, in the presence of enzymes, the pigment chlorophyll, and sunlight, are converted to *carbohydrates*. These are compounds with formulas $C_m(H_2O)_n$, where m and n are integers. For example, in the sugar glucose $m = n = 6$, that is, $C_6(H_2O)_6 = C_6H_{12}O_6$. Its formation through photosynthesis is an *endothermic* process, represented as

◀ Although the formula $C_m(H_2O)_n$ suggests a "hydrate" of carbon, in carbohydrates, there are no H_2O units, as there are in hydrates, such as $CuSO_4 \cdot 5\,H_2O$. H and O atoms are simply found in the same numerical ratio as in H_2O.

$$6\,CO_2(g) + 6\,H_2O(l) \xrightarrow[\text{sunlight}]{\text{chlorophyll}} C_6H_{12}O_6(s) + 6\,O_2(g) \quad \Delta H° = +2.8 \times 10^3\,\text{kJ} \tag{4.23}$$

When reaction (4.23) is reversed, as in the combustion of glucose, heat is evolved. The combustion reaction is *exothermic*.

The complex carbohydrate cellulose, with molecular masses ranging up to 500,000 u, is the principal structural material of plants. When plant life decomposes in the presence of bacteria and out of contact with air, O and H atoms are removed and the approximate carbon content of the residue increases in the progression

$$\text{Peat} \longrightarrow \text{lignite (32\% C)} \longrightarrow \text{sub-bituminous coal (40\% C)} \longrightarrow \text{bituminous coal (60\% C)} \longrightarrow \text{anthracite coal (80\% C)}$$

For this process to progress all the way to anthracite coal may take about 300 million years. Coal, then, is a combustible organic rock consisting of carbon, hydrogen, and oxygen, together with small quantities of nitrogen, sulfur, and mineral matter (ash). (One proposed formula for a "molecule" of bituminous coal is $C_{153}H_{115}N_3O_{13}S_2$.)

Petroleum and natural gas formed in a different way. The remains of plants and animals living in ancient seas fell to the ocean floor, where they were decomposed by bacteria and covered with sand and mud. Over time, the sand and mud were converted to sandstone by the weight of overlying layers of sand and mud. The high pressures and temperatures resulting from this overlying sandstone rock formation transformed the original organic matter into petroleum and natural gas. The ages of these deposits range from about 250 million to 500 million years.

A typical natural gas consists of about 85% methane (CH_4), 10% ethane (C_2H_6), 3% propane (C_3H_8), and small quantities of other combustible and noncombustible gases. A typical petroleum consists of several hundred different hydrocarbons that range in complexity from C_1 molecules (CH_4) to C_{40} or higher (such as $C_{40}H_{82}$).

TABLE 4.4 Approximate Heats of Combustion of Some Fuels

Heat of Combustion	
Fuel	**kJ/g**
Municipal waste	−12.7
Cellulose	−17.5
Pinewood	−21.2
Methanol	−22.7
Peat	−20.8
Bituminous coal	−28.3
Isooctane (a component of gasoline)	−47.8
Natural gas	−49.5

One way to compare different fuels is through their heats of combustion: In general, *the higher the heat of combustion, the better the fuel*. Table 4.4 lists approximate heats of combustion for the fossil fuels. These data show that *biomass* (living matter or materials derived from it—wood, alcohols, municipal waste) is a viable fuel, but that fossil fuels yield more energy per unit mass.

Problems Posed by Fossil Fuel Use There are two fundamental problems with the use of fossil fuels. First, fossil fuels are essentially *nonrenewable* energy sources. The world consumption of fossil fuels is expected to increase for the foreseeable future (Fig. 4-22), but when will Earth's supply of these fuels run out? There is currently a debate about whether oil production has peaked now and is about to decline, or whether it will peak more toward the middle of the this century. The second problem with fossil fuels is their environmental effect. Sulfur impurities in fuels produce oxides of sulfur. The high temperatures associated with combustion cause the reaction of N_2 and O_2 in air to form oxides of nitrogen. Oxides of sulfur and nitrogen are implicated in air pollution and are important contributors to the environmental problem known as acid rain. Another inevitable product of the combustion of fossil fuels is carbon dioxide, one of the "greenhouse" gases leading to *global warming* and potential changes in Earth's climate.

▶ Environmental issues associated with oxides of sulfur and nitrogen are discussed more fully in later chapters.

Global Warming—An Environmental Issue Involving Carbon Dioxide We do not normally think of CO_2 as an air pollutant because it is essentially nontoxic and is a natural and necessary component of air. Its ultimate effect on the environment, however, could be very significant. A buildup of $CO_2(g)$ in the atmosphere may disturb the energy balance on Earth.

Earth's atmosphere is largely transparent to visible and UV radiation from the sun. This radiation is absorbed at Earth's surface, which is warmed

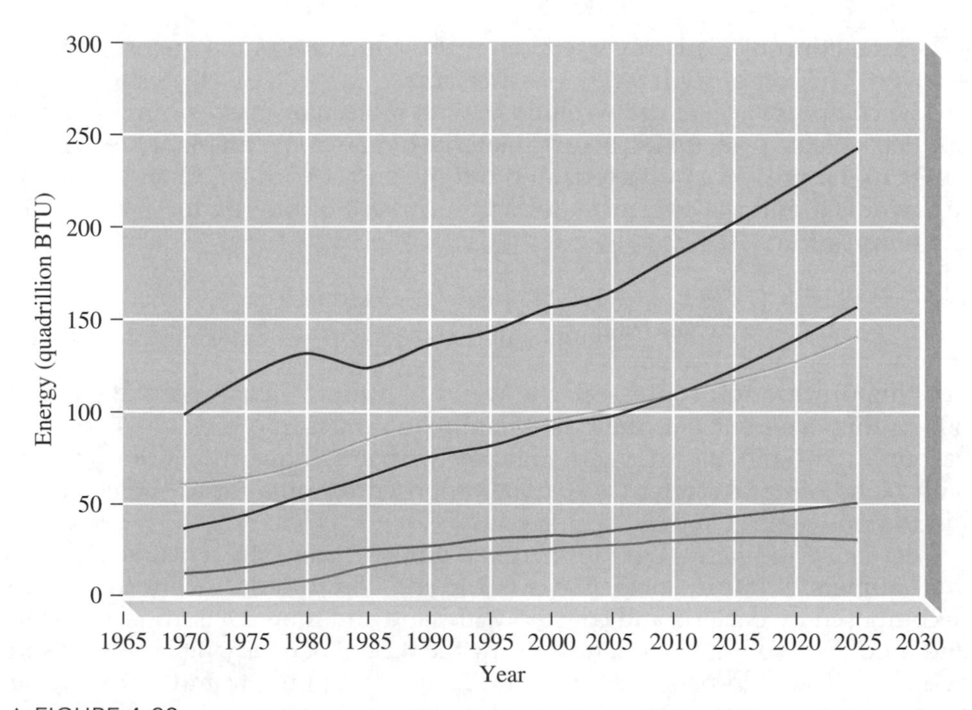

▲ FIGURE 4-22
World primary energy consumption by energy source
These graphs show the history of energy consumption since 1970, with predictions to 2025. Petroleum (dark blue line) is seen to be the major source of energy for the foreseeable future, followed by coal (yellow) and natural gas (pink), which are about the same. Other sources of energy included are wind power (purple) and nuclear power (light blue). The unit BTU is a measure of energy and stands for British thermal unit (see Exercise 95). [*Source: www.eia.doe.gov/oiaf/ieo/pdf/ieoreftab_2.pdf*]

by it. Some of this absorbed energy is reradiated as infrared radiation. Certain atmospheric gases, primarily CO_2, methane, and water vapor, absorb some of this infrared radiation, and the energy thus retained in the atmosphere produces a warming effect. This process, outlined in Figure 4-23, is often compared to the retention of thermal energy in a greenhouse and is called the "greenhouse effect."* The natural greenhouse effect is essential in maintaining the proper temperature for life on Earth. Without it, Earth would be permanently covered with ice.

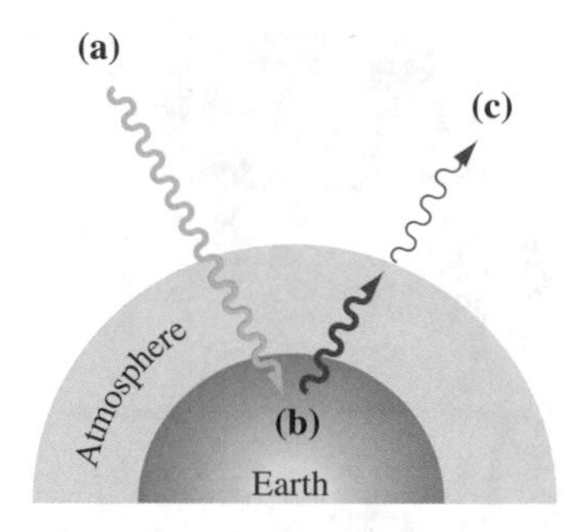

▲ FIGURE 4-23
The "greenhouse" effect
(a) Some incoming radiation from sunlight is reflected back into space by the atmosphere, and some, such as certain UV light, is absorbed by stratospheric ozone. Much of the radiation from sunlight, however, reaches Earth's surface. **(b)** Earth's surface re-emits some of this energy as infrared radiation. **(c)** Some of the infrared radiation leaving the Earth's surface is absorbed by CO_2 and other greenhouse gases and is redirected back towards the Earth's surface. The redirected infrared radiation warms the atmosphere.

Over the past 400,000 years, the atmospheric carbon dioxide concentration has varied from 180 to 300 parts per million with the preindustrial-age concentration at about 285 ppm. By 2005, the level had increased to about 376 ppm and is still rising (Fig. 4-24). Increasing atmospheric carbon dioxide concentrations result from the burning of carbon-containing fuels such as wood, coal, natural gas, and gasoline (Fig. 4-24) and from the deforestation of tropical regions (plants, through photosynthesis, consume CO_2 from the atmosphere). The expected effect of a CO_2 buildup is an increase in Earth's average temperature, a **global warming**. Some estimates are that a doubling of the CO_2 content over that of preindustrial times could occur before the end of the present century and that this doubling could produce an average global temperature increase of 1.5 to 4.5 °C.

Predicting the probable effects of a CO_2 buildup in the atmosphere is done largely through computer models, and it is very difficult to know all the factors that should be included in these models and the relative importance of these factors. For example, global warming could lead to the increased evaporation of water and increased cloud formation. In turn, an increased cloud cover could reduce the amount of solar radiation reaching Earth's surface and, to some extent, offset global warming.

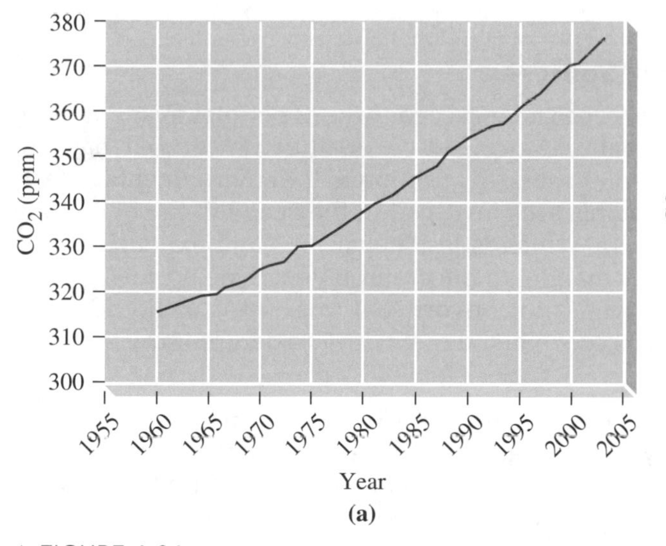

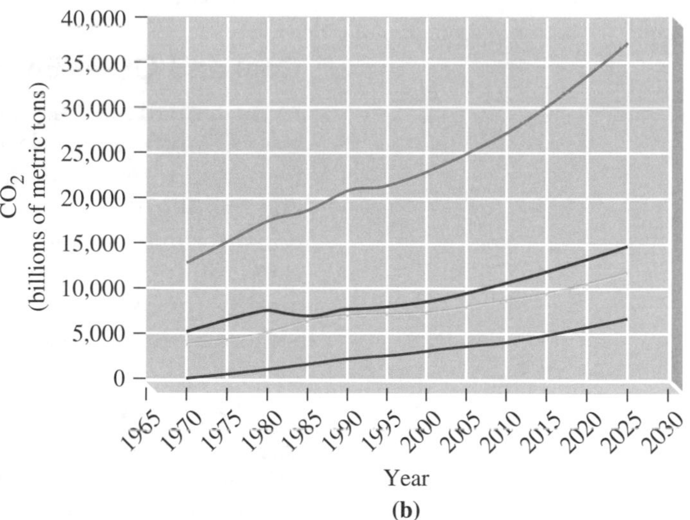

▲ FIGURE 4-24
Increasing carbon dioxide content of the atmosphere
(a) The global average atmospheric carbon dioxide level over a 50-year span, expressed in parts per million by volume, as measured by a worldwide cooperative sampling network. **(b)** The actual and predicted CO_2 emissions for a 55-year span due to the combustion of natural gas (pink line), coal (yellow), and petroleum (dark blue), together with the total of all CO_2 emissions (light blue). The CO_2 content of the atmosphere continues to increase, from approximately 375 ppm in 2003 to 385 ppm in 2008.

*Glass, like CO_2, is transparent to visible and some UV light but absorbs infrared radiation. The glass in a greenhouse, though, acts primarily to prevent the bulk flow of warm air out of the greenhouse.

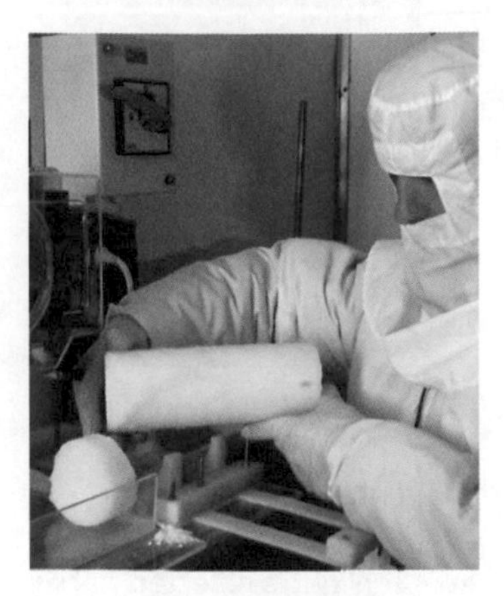

▲ An ice core from the ice sheet in Antarctica is cut into sections in a refrigerated clean room. The ice core is then analyzed to determine the amount and type of trapped gases and trace elements it contains. These data provide information regarding past changes in climate and current trends in the pollution of the atmosphere.

Some of the significant possible effects of global warming are

- local temperature changes. The average annual temperature for Alaska and Northern Canada has increased by 1.9 °C over the past 50 years. Alaskan winter temperatures have increased by an average of 3.5 °C over this same time period.
- a rise in sea level caused by the thermal expansion of seawater and increased melting of continental ice caps. A potential increase in sea level of up to 1 m by 2100 would displace tens of millions of inhabitants in Bangladesh alone.
- the migration of plant and animal species. Vegetation now characteristic of certain areas of the globe could migrate into regions several hundred kilometers closer to the poles. The areas in which diseases, such as malaria, are endemic could also expand.

Although some of the current thinking involves speculation, a growing body of evidence supports the likelihood of global warming, also called climate change. For example, analyses of tiny air bubbles trapped in the Antarctic ice cap show a strong correlation between the atmospheric CO_2 content and temperature for the past 160,000 years—low temperatures during periods of low CO_2 levels and higher temperatures with higher levels of CO_2.

CO_2 is not the only greenhouse gas. Several gases are even stronger infrared absorbers—specifically, methane (CH_4), ozone (O_3), nitrous oxide (N_2O), and chlorofluorocarbons (CFCs). Furthermore, atmospheric concentrations of some of these gases have been growing at a faster rate than that of CO_2. No strategies beyond curtailing the use of chlorofluorocarbons and fossil fuels have emerged for countering a possible global warming. Like several other major environmental issues, some aspects of climate change are not well understood, and research, debate, and action are all likely to occur simultaneously for a long time to come.

Coal and Other Energy Sources

In the United States, reserves of coal far exceed those of petroleum and natural gas. Despite this relative abundance, however, the use of coal has not increased significantly in recent years. In addition to the environmental effects cited above, the expense and hazards involved in the deep mining of coal are considerable. Surface mining, which is less hazardous and expensive than deep mining, is also more damaging to the environment. One promising possibility for using coal reserves is to convert coal to gaseous or liquid fuels, either in surface installations or while the coal is still underground.

Gasification of Coal Before cheap natural gas became available in the 1940s, gas produced from coal (variously called producer gas, town gas, or city gas) was widely used in the United States. This gas was manufactured by passing steam and air through heated coal and involved such reactions as

$$\text{C(graphite)} + H_2O(g) \longrightarrow CO(g) + H_2(g) \qquad \Delta H^\circ = +131.3\text{ kJ} \qquad \textbf{(4.24)}$$

$$CO(g) + H_2O(g) \longrightarrow CO_2(g) + H_2(g) \qquad \Delta H^\circ = -41.2\text{ kJ} \qquad \textbf{(4.25)}$$

$$2\text{C(graphite)} + O_2(g) \longrightarrow 2\,CO(g) \qquad \Delta H^\circ = -221.0\text{ kJ} \qquad \textbf{(4.26)}$$

$$\text{C(graphite)} + 2\,H_2(g) \longrightarrow CH_4(g) \qquad \Delta H^\circ = -74.8\text{ kJ} \qquad \textbf{(4.27)}$$

The principal gasification reaction (4.24) is highly endothermic. The heat requirements for this reaction are met by the carefully controlled partial burning of coal (reaction 4.26).

A typical producer gas consists of about 23% CO, 18% H_2, 8% CO_2, and 1% CH_4 by volume. It also contains about 50% N_2 because air is used in its production. Because the N_2 and CO_2 are noncombustible, producer gas has only about 10% to 15% of the heat value of natural gas. Modern gasification processes include several features:

1. They use $O_2(g)$ instead of air, thereby eliminating $N_2(g)$ in the product.
2. They provide for the removal of noncombustible $CO_2(g)$ and sulfur impurities. For example,

$$CaO(s) + CO_2(g) \longrightarrow CaCO_3(s)$$
$$2\,H_2S(g) + SO_2(g) \longrightarrow 3\,S(s) + 2\,H_2O(g)$$

3. They include a step (called *methanation*) to convert CO and H_2, in the presence of a catalyst, to CH_4.

$$CO(g) + 3\,H_2(g) \xrightarrow{\text{catalyst}} CH_4(g) + H_2O(l)$$

The product is called *substitute natural gas* (SNG), a gaseous mixture with composition and heat value similar to that of natural gas.

Liquefaction of Coal The first step in obtaining liquid fuels from coal generally involves gasification of coal, as in reaction (4.24). This step is followed by catalytic reactions in which liquid hydrocarbons are formed.

$$n\,CO + (2n + 1)H_2 \longrightarrow C_nH_{2n+2} + n\,H_2O$$

In still another process, liquid methanol is formed.

$$CO(g) + 2\,H_2(g) \longrightarrow CH_3OH(l) \qquad \textbf{(4.28)}$$

In 1942, some 32 million gallons of aviation fuel were made from coal in Germany. In South Africa, the Sasol process for coal liquefaction has been a major source of gasoline and a variety of other petroleum products and chemicals for more than 50 years.

Methanol

Methanol, CH_3OH, can be obtained from coal by reaction (4.28). It can also be produced by thermal decomposition (pyrolysis) of wood, manure, sewage, or municipal waste. The heat of combustion of methanol is only about one-half that of a typical gasoline on a mass basis, but methanol has a high octane number—106—compared with 100 for the gasoline hydrocarbon isooctane and about 92 for premium gasoline. Methanol has been tested and used as a fuel in internal combustion engines and is cleaner burning than gasoline. Methanol can also be used for space heating, electric power generation, fuel cells, and as a reactant to make a variety of other organic compounds.

Ethanol

Ethanol, C_2H_5OH, is produced mostly from ethylene, C_2H_4, which in turn is derived from petroleum. Current interest centers on the production of ethanol by the fermentation of organic matter, a process known throughout recorded history. Ethanol production by fermentation is probably most advanced in Brazil, where sugarcane and cassava (manioc) are the plant matter (biomass) used. In the United States, corn-based ethanol is used chiefly as an additive to gasoline to improve its octane rating and reduce air pollution. Also, a 90% gasoline–10% ethanol mixture is used as an automotive fuel under the name *gasohol*.

Biofuels

Biofuels are renewable energy sources that are similar to fossil fuels. Biofuels are fuels derived from dead biological material, most commonly plants. Fossil fuels are derived from biological material that has been dead for a very long time. The use of biofuels is not new; several car inventors had envisioned their vehicles running on such fuels as peanut oil, hemp-derived fuel, and ethanol. Reacting vegetable oil with a base–alcohol mixture produces a compound commonly called a biodiesel. A typical petro–diesel compound is the hydrocarbon cetane ($C_{16}H_{34}$), and the typical biodiesel compound contains oxygen atoms, as illustrated in the figure below. The standard enthalpies of combustion of the petro–diesel and the biodiesel are very similar.

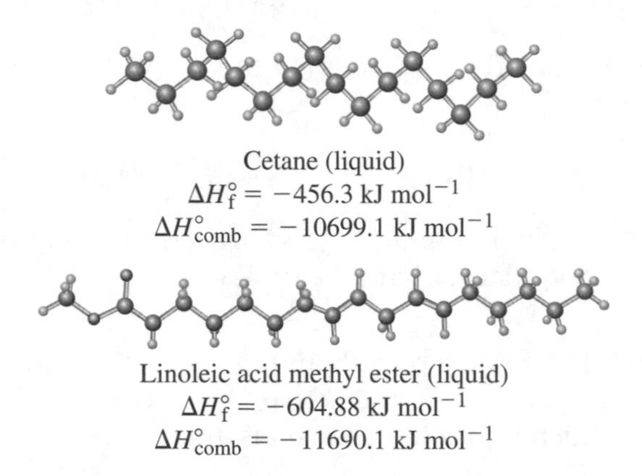

Cetane (liquid)
$\Delta H_f^\circ = -456.3 \text{ kJ mol}^{-1}$
$\Delta H_{comb}^\circ = -10699.1 \text{ kJ mol}^{-1}$

Linoleic acid methyl ester (liquid)
$\Delta H_f^\circ = -604.88 \text{ kJ mol}^{-1}$
$\Delta H_{comb}^\circ = -11690.1 \text{ kJ mol}^{-1}$

Although biofuels are appealing replacements for fossil fuels, their widespread adoption has several potential drawbacks. One major concern is the food-versus-fuel issue. Typical plants used for food (e.g., sugar cane) are sources of biofuels, which drives up the cost of food. A positive aspect of biofuels is that they are carbon neutral; that is, the $CO_2(g)$ produced by the burning of a biofuel is then used by plants for new growth, resulting in no net gain of carbon in the atmosphere. Biofuels and their use have many other advantages and disadvantages. Importantly, chemical knowledge of these compounds is needed to address these issues.

Hydrogen

Another fuel with great potential is hydrogen. Its most attractive features are that

- on a per gram basis, its heat of combustion is more than twice that of methane and about three times that of gasoline;
- the product of its combustion is H_2O, not CO and CO_2 as with gasoline.

Currently, the bulk of hydrogen used commercially is made from petroleum and natural gas, but for hydrogen to be a significant fuel of the future, efficient methods must be perfected for obtaining hydrogen from other sources, especially water. Alternative methods of producing hydrogen and the prospects of developing an economy based on hydrogen are discussed later in the text.

Alternative Energy Sources

Combustion reactions are only one means of extracting useful energy from materials. An alternative, for example, is to carry out reactions that yield the same products as combustion reactions in electrochemical cells called *fuel cells*. The energy is released as electricity rather than as heat. Solar energy can be used directly, without recourse to photosynthesis. Nuclear processes can be used in place of chemical reactions. Other alternative sources in various stages of development and use include hydroelectric energy, geothermal energy, and tidal and wind power.

Summary

4-1 Getting Started: Some Terminology—The subject of a thermochemical study is broken down into the **system** of interest and the portions of the universe with which the system may interact, the **surroundings**. An **open system** can exchange both energy and matter with its surroundings. A **closed system** can exchange only energy and not matter. An **isolated system** can exchange neither energy nor matter with its surroundings (Fig. 4-1). **Energy** is the capacity to do work, and **work** is performed when a force acts through a distance. Energy can be further characterized (Fig. 4-2) as **kinetic energy** (energy associated with matter in motion) or **potential energy** (energy resulting from the position or composition of matter). Kinetic energy associated with random molecular motion is sometimes called **thermal energy**.

4-2 Heat—**Heat** is energy transferred between a system and its surroundings as a result of a temperature difference between the two. In some cases, heat can be transferred at constant temperature, as in a change in state of matter in the system. A quantity of heat is the product of the heat capacity of the system and the temperature change (equation 4.5). In turn, **heat capacity** is the product of mass and **specific heat**, the amount of heat required to change the temperature of one gram of substance by one degree Celsius. Historically, the unit for measuring heat has been the **calorie (cal)**, but the SI unit of heat is the joule, the same as for other forms of energy (equation 4.2). Energy transfers between a system and its surroundings must conform to the **law of conservation of energy**, meaning that all heat lost by a system is gained by its surroundings (equation 4.6).

4-3 Heats of Reaction and Calorimetry—In a chemical reaction, a change in the **chemical energy** associated with the reactants and products may appear as heat. The **heat of reaction** is the quantity of heat exchanged between a system and its surroundings when the reaction occurs at a constant temperature. In an **exothermic reaction**, heat is given off by the system; in an **endothermic reaction** the system absorbs heat. Heats of reaction are determined in a **calorimeter**, a device for measuring quantities of heat (equation 4.10). Exothermic combustion reactions are usually studied in a **bomb calorimeter** (Fig. 4-5). A common type of calorimeter used in the general chemistry laboratory is constructed from ordinary Styrofoam cups (Fig. 4-6).

4-4 Work—In some reactions an energy transfer between a system and its surroundings occurs as work. This is commonly the work involved in the expansion or compression of gases (Fig. 4-8) and is called **pressure–volume work** (equation 4.11).

4-5 The First Law of Thermodynamics—**Internal energy** (U) is the total energy (both kinetic and potential) in a system. The **first law of thermodynamics** relates changes in the internal energy of a system (ΔU) to the quantities of heat (q) and work (w) exchanged between the system and its surroundings. The relationship is $\Delta U = q + w$ (equation 4.12) and requires that a set of sign conventions be consistently followed. A **function of state (state function)** has a value that depends only on the exact condition or state in which a system is found and not on how that state was reached. Internal energy is a state function. A path-dependent function, such as heat or work, depends on how a change in a system is achieved. A change that is accomplished through an infinite number of infinitesimal steps is a **reversible process** (Fig. 4-12), whereas a change accomplished in one step or a series of finite steps is **irreversible**.

4-6 Heats of Reaction: ΔU and ΔH—In a chemical reaction with work limited to pressure–volume work and conducted at constant volume, the heat of reaction is equal to the change in internal energy (equation 4.13). For reactions at constant pressure a more useful function is **enthalpy** (H), defined as the internal energy (U) of a system plus the pressure–volume product (PV). The **enthalpy change** (ΔH) in a reaction proves to be the heat of reaction at constant pressure (equation 4.14). Most heats of reaction are reported as ΔH values. A substance under a pressure of 1 bar (10^5 Pa) and at the temperature of interest is said to be in its **standard state**. If the reactants and products of a reaction are in their standard states, the enthalpy change in a reaction is called the **standard enthalpy of reaction** and designated as $\Delta H°$. Enthalpy changes can be represented schematically through **enthalpy diagrams** (Fig. 4-15).

4-7 Indirect Determination of ΔH: Hess's Law—Often an unknown ΔH value can be established indirectly through **Hess's law**, which states that an overall enthalpy change is the sum of the enthalpy changes of the individual steps leading to the overall process (Fig. 4-17).

4-8 Standard Enthalpies of Formation—By arbitrarily assigning an enthalpy of zero to the reference forms of the elements in their standard states, the enthalpy change in the formation of a compound from its elements becomes a **standard enthalpy of formation** (ΔH_f°). Using tabulated standard enthalpies of formation (Table 4.2), it is possible to calculate standard enthalpies of reactions without having to perform additional experiments (equation 4.21).

4-9 Fuels as Sources of Energy—One of the chief applications of thermochemistry is in the study of the combustion of fuels as energy sources. Currently, the principal fuels are the fossil fuels, but potential alternative fuels are also mentioned in this chapter and discussed in more depth later in the text. One of the problems with the use of fossil fuels is the potential for **global warming**.

Integrative Example

When charcoal is burned in a limited supply of oxygen in the presence of H_2O, a mixture of CO, H_2, and other noncombustible gases (mostly CO_2) is obtained. Such a mixture is called *synthesis gas*. This gas can be used to synthesize organic compounds, or it can be burned as a fuel. A typical synthesis gas consists of 55.0% CO(g), 33.0% $H_2(g)$, and 12.0% noncombustible gases (mostly CO_2), *by volume*. To what temperature can 25.0 kg water at 25.0 °C be heated with the heat liberated by the combustion of 0.205 m^3 of this typical synthesis gas, measured at 25.0 °C and 102.6 kPa pressure?

Analyze

First, use the ideal gas equation to calculate the total number of moles of gas, and then use equation (2.17) to establish the number of moles of each combustible gas. Next, write an equation for the combustion of each gas. Use these equations and enthalpy of formation data to calculate the total amount of heat released by the combustion. Finally, use equation (4.5) to calculate the temperature increase when this quantity of heat is absorbed by the 25.0 kg of water. The final water temperature is then easily established.

Solve

Substitute the applicable data into the ideal gas equation using SI units, with $R = 8.3145\ m^3\ Pa\ mol^{-1}\ K^{-1}$. Solve for n.

$$n = \frac{PV}{RT} = \frac{102.6\ \text{kPa} \times 1000\ \text{Pa}/1\ \text{kPa} \times 0.205\ \text{m}^3}{8.3145\ \text{m}^3\ \text{Pa mol}^{-1}\ \text{K}^{-1} \times 298.2\ \text{K}}$$
$$= 8.48\ \text{mol gas}$$

Now, apportion the 8.48 moles among the three gases present, converting the volume percents to mole fractions and using equation (2.17).

$$n_{CO} = n_{tot} \times x_{CO} = 8.48\ \text{mol} \times 0.550 = 4.66\ \text{mol CO}$$
$$n_{H_2} = n_{tot} \times x_{H_2} = 8.48\ \text{mol} \times 0.330 = 2.80\ \text{mol H}_2$$

(remaining gas noncombustible)

Write an equation for the combustion of CO(g), list ΔH_f° data beneath the equation, and determine ΔH_{comb}° per mole of CO(g).

$$\text{CO(g)} + \frac{1}{2}\text{O}_2\text{(g)} \longrightarrow \text{CO}_2\text{(g)}$$

ΔH_f°: −110.5 kJ/mol   −393.5 kJ/mol

$$\Delta H_{comb}^\circ = 1\ \text{mol CO}_2 \times (-393.5\ \text{kJ/mol CO}_2) - 1\ \text{mol CO} \times (-110.5\ \text{kJ/mol CO})$$
$$= -283.0\ \text{kJ}$$

Write another equation for the combustion of $H_2(g)$, again listing ΔH_f° data beneath the equation, and determining ΔH_{comb}° per mole of $H_2(g)$.

$$\text{H}_2\text{(g)} + \frac{1}{2}\text{O}_2\text{(g)} \longrightarrow \text{H}_2\text{O(l)}$$

ΔH_f°: 0 kJ/mol   −285.8 kJ/mol

$$\Delta H_{comb}^\circ = 1\ \text{mol H}_2\text{O} \times (-285.8\ \text{kJ/mol H}_2\text{O}) = -285.8\ \text{kJ}$$

Determine the total heat released in the combustion of the amounts of CO and H_2 in the 0.205 m^3 of gas.

$$4.66\ \text{mol CO} \times (-283.0\ \text{kJ/mol CO}) + 2.80\ \text{mol H}_2 \times (-285.8\ \text{kJ/mol H}_2)$$
$$= -2.12 \times 10^3\ \text{kJ}$$

The quantity of heat absorbed by the 25.0 kg of water is

$$q_{water} = -q_{comb}$$
$$= -\left(-2.12 \times 10^3\ \text{kJ} \times \frac{1000\ \text{J}}{1\ \text{kJ}}\right) = 2.12 \times 10^6\ \text{J}$$

Rearrange equation (4.5) to solve for the temperature change in the 2.50×10^4 g (25.0 kg) of water.

$$\Delta T = \frac{q_{water}}{\text{mass water} \times \text{sp ht water}}$$

$$\Delta T = \frac{2.12 \times 10^6\ \text{J}}{\left(2.50 \times 10^4\ \text{g H}_2\text{O} \times \frac{4.18\ \text{J}}{\text{g H}_2\text{O}\,^\circ\text{C}}\right)} = 20.3\ ^\circ\text{C}$$

From the initial temperature and the temperature change, determine the final temperature.

$$T_f = T_i + \Delta T = 25.0\ ^\circ\text{C} + 20.3\ ^\circ\text{C} = 45.3\ ^\circ\text{C}$$

Assess

The assumption that the gas sample obeys the ideal gas law is probably valid since the temperature of the gas (25.0 °C) is not particularly low and the gas pressure, about 1 atm, is not particularly high. However, the implicit assumption that all the heat of combustion could be transferred to the water was probably not valid. If the transfer were to occur in an ordinary gas-fired water heater, some of the heat would undoubtedly be lost through the exhaust vent. Thus, our calculation was of the highest temperature that could possibly be attained. Note that in using the ideal gas equation the simplest approach was to work with SI units because those were the units of the data that were given.

PRACTICE EXAMPLE A: The enthalpy of combustion for 1-hexadecene, $C_{16}H_{32}$, is $-10539.0\ \text{kJ mol}^{-1}$, and that of hexadecane, $C_{16}H_{34}$, is $-10699.1\ \text{kJ mol}^{-1}$. What is the enthalpy of hydrogenation of 1-hexadecene to hexadecane?

PRACTICE EXAMPLE B: A chemist mixes 56 grams of CaO, powdered lime, with 100 mL of water at 20 °C. After the completion of the reaction, $CaO(s) + H_2O(l) \rightarrow Ca(OH)_2(s)$, what are the contents of the reaction vessel? [*Hint:* Assume that the heat released by the reaction is absorbed by the water.]

Exercises

Heat Capacity (Specific Heat)

1. Calculate the quantity of heat, in kilojoules, **(a)** required to raise the temperature of 9.25 L of water from 22.0 to 29.4 °C; **(b)** associated with a 33.5 °C decrease in temperature in a 5.85 kg aluminum bar (specific heat of aluminum = $0.903\ \text{J g}^{-1}\ {}^{\circ}\text{C}^{-1}$).
2. Calculate the final temperature that results when **(a)** a 12.6 g sample of water at 22.9 °C absorbs 875 J of heat; **(b)** a 1.59 kg sample of platinum at 78.2 °C gives off 1.05 kcal of heat (sp ht of Pt = $0.032\ \text{cal g}^{-1}\ {}^{\circ}\text{C}^{-1}$).
3. Refer to Example 4-2. The experiment is repeated with several different metals substituting for the lead. The masses of metal and water and the initial temperatures of the metal and water are the same as in Figure 4-3. The final temperatures are **(a)** Zn, 38.9 °C; **(b)** Pt, 28.8 °C; **(c)** Al, 52.7 °C. What is the specific heat of each metal, expressed in $\text{J g}^{-1}\ {}^{\circ}\text{C}^{-1}$?
4. A 75.0 g piece of Ag metal is heated to 80.0 °C and dropped into 50.0 g of water at 23.2 °C. The final temperature of the Ag–H_2O mixture is 27.6 °C. What is the specific heat of silver?
5. A 465 g chunk of iron is removed from an oven and plunged into 375 g water in an insulated container. The temperature of the water increases from 26 to 87 °C. If the specific heat of iron is $0.449\ \text{J g}^{-1}\ {}^{\circ}\text{C}^{-1}$, what must have been the original temperature of the iron?
6. A piece of stainless steel (sp ht = $0.50\ \text{J g}^{-1}\ {}^{\circ}\text{C}^{-1}$) is transferred from an oven at 183 °C into 125 mL of water at 23.2 °C. The water temperature rises to 51.5 °C. What is the mass of the steel? How precise is this method of mass determination? Explain.
7. A 1.00 kg sample of magnesium at 40.0 °C is added to 1.00 L of water maintained at 20.0 °C in an insulated container. What will be the final temperature of the Mg–H_2O mixture (specific heat of Mg = $1.024\ \text{J g}^{-1}\ {}^{\circ}\text{C}^{-1}$)?
8. Brass has a density of $8.40\ \text{g/cm}^3$ and a specific heat of $0.385\ \text{J g}^{-1}\ {}^{\circ}\text{C}^{-1}$. A $15.2\ \text{cm}^3$ piece of brass at an initial temperature of 163 °C is dropped into an insulated container with 150.0 g water initially at 22.4 °C. What will be the final temperature of the brass–water mixture?
9. A 74.8 g sample of copper at 143.2 °C is added to an insulated vessel containing 165 mL of glycerol, $C_3H_8O_3(l)$ (d = 1.26 g/mL), at 24.8 °C. The final temperature is 31.1°C. The specific heat of copper is $0.385\ \text{J g}^{-1}\ {}^{\circ}\text{C}^{-1}$. What is the heat capacity of glycerol in $\text{J mol}^{-1}\ {}^{\circ}\text{C}^{-1}$?
10. What volume of 18.5 °C water must be added, together with a 1.23 kg piece of iron at 68.5 °C, so that the temperature of the water in the insulated container shown in the figure remains constant at 25.6 °C?

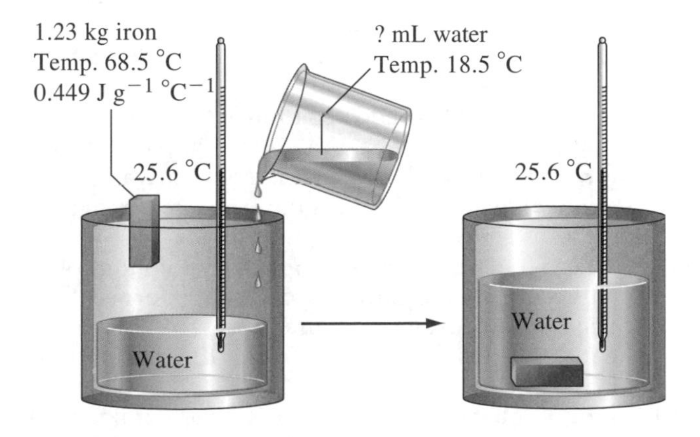

11. In the form of heat, 6.052 J of energy is transferred to a 1.0 L sample of air ($d = 1.204\ \mathrm{mg/cm^3}$) at 20.0 °C. The final temperature of the air is 25.0 °C. What is the heat capacity of air in J/K?

12. What is the final temperature (in °C) of 1.24 g of water with an initial temperature of 20.0 °C after 6.052 J of heat is added to it?

Heats of Reaction

13. How much heat, in kilojoules, is associated with the production of 283 kg of slaked lime, $Ca(OH)_2$?

$$CaO(s) + H_2O(l) \longrightarrow Ca(OH)_2(s) \qquad \Delta H° = -65.2\ \mathrm{kJ}$$

14. The standard enthalpy change in the combustion of the hydrocarbon octane is $\Delta H° = -5.48 \times 10^3\ \mathrm{kJ/mol}$ $C_8H_{18}(l)$. How much heat, in kilojoules, is liberated *per gallon* of octane burned? (Density of octane = 0.703 g/mL; 1 gal = 3.785 L.)

15. How much heat, in kilojoules, is evolved in the complete combustion of **(a)** 1.325 g $C_4H_{10}(g)$ at 25 °C and 1 atm; **(b)** 28.4 L $C_4H_{10}(g)$ at STP; **(c)** 12.6 L $C_4H_{10}(g)$ at 23.6 °C and 738 mmHg? Assume that the enthalpy change for the reaction does not change significantly with temperature or pressure. The complete combustion of butane, $C_4H_{10}(g)$, is represented by the equation

$$C_4H_{10}(g) + \frac{13}{2}O_2(g) \longrightarrow 4\,CO_2(g) + 5\,H_2O(l) \qquad \Delta H° = -2877\ \mathrm{kJ}$$

16. Upon complete combustion, the indicated substances evolve the given quantities of heat. Write a balanced equation for the combustion of 1.00 mol of each substance, including the enthalpy change, ΔH, for the reaction.
(a) 0.584 g of propane, $C_3H_8(g)$, yields 29.4 kJ
(b) 0.136 g of camphor, $C_{10}H_{16}O(s)$, yields 5.27 kJ
(c) 2.35 mL of acetone, $(CH_3)_2CO(l)$ ($d = 0.791$ g/mL), yields 58.3 kJ

17. The combustion of methane gas, the principal constituent of natural gas, is represented by the equation

$$CH_4(g) + 2\,O_2(g) \longrightarrow CO_2(g) + 2\,H_2O(l) \qquad \Delta H° = -890.3\ \mathrm{kJ}$$

(a) What mass of methane, in kilograms, must be burned to liberate 2.80×10^7 kJ of heat?
(b) What quantity of heat, in kilojoules, is liberated in the complete combustion of 1.65×10^4 L of $CH_4(g)$, measured at 18.6 °C and 768 mmHg?
(c) If the quantity of heat calculated in part **(b)** could be transferred with 100% efficiency to water, what volume of water, in liters, could be heated from 8.8 to 60.0 °C as a result?

18. Refer to the Integrative Example. What volume of the synthesis gas, measured at STP and burned in an open flame (constant-pressure process), is required to heat 40.0 gal of water from 15.2 to 65.0 °C? (1 gal = 3.785 L.)

19. The combustion of hydrogen–oxygen mixtures is used to produce very high temperatures (approximately 2500 °C) needed for certain types of welding operations. Consider the reaction to be

$$H_2(g) + \frac{1}{2}O_2(g) \longrightarrow H_2O(g) \quad \Delta H° = -241.8\ \mathrm{kJ}$$

What is the quantity of heat evolved, in kilojoules, when a 180 g mixture containing equal parts of H_2 and O_2 by mass is burned?

20. Thermite mixtures are used for certain types of welding, and the thermite reaction is highly exothermic.

$$Fe_2O_3(s) + 2\,Al(s) \longrightarrow Al_2O_3(s) + 2\,Fe(s) \qquad \Delta H° = -852\ \mathrm{kJ}$$

1.00 mol of granular Fe_2O_3 and 2.00 mol of granular Al are mixed at room temperature (25 °C), and a reaction is initiated. The liberated heat is retained within the products, whose combined specific heat over a broad temperature range is about $0.8\ \mathrm{J\,g^{-1}\,°C^{-1}}$. (The melting point of iron is 1530 °C.) Show that the quantity of heat liberated is more than sufficient to raise the temperature of the products to the melting point of iron.

21. A 0.205 g pellet of potassium hydroxide, KOH, is added to 55.9 g water in a Styrofoam coffee cup. The water temperature rises from 23.5 to 24.4 °C. [Assume that the specific heat of dilute KOH(aq) is the same as that of water.]
(a) What is the approximate heat of solution of KOH, expressed as kilojoules per mole of KOH?
(b) How could the precision of this measurement be improved *without* modifying the apparatus?

22. The heat of solution of KI(s) in water is +20.3 kJ/mol KI. If a quantity of KI is added to sufficient water at 23.5 °C in a Styrofoam cup to produce 150.0 mL of 2.50 M KI, what will be the final temperature? (Assume a density of 1.30 g/mL and a specific heat of $2.7\ \mathrm{J\,g^{-1}\,°C^{-1}}$ for 2.50 M KI.)

23. You are planning a lecture demonstration to illustrate an endothermic process. You want to lower the temperature of 1400 mL water in an insulated container from 25 to 10 °C. Approximately what mass of $NH_4Cl(s)$ should you dissolve in the water to achieve this result? The heat of solution of NH_4Cl is +14.7 kJ/mol NH_4Cl.

24. Care must be taken in preparing solutions of solutes that liberate heat on dissolving. The heat of solution of NaOH is −44.5 kJ/mol NaOH. To what maximum temperature may a sample of water, originally at 21 °C, be raised in the preparation of 500 mL of 7.0 M NaOH? Assume the solution has a density of 1.08 g/mL and specific heat of $4.00\ \mathrm{J\,g^{-1}\,°C^{-1}}$.

25. Refer to Example 4-4. The product of the neutralization is 0.500 M NaCl. For this solution, assume a density of 1.02 g/mL and a specific heat of $4.02\ \mathrm{J\,g^{-1}\,°C^{-1}}$. Also, assume a heat capacity for the Styrofoam cup of 10 J/°C, and recalculate the heat of neutralization.

26. The heat of neutralization of HCl(aq) by NaOH(aq) is −55.84 kJ/mol H_2O produced. If 50.00 mL of 1.05 M NaOH is added to 25.00 mL of 1.86 M HCl, with both solutions originally at 24.72 °C, what will be the final solution temperature? (Assume that no heat is lost to the surrounding air and that the solution produced in the neutralization reaction has a density of 1.02 g/mL and a specific heat of $3.98\ \mathrm{J\,g^{-1}\,°C^{-1}}$.)

27. Acetylene (C_2H_2) torches are used in welding. How much heat (in kJ) evolves when 5.0 L of C_2H_2 ($d = 1.0967\ kg/m^3$) is mixed with a stoichiometric amount of oxygen gas? The combustion reaction is

$$C_2H_2(g) + \frac{5}{2}O_2(g) \longrightarrow 2\,CO_2(g) + H_2O(l) \qquad \Delta H° = -1299.5\ kJ$$

28. Propane (C_3H_8) gas ($d = 1.83\ kg/m^3$) is used in most gas grills. What volume (in liters) of propane is needed to generate 273.8 kJ of heat?

$$C_3H_8(g) + 5\,O_2(g) \longrightarrow 3\,CO_2(g) + 4\,H_2O(l) \qquad \Delta H° = -2219.9\ kJ$$

Enthalpy Changes and States of Matter

29. What mass of ice can be melted with the same quantity of heat as required to raise the temperature of 3.50 mol $H_2O(l)$ by 50.0 °C? [$\Delta H°_{fusion} = 6.01\ kJ/mol\ H_2O(s)$]

30. What will be the final temperature of the water in an insulated container as the result of passing 5.00 g of steam, $H_2O(g)$, at 100.0 °C into 100.0 g of water at 25.0 °C? ($\Delta H°_{vap} = 40.6\ kJ/mol\ H_2O$)

31. A 125 g stainless steel ball bearing (sp ht = $0.50\ J\ g^{-1}\ °C^{-1}$) at 525 °C is dropped into 75.0 mL of water at 28.5 °C in an open Styrofoam cup. As a result, the water is brought to a boil when the temperature reaches 100.0 °C. What mass of water vaporizes while the boiling continues? ($\Delta H°_{vap} = 40.6\ kJ/mol\ H_2O$)

32. If the ball bearing described in Exercise 31 is dropped onto a large block of ice at 0 °C, what mass of liquid water will form? ($\Delta H°_{fusion} = 6.01\ kJ/mol\ H_2O(s)$)

33. The enthalpy of sublimation (solid → gas) for dry ice (i.e., CO_2) is $\Delta H°_{sub} = 571\ kJ/kg$ at −78.5 °C. If 125.0 J of heat is transferred to a block of dry ice that is −78.5°C, what volume of CO_2 gas ($d = 1.98\ g/L$) will be generated?

34. The enthalpy of vaporization for $N_2(l)$ is 5.56 kJ/mol. How much heat (in J) is required to produce 1.0 L of $N_2(g)$ at 77.36 K and 1.0 atm?

Calorimetry

35. A sample gives off 5228 cal when burned in a bomb calorimeter. The temperature of the calorimeter assembly increases by 4.39 °C. Calculate the heat capacity of the calorimeter, in kilojoules per degree Celsius.

36. The following substances undergo complete combustion in a bomb calorimeter. The calorimeter assembly has a heat capacity of 5.136 kJ/°C. In each case, what is the final temperature if the initial water temperature is 22.43 °C?
(a) 0.3268 g caffeine, $C_8H_{10}O_2N_4$ (heat of combustion = −1014.2 kcal/mol caffeine);
(b) 1.35 mL of methyl ethyl ketone, $C_4H_8O(l)$, $d = 0.805\ g/mL$ (heat of combustion = −2444 kJ/mol methyl ethyl ketone).

37. A bomb calorimetry experiment is performed with xylose, $C_5H_{10}O_5(s)$, as the combustible substance. The data obtained are

mass of xylose burned:	1.183 g
heat capacity of calorimeter:	4.728 kJ/°C
initial calorimeter temperature:	23.29 °C
final calorimeter temperature:	27.19 °C

(a) What is the heat of combustion of xylose, in kilojoules per mole? **(b)** Write the chemical equation for the complete combustion of xylose, and represent the value of ΔH in this equation. (Assume for this reaction that $\Delta U \approx \Delta H$.)

38. A coffee-cup calorimeter contains 100.0 mL of 0.300 M HCl at 20.3 °C. When 1.82 g Zn(s) is added, the temperature rises to 30.5 °C. What is the heat of reaction per mol Zn? Make the same assumptions as in Example 4-4, and also assume that there is no heat lost with the $H_2(g)$ that escapes.

$$Zn(s) + 2\,H^+(aq) \longrightarrow Zn^{2+}(aq) + H_2(g)$$

39. A 0.75 g sample of KCl is added to 35.0 g H_2O in a Styrofoam cup and stirred until it dissolves. The temperature of the solution drops from 24.8 to 23.6 °C. **(a)** Is the process endothermic or exothermic? **(b)** What is the heat of solution of KCl expressed in kilojoules per mole of KCl?

40. The heat of solution of potassium acetate in water is $-15.3\ kJ/mol\ KC_2H_3O_2$. What will be the final temperature when 0.136 mol $KC_2H_3O_2$ is dissolved in 525 mL water that is initially at 25.1 °C?

41. A 1.620 g sample of naphthalene, $C_{10}H_8(s)$, is completely burned in a bomb calorimeter assembly and a temperature increase of 8.44 °C is noted. If the heat of combustion of naphthalene is $-5156\ kJ/mol\ C_{10}H_8$, what is the heat capacity of the bomb calorimeter?

42. Salicylic acid, $C_7H_6O_3$, has been suggested as a calorimetric standard. Its heat of combustion is $-3.023 \times 10^3\ kJ/mol\ C_7H_6O_3$. From the following data determine the heat capacity of a bomb calorimeter assembly (that is, the bomb, water, stirrer, thermometer, wires, and so forth).

mass of salicylic acid burned:	1.201 g
initial calorimeter temperature:	23.68 °C
final calorimeter temperature:	29.82 °C

43. Refer to Example 4-3. Based on the heat of combustion of sucrose established in the example, what should be the temperature change (ΔT) produced by the combustion of 1.227 g $C_{12}H_{22}O_{11}$ in a bomb calorimeter assembly with a heat capacity of 3.87 kJ/°C?

44. A 1.397 g sample of thymol, $C_{10}H_{14}O(s)$ (a preservative and a mold and mildew preventative), is burned in a bomb calorimeter assembly. The temperature increase is 11.23 °C, and the heat capacity of the bomb calorimeter is 4.68 kJ/°C. What is the heat of combustion of thymol, expressed in kilojoules per mole of $C_{10}H_{14}O$?

45. A 5.0 g sample of NaCl is added to a Styrofoam cup of water, and the change in water temperature is 5.0 °C. The heat of solution of NaCl is 3.76 kJ/mol. What is the mass (in g) of water in the Styrofoam cup?

46. We can determine the purity of solid materials by using calorimetry. A gold ring (for pure gold, specific heat $= 0.1291\ \text{J g}^{-1}\ \text{K}^{-1}$) with mass of 10.5 g is heated to 78.3 °C and immersed in 50.0 g of 23.7 °C water in a constant-pressure calorimeter. The final temperature of the water is 31.0 °C. Is this a pure sample of gold?

Pressure–Volume Work

47. Calculate the quantity of work associated with a 3.5 L expansion of a gas (ΔV) against a pressure of 748 mmHg in the units **(a)** atm L; **(b)** joules (J); **(c)** calories (cal).

48. Calculate the quantity of work, in joules, associated with the compression of a gas from 5.62 L to 3.37 L by a constant pressure of 1.23 atm.

49. A 1.00 g sample of Ne(g) at 1 atm pressure and 27 °C is allowed to expand into an *evacuated* vessel of 2.50 L volume. Does the gas do work? Explain.

50. Compressed air in aerosol cans is used to free electronic equipment of dust. Does the air do any work as it escapes from the can?

51. In each of the following processes, is any work done when the reaction is carried out at constant pressure in a vessel open to the atmosphere? If so, is work done by the reacting system or on it? **(a)** Neutralization of $Ba(OH)_2(aq)$ by HCl(aq); **(b)** conversion of gaseous nitrogen dioxide to gaseous dinitrogen tetroxide; **(c)** decomposition of calcium carbonate to calcium oxide and carbon dioxide gas.

52. In each of the following processes, is any work done when the reaction is carried out at constant pressure in a vessel open to the atmosphere? If so, is work done by the reacting system or on it? **(a)** Reaction of nitrogen monoxide and oxygen gases to form gaseous nitrogen dioxide; **(b)** precipitation of magnesium hydroxide by the reaction of aqueous solutions of NaOH and $MgCl_2$; **(c)** reaction of copper(II) sulfate and water vapor to form copper(II) sulfate pentahydrate.

53. If 325 J of work is done by a system at a pressure of 1.0 atm and 298 K, what is the change in the volume of the system?

54. A movable piston in a cylinder holding 5.0 L $N_2(g)$ is used to lift a 1.23 kg object to a height of 4.5 meters. How much work (in J) was done by the gas?

First Law of Thermodynamics

55. What is the change in internal energy of a system if the system **(a)** absorbs 58 J of heat and does 58 J of work; **(b)** absorbs 125 J of heat and does 687 J of work; **(c)** evolves 280 cal of heat and has 1.25 kJ of work done on it?

56. What is the change in internal energy of a system if the *surroundings* **(a)** transfer 235 J of heat and 128 J of work to the system; **(b)** absorb 145 J of heat from the system while doing 98 J of work on the system; **(c)** exchange no heat, but receive 1.07 kJ of work from the system?

57. The internal energy of a fixed quantity of an ideal gas depends only on its temperature. A sample of an ideal gas is allowed to expand at a constant temperature (isothermal expansion). **(a)** Does the gas do work? **(b)** Does the gas exchange heat with its surroundings? **(c)** What happens to the temperature of the gas? **(d)** What is ΔU for the gas?

58. In an *adiabatic* process, a system is thermally insulated—there is no exchange of heat between system and surroundings. For the adiabatic expansion of an ideal gas **(a)** does the gas do work? **(b)** Does the internal energy of the gas increase, decrease, or remain constant? **(c)** What happens to the temperature of the gas? [*Hint*: Refer to Exercise 57.]

59. Do you think the following observation is in any way possible? An ideal gas is expanded isothermally and is observed to do twice as much work as the heat absorbed from its surroundings. Explain your answer. [*Hint:* Refer to Exercises 57 and 58.]

60. Do you think the following observation is any way possible? A gas absorbs heat from its surroundings while being compressed. Explain your answer. [*Hint:* Refer to Exercises 55 and 56.]

61. There are other forms of work besides P–V work. For example, electrical work is defined as the potential × change in charge, $w = \text{£}\, dq$. If a charge in a system is changed from 10 C to 5 C in a potential of 100 V and 45 J of heat is liberated, what is the change in the internal energy? (Note: 1 V = 1 J/C)

62. Another form of work is extension, defined as the tension × change in length, $w = f\,\Delta l$. A piece of DNA has an approximate tension of $f = 10$ pN. What is the change in the internal energy of the adiabatic stretching of DNA by 10 pm?

Relating ΔH and ΔU

63. Only one of the following expressions holds true for the heat of a chemical reaction, *regardless of how the reaction is carried out*. Which is the correct expression and why? **(a)** q_V; **(b)** q_P; **(c)** $\Delta U - w$; **(d)** ΔU; **(e)** ΔH.

64. Determine whether ΔH is equal to, greater than, or less than ΔU for the following reactions. Keep in mind that "greater than" means more positive or less negative, and "less than" means less positive or more negative. Assume that the only significant change in volume during a reaction at constant pressure is that associated with changes in the amounts of gases.
(a) The complete combustion of one mole of 1-butanol(l).
(b) The complete combustion of one mole of glucose, $C_6H_{12}O_6(s)$.

(c) The decomposition of solid ammonium nitrate to produce liquid water and gaseous dinitrogen monoxide.

65. The heat of combustion of 2-propanol at 298.15 K, determined in a bomb calorimeter, is -33.41 kJ/g. For the combustion of one mole of 2-propanol, determine **(a)** ΔU, and **(b)** ΔH.

66. Write an equation to represent the combustion of thymol referred to in Exercise 44. Include in this equation the values for ΔU and ΔH.

Hess's Law

67. The standard enthalpy of formation of $NH_3(g)$ is -46.11 kJ/mol NH_3. What is $\Delta H°$ for the following reaction?

$$\frac{2}{3}NH_3(g) \longrightarrow \frac{1}{3}N_2(g) + H_2(g) \qquad \Delta H° =$$

68. Use Hess's law to determine $\Delta H°$ for the reaction $CO(g) + \frac{1}{2}O_2(g) \longrightarrow CO_2(g)$, given that

$$C(graphite) + \frac{1}{2}O_2(g) \longrightarrow CO(g) \qquad \Delta H° = -110.54\ kJ$$

$$C(graphite) + O_2(g) \longrightarrow CO_2(g) \qquad \Delta H° = -393.51\ kJ$$

69. Use Hess's law to determine $\Delta H°$ for the reaction $C_3H_4(g) + 2H_2(g) \longrightarrow C_3H_8(g)$, given that

$$H_2(g) + \frac{1}{2}O_2(g) \longrightarrow H_2O(l) \quad \Delta H° = -285.8\ kJ$$

$$C_3H_4(g) + 4O_2(g) \longrightarrow 3CO_2(g) + 2H_2O(l) \qquad \Delta H° = -1937\ kJ$$

$$C_3H_8(g) + 5O_2(g) \longrightarrow 3CO_2(g) + 4H_2O(l) \qquad \Delta H° = -2219.1\ kJ$$

70. Given the following information:

$$\frac{1}{2}N_2(g) + \frac{3}{2}H_2(g) \longrightarrow NH_3(g) \qquad \Delta H_1°$$

$$NH_3(g) + \frac{5}{4}O_2(g) \longrightarrow NO(g) + \frac{3}{2}H_2O(l) \qquad \Delta H_2°$$

$$H_2(g) + \frac{1}{2}O_2(g) \longrightarrow H_2O(l) \qquad \Delta H_3°$$

Determine $\Delta H°$ for the following reaction, expressed in terms of $\Delta H_1°$, $\Delta H_2°$, and $\Delta H_3°$.

$$N_2(g) + O_2(g) \longrightarrow 2NO(g) \qquad \Delta H° = ?$$

71. For the reaction $C_2H_4(g) + Cl_2(g) \longrightarrow C_2H_4Cl_2(l)$, determine $\Delta H°$, given that

$$4HCl(g) + O_2(g) \longrightarrow 2Cl_2(g) + 2H_2O(l) \qquad \Delta H° = -202.4\ kJ$$

$$2HCl(g) + C_2H_4(g) + \frac{1}{2}O_2(g) \longrightarrow C_2H_4Cl_2(l) + H_2O(l) \quad \Delta H° = -318.7\ kJ$$

72. Determine $\Delta H°$ for this reaction from the data below.
$N_2H_4(l) + 2H_2O_2(l) \longrightarrow N_2(g) + 4H_2O(l)$

$$N_2H_4(l) + O_2(g) \longrightarrow N_2(g) + 2H_2O(l) \qquad \Delta H° = -622.2\ kJ$$

$$H_2(g) + \frac{1}{2}O_2(g) \longrightarrow H_2O(l) \qquad \Delta H° = -285.8\ kJ$$

$$H_2(g) + O_2(g) \longrightarrow H_2O_2(l) \qquad \Delta H° = -187.8\ kJ$$

73. Substitute natural gas (SNG) is a gaseous mixture containing $CH_4(g)$ that can be used as a fuel. One reaction for the production of SNG is

$$4CO(g) + 8H_2(g) \longrightarrow 3CH_4(g) + CO_2(g) + 2H_2O(l) \quad \Delta H° = ?$$

Use appropriate data from the following list to determine $\Delta H°$ for this SNG reaction.

$$C(graphite) + \frac{1}{2}O_2(g) \longrightarrow CO(g) \qquad \Delta H° = -110.5\ kJ$$

$$CO(g) + \frac{1}{2}O_2(g) \longrightarrow CO_2(g) \qquad \Delta H° = -283.0\ kJ$$

$$H_2(g) + \frac{1}{2}O_2(g) \longrightarrow H_2O(l) \qquad \Delta H° = -285.8\ kJ$$

$$C(graphite) + 2H_2(g) \longrightarrow CH_4(g) \qquad \Delta H° = -74.81\ kJ$$

$$CH_4(g) + 2O_2(g) \longrightarrow CO_2(g) + 2H_2O(l) \qquad \Delta H° = -890.3\ kJ$$

74. CCl_4, an important commercial solvent, is prepared by the reaction of $Cl_2(g)$ with a carbon compound. Determine $\Delta H°$ for the reaction

$$CS_2(l) + 3Cl_2(g) \longrightarrow CCl_4(l) + S_2Cl_2(l).$$

Use appropriate data from the following listing.

$$CS_2(l) + 3O_2(g) \longrightarrow CO_2(g) + 2SO_2(g) \qquad \Delta H° = -1077\ kJ$$

$$2S(s) + Cl_2(g) \longrightarrow S_2Cl_2(l) \qquad \Delta H° = -58.2\ kJ$$

$$C(s) + 2Cl_2(g) \longrightarrow CCl_4(l) \qquad \Delta H° = -135.4\ kJ$$

$$S(s) + O_2(g) \longrightarrow SO_2(g) \qquad \Delta H° = -296.8\ kJ$$

$$SO_2(g) + Cl_2(g) \longrightarrow SO_2Cl_2(l) \qquad \Delta H° = +97.3\ kJ$$

$$C(s) + O_2(g) \longrightarrow CO_2(g) \qquad \Delta H° = -393.5\ kJ$$

$$CCl_4(l) + O_2(g) \longrightarrow COCl_2(g) + Cl_2O(g) \qquad \Delta H° = -5.2\ kJ$$

75. Use Hess's law and the following data

$$CH_4(g) + 2O_2(g) \longrightarrow CO_2(g) + 2H_2O(g) \qquad \Delta H° = -802\ kJ$$

$$CH_4(g) + CO_2(g) \longrightarrow 2CO(g) + 2H_2(g) \qquad \Delta H° = +247\ kJ$$

$$CH_4(g) + H_2O(g) \longrightarrow CO(g) + 3H_2(g) \qquad \Delta H° = +206\ kJ$$

to determine $\Delta H°$ for the following reaction, an important source of hydrogen gas

$$CH_4(g) + \frac{1}{2}O_2(g) \longrightarrow CO(g) + 2H_2(g)$$

76. The standard heats of combustion ($\Delta H°$) per mole of 1,3-butadiene, $C_4H_6(g)$; butane, $C_4H_{10}(g)$; and $H_2(g)$ are −2540.2, −2877.6, and −285.8 kJ, respectively. Use these data to calculate the heat of hydrogenation of 1,3-butadiene to butane.

$$C_4H_6(g) + 2\,H_2(g) \longrightarrow C_4H_{10}(g) \qquad \Delta H° = ?$$

[*Hint:* Write equations for the combustion reactions. In each combustion, the products are $CO_2(g)$ and $H_2O(l)$.]

77. One glucose molecule, $C_6H_{12}O_6(s)$, is converted to two lactic acid molecules, $CH_3CH(OH)COOH(s)$ during glycolysis. Given the combustion reactions of glucose and lactic acid, determine the standard enthalpy for glycolysis.

$$C_6H_{12}O_6(s) + 6\,O_2(g) \longrightarrow 6\,CO_2(g) + 6\,H_2O(l) \qquad \Delta H° = -2808\text{ kJ}$$

$$CH_3CH(OH)COOH(s) + 3\,O_2(g) \longrightarrow 3\,CO_2(g) + 3\,H_2O(l) \qquad \Delta H° = -1344\text{ kJ}$$

78. The standard enthalpy of fermentation of glucose to ethanol is

$$C_6H_{12}O_6(s) \rightarrow 2\,CH_3CH_2OH(l) + 2\,CO_2(g) \qquad \Delta H° = -72\text{ kJ}$$

Use the standard enthalpy of combustion for glucose to calculate the enthalpy of combustion for ethanol.

Standard Enthalpies of Formation

79. Use standard enthalpies of formation from Table 4.2 and equation (4.21) to determine the standard enthalpy changes in the following reactions.
(a) $C_3H_8(g) + H_2(g) \longrightarrow C_2H_6(g) + CH_4(g)$;
(b) $2\,H_2S(g) + 3\,O_2(g) \longrightarrow 2\,SO_2(g) + 2\,H_2O(l)$.

80. Use standard enthalpies of formation from Tables 4.2 and 4.3 and equation (4.21) to determine the standard enthalpy change in the following reaction.

$$NH_4^+(aq) + OH^-(aq) \longrightarrow H_2O(l) + NH_3(g).$$

81. Use the information given here, data from Appendix A, and equation (4.21) to calculate the standard enthalpy of formation per mole of ZnS(s).

$$2\,ZnS(s) + 3\,O_2(g) \longrightarrow 2\,ZnO(s) + 2\,SO_2(g) \qquad \Delta H° = -878.2\text{ kJ}$$

82. Use the data in Figure 4-18 to establish possible relationships between the molecular structure of the hydrocarbons and their standard enthalpies of formation.

83. Use standard enthalpies of formation from Table 4.2 to determine the enthalpy change at 25 °C for the following reaction.

$$2\,Cl_2(g) + 2\,H_2O(l) \longrightarrow 4\,HCl(g) + O_2(g) \qquad \Delta H° = ?$$

84. Use data from Appendix A to calculate the standard enthalpy change for the following reaction at 25 °C.

$$Fe_2O_3(s) + 3\,CO(g) \longrightarrow 2\,Fe(s) + 3\,CO_2(g) \qquad \Delta H° = ?$$

85. Use data from Table 4.2 to determine the standard heat of combustion of $C_2H_5OH(l)$, if reactants and products are maintained at 25 °C and 1 bar.

86. Use data from Table 4.2, together with the fact that $\Delta H° = -3509$ kJ for the complete combustion of one mole of pentane, $C_5H_{12}(l)$, to calculate $\Delta H°$ for the synthesis of 1 mol $C_5H_{12}(l)$ from CO(g) and $H_2(g)$.

$$5\,CO(g) + 11\,H_2(g) \longrightarrow C_5H_{12}(l) + 5\,H_2O(l) \qquad \Delta H° = ?$$

87. Use data from Table 4.2 and $\Delta H°$ for the following reaction to determine the standard enthalpy of formation of $CCl_4(g)$ at 25 °C and 1 bar.

$$CH_4(g) + 4\,Cl_2(g) \longrightarrow CCl_4(g) + 4\,HCl(g) \qquad \Delta H° = -397.3\text{ kJ}$$

88. Use data from Table 4.2 and $\Delta H°$ for the following reaction to determine the standard enthalpy of formation of hexane, $C_6H_{14}(l)$, at 25 °C and 1 bar.

$$2\,C_6H_{14}(l) + 19\,O_2(g) \longrightarrow 12\,CO_2(g) + 14\,H_2O(l) \qquad \Delta H° = -8326\text{ kJ}$$

89. Use data from Table 4.3 and Appendix A to determine the standard enthalpy change in the following reaction.

$$Al^{3+}(aq) + 3\,OH^-(aq) \longrightarrow Al(OH)_3(s) \qquad \Delta H° = ?$$

90. Use data from Table 4.3 and Appendix A to determine the standard enthalpy change in the following reaction.

$$Mg(OH)_2(s) + 2\,NH_4^+(aq) \longrightarrow Mg^{2+}(aq) + 2\,H_2O(l) + 2\,NH_3(g) \qquad \Delta H° = ?$$

91. The decomposition of limestone, $CaCO_3(s)$, into quicklime, CaO(s), and $CO_2(g)$ is carried out in a gas-fired kiln. Use data from Appendix A to determine how much heat is required to decompose 1.35×10^3 kg $CaCO_3(s)$. (Assume that heats of reaction are the same as at 25 °C and 1 bar.)

92. Use data from Table 4.2 to calculate the volume of butane, $C_4H_{10}(g)$, measured at 24.6 °C and 756 mmHg, that must be burned to liberate 5.00×10^4 kJ of heat.

93. Ants release formic acid (HCOOH) when they bite. Use the data in Table 4.2 and the standard enthalpy of combustion for formic acid ($\Delta H° = -255$ kJ/mol) to calculate the standard enthalpy of formation for formic acid.

94. Calculate the enthalpy of combustion for lactic acid by using the data in Table 4.2 and the standard enthalpy of formation for lactic acid [$CH_3CH(OH)COOH(s)$]: $\Delta H_f^\circ = -694.0$ kJ/mol.

Integrative and Advanced Exercises

95. A British thermal unit (Btu) is defined as the quantity of heat required to change the temperature of 1 lb of water by 1 °F. Assume the specific heat of water to be independent of temperature. How much heat is required to raise the temperature of the water in a 40 gal water heater from 48 to 145 °F in **(a)** Btu; **(b)** kcal; **(c)** kJ?

96. A 7.26 kg shot (as used in the sporting event, the shot put) is dropped from the top of a building 168 m high. What is the maximum temperature increase that could occur in the shot? Assume a specific heat of $0.47\ \text{J g}^{-1}\ °\text{C}^{-1}$ for the shot. Why would the actual measured temperature increase likely be less than the calculated value?

97. An alternative approach to bomb calorimetry is to establish the heat capacity of the calorimeter, *exclusive* of the water it contains. The heat absorbed by the water and by the rest of the calorimeter must be calculated separately and then added together. A bomb calorimeter assembly containing 983.5 g water is calibrated by the combustion of 1.354 g anthracene. The temperature of the calorimeter rises from 24.87 to 35.63 °C. When 1.053 g citric acid is burned in the same assembly, but with 968.6 g water, the temperature increases from 25.01 to 27.19 °C. The heat of combustion of anthracene, $C_{14}H_{10}(s)$, is -7067 kJ/mol $C_{14}H_{10}$. What is the heat of combustion of citric acid, $C_6H_8O_7$, expressed in kJ/mol?

98. The method of Exercise 97 is used in some bomb calorimetry experiments. A 1.148 g sample of benzoic acid is burned in excess $O_2(g)$ in a bomb immersed in 1181 g of water. The temperature of the water rises from 24.96 to 30.25 °C. The heat of combustion of benzoic acid is -26.42 kJ/g. In a second experiment, a 0.895 g powdered coal sample is burned in the same calorimeter assembly. The temperature of 1162 g of water rises from 24.98 to 29.81 °C. How many metric tons (1 metric ton = 1000 kg) of this coal would have to be burned to release 2.15×10^9 kJ of heat?

99. A handbook lists two different values for the heat of combustion of hydrogen: 33.88 kcal/g H_2 if $H_2O(l)$ is formed, and 28.67 kcal/g H_2 if $H_2O(g)$ is formed. Explain why these two values are different, and indicate what property this difference represents. Devise a means of verifying your conclusions.

100. Determine the missing values of $\Delta H°$ in the diagram shown below.

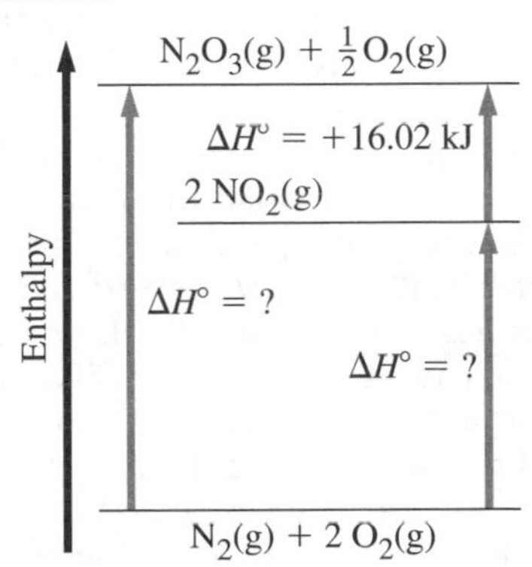

101. A particular natural gas consists, in mole percents, of 83.0% CH_4, 11.2% C_2H_6, and 5.8% C_3H_8. A 385 L sample of this gas, measured at 22.6 °C and 739 mmHg, is burned at constant pressure in an excess of oxygen gas. How much heat, in kilojoules, is evolved in the combustion reaction?

102. An overall reaction for a coal gasification process is

$$2\,C(\text{graphite}) + 2\,H_2O(g) \longrightarrow CH_4(g) + CO_2(g)$$

Show that this overall equation can be established by an appropriate combination of equations from Section 4-9.

103. Which of the following gases has the greater fuel value on a per liter (STP) basis? That is, which has the greater heat of combustion? [*Hint:* The only combustible gases are CH_4, C_3H_8, CO, and H_2.]
(a) coal gas: 49.7% H_2, 29.9% CH_4, 8.2% N_2, 6.9% CO, 3.1% C_3H_8, 1.7% CO_2, and 0.5% O_2, by volume.
(b) sewage gas, 66.0% CH_4, 30.0% CO_2, and 4.0% N_2, by volume.

104. A calorimeter that measures an exothermic heat of reaction by the quantity of ice that can be melted is called an ice calorimeter. Now consider that 0.100 L of methane gas, $CH_4(g)$, at 25.0 °C and 744 mmHg is burned at constant pressure in air. The heat liberated is captured and used to melt 9.53 g ice at 0 °C (ΔH_{fusion} of ice = 6.01 kJ/mol).
(a) Write an equation for the complete combustion of CH_4, and show that combustion is incomplete in this case.

(b) Assume that $CO(g)$ is produced in the incomplete combustion of CH_4, and represent the combustion as best you can through a single equation with small whole numbers as coefficients. ($H_2O(l)$ is another product of the combustion.)

105. For the reaction

$$C_2H_4(g) + 3\,O_2(g) \longrightarrow 2\,CO_2(g) + 2\,H_2O(l) \qquad \Delta H^\circ = -1410.9\ \text{kJ}$$

if the H_2O were obtained as a gas rather than a liquid, **(a)** would the heat of reaction be greater (more negative) or smaller (less negative) than that indicated in the equation? **(b)** Explain your answer. **(c)** Calculate the value of ΔH° in this case.

106. Some of the butane, $C_4H_{10}(g)$, in a 200.0 L cylinder at 26.0 °C is withdrawn and burned at a constant pressure in an excess of air. As a result, the pressure of the gas in the cylinder falls from 2.35 atm to 1.10 atm. The liberated heat is used to raise the temperature of 132.5 L of water in a heater from 26.0 to 62.2 °C. Assume that the combustion products are $CO_2(g)$ and $H_2O(l)$ exclusively, and determine the efficiency of the water heater. (That is, what percent of the heat of combustion was absorbed by the water?)

107. The metabolism of glucose, $C_6H_{12}O_6$, yields $CO_2(g)$ and $H_2O(l)$ as products. Heat released in the process is converted to useful work with about 70% efficiency. Calculate the mass of glucose metabolized by a 58.0 kg person in climbing a mountain with an elevation gain of 1450 m. Assume that the work performed in the climb is about four times that required to simply lift 58.0 kg by 1450 m. (ΔH_f° of $C_6H_{12}O_6(s)$ is -1273.3 kJ/mol.)

108. An alkane hydrocarbon has the formula C_nH_{2n+2}. The enthalpies of formation of the alkanes decrease (become more negative) as the number of C atoms increases. Starting with butane, $C_4H_{10}(g)$, for each additional CH_2 group in the formula, the enthalpy of formation, ΔH_f°, changes by about -21 kJ/mol. Use this fact and data from Table 4.2 to estimate the heat of combustion of heptane, $C_7H_{16}(l)$.

109. Upon complete combustion, a 1.00 L sample (at STP) of a natural gas gives off 43.6 kJ of heat. If the gas is a mixture of $CH_4(g)$ and $C_2H_6(g)$, what is its percent composition, *by volume*?

110. Under the entry H_2SO_4, a reference source lists many values for the standard enthalpy of formation. For example, for pure $H_2SO_4(l)$, $\Delta H_f^\circ = -814.0$ kJ/mol; for a solution with 1 mol H_2O per mole of H_2SO_4, -841.8; with 10 mol H_2O, -880.5; with 50 mol H_2O; -886.8; with 100 mol H_2O, -887.7; with 500 mol H_2O, -890.5; with 1000 mol H_2O, -892.3; with 10,000 mol H_2O, -900.8; and with 100,000 mol H_2O, -907.3. **(a)** Explain why these values are not all the same. **(b)** The value of $\Delta H_f^\circ[H_2SO_4(aq)]$ in an infinitely dilute solution is -909.3 kJ/mol. What data from this chapter can you cite to confirm this value? Explain. **(c)** If 500.0 mL of 1.00 M $H_2SO_4(aq)$ is prepared from pure $H_2SO_4(l)$, what is the approximate change in temperature that should be observed? Assume that the $H_2SO_4(l)$ and $H_2O(l)$ are at the same temperature initially and that the specific heat of the $H_2SO_4(aq)$ is about 4.2 J g^{-1} °C^{-1}.

111. Refer to the discussion of the gasification of coal (page 150), and show that some of the heat required in the gasification reaction (equation 4.24) can be supplied by the *methanation* reaction. This fact contributes to the success of modern processes that produce *synthetic natural gas* (SNG).

112. A 1.103 g sample of a gaseous carbon–hydrogen–oxygen compound that occupies a volume of 582 mL at 765.5 Torr and 25.00 °C is burned in an excess of $O_2(g)$ in a bomb calorimeter. The products of the combustion are 2.108 g $CO_2(g)$, 1.294 g $H_2O(l)$, and enough heat to raise the temperature of the calorimeter assembly from 25.00 to 31.94 °C. The heat capacity of the calorimeter is 5.015 kJ/°C. Write an equation for the combustion reaction, and indicate ΔH° for this reaction at 25.00 °C.

113. Several factors are involved in determining the cooking times required for foods in a microwave oven. One of these factors is specific heat. Determine the approximate time required to warm 250 mL of chicken broth from 4 °C (a typical refrigerator temperature) to 50 °C in a 700 W microwave oven. Assume that the density of chicken broth is about 1 g/mL and that its specific heat is approximately 4.2 J g^{-1} °C^{-1}.

114. Suppose you have a setup similar to the one depicted in Figure 4-8 except that there are two different weights rather than two equal weights. One weight is a steel cylinder 10.00 cm in diameter and 25 cm long, the other weight produces a pressure of 745 Torr. The temperature of the gas in the cylinder in which the expansion takes place is 25.0 °C. The piston restraining the gas has a diameter of 12.00 cm, and the height of the piston above the base of the gas expansion cylinder is 8.10 cm. The density of the steel is 7.75 g/cm^3. How much work is done when the steel cylinder is suddenly removed from the piston?

115. When one mole of sodium carbonate decahydrate (washing soda) is gently warmed, 155.3 kJ of heat is absorbed, water vapor is formed, and sodium carbonate heptahydrate remains. On more vigorous heating, the heptahydrate absorbs 320.1 kJ of heat and loses more water vapor to give the monohydrate. Continued heating gives the anhydrous salt (soda ash) while 57.3 kJ of heat is absorbed. Calculate ΔH for the conversion of one mole of washing soda into soda ash. Estimate ΔU for this process. Why is the value of ΔU only an estimate?

116. The oxidation of $NH_3(g)$ to $NO(g)$ in the Ostwald process must be very carefully controlled in terms of temperature, pressure, and contact time with the catalyst. This is because the oxidation of $NH_3(g)$ can yield any one of the products $N_2(g)$, $N_2O(g)$, $NO(g)$, and $NO_2(g)$, depending on conditions. Show that oxidation of $NH_3(g)$ to $N_2(g)$ is the most exothermic of the four possible reactions.

117. In the Are You Wondering 4-1 box, the temperature variation of enthalpy is discussed, and the equation q_P = heat capacity × temperature change = $C_P \times \Delta T$ was introduced to show how enthalpy changes with temperature for a constant-pressure process. Strictly speaking, the heat capacity of a substance at constant pressure is the slope of the line representing the variation of enthalpy (H) with temperature, that is

$$C_P = \frac{dH}{dT} \quad \text{(at constant pressure)}$$

where C_P is the heat capacity of the substance in question. Heat capacity is an extensive quantity and heat capacities are usually quoted as molar heat capacities $C_{P,m}$, the heat capacity of one mole of substance; an intensive property. The heat capacity at constant pressure is used to estimate the change in enthalpy due to a change in temperature. For infinitesimal changes in temperature,

$$dH = C_P dT \quad \text{(at constant pressure)}$$

To evaluate the change in enthalpy for a particular temperature change, from T_1 to T_2, we write

$$\int_{H(T_1)}^{H(T_2)} dH = H(T_2) - H(T_1) = \int_{T_1}^{T_2} C_P dT$$

If we assume that C_P is independent of temperature, then we recover equation (4.5)

$$\Delta H = C_P \times \Delta T$$

On the other hand, we often find that the heat capacity is a function of temperature; a convenient empirical expression is

$$C_{P,m} = a + bT + \frac{c}{T^2}$$

What is the change in molar enthalpy of N_2 when it is heated from 25.0 °C to 100.0 °C? The molar heat capacity of nitrogen is given by

$$C_{P,m} = 28.58 + 3.77 \times 10^{-3}\,T - \frac{0.5 \times 10^5}{T^2}\,\text{J K}^{-1}\,\text{mol}^{-1}$$

118. How much heat is required to convert 10.0 g of ice at −5.0 °C to steam at 100.0 °C? The temperature-dependent constant-pressure specific heat of ice is $C_p(T)/(\text{kJ kg}^{-1}\,\text{K}^{-1}) = 1.0187T - 1.49 \times 10^{-2}$. The temperature-dependent constant-pressure specific heat for water is $C_p(T)/(\text{kJ kg}^{-1}\,\text{K}^{-1}) = -1.0 \times 10^{-7}T^3 + 1.0 \times 10^{-4}T^2 - 3.92 \times 10^{-2}T + 8.7854$.

119. The standard enthalpy of formation of gaseous H_2O at 298.15 K is −241.82 kJ mol^{-1}. Using the ideas contained in Figure 4-16, estimate its value at 100.0 °C given the following values of the molar heat capacities at constant pressure: $H_2O(g)$: 33.58 J K^{-1} mol^{-1}; $H_2(g)$: 28.84 J K^{-1} mol^{-1}; $O_2(g)$: 29.37 J K^{-1} mol^{-1}. Assume the heat capacities are independent of temperature.

Feature Problems

120. James Joule published his definitive work related to the first law of thermodynamics in 1850. He stated that "the quantity of heat capable of increasing the temperature of one pound of water by 1 °F requires for its evolution the expenditure of a mechanical force represented by the fall of 772 lb through the space of one foot." Validate this statement by relating it to information given in this text.

121. Based on specific heat measurements, Pierre Dulong and Alexis Petit proposed in 1818 that the specific heat of an element is inversely related to its atomic weight (atomic mass). Thus, by measuring the specific heat of a new element, its atomic weight could be readily established.

(a) Use data from Table 4.1 and inside the front cover to plot a *straight-line* graph relating atomic mass and specific heat. Write the equation for this straight line.

(b) Use the measured specific heat of 0.23 J g^{-1} °C^{-1} and the equation derived in part **(a)** to obtain an approximate value of the atomic mass of cadmium, an element discovered in 1817.

(c) To raise the temperature of 75.0 g of a particular metal by 15 °C requires 450 J of heat. What might this metal be?

122. We can use the heat liberated by a neutralization reaction as a means of establishing the stoichiometry of the reaction. The data in the table are for the reaction of 1.00 M NaOH with 1.00 M citric acid, $C_6H_8O_7$, in a total solution volume of 60.0 mL.

mL 1.00 M NaOH Used	mL 1.00 M Citric Acid Used	ΔT, °C
20.0	40.0	4.7
30.0	30.0	6.3
40.0	20.0	8.2
50.0	10.0	6.7
55.0	5.0	2.7

(a) Plot ΔT versus mL 1.00 M NaOH, and identify the exact stoichiometric proportions of NaOH and citric acid at the equivalence point of the neutralization reaction.
(b) Why is the temperature change in the neutralization greatest when the reactants are in their exact stoichiometric proportions? That is, why not use an excess of one of the reactants to ensure that the neutralization has gone to completion to achieve the maximum temperature increase?
(c) Rewrite the formula of citric acid to reflect more precisely its acidic properties. Then write a balanced net ionic equation for the neutralization reaction.

123. In a student experiment to confirm Hess's law, the reaction

$$NH_3(\text{concd aq}) + HCl(aq) \longrightarrow NH_4Cl(aq)$$

was carried out in two different ways. First, 8.00 mL of concentrated $NH_3(aq)$ was added to 100.0 mL of 1.00 M HCl in a calorimeter. [The $NH_3(aq)$ was slightly in excess.] The reactants were initially at 23.8 °C, and the final temperature after neutralization was 35.8 °C. In the second experiment, air was bubbled through 100.0 mL of concentrated $NH_3(aq)$, sweeping out $NH_3(g)$ (see sketch). The $NH_3(g)$ was neutralized in 100.0 mL of 1.00 M HCl. The temperature of the concentrated $NH_3(aq)$ fell from 19.3 to 13.2 °C. At the same time, the temperature of the 1.00 M HCl rose from 23.8 to 42.9 °C as it was neutralized by $NH_3(g)$. Assume that all solutions have densities of 1.00 g/mL and specific heats of 4.18 J g^{-1} $°C^{-1}$.
(a) Write the two equations and ΔH values for the processes occurring in the second experiment. Show that the sum of these two equations is the same as the equation for the reaction in the first experiment.
(b) Show that, within the limits of experimental error, ΔH for the overall reaction is the same in the two experiments, thereby confirming Hess's law.

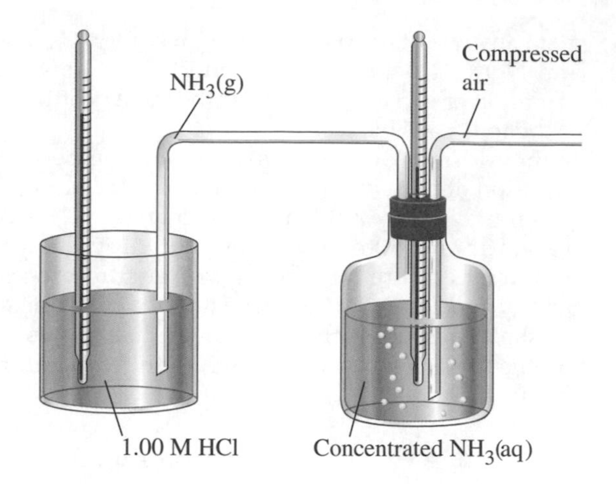

124. When an ideal gas is heated, the change in internal energy is limited to increasing the average translational kinetic energy of the gas molecules. Thus, there is a simple relationship between ΔU of the gas and the change in temperature that occurs. Derive this relationship with the help of ideas about the kinetic-molecular theory of gases developed in Chapter 2. After doing so, obtain numerical values (in J mol^{-1} K^{-1}) for the following molar heat capacities.
(a) The heat capacity, C_V, for one mole of gas under constant-volume conditions
(b) The heat capacity, C_P, for one mole of gas under constant-pressure conditions

125. Refer to Example 4-5 dealing with the work done by 0.100 mol He at 298 K in expanding in a single step from 2.40 to 1.20 atm. Review also the two-step expansion (2.40 atm $\longrightarrow$ 1.80 atm $\longrightarrow$ 1.20 atm) described on page 129 (see Figure 4-11).
(a) Determine the total work that would be done if the He expanded in a series of steps, at 0.10 atm intervals, from 2.40 to 1.20 atm.
(b) Represent this total work on the graph below, in which the quantity of work done in the two-step expansion is represented by the sum of the colored rectangles.
(c) Show that the maximum amount of work would occur if the expansion occurred in an infinite number of steps. To do this, express each infinitesimal quantity of work as $dw = P\,dV$ and use the methods of integral calculus (integration) to sum these quantities. Assume ideal behavior for the gas.
(d) Imagine reversing the process, that is, compressing the He from 1.20 to 2.40 atm. What are the maximum and minimum amounts of work required to produce this compression? Explain.
(e) In the isothermal compression described in part (d), what is the change in internal energy assuming ideal gas behavior? What is the value of q?
(f) Using the formula for the work derived in part (c), obtain an expression for q/T. Is this new function a state function? Explain.

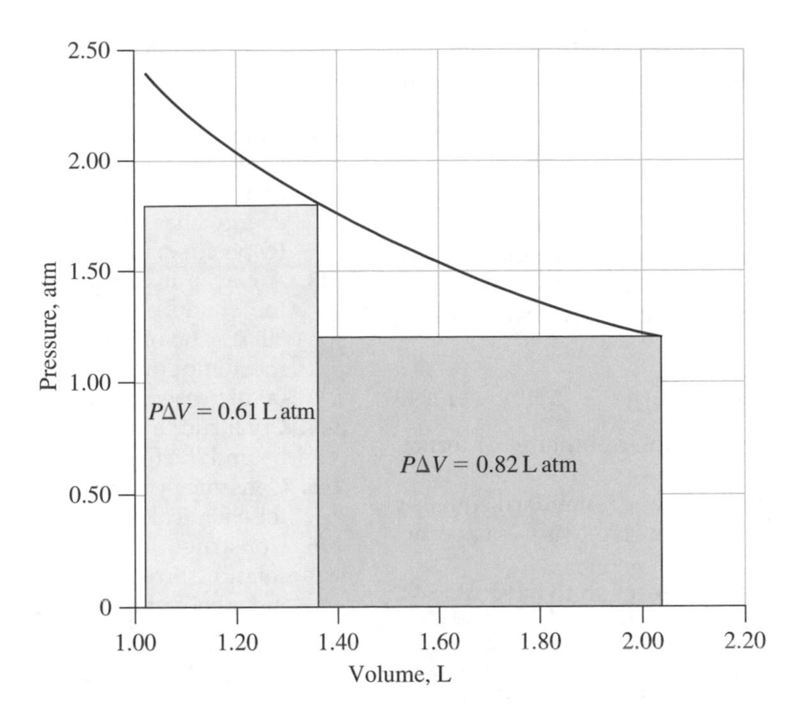

126. Look up the specific heat of several elements, and plot the products of the specific heats and atomic masses as a function of the atomic masses. Based on the plot, develop a hypothesis to explain the data. How could you test your hypothesis?

Self-Assessment Exercises

127. In your own words, define or explain the following terms or symbols: **(a)** ΔH; **(b)** $P\Delta V$; **(c)** ΔH_f°; **(d)** standard state; **(e)** fossil fuel.

128. Briefly describe each of the following ideas or methods: **(a)** law of conservation of energy; **(b)** bomb calorimetry; **(c)** function of state; **(d)** enthalpy diagram; **(e)** Hess's law.

129. Explain the important distinctions between each pair of terms: **(a)** system and surroundings; **(b)** heat and work; **(c)** specific heat and heat capacity; **(d)** endothermic and exothermic; **(e)** constant-volume process and constant-pressure process.

130. The temperature increase of 225 mL of water at 25 °C contained in a Styrofoam cup is noted when a 125 g sample of a metal at 75 °C is added. With reference to Table 4.1, the greatest temperature increase will be noted if the metal is **(a)** lead; **(b)** aluminum; **(c)** iron; **(d)** copper.

131. A plausible final temperature when 75.0 mL of water at 80.0 °C is added to 100.0 mL of water at 20 °C is **(a)** 28 °C; **(b)** 40 °C; **(c)** 46 °C; **(d)** 50 °C.

132. $\Delta U = 100$ J for a system that gives off 100 J of heat and **(a)** does no work; **(b)** does 200 J of work; **(c)** has 100 J of work done on it; **(d)** has 200 J of work done on it.

133. The heat of solution of NaOH(s) in water is -41.6 kJ/mol NaOH. When NaOH(s) is dissolved in water the solution temperature **(a)** increases; **(b)** decreases; **(c)** remains constant; **(d)** either increases or decreases, depending on how much NaOH is dissolved.

134. The standard molar enthalpy of formation of $CO_2(g)$ is equal to **(a)** 0; **(b)** the standard molar heat of combustion of graphite; **(c)** the sum of the standard molar enthalpies of formation of CO(g) and $O_2(g)$; **(d)** the standard molar heat of combustion of CO(g).

135. Which two of the following statements are false? **(a)** $q_V = q_P$ for the reaction $N_2(g) + O_2(g) \longrightarrow 2\,NO(g)$; **(b)** $\Delta H > 0$ for an endothermic reaction; **(c)** By convention, the most stable form of an element must always be chosen as the reference form and assigned the value $\Delta H_f^\circ = 0$; **(d)** ΔU and ΔH for a reaction can never have the same value; **(e)** $\Delta H < 0$ for the neutralization of a strong acid by a strong base.

136. A 1.22 kg piece of iron at 126.5 °C is dropped into 981 g water at 22.1 °C. The temperature rises to 34.4 °C. What will be the final temperature if this same piece of iron at 99.8 °C is dropped into 325 mL of glycerol, $HOCH_2CH(OH)CH_2OH(l)$ at 26.2 °C?

For glycerol, $d = 1.26\ g/mL$; $C_p = 219\ J\ K^{-1}\ mol^{-1}$.

137. Write the balanced chemical equations for reactions that have the following as their standard enthalpy changes.
(a) $\Delta H_f^\circ = +82.05\ kJ/mol\ N_2O(g)$
(b) $\Delta H_f^\circ = -394.1\ kJ/mol\ SO_2Cl_2(l)$
(c) $\Delta H_{comb}^\circ = -1527\ kJ/mol\ CH_3CH_2COOH(l)$

138. The standard molar heats of combustion of C(graphite) and CO(g) are −393.5 and −283 kJ/mol, respectively. Use those data and that for the following reaction

$$CO(g) + Cl_2(g) \longrightarrow COCl_2(g) \qquad \Delta H^\circ = -108\ kJ$$

to calculate the standard molar enthalpy of formation of $COCl_2(g)$.

139. Can a chemical compound have a standard enthalpy of formation of zero? If so, how likely is this to occur? Explain.

140. Is it possible for a chemical reaction to have $\Delta U < 0$ and $\Delta H > 0$? Explain.

141. Use principles from this chapter to explain the observation that professional chefs prefer to cook with a gas stove rather than an electric stove.

142. Hot water and a piece of cold metal come into contact in an isolated container. When the final temperature of the metal and water are identical, is the total energy change in this process **(a)** zero; **(b)** negative; **(c)** positive; **(d)** not enough information.

143. A clay pot containing water at 25 °C is placed in the shade on a day in which the temperature is 30 °C. The outside of the clay pot is kept moist. Will the temperature of the water inside the clay pot **(a)** increase; **(b)** decrease; **(c)** remain the same?

144. Construct a concept map encompassing the ideas behind the first law of thermodynamics.

145. Construct a concept map to show the use of enthalpy for chemical reactions.

146. Construct a concept map to show the interrelationships between path-dependent and path-independent quantities in thermodynamics.

Spontaneous Change: Entropy and Gibbs Energy

5

CONTENTS

Thermodynamics originated in the early nineteenth century with attempts to improve the efficiency of steam engines. However, the laws of thermodynamics are widely useful throughout the field of chemistry and in biology as well, as we discover in this chapter.

The reaction of nitrogen and oxygen gases, which does not occur appreciably in the forward direction at room temperature, produces significant equilibrium amounts of NO(g) at *high* temperatures.

$$N_2(g) + O_2(g) \rightleftharpoons 2\,NO(g)$$

Another reaction involving oxides of nitrogen is the conversion of NO(g) to NO_2(g):

$$2\,NO(g) + O_2(g) \rightleftharpoons 2\,NO_2(g)$$

This reaction, unlike the first, yields its greatest equilibrium amounts of NO_2(g) at *low* temperatures.

What is there about these two reactions that causes the forward reaction of one to be favored at high temperatures but the forward reaction of the other to be favored at low temperatures? Our primary objective in this chapter is to develop concepts to help us answer questions like this. This chapter shows the great power of thermodynamics to provide explanations of many chemical phenomena.

◀ Throughout the text we have adopted the IUPAC recommended name of "Gibbs energy" to replace the terms *free energy* or *Gibbs free energy*.

▲ When the spring powering this mechanical toy unwinds, the toy stops moving. The spring cannot spontaneously rewind.

▶ Spontaneous: "proceeding from natural feeling or native tendency without external constraint . . . ; developing without apparent external influence, force, cause, or treatment." *Merriam-Webster's Collegiate Dictionary*, online, 2000.

5-1 Spontaneity: The Meaning of Spontaneous Change

Most of us have played with spring-wound toys, whether a toy automobile, top, or music box. In every case, once the wound-up toy is released, it keeps running until the stored energy in the spring has been released; then the toy stops. The toy never rewinds itself. Human intervention is necessary (winding by hand). The running down of a wound-up spring is an example of a *spontaneous* process. The rewinding of the spring is a *nonspontaneous* process. Let's explore the scientific meaning of these two terms.

A **spontaneous process** is a process that occurs in a system left to itself; once started, no action from outside the system (external action) is necessary to make the process continue. Conversely, a **nonspontaneous process** will not occur *unless* some external action is continuously applied. Consider the rusting of an iron pipe exposed to the atmosphere. Although the process occurs slowly, it does so continuously. As a result, the amount of iron decreases and the amount of rust increases until a final state of equilibrium is reached in which essentially all the iron has been converted to iron(III) oxide. We say that the reaction

$$4\,Fe(s) + 3\,O_2(g) \longrightarrow 2\,Fe_2O_3(s)$$

is *spontaneous*. Now consider the reverse situation: the extraction of pure iron from iron(III) oxide. We should not say that the process is impossible, but it is certainly *nonspontaneous*. In fact, this nonspontaneous reverse process is involved in the manufacture of iron from iron ore.

We will consider specific quantitative criteria for spontaneous change later in the chapter, but even now we can identify some spontaneous processes intuitively. For example, in the neutralization of NaOH(aq) with HCl(aq), the net change that occurs is

$$H_3O^+(aq) + OH^-(aq) \longrightarrow 2\,H_2O(l)$$

There is very little tendency for the reverse reaction (self-ionization) to occur, so the neutralization reaction is a spontaneous reaction. The melting of ice, however, is spontaneous at temperatures above 0 °C but nonspontaneous below 0 °C.

From our discussion of spontaneity to this point, we can reach these conclusions at ambient pressures.

- If a process is spontaneous, the reverse process is nonspontaneous.
- Both spontaneous and nonspontaneous processes are possible, but only spontaneous processes will occur *without intervention*. Nonspontaneous processes require the system to be acted on by an external agent.
- Some spontaneous processes occur very slowly and others occur rather rapidly. For example, the melting of an ice cube that has been dropped into cold water at 1 °C is a spontaneous process that occurs slowly. The melting of an ice cube that has been dropped into hot water at 99 °C is a spontaneous process that occurs rapidly. The main point is that spontaneous does not mean fast.

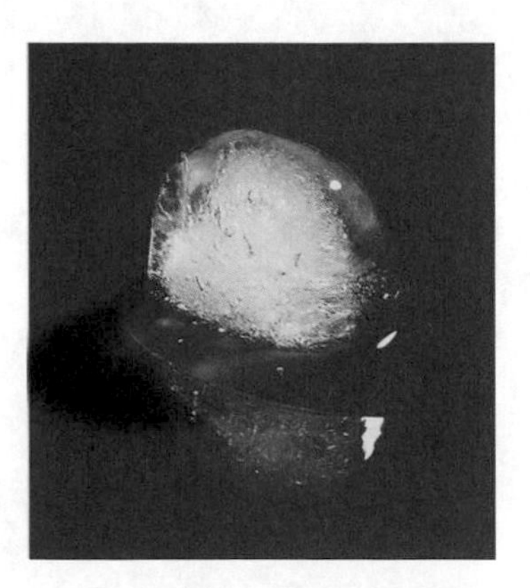

▲ The melting of an ice cube occurs spontaneously at temperatures above 0 °C.

We would like to do more, however. We want to be able to predict whether the forward or the reverse direction is the direction of spontaneous change in a process, so we need a criterion for spontaneous change. To begin, let's look to mechanical systems for a clue. A ball rolls downhill, and water flows to a lower level. A common feature of these processes is that *potential energy decreases*.

For chemical systems, the property analogous to the potential energy of a mechanical system is the internal energy (U) or the closely related property enthalpy (H). In the 1870s, P. Berthelot and J. Thomsen proposed that the direction of spontaneous change is the direction in which the enthalpy of a system decreases. In a system in which enthalpy decreases, heat is given off by the system to the surroundings. Bertholet and Thomsen concluded that exothermic reactions should be spontaneous. In fact, many exothermic processes are spontaneous, but some are not. Also, some endothermic reactions *are* spontaneous. Thus, we cannot predict whether a process is spontaneous from its enthalpy change alone. Here are three examples of spontaneous, *endothermic* processes:

- the melting of ice at room temperature
- the evaporation of liquid diethyl ether from an open beaker
- the dissolving of ammonium nitrate in water

We will have to look to thermodynamic functions other than enthalpy change (ΔH) as criteria for spontaneous change.

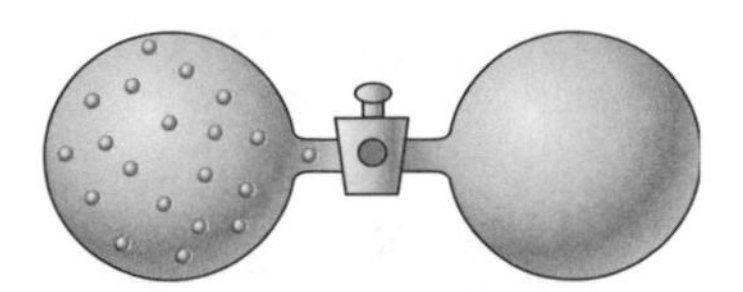

(a) Initial condition

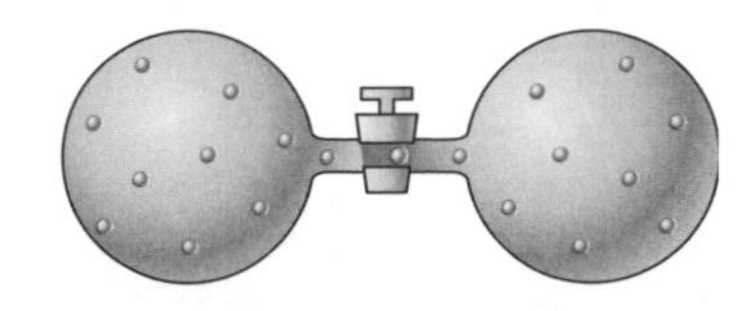

(b) After expansion into vacuum

▲ FIGURE 5-1
Expansion of an ideal gas into a vacuum
(a) Initially, an ideal gas is confined to the bulb on the left at 1.00 atm pressure.
(b) When the stopcock is opened, the gas expands into the identical bulb on the right. The final condition is one in which the gas is equally distributed between the two bulbs at a pressure of 0.50 atm.

 5-1 CONCEPT ASSESSMENT

Is it correct to say that a spontaneous process is a fast process and a nonspontaneous process is a very slow one? Explain.

5-2 The Concept of Entropy

To continue our search for criteria for spontaneous change, consider Figure 5-1, which depicts two identical glass bulbs joined by a stopcock. Initially, the bulb on the left contains an ideal gas at 1.00 atm pressure, and the bulb on the right is evacuated. When the valve is opened, the gas immediately expands into the evacuated bulb. After this expansion, the molecules are dispersed throughout the apparatus, with essentially equal numbers of molecules in both bulbs and a pressure of 0.50 atm. What causes this spontaneous expansion of the gas at a constant temperature?

One of the characteristics of an ideal gas is that its internal energy (U) does not depend on the gas pressure, but only on the temperature. Therefore, in this expansion $\Delta U = 0$. Also, the enthalpy change is zero: $\Delta H = 0$. This means that the expansion is not caused by the system dropping to a lower energy state. A convenient mental image to "explain" the expansion is that the gas molecules tend to spread out into the larger volume available to them at the reduced pressure. A more fundamental description of the underlying cause is that, for the same total energy, in the expanded volume there are more available translational energy levels among which the gas molecules can be distributed. The tendency is for the energy of the system to spread out over a larger number of energy levels.

A similar situation—the mixing of ideal gases—is depicted in Figure 5-2. In this case, the two bulbs initially are filled with different ideal gases at 1.00 atm. When the stopcock is opened, the gases mix. The resulting change is essentially that of the expansion of the ideal gas pictured in Figure 5-1, but twice over. That is, each gas expands into the new volume available to it, without regard for the other gas (recall Dalton's law of partial pressures. Again, each expanded gas has more translational energy levels available to its molecules—the energy of the system has spread out. And again, the internal energy and enthalpy of the system are not changed by the expansion.

KEEP IN MIND

that U and H are related as follows: $H = U + PV$, and $\Delta H = \Delta U + \Delta(PV)$. For a fixed amount of an ideal gas at a constant temperature, PV = constant, $\Delta(PV) = 0$, and $\Delta H = \Delta U$.

Entropy

The thermodynamic property related to the way in which the energy of a system is distributed among the available microscopic energy levels is called **entropy**.

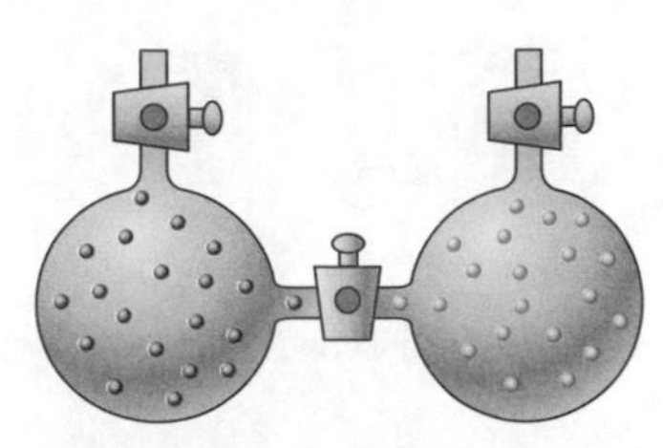

(a) Before mixing

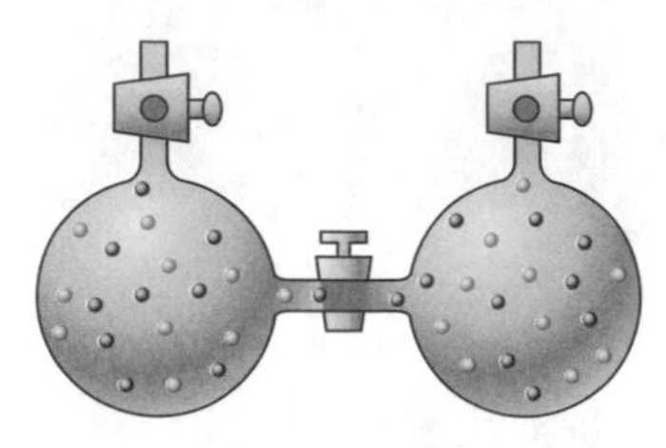

(b) After mixing

• Gas A • Gas B

▲ FIGURE 5-2
The mixing of ideal gasses
The total volume of the system and the total gas pressure remain fixed. The net change is that **(a)** before mixing, each gas is confined to half the total volume (a single bulb) at a pressure of 1.00 atm, and **(b)** after mixing, each gas has expanded into the total volume (both bulbs) and exerts a partial pressure of 0.50 atm.

The greater the number of arrangements (i.e., microstates) of the microscopic particles (atoms, ions, molecules) among the energy levels in a particular state of a system, the greater the entropy of the system.

Entropy is denoted by the symbol S. Like internal energy and enthalpy, entropy is a function of state. It has a unique value for a system whose temperature, pressure, and composition are specified. The **entropy change, ΔS,** is the difference in entropy between two states of a system, and it also has a unique value.

In the gas expansion of Figure 5-1, the entropy of the gas *increases* and $\Delta S > 0$. In the mixing of gases as carried out in Figure 5-2, entropy also increases, a fact that we can represent symbolically.

$$A(g) + B(g) \longrightarrow \text{mixture of } A(g) \text{ and } B(g)$$

$$\Delta S = S_{\text{mix of gases}} - [S_{A(g)} + S_{B(g)}] > 0$$

Because both of these expansions occur spontaneously and neither is accompanied by a change in internal energy or enthalpy, it seems possible that *increases in entropy underlie spontaneous processes*. This is a proposition that we will have to examine more closely later, but let's accept it for now.

The Boltzmann Equation for Entropy

The connection between macroscopic changes, such as the mixing of gases, and the microscopic nature of matter was enunciated by Ludwig Boltzmann. The conceptual breakthrough that Boltzmann made was to associate the number of energy levels in the system with the number of ways of arranging the particles (atoms, ions, or molecules) in these energy levels. The microscopic energy levels are also called *states*, and the particular way a number of particles is distributed among these states is called a *microstate*. The more states a given number of particles can occupy, the more microstates the system has. The more microstates that exist, the greater the entropy. Boltzmann derived the relationship

$$S = k \ln W \tag{5.1}$$

where S is the entropy, k is the Boltzmann constant, and W is the number of microstates. We can think of the Boltzmann constant as the gas constant per molecule; that is, $k = R/N_A$. [Although we didn't specifically introduce k in the discussion of kinetic-molecular theory, R/N_A appears in equation (2.21).] The number of microstates, W, is the number of ways that the atoms or molecules can be positioned in the states available and still give rise to the same total energy. Each permissible arrangement of the particles constitutes one of the microstates, so W is the total number of microstates that correspond to the same energy.

▲ **A bust marking Ludwig Boltzmann's tomb in Vienna**
Boltzmann's famous equation is inscribed on the tomb. At the time of Boltzmann's death, the term *log* was used for both natural logarithms and logarithms to the base ten; the symbol "ln" had not yet been adopted.

Let us explore the connection between the number of microstates (W) and entropy (S) a little further by using a small one-dimensional crystal of four nitrous oxide molecules, NO. At $T = 0$ K, the four NO molecules are aligned as NO···NO···NO···NO, which is the only microstate possible. Therefore, $W = 1$ and $S = 0$. Now consider what happens when the temperature is raised just enough to allow a single NO to rotate. Such an increase in temperature corresponds to an increase in the internal energy of the system. Now four microstates are possible, NO···NO···NO···ON; NO···NO···ON···NO; NO···ON···NO···NO; and ON···NO···NO···NO; W equals 4. By using Boltzmann's equation, we find that $S = k \ln 4 = (1.3807 \times 10^{-23}\ \text{J K}^{-1})\ln 4 = 1.9141 \times 10^{-23}\ \text{J K}^{-1}$. As the energy of the system increases, the number of microstates increases; therefore, entropy of the system will increase.

How can we use Boltzmann's equation to think about the distribution of microscopic particles among the energy levels of a system? Let's consider again the particle-in-a-box model for a matter wave. Specifically, we can use the equation $E = n^2h^2/8mL^2$ to calculate a few energy levels for a matter wave in a one-dimensional box. Representative energy levels are shown in the energy-level diagrams in Figure 5-3(a) for a particle in boxes of lengths L, $2L$, and $3L$. We see the following relationship between the length of the box and the number of levels: L, *three* levels; $2L$, *six* levels; and $3L$, *nine* levels. As the boundaries of the box are expanded, the separation between the energy levels decreases resulting in an increase of accessible energy levels. Extending this model to three-dimensional space and large numbers of gas molecules, we find less crowding of molecules into a limited number of energy levels when the pressure of the gas drops and the molecules expand into a larger volume. Thus, there is a greater spreading of the energy, and the entropy increases.

We can use the same particle-in-a-box model to understand the effect of raising the temperature of a substance on the entropy of the system. We will consider a gas, but our conclusions are equally valid for a liquid or solid. At low temperatures, the molecules have a low energy, and the gas molecules can occupy only a few of the energy levels; the value of W is small, and the entropy is low. As the temperature is raised, the energy of the molecules increases and the molecules have access to a larger number of energy levels. Thus the number of accessible microstates (W) increases and the entropy rises (Fig. 5-3(b)).

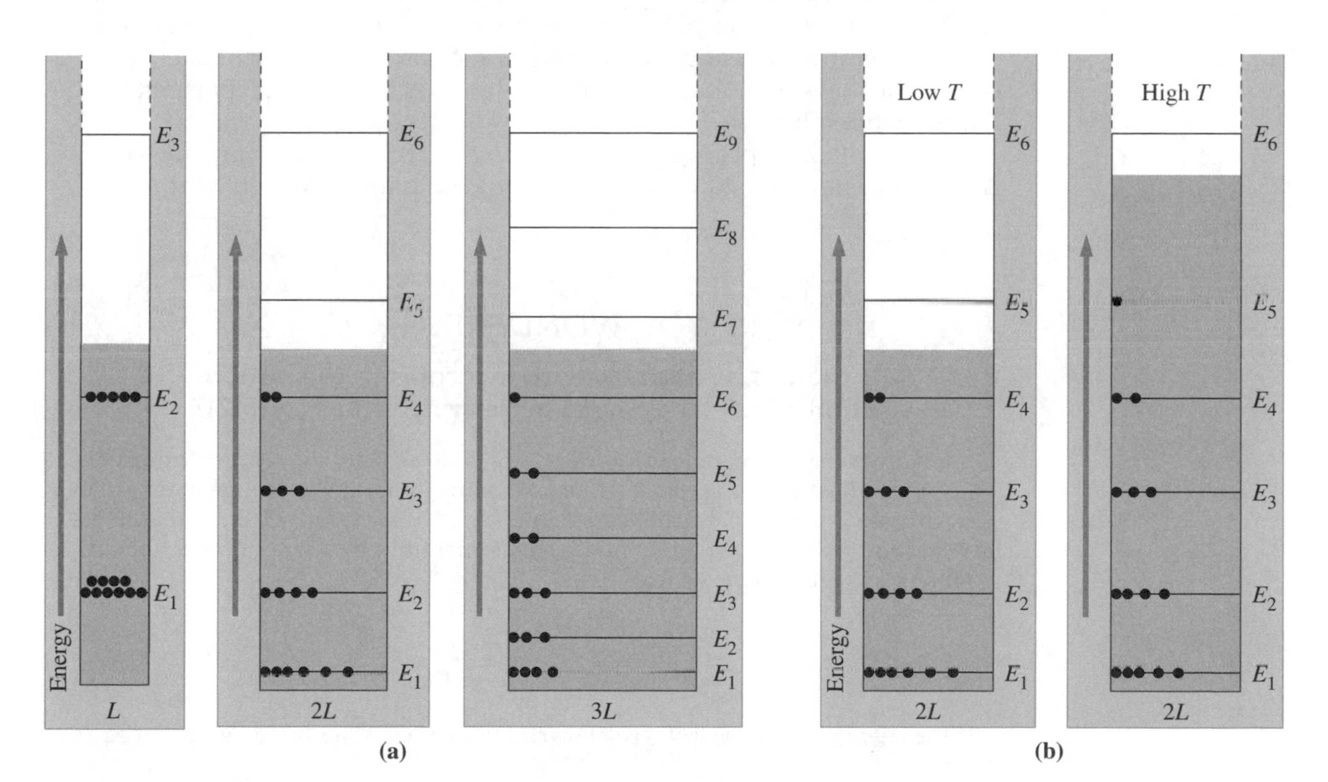

▲ FIGURE 5-3
Energy levels for a particle in a one-dimensional box
(a) The energy levels of a particle in a box become more numerous and closer together as the length of the box increases. The range of thermally accessible levels is indicated by the tinted band. The solid circles signify a system consisting of 15 particles. Each drawing represents a single microstate of the system. Can you see that as the box length increases there are many more microstates available to the particles for a given amount of thermal energy? As the number of possible microstates for a given total energy increases, so does the entropy. **(b)** More energy levels become accessible in a box of fixed length as the temperature is raised. Because the average energy of the particles also increases, the internal energy and entropy both increase as the temperature is raised.

In summary, the state of a thermodynamic system can be described in two ways: the macroscopic description, in terms of state functions P, V, and T; and the microscopic description, requiring a knowledge of the position and velocity of every particle (atom or molecule) in the system. Boltzmann's equation provides the connection between the two.

Entropy Change

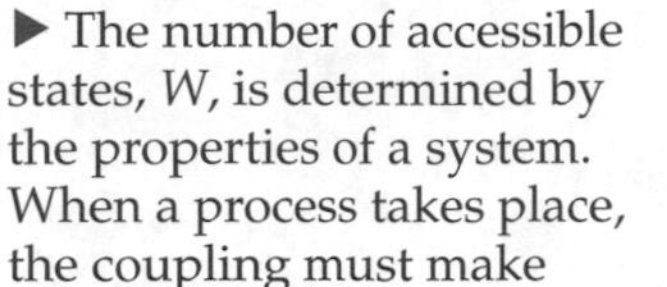

▶ The number of accessible states, W, is determined by the properties of a system. When a process takes place, the coupling must make the system larger; hence W must increase as the system spontaneously moves to a different equilibrium.

An entropy change is based on two measurable quantities: heat (q) and temperature (T). Both of these factors affect the availability of energy levels to the microscopic particles of a system. The following equation relates these factors to an entropy change,

$$\Delta S = \frac{q_{rev}}{T} \tag{5.2}$$

where T is the Kelvin temperature. Notice that ΔS is directly proportional to the quantity of heat because the more energy added to a system (as heat), the greater the number of energy levels available to the microscopic particles. Raising the temperature also increases the availability of energy levels, but for a given quantity of heat the proportional increase in number of energy levels is greatest at low temperatures. That is why ΔS is inversely proportional to the Kelvin temperature.

Equation (5.2) appears simple, but it is not. If S is to be a function of state, ΔS for a system must be independent of the path by which heat is lost or

5-1 ARE YOU WONDERING...

If there is a natural way to incorporate the notion of infinitesimal changes in deriving equation (5.2)?

The infinitesimal change in entropy, dS, that accompanies an infinitesimal reversible heat flow, dq_{rev}, is $dS = dq_{rev}/T$. Now imagine the change in a system from state 1 to state 2 is carried out in a series of such infinitesimal reversible steps. Summation of all these infinitesimal quantities through the calculus technique of integration yields ΔS.

$$\Delta S = \int \frac{dq_{rev}}{T}$$

If the change of state is isothermal (carried out at constant temperature), we can write

$$\Delta S = \int \frac{dq_{rev}}{T} = \frac{1}{T}\int dq_{rev} = \frac{q_{rev}}{T}$$

and we have recovered the definition of entropy change in (5.2.)

Starting with equivalent expressions for dq_{rev}, ΔS can be related to other system properties. For the isothermal, reversible expansion of an ideal gas, $dq_{rev} = -dw_{rev}$, leading to equation (5.10) on page 187, which describes ΔS in terms of gas volumes. For a reversible change in temperature, $dq_{rev} = C_p\,dT$, which leads to the entropy change for a change in temperature (see Exercise 86).

gained. Conversely, because the value of q ordinarily depends on the path chosen (recall page 260), equation (5.2) holds only for a carefully defined path. The path must be *reversible*, that is, $q = q_{rev}$. As we learned in Chapter 4, a reversible process can be made to reverse its direction when just an infinitesimal change in the opposite direction is made in a system property (review Figure 4-12). Because q has the unit J and $1/T$ has the unit K^{-1}, the unit of entropy change, ΔS, is J/K, or J K^{-1}.

In some instances, it is difficult to construct mental pictures to assess how the entropy of a system changes during a process. However, in many cases, an increase or a decrease in the accessibility of energy levels for the microscopic particles of a system parallels an increase or decrease in the *number* of microscopic particles and the *space* available to them. As a consequence, we can often make qualitative predictions about entropy change by focusing on those two factors. Let's test this idea by considering again the three spontaneous, endothermic processes listed at the conclusion of Section 5-1 and illustrated in Figure 5-4.

In the melting of ice, a crystalline solid is replaced by a less structured liquid. Molecules that were relatively fixed in position in the solid, being limited to vibrational motion, are now free to move about a bit. The molecules have gained some translational and rotational motion. The number of accessible microscopic energy levels has increased, and so has the entropy.

In the vaporization process, a liquid is replaced by the even less structured gas. Molecules in the gaseous state, because they can move within a large free volume, have many more accessible energy levels than do those in the liquid state. In the gas, energy can be spread over a much greater number of microscopic energy levels than in the liquid. The entropy of the gaseous state is much higher than that of the liquid state.

In the dissolving of ammonium nitrate in water, for example, a crystalline solid and a pure liquid are replaced by a mixture of ions and water molecules in the liquid (solution) state. This situation is somewhat more involved than the first two because some decrease in entropy is associated with the clustering of water molecules around the ions because of ion–dipole forces. The increase in entropy that accompanies the destruction of the solid's crystalline lattice predominates, however, and for the overall dissolution process, $\Delta S > 0$.

In each of the three spontaneous, endothermic processes discussed here, the increase in entropy ($\Delta S > 0$) outweighs the fact that heat must be absorbed ($\Delta H > 0$), and each process is spontaneous.

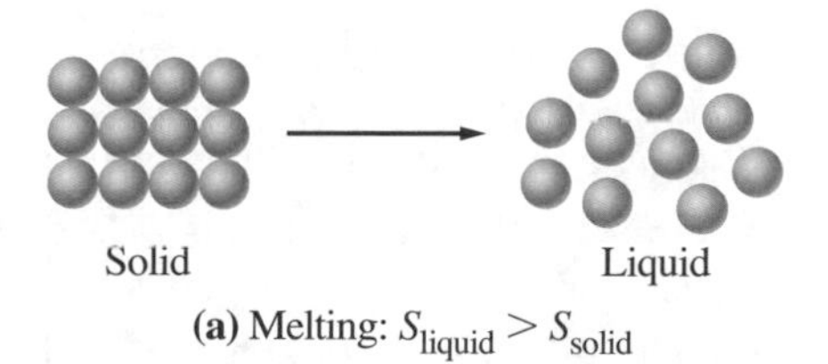

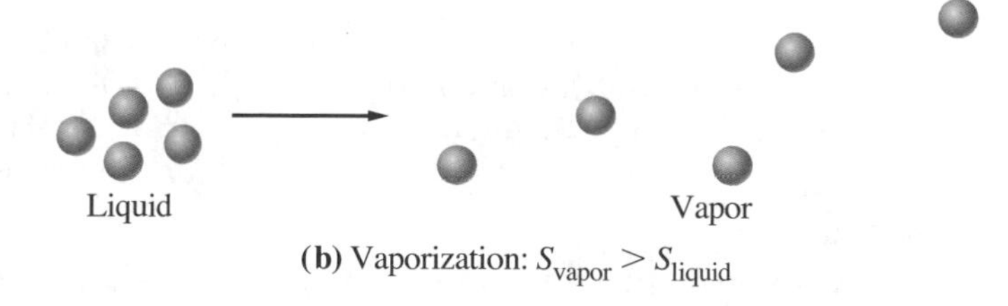

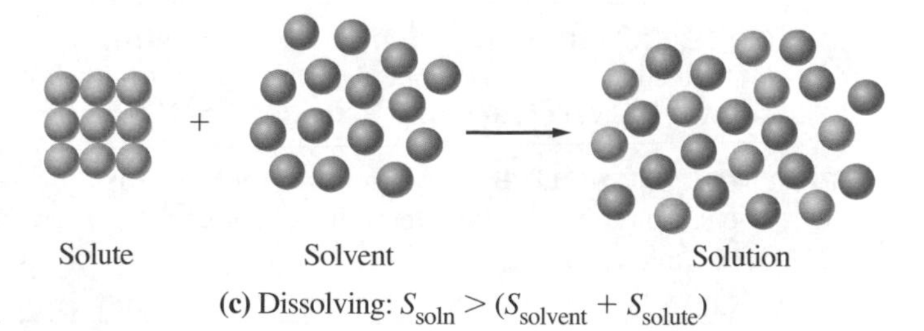

▲ FIGURE 5-4
Three processes in which entropy increases
Each of the processes pictured—**(a)** the melting of a solid, **(b)** the evaporation of a liquid, and **(c)** the dissolving of a solute—results in an increase in entropy. For part (c), the generalization works best for nonelectrolyte solutions, in which ion–dipole forces do not exist.

In summary, four situations generally produce an *increase* in entropy:

- Pure liquids or liquid solutions are formed from solids.
- Gases are formed from either solids or liquids.
- The number of molecules of gas increases as a result of a chemical reaction.
- The temperature of a substance increases. (Increased temperature means an increased number of accessible energy levels for the increased molecular motion, whether it be vibrational motion of atoms or ions in a solid, or translational and rotational motion of molecules in a liquid or gas.)

We apply these generalizations in Example 5-1.

EXAMPLE 5-1 Making Qualitative Predictions of Entropy Changes in Physical and Chemical Processes

Predict whether each of the following processes involves an increase or a decrease in entropy or whether the outcome is uncertain.

(a) The decomposition of ammonium nitrate (a fertilizer and a highly explosive compound): $2\,NH_4NO_3(s) \longrightarrow 2\,N_2(g) + 4\,H_2O(g) + O_2(g)$.

(b) The conversion of SO_2 to SO_3 (a key step in the manufacture of sulfuric acid): $2\,SO_2(g) + O_2(g) \longrightarrow 2\,SO_3(g)$.

(c) The extraction of sucrose from cane sugar juice: $C_{12}H_{22}O_{11}(aq) \longrightarrow C_{12}H_{22}O_{11}(s)$.

(d) The "water gas shift" reaction (involved in the gasification of coal): $CO(g) + H_2O(g) \longrightarrow CO_2(g) + H_2(g)$.

Analyze

Apply the generalizations summarized above. Three of the processes are chemical reactions, and for those processes, we should first consider whether the number of molecules of gas increases or decreases.

Solve

(a) Here, a solid yields a large quantity of gas. Entropy increases.

(b) Three moles of gaseous reactants produce two moles of gaseous products. The loss of one mole of gas indicates a loss of volume available to a smaller number of gas molecules. This loss reduces the number of possible configurations for the molecules in the system and the number of accessible microscopic energy levels. Entropy decreases.

(c) The sucrose molecules are reduced in mobility and in the number of forms in which their energy can be stored when they leave the solution and arrange themselves into a crystalline state. Entropy decreases.

(d) The entropies of the four gases are likely to be different because their molecular structures are different. The number of moles of gases is the same on both sides of the equation, however, so the entropy change is likely to be small if the temperature is constant. On the basis of just the generalizations listed above, we cannot determine whether entropy increases or decreases.

Assess

As we shall soon see, the ability to predict increases or decreases in entropy will help us to understand when a process will proceed spontaneously in the forward direction.

PRACTICE EXAMPLE A: Predict whether entropy increases or decreases in each of the following reactions. **(a)** The Claus process for removing H_2S from natural gas: $2\,H_2S(g) + SO_2(g) \longrightarrow 3\,S(s) + 2\,H_2O(g)$; **(b)** the decomposition of mercury(II) oxide: $2\,HgO(s) \longrightarrow 2\,Hg(l) + O_2(g)$.

PRACTICE EXAMPLE B: Predict whether entropy increases or decreases or whether the outcome is uncertain in each of the following reactions. **(a)** $Zn(s) + Ag_2O(s) \longrightarrow ZnO(s) + 2\,Ag(s)$; **(b)** the chlor-alkali process, $2\,Cl^-(aq) + 2\,H_2O(l) \xrightarrow{\text{electrolysis}} 2\,OH^-(aq) + H_2(g) + Cl_2(g)$.

5-2 CONCEPT ASSESSMENT

Figure 5-1 illustrates a spontaneous process through the expansion of an ideal gas into an evacuated bulb. Use the one-dimensional particle-in-a-box model to represent the initial condition of Figure 5-1. Use a second particle-in-a-box model to represent the system after expansion into the vacuum.
Use these models to explain on a microscopic basis why this expansion is spontaneous. [*Hint:* Assume that the volume of the bulbs is analogous to the length of the box.]

5-3 Evaluating Entropy and Entropy Changes

The difficulty of calculating an entropy change with equation (5.2) was mentioned on page 172. The emphasis then shifted to making qualitative predictions about entropy changes. In this section we will see that in a few instances a simple direct calculation of ΔS is possible. Also, we will find that, unlike the case with internal energy and enthalpy, it is possible to determine *absolute* entropy values.

Phase Transitions

In the equilibrium between two phases, the exchange of heat can be carried out reversibly, and the quantity of heat proves to be equal to the enthalpy change for the transition, ΔH_{tr}. In this case, equation (5.2) can be written as

$$\Delta S_{tr} = \frac{\Delta H_{tr}}{T_{tr}} \qquad (5.3)$$

Rather than use the general symbol "tr" to represent a transition, we can be more specific about just which phases are involved, such as "fus" for the melting of a solid and "vap" for the vaporization of a liquid. If the transitions involve standard state conditions (1 bar ≈ 1 atm pressure), we also use the degree sign (°). Thus for the melting (fusion) of ice at its normal melting point,

$$H_2O(s, 1\text{ atm}) \rightleftharpoons H_2O(l, 1\text{ atm}) \qquad \Delta H^\circ_{fus} = 6.02\text{ kJ mol}^{-1}\text{ at }273.15\text{ K}$$

the standard entropy change is

$$\Delta S^\circ_{fus} = \frac{\Delta H^\circ_{fus}}{T_{mp}} = \frac{6.02\text{ kJ mol}^{-1}}{273.15\text{ K}} = 2.20 \times 10^{-2}\text{ kJ mol}^{-1}\text{ K}^{-1}$$
$$= 22.0\text{ J mol}^{-1}\text{ K}^{-1}$$

KEEP IN MIND

that the normal melting point and normal boiling point are determined at 1 atm pressure. The difference between 1 atm and the standard state pressure of 1 bar is so small that we can usually ignore it.

Entropy changes depend on the quantities of substances involved and are usually expressed on a per-mole basis.

A useful generalization known as **Trouton's rule** states that for many liquids at their normal boiling points, the standard molar *entropy of vaporization* has a value of about 87 J mol^{-1} K^{-1}.

$$\Delta S^\circ_{vap} = \frac{\Delta H^\circ_{vap}}{T_{bp}} \approx 87\text{ J mol}^{-1}\text{ K}^{-1} \qquad (5.4)$$

For instance, the values of ΔS°_{vap} for benzene (C_6H_6) and octane (C_8H_{18}) are 87.1 and 86.2 J mol^{-1} K^{-1}, respectively. If the increased accessibility of microscopic energy levels produced in transferring one mole of molecules from liquid

5-2 ARE YOU WONDERING...

If the thermodynamic entropy (equation 5.2), $\Delta S = q_{rev}/T$, can be derived from the statistical entropy (equation 5.1), $S = k \ln W$?

It can, but a rigorous derivation is very complex. However, by using a system of evenly spaced energy levels for the surroundings, a simplified derivation can be shown. Consider just two energy levels from the numerous energy levels representing the surroundings. Now, as suggested in Figure 5-5, construct two states, **A** and **B**, which are the most probable initial state (state **A**) and final state (state **B**) after the addition of an infinitesimal amount of heat (q_{rev}).

The temperature of **B** is slightly higher than the temperature of **A**. The amount of heat (q) used is just the energy difference ($\Delta\varepsilon$) between the two levels and therefore a single particle jumps from level i to level j. The number of **A** microstates, W_A, is almost exactly the same as the number of **B** microstates, W_B. The entropy change for the surroundings is

$$\Delta S_{sur} = k \ln\left(\frac{W_B}{W_A}\right)$$

However, the ratio of probabilities is related to the population of each state as shown in the following relationship:

$$\frac{W_B}{W_A} = \frac{n_i}{n_j + 1} \approx \frac{n_i}{n_j}$$

Boltzmann derived the following distribution law

$$\frac{n_j}{n_i} = e^{-\Delta\varepsilon/kT}$$

which relates the population of level i to that of level j. We use this to determine the entropy change of the surroundings along with the substitution of q_{rev} for $\Delta\varepsilon$.

$$\Delta S_{sur} = k \ln\left(\frac{W_B}{W_A}\right) = k \ln\left(e^{q_{rev}/kT}\right) = k\frac{q_{rev}}{kT} = \frac{q_{rev}}{T}$$

We have shown the relationship of the statistical entropy (equation 5.1) to the thermodynamic entropy (equation 5.2) to be true for the entropy change of the surroundings; however, this can be shown to hold for the system as well.

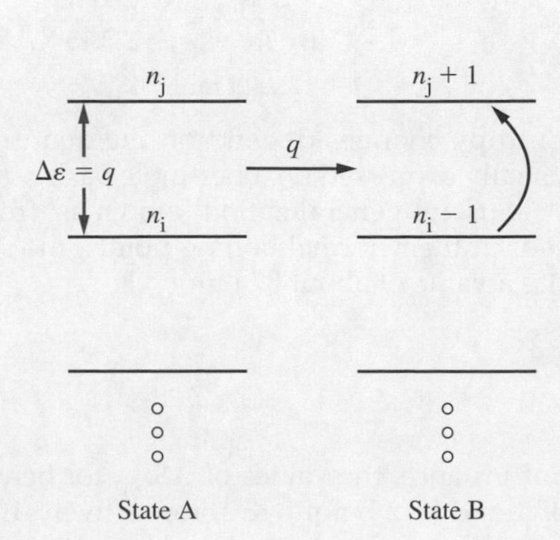

▶ FIGURE 5-5
Energy levels and populations representing the initial state of the surroundings (State **A**) and the state of the surroundings (State **B**) upon the addition of a quantity of heat (q). The spacing between the energy levels is $\Delta\varepsilon$. The populations of the energy levels are indicated by n_i and n_j.

EXAMPLE 5-2 Determining the Entropy Change for a Phase Transition

What is the standard molar entropy for the vaporization of water at 373 K given that the standard molar enthalpy of vaporization is 40.7 kJ mol^{-1}?

Analyze

This is an example of a phase transition, which means we can make use of $\Delta S° = \dfrac{\Delta H°_{transition}}{T_{transition}}$.

Solve

Although a chemical equation is not necessary, writing one can help us see the process we use to find the value of $\Delta S°_{vap}$.

$$H_2O(l, 1 \text{ atm}) \rightleftharpoons H_2O(g, 1 \text{ atm}) \qquad \Delta H°_{vap} = 40.7 \text{ kJ/mol } H_2O$$
$$\Delta S°_{vap} = ?$$

$$\Delta S°_{vap} = \frac{\Delta H°_{vap}}{T_{bp}} = \frac{40.7 \text{ kJ mol}^{-1}}{373 \text{ K}} = 0.109 \text{ kJ mol}^{-1} \text{ K}^{-1}$$
$$= 109 \text{ J mol}^{-1} \text{ K}$$

Assess

When solving this type of problem, we should check the sign of ΔS. Here, we expect an increase in entropy (ΔS is positive) because, as discussed on page 173, the entropy of a gas is much higher than that of a liquid.

PRACTICE EXAMPLE A: What is the standard molar entropy of vaporization, $\Delta S°_{vap}$, for CCl_2F_2, a chlorofluorocarbon that once was heavily used in refrigeration systems? Its normal boiling point is −29.79 °C, and $\Delta H°_{vap} = 20.2$ kJ mol^{-1}.

PRACTICE EXAMPLE B: The entropy change for the transition from solid rhombic sulfur to solid monoclinic sulfur at 95.5 °C is $\Delta S°_{tr} = 1.09$ J mol^{-1} K^{-1}. What is the standard molar enthalpy change, $\Delta H°_{tr}$, for this transition?

to vapor at 1 atm pressure is roughly comparable for different liquids, then we should expect similar values of $\Delta S°_{vap}$.

Instances in which Trouton's rule fails are also understandable. In water and in ethanol, for example, hydrogen bonding among molecules produces a lower entropy than would otherwise be expected in the liquid state. Consequently, the entropy increase in the vaporization process is greater than normal, and so $\Delta S°_{vap} > 87$ J mol^{-1} K^{-1}.

The entropy concept helps explain Raoult's law. Recall that for an ideal solution, $\Delta H_{soln} = 0$ and intermolecular forces of attraction are the same as in the pure liquid solvent. Thus, we expect the molar ΔH_{vap} to be the same whether vaporization of solvent occurs from an ideal solution or from the pure solvent at the same temperature. So, too, should ΔS_{vap} be the same because $\Delta S_{vap} = \Delta H_{vap}/T$. When one mole of solvent is transferred from liquid to vapor at the equilibrium vapor pressure $P°$, entropy increases by the amount ΔS_{vap}. As shown in Figure 5-6, because the entropy of the ideal solution is greater than that of the pure solvent, the entropy of the vapor produced by the vaporization of solvent from the ideal solution is also greater than the entropy of the vapor obtained from the pure solvent. For the vapor above the solution to have the higher entropy, its molecules must have a greater number of accessible microscopic energy levels. In turn, the vapor must be present in a larger volume and, hence, must be at a lower pressure than the vapor coming from the pure solvent. This relationship corresponds to Raoult's law: $P_A = x_A P°_A$.

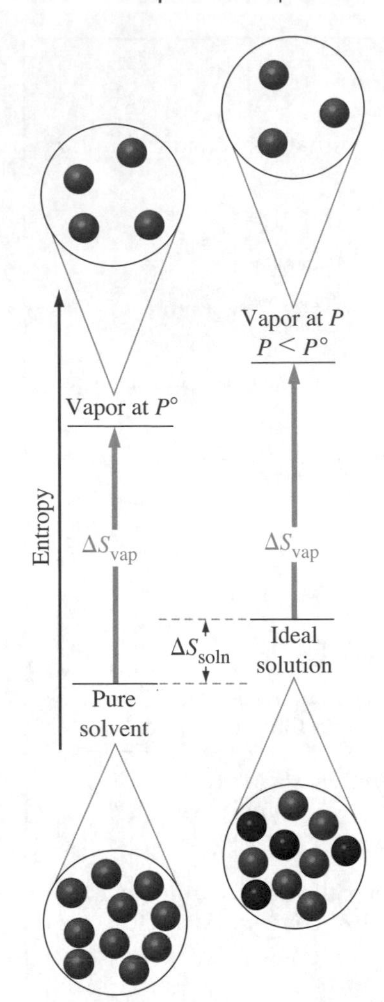

▲ FIGURE 5-6
An entropy-based rationale of Raoult's law
If ΔS_{vap} has the same value for vaporization from the pure solvent and from an ideal solution, the equilibrium vapor pressure is lower above the solution: $P < P°$.

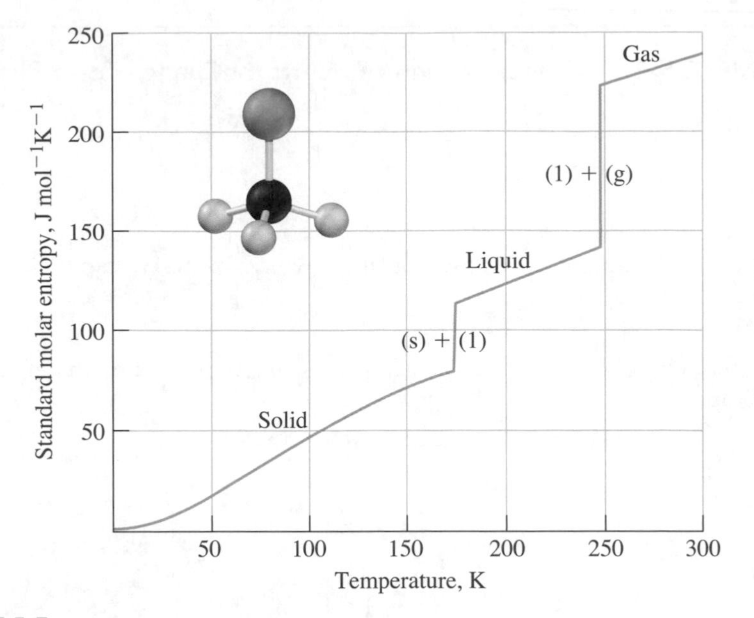

▲ FIGURE 5-7
Molar entropy as a function of temperature
The standard molar entropy of methyl chloride, CH_3Cl, is plotted at various temperatures from 0 to 300 K, with the phases noted. The vertical segment between the solid and liquid phases corresponds to ΔS_{fus}; the other vertical segment, to ΔS_{vap}. By the third law of thermodynamics, an entropy of *zero* is expected at 0 K. Experimental methods cannot be carried to that temperature, however, so an extrapolation is required.

Absolute Entropies

To establish an *absolute* value of the entropy of a substance, we look for a condition in which the substance is in its lowest possible energy state, called the *zero-point energy*. The entropy of this state is taken to be zero. Then we evaluate entropy changes as the substance is brought to other conditions of temperature and pressure. We add together these entropy changes and obtain a numerical value of the absolute entropy. The principle that permits this procedure is the **third law of thermodynamics,** which can be stated as follows:

> The entropy of a pure perfect crystal at 0 K is zero.

Figure 5-7 illustrates the method outlined in the preceding paragraph for determining absolute entropy as a function of temperature. Where phase transitions occur, equation (5.3) is used to evaluate the corresponding entropy changes. Over temperature ranges in which there are no transitions, $\Delta S°$ values are obtained from measurements of specific heats as a function of temperature.

The absolute entropy of one mole of a substance in its standard state is called the **standard molar entropy,** $S°$. Standard molar entropies of a number of substances at 25 °C are tabulated in Appendix A. To use these values to calculate the entropy change of a reaction, we use an equation with a familiar form (recall equation 4.21).

$$\Delta S° = \left[\sum \nu_p S°(\text{products}) - \sum \nu_r S°(\text{reactants}) \right] \quad \textbf{(5.5)}$$

The symbol Σ means "the sum of," and the terms added are the products of the standard molar entropies and the corresponding stoichiometric coefficients, ν. Example 5-3 shows how to use this equation.

KEEP IN MIND
that there are no units of the stoichiometric coefficient, n.

EXAMPLE 5-3 Calculating Entropy Changes from Standard Molar Entropies

Use data from Appendix D to calculate the standard molar entropy change for the conversion of nitrogen monoxide to nitrogen dioxide (a step in the manufacture of nitric acid).

$$2\,NO(g) + O_2(g) \longrightarrow 2\,NO_2(g) \qquad \Delta S^\circ_{298\,K} = ?$$

Analyze

In this example we are applying equation (5.5).

Solve

Equation (5.5) takes the form

$$\Delta S^\circ = 2S^\circ_{NO_2(g)} - 2S^\circ_{NO(g)} - S^\circ_{O_2(g)}$$
$$= (2 \times 240.1) - (2 \times 210.8) - 205.1 = -146.5\ J\ K^{-1}$$

Assess

Some qualitative reasoning can be applied as a useful check on this calculation. Because three moles of gaseous reactants produce only two moles of gaseous products, the entropy should decrease; that is, ΔS° should be negative.

PRACTICE EXAMPLE A: Use data from Appendix A to calculate the standard molar entropy change for the synthesis of ammonia from its elements.

$$N_2(g) + 3\,H_2(g) \longrightarrow 2\,NH_3(g) \qquad \Delta S^\circ_{298\,K} = ?$$

PRACTICE EXAMPLE B: N_2O_3 is an unstable oxide that readily decomposes. The decomposition of 1.00 mol of N_2O_3 to nitrogen monoxide and nitrogen dioxide at 25 °C is accompanied by the entropy change $\Delta S^\circ = 138.5\ J\ K^{-1}$. What is the standard molar entropy of $N_2O_3(g)$ at 25 °C?

Example 5-3 used the standard molar entropies of $NO_2(g)$ and NO(g). Why is the value for $NO_2(g)$, 240.1 J mol^{-1} K^{-1}, greater than that of NO(g), 210.8 J mol^{-1} K^{-1}? Entropy increases when a substance absorbs heat (recall that $\Delta S = q_{rev}/T$), and some of this heat goes into raising the average translational kinetic energies of molecules. But there are other ways for heat energy to be used. One possibility, pictured in Figure 5-8, is that the vibrational energies of molecules can be increased. In the *diatomic* molecule NO(g), only one type of vibration is possible; in the *triatomic* molecule $NO_2(g)$, *three* types are possible. Because there are more possible ways of distributing energy among NO_2 molecules than among NO molecules, $NO_2(g)$ has a higher molar entropy than does NO(g) at the same temperature. Thus the following statement should be added to the generalizations about entropy on page 174.

In general, more complex molecules (e.g., with more atoms per molecule) produce greater molar entropies.

◀ In general, at low temperatures, because the quanta of energy are so small, translational energies are most important in establishing the entropy of gaseous molecules. As the temperature increases and the quanta of energy become larger, first rotational energies become important, and finally, at still higher temperatures, vibrational modes of motion start to contribute to the entropy.

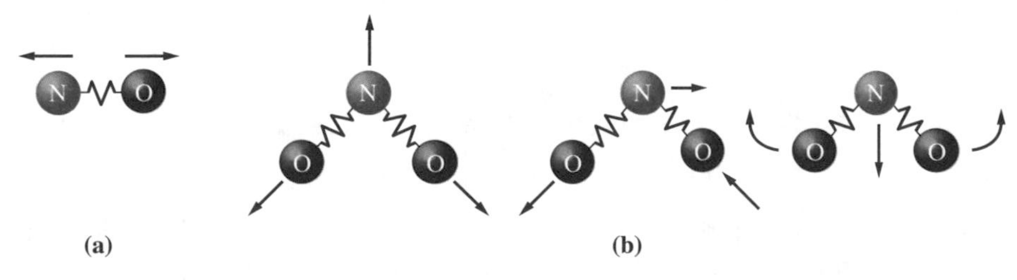

▲ FIGURE 5-8
Vibrational energy and entropy
The movement of atoms is suggested by the arrows. **(a)** The NO molecule has only one type of vibrational motion, whereas **(b)** the NO_2 molecule has three. This difference helps account for the fact that the molar entropy of $NO_2(g)$ is greater than that of NO(g).

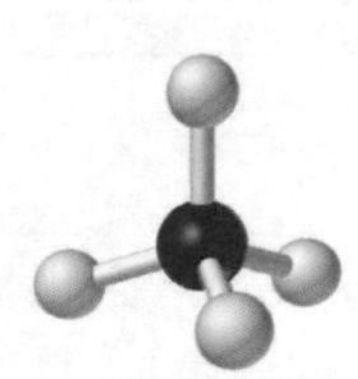

Methane, CH_4
$S° = 186.3 \text{ J mol}^{-1} \text{ K}^{-1}$

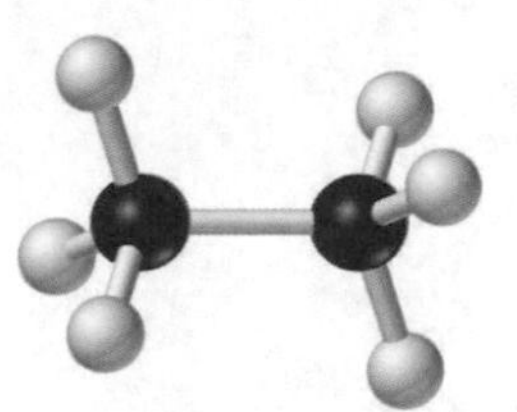

Ethane, C_2H_6
$S° = 229.6 \text{ J mol}^{-1} \text{ K}^{-1}$

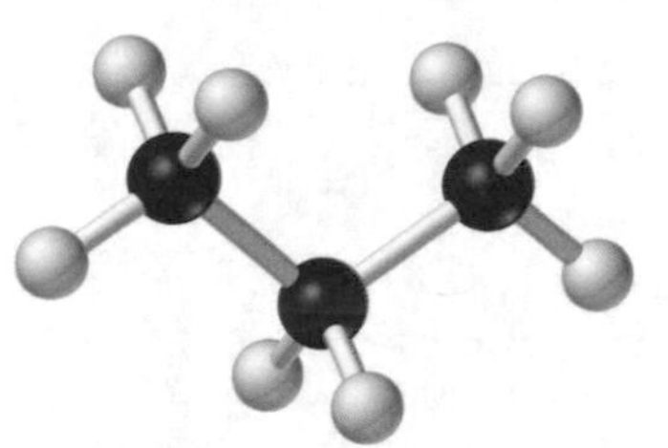

Propane, C_3H_8
$S° = 270.3 \text{ J mol}^{-1} \text{ K}^{-1}$

5-3 ARE YOU WONDERING...

Whether there is a correlation between standard entropy and enthalpy?

The answer to this question is yes, at least for solids heated to 298.15 K at 1 bar. To see why this is so we begin with the temperature variation of entropy and enthalpy written as

$$S° = \int_0^{298.15 \text{ K}} \frac{C_p(T)}{T} dT$$

$$\Delta H° = \int_0^{298.15} C_p(T) dT$$

If we assume that the constant pressure heat capacity, C_p, of a solid is a linear function of temperature, $C_p = AT$, then the ratio of the entropy to enthalpy is

$$\frac{S°}{\Delta H°} = \frac{\int_{0 \text{ K}}^{298.15 \text{ K}} \frac{C_p(T)}{T} dT}{\int_{0 \text{ K}}^{298.15 \text{ K}} T\frac{C_p(T)}{T} dT} \approx \frac{\int_{0 \text{ K}}^{298.15 \text{ K}} A dT}{\int_{0 \text{ K}}^{298.15 \text{ K}} TA dT} = \frac{1}{149.075 \text{ K}} = 0.0067 \text{ K}^{-1}$$

This result suggests that a simple (linear) correlation exists between entropy and enthalpy. Do experimental facts support this conclusion? The following figure is a plot of standard entropy versus standard enthalpy change at 298.15 K and 1 bar for several monatomic solids.

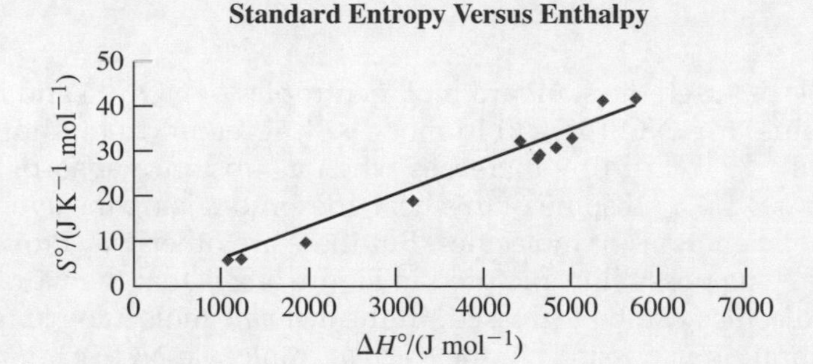

The slope of the line is equal to the predicted ratio (0.0067 K^{-1}). Notice that the points lie close to this line. So what does this mean? As we heat the solid from nearly absolute zero to 298.15 K, the solid gains energy, represented here as a standard enthalpy change. This energy is dispersed throughout the various energy levels of the solid. The standard entropy value, $S°$, of the solid at 298.15 K and 1 bar is proportional to the quantity of energy stored in the solid at that temperature with the proportionality constant of 0.0067 K^{-1}.

5-4 Criteria for Spontaneous Change: The Second Law of Thermodynamics

In Section 5-2, we came to the tentative conclusion that processes in which the entropy of a system increases should be spontaneous and that processes in which entropy decreases should be nonspontaneous. But this statement can present difficulties, for example, of how to explain the spontaneous freezing of water at −10 °C. Because crystalline ice has a lower molar entropy than does liquid water, the freezing of water is a process for which entropy *decreases*. The way out of this dilemma is to recognize that *two* entropy changes must always be considered simultaneously—the entropy change of the system itself and the entropy change of the surroundings. The criteria for spontaneous change must be based on the sum of the two, called the entropy change of the "universe":

$$\Delta S_{\text{total}} = \Delta S_{\text{universe}} = \Delta S_{\text{system}} + \Delta S_{\text{surroundings}} \quad \textbf{(5.6)}$$

Although it is beyond the scope of this discussion to verify the following expression, the expression provides the basic criterion for spontaneous change. In a spontaneous change,

$$\Delta S_{\text{univ}} = \Delta S_{\text{sys}} + \Delta S_{\text{surr}} > 0 \quad \textbf{(5.7)}$$

Equation (5.7) is one way of stating the **second law of thermodynamics**. Another way is through the following statement.

> All spontaneous processes produce an increase in the entropy of the universe.

According to expression (5.7), if a process produces positive entropy changes in both the system and its surroundings, the process is surely spontaneous. And if both these entropy changes are negative, the process is just as surely nonspontaneous. If one of the entropy changes is positive, and the other negative, whether the sum of the two is positive or negative depends on the relative magnitudes of the two changes. The freezing of water produces a negative entropy change in the system, but in the surroundings, which absorb heat, the entropy change is positive. As long as the temperature is below 0 °C, the entropy of the surroundings increases more than the entropy of the system decreases. Because the *total* entropy change is positive, the freezing of water below 0 °C is indeed spontaneous.

Gibbs Energy and Gibbs Energy Change

We could use expression (5.7) as the basic criterion for spontaneity (spontaneous change), but it would be very difficult to apply. To evaluate a total entropy change (ΔS_{univ}), we always have to evaluate ΔS for the surroundings. At best, this process is tedious, and in many cases it is not even possible, because we cannot figure out all the interactions between a system and its surroundings. Surely it is preferable to have a criterion that can be applied to *the system itself*, without having to worry about changes in the surroundings.

To develop this new criterion, let us explore a hypothetical process conducted at constant temperature and pressure and with work limited to pressure–volume work. This process is accompanied by a heat effect, q_p, which is equal to ΔH for the system (ΔH_{sys}) as seen in Section 4-6. The heat effect experienced by the surroundings is the *negative* of that for the system: $q_{\text{surr}} = -q_p = -\Delta H_{\text{sys}}$. Furthermore, if the hypothetical surroundings are large enough, the path by which heat enters or leaves the surroundings can be made *reversible*. That is, the quantity of heat can be made to produce only an infinitesimal change in the temperature of the surroundings. In this case, according to equation (5.2), the entropy change in the surroundings is $\Delta S_{\text{surr}} = -\Delta H_{\text{sys}}/T$.* Now substitute this value of ΔS_{surr} into equation (5.6), then multiply by T to obtain

$$T\,\Delta S_{\text{univ}} = T\,\Delta S_{\text{sys}} - \Delta H_{\text{sys}} = -(\Delta H_{\text{sys}} - T\,\Delta S_{\text{sys}})$$

*We cannot similarly substitute $\Delta H_{\text{sys}}/T$ for ΔS_{sys}. A process that occurs spontaneously is generally far removed from an equilibrium condition and is therefore *irreversible*. We cannot substitute q for an irreversible process into equation (5.2).

▲ **J. Willard Gibbs (1839–1903)—a great "unknown" scientist**
Gibbs, a Yale University professor of mathematical physics, spent most of his career without recognition, partly because his work was abstract and partly because his important publications were in little-read journals. Yet today, Gibbs's ideas serve as the basis of most of chemical thermodynamics.

Finally, multiply by −1 (change signs).

$$-T\,\Delta S_{univ} = \Delta H_{sys} - T\,\Delta S_{sys} \tag{5.8}$$

This is the significance of equation (5.8). The right side of this equation has terms involving *only the system*. On the left side appears the term ΔS_{univ}, which embodies the criterion for spontaneous change, that for a spontaneous process, $\Delta S_{univ} > 0$.

Equation (5.8) is generally cast in a somewhat different form that requires a new thermodynamic function, called the **Gibbs energy**, G. The Gibbs energy for a system is defined by the equation

$$G = H - TS$$

The **Gibbs energy change, ΔG,** for a process at constant T is

$$\Delta G = \Delta H - T\,\Delta S \tag{5.9}$$

In equation (5.9), all the terms apply to measurements *on the system*. All reference to the surroundings has been eliminated. Also, when we compare equations (5.8) and (5.9), we get

$$\Delta G = -T\,\Delta S_{univ}$$

Now, by noting that ΔG is *negative* when ΔS_{univ} is *positive*, we have our final criterion for spontaneous change based on properties of only the system itself.

For a process occurring at constant T and P, these statements hold true.

- If $\Delta G < 0$ (*negative*), the process is *spontaneous*.
- If $\Delta G > 0$ (*positive*), the process is *nonspontaneous*.
- If $\Delta G = 0$ (*zero*), the process is *at equilibrium*.

Evaluation of the units in equation (5.9) shows that Gibbs energy is indeed an energy term. ΔH has the unit joules per mole (J mol^{-1}), and the product $T\,\Delta S$ has the units $\text{K} \times \text{J mol}^{-1}\,\text{K}^{-1} = \text{J mol}^{-1}$. ΔG is the difference in two quantities with units of energy.

Applying the Gibbs Energy Criteria for Spontaneous Change

▶ Sometimes the term "$T\,\Delta S$" is referred to as "organizational energy," because ΔS is related to the way the energy of a system is distributed among the available energy levels.

Later, we will look at quantitative applications of equation (5.9), but for now we can use the equation to make some qualitative predictions. Altogether there are four possibilities for ΔG on the basis of the signs of ΔH and ΔS. These possibilities are outlined in Table 5.1 and demonstrated in Example 5-4.

If ΔH is *negative* and ΔS is *positive*, the expression $\Delta G = \Delta H - T\,\Delta S$ is negative at all temperatures. The process is spontaneous at all temperatures. This corresponds to the situation noted previously in which both ΔS_{sys} and ΔS_{surr} are positive and ΔS_{univ} is also positive.

Unquestionably, if a process is accompanied by an *increase* in enthalpy (heat is absorbed) and a *decrease* in entropy, ΔG is positive at all temperatures

TABLE 5.1 Criteria for Spontaneous Change: $\Delta G - \Delta H - T\Delta S$

Case	ΔH	ΔS	ΔG	Result	Example
1.	−	+	−	spontaneous at all temp.	$2\,N_2O(g) \longrightarrow 2\,N_2(g) + O_2(g)$
2.	−	−	− +	spontaneous at low temp. nonspontaneous at high temp.	$H_2O(l) \longrightarrow H_2O(s)$
3.	+	+	+ −	nonspontaneous at low temp. spontaneous at high temp.	$2\,NH_3(g) \longrightarrow N_2(g) + 3\,H_2(g)$
4.	+	−	+	nonspontaneous at all temp.	$3\,O_2(g) \longrightarrow 2\,O_3(g)$

and the process is nonspontaneous. This corresponds to a situation in which both ΔS_{sys} and ΔS_{surr} are negative and ΔS_{univ} is also negative.

The questionable cases are those in which the entropy and enthalpy factors work in opposition—that is, with ΔH and ΔS *both* negative or *both* positive. In these cases, whether a reaction is spontaneous or not (that is, whether ΔG is negative or positive) depends on temperature. In general, if a reaction has negative values for both ΔH and ΔS, it is spontaneous at *lower* temperatures, whereas if ΔH and ΔS are both positive, the reaction is spontaneous at *higher* temperatures.

◀ For cases 2 and 3, there is a particular temperature at which a process switches from being spontaneous to being nonspontaneous. Section 5-6 explains how to determine such a temperature.

EXAMPLE 5-4 Using Enthalpy and Entropy Changes to Predict the Direction of Spontaneous Change

Under what temperature conditions would the following reactions occur spontaneously?

(a) $2\,NH_4NO_3(s) \longrightarrow 2\,N_2(g) + 4\,H_2O(g) + O_2(g) \qquad \Delta H^\circ = -236.0 \text{ kJ mol}^{-1}$

(b) $I_2(g) \longrightarrow 2\,I(g)$

Analyze

(a) The reaction is exothermic, and in Example 5-1(a) we concluded that $\Delta S > 0$ because large quantities of gases are produced.

(b) Because one mole of gaseous reactant produces two moles of gaseous product, we expect entropy to increase. But what is the sign of ΔH? We could calculate ΔH from enthalpy of formation data, but there is no need to. In the reaction, covalent bonds in $I_2(g)$ are broken and no new bonds are formed. Because energy is absorbed to break bonds, ΔH must be positive. With $\Delta H > 0$ and $\Delta S > 0$, case 3 in Table 5.1 applies.

Solve

(a) With $\Delta H < 0$ and $\Delta S > 0$, this reaction should be spontaneous at all temperatures (case 1 in Table 5.1). $NH_4NO_3(s)$ exists only because the decomposition has very high activation energy.

(b) ΔH is larger than $T\,\Delta S$ at low temperatures, and the reaction is nonspontaneous. At high temperatures, the $T\,\Delta S$ term becomes larger than ΔH, ΔG becomes negative, and the reaction is spontaneous.

Assess

We observe that reaction spontaneity depends on a balance of enthalpy, entropy, and temperature. Table 5.1 is a good summary of the conditions in which reactions will be spontaneous or nonspontaneous.

PRACTICE EXAMPLE A: Which of the four cases in Table 5.1 would apply to each of the following reactions:

(a) $N_2(g) + 3\,H_2(g) \longrightarrow 2\,NH_3(g), \qquad \Delta H^\circ = -92.22 \text{ kJ};$

(b) $2\,C(\text{graphite}) + 2\,H_2(g) \longrightarrow C_2H_4(g), \qquad \Delta H^\circ = 52.26 \text{ kJ}?$

PRACTICE EXAMPLE B: Under what temperature conditions would the following reactions occur spontaneously? **(a)** The decomposition of calcium carbonate into calcium oxide and carbon dioxide. **(b)** The "roasting" of zinc sulfide in oxygen to form zinc oxide and sulfur dioxide. This exothermic reaction releases 439.1 kJ for every mole of zinc sulfide that reacts.

▲ Only because of the high activation energy for the $NH_4NO_3(s)$ decomposition reaction does $NH_4NO_3(s)$ exist at all.

Example 5-4(b) illustrates why there is an upper temperature limit for the stabilities of chemical compounds. No matter how positive the value of ΔH for dissociation of a molecule into its atoms, the term $T\,\Delta S$ will eventually exceed ΔH in magnitude as the temperature increases. Known temperatures range from near absolute zero to the interior temperatures of stars (about 3×10^7 K). Molecules exist only at limited temperatures (up to about 1×10^4 K or about 0.03% of this total temperature range).

◀ A related observation is that only a small fraction of the mass of the universe is in molecular form.

The method of Example 5-4 is adequate for making predictions about the sign of ΔG, but we will also want to use equation (5.9) to calculate numerical values. We will do that in Section 5-5.

Gibbs Energy Change and Work

We might think that the quantity of energy available to do work in the surroundings as a result of a chemical process is $-\Delta H$. This would be the same as the quantity of heat that an exothermic reaction releases to the surroundings. (In thinking along those lines, we would say that an endothermic reaction is incapable of doing work.) However, that quantity of heat must be adjusted for the heat requirement in producing the entropy change in the system ($q_{rev} = T\,\Delta S$). If an exothermic reaction is accompanied by an *increase* in entropy, the amount of energy available to do work in the surroundings is *greater* than $-\Delta H$. If entropy *decreases* in the exothermic reaction, the amount of energy available to do work is *less* than $-\Delta H$. But notice that in either case, this amount of energy is equal to $-\Delta G$. Thus, the amount of work that can be extracted from a chemical process is $-\Delta G$. Because $-\Delta G$ represents the energy freely available for doing work, G was once called *Gibbs free energy*, or *simply free energy*, by most chemists. Notice also that this interpretation of Gibbs energy allows for the possibility of work being done in an endothermic process if $T\,\Delta S$ exceeds ΔH. In Chapter 7, we will see how the Gibbs energy change of a reaction can be converted to electrical work. In any case, do not think of Gibbs energy as being free. Costs are always involved in tapping an energy source.

5-5 Standard Gibbs Energy Change, $\Delta G°$

Because Gibbs energy is related to enthalpy ($G = H - TS$), we cannot establish absolute values of G any more than we can for H. We must work with Gibbs energy changes, ΔG. We will find a special use for the Gibbs energy change corresponding to reactants and products in their standard states—the **standard Gibbs energy change, $\Delta G°$**. The standard state conventions were introduced and applied to enthalpy change in Chapter 4.

KEEP IN MIND

that a pressure of 1 bar is very nearly the same as 1 atm. The differences in these two pressures on the values of properties is generally so small that we can use the two pressure units almost interchangeably.

The **standard Gibbs energy of formation**, ΔG_f°, is the Gibbs energy change for a reaction in which a substance in its standard state is formed from its elements in their reference forms in their standard states. And, as was the case when we established enthalpies of formation in Section 4-8, this definition leads to values of *zero* for the Gibbs energies of formation of the elements in their reference forms at a pressure of 1 bar. Other Gibbs energies of formation are related to this condition of zero and are generally tabulated per mole of substance (see Appendix A).

Some additional relationships involving Gibbs energy changes are similar to those presented for enthalpy in Section 7-7: (1) ΔG changes sign when a process is reversed; and (2) ΔG for an overall process can be obtained by summing the ΔG values for the individual steps. The two expressions that follow are useful in calculating $\Delta G°$ values, depending on the data available. We can use the first expression at any temperature for which $\Delta H°$ and $\Delta S°$ values are known. We can use the second expression only at temperatures at which ΔG_f° values are known. The only temperature at which tabulated data are commonly given is 298.15 K. The first expression is applied in Example 5-5 and Practice Example 5-5A, and the second expression in Practice Example 5-5B.

▶ Many substances do not exist at the standard conditions that define their Gibbs energy. This does not matter since we can calculate the standard Gibbs energy from nonstandard conditions. Dealing with nonstandard conditions is discussed on page 187. Gibbs energies are listed under standard conditions for ease and conciseness.

$$\Delta G° = \Delta H° - T\Delta S°$$

$$\Delta G° = \left[\sum \nu_p\, \Delta G_f^\circ(\text{products}) - \sum \nu_r \Delta G_f^\circ(\text{reactants})\right]$$

EXAMPLE 5-5 Calculating ΔG° for a Reaction

Determine ΔG° at 298.15 K for the reaction

$$2\,NO(g) + O_2(g) \longrightarrow 2\,NO_2(g) \quad \text{(at 298.15 K)} \qquad \Delta H^\circ = -114.1\text{ kJ}$$
$$\Delta S^\circ = -146.5\text{ J K}^{-1}$$

Analyze

Because we have values of ΔH° and ΔS°, the most direct method of calculating ΔG° is to use the expression $\Delta G^\circ = \Delta H^\circ - T\,\Delta S^\circ$.

Solve

First we must convert all the data to a common energy unit (for instance, kJ).

$$\begin{aligned}\Delta G^\circ &= -114.1\text{ kJ} - (298.15\text{ K} \times -0.1465\text{ kJ K}^{-1})\\ &= -114.1\text{ kJ} + 43.68\text{ kJ}\\ &= -70.4\text{ kJ}\end{aligned}$$

Assess

In this type of problem, one of the most common mistakes is not keeping the units straight. Note that the unit for the standard molar enthalpy is kJ mol^{-1}, and for the standard molar entropy it is J mol^{-1} K^{-1}. This example says that all the reactants and products are maintained at 25 °C and 1 bar pressure. Under these conditions, the Gibbs energy change is −70.4 kJ for oxidizing two moles of NO to two moles of NO_2. To do this, it is necessary to replenish the NO so as to maintain the standard conditions.

PRACTICE EXAMPLE A: Determine ΔG° at 298.15 K for the reaction $4\,Fe(s) + 3O_2(g) \longrightarrow 2\,Fe_2O_3(s)$. $\Delta H^\circ = -1648$ kJ and $\Delta S^\circ = -549.3$ J K^{-1}.

PRACTICE EXAMPLE B: Determine ΔG° for the reaction in Example 5-5 by using data from Appendix A. Compare the two results.

5-6 Gibbs Energy Change and Equilibrium

We have seen that $\Delta G < 0$ for spontaneous processes and that $\Delta G > 0$ for nonspontaneous processes. If $\Delta G = 0$, the forward and reverse processes show an equal tendency to occur, and the system is at *equilibrium*. At this point, even an infinitesimal change in one of the system variables (such as temperature or pressure) will cause a net change to occur. But if a system at equilibrium is left undisturbed, no net change occurs with time.

Figure 5-9 illustrates a hypothetical process in which ΔH and ΔS are independent of temperature, and both are positive. This corresponds to case 3

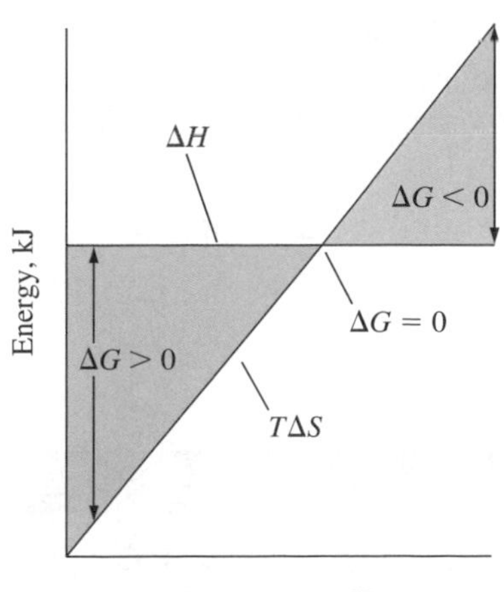

◀ FIGURE 5-9
Gibbs energy change as a function of temperature
The green shaded region corresponds to ΔG at temperatures in which the process is *nonspontaneous*. The orange shaded region corresponds to ΔG at temperatures in which the process is *spontaneous*.

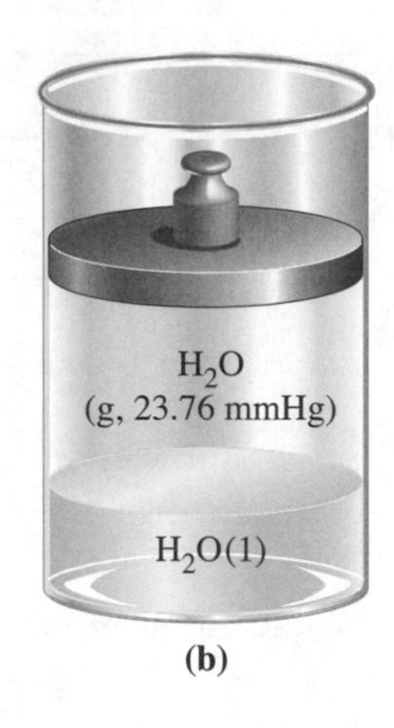

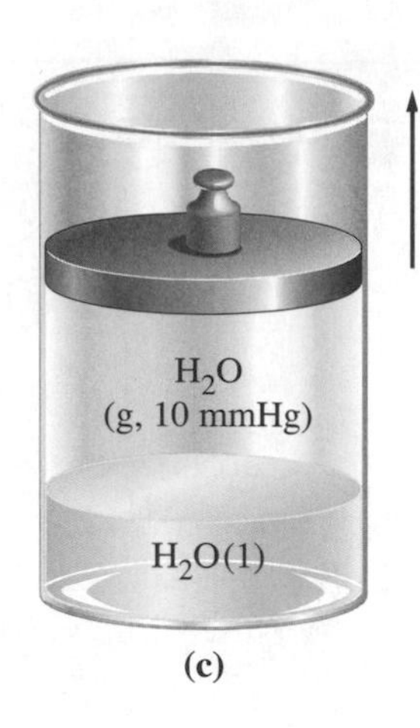

▲ FIGURE 5-10
Liquid–vapor equilibrium and the direction of spontaneous change
(a) For the vaporization of water at 298.15 K and 1 atm, $H_2O(l, 1\text{ atm}) \longrightarrow H_2O(g, 1\text{ atm})$, $\Delta G° = 8.590$ kJ. The direction of spontaneous change is the *condensation* of $H_2O(g)$. **(b)** At 298.15 K and 23.76 mmHg, the liquid and vapor are in equilibrium and $\Delta G° = 0$. **(c)** At 298.15 K and 10 mmHg, the vaporization of $H_2O(l)$ occurs spontaneously: $H_2O(l, 10\text{ mmHg}) \longrightarrow H_2O(g, 10\text{ mmHg})$, and $\Delta G < 0$.

in Table 5.1. If we start at the left side of the figure (i.e., at a relatively low temperature), we see that the magnitude of ΔH exceeds the magnitude of $T\,\Delta S$ and that $\Delta H - T\,\Delta S$, which was defined as ΔG, is positive; the process is *nonspontaneous*. As the temperature increases, the magnitude of ΔG decreases. At the right side of the figure (i.e., at a relatively high temperature), the magnitude of $T\,\Delta S$ exceeds the magnitude of ΔH; therefore, ΔG is negative; the process is *spontaneous*. The temperature at which the two lines (ΔH and $T\,\Delta S$) intersect, $\Delta G = 0$, and the system is at equilibrium.

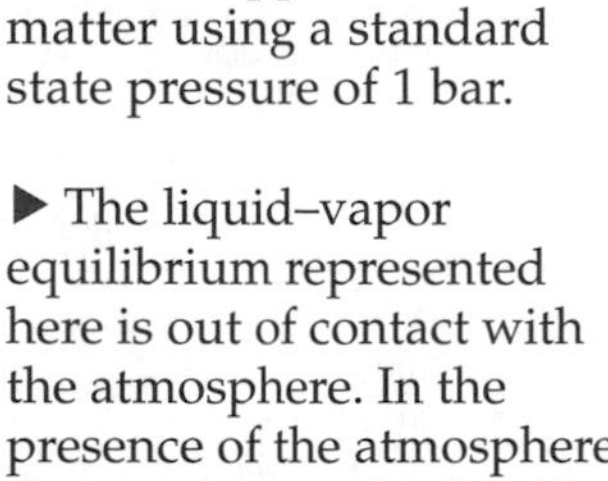

▶ Here, we have used a standard state pressure of 1 atm. See Feature Problem 93 for an appraisal of this matter using a standard state pressure of 1 bar.

▶ The liquid–vapor equilibrium represented here is out of contact with the atmosphere. In the presence of the atmosphere, the pressure on the liquid would be barometric pressure, whereas that of the vapor would remain essentially unchanged at 0.03126 atm.

For the vaporization of water, *with both liquid and vapor in their standard states* (which means that $\Delta G = \Delta G°$), the intersection of the two lines in Figure 5-9 is at $T = 373.15$ K (100.00 °C). That is, for the vaporization of water at 1 atm,

$$H_2O(l, 1\text{ atm}) \rightleftharpoons H_2O(g, 1\text{ atm}) \qquad \Delta G° = 0 \text{ at } 373.15\text{ K}$$

At 25 °C, the $\Delta H°$ line lies above the $T\,\Delta S$ line in Figure 5-9. This means that $\Delta G° > 0$.

$$H_2O(l, 1\text{ atm}) \longrightarrow H_2O(g, 1\text{ atm}) \qquad \Delta G° = +8.590\text{ kJ at } 298.15\text{ K}$$

The positive value of $\Delta G°$ does not mean that vaporization of water will not occur. From common experience, we know that water spontaneously evaporates at room temperature. What the positive value means is that liquid water will not spontaneously produce $H_2O(g)$ at 1 atm pressure at 25 °C. Instead, $H_2O(g)$ is produced with a vapor pressure that is less than 1 atm pressure. The equilibrium vapor pressure of water at 25 °C is 23.76 mmHg = 0.03126 atm; that is,

$$H_2O(l, 0.03126\text{ atm}) \rightleftharpoons H_2O(g, 0.03126\text{ atm}) \qquad \Delta G = 0$$

Figure 5-10 offers a schematic summary of ideas concerning the transition between liquid and gaseous water at 25 °C.

5-3 CONCEPT ASSESSMENT

Redraw Figure 5-9 for case 2 in Table 5.1. How does your drawing compare with Figure 5-9? State the similarities and differences.

Relationship of $\Delta G°$ To ΔG for Nonstandard Conditions

If you think about the situation just described for the vaporization of water, there is not much value in describing equilibrium in a process in terms of its $\Delta G°$ value. At only one temperature are the reactants in their standard states in equilibrium with products in their standard states; that is, at only one temperature does $\Delta G° = 0$. We want to be able to describe equilibrium for a variety of conditions, typically *nonstandard* conditions. Many reactions, such as processes occurring under physiological conditions, take place under nonstandard conditions. How, under such circumstances, can a biochemist decide which processes are spontaneous? For this we need to work with ΔG, not $\Delta G°$.

To obtain the relationship between ΔG and $\Delta G°$, we will consider a reaction between ideal gas molecules. We assume this is the case in the reaction of nitrogen with hydrogen to produce ammonia.

$$N_2(g) + 3\,H_2(g) \rightleftharpoons 2\,NH_3(g)$$

The expressions for ΔG and $\Delta G°$ are $\Delta G = \Delta H - T\,\Delta S$ and $\Delta G° = \Delta H° - T\,\Delta S°$, respectively. First consider how the enthalpy terms ΔH and $\Delta H°$ are related for an ideal gas. The enthalpy of an ideal gas is a function of temperature only; it is independent of pressure. Thus, under any mixing conditions for an ideal gas, $\Delta H = \Delta H°$. We can write

$$\Delta G = \Delta H° - T\,\Delta S \qquad \textit{(ideal gas)}$$

We now need to obtain a relationship between ΔS and $\Delta S°$. To do so, we consider the isothermal expansion of an ideal gas for which $q = -w$ and $\Delta U = 0$.

$$w = -RT\ln\frac{V_f}{V_i} \qquad \textit{(reversible, isothermal)}$$

The reversible, isothermal heat of expansion is

$$q_{rev} = -w = RT\ln\frac{V_f}{V_i}$$

From equation (5.2), we obtain the entropy change for the isothermal expansion of one mole of an ideal gas.

$$\Delta S = \frac{q_{rev}}{T} = R\ln\frac{V_f}{V_i} \qquad \textbf{(5.10)}$$

Using equation (5.10), we can now evaluate the entropy of an ideal gas under any conditions of pressure. From the ideal gas equation, we know that the volume of an ideal gas is inversely proportional to the pressure, so we can recast equation (5.10) as

$$\Delta S = S_f - S_i = R\ln\frac{V_f}{V_i} = R\ln\frac{P_i}{P_f} = -R\ln\frac{P_f}{P_i}$$

where P_i and P_f are the initial and final pressures, respectively. If we set $P_i = 1$ bar and designate P_i as $P°$ and S_i as $S°$, we obtain for the entropy at any pressure P

$$S = S° - R\ln\frac{P}{P°} = S° - R\ln\frac{P}{1} = S° - R\ln P \qquad \textbf{(5.11)}$$

Now, let's return to the ammonia synthesis reaction and calculate the entropy change for that reaction. We begin by applying equation (5.11) to each of the three gases.

$$S_{NH_3} = S°_{NH_3} - R\ln P_{NH_3} \qquad S_{N_2} = S°_{N_2} - R\ln P_{N_2} \quad S_{H_2} = S°_{H_2} - R\ln P_{H_2}$$

Then we substitute the above values into the equation $\Delta S = 2S_{NH_3} - S_{N_2} - 3S_{H_2}$ to obtain

$$\Delta S = 2S^\circ_{NH_3} - 2R \ln P_{NH_3} - S^\circ_{N_2} + R \ln P_{N_2} - 3S^\circ_{H_2} + 3R \ln P_{H_2}$$

By rearranging the terms, we get

$$\Delta S = 2S^\circ_{NH_3} - S^\circ_{N_2} - 3S^\circ_{H_2} - 2R \ln P_{NH_3} + R \ln P_{N_2} + 3R \ln P_{H_2}$$

and, since the first three terms on the right-hand side of the above equation represent ΔS°, we have

$$\Delta S = \Delta S^\circ - 2R \ln P_{NH_3} + R \ln P_{N_2} + 3R \ln P_{H_2}$$
$$\Delta S = \Delta S^\circ - R \ln P^2_{NH_3} + R \ln P_{N_2} + R \ln P^3_{H_2}$$
$$\Delta S = \Delta S^\circ + R \ln \frac{P_{N_2} P^3_{H_2}}{P^2_{NH_3}}$$

Finally, we can write the equation for ΔG by substituting the expression for ΔS into the equation

$$\Delta G = \Delta H^\circ - T\,\Delta S \qquad \textit{(ideal gas)}$$

▶ It is commonly stated that we are headed for a state of maximum entropy. Although this is true, it gives the incorrect notion that entropy, as defined here, and time are related. They are not. Entropy is a property of an equilibrium state. Here we calculate the difference between the entropies of two different equilibrium states.

5-4 ARE YOU WONDERING...

If there is a microscopic approach to obtaining equation (5.10)?

To do this, we use the ideas of Ludwig Boltzmann. Consider an ideal gas at an initial volume V_i and allow the gas to expand isothermally to a final volume V_f. By using the Boltzmann equation, we find that for the change in entropy,

$$\Delta S = S_f - S_i = k \ln W_f - k \ln W_i$$
$$\Delta S = k \ln \frac{W_f}{W_i}$$

where k is the Boltzmann constant, S_i and S_f are the initial and final entropies, respectively, and W_i and W_f are the number of microstates for the initial and final macroscopic states of the gas, respectively. We must now obtain a value for the ratio W_f/W_i. To do that, suppose that there is only a single gas molecule in a container. The number of microstates available to this single molecule should be proportional to the number of positions where the molecule can be and, hence, to the volume of the container. That is also true for each molecule in a system of N_A particles—Avogadro's number of particles. The number of microstates available to the whole system is

$$W_{total} = W_{particle\,1} \times W_{particle\,2} \times W_{particle\,3} \times \cdots$$

Because the number of microstates for each particle is proportional to the volume V of the container, the number of microstates for N_A (Avogadro's number) ideal gas molecules is

$$W \propto V^{N_A}$$

Thus, the ratio of the microstates for isothermal expansion is

$$\frac{W_f}{W_i} = \left(\frac{V_f}{V_i}\right)^{N_A}$$

We can now calculate ΔS as follows:

$$\Delta S = k \ln \frac{W_f}{W_i} = k \ln\left(\frac{V_f}{V_i}\right)^{N_A} = N_A k \ln\left(\frac{V_f}{V_i}\right) = R \ln\left(\frac{V_f}{V_i}\right)$$

where R is the ideal gas constant. This equation, which gives the entropy change for the expansion of one mole of ideal gas, is simply equation (5.10).

This leads to

$$\Delta G = \Delta H^\circ - T\,\Delta S^\circ - RT\ln\frac{P_{N_2}P^3_{H_2}}{P^2_{NH_3}}$$

$$\Delta G = \underbrace{\Delta H^\circ - T\,\Delta S^\circ}\, + RT\ln\frac{P^2_{NH_3}}{P_{N_2}P^3_{H_2}}$$

$$\Delta G = \Delta G^\circ + RT\ln\frac{P^2_{NH_3}}{P_{N_2}P^3_{H_2}}$$

To simplify, we designate the quotient in the logarithmic term as the *reaction quotient Q*.

$$\Delta G = \Delta G^\circ + RT\ln Q \qquad \textbf{(5.12)}$$

◀ Equation (5.12) shows that the value of the reaction quotient affects whether the forward or reverse reaction is favored under a particular set of conditions. Recall that all reactions proceed toward equilibrium where Gibbs energy change is equal to zero.

Equation (5.12) is the relationship between ΔG and ΔG° that we have been seeking in this section, and we see that the key term in the equation is the reaction quotient formulated for the actual, nonstandard conditions. We can use equation (5.12) to decide on the spontaneity of a reaction under any conditions of composition, provided that the temperature and pressure at which we observe the reaction are constant. We turn now to describing how the standard Gibbs energy change is related to the equilibrium constant.

Relationship of ΔG° to the Equilibrium Constant K

We encounter an interesting situation when we apply equation (5.12) to a reaction at equilibrium. We have learned that at equilibrium $\Delta G = 0$, and if a system is at equilibrium $Q = K$. So, we can write that, *at equilibrium*,

$$\Delta G = \Delta G^\circ + RT\ln K = 0$$

which means that

$$\Delta G^\circ = -RT\ln K \qquad \textbf{(5.13)}$$

If we have a value of ΔG° at a given temperature, we can use equation (5.13) to calculate an equilibrium constant K. This means that the tabulation of thermodynamic data in Appendix A can serve as a direct source of countless equilibrium constant values at 298.15 K.

We need to say a few words about the units required in equation (5.13). Because logarithms can be taken of dimensionless numbers only, K has no units; neither does $\ln K$. The right-hand side of equation (5.13) has the unit of "RT": $\text{J mol}^{-1}\,\text{K}^{-1} \times \text{K} = \text{J mol}^{-1}$. ΔG°, on the left-hand side of the equation, must have the same unit: J mol^{-1}. The "mol^{-1}" part of this unit means "per mole of reaction." One mole of reaction is simply the reaction based on the stoichiometric coefficients chosen for the balanced equation. Strictly speaking the "mol^{-1}" should be included. Remember that the "mol^{-1}" is of reaction not per mole of substance.

◀ When a ΔG° value is accompanied by a chemical equation, the "mol^{-1}" portion of the unit is often dropped.

5-4 CONCEPT ASSESSMENT

For the reaction below, $\Delta G^\circ = 326.4\ \text{kJ mol}^{-1}$:

$$3\,O_2(g) \longrightarrow 2\,O_3(g)$$

What is the Gibbs energy change for the system when 1.75 mol $O_2(g)$ at 1 bar reacts completely to give $O_3(g)$ at 1 bar?

5-5 ARE YOU WONDERING...

Whether there is a relationship between thermodynamics and the reaction rates?

Recall that when a reaction achieves equilibrium, the forward rate and reverse rate are equal. When the elementary reaction $A \underset{k_{-1}}{\overset{k_1}{\rightleftharpoons}} B$ reaches equilibrium we can write $k_1[A] = k_{-1}[B]$. Let us rearrange this expression such that the rate constants are on one side, and the concentrations are on the other.

$$\frac{k_1}{k_{-1}} = \frac{[B]}{[A]}$$

The right side of the above equation is what we have defined as the equilibrium constant expression, $K = [B]/[A]$. The equilibrium constant is related to Gibbs energy by the expression $K = e^{-\Delta G°/RT}$, showing that $\frac{k_1}{k_{-1}} = e^{-\Delta G°/RT}$. This expression is valid only when the overall reaction mechanism is one step.

▶ From a theoretical standpoint, as can be seen from Figure 5-11, all chemical reactions reach equilibrium and no chemical reaction goes totally to completion.

Criteria for Spontaneous Change: Our Search Concluded

The graphs plotted in Figure 5-11 represent the culmination of our quest for criteria for spontaneous change. Unfortunately, to construct these plots in all their detail is beyond the scope of this text. However, we can rationalize their

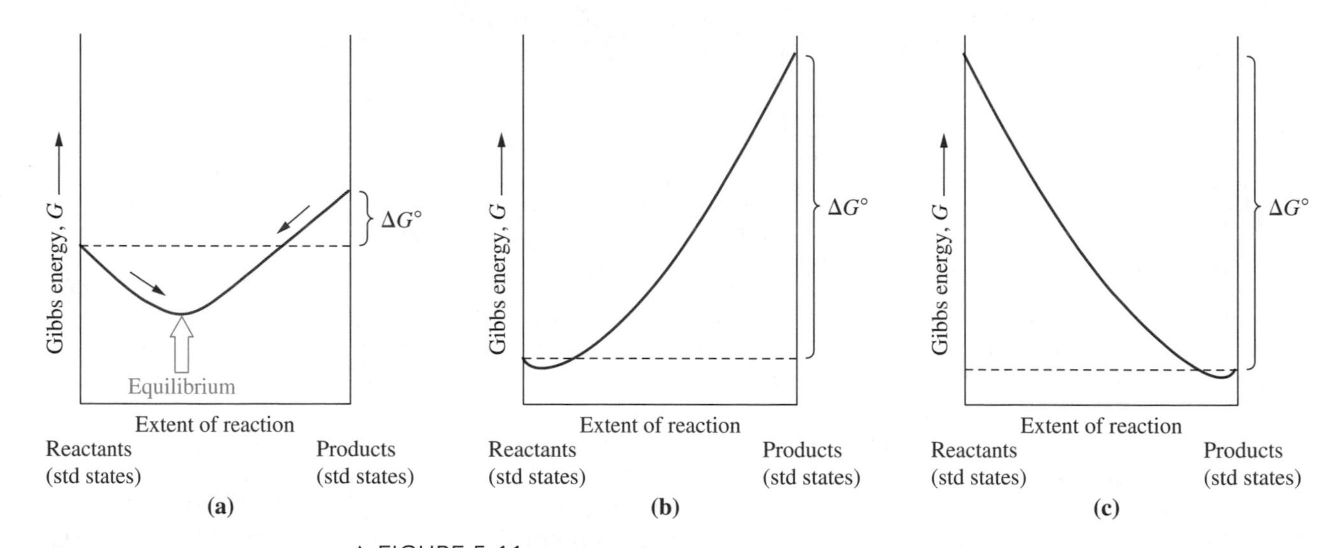

▶ Here the system starts at standard conditions and runs down to equilibrium because the reactants are not replenished. At equilibrium there is no driving force for the reaction, so there is no further reaction and the Gibbs energy must be at a minimum.

▲ FIGURE 5-11
Gibbs energy change, equilibrium, and the direction of spontaneous change
Gibbs energy is plotted against the extent of reaction for a hypothetical reaction. $\Delta G°$ is the difference between the standard Gibbs energies of formation of products and reactants. The equilibrium point lies somewhere between pure reactants and pure products. **(a)** $\Delta G°$ is small, so the equilibrium mixture lies about midway between the two extremes of pure products or reactants in their standard states. The effect of nonstandard conditions can be deduced from the slope of the curve. Mixtures with $Q > K$ are to the right of the equilibrium point and undergo spontaneous change in the direction of lower Gibbs energy, eventually coming to equilibrium. Similarly, mixtures with $Q < K$ are to the left of the equilibrium point and spontaneously yield more products before reaching equilibrium. **(b)** $\Delta G°$ is large and positive, so the equilibrium point lies close to the extreme of pure reactants in their standard states. Consequently, very little reaction takes place before equilibrium is reached. **(c)** $\Delta G°$ is large and negative, so the equilibrium point lies close to the extreme of pure products in their standard states; the reaction goes essentially to completion.

TABLE 5.2 Significance of the Magnitude of $\Delta G°$ (at 298 K)

$\Delta G°$	K	Significance
+200 kJ/mol	9.1×10^{-36}	Equilibrium favors reactants
+100	3.0×10^{-18}	
+50	1.7×10^{-9}	
+10	1.8×10^{-2}	Equilibrium calculation is necessary
+1.0	6.7×10^{-1}	
0	1.0	
−1.0	1.5	
−10	5.6×10^{1}	
−50	5.8×10^{8}	Equilibrium favors products
−100	3.3×10^{17}	
−200	1.1×10^{35}	

general shape on the basis of two ideas: (1) Every chemical reaction consists of both a forward and a reverse reaction, even if one of these occurs only to a very slight extent. (2) The direction of spontaneous change in both the forward and reverse reactions is the direction in which Gibbs energy decreases ($\Delta G < 0$). As a consequence, Gibbs energy reaches a minimum at some point between the left-hand and right-hand sides of the graph. This minimum is the equilibrium point in the reaction.

Now consider the vertical distance between the two end points of the graph; this distance represents $\Delta G°$ of the reaction. If, as in Figure 5-11(a), $\Delta G°$ of a reaction is small, either positive or negative, the equilibrium condition is one in which significant amounts of both reactants and products will be found. If $\Delta G°$ is a *large, positive* quantity, as in Figure 5-11(b), the equilibrium point lies far to the left—that is, very close to the reactants side. If $\Delta G°$ is a *large, negative* quantity, as in Figure 5-11(c), the equilibrium point lies far to the right—that is, very close to the products side. Table 5.2 summarizes the conclusions of this discussion, gives approximate magnitudes to the terms *small* and *large*, and relates $\Delta G°$ values to values of K.

$\Delta G°$ and ΔG: Predicting the Direction of Chemical Change

We have considered both $\Delta G°$ and ΔG in relation to the spontaneity of chemical reactions, and this is a good time to summarize some ideas about them.

$\Delta G < 0$ signifies that a reaction or process is spontaneous in the forward direction (to the right) for the stated conditions.

$\Delta G° < 0$ signifies that the forward reaction is spontaneous when reactants and products are in their standard states. It further signifies that $K > 1$, whatever the initial concentrations or pressures of reactants and products.

$\Delta G = 0$ signifies that the reaction is at equilibrium under the stated conditions.

$\Delta G° = 0$ signifies that the reaction is at equilibrium when reactants and products are in their standard states. It further signifies that $K = 1$, which can occur only at a particular temperature.

$\Delta G > 0$ signifies that the reaction or process is nonspontaneous in the forward direction under the stated conditions.

$\Delta G° > 0$ signifies that the forward reaction is nonspontaneous when reactants and products are in their standard states. It further signifies that $K < 1$, whatever the initial concentrations or pressures of reactants and products.

$\Delta G = \Delta G°$ only when all reactants and products are in their standard states. Otherwise, $\Delta G = \Delta G° + RT \ln Q$.

The Thermodynamic Equilibrium Constant: Activities

When we derived the equation $\Delta G = \Delta G^\circ + RT \ln Q$, we used the relationship given in equation (5.11),

$$S = S^\circ - R \ln \frac{P}{P^\circ} = S^\circ - R \ln \frac{P}{1}$$

where for a gas, we defined a standard state of 1 bar, the reference state for values of entropy. The ratio P/P° is dimensionless, which is essential for a term appearing in a logarithm. At the time, we were considering a gas-phase reaction, but we must be able to discuss reactions in solutions also, so we need a more general approach. For this, we need to turn to the concept of *activity*, which requires us to write

$$S = S^\circ - R \ln a$$

where a is the activity, defined as

$$a = \frac{\text{the effective concentration of a substance in the system}}{\text{the effective concentration of that substance in a standard reference state}}$$

KEEP IN MIND

that the ideal gas equation $PV = nRT$ can be rewritten as $(n/V) = [\text{concentration}] = (P/RT)$ so that pressure is an effective concentration.

In a gas-phase reaction, we express pressure in bars and take the reference state to be 1 bar. In this way and as expected, activity is a dimensionless quantity.

In extending the activity concept to solutions, we define the reference state as a 1 M solution, so the activity of a substance is the numerical value of its molarity. Thus, the activity of protons in a 0.1 M solution of HCl in water is

$$a_{H^+} = \frac{0.1\ \text{M}}{1\ \text{M}} = 0.1$$

KEEP IN MIND

that the precise definition of pH is

$$\text{pH} = -\log a_{H^+} \approx -\log\left(\frac{[H^+]}{1\ \text{M}}\right)$$

We often use a simplified version of the expression above, namely $\text{pH} = -\log[H^+]$. When we do, we must remember to use only the numerical part of $[H^+]$ in the logarithm.

Another situation that we have encountered is that of a heterogeneous equilibrium, such as

$$CaCO_3(s) \rightleftharpoons CaO(s) + CO_2(g)$$

Recall that we choose the pure solids as the reference states, but the effective concentrations of the $CaCO_3(s)$ and CaO(s) in the system are also those of the pure solids. Consequently, the activity of a solid is unity. This conclusion agrees with our observation in Figure 15-4 that the addition of either CaO(s) or $CaCO_3(s)$ to an equilibrium mixture of $CaCO_3(s)$, $CO_2(g)$, and CaO(s) has no effect on the pressure of $CO_2(g)$. The activities of CaO(s) and $CaCO_3(s)$ are constant (unity).

5-6 ARE YOU WONDERING...

How to deal with activities under nonideal conditions?

For nonideal conditions, we sweep all deviations from ideality into an experimentally determined correction factor called the *activity coefficient*, γ. Thus, for real (nonideal) systems, we write

For a gas: $a_G = \gamma P_G$
For a solute: $a_X = \gamma[X]$
For a pure solid or liquid: $a_L = a_S = 1$

More advanced treatments of this topic show how γ is related to the composition of the system. For dilute solutions or near ideal gases, we will assume that $\gamma = 1$. However, keep in mind that the results we obtain are limited by the validity of this assumption.

In summary, we can make these statements:

- *For pure solids and liquids:* The activity $a = 1$. The reference state is the pure solid or liquid.
- *For gases:* With ideal gas behavior assumed, the activity is replaced by the numerical value of the gas pressure in bars. The reference state is the gas at 1 bar at the temperature of interest. Thus, the activity of a gas at 0.50 bar pressure is $a = (0.50\text{ bar})/(1\text{ bar}) = 0.50$. (Recall also, that 1 bar of pressure is almost identical to 1 atm.)
- *For solutes in aqueous solution:* With ideal solution behavior assumed (for example, no interionic attractions), the activity is replaced by the numerical value of the molarity. The reference state is a 1 M solution. Thus, the activity of the solute in a 0.25 M solution is $a = (0.25\text{ M})/(1\text{ M}) = 0.25$.

When an equilibrium expression is written in terms of activities, the equilibrium constant is called the **thermodynamic equilibrium constant**. The thermodynamic equilibrium constant is dimensionless and thus appropriate for use in equation (5.13).

Thermodynamic equilibrium constants, K, are sometimes identical to K_c and K_p values, as in parts **(a)** and **(b)** of Example 5-6. In other instances, as in part **(c)**, this is not the case. In working through Example 5-6, keep in mind that the sole reason for writing thermodynamic equilibrium constants in this text is to get the proper value to use in equation (5.13). Note that the reaction quotient Q must also be written in the same manner as K when used in equation (5.12), as demonstrated in Example 5-7.

EXAMPLE 5-6 Writing Thermodynamic Equilibrium Constant Expressions

For the following reversible reactions, write thermodynamic equilibrium constant expressions, making appropriate substitutions for activities. Then equate K to K_c or K_p, where this can be done.

(a) The water gas reaction

$$C(s) + H_2O(g) \rightleftharpoons CO(g) + H_2(g)$$

(b) Formation of a saturated aqueous solution of lead(II) iodide, a very slightly soluble solute

$$PbI_2(s) \rightleftharpoons Pb^{2+}(aq) + 2\,I^-(aq)$$

(c) Oxidation of sulfide ion by oxygen gas (used in removing sulfides from wastewater, as in pulp and paper mills)

$$O_2(g) + 2\,S^{2-}(aq) + 2\,H_2O(l) \rightleftharpoons 4\,OH^-(aq) + 2\,S(s)$$

Analyze

In each case, once we have made the appropriate substitutions for activities, if all terms are molarities, the thermodynamic equilibrium constant is the same as K_c. If all terms are partial pressures, $K = K_p$. If both molarities *and* partial pressures appear in the expression, however, the equilibrium constant expression can be designated only as K.

Solve

(a) The activity of solid carbon is 1. Partial pressures are substituted for the activities of the gases.

$$K = \frac{a_{CO(g)}a_{H_2(g)}}{a_{C(s)}a_{H_2O(g)}} = \frac{(P_{CO})(P_{H_2})}{1 \times (P_{H_2O})} = \frac{(P_{CO})(P_{H_2})}{(P_{H_2O})} = K_p$$

(b) The activity of solid lead(II) iodide is 1. Molarities are substituted for activities of the ions in aqueous solution.

$$K = \frac{a_{Pb^{2+}(aq)}a^2_{I^-(aq)}}{a_{PbI_2(s)}} = [Pb^{2+}][I^-]^2 = K_c = K_{sp}$$

(continued)

(c) The activity of both the solid sulfur and the liquid water is 1. Molarities are substituted for the activities of $OH^-(aq)$ and $S^{2-}(aq)$. The partial pressure of $O_2(g)$ is substituted for its activity. Thus, the resulting K is neither a K_c nor a K_p.

$$K = \frac{a^4_{OH^-(aq)} a^2_{S(s)}}{a_{O_2(g)} a^2_{S^{2-}(aq)} a^2_{H_2O(l)}} = \frac{[OH^-]^4 \cdot (1)^2}{P_{O_2} \cdot [S^{2-}]^2 \cdot (1)^2} = \frac{[OH^-]^4}{P_{O_2} \cdot [S^{2-}]^2}$$

Assess

These are thermodynamic equilibrium expressions since they are written in terms of their activities. The values of the thermodynamic equilibrium constant will be dimensionless. The standard pressure and concentration terms have been left out for clarity.

PRACTICE EXAMPLE A: Write thermodynamic equilibrium constant expressions for each of the following reactions. Relate these to K_c or K_p where appropriate.

(a) $Si(s) + 2\,Cl_2(g) \rightleftharpoons SiCl_4(g)$

(b) $Cl_2(g) + H_2O(l) \rightleftharpoons HOCl(aq) + H^+(aq) + Cl^-(aq)$

PRACTICE EXAMPLE B: Write a thermodynamic equilibrium constant expression to represent the reaction of solid lead(II) sulfide with aqueous nitric acid to produce solid sulfur, a solution of lead(II) nitrate, and nitrogen monoxide gas. Base the expression on the balanced net ionic equation for the reaction.

EXAMPLE 5-7 Assessing Spontaneity for Nonstandard Conditions

For the decomposition of 2-propanol to form propanone (acetone) and hydrogen,

$$(CH_3)_2CHOH(g) \rightleftharpoons (CH_3)_2CO(g) + H_2(g)$$

the equilibrium constant is 0.444 at 452 K. Is this reaction spontaneous under standard conditions? Will the reaction be spontaneous when the partial pressures of 2-propanol, propanone, and hydrogen are 0.1 bar, respectively?

Analyze

We are asked two questions. The first is whether this reaction is spontaneous under standard conditions, which means the reactants and products are at 1 bar. We can easily answer by applying the equation $\Delta G° = -RT \ln K$. The second part asks whether this reaction is spontaneous under a set of nonstandard conditions. We are asked to determine ΔG.

Solve

In each case, we first must obtain the value of $\Delta G°$, which we can get from equation (5.13).

$$\Delta G° = -RT \ln K = -8.3145\ \text{J mol}^{-1}\ \text{K}^{-1} \times 452\ \text{K} \times \ln(0.444) = 3.05 \times 10^3\ \text{J mol}^{-1}$$

This result enables us to state categorically that the reaction will not proceed spontaneously if all reactants and products are in their standard states—that is, with the partial pressures of reactants and products at 1 bar.

To determine whether the reaction is spontaneous under the nonstandard-state conditions given, we must calculate ΔG. We first write Q in terms of activities and then substitute the partial pressures of the gases for the activities of the gases.

$$Q = \frac{a_{(CH_3)_2CO} a_{H_2}}{a_{(CH_3)_2CHOH}} = \frac{P_{(CH_3)_2CO} P_{H_2}}{P_{(CH_3)_2CHOH}}$$

Then use this expression in equation (5.12).

$$\Delta G = \Delta G° + RT \ln \frac{P_{(CH_3)_2CO} P_{H_2}}{P_{(CH_3)_2CHOH}}$$
$$= 3.05 \times 10^3\ \text{J mol}^{-1} + 8.3145\ \text{J mol}^{-1}\ \text{K}^{-1} \times 452\ \text{K} \times \ln \frac{0.1 \times 0.1}{0.1}$$
$$= -5.60 \times 10^3\ \text{J mol}^{-1}$$

The value of ΔG is negative, so we can conclude that under this second set of conditions the reaction should proceed spontaneously.

Assess

Remember, however, that thermodynamics says nothing about the rate of the reaction, only that the reaction will proceed in its own good time!

PRACTICE EXAMPLE A: Use the data in Appendix A to decide whether the following reaction is spontaneous under standard conditions at 298.15 K.

$$N_2O_4(g) \longrightarrow 2\,NO_2(g)$$

PRACTICE EXAMPLE B: If a gaseous mixture of N_2O_4 and NO_2, both at a pressure of 0.5 bar, is introduced into a previously evacuated vessel, which of the two gases will spontaneously convert into the other at 298.15 K?

We have now acquired all the tools with which to perform one of the most practical calculations of chemical thermodynamics: *determining the equilibrium constant for a reaction from tabulated data*. Example 5-8, which demonstrates this application, uses thermodynamic properties of ions in aqueous solution as well as of compounds. An important idea to note about the thermodynamic properties of ions is that they are relative to $H^+(aq)$, which, by convention, is assigned values of *zero* for ΔH_f°, ΔG_f°, and S°. This means that entropies listed

EXAMPLE 5-8 Calculating the Equilibrium Constant of a Reaction from the Standard Gibbs Energy Change

Determine the equilibrium constant at 298.15 K for the dissolution of magnesium hydroxide in an acidic solution.

$$Mg(OH)_2(s) + 2\,H^+(aq) \rightleftharpoons Mg^{2+}(aq) + 2\,H_2O(l)$$

Analyze

The key to solving this problem is to find a value of ΔG° and then to use the expression $\Delta G^\circ = -RT \ln K$.

Solve

We can obtain ΔG° from standard Gibbs energies of formation listed in Appendix D. Note that because its value is zero, the term $\Delta G_f^\circ[H^+(aq)]$ is not included.

$$\Delta G^\circ = 2\,\Delta G_f^\circ[H_2O(l)] + \Delta G_f^\circ[Mg^{2+}(aq)] - \Delta G_f^\circ[Mg(OH)_2(s)]$$
$$= 2(-237.1\text{ kJ mol}^{-1}) + (-454.8\text{ kJ mol}^{-1}) - (-833.5\text{ kJ mol}^{-1})$$

Now solve for $\ln K$ and K.

$$\Delta G^\circ = -RT \ln K = -95.5\text{ kJ mol}^{-1} = -95.5 \times 10^3\text{ J mol}^{-1}$$
$$\ln K = \frac{-\Delta G^\circ}{RT} = \frac{-(-95.5 \times 10^3\text{ J mol}^{-1})}{8.3145\text{ J mol}^{-1}\text{ K}^{-1} \times 298.15\text{ K}} = 38.5$$
$$K = e^{38.5} = 5 \times 10^{16}$$

Assess

The value of K obtained here is the thermodynamic equilibrium constant. According to the conventions we have established, the activities of both $Mg(OH)_2(s)$ and $H_2O(l)$ are 1, and molarities can be substituted for the activities of the ions.

$$K = \frac{a_{Mg^{2+}(aq)}\,a^2_{H_2O(l)}}{a_{Mg(OH)_2(s)}\,a^2_{H^+(aq)}} = \frac{[Mg^{2+}]}{[H^+]^2} = K_c = 5 \times 10^{16}$$

PRACTICE EXAMPLE A: Determine the equilibrium constant at 298.15 K for $AgI(s) \rightleftharpoons Ag^+(aq) + I^-(aq)$. Compare your answer to the K_{sp} for AgI in Appendix A.

PRACTICE EXAMPLE B: At 298.15 K, should manganese dioxide react to an appreciable extent with 1 M HCl(aq), producing manganese(II) ion in solution and chlorine gas?

for ions are not absolute entropies, as they are for compounds. Negative values of $S°$ simply denote an entropy less than that of $H^+(aq)$.

When a question requires the use of thermodynamic properties, it is a good idea to think qualitatively about the problem before diving into calculations. The dissolution of $Mg(OH)_2(s)$ in acidic solution considered in Example 5-8 is an acid–base reaction that illustrates the effect of pH on solubility. We should certainly expect the reaction to be spontaneous. This means that the value of K should be large, which we found to be the case. If we had made an error in sign in our calculation (an easy thing to do using the expression $\Delta G° = -RT \ln K$), we would have obtained $K = 2 \times 10^{-17}$. But we would have seen immediately that this is the wrong answer. This erroneous value suggests a reaction in which the concentration of products is extremely low at equilibrium.

The data listed in Appendix A are for 25 °C. Thus, values of $\Delta G°$ and K obtained with these data are also at 25 °C. Most chemical reactions are carried out at temperatures other than 25 °C, however. In Section 5-7, we will learn how to calculate values of equilibrium constants at various temperatures.

5-7 $\Delta G°$ and K as Functions of Temperature

▶ In general, equilibrium constants for exothermic reactions will be lower at higher temperatures and higher at lower temperatures. Alternatively, equilibrium constants for endothermic reactions are lower at lower temperatures and higher at higher temperatures. This is seen by evaluating equation (5.15).

We use Le Châtelier's principle to make qualitative predictions of the effect of temperature on an equilibrium condition. We can now describe a *quantitative* relationship between the equilibrium constant and temperature. In the method illustrated in Example 5-9, we assume that $\Delta H°$ is practically independent of temperature. Although absolute entropies depend on temperature, we assume that the entropy *change* $\Delta S°$ for a reaction is also independent of temperature. Yet, the term "$T\Delta S$" is strongly temperature-dependent because of the temperature factor T. As a result, $\Delta G°$, which is equal to $\Delta H° - T\Delta S°$, is also dependent on temperature.

EXAMPLE 5-9 **Determining the Relationship Between an Equilibrium Constant and Temperature by Using Equations for Gibbs Energy Change**

At what temperature will the equilibrium constant for the formation of NOCl(g) be $K = K_p = 1.00 \times 10^3$? Data for this reaction at 25 °C are

$$2\,NO(g) + Cl_2(g) \rightleftharpoons 2\,NOCl(g)$$

$$\Delta G° = -40.9\ \text{kJ mol}^{-1} \qquad \Delta H = -77.1\ \text{kJ mol}^{-1}$$

$$\Delta S° = -121.3\ \text{J mol}^{-1}\,\text{K}^{-1}$$

Analyze

To determine an unknown temperature from a known equilibrium constant, we need an equation in which both of these terms appear. The required equation is $\Delta G° = -RT \ln K$. However, to solve for the unknown temperature, we need the value of $\Delta G°$ at that temperature. We know the value of $\Delta G°$ at 25 °C (-40.9 kJ mol^{-1}), but we also know that this value will be different at other temperatures. We can assume, however, that the values of $\Delta H°$ and $\Delta S°$ will not change much with temperature. This means that we can obtain a value of $\Delta G°$ from the equation $\Delta G° = \Delta H° - T\,\Delta S°$, where T is the *unknown* temperature and the values of $\Delta H°$ and $\Delta S°$ are those at 25 °C. Now we have two equations that we can set equal to each other.

Solve

That is,

$$\Delta G° = \Delta H° - T\,\Delta S° = -RT \ln K$$

We can gather the terms with T on the right,

$$\Delta H° = T\,\Delta S° - RT \ln K = T(\Delta S° - R \ln K)$$

and solve for T.

$$T = \frac{\Delta H°}{\Delta S° - R \ln K}$$

Now substitute values for $\Delta H°$, $\Delta S°$, R, and $\ln K$.

$$T = \frac{-77.1 \times 10^3\ \text{J mol}^{-1}}{-121.3\ \text{J mol}^{-1}\,\text{K}^{-1} - [8.3145\ \text{J mol}^{-1}\,\text{K}^{-1} \times \ln(1.00 \times 10^3)]}$$
$$= \frac{-77.1 \times 10^3\ \text{J mol}^{-1}}{-121.3\ \text{J mol}^{-1}\,\text{K}^{-1} - (8.3145 \times 6.908)\ \text{J mol}^{-1}\,\text{K}^{-1}}$$
$$= \frac{-77.1 \times 10^3\ \text{J mol}^{-1}}{-178.7\ \text{J mol}^{-1}\,\text{K}^{-1}} = 431\ \text{K}$$

Assess

Although the answer shows three significant figures, the final result should probably be rounded to just two significant figures. The assumption we made about the constancy of $\Delta H°$ and $\Delta S°$ is probably no more valid than that.

PRACTICE EXAMPLE A: At what temperature will the formation of $NO_2(g)$ from NO(g) and $O_2(g)$ have $K_p = 1.50 \times 10^2$? For the reaction $2\,NO(g) + O_2(g) \rightleftharpoons 2\,NO_2(g)$ at 25 °C, $\Delta H° = -114.1$ kJ mol^{-1} and $\Delta S° = -146.5$ J mol^{-1}K^{-1}.

PRACTICE EXAMPLE B: For the reaction $2\,NO(g) + Cl_2(g) \rightleftharpoons 2\,NOCl(g)$, what is the value of K at **(a)** 25 °C; **(b)** 75 °C? Use data from Example 5-9. [*Hint:* The solution to part (a) can be done somewhat more simply than that for (b).]

An alternative to the method outlined in Example 5-9 is to relate the equilibrium constant and temperature directly, without specific reference to a Gibbs energy change. We start with the same two expressions as in Example 5-9,

$$-RT \ln K = \Delta G° = \Delta H° - T\,\Delta S°$$

and divide by $-RT$.

$$\ln K = \frac{-\Delta H°}{RT} + \frac{\Delta S°}{R} \qquad \textbf{(5.14)}$$

If we assume that $\Delta H°$ and $\Delta S°$ are constant, equation (5.14) describes a straight line with a slope of $-\Delta H°/R$ and a y-intercept of $\Delta S°/R$. Table 5.3 lists equilibrium constants as a function of the reciprocal of Kelvin temperature for

TABLE 5.3 Equilibrium Constants, K_p, for the Reaction $2\,SO_2(g) + O_2(g) \rightleftharpoons 2\,SO_3(g)$ at Several Temperatures

T, K	$1/T$, K^{-1}	K_p	$\ln K_p$
800	12.5×10^{-4}	9.1×10^2	6.81
850	11.8×10^{-4}	1.7×10^2	5.14
900	11.1×10^{-4}	4.2×10^1	3.74
950	10.5×10^{-4}	1.0×10^1	2.30
1000	10.0×10^{-4}	3.2×10^0	1.16
1050	9.52×10^{-4}	1.0×10^0	0.00
1100	9.09×10^{-4}	3.9×10^{-1}	−0.94
1170	8.5×10^{-4}	1.2×10^{-1}	−2.12

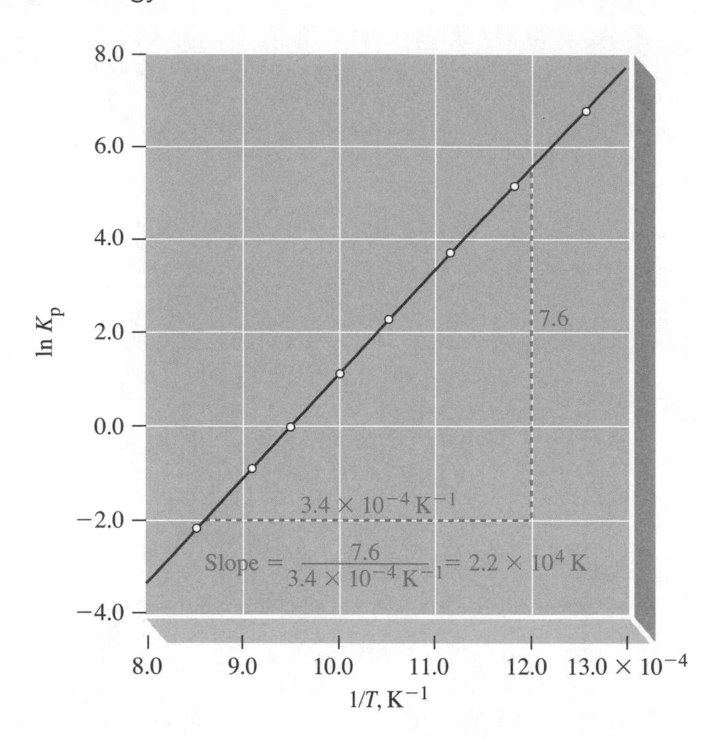

▶ FIGURE 5-12
Temperature dependence of the equilibrium constant K_p for the reaction

$$2\,SO_2(g) + O_2(g) \rightleftharpoons 2\,SO_3(g)$$

This graph can be used to establish the enthalpy of reaction, $\Delta H°$ (see equation 5.14).

$$\text{slope} = \Delta H°/R = 2.2 \times 10^4\ \text{K}$$
$$\Delta H° = -8.3145\ \text{J mol}^{-1}\ \text{K}^{-1} \times 2.2 \times 10^4\ \text{K}$$
$$= -1.8 \times 10^5\ \text{J mol}^{-1}$$
$$= -1.8 \times 10^2\ \text{kJ mol}^{-1}$$

the reaction of $SO_2(g)$ and $O_2(g)$ that forms $SO_3(g)$. The ln K_p and $1/T$ data from Table 5.3 are plotted in Figure 5-12 and yield the expected straight line.

Now we can follow the procedure used in Appendix A-4 to derive the Clausius–Clapeyron equation. We can write equation (5.14) twice, for two different temperatures and with the corresponding equilibrium constants. Then, if we subtract one equation from the other, we obtain the result shown here,

$$\ln\frac{K_2}{K_1} = -\frac{\Delta H°}{R}¢\frac{1}{T_2} - \frac{1}{T_1}† \qquad \textbf{(5.15)}$$

where T_2 and T_1 are two Kelvin temperatures; K_2 and K_1 are the equilibrium constants at those temperatures; $\Delta H°$ is the enthalpy of reaction, expressed in J mol^{-1}; and R is the gas constant, expressed as 8.3145 J mol^{-1} K^{-1}. Jacobus van't Hoff (1852–511) derived equation (5.15), which is often referred to as *the van't Hoff equation.*

KEEP IN MIND

that the Clausius–Clapeyron equation (3.2) is just a special case of equation (5.15) in which the equilibrium constants are equilibrium vapor pressures and $\Delta H° = \Delta H_{vap}$.

5-5 CONCEPT ASSESSMENT

The normal boiling point of water is 100 °C. At 120 °C and 1 atm, is ΔH or T Δ S greater for the vaporization of water?

EXAMPLE 5-10 Relating Equilibrium Constants and Temperature Through the Van't Hoff Equation

Use data from Table 5.3 and Figure 5-12 to estimate the temperature at which $K_p = 1.0 \times 10^6$ for the reaction

$$2\,SO_2(g) + O_2(g) \rightleftharpoons 2\,SO_3(g)$$

Analyze

To use the van't Hoff equation select one known temperature and equilibrium constant from Table 5.3 and the enthalpy change of the reaction, $\Delta H°$, from Figure 5-12.

Solve

The data to be substituted into equation (5.15) are $T_1 = ?, K_1 = 1.0 \times 10^6$; $T_2 = 800$ K, $K_2 = 9.1 \times 10^2$; and $\Delta H° = -1.8 \times 10^5$ J mol^{-1}.

In the following setup, we have dropped the units for simplicity. However, you should be able to show that units cancel properly.

$$\ln\frac{K_2}{K_1} = \frac{\Delta H°}{R}\left(\frac{1}{T_1} - \frac{1}{T_2}\right)$$

$$\ln\frac{9.1 \times 10^2}{1.0 \times 10^6} = \frac{-1.8 \times 10^5}{8.3145}\left(\frac{1}{T_1} - \frac{1}{800}\right)$$

$$-7.00 = -2.2 \times 10^4\left(\frac{1}{T_1} - \frac{1}{800}\right)$$

$$\frac{-7.00}{-2.2 \times 10^4} + \frac{1}{800} = \frac{1}{T_1}$$

$$\frac{1}{T_1} = (3.2 \times 10^{-4}) + (1.25 \times 10^{-3}) = 1.57 \times 10^{-3}$$

$$T_1 = \frac{1}{1.57 \times 10^{-3}} = 6.37 \times 10^2 \text{ K}$$

Assess

A common error in this type of problem is the use of incorrect temperature units. It should be Kelvin (K).

PRACTICE EXAMPLE A: Estimate the temperature at which $K_p = 5.8 \times 10^{-2}$ for the reaction in Example 5-10. Use data from Table 5.3 and Figure 5-12.

PRACTICE EXAMPLE B: What is the value of K_p for the reaction $2\,SO_2(g) + O_2(g) \rightleftharpoons 2\,SO_3(g)$ at 235 °C? Use data from Table 5.3, Figure 5-12 and the van't Hoff equation (5.15).

5-8 Coupled Reactions

We have seen two ways to obtain product from a nonspontaneous reaction: (1) Change the reaction conditions to ones that make the reaction spontaneous (mostly by changing the temperature), and (2) carry out the reaction by electrolysis. But there is a third way also. Combine a pair of reactions, one with a positive ΔG and one with a negative ΔG, to obtain a spontaneous overall reaction. Such paired reactions are called **coupled reactions**. Consider the extraction of a metal from its oxide.

When copper(I) oxide is heated to 673 K, no copper metal is obtained. The decomposition of Cu_2O to form products in their standard states (for instance, $P_{O_2} = 1.00$ bar) is nonspontaneous at 673 K.

$$Cu_2O(s) \xrightarrow{\Delta} 2\,Cu(s) + \frac{1}{2}O_2(g) \qquad \Delta G°_{673K} = +125 \text{ kJ} \qquad \textbf{(5.16)}$$

◀ In general chemistry, simple examples of reactions are generally used. In fact, in almost all interesting cases, one reaction is coupled to another, and so forth. No better example exists than the complex cycles of coupled chemical reactions in biological processes.

Suppose this nonspontaneous decomposition reaction is coupled with the partial oxidation of carbon to carbon monoxide—a spontaneous reaction. The overall reaction (5.17), because it has a negative value of $\Delta G°$, is spontaneous when reactants and products are in their standard states.

$$Cu_2O(s) \longrightarrow 2\,Cu(s) + \cancel{\tfrac{1}{2}O_2(g)} \qquad \Delta G°_{673\,K} = +125 \text{ kJ}$$

$$C(s) + \cancel{\tfrac{1}{2}O_2(g)} \longrightarrow CO(g) \qquad \Delta G°_{673\,K} = -175 \text{ kJ}$$

$$Cu_2O(s) + C(s) \longrightarrow 2\,Cu(s) + CO(g) \qquad \Delta G°_{673\,K} = -50 \text{ kJ} \qquad \textbf{(5.17)}$$

Note that reactions (5.16) and (5.17) are not the same, even though each has Cu(s) as a product. The purpose of coupled reactions, then, is to produce a spontaneous overall reaction by combining two other processes: one nonspontaneous and one spontaneous. Many metallurgical processes employ coupled reactions, especially those that use carbon or hydrogen as reducing agents.

To sustain life, organisms must synthesize complex molecules from simpler ones. If carried out as single-step reactions, these syntheses would generally be accompanied by increases in enthalpy, decreases in entropy, and increases in Gibbs energy—in short, they would be nonspontaneous and would not occur. In living organisms, changes in temperature and electrolysis are not viable options for dealing with nonspontaneous processes. Here, coupled reactions are crucial.

Summary

5-1 Spontaneity: The Meaning of Spontaneous Change—A process that proceeds without need of external intervention is said to be a **spontaneous process**. A **nonspontaneous process** cannot occur without external intervention. A process that is spontaneous in one direction is nonspontaneous in the reverse direction. Some spontaneous processes are exothermic, others are endothermic so that criteria other than enthalpy change are needed to define spontaneity.

5-2 The Concept of Entropy—**Entropy** is a thermodynamic property related to the distribution of a system's energy among the available microscopic energy levels. Boltzmann's formula (equation 5.1) illustrates the relationship between entropy and the number of microstates of a system. The thermodynamic definition of an **entropy change, ΔS,** is of a quantity of heat (q_{rev}) divided by a Kelvin temperature (equation 5.2), and having the units $J\ K^{-1}$. The quantity of heat released (or absorbed) during the process must be from a reversible process in order for the entropy change to be path-independent.

5-3 Evaluating Entropy and Entropy Changes—The **third law of thermodynamics states** that the entropy of a pure, perfect crystal at 0 K is zero. Thus there are absolute entropies, unlike internal energy and enthalpy. The entropy of a substance in its standard state is called **standard molar entropy**, S°. Standard molar entropies of **reactants** and products can be used to calculate standard entropy changes in chemical reactions (equation 5.5). Another important entropy-related relationship is **Trouton's rule**, which states that the standard entropy of vaporization at the normal boiling point is approximately constant at 87 $J\ mol^{-1}\ K^{-1}$ (equation 5.4).

5-4 Criteria for Spontaneous Change: The Second Law of Thermodynamics—The basic criterion for spontaneous change is that the entropy change of the universe, which is the sum of the entropy change of the system plus that of the surroundings (equation 5.6), must be greater than zero (equation 5.7). This statement is known as the **second law of thermodynamics**. An equivalent criterion applied to the system alone is based on a thermodynamic function known as the **Gibbs energy**. The **Gibbs energy change, ΔG,** is the enthalpy change for the system (ΔH) minus the product of the temperature and entropy change for the system ($T\ \Delta S$) (equation 5.9). Table 5.1 summarizes the criteria for spontaneous change based on Gibbs energy change.

5-5 Standard Gibbs Energy Change, ΔG°—The **standard Gibbs energy change, ΔG°,** is based on the conversion of reactants in their standard states to products in their standard states. Tabulated Gibbs energy data are usually **standard Gibbs energies of formation**, ΔG_f°, and usually at 298.15 K.

5-6 Gibbs Energy Change and Equilibrium—The relationship between the standard Gibbs energy change and the equilibrium constant for a reaction is $\Delta G^\circ = -RT \ln K$. The constant, K, is called a **thermodynamic equilibrium constant**. It is based on the activities of reactants and products, but these activities can be related to solution molarities and gas partial pressures by means of a few simple conventions.

5-7 ΔG° and K as Functions of Temperature—By starting with the relationship between standard Gibbs energy change and the equilibrium constant, the van't Hoff equation—relating the equilibrium constant and temperature—can be written. With this equation, tabulated data at 25 °C can be used to determine equilibrium constants not just at 25 °C but at other temperatures as well.

5-8 Coupled Reactions—Nonspontaneous processes can be made spontaneous by coupling them with spontaneous reactions and by taking advantage of the state function property of G. **Coupled reactions**, that is, paired reactions that yield a spontaneous overall reaction, occur in metallurgical processes and in biochemical transformations.

Integrative Example

The synthesis of methanol is of great importance because methanol can be used directly as a motor fuel, mixed with gasoline for fuel use, or converted to other organic compounds. The synthesis reaction, carried out at about 500 K, is

$$CO(g) + 2\,H_2(g) \rightleftharpoons CH_3OH(g)$$

What is the value of K_p at 500 K?

Analyze

Our approach to this problem begins with determining $\Delta G°$ from Gibbs energy of formation data and using $\Delta G°$ to find K_p at 298 K. The next step is to calculate $\Delta H°$ from enthalpy of formation data, and use this value together with K_p at 298 K in expression (5.15) to find K_p at 500 K.

Solve

Write the equation for methanol synthesis; place Gibbs energy of formation data from Appendix D under formulas in the equation, and use these data to calculate $\Delta G°$ at 298 K.

$$\begin{array}{lccc} & CO(g) & +\ 2\,H_2(g) \rightleftharpoons & CH_3OH(g) \\ \Delta G_f^\circ,\ \text{kJ mol}^{-1} & -137.2 & 0 & -162.0 \end{array}$$

$$\Delta G° = 1\text{ mol }CH_3OH \times (-162.0\text{ kJ/mol }CH_3OH) - 1\text{ mol CO} \times (-137.2\text{ kJ/mol CO}) = -24.8\text{ kJ}$$

To calculate K_p at 298 K, use $\Delta G°$ at 298 K, written as $-24.8 \times 10^3\text{ J mol}^{-1}$, in the expression $\Delta G° = -RT\ln K_p$.

$$\ln K_p = -\Delta G°/RT = \frac{-(-24.8 \times 10^3\text{ J mol}^{-1})}{8.3145\text{ J mol}^{-1}\text{ K}^{-1} \times 298\text{ K}} = 10.0$$

$$K_p = e^{10.0} = 2.2 \times 10^4$$

To determine $\Delta H°$ at 298 K, use standard enthalpy of formation data from Appendix A, applied in the same manner as was previously used for $\Delta G°$.

$$\begin{array}{lccc} & CO(g) & +\ 2\,H_2(g) \rightleftharpoons & CH_3OH(g) \\ \Delta H_f^\circ,\ \text{kJ mol}^{-1} & -110.5 & 0 & -200.7 \end{array}$$

$$\Delta H° = 1\text{ mol }CH_3OH \times (-200.7\text{ kJ/mol }CH_3OH) - 1\text{ mol CO} \times (-110.5\text{ kJ/mol CO}) = -90.2\text{ kJ}$$

Use the van't Hoff equation with $K_p = 2.2 \times 10^4$ at 298 K and $\Delta H° = -90.2 \times 10^3\text{ J mol}^{-1}$. Solve for K_p at 500 K.

$$\ln\frac{K_p}{2.2 \times 10^4} = \frac{-90.2 \times 10^3\text{ J mol}^{-1}}{8.3145\text{ J mol}^{-1}\text{ K}^{-1}}\left(\frac{1}{298\text{ K}} - \frac{1}{500\text{ K}}\right) = -14.7$$

$$\frac{K_p}{2.2 \times 10^4} = e^{-14.7} = 4 \times 10^{-7} \qquad K_p = 9 \times 10^{-3}$$

Assess

We have been successful in determining the equilibrium constant for the synthesis of methanol at 500 K by using tabulated thermodynamic data and the van't Hoff equation. Note that increasing the temperature favors the reverse reaction, as we should expect from Le Châtelier's principle. That is, an increase in temperature in a reversible reaction favors the heat absorbing (endothermic) reaction. Here, the forward reaction is exothermic and the reverse reaction is endothermic.

PRACTICE EXAMPLE A: Dinitrogen pentoxide, N_2O_5, is a solid with a high vapor pressure. Its vapor pressure at 7.5 °C is 100 mmHg, and the solid sublimes at a pressure of 1.00 atm at 32.4 °C. What is the standard Gibbs energy change for the process at $N_2O_5(s) \longrightarrow N_2O_5(g)$ at 25 °C?

PRACTICE EXAMPLE B: A plausible reaction for the production of ethylene glycol (used as antifreeze) is

$$2\,CO(g) + 3H_2(g) \longrightarrow CH_2OHCH_2OH(l)$$

The following thermodynamic properties of $CH_2OHCH_2OH(l)$ at 25 °C are given: $\Delta H_f^\circ = -454.8\text{ kJ mol}^{-1}$ and $\Delta G_f^\circ = -323.1\text{ kJ mol}^{-1}$. Use these data, together with values from Appendix D, to obtain a value of $S°$, the standard molar entropy of $CH_2OHCH_2OH(l)$ at 25 °C.

Exercises

Spontaneous Change and Entropy

1. Indicate whether each of the following changes represents an increase or a decrease in entropy in a system, and explain your reasoning: **(a)** the freezing of ethanol; **(b)** the sublimation of dry ice; **(c)** the burning of a rocket fuel.
2. Arrange the entropy changes of the following processes, all at 25 °C, in the expected order of increasing ΔS, and explain your reasoning:
   (a) $H_2O(l, 1\ atm) \longrightarrow H_2O(g, 1\ atm)$
   (b) $CO_2(s, 1\ atm) \longrightarrow CO_2(g, 10\ mmHg)$
   (c) $H_2O(l, 1\ atm) \longrightarrow H_2O(g, 10\ mmHg)$
3. Use ideas from this chapter to explain this famous remark attributed to Rudolf Clausius (1865): "Die Energie der Welt ist konstant; die Entropie der Welt strebt einem Maximum zu." ("The energy of the world is constant; the entropy of the world increases toward a maximum.")
4. Comment on the difficulties of solving environmental pollution problems from the standpoint of entropy changes associated with the formation of pollutants and with their removal from the environment.
5. Indicate whether the entropy of the system would increase or decrease in each of the following reactions. If you cannot be certain simply by inspecting the equation, explain why.
   (a) $CCl_4(l) \longrightarrow CCl_4(g)$
   (b) $CuSO_4 \cdot 3\,H_2O(s) + 2\,H_2O(g) \longrightarrow CuSO_4 \cdot 5\,H_2O(s)$
   (c) $SO_3(g) + H_2(g) \longrightarrow SO_2(g) + H_2O(g)$
   (d) $H_2S(g) + O_2(g) \longrightarrow H_2O(g) + SO_2(g)$ (not balanced)
6. Which substance in each of the following pairs would have the greater entropy? Explain.
   (a) at 75 °C and 1 atm: 1 mol $H_2O(l)$ or 1 mol $H_2O(g)$
   (b) at 5 °C and 1 atm: 50.0 g Fe(s) or 0.80 mol Fe(s)
   (c) 1 mol Br_2 (l, 1 atm, 8 °C) or 1 mol Br_2 (s, 1 atm, −8 °C)
   (d) 0.312 mol SO_2 (g, 0.110 atm, 32.5 °C) or 0.284 mol O_2 (g, 15.0 atm, 22.3 °C)
7. For each of the following reactions, indicate whether ΔS for the reaction should be positive or negative. If it is not possible to determine the sign of ΔS from the information given, indicate why.
   (a) $CaO(s) + H_2O(l) \longrightarrow Ca(OH)_2(s)$
   (b) $2\,HgO(s) \longrightarrow 2\,Hg(l) + O_2(g)$
   (c) $2\,NaCl(l) \longrightarrow 2\,Na(l) + Cl_2(g)$
   (d) $Fe_2O_3(s) + 3\,CO(g) \longrightarrow 2\,Fe(s) + 3\,CO_2(g)$
   (e) $Si(s) + 2\,Cl_2(g) \longrightarrow SiCl_4(g)$
8. By analogy to ΔH_f° and ΔG_f° how would you define entropy of formation? Which would have the largest entropy of formation: $CH_4(g)$, $CH_3CH_2OH(l)$, or $CS_2(l)$? First make a qualitative prediction; then test your prediction with data from Appendix A.

Phase Transitions

9. In Example 5-2, we dealt with ΔH°_{vap} and ΔS°_{vap} for water at 100 °C.
   (a) Use data from Appendix A to determine values for these two quantities at 25 °C.
   (b) From your knowledge of the structure of liquid water, explain the differences in ΔH°_{vap} values and in ΔS°_{vap} values between 25 °C and 100 °C.
10. Pentane is one of the most volatile of the hydrocarbons in gasoline. At 298.15 K, the following enthalpies of formation are given for pentane: $\Delta H_f^\circ C_5H_{12}(l) = -173.5\ kJ\ mol^{-1}$; $\Delta H_f^\circ[C_5H_{12}(g)] = -146.9\ kJ\ mol^{-1}$.
    (a) Estimate the normal boiling point of pentane.
    (b) Estimate ΔG° for the vaporization of pentane at 298 K.
    (c) Comment on the significance of the sign of ΔG° at 298 K.
11. Which of the following substances would obey Trouton's rule most closely: HF, $C_6H_5CH_3$ (toluene), or CH_3OH (methanol)? Explain your reasoning.
12. Estimate the normal boiling point of bromine, Br_2, in the following way: Determine ΔH°_{vap} for Br_2 from data in Appendix A. Assume that ΔH°_{vap} remains constant and that Trouton's rule is obeyed.
13. In what temperature range can the following equilibrium be established? Explain.
    $$H_2O(l, 0.50\ atm) \rightleftharpoons H_2O(g, 0.50\ atm)$$
14. Refer to Figures 3-28 and 5-9. Which has the lowest Gibbs energy at 1 atm and −60 °C: solid, liquid, or gaseous carbon dioxide? Explain.

Gibbs Energy and Spontaneous Change

15. Which of the following changes in a thermodynamic property would you expect to find for the reaction $Br_2(g) \longrightarrow 2\,Br(g)$ *at all temperatures:* **(a)** $\Delta H < 0$; **(b)** $\Delta S > 0$; **(c)** $\Delta G < 0$; **(d)** $\Delta S < 0$? Explain.
16. If a reaction can be carried out only by electrolysis, which of the following changes in a thermodynamic property *must* apply: **(a)** $\Delta H > 0$; **(b)** $\Delta S > 0$; **(c)** $\Delta G = \Delta H$; **(d)** $\Delta G > 0$? Explain.
17. Indicate which of the four cases in Table 5.1 applies to each of the following reactions. If you are unable to decide from only the information given, state why.
    (a) $PCl_3(g) + Cl_2(g) \longrightarrow PCl_5(g)\ \Delta H^\circ = -87.9\ kJ$
    (b) $CO_2(g) + H_2(g) \longrightarrow CO(g) + H_2O(g)\ \Delta H^\circ = +41.2\ kJ$
    (c) $NH_4CO_2NH_2(s) \longrightarrow 2\,NH_3(g) + CO_2(g)\ \Delta H^\circ = +159.2\ kJ$

18. Indicate which of the four cases in Table 5.1 applies to each of the following reactions. If you are unable to decide from only the information given, state why.

(a) $H_2O(g) + \frac{1}{2}O_2(g) \longrightarrow H_2O_2(g)$

$\Delta H° = +105.5\ kJ$

(b) $C_6H_6(l) + \frac{15}{2}O_2(g) \longrightarrow 6\,CO_2(g) + 3\,H_2O(g)$

$\Delta H° = -3135\ kJ$

(c) $NO(g) + \frac{1}{2}Cl_2(g) \longrightarrow NOCl(g)$

$\Delta H° = -38.54\ kJ$

19. For the mixing of ideal gases (see Figure 5-2), explain whether a positive, negative, or zero value is expected for ΔH, ΔS, and ΔG.

20. What values of ΔH, ΔS, and ΔG would you expect for the formation of an ideal solution of liquid components? (Is each value positive, negative, or zero?)

21. Explain why **(a)** some exothermic reactions do not occur spontaneously, and **(b)** some reactions in which the entropy of the system increases do not occur spontaneously.

22. Explain why you would expect a reaction of the type $AB(g) \longrightarrow A(g) + B(g)$ always to be spontaneous at *high* rather than at low temperatures.

Standard Gibbs Energy Change

23. From the data given in the following table, determine $\Delta S°$ for the reaction $NH_3(g) + HCl(g) \longrightarrow NH_4Cl(s)$. All data are at 298 K.

	$\Delta H_f°$, kJ mol^{-1}	$\Delta G_f°$, kJ mol^{-1}
$NH_3(g)$	−46.11	−16.48
$HCl(g)$	−92.31	−95.30
$NH_4Cl(s)$	−314.4	−202.9

24. Use data from Appendix A to determine values of $\Delta G°$ for the following reactions at 25 °C.

(a) $C_2H_2(g) + 2\,H_2(g) \longrightarrow C_2H_6(g)$

(b) $2\,SO_3(g) \longrightarrow 2\,SO_2(g) + O_2(g)$

(c) $Fe_3O_4(s) + 4\,H_2(g) \longrightarrow 3\,Fe(s) + 4\,H_2O(g)$

(d) $2\,Al(s) + 6\,H^+(aq) \longrightarrow 2\,Al^{3+}(aq) + 3\,H_2(g)$

25. At 298 K, for the reaction $2\,PCl_3(g) + O_2(g) \longrightarrow 2\,POCl_3(l)$, $\Delta H° = -620.2\ kJ$ and the standard molar entropies are $PCl_3(g)$, 311.8 J K^{-1}; $O_2(g)$, 205.1 J K^{-1}; and $POCl_3(l)$, 222.4 J K^{-1}. Determine **(a)** $\Delta G°$ at 298 K and **(b)** whether the reaction proceeds spontaneously in the forward or the reverse direction when reactants and products are in their standard states.

26. At 298 K, for the reaction $2\,H^+(aq) + 2\,Br^-(aq) + 2\,NO_2(g) \longrightarrow Br_2(l) + 2\,HNO_2(aq)$, $\Delta H° = -61.6\ kJ$ and the standard molar entropies are $H^+(aq)$, 0 J K^{-1}; $Br^-(aq)$, 82.4 J K^{-1}; $NO_2(g)$, 240.1 J K^{-1}; $Br_2(l)$, 152.2 J K^{-1}; $HNO_2(aq)$, 135.6 J K^{-1}. Determine **(a)** $\Delta G°$ at 298 K and **(b)** whether the reaction proceeds spontaneously in the forward or the reverse direction when reactants and products are in their standard states.

27. The following standard Gibbs energy changes are given for 25 °C.

(1) $N_2(g) + 3\,H_2(g) \longrightarrow 2\,NH_3(g)$ $\quad \Delta G° = -33.0\ kJ$

(2) $4\,NH_3(g) + 5\,O_2(g) \longrightarrow 4\,NO(g) + 6\,H_2O(l)$ $\quad \Delta G° = -1010.5\ kJ$

(3) $N_2(g) + O_2(g) \longrightarrow 2\,NO(g)$ $\quad \Delta G° = +173.1\ kJ$

(4) $N_2(g) + 2\,O_2(g) \longrightarrow 2\,NO_2(g)$ $\quad \Delta G° = +102.6\ kJ$

(5) $2\,N_2(g) + O_2(g) \longrightarrow 2\,N_2O(g)$ $\quad \Delta G° = +208.4\ kJ$

Combine the preceding equations, as necessary, to obtain $\Delta G°$ values for each of the following reactions.

(a) $N_2O(g) + \frac{3}{2}O_2(g) \longrightarrow 2\,NO_2(g)$ $\quad \Delta G° = ?$

(b) $2\,H_2(g) + O_2(g) \longrightarrow 2\,H_2O(l)$ $\quad \Delta G° = ?$

(c) $2\,NH_3(g) + 2\,O_2(g) \longrightarrow N_2O(g) + 3\,H_2O(l)$ $\quad \Delta G° = ?$

Of reactions (a), (b), and (c), which would tend to go to completion at 25 °C, and which would reach an equilibrium condition with significant amounts of all reactants and products present?

28. The following standard Gibbs energy changes are given for 25 °C.

(1) $SO_2(g) + 3\,CO(g) \longrightarrow COS(g) + 2\,CO_2(g)$ $\quad \Delta G° = -246.4\ kJ$

(2) $CS_2(g) + H_2O(g) \longrightarrow COS(g) + H_2S(g)$ $\quad \Delta G° = -41.5\ kJ$

(3) $CO(g) + H_2S(g) \longrightarrow COS(g) + H_2(g)$ $\quad \Delta G° = +1.4\ kJ$

(4) $CO(g) + H_2O(g) \longrightarrow CO_2(g) + H_2(g)$ $\quad \Delta G° = -28.6\ kJ$

Combine the preceding equations, as necessary, to obtain $\Delta G°$ values for the following reactions.

(a) $COS(g) + 2\,H_2O(g) \longrightarrow SO_2(g) + CO(g) + 2\,H_2(g)$ $\quad \Delta G° = ?$

(b) $COS(g) + 3\,H_2O(g) \longrightarrow SO_2(g) + CO_2(g) + 3\,H_2(g)$ $\quad \Delta G° = ?$

(c) $COS(g) + H_2O(g) \longrightarrow CO_2(g) + H_2S(g)$ $\quad \Delta G° = ?$

Of reactions (a), (b), and (c), which is spontaneous in the forward direction when reactants and products are present in their standard states?

29. Write an equation for the combustion of one mole of benzene, $C_6H_6(l)$, and use data from Appendix A to determine $\Delta G°$ at 298 K if the products of the combustion are **(a)** $CO_2(g)$ and $H_2O(l)$, and **(b)** $CO_2(g)$ and $H_2O(g)$. Describe how you might determine the *difference* between the values obtained in (a) and (b) without having either to write the combustion equation or to determine $\Delta G°$ values for the combustion reactions.

30. Use molar entropies from Appendix A, together with the following data, to estimate the bond-dissociation energy of the F_2 molecule.

$$F_2(g) \longrightarrow 2\,F(g) \quad \Delta G° = 123.9\ kJ$$

31. Assess the feasibility of the reaction

$$N_2H_4(g) + 2\,OF_2(g) \longrightarrow N_2F_4(g) + 2\,H_2O(g)$$

by determining each of the following quantities for this reaction at 25 °C.
(a) $\Delta S°$ (The standard molar entropy of $N_2F_4(g)$ is 301.2 J K^{-1}.)
(b) $\Delta H°$ (Use F—O and N—F bond energies of 222 and 301 kJ mol^{-1}, respectively.)
(c) $\Delta G°$

Is the reaction feasible? If so, is it favored at high or low temperatures?

32. Solid ammonium nitrate can decompose to dinitrogen oxide gas and liquid water. What is $\Delta G°$ at 298 K? Is the decomposition reaction favored at temperatures above or below 298 K?

The Thermodynamic Equilibrium Constant

33. For one of the following reactions, $K_cK_p = K$. Identify that reaction. For the other two reactions, what is the relationship between K_c, K_p, and K? Explain.
(a) $2\,SO_2(g) + O_2(g) \rightleftharpoons 2\,SO_3(g)$
(b) $HI(g) \rightleftharpoons \frac{1}{2}H_2(g) + \frac{1}{2}I_2(g)$
(c) $NH_4HCO_3(s) \rightleftharpoons NH_3(g) + CO_2(g) + H_2O(l)$

34. $H_2(g)$ can be prepared by passing steam over hot iron: $3\,Fe(s) + 4\,H_2O(g) \rightleftharpoons Fe_3O_4(s) + 4\,H_2(g)$.
(a) Write an expression for the thermodynamic equilibrium constant for this reaction.
(b) Explain why the partial pressure of $H_2(g)$ is independent of the amounts of Fe(s) and $Fe_3O_4(s)$ present.
(c) Can we conclude that the production of $H_2(g)$ from $H_2O(g)$ could be accomplished regardless of the proportions of Fe(s) and $Fe_3O_4(s)$ present? Explain.

35. In the synthesis of gaseous methanol from carbon monoxide gas and hydrogen gas, the following equilibrium concentrations were determined at 483 K: $[CO(g)] = 0.0911$ M, $[H_2O(g)] = 0.0822$ M, and $[CH_3OH(g)] = 0.00892$ M. Calculate the equilibrium constant and Gibbs energy for this reaction.

36. Calculate the equilibrium constant and Gibbs energy for the reaction $CO(g) + 2\,H_2(g) \longrightarrow CH_3OH(g)$ at 483 K by using the data tables from Appendix A. Are the values determined here different from or the same as those in exercise 35? Explain.

Relationships Involving ΔG, $\Delta G°$, Q, and K

37. Use data from Appendix A to determine K_p at 298 K for the reaction $N_2O(g) + \frac{1}{2}O_2(g) \rightleftharpoons 2\,NO(g)$.

38. Use data from Appendix D to establish for the reaction $2\,N_2O_4(g) + O_2(g) \rightleftharpoons 2\,N_2O_5(g)$:
(a) $\Delta G°$ at 298 K for the reaction as written;
(b) K_p at 298 K.

39. Use data from Appendix A to determine values at 298 K of $\Delta G°$ and K for the following reactions. (*Note:* The equations are not balanced.)
(a) $HCl(g) + O_2(g) \rightleftharpoons H_2O(g) + Cl_2(g)$
(b) $Fe_2O_3(s) + H_2(g) \rightleftharpoons Fe_3O_4(s) + H_2O(g)$
(c) $Ag^+(aq) + SO_4^{2-}(aq) \rightleftharpoons Ag_2SO_4(s)$

40. In Example 5-1, we were unable to conclude by inspection whether $\Delta S°$ for the reaction $CO(g) + H_2O(g) \longrightarrow CO_2(g) + H_2(g)$ should be positive or negative. Use data from Appendix A to obtain $\Delta S°$ at 298 K.

41. Use thermodynamic data at 298 K to decide in which direction the reaction

$$2\,SO_2(g) + O_2(g) \rightleftharpoons 2\,SO_3(g)$$

is spontaneous when the partial pressures of SO_2, O_2, and SO_3 are 1.0×10^{-4}, 0.20, and 0.10 atm, respectively.

42. Use thermodynamic data at 298 K to decide in which direction the reaction

$$H_2(g) + Cl_2(g) \rightleftharpoons 2\,HCl(g)$$

is spontaneous when the partial pressures of H_2, Cl_2, and HCl are all 0.5 atm.

43. The standard Gibbs energy change for the reaction

$$CH_3CO_2H(aq) + H_2O(l) \rightleftharpoons CH_3CO_2^-(aq) + H_3O^+(aq)$$

is 27.07 kJ mol^{-1} at 298 K. Use this thermodynamic quantity to decide in which direction the reaction is spontaneous when the concentrations of $CH_3CO_2H(aq)$, $CH_3CO_2^-(aq)$, and $H_3O^+(aq)$ are 0.10 M, 1.0×10^{-3} M, and 1.0×10^{-3} M, respectively.

44. The standard Gibbs energy change for the reaction

$$NH_3(aq) + H_2O(l) \rightleftharpoons NH_4^+(aq) + OH^-(aq)$$

is 29.05 kJ mol^{-1} at 298 K. Use this thermodynamic quantity to decide in which direction the reaction is spontaneous when the concentrations of $NH_3(aq)$, $NH_4^+(aq)$, and $OH^-(aq)$ are 0.10 M, 1.0×10^{-3} M, and 1.0×10^{-3} M, respectively.

45. For the reaction $2\,NO(g) + O_2(g) \longrightarrow 2\,NO_2(g)$ all but one of the following equations is correct. Which is *incorrect*, and why? **(a)** $K = K_p$; **(b)** $\Delta S° = (\Delta G° - \Delta H°)/T$; **(c)** $K_p = e^{-\Delta G°/RT}$; **(d)** $\Delta G = \Delta G° + RT \ln Q$.

46. Why is $\Delta G°$ such an important property of a chemical reaction, even though the reaction is generally carried out under *nonstandard* conditions?

47. At 1000 K, an equilibrium mixture in the reaction $CO_2(g) + H_2(g) \rightleftharpoons CO(g) + H_2O(g)$ contains 0.276 mol H_2, 0.276 mol CO_2, 0.224 mol CO, and 0.224 mol H_2O.
(a) What is K_p at 1000 K?

(b) Calculate $\Delta G°$ at 1000 K.
(c) In which direction would a spontaneous reaction occur if the following were brought together at 1000 K: 0.0750 mol CO_2, 0.095 mol H_2, 0.0340 mol CO, and 0.0650 mol H_2O?

48. For the reaction $2\,SO_2(g) + O_2(g) \rightleftharpoons 2\,SO_3(g)$, $K_c = 2.8 \times 10^2$ at 1000 K.
(a) What is $\Delta G°$ at 1000 K? [*Hint:* What is K_p?]
(b) If 0.40 mol SO_2, 0.18 mol O_2, and 0.72 mol SO_3 are mixed in a 2.50 L flask at 1000 K, in what direction will a net reaction occur?

49. For the following equilibrium reactions, calculate $\Delta G°$ at the indicated temperature. [*Hint:* How is each equilibrium constant related to a thermodynamic equilibrium constant, *K*?]
(a) $H_2(g) + I_2(g) \rightleftharpoons 2\,HI(g) \quad K_c = 50.2$ at 445 °C
(b) $N_2O(g) + \frac{1}{2}O_2(g) \rightleftharpoons 2NO(g)$
$K_c = 1.7 \times 10^{-13}$ at 25 °C
(c) $N_2O_4(g) \rightleftharpoons 2NO_2(g)$
$K_c = 4.61 \times 10^{-3}$ at 25 °C
(d) $2\,Fe^{3+}(aq) + Hg_2{}^{2+}(aq) \rightleftharpoons 2\,Fe^{2+}(aq) + 2\,Hg^{2+}(aq)$
$K_c = 9.14 \times 10^{-6}$ at 25 °C

50. Two equations can be written for the dissolution of $Mg(OH)_2(s)$ in acidic solution.

$$Mg(OH)_2(s) + 2\,H^+(aq) \rightleftharpoons Mg^{2+}(aq) + 2\,H_2O(l) \qquad \Delta G° = -95.5 \text{ kJ mol}^{-1}$$

$$\frac{1}{2}Mg(OH)_2(s) + H^+(aq) \rightleftharpoons \frac{1}{2}Mg^{2+}(aq) + H_2O(l) \qquad \Delta G° = -47.8 \text{ kJ mol}^{-1}$$

(a) Explain why these two equations have different $\Delta G°$ values.
(b) Will *K* for these two equations be the same or different? Explain.
(c) Will the solubilities of $Mg(OH)_2(s)$ in a buffer solution at pH = 8.5 depend on which of the two equations is used as the basis of the calculation? Explain.

51. At 298 K, $\Delta G_f^\circ[CO(g)] = -137.2$ kJ/mol and $K_p = 6.5 \times 10^{11}$ for the reaction $CO(g) + Cl_2(g) \rightleftharpoons COCl_2(g)$. Use these data to determine $\Delta G_f^\circ[COCl_2(g)]$, and compare your result with the value in Appendix A.

52. Use thermodynamic data from Appendix A to calculate values of K_{sp} for the following sparingly soluble solutes: **(a)** AgBr; **(b)** $CaSO_4$; **(c)** $Fe(OH)_3$. [*Hint:* Begin by writing solubility equilibrium expressions.]

53. To establish the law of conservation of mass, Lavoisier carefully studied the decomposition of mercury(II) oxide:

$$HgO(s) \longrightarrow Hg(l) + \frac{1}{2}O_2(g)$$

At 25 °C, $\Delta H° = +90.83$ kJ and $\Delta G° = +58.54$ kJ.
(a) Show that the partial pressure of $O_2(g)$ in equilibrium with HgO(s) and Hg(l) at 25 °C is extremely low.
(b) What conditions do you suppose Lavoisier used to obtain significant quantities of oxygen?

54. Currently, CO_2 is being studied as a source of carbon atoms for synthesizing organic compounds. One possible reaction involves the conversion of CO_2 to methanol, CH_3OH.

$$CO_2(g) + 3\,H_2(g) \longrightarrow CH_3OH(g) + H_2O(g)$$

With the aid of data from Appendix A, determine
(a) if this reaction proceeds to any significant extent at 25 °C;
(b) if the production of $CH_3OH(g)$ is favored by raising or lowering the temperature from 25 °C;
(c) K_p for this reaction at 500 K;
(d) the partial pressure of $CH_3OH(g)$ at equilibrium if $CO_2(g)$ and $H_2(g)$, each initially at a partial pressure of 1 atm, react at 500 K.

$\Delta G°$ and *K* as Functions of Temperature

55. Use data from Appendix A to establish at 298 K for the reaction:

$$2\,NaHCO_3(s) \longrightarrow Na_2CO_3(s) + H_2O(l) + CO_2(g)$$

(a) $\Delta S°$; **(b)** $\Delta H°$; **(c)** $\Delta G°$; **(d)** K.

56. A possible reaction for converting methanol to ethanol is

$$CO(g) + 2\,H_2(g) + CH_3OH(g) \longrightarrow C_2H_5OH(g) + H_2O(g)$$

(a) Use data from Appendix A to calculate $\Delta H°$, $\Delta S°$, and $\Delta G°$ for this reaction at 25 °C.
(b) Is this reaction thermodynamically favored at high or low temperatures? At high or low pressures? Explain.
(c) Estimate K_p for the reaction at 750 K.

57. What must be the temperature if the following reaction has $\Delta G° = -45.5$ kJ, $\Delta H° = -24.8$ kJ, and $\Delta S° = 15.2\text{ J K}^{-1}$?

$$Fe_2O_3(s) + 3\,CO(g) \longrightarrow 2\,Fe(s) + 3\,CO_2(g)$$

58. Estimate K_p at 100 °C for the reaction $2\,SO_2(g) + O_2(g) \rightleftharpoons 2\,SO_3(g)$. Use data from Table 5.3 and Figure 5-12.

59. The synthesis of ammonia by the Haber process occurs by the reaction $N_2(g) + 3\,H_2(g) \rightleftharpoons 2\,NH_3(g)$ at 400 °C. Using data from Appendix A and assuming that $\Delta H°$ and $\Delta S°$ are essentially unchanged in the temperature interval from 25 to 400 °C, estimate K_p at 400 °C.

60. Use data from Appendix A to determine **(a)** $\Delta H°$, $\Delta S°$, and $\Delta G°$ at 298 K and **(b)** K_p at 875 K for the water gas shift reaction, used commercially to produce $H_2(g)$: $CO(g) + H_2O(g) \rightleftharpoons CO_2(g) + H_2(g)$.
[*Hint:* Assume that $\Delta H°$ and $\Delta S°$ are essentially unchanged in this temperature interval.]

61. In Example 5-10, we used the van't Hoff equation to determine the temperature at which $K_p = 1.0 \times 10^6$ for the reaction $2\,SO_2(g) + O_2(g) \rightleftharpoons 2\,SO_3(g)$. Obtain another estimate of this temperature with data from Appendix A and equations (5.9) and (5.13). Compare your result with that obtained in Example 5-10.

62. The following equilibrium constants have been determined for the reaction $H_2(g) + I_2(g) \rightleftharpoons 2\,HI(g)$: $K_p = 50.0$ at 448 °C and 66.9 at 350 °C. Use these data to estimate $\Delta H°$ for the reaction.

63. For the reaction $N_2O_4(g) \rightleftharpoons 2\,NO_2(g)$, $\Delta H° = +57.2\ \text{kJ mol}^{-1}$ and $K_p = 0.113$ at 298 K.
(a) What is K_p at 0 °C?
(b) At what temperature will $K_p = 1.00$?

64. Use data from Appendix A and the van't Hoff equation (5.15) to estimate a value of K_p at 100 °C for the reaction $2\,NO(g) + O_2(g) \rightleftharpoons 2\,NO_2(g)$. [*Hint:* First determine K_p at 25 °C. What is $\Delta H°$ for the reaction?]

65. For the reaction

$$CO(g) + 3\,H_2(g) \rightleftharpoons CH_4(g) + H_2O(g),$$
$$K_p = 2.15 \times 10^{11} \text{ at } 200\ °C$$
$$K_p = 4.56 \times 10^{8} \text{ at } 260\ °C$$

determine $\Delta H°$ by using the van't Hoff equation (5.15) and by using tabulated data in Appendix A. Compare the two results, and comment on how good the assumption is that $\Delta H°$ is essentially independent of temperature in this case.

66. Sodium carbonate, an important chemical used in the production of glass, is made from sodium hydrogen carbonate by the reaction

$$2\,NaHCO_3(s) \rightleftharpoons Na_2CO_3(s) + CO_2(g) + H_2O(g)$$

Data for the temperature variation of K_p for this reaction are $K_p = 1.66 \times 10^{-5}$ at 30 °C; 3.90×10^{-4} at 50 °C; 6.27×10^{-3} at 70 °C; and 2.31×10^{-1} at 100 °C.
(a) Plot a graph similar to Figure 5-12, and determine $\Delta H°$ for the reaction.
(b) Calculate the temperature at which the total gas pressure above a mixture of $NaHCO_3(s)$ and $Na_2CO_3(s)$ is 2.00 atm.

Coupled Reactions

67. Titanium is obtained by the reduction of $TiCl_4(l)$, which in turn is produced from the mineral rutile (TiO_2).
(a) With data from Appendix A, determine $\Delta G°$ at 298 K for this reaction.

$$TiO_2(s) + 2\,Cl_2(g) \longrightarrow TiCl_4(l) + O_2(g)$$

(b) Show that the conversion of $TiO_2(s)$ to $TiCl_4(l)$, with reactants and products in their standard states, is spontaneous at 298 K if the reaction in (a) is coupled with the reaction

$$2\,CO(g) + O_2(g) \longrightarrow 2\,CO_2(g)$$

68. Following are some standard Gibbs energies of formation, $\Delta G_f°$, per mole of metal oxide at 1000 K: NiO, −115 kJ; MnO, −280 kJ; TiO_2, −630 kJ. The standard Gibbs energy of formation of CO at 1000 K is −250 kJ per mol CO. Use the method of coupled reactions (page 199) to determine which of these metal oxides can be reduced to the metal by a spontaneous reaction with carbon at 1000 K and with all reactants and products in their standard states.

69. In biochemical reactions the phosphorylation of amino acids is an important step. Consider the following two reactions and determine whether the phosphorylation of arginine with ATP is spontaneous.

$$\text{ATP} + H_2O \longrightarrow \text{ADP} + \text{P} \quad \Delta G°' = -31.5\ \text{kJ mol}^{-1}$$
$$\text{arginine} + \text{P} \longrightarrow \text{phosphorarginine} + H_2O \quad \Delta G°' = 33.2\ \text{kJ mol}^{-1}$$

70. The synthesis of glutamine from glutamic acid is given by $\text{Glu}^- + NH_4^+ \longrightarrow \text{Gln} + H_2O$. The Gibbs energy for this reaction at pH = 7 and $T = 310$ K is $\Delta G°' = 14.8\ \text{kJ mol}^{-1}$. Will this reaction be spontaneous if coupled with the hydrolysis of ATP?

$$\text{ATP} + H_2O \longrightarrow \text{ADP} + \text{P} \quad \Delta G°' = -31.5\ \text{kJ mol}-1$$

Integrative and Advanced Exercises

71. Use data from Appendix A to estimate **(a)** the normal boiling point of mercury and **(b)** the vapor pressure of mercury at 25 °C.

72. Consider the vaporization of water: $H_2O(l) \longrightarrow H_2O(g)$ at 100 °C, with $H_2O(l)$ in its standard state, but with the partial pressure of $H_2O(g)$ at 2.0 atm. Which of the following statements about this vaporization at 100 °C are true? **(a)** $\Delta G° = 0$, **(b)** $\Delta G = 0$, **(c)** $\Delta G° > 0$, **(d)** $\Delta G > 0$? Explain.

73. At 298 K, 1.00 mol BrCl(g) is introduced into a 10.0 L vessel, and equilibrium is established in the reaction $BrCl(g) \rightleftharpoons \frac{1}{2}Br_2(g) + \frac{1}{2}Cl_2(g)$. Calculate the amounts of each of the three gases present when equilibrium is established. [*Hint:* Use data from Appendix A as necessary.]

74. Use data from Appendix A and other information from this chapter to estimate the temperature at which the dissociation of $I_2(g)$ becomes appreciable [for example, with the $I_2(g)$ 50% dissociated into I(g) at 1 atm total pressure].

75. The following table shows the enthalpies and Gibbs energies of formation of three metal oxides at 25 °C.
(a) Which of these oxides can be most readily decomposed to the free metal and $O_2(g)$?
(b) For the oxide that is most easily decomposed, to what temperature must it be heated to produce $O_2(g)$ at 1.00 atm pressure?

	$\Delta H_f°$, kJ mol^{-1}	$\Delta G_f°$, kJ mol^{-1}
PbO(red)	−219.0	−188.9
Ag_2O	−31.05	−11.20
ZnO	−348.3	−318.3

76. The following data are given for the two solid forms of HgI_2 at 298 K.

	ΔH_f°, kJ mol^{-1}	ΔG_f°, kJ mol^{-1}	S°, J mol^{-1} K^{-1}
HgI_2(red)	−105.4	−101.7	180
HgI_2(yellow)	−102.9	(?)	(?)

Estimate values for the two missing entries. To do this, assume that for the transition $HgI_2(red) \longrightarrow HgI_2(yellow)$, the values of ΔH° and ΔS° at 25 °C have the same values that they do at the equilibrium temperature of 127 °C.

77. Oxides of nitrogen are produced in high-temperature combustion processes. The essential reaction is $N_2(g) + O_2(g) \rightleftharpoons 2\,NO(g)$. At what approximate temperature will an *equimolar* mixture of $N_2(g)$ and $O_2(g)$ be 1.0% converted to NO(g)? [*Hint:* Use data from Appendix A as necessary.]

78. Use the following data, as appropriate, to estimate the molarity of a saturated aqueous solution of $Sr(IO_3)_2$.

	ΔH_f°, kJ mol^{-1}	ΔG_f°, kJ mol^{-1}	S°, J mol^{-1} K^{-1}
$Sr(IO_3)_2(s)$	−1019.2	−855.1	234
$Sr^{2+}(aq)$	−545.8	−599.5	−32.6
$IO_3^-(aq)$	−221.3	−128.0	118.4

79. Use the following data together with other data from the text to determine the temperature at which the equilibrium pressure of water vapor above the two solids in the following reaction is 75 Torr.

$$CuSO_4 \cdot 3\,H_2O(s) \rightleftharpoons CuSO_4 \cdot H_2O(s) + 2\,H_2O(g)$$

	ΔH_f°, kJ mol^{-1}	ΔG_f°, kJ mol^{-1}	S°, J mol^{-1} K^{-1}
$CuSO_4 \cdot 3\,H_2O(s)$	−1684.3	−1400.0	221.3
$CuSO_4 \cdot H_2O(s)$	−1085.8	−918.1	146.0

80. For the dissociation of $CaCO_3(s)$ at 25 °C, $CaCO_3(s) \rightleftharpoons CaO(s) + CO_2(g)$ $\Delta G^\circ = +131$ kJ mol^{-1}. A sample of pure $CaCO_3(s)$ is placed in a flask and connected to an ultrahigh vacuum system capable of reducing the pressure to 10^{-9} mmHg.
(a) Would $CO_2(g)$ produced by the decomposition of $CaCO_3(s)$ at 25 °C be detectable in the vacuum system at 25 °C?
(b) What additional information do you need to determine P_{CO_2} as a function of temperature?
(c) With necessary data from Appendix A, determine the minimum temperature to which $CaCO_3(s)$ would have to be heated for $CO_2(g)$ to become detectable in the vacuum system.

81. Introduced into a 1.50 L flask is 0.100 mol of $PCl_5(g)$; the flask is held at a temperature of 227 °C until equilibrium is established. What is the total pressure of the gases in the flask at this point?

$$PCl_5(g) \rightleftharpoons PCl_3(g) + Cl_2(g)$$

[*Hint:* Use data from Appendix A and appropriate relationships from this chapter.]

82. From the data given in Exercise 66, estimate a value of ΔS° at 298 K for the reaction

$$2\,NaHCO_3(s) \longrightarrow Na_2CO_3(s) + H_2O(g) + CO_2(g)$$

83. The normal boiling point of cyclohexane, C_6H_{12}, is 80.7 °C. Estimate the temperature at which the vapor pressure of cyclohexane is 100.0 mmHg.

84. The term *thermodynamic stability* refers to the sign of ΔG_f°. If ΔG_f° is negative, the compound is stable with respect to decomposition into its elements. Use the data in Appendix A to determine whether $Ag_2O(s)$ is thermodynamically stable at **(a)** 25 °C and **(b)** 200 °C.

85. At 0 °C, ice has a density of 0.917 g mL^{-1} and an absolute entropy of 37.95 J mol^{-1} K^{-1}. At this temperature, liquid water has a density of 1.000 g mL^{-1} and an absolute entropy of 59.94 J mol^{-1} K^{-1}. The pressure corresponding to these values is 1 bar. Calculate ΔG, ΔG°, ΔS°, and ΔH° for the melting of two moles of ice at its normal melting point.

86. The decomposition of the poisonous gas phosgene is represented by the equation $COCl_2(g) \rightleftharpoons CO(g) + Cl_2(g)$. Values of K_p for this reaction are $K_p = 6.7 \times 10^{-9}$ at 99.8 °C and $K_p = 4.44 \times 10^{-2}$ at 395 °C. At what temperature is $COCl_2$ 15% dissociated when the total gas pressure is maintained at 1.00 atm?

87. Use data from Appendix A to estimate the aqueous solubility, in milligrams per liter, of AgBr(s) at 100 °C.

88. The standard molar entropy of solid hydrazine at its melting point of 1.53 °C is 67.15 J mol^{-1} K^{-1}. The enthalpy of fusion is 12.66 kJ mol^{-1}. For $N_2H_4(l)$ in the interval from 1.53 °C to 298.15 K, the molar heat capacity at constant pressure is given by the expression $C_p = 97.78 + 0.0586(T - 280)$. Determine the standard molar entropy of $N_2H_4(l)$ at 298.15 K. [*Hint:* The heat absorbed to produce an infinitesimal change in the temperature of a substance is $dq_{rev} = C_p\,dT$.]

89. Use the following data to estimate the standard molar entropy of gaseous benzene at 298.15 K; that is, $S^\circ[C_6H_6(g, 1\text{ atm})]$. For C_6H_6 (s, 1 atm) at its melting point of 5.53 °C, S° is 128.82 J mol^{-1} K^{-1}. The enthalpy of fusion is 9.866 kJ mol^{-1}. From the melting point to 298.15 K, the average heat capacity of liquid benzene is 134.0 J K^{-1} mol^{-1}. The enthalpy of vaporization of $C_6H_6(l)$ at 298.15 K is 33.85 kJ mol^{-1}, and in the vaporization, $C_6H_6(g)$ is produced at a pressure of 95.13 Torr. Imagine that this vapor could be compressed to 1 atm pressure without condensing and while behaving as an ideal gas. Calculate $S^\circ[C_6H_6(g, 1\text{ atm})]$. [*Hint:* Refer to Exercise 88, and note the following: For infinitesimal quantities, $dS = dq/dT$; for the compression of an ideal gas, $dq = -dw$; and for pressure–volume work, $dw = -P\,dV$.]

90. On page 170 the terms *states* and *microstates* were introduced. Consider a system that has four states (i.e., energy levels), with energy $\varepsilon = 0, 1, 2,$ and 3 energy units, and three particles labeled A, B, and C. The total energy of the system, in energy units, is 3. How many microstates can be generated?

91. In Figure 5-7, page 178, the temperature dependence of the standard molar entropy for chloroform is plotted. **(a)** Explain why the slope for the standard molar entropy of the solid is greater than the slope for the standard molar entropy of the liquid, which is greater than the slope for the standard molar entropy of the gas. **(b)** Explain why the change in the standard molar entropy from solid to liquid is smaller than that for the liquid to gas.

92. The following data are from a laboratory experiment that examines the relationship between solubility and thermodynamics. In this experiment $KNO_3(s)$ is placed in a test tube containing some water. The solution is heated until all the $KNO_3(s)$ is dissolved and then allowed to cool. The temperature at which crystals appear is then measured. From this experiment we can determine the equilibrium constant, Gibbs energy, enthalpy, and entropy for the reaction. Use the following data to calculate ΔG, ΔH, and ΔS for the dissolution of $KNO_3(s)$. (Assume the initial mass of $KNO_3(s)$ was 20.2 g.)

Total Volume, mL	Temperature Crystals Formed, K
25.0	340
29.2	329
33.4	320
37.6	313
41.8	310
46.0	306
51.0	303

Data reported by J. O. Schreck, *J. Chem. Educ.*, **73**, 426 (1996).

Feature Problems

93. A tabulation of more precise thermodynamic data than are presented in Appendix A lists the following values for $H_2O(l)$ and $H_2O(g)$ at 298.15 K, at a standard state pressure of 1 bar.

	ΔH_f°, kJ mol^{-1}	ΔG_f°, kJ mol^{-1}	S°, J mol^{-1} K^{-1}
$H_2O(l)$	−285.830	−237.129	69.91
$H_2O(g)$	−241.818	−228.572	188.825

(a) Use these data to determine, in two different ways, ΔG° at 298.15 K for the vaporization: $H_2O\,(l, 1\text{ bar}) \rightleftharpoons H_2O(g, 1\text{ bar})$. The value you obtain will differ slightly from that on page 186, because here, the standard state pressure is 1 bar, and there, it is 1 atm.
(b) Use the result of part (a) to obtain the value of K for this vaporization and, hence, the vapor pressure of water at 298.15 K.
(c) The vapor pressure in part (b) is in the unit bar. Convert the pressure to millimeters of mercury.
(d) Start with the value $\Delta G^\circ = 8.590$ kJ, given on page 186 and calculate the vapor pressure of water at 298.15 K in a fashion similar to that in parts (b) and (c). In this way, demonstrate that the results obtained in a thermodynamic calculation do not depend on the convention we choose for the standard state pressure, as long as we use standard state thermodynamic data consistent with that choice.

94. The graph shows how ΔG° varies with temperature for three different oxidation reactions: the oxidations of C(graphite), Zn, and Mg to CO, ZnO, and MgO, respectively. Such graphs as these can be used to show the temperatures at which carbon is an effective reducing agent to reduce metal oxides to the free metals. As a result, such graphs are important to metallurgists. Use these graphs to answer the following questions.
(a) Why can Mg be used to reduce ZnO to Zn at all temperatures, but Zn cannot be used to reduce MgO to Mg at any temperature?
(b) Why can C be used to reduce ZnO to Zn at some temperatures but not at others? At what temperatures can carbon be used to reduce zinc oxide?
(c) Is it possible to produce Zn from ZnO by its direct decomposition without requiring a coupled reaction? If so, at what approximate temperatures might this occur?
(d) Is it possible to decompose CO to C and O_2 in a spontaneous reaction? Explain.

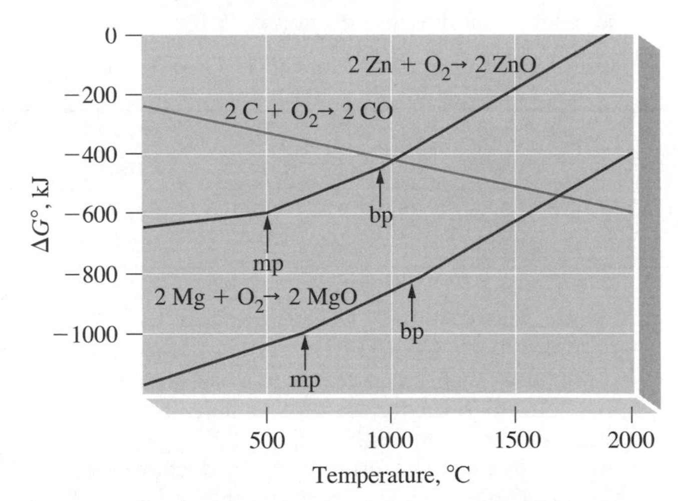

▲ ΔG° for three reactions as a function of temperature. The reactions are indicated by the equations written above the graphs. The points noted by arrows are the melting points (mp) and boiling points (bp) of zinc and magnesium.

(e) To the set of graphs, add straight lines representing the reactions

$$C(\text{graphite}) + O_2(g) \longrightarrow CO_2(g)$$
$$2\,CO(g) + O_2(g) \longrightarrow 2\,CO_2(g)$$

given that the three lines representing the formation of oxides of carbon intersect at about 800 °C. [*Hint:* At what other temperature can you relate ΔG° and temperature?]

The slopes of the three lines described above differ sharply. Explain why this is so—that is, explain the slope of each line in terms of principles governing Gibbs energy change.

(f) The graphs for the formation of oxides of other metals are similar to the ones shown for Zn and Mg; that is, they all have positive slopes. Explain why carbon is such a good reducing agent for the reduction of metal oxides.

95. In a heat engine, heat (q_h) is absorbed by a working substance (such as water) at a high temperature (T_h). Part of this heat is converted to work (w), and the rest (q_l) is released to the surroundings at the lower temperature (T_l). The *efficiency* of a heat engine is the ratio w/q_h. The second law of thermodynamics establishes the following equation for the maximum efficiency of a heat engine, expressed on a percentage basis.

$$\text{efficiency} = \frac{w}{q_h} \times 100\% = \frac{T_h - T_l}{T_h} \times 100\%$$

In a particular electric power plant, the steam leaving a steam turbine is condensed to liquid water at 41 °C(T_l) and the water is returned to the boiler to be regenerated as steam. If the system operates at 36% efficiency,

(a) What is the minimum temperature of the steam [$H_2O(g)$] used in the plant?

(b) Why is the actual steam temperature probably higher than that calculated in part (a)?

(c) Assume that at T_h the $H_2O(g)$ is in equilibrium with $H_2O(l)$. Estimate the steam pressure at the temperature calculated in part (a).

(d) Is it possible to devise a heat engine with greater than 100 percent efficiency? With 100 percent efficiency? Explain.

96. The Gibbs energy available from the complete combustion of 1 mol of glucose to carbon dioxide and water is

$$C_6H_{12}O_6(aq) + 6\,O_2(g) \longrightarrow 6\,CO_2(g) + 6\,H_2O(l) \qquad \Delta G° = -2870\ \text{kJ mol}^{-1}$$

(a) Under biological standard conditions, compute the maximum number of moles of ATP that could form from ADP and phosphate if all the energy of combustion of 1 mol of glucose could be utilized.

(b) The actual number of moles of ATP formed by a cell under aerobic conditions (that is, in the presence of oxygen) is about 38. Calculate the efficiency of energy conversion of the cell.

(c) Consider these typical physiological conditions.

$$P_{CO_2} = 0.050\ \text{bar};\ P_{O_2} = 0.132\ \text{bar};$$
$$[\text{glucose}] = 1.0\ \text{mg/mL};\ \text{pH} = 7.0;$$
$$[\text{ATP}] = [\text{ADP}] = [P_i] = 0.00010\ \text{M}.$$

Calculate ΔG for the conversion of 1 mol ADP to ATP and ΔG for the oxidation of 1 mol glucose under these conditions.

(d) Calculate the efficiency of energy conversion for the cell under the conditions given in part (c). Compare this efficiency with that of a diesel engine that attains 78% of the theoretical efficiency operating with $T_h = 1923$ K and $T_l = 873$ K. Suggest a reason for your result. [*Hint:* See Feature Problem 95.]

97. The entropy of materials at $T = 0$ K should be zero; however, for some substances, such as CO and H_2O, this is not true. The difference between the measured value and expected value of zero is known as residual entropy. **(a)** Calculate the residual entropy for one mole of CO by using the Boltzmann equation for entropy. **(b)** Calculate the residual entropy for one mole of H_2O in the same manner.

Self-Assessment Exercises

98. In your own words, define the following symbols: **(a)** ΔS_{univ}; **(b)** ΔG_f°; **(c)** K.

99. Briefly describe each of the following ideas, methods, or phenomena: **(a)** absolute molar entropy; **(b)** coupled reactions; **(c)** Trouton's rule; **(d)** evaluation of an equilibrium constant from tabulated thermodynamic data.

100. Explain the important distinctions between each of the following pairs: **(a)** spontaneous and nonspontaneous processes; **(b)** the second and third laws of thermodynamics; **(c)** ΔG and $\Delta G°$.

101. For a process to occur spontaneously, **(a)** the entropy of the system must increase; **(b)** the entropy of the surroundings must increase; **(c)** both the entropy of the system and the entropy of the surroundings must increase; **(d)** the net change in entropy of the system and surroundings considered together must be a positive quantity; **(e)** the entropy of the universe must remain constant.

102. The Gibbs energy change of a reaction can be used to assess **(a)** how much heat is absorbed from the surroundings; **(b)** how much work the system does on the surroundings; **(c)** the net direction in which the reaction occurs to reach equilibrium; **(d)** the proportion of the heat evolved in an exothermic reaction that can be converted to various forms of work.

103. The reaction, $2\,Cl_2O(g) \longrightarrow 2\,Cl_2(g) + O_2(g)$ $\Delta H = -161$ kJ, is expected to be **(a)** spontaneous at all temperatures; **(b)** spontaneous at low temperatures, but nonspontaneous at high temperatures; **(c)** nonspontaneous at all temperatures; **(d)** spontaneous at high temperatures only.

104. If $\Delta G° = 0$ for a reaction, it must also be true that **(a)** $K = 0$; **(b)** $K = 1$; **(c)** $\Delta H° = 0$; **(d)** $\Delta S° = 0$; **(e)** the equilibrium activities of the reactants and products do not depend on the initial conditions.

105. Two correct statements about the reversible reaction $N_2(g) + O_2(g) \rightleftharpoons 2\,NO(g)$ are **(a)** $K = K_p$; **(b)** the equilibrium amount of NO increases with an increased total gas pressure; **(c)** the equilibrium amount of NO increases if an equilibrium mixture is transferred from a 10.0 L container to a 20.0 L container; **(d)** $K = K_c$; **(e)** the composition of an equilibrium mixture of the gases is independent of the temperature.

106. Suppose a graph similar to (Figure 5-9) were drawn for the process $I_2(s) \longrightarrow I_2(l)$ at 1 atm.
(a) Refer to Figure 3-27 and determine the temperature at which the two lines would intersect.
(b) What would be the value of $\Delta G°$ at this temperature? Explain.

107. *Without performing detailed calculations,* indicate whether any of the following reactions would occur to a measurable extent at 298 K.
(a) Conversion of dioxygen to ozone:
$$3\,O_2(g) \longrightarrow 2\,O_3(g)$$
(b) Dissociation of N_2O_4 to NO_2:
$$N_2O_4(g) \longrightarrow 2\,NO_2(g)$$
(c) Formation of BrCl:
$$Br_2(l) + Cl_2(g) \longrightarrow 2\,BrCl(g)$$

108. Explain briefly why
(a) the change in entropy in a system is not always a suitable criterion for spontaneous change;
(b) $\Delta G°$ is so important in dealing with the question of spontaneous change, even though the conditions employed in a reaction are very often nonstandard.

109. A handbook lists the following standard enthalpies of formation at 298 K for cyclopentane, C_5H_{10}: $\Delta H_f°[C_5H_{10}(l)] = -105.9$ kJ/mol and $\Delta H_f°[C_5H_{10}(g)] = -77.2$ kJ/mol.
(a) Estimate the normal boiling point of cyclopentane.
(b) Estimate $\Delta G°$ for the vaporization of cyclopentane at 298 K.
(c) Comment on the significance of the sign of $\Delta G°$ at 298 K.

110. Consider the reaction $NH_4NO_3(s) \longrightarrow N_2O(g) + 2\,H_2O(l)$ at 298 K.
(a) Is the forward reaction endothermic or exothermic?
(b) What is the value of $\Delta G°$ at 298 K?
(c) What is the value of K at 298 K?
(d) Does the reaction tend to occur spontaneously at temperatures above 298 K, below 298 K, both, or neither?

111. Which of the following diagrams represents an equilibrium constant closest to 1?

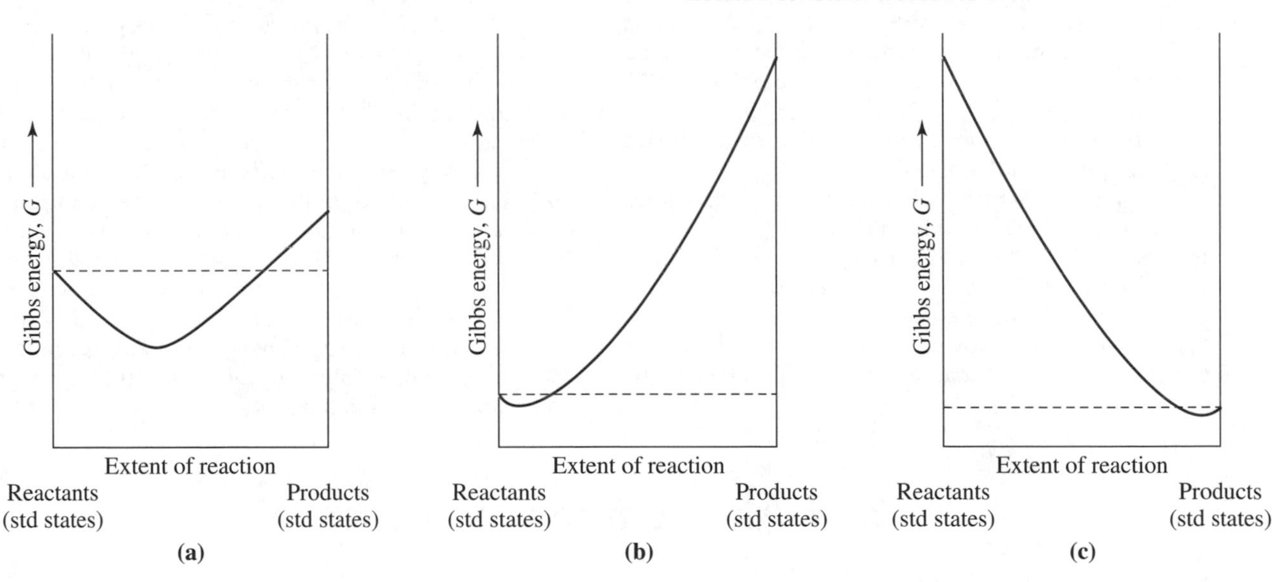

112. At room temperature and normal atmospheric pressure, is the entropy of the universe positive, negative, or zero for the transition of carbon dioxide solid to liquid?

Principles of Chemical Equilibrium

6

A vital natural reaction is in progress in the lightning bolt seen here: $N_2(g) + O_2(g) \rightleftharpoons 2NO(g)$. Usually this reversible reaction does not occur to any significant extent in the forward direction, but in the high-temperature lightning bolt it does. At equilibrium at high temperatures, measurable conversion of $N_2(g)$ and $O_2(g)$ to $NO(g)$ occurs. In this chapter we study the equilibrium condition in a reversible reaction and the factors affecting it.

CONTENTS

Until now, we have stressed reactions that go to completion and the concepts of stoichiometry that allow us to calculate the outcomes of such reactions. We have made occasional references to situations involving both a forward and a reverse reaction—*reversible reactions*—but in this chapter, we will look at them in a detailed and systematic way.

Our emphasis will be on the equilibrium condition reached when forward and reverse reactions proceed at the same rate. Our main tool in dealing with equilibrium will be the equilibrium constant. We will begin with some key relationships involving equilibrium constants; then we will make qualitative predictions about the condition of equilibrium; and finally we will do various equilibrium calculations. As we will discover throughout the remainder of the text, the equilibrium condition plays a role in numerous natural phenomena and affects the methods used to produce many important industrial chemicals.

6-1 Dynamic Equilibrium

Let's begin by describing three simple physical and one chemical phenomena that will help us to establish the core attribute of a system at **equilibrium**—two opposing processes take place at equal rates.

1. When a liquid vaporizes within a closed container, after a time, vapor molecules condense to the liquid state at the same rate at which liquid molecules vaporize. Even though molecules continue to pass back and forth between liquid and vapor (a *dynamic* process), the pressure exerted by the vapor remains constant with time. *The vapor pressure of a liquid is a property resulting from an equilibrium condition.*
2. When a solute is added to a solvent, the system may reach a point at which the rate of dissolution is just matched by the rate at which dissolved solute crystallizes—that is, the solution is saturated. Even though solute particles continue to pass back and forth between the saturated solution and the undissolved solute, the concentration of dissolved solute remains constant. *The solubility of a solute is a property resulting from an equilibrium condition.*
3. When an aqueous solution of iodine, I_2, is shaken with pure carbon tetrachloride, $CCl_4(l)$, the I_2 molecules move into the CCl_4 layer. As the concentration of I_2 builds up in the CCl_4, the rate of return of I_2 to the water layer becomes significant. When I_2 molecules pass between the two liquids at equal rates—a condition of dynamic equilibrium—the concentration of I_2 in each layer remains constant. At this point, the concentration of I_2 in the CCl_4 is about 85 times as great as in the H_2O (Fig. 6-1). The ratio of concentrations of a solute in two immiscible solvents is called the distribution coefficient. *The distribution coefficient, which represents the partitioning of a solute between two immiscible solvents, is a property resulting from an equilibrium condition.*
4. When gaseous phosphorus pentachloride is heated, it decomposes to phosphorus trichloride and chlorine gases: $PCl_5(g) \longrightarrow PCl_3(g) + Cl_2(g)$. Consider a sample of $PCl_5(g)$ initially exerting a pressure of 1.0 atm in a closed container at 250 °C. The gas pressure in the container first rises rapidly and then ever more slowly, reaching a maximum, unchanging pressure of 1.7 atm. Because two moles of gas are produced for each mole of $PCl_5(g)$ that decomposes, if the reaction went to completion the final pressure would have been 2.0 atm. We conclude that *the decomposition of PCl_5 is a reversible reaction that reaches an equilibrium condition.*

▲ FIGURE 6-1
Dynamic equilibrium in a physical process
(a) A yellow-brown saturated solution of I_2 in water (top layer) is brought into contact with colorless $CCl_4(l)$ (bottom layer), **(b)** I_2 molecules distribute themselves between the H_2O and CCl_4. When equilibrium is reached, $[I_2]$ in the CCl_4 (violet, bottom layer) is about 85 times as great as in the water (colorless, top layer).

The properties in the first three situations just described—vapor pressure, solubility, and distribution coefficient—are examples of physical equilibria. The fourth situation is an example of chemical equilibrium. All four are described through a general quantity known as an *equilibrium constant*, the subject of the next section.

6-1 CONCEPT ASSESSMENT

For each chemical equation state whether it represents physical or chemical equilibrium: **(a)** $CaCO_3(s) \rightleftharpoons Ca^{2+}(aq) + CO_3{}^{2-}(aq)$; **(b)** $I_2(s) \rightleftharpoons I_2(g)$; **(c)** $Fe(s) + 4H_2O(l) \rightleftharpoons Fe_3O_4(s) + 4H_2(g)$.

6-2 The Equilibrium Constant Expression

The oxidation–reduction reaction of copper(II) and tin(II) in aqueous solution is a reversible reaction, which means that at the same time as copper(I) and tin(IV) are being formed,

$$2\,Cu^{2+}(aq) + Sn^{2+}(aq) \longrightarrow 2\,Cu^{+}(aq) + Sn^{4+}(aq) \qquad \textbf{(6.1)}$$

copper(I) and tin(IV) ions elsewhere in the solution are being consumed to form copper(II) and tin(II):

$$2\,Cu^{+}(aq) + Sn^{4+}(aq) \longrightarrow 2\,Cu^{2+}(aq) + Sn^{2+}(aq) \qquad \textbf{(6.2)}$$

6-1 ARE YOU WONDERING...

How we know that an equilibrium is dynamic—that forward and reverse reactions continue even after equilibrium is reached?

Suppose we have an equilibrium mixture of AgI(s) and its saturated aqueous solution.

$$AgI(s) \rightleftharpoons Ag^{+}(aq) + I^{-}(aq)$$

Now let's add to this mixture some saturated solution of AgI made from AgI containing radioactive iodine-131 as iodide ion, as illustrated in Figure 6-2. If both the forward and reverse processes stopped at equilibrium, radioactivity would be confined to the solution. What we find, though, is that radioactivity shows up in the solid in contact with the saturated solution. Over time, the radioactive "hot" spots distribute themselves throughout the solution and undissolved solid. The only way this can happen is if the dissolving of the solid solute and its crystallization from the saturated solution continue indefinitely. The equilibrium condition is *dynamic*.

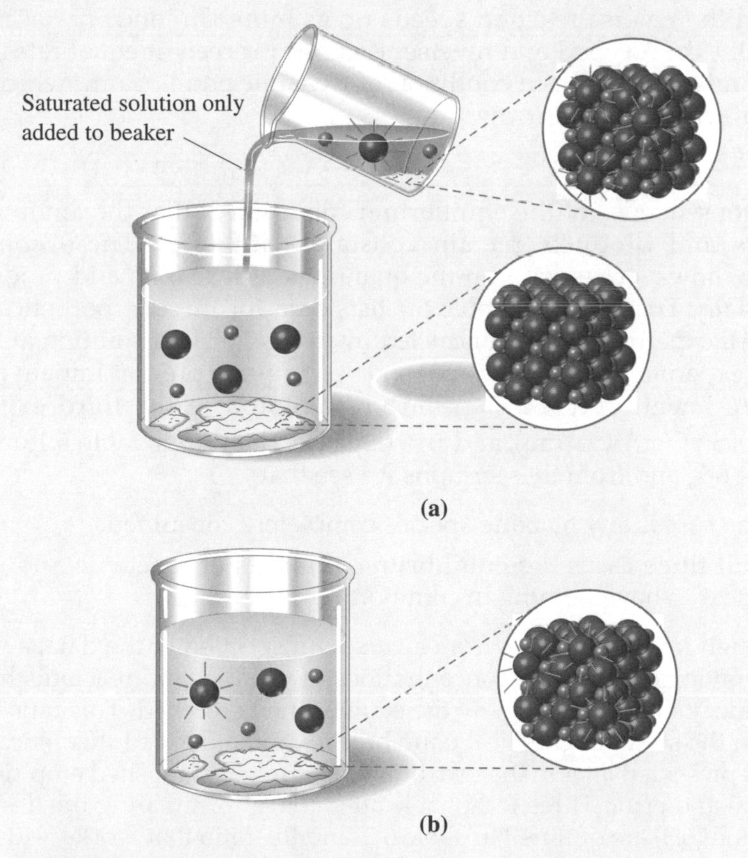

▲ FIGURE 6-2
Dynamic equilibrium illustrated
(a) A saturated solution of radioactive AgI is added to a saturated solution of AgI. **(b)** The radioactive iodide ions distribute themselves throughout the solution and the solid AgI, showing that the equilibrium is dynamic.

▶ The equilibrium state can be obtained by starting with any combination of reactants and products.

TABLE 6.1 Three Approaches to Equilibrium in the Reaction[a] $2\,Cu^{2+}(aq) + Sn^{2+}(aq) \rightleftharpoons 2\,Cu^{+}(aq) + Sn^{4+}(aq)$

	$Cu^{2+}(aq)$	$Sn^{2+}(aq)$	$Cu^{+}(aq)$	$Sn^{4+}(aq)$
Experiment 1				
Initial amounts, mol	0.100	0.100	0.000	0.000
Equilibrium amounts, mol	0.0360	0.0680	0.0640	0.0320
Equilibrium concentrations, mol/L	0.0360	0.0680	0.0640	0.0320
Experiment 2				
Initial amounts, mol	0.000	0.000	0.100	0.100
Equilibrium amounts, mol	0.0567	0.0283	0.0433	0.0717
Equilibrium concentrations, mol/L	0.0567	0.0283	0.0433	0.0717
Experiment 3				
Initial amounts, mol	0.100	0.100	0.100	0.100
Equilibrium amounts, mol	0.0922	0.0961	0.1078	0.1039
Equilibrium concentrations, mol/L	0.0922	0.0961	0.1078	0.1039

The concentrations printed in blue are used in the calculations in Table 6.2.
[a] Reaction carried out in 1.00 L of solution at 298 K.

▶ The rates of reactions (forward and reverse) are affected by the concentration of reactants.

Initially, only the forward reaction (6.1) occurs, but as soon as some Cu^{+} and Sn^{4+} form, the reverse reaction (6.2) begins. With passing time, the forward reaction slows because of the decreasing concentrations of Cu^{2+} and Sn^{2+} and the reverse reaction speeds up as more Cu^{+} and Sn^{4+} accumulate. Eventually, the forward and reverse reactions proceed at equal rates, and the reaction mixture reaches a condition of dynamic equilibrium, which we can represent with a double arrow $\rightleftharpoons$.

$$2\,Cu^{2+}(aq) + Sn^{2+}(aq) \rightleftharpoons 2\,Cu^{+}(aq) + Sn^{4+}(aq) \tag{6.3}$$

One consequence of the equilibrium condition is that the amounts of the reactants and products remain constant with time. These equilibrium amounts, however, depend on the quantities of reactants and products present initially. For example, Table 6.1 lists data for three hypothetical experiments. All experiments are conducted by using 1.00 L of solution at 298 K. In the first experiment, only $Cu^{2+}(aq)$ and $Sn^{2+}(aq)$ are present initially; in a second experiment, only $Cu^{+}(aq)$ and $Sn^{4+}(aq)$; and in the third experiment, $Cu^{2+}(aq)$, $Sn^{2+}(aq)$, $Cu^{+}(aq)$, and $Sn^{4+}(aq)$. The data from Table 6.1 are plotted in Figure 6-3, and from these graphs we see that

- in no case is any reacting species completely consumed.
- in all three cases the equilibrium amounts of reactants and products appear to have nothing in common.

Although it is not obvious from a cursory inspection of the data, a particular ratio involving equilibrium concentrations of product and reactants has a constant value, independent of how the equilibrium is reached. This ratio, which is central to the study of chemical equilibrium, can be derived theoretically using concepts presented later in the text, but it can also be established empirically, that is, by trial and error. Three reasonable attempts at formulating the desired ratio for reaction (6.3) are outlined in Table 6.2, and the ratio that works is identified.

For the copper–tin oxidation–reduction reaction, the ratio of equilibrium concentrations in the following equation has a constant value of 1.48 at 300 K.

▶ The representation of the equilibrium expression in terms of concentrations is valid only at low concentrations, usually less than a few moles per liter.

$$K = \frac{[Cu^{+}]^2_{eq}[Sn^{4+}]_{eq}}{[Cu^{2+}]^2_{eq}[Sn^{2+}]_{eq}} = 1.48 \tag{6.4}$$

This ratio is called the **equilibrium constant expression** and its numerical value is the **equilibrium constant**.

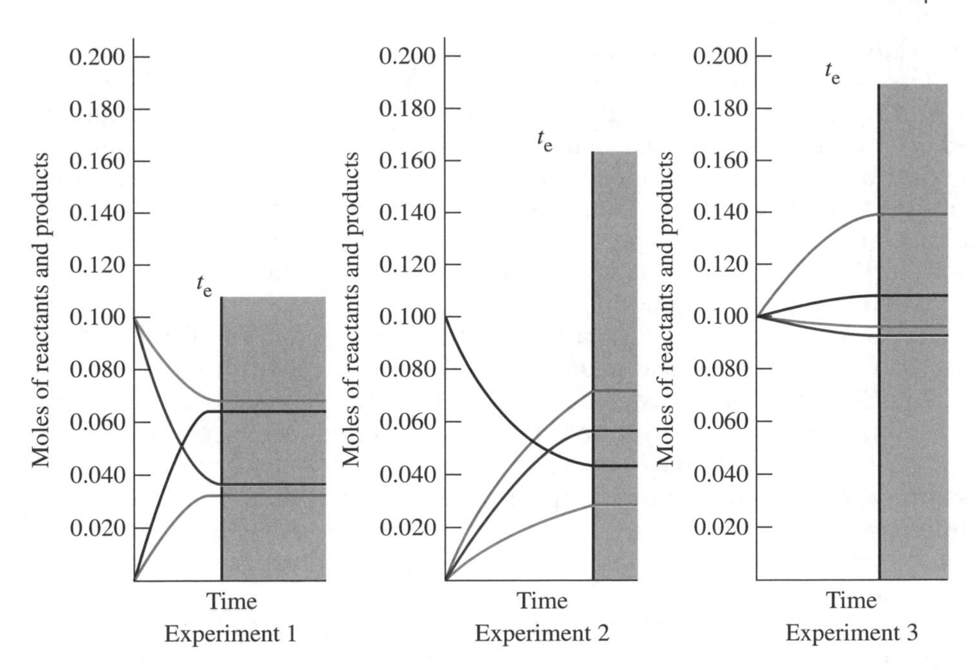

t_e = time for equilibrium to be reached
— mol Cu^{2+}
— mol Sn^{2+}
— mol Cu^{+}
— mol Sn^{4+}

▲ FIGURE 6-3
Three approaches to equilibrium in the reaction

$$2\,Cu^{2+}(aq) + Sn^{2+}(aq) \rightleftharpoons 2\,Cu^{+}(aq) + Sn^{4+}(aq)$$

The initial and equilibrium amounts for each of these three cases are listed in Table 6.1. t_e = time for equilibrium to be reached.

The Equilibrium Constant and Activities

We have discovered that the equilibrium constant expression is written as a ratio of the product concentrations divided by the reactant concentrations. G. N. Lewis* proposed a more appropriate way to represent the equilibrium constant expression that uses the activities of the reactants and products. **Activity** is a thermodynamic concept. Here, we summarize only a few

◀ "Equilibrium" means equal rates of forward and reverse reactions, *not* equal concentrations of reactants and products.

TABLE 6.2

Expt	Trial 1: $\dfrac{[Cu^+][Sn^{4+}]}{[Cu^{2+}][Sn^{2+}]}$	Trial 2: $\dfrac{(2 \times [Cu^+])[Sn^{4+}]}{(2 \times [Cu^{2+}])[Sn^{2+}]}$	Trial 3: $\dfrac{[Cu^+]^2[Sn^{4+}]}{[Cu^{2+}]^2[Sn^{2+}]}$
1	$\dfrac{0.0640 \times 0.0320}{0.0360 \times 0.0680} = 0.837$	$\dfrac{(2 \times 0.0640) \times 0.0320}{(2 \times 0.0360) \times 0.0680} = 0.837$	$\dfrac{0.0640^2 \times 0.0320}{0.0360^2 \times 0.0680} = 1.49$
2	$\dfrac{0.0433 \times 0.0717}{0.0567 \times 0.0283} = 1.93$	$\dfrac{(2 \times 0.0433) \times 0.0717}{(2 \times 0.0567) \times 0.0283} = 1.93$	$\dfrac{0.0433^2 \times 0.0717}{0.0567^2 \times 0.0283} = 1.48$
3	$\dfrac{0.1078 \times 0.1039}{0.0922 \times 0.0961} = 1.26$	$\dfrac{(2 \times 0.1078) \times 0.1039}{(2 \times 0.0922) \times 0.0961} = 1.26$	$\dfrac{0.1078^2 \times 0.1039}{0.0922^2 \times 0.0961} = 1.48$

Equilibrium concentration data are from Table 6.1. In Trial 1, the equilibrium concentration of Cu^+ and Sn^{2+} are placed in the numerator and the equilibrium concentration of Cu^{2+} and Sn^{4+}, in the denominator. In Trial 2, each concentration is multiplied by its stoichiometric coefficient. In Trial 3, each concentration is raised to a power equal to its stoichiometric coefficient. Trial 3 has essentially the same value for each experiment. This value is the equilibrium constant K.

*G. N. Lewis and M. Randall, *Thermodynamics*, McGraw Hill, New York, 1923.

▶Because of interactions between particles, the "effective" or "active" concentration (activity) of a substance is usually different from the stoichiometric concentration. The activity coefficient, γ, takes into account the effect of particle interactions.

important points. For a substance in solution, activity is equal to the dimensionless ratio $\gamma[X]/c°$, where γ is referred to as the *activity coefficient*, $[X]$ represents a particular concentration and $c°$ corresponds to the concentration in a chosen reference state. Our usual choice of reference state for a substance in solution is a concentration of one mole per liter (1 mol L^{-1}). For gases, activity is equal to the dimensionless ratio $\gamma P/P°$, where P is a particular partial pressure and $P°$ is the partial pressure in the reference state; our usual choice of $P°$ is 1 bar (essentially equal to 1 atm). Pure solids and pure liquids are usually assigned activities of 1.

Why base equilibrium constants on activities? Under conditions where gases do not obey the ideal gas law or solutions depart from ideal behavior, equilibrium constant values may vary with total concentration or pressure. This problem is eliminated when activities are used. Activities are "effective" or "active" concentrations. In this text we will generally assume that systems are ideal, and that activities can be replaced by the numerical values of concentrations or partial pressures. Later on in this text we will establish the relationship between equilibrium and thermodynamic quantities.

Let us reconsider expression (6.4), this time by using activities. We will replace equation (6.4) with the following expression:

$$K = \frac{a^2_{Cu^+} a_{Sn^{4+}}}{a^2_{Cu^{2+}} a_{Sn^{2+}}} = 1.48 \qquad \textbf{(6.5)}$$

To establish the relationship between an equilibrium constant expressed in activities and the corresponding one expressed in concentration, we begin by writing the activity of each species, using the [ ] symbol for the equilibrium concentration and $c°$ for the concentration in the reference state.

$$a_{Cu^+} = \frac{\gamma_{Cu^+}[Cu^+]}{c°}; \qquad a_{Sn^{4+}} = \frac{\gamma_{Sn^{4+}}[Sn^{4+}]}{c°}$$

$$a_{Cu^{2+}} = \frac{\gamma_{Cu^{2+}}[Cu^{2+}]}{c°}; \qquad a_{Sn^{2+}} = \frac{\gamma_{Sn^{2+}}[Sn^{2+}]}{c°}$$

Then we choose the value $c° = 1\ \text{mol L}^{-1}$, we substitute these relationships into the equilibrium constant expression (6.5), and we have

▶ The activity coefficients for ions will not be equal to 1 because the interactions between the ions are significant, even at low concentrations.

$$K = \frac{\left(\dfrac{\gamma_{Cu^+}[Cu^+]_{eq}}{c°}\right)^2 \dfrac{\gamma_{Sn^{4+}}[Sn^{4+}]_{eq}}{c°}}{\left(\dfrac{\gamma_{Cu^{2+}}[Cu^{2+}]_{eq}}{c°}\right)^2 \dfrac{\gamma_{Sn^{2+}}[Sn^{2+}]_{eq}}{c°}} \approx \frac{[Cu^+]^2_{eq}[Sn^{4+}]_{eq}}{[Cu^{2+}]^2_{eq}[Sn^{2+}]_{eq}} = 1.48 \qquad \textbf{(6.6)}$$

The approximation made in writing expression (6.6) is that the values of all the γ are equal to one. This is equivalent to assuming that the ions behave ideally in solution. Notice that we have arrived at exactly the expression in equation (6.4).

6-2 CONCEPT ASSESSMENT

How would you write the equilibrium constant expression for $Cu(s) + 2\,H^+(aq) \longrightarrow Cu^{+2}(aq) + H_2(g)$? Write this first in terms of activities and then convert to pressures and concentrations.

A General Expression for K

Before proceeding to other matters, let us emphasize that the equilibrium constant expression for the oxidation–reduction reaction of copper(II) and tin(II)

EXAMPLE 6-1 Relating Equilibrium Concentrations of Reactants and Products

These equilibrium concentrations are measured in reaction (6.3) at 300 K: $[Cu^+]_{eq} = 0.148\ M$, $[Sn^{2+}]_{eq} = 0.124\ M$, and $[Sn^{4+}]_{eq} = 0.176\ M$. What is the equilibrium concentration of $Cu^{2+}(aq)$?

Analyze

First, we write the equilibrium constant expression for reaction (6.3) in terms of activities, along with the value of the equilibrium constant. Then, we convert the activities to concentrations and replace the concentrations with the given data.

Solve

Write the equilibrium constant expression.

$$K = \frac{a^2_{Cu^+} a_{Sn^{4+}}}{a^2_{Cu^{2+}} a_{Sn^{2+}}} = 1.48$$

Assume that the reaction conditions are such that the activities can be replaced by their concentration values, allowing concentration units to be canceled, as in expression (6.6).

$$K = \frac{[Cu^+]^2_{eq}[Sn^{4+}]_{eq}}{[Cu^{2+}]^2_{eq}[Sn^{2+}]_{eq}} = 1.48$$

Substitute the known equilibrium concentrations into the equilibrium constant expression.

$$K = \frac{[Cu^+]^2_{eq}[Sn^{4+}]_{eq}}{[Cu^{2+}]^2_{eq}[Sn^{2+}]_{eq}} = \frac{(0.148)^2(0.176)}{[Cu^{2+}]^2_{eq}(0.124)} = 1.48$$

Solve for the unknown concentration, $[Cu^{2+}]$. (An implicit calculation to restore the concentration unit is $[Cu^{2+}] = a_{Cu^{2+}} \times c° = 0.145 \times 1.000\ M = 0.145\ M$.)

$$[Cu^{2+}]^2 = \frac{0.148^2 \times 0.176}{0.124 \times 1.48} = 0.0210$$

$$[Cu^{2+}] = \sqrt{0.0210} = 0.145\ M$$

Assess

When solving equilibrium problems, we should examine the results to ensure they make sense. We can do this easily by placing the solution back into the equilibrium constant expression and calculating the equilibrium constant to see whether it agrees with the value stated in the problem, as shown below.

$$K = \frac{0.148^2 \times 0.176}{0.145^2 \times 0.124} = 1.48$$

PRACTICE EXAMPLE A: In another experiment, equal concentrations of $[Cu^+]$, $[Sn^{4+}]$, and $[Sn^{2+}]$ are found to be in equilibrium in reaction (6.3). What must be the equilibrium concentration of $[Cu^{2+}]$?

PRACTICE EXAMPLE B: At 25 °C, $K = 9.14 \times 10^{-6}$ for the reaction $2\ Fe^{3+}(aq) + Hg_2{}^{2+}(aq) \rightleftharpoons 2\ Fe^{2+}(aq) + 2\ Hg^{2+}(aq)$. If the equilibrium concentrations of Fe^{3+}, and Hg^{2+} are 0.015 M, 0.0025 M and 0.0018 M, Fe^{2+} respectively, what is the equilibrium concentration of $Hg_2{}^{2+}$?

summarized through expression (6.6) is just a specific example of a more general case. For the hypothetical, generalized reaction

$$aA(aq) + bB(aq) \cdots \rightleftharpoons gG(aq) + hH(aq) \cdots$$

The equilibrium constant expression has the form

$$K = \frac{(a_G)^g(a_H)^h \cdots}{(a_A)^a(a_B)^b \cdots} \approx \left(\frac{1}{c°}\right)^{\Delta n} \frac{[G]^g[H]^h \cdots}{[A]^a[B]^b \cdots} = \left(\frac{1}{c°}\right)^{\Delta n} K_c \quad \textbf{(6.7)}$$

where $\Delta n = (g + h + \cdots) - (a + b + \cdots)$ and K_c is an equilibrium constant expression written in terms of concentrations. The factor $(1/c°)^{\Delta n}$ ensures that K is a dimensionless quantity.

The *numerator* of an equilibrium constant expression is the product of the activities of the species on the *right* side of the equation $(a_G, a_H, \ldots)$, with each activity raised to a power given by the stoichiometric coefficient $(g, h, \ldots)$. The *denominator* is the product of the activities of the species on the *left* side of the

◀ In principle, when using equation (6.7), we can express concentrations in any unit. However, the use of a unit other than mol/L will require an "extra" calculation, that is, the calculation of the value of $(1/c°)^{\Delta n}$. When we express concentrations, in mol/L, the factor $(1/c°)^{\Delta n}$ has a numerical value of 1. For this reason, when using equation (6.7), we will express concentrations in mol/L and substitute their values (without units) into the expression to obtain the correct value of K.

6-3 CONCEPT ASSESSMENT

Consider a hypothetical reaction in which one molecule, A, is converted to its isomer, B, that is, the reversible reaction $A \rightleftharpoons B$. Start with a flask containing 54 molecules of A, represented by open circles. Convert the appropriate number of open circles to filled circles to represent the isomer B and portray the equilibrium condition if $K = 0.02$. Repeat the process for $K = 0.5$ and then for $K = 1$.

equation ($a_A, a_B, \dots$), and again, with each activity raised to a power given by the stoichiometric coefficient ($a, b, \dots$). As previously noted, where equilibrium systems are sufficiently close to ideal in their behavior, equilibrium concentrations are acceptable approximations to true activities.

The numerical value of an equilibrium constant, K, depends on the particular reaction and on the temperature. We will explore the significance of these numerical values in Section 6-4.

Relationship Between the Equilibrium Constant and Rate Constants

Given the requirement that the rates of the forward and reverse reactions become equal at equilibrium, it seems that a relationship should exist between the equilibrium constant and the rate constants for the forward and reverse reactions. That such a relationship does exist can be demonstrated easily for elementary reactions. Consider again the hypothetical generalized reaction

$$aA + bB + \cdots \underset{k_{-1}}{\overset{k_1}{\rightleftharpoons}} gG + hH + \cdots$$

k_1 and k_{-1} are the rate constants for the forward and reverse reactions. *With the assumption that both the forward and reverse reactions are elementary reactions*, we can write

$$\text{rate of forward reaction} = k_1[A]^a[B]^b \cdots$$
$$\text{rate of reverse reaction} = k_{-1}[G]^g[H]^h \dots$$

At equilibrium, these two rates become equal; thus,

$$k_1[A]^a[B]^b \cdots = k_{-1}[G]^g[H]^h \cdots$$

which can be rearranged into an expression having rate constants on one side and concentrations on the other:

$$\frac{k_1}{k_{-1}} = \frac{[G]^g[H]^h \cdots}{[A]^a[B]^b \cdots}$$

Because the right side of the equation above is the equilibrium constant expression for the reaction, we arrive at the following result:

$$\frac{k_1}{k_{-1}} = K$$

Keep in mind that this result is based on the assumption that the forward and reverse reactions are elementary reactions. For reactions that involve a multistep mechanism, the relationship between K and the rate constants is more complicated. For a mechanism involving n steps, it can be demonstrated (in the manner described in Exercise 95) that the relationship between K and the rate constants is

$$\frac{k_1}{k_{-1}} \times \frac{k_2}{k_{-2}} \times \cdots \times \frac{k_n}{k_{-n}} = K$$

Although the expression above shows that there is indeed a relationship between the equilibrium constant and rate constants, it is generally easier to obtain K directly from measurements on equilibrium conditions than to attempt a calculation based on rate constants.

6-3 Relationships Involving Equilibrium Constants

Before assessing an equilibrium situation, it may be necessary to make some preliminary calculations or decisions to get the appropriate equilibrium constant expression. This section presents some useful ideas in working with equilibrium constants.

Relationship of K to the Balanced Chemical Equation

We must always make certain that the expression for K matches the corresponding balanced equation. In doing so, the following hold true.

- When we *reverse* an equation, we *invert* the value of K.
- When we *multiply* the coefficients in a balanced equation by a common factor (2, 3, . . .), we raise the equilibrium constant to the *corresponding power* (2, 3, . . .).
- When we *divide* the coefficients in a balanced equation by a common factor (2, 3, . . .), we take the *corresponding root* of the equilibrium constant (square root, cube root, . . .).

To illustrate these points, let us consider the synthesis of methanol (methyl alcohol) from a carbon monoxide–hydrogen mixture called synthesis gas. This reaction is likely to become increasingly important as methanol and its mixtures with gasoline find greater use as motor fuels. The balanced reaction is

$$CO(g) + 2\,H_2(g) \rightleftharpoons CH_3OH(g) \quad K = 9.23 \times 10^{-3}$$

▲ Methanol is actively being considered as an alternative fuel to gasoline.

Suppose that in discussing the synthesis of CH_3OH from CO and H_2, we had written the reverse reaction, that is,

$$CH_3OH(g) \rightleftharpoons CO(g) + 2\,H_2(g) \qquad K' = ?$$

Now, according to the generalized equilibrium constant expression (6.7), we should write

$$K' = \frac{a_{CO}\,a_{H_2}^2}{a_{CH_3OH}} = \frac{1}{\dfrac{a_{CH_3OH}}{a_{CO}\,a_{H_2}^2}} = \frac{1}{K} = \frac{1}{9.23 \times 10^{-3}} = 1.08 \times 10^2$$

In the preceding expression, the equilibrium constant expression and K value for the reaction, as originally written, are printed in blue. We see that $K' = 1/K$.

Suppose that for a certain application we want an equation based on synthesizing *two* moles of $CH_3OH(g)$.

$$2\,CO(g) + 4\,H_2(g) \rightleftharpoons 2\,CH_3OH(g) \qquad K'' = ?$$

Here, $K'' = K^2$. That is,

$$K'' = \frac{a_{CH_3OH}^2}{a_{CO}^2\,a_{H_2}^4} = \left(\frac{a_{CH_3OH}}{a_{CO}\,a_{H_2}^2}\right)^2 = (K)^2 = (9.23 \times 10^{-3})^2 = 8.52 \times 10^{-5}$$

6-4 CONCEPT ASSESSMENT

Can you conclude whether the numerical value of K for the reaction $2\,ICl(g) \rightleftharpoons I_2(g) + Cl_2(g)$ is greater or less than the numerical value of K for the reaction $ICl(g) \rightleftharpoons \frac{1}{2}I_2(g) + \frac{1}{2}Cl_2(g)$? Explain.

EXAMPLE 6-2 Relating *K* to the Balanced Chemical Equation

The following *K* value is given at 298 K for the synthesis of $NH_3(g)$ from its elements.

$$N_2(g) + 3H_2(g) \rightleftharpoons 2NH_3(g) \qquad K = 5.8 \times 10^5$$

What is the value of *K* at 298 K for the following reaction?

$$NH_3(g) \rightleftharpoons \frac{1}{2}N_2(g) + \frac{3}{2}H_2(g) \qquad K = ?$$

Analyze

The solution to this problem lies in recognizing that the reaction is the reverse and one-half of the given reaction. In this example we apply two of the rules given above that relate *K* to balanced chemical reactions.

Solve

First, reverse the given equation. This puts $NH_3(g)$ on the left side of the equation, where we need it.

$$2NH_3(g) \rightleftharpoons N_2(g) + 3H_2(g)$$

The equilibrium constant K' becomes

$$K' = 1/(5.8 \times 10^5) = 1.7 \times 10^{-6}$$

Then, to base the equation on 1 mol $NH_3(g)$, divide all coefficients by 2.

$$NH_3(g) \rightleftharpoons \frac{1}{2}N_2(g) + \frac{3}{2}H_2(g)$$

This requires the square root of K'.

$$K = \sqrt{1.7 \times 10^{-6}} = 1.3 \times 10^{-3}$$

Assess

Because the rules given on page 219 are used extensively throughout this book, memorizing them will be helpful.

PRACTICE EXAMPLE A: Use data from Example 6-2 to determine the value of *K* at 298 K for the reaction

$$\frac{1}{3}N_2(g) + H_2(g) \rightleftharpoons \frac{2}{3}NH_3(g)$$

PRACTICE EXAMPLE B: For the reaction $NO(g) + \frac{1}{2}O_2(g) \rightleftharpoons NO_2(g)$ at 184 °C, $K = 1.2 \times 10^2$. What is the value of *K* at 184 °C for the reaction $2\,NO_2(g) \rightleftharpoons 2\,NO(g) + O_2(g)$?

Combining Equilibrium Constant Expressions

Through Hess's law, we show how to combine a series of equations into a single overall equation. The enthalpy change of the overall reaction was obtained by adding together the enthalpy changes of the individual reactions. A similar procedure can be used with equilibrium constants, but with this important difference:

> When individual equations are combined (that is, added), their equilibrium constants are *multiplied* to obtain the equilibrium constant for the overall reaction.

Suppose we need the equilibrium constant for the reaction

$$N_2O(g) + \frac{1}{2}O_2(g) \rightleftharpoons 2\,NO(g) \qquad K = ? \tag{6.8}$$

and know the *K* values of these two equilibria.

$$N_2(g) + \frac{1}{2}O_2(g) \rightleftharpoons N_2O(g) \qquad K = 5.4 \times 10^{-19} \tag{6.9}$$

$$N_2(g) + O_2(g) \rightleftharpoons 2\,NO(g) \qquad K = 4.6 \times 10^{-31} \tag{6.10}$$

Equation (6.8) is obtained by reversing equation (6.9) and adding it to (6.10). This requires that we also take the *reciprocal* of the *K* value of equation (6.9).

(a) $$N_2O(g) \rightleftharpoons N_2(g) + \frac{1}{2}O_2(g) \qquad K(a) = 1/(5.4 \times 10^{-19}) = 1.9 \times 10^{18}$$

(b) $$N_2(g) + O_2(g) \rightleftharpoons 2\,NO(g) \qquad K(b) = 4.6 \times 10^{-31}$$

Overall: $$N_2O(g) + \frac{1}{2}O_2(g) \rightleftharpoons 2\,NO(g) \qquad K(\text{overall}) = ?$$

The overall equation is expression (6.8), and according to the general expression (6.7),

$$K(\text{overall}) = \frac{a_{NO}^2}{a_{N_2O}\,a_{O_2}^{1/2}} = \underbrace{\frac{a_{N_2}a_{O_2}^{1/2}}{a_{N_2O}}}_{K(a)} \times \underbrace{\frac{a_{NO}^2}{a_{N_2}\,a_{O_2}}}_{K(b)} = K(a) \times K(b)$$

$$= 1.9 \times 10^{18} \times 4.6 \times 10^{-31} = 8.5 \times 10^{-13}$$

6-5 CONCEPT ASSESSMENT

You want to calculate *K* for the reaction

$$CH_4(g) + 2\,H_2O(g) \rightleftharpoons CO_2(g) + 4\,H_2(g)$$

and you have available a *K* value for the reaction

$$CO_2(g) + H_2(g) \rightleftharpoons CO(g) + H_2O(g)$$

What additional *K* value do you need, assuming that all *K* values are at the same temperature?

Equilibria Involving Gases

Mixtures of gases are as much solutions as are mixtures in a liquid solvent. Thus, concentrations in a gaseous mixture can be expressed on a mole-per-liter basis. However, the activity of a gas is not defined in terms of its concentration, but rather, in terms of its partial pressure relative to a reference pressure of $P° = 1$ bar. Let us investigate equilibria involving gases by considering a specific gas-phase reaction.

A key step in the manufacture of sulfuric acid is the following reversible reaction.

◀ The reaction of sulfur dioxide with oxygen gas to form sulfur trioxide is a reaction that takes place in the atmosphere. This results in the formation of sulfuric acid, which contributes to acid rain.

$$2\,SO_2(g) + O_2(g) \rightleftharpoons 2\,SO_3(g) \tag{6.11}$$

Since all the reaction species are in the gas phase it seems reasonable to use a partial-pressure reference state. We begin by writing the equilibrium constant expression in terms of activities

$$K = \left(\frac{(a_{SO_3})^2}{(a_{SO_2})^2 a_{O_2}}\right)_{eq} \tag{6.12}$$

where the activities are

$$a_{SO_2} = \frac{\gamma_{SO_2} P_{SO_2}}{P°_{SO_2}}; \qquad a_{O_2} = \frac{\gamma_{O_2} P_{O_2}}{P°_{O_2}}; \qquad a_{SO_3} = \frac{\gamma_{SO_3} P_{SO_3}}{P°_{SO_3}}$$

The reference-state partial pressure is $P° = 1$ bar, which we will take to be essentially the same as 1 atm. Substituting these relationships into equation (6.12) and setting all the γ values equal to 1, we obtain

$$K = \left(\frac{\left(\frac{P_{SO_3}}{P^\circ}\right)^2}{\left(\frac{P_{SO_2}}{P^\circ}\right)^2 \frac{P_{O_2}}{P^\circ}} \right)_{eq} = P^\circ \left(\frac{(P_{SO_3})^2}{(P_{SO_2})^2 P_{O_2}} \right)_{eq} = P^\circ \times K_p \quad (6.13)$$

As always, the equilibrium constant, K, is dimensionless. The quantity multiplying P° on the right hand side of equation (6.13) is an equilibrium constant expressions written in terms of partial pressures; it is given the symbol K_p:

$$K_p = \left(\frac{(P_{SO_3})^2}{(P_{SO_2})^2 P_{O_2}} \right)_{eq}$$

To establish the equilibrium constant based on concentrations, we first use the ideal gas law, $PV = nRT$, to relate gas concentrations and partial pressures,

$$[SO_2] = \frac{n}{V} = \frac{P_{SO_2}}{RT}; \qquad [O_2] = \frac{n}{V} = \frac{P_{O_2}}{RT}; \qquad [SO_3] = \frac{n}{V} = \frac{P_{SO_3}}{RT}$$

and then substitute into the expression for K_p. We obtain

$$K_p = \left(\frac{(P_{SO_3})^2}{(P_{SO_2})^2 P_{O_2}} \right)_{eq} = \left(\frac{([SO_3]RT)^2}{([SO_2]RT)^2 [O_2]RT} \right)_{eq} = \frac{1}{RT} \left(\frac{[SO_3]^2}{[SO_2]^2[O_2]} \right)_{eq} \quad (6.14)$$

The final parenthetical factor in equation (6.14) is given the symbol K_c, where the subscript "c" emphasizes that this equilibrium constant expression is written in terms of concentrations. Equation (6.14) makes it clear that, in general, K_p and K_c have different values. This result is not wrong. It stems from the fact that for gases, we can choose to express the equilibrium constants in terms of either pressures or concentrations.

Thus, the relationship between K_p and K_c for reaction (6.11) is

$$K_p = K_c(RT)^{-1}$$

If we carried out a similar derivation for the general reaction,

$$aA(g) + bB(g) + \cdots \rightleftharpoons gG(g) + hH(g) + \cdots$$

the results would be

$$K = \frac{(a_G)^g (a_H)^h \cdots}{(a_A)^a (a_B)^b \cdots} \approx \left(\frac{1}{P^\circ}\right)^{\Delta n} \frac{P_G^g P_H^h \cdots}{P_A^a P_B^b \cdots} = \left(\frac{1}{P^\circ}\right)^{\Delta n} K_p \quad (6.15)$$

and

$$K_p = K_c(RT)^{\Delta n_{gas}} \quad (6.16)$$

where Δn_{gas} is the difference in the stoichiometric coefficients of *gaseous* products and reactants; that is, $\Delta n_{gas} = (g + h + \cdots) - (a + b + \cdots)$. In reaction (6.11), $\Delta n_{gas} = 2 - (2 + 1) = -1$, and thus, $K_p = K_c(RT)^{-1}$, as we established previously. It is important to note that, when applying equation (6.16), we must use $R = 0.08314472$ bar L K^{-1} mol^{-1}. This value of R is required because, as discussed previously, partial pressures are to be expressed in bar and concentrations in mol/L.

KEEP IN MIND

that $K_p = K_c$ only if $\Delta n_{gas} = 0$. That is, $K_p = K_c(RT)^0 = K_c$ because any number raised to the zero power equals one.

Let us address another very important fact concerning the equilibrium constants we have encountered. The equilibrium constant K, expressed in terms of activities, is a dimensionless quantity. Unlike K, the equilibrium constants K_p and K_c have units of (bar)$^{\Delta n}$ and (mol/L)$^{\Delta n}$, respectively. The factors $(1/c^\circ)^{\Delta n}$ and $(1/P^\circ)^{\Delta n}$ appearing in equations (6.7) and (6.15) ensure that K is a dimensionless quantity. Throughout this text, we will use K_p and K_c expressions in solving problems. To avoid the clutter of units in these calculations, and to simplify the

EXAMPLE 6-3 Illustrating the Dependence of *K* on the Reference State

Complete the calculation of K_p for reaction (6.11) knowing that $K_c = 2.8 \times 10^2$ (at 1000 K).

Analyze

We use equation (6.16), with $R = 0.08314$ bar L K^{-1} mol^{-1}. For reasons outlined on page 222, units are omitted from our calculations.

Solve

Write the equation relating the two equilibrium constants with different reference states.

$$K_c = RT \times K_p$$

Rearrange the expression to obtain the quantity desired, K_p.

$$K_p = \frac{K_c}{RT}$$

Substitute the given data and solve.

$$K_p = \frac{2.8 \times 10^2}{0.08314 \times 1000} = 3.4$$

Assess

In this example the equilibrium constant depends on the reference state used. When working this type of problem, keep in mind that Δn is equal to the sum of coefficients of products in the gas phase minus the sum of coefficients of reactants in the gas phase. That is, for the purposes of converting a K_p value to K_c value (or vice versa), Δn is obtained from the coefficients in the chemical equation, not from the actual amounts of gases present in an equilibrium mixture.

PRACTICE EXAMPLE A: For the reaction $2\,NH_3(g) \rightleftharpoons N_2(g) + 3\,H_2(g)$ at 298 K, $K_c = 2.8 \times 10^{-9}$. What is the value of K_p for this reaction?

PRACTICE EXAMPLE B: At 1065 °C, for the reaction $2\,H_2S(g) \rightleftharpoons 2\,H_2(g) + S_2(g)$, $K_p = 1.2 \times 10^{-2}$. What is the value of K_c for the reaction $H_2(g) + \frac{1}{2}S_2(g) \rightleftharpoons H_2S(g)$ at 1065 °C?

conversion of a K_c or K_p value to a K value, we will always use the numerical values of partial pressures or concentrations in the expressions without including the units bar or mol/L explicitly.

Equilibria Involving Pure Liquids and Solids

Up to this point in the chapter, all our examples have involved gas phase reactions or reactions occurring in aqueous solutions. Gas-phase reactions and reactions in aqueous solution are *homogeneous* reactions: They occur within a single phase. Let's extend our coverage now to include reactions involving one or more condensed phases—solids and liquids—in contact with a gas or solution phase. These are called *heterogeneous* reactions. One of the most important ideas about heterogeneous reactions is that

> Equilibrium constant expressions *do not* contain concentration terms for solid or liquid phases of a single component (that is, for pure solids and liquids).

◀ Still another way to think about solids and liquids is through their densities. Density, the mass per unit volume of a substance, can be expressed in moles per liter by converting the unit volume from milliliter to liter and dividing the mass in grams by the molar mass. The resultant molar density (mol/L) is a concentration term and, at a fixed temperature, is a constant that would be incorporated in the K_c value.

We can think about this statement in either of two ways: (1) An equilibrium constant expression includes terms only for reactants and products whose concentrations and/or partial pressures *can change* during a chemical reaction. The concentration of the single component within a pure solid or liquid phase *cannot change*. (2) Alternatively, recall that the activities of pure liquids and solids are set equal to 1; thus the effect on the numerical value of the equilibrium constant is the same as not including terms for pure solids and liquids at all.

The water–gas reaction, used to make combustible gases from coal, has reacting species in both gaseous and solid phases.

$$C(s) + H_2O(g) \rightleftharpoons CO(g) + H_2(g)$$

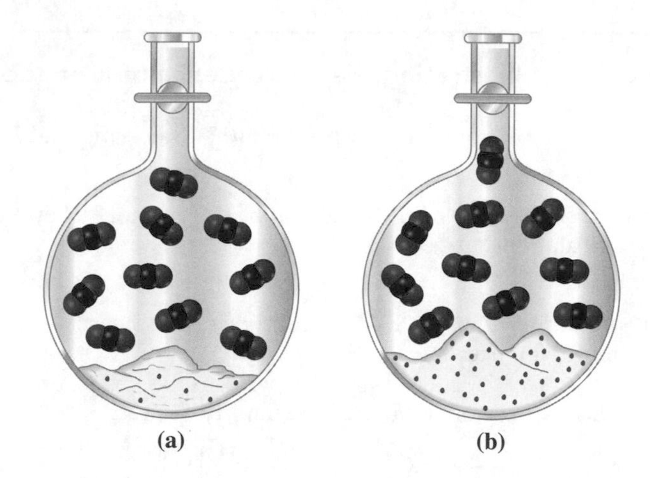

▶ FIGURE 6-4
Equilibrium in the reaction
$CaCO_3(s) \rightleftharpoons CaO(s) + CO_2(g)$
(a) Decomposition of $CaCO_3(s)$ upon heating in a closed vessel yields a few granules CaO(s), together with $CO_2(g)$, which soon exerts its equilibrium partial pressure. **(b)** Introduction of additional $CaCO_3(s)$ and/or more CaO(s) has no effect on the partial pressure of the $CO_2(g)$, which remains the same as in (a).

Although solid carbon must be present for the reaction to occur, the equilibrium constant expression contains terms only for the species in the homogeneous gas phase: H_2O, CO, and H_2.

$$K = \frac{a_{CO}a_{H_2}}{a_{C(s)}a_{H_2O}} \approx \frac{P_{CO}P_{H_2}}{P_{H_2O}} = K_p$$

The activity of solid carbon is $a_{C(s)} = 1$, and we have implicitly divided through each of the remaining pressures by the reference-state pressure, $P° = 1$ bar, to obtain a dimensionless K.

The decomposition of calcium carbonate (limestone) is also a heterogeneous reaction. The equilibrium constant expression, K_c, contains just a single term.

$$CaCO_3(s) \rightleftharpoons CaO(s) + CO_2(g) \qquad K_c = [CO_2] \tag{6.17}$$

We can write K_p for reaction (6.17) by using equation (6.16), with $\Delta n_{gas} = 1$.

$$K_p = P_{CO_2} \quad \text{and} \quad K_p = K_c(RT) \tag{6.18}$$

Equation (6.18) indicates that the equilibrium pressure of $CO_2(g)$ in contact with $CaCO_3(s)$ and CaO(s) is a constant equal to K_p. Its value is *independent* of the quantities of $CaCO_3$ and CaO (as long as both solids are present). Figure 6-4 offers a conceptualization of this decomposition reaction.

One of our examples in Section 6-1 was liquid–vapor equilibrium. This is a physical equilibrium because no chemical reactions are involved. Consider the liquid–vapor equilibrium for water.

$$H_2O(l) \rightleftharpoons H_2O(g)$$
$$K_c = [H_2O(g)] \qquad K_p = P_{H_2O} \qquad K_p = K_cRT$$

So, equilibrium vapor pressures such as P_{H_2O} are just values of K_p. As we have seen before, these values do *not* depend on the quantities of liquid or vapor at equilibrium, as long as some of each is present.

EXAMPLE 6-4 Writing Equilibrium Constant Expressions for Reactions Involving Pure Solids or Liquids

At equilibrium in the following reaction at 60 °C, the partial pressures of the gases are found to be $P_{HI} = 3.70 \times 10^{-3}$ bar and $P_{H_2S} = 1.01$ bar. What is the value of K for the reaction?

$$H_2S(g) + I_2(s) \rightleftharpoons 2\,HI(g) + S(s) \qquad K = ?$$

Analyze

We need to first write the equilibrium constant expression in terms of activities, and then eliminate the activities of pure solids and pure liquids by setting their activities to 1.

Solve

Write the equilibrium constant expression in terms of activities. Note that activities for the iodine and sulfur are not included, since the activity of a pure solid is 1.

$$K = \frac{(a_{HI})^2}{(a_{H_2S})}$$

The partial pressures are given in bar. The activity of each gas is equal to the numerical value of its partial pressure.

$$a_{HI} = 3.70 \times 10^{-3} \text{ and } a_{H_2S} = 1.01$$

Substitute the given equilibrium data into the equilibrium constant expression.

$$K = \frac{(3.70 \times 10^{-3})^2}{1.01} = 1.36 \times 10^{-5}$$

Assess

Note that the equilibrium constant, K, has no units. You must remember that activities are dimensionless quantities, and that when the partial pressure of a gas is expressed in bar, the activity is equal to the numerical value of its pressure.

PRACTICE EXAMPLE A: Teeth are made principally from the mineral hydroxyapatite, $Ca_5(PO_4)_3OH$, which can be dissolved in acidic solution such as that produced by bacteria in the mouth. The reaction that occurs is $Ca_5(PO_4)_3OH(s) + 4\,H^+(aq) \rightleftharpoons 5\,Ca^{2+}(aq) + 3\,HPO_4^{2-}(aq) + H_2O(l)$. Write the equilibrium constant expression K_c for this reaction.

PRACTICE EXAMPLE B: The steam–iron process is used to generate $H_2(g)$, mostly for use in hydrogenating oils. Iron metal and steam $[H_2O(g)]$ react to produce $Fe_3O_4(s)$ and $H_2(g)$. Write expressions for K_c and K_p for this reversible reaction. How are the values of K_c and K_p related to each other? Explain.

6-4 The Magnitude of an Equilibrium Constant

In principle, every chemical reaction has an equilibrium constant, but often the constants are not used. Why is this so? Table 6.3 lists equilibrium constants for several reactions mentioned in this chapter or previously in the text. The first of these reactions is the synthesis of H_2O from its elements. We have always assumed that this reaction goes to completion, that is, that the reverse reaction is negligible and the overall reaction proceeds only in the forward direction. If a reaction goes to completion, one (or more) of the reactants is used up. A term in the *denominator* of the equilibrium constant expression approaches *zero* and makes the value of the equilibrium constant very large. A very large numerical value of K signifies that the forward reaction, as written, *goes to completion* or very nearly so. Because the value of K_p for the water synthesis reaction is 1.4×10^{83}, we are entirely justified in saying that the reaction goes to completion at 298 K.

If the equilibrium constant is so large, why is a mixture of hydrogen and oxygen gases stable at room temperature? The value of the equilibrium

TABLE 6.3 Equilibrium Constants of Some Common Reactions

Reaction	Equilibrium Constant, K_p
$2\,H_2(g) + O_2(g) \rightleftharpoons 2\,H_2O(l)$	1.4×10^{83} at 298 K
$CaCO_3(s) \rightleftharpoons CaO(s) + CO_2(g)$	1.9×10^{-23} at 298 K 1.0 at about 1200 K
$2\,SO_2(g) + O_2(g) \rightleftharpoons 2\,SO_3(g)$	3.4 at 1000 K
$C(s) + H_2O(g) \rightleftharpoons CO(g) + H_2(g)$	1.6×10^{-21} at 298 K 10.0 at about 1100 K

constant relates to thermodynamic stability: $H_2O(l)$ is much more thermodynamically stable than a mixture of $H_2(g)$ and $O_2(g)$ because it lies at a lower energy state. However, the rate of a chemical reaction is strongly governed by the activation energy, E_a. Because E_a is very high for the synthesis of $H_2O(l)$ from $H_2(g)$ and $O_2(g)$, the rate of reaction is inconsequential at 298 K. To get the reaction to occur at a measurable rate, we must either raise the temperature or use a catalyst. A chemist would say that the synthesis of $H_2O(l)$ at 298 K is a *kinetically* controlled reaction (as opposed to *thermodynamically* controlled).

▶ The products formed in a reaction under *kinetic control* are determined by reaction rates. The products formed in a reaction under *thermodynamic control* will depend on the stability of the products.

From Table 6.3, we see that K_p for the decomposition of $CaCO_3(s)$ (limestone) is very small at 298 K (only 1.9×10^{-23}). To account for a very small numerical value of an equilibrium constant, the *numerator* must be very small (approaching zero). A very small numerical value of K signifies that the forward reaction, as written, *does not occur to any significant extent*. Although limestone does not decompose at ordinary temperatures, the partial pressure of $CO_2(g)$ in equilibrium with $CaCO_3(s)$ and $CaO(s)$ increases with temperature. It becomes 1 atm at about 1200 K. An important application of this decomposition reaction is in the commercial production of quicklime (CaO).

The conversion of $SO_2(g)$ and $O_2(g)$ to $SO_3(g)$ at 1000 K has an equilibrium constant such that we expect significant amounts of both reactants and products to be present at equilibrium (see Table 6.3). Both the forward and reverse reactions are important. A similar situation exists for the reaction of C(s) and $H_2O(g)$ at 1100 K, but not at 298 K where the forward reaction does not occur to any significant extent ($K_p = 1.6 \times 10^{-21}$).

In light of the several cases from Table 6.3, we can conclude the following:

> We consider a reaction going to completion if $K > 10^{10}$ or a reaction not occurring in the forward direction if $K < 10^{-10}$.

Thus, we see that equilibrium calculations are not required for all reactions. At times, we can use simple stoichiometric calculations to determine the outcome of a reaction, and in some cases there may be no reaction at all.

6-6 CONCEPT ASSESSMENT

Why is having a balanced equation a necessary condition for predicting the outcome of a chemical reaction, but often not a sufficient condition?

6-5 The Reaction Quotient, Q: Predicting the Direction of Net Change

Let's return briefly to the set of three experiments that we discussed in Section 6-2, involving the reaction

$$2\,Cu^{2+}(aq) + Sn^{2+}(aq) \longrightarrow 2\,Cu^{+}(aq) + Sn^{4+}(aq) \qquad K_c = 1.48 \qquad \textbf{(6.19)}$$

Experiment 1 starts with just the reactants, Cu^{2+} and Sn^{2+}. An overall, or net, change has to occur in which some Cu^{+} and Sn^{4+} forms. Only in this way can an equilibrium condition be reached in which all reacting species are present. We say that a net change occurs in the *forward* direction (*to the right*).

Experiment 2 starts with just the product, Cu^{+} and Sn^{4+}. Here, some of the Cu^{+} and Sn^{4+} must decompose back to Cu^{2+} and Sn^{2+} before equilibrium can be established. We say that a net change occurs in the *reverse* direction (*to the left*).

Experiment 3 starts with all the reacting species present: Cu^{2+}, Sn^{2+}, Cu^{+}, and Sn^{4+}. In this system, it is not obvious in what direction a net change occurs to establish equilibrium.

The ability to predict the direction of net change in establishing equilibrium is important for two reasons.

- At times we do not need detailed equilibrium calculations. We may need only a qualitative description of the changes that occur in establishing equilibrium from a given set of initial conditions.
- In some equilibrium calculations, it is helpful to determine the direction of net change as a first step.

For any set of *initial* activities in a reaction mixture, we can set up a ratio of activities having the same form as the equilibrium constant expression. This ratio is called the **reaction quotient** and is designated Q. For a hypothetical generalized reaction, the reaction quotient, first written in terms of activities, and then as concentrations assuming a concentration reference state, is

$$Q_c = \frac{(a_{\text{init}})^g (a_{\text{init}})^h}{(a_{\text{init}})^a (a_{\text{init}})^b} \qquad Q_c = \frac{[\text{G}]^g_{\text{init}}[\text{H}]^h_{\text{init}}}{[\text{A}]^a_{\text{init}}[\text{B}]^b_{\text{init}}} \tag{6.20}$$

If $Q = K$, a reaction is at equilibrium, but our primary interest in the relationship between Q and K is for a reaction mixture that is not at equilibrium. To see what this relationship is, let's turn again to the experiments in Table 6.1.

In Experiment 1, the initial concentrations of Cu^{2+} and Sn^{2+} are 0.100 mol/1.00 L = 0.100 M. Initially there is no Cu^{+} and Sn^{4+}. The expression for Q_c is

$$Q_c = \frac{[\text{Cu}^+]^2_{\text{init}}[\text{Sn}^{4+}]_{\text{init}}}{[\text{Cu}^{2+}]^2_{\text{init}}[\text{Sn}^{2+}]_{\text{init}}} = \frac{0 \times 0}{(0.100)^2(0.100)} = 0 \tag{6.21}$$

We know that a net reaction occurs *to the right*, producing some Cu^{+} and Sn^{4+}. As it does, the numerator in expression (6.21) increases, the denominator decreases, and the value of Q_c increases; eventually $Q_c = K_c$.

If $Q_c < K_c$, then a net change occurs from left to right (the direction of the forward reaction).

In Experiment 2, the initial concentrations of Cu^{+} and Sn^{4+} are 0.100 mol/1.00 L = 0.100 M. Initially, there is no Cu^{2+} and Sn^{2+}. The expression for Q_c is

$$Q_c = \frac{[\text{Cu}^+]^2_{\text{init}}[\text{Sn}^{4+}]_{\text{init}}}{[\text{Cu}^{2+}]^2_{\text{init}}[\text{Sn}^{4+}]_{\text{init}}} = \frac{(0.100)^2(0.100)}{0 \times 0} = \infty \tag{6.22}$$

◀ Strictly speaking, we cannot evaluate Q_c in this case. Any value divided by zero is undefined. By writing $Q_c = \infty$, we mean the following: As the concentrations of reactants approach a value of zero, Q_c approaches ∞.

We know that a net reaction occurs *to the left*, producing some Cu^{2+} and Sn^{2+}. As it does, the numerator in expression (6.22) decreases, the denominator increases, and the value of Q_c decreases; eventually $Q_c = K_c$.

If $Q_c > K_c$, a net change occurs from right to left (the direction of the reverse reaction).

Now let us turn to a case where direction of net change is not immediately obvious. In Experiment 3, the initial concentrations of all four species are 0.100 mol/1.00 L = 0.100 M. The value of Q_c is

$$Q_c = \frac{[\text{Cu}^+]^2_{\text{init}}[\text{Sn}^{4+}]_{\text{init}}}{[\text{Cu}^{2+}]^2_{\text{init}}[\text{Sn}^{2+}]_{\text{init}}} = \frac{(0.100)^2(0.100)}{(0.100)^2(0.100)} = 1.00$$

Because $Q_c < K_c$ (1.00 compared with 1.48), a net change occurs in the *forward direction*. Note that you can verify this conclusion from Figure 6-3. The

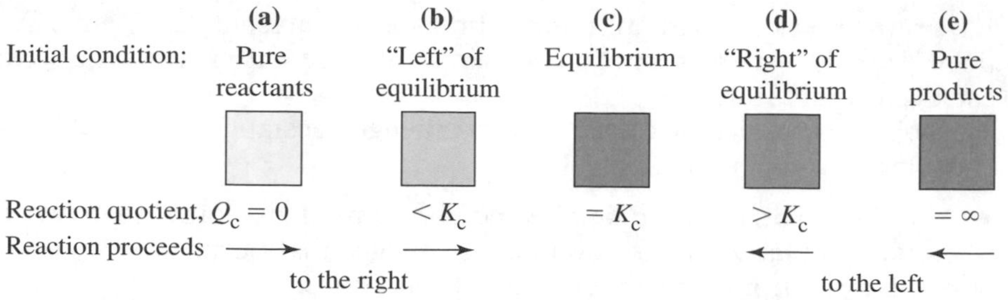

	(a)	(b)	(c)	(d)	(e)
Initial condition:	Pure reactants	"Left" of equilibrium	Equilibrium	"Right" of equilibrium	Pure products
Reaction quotient, Q_c	$= 0$	$< K_c$	$= K_c$	$> K_c$	$= \infty$
Reaction proceeds	$\longrightarrow$	$\longrightarrow$		$\longleftarrow$	$\longleftarrow$
	to the right			to the left	

▲ FIGURE 6-5
Predicting the direction of net change in a reversible reaction
Five possibilities for the relationship of initial and equilibrium conditions are shown. From Table 6.1 and Figure 6-3, Experiment 1 corresponds to initial condition (a); Experiment 2 to condition (e); and Experiment 3 to (d). The situation in Example 6-5 also corresponds to condition (d).

amounts of Cu^{2+} and Sn^{2+} at equilibrium are less than they were initially, and the amounts of Cu^{+} and Sn^{4+} are greater.

The criteria for predicting the direction of a net chemical change in a reversible reaction are summarized in Figure 6-5 and applied in Example 6-5.

EXAMPLE 6-5 Predicting the Direction of a Net Chemical Change in Establishing Equilibrium

To increase the yield of $H_2(g)$ in the water–gas reaction—the reaction of C(g) and $H_2O(g)$ to form CO(g) and $H_2(g)$—a follow-up reaction called the "water–gas shift reaction" is generally used. In this reaction, some of the CO(g) of the water gas is replaced by $H_2(g)$.

$$CO(g) + H_2O(g) \rightleftharpoons CO_2(g) + H_2(g)$$

$K_c = 1.00$ at about 1100 K. The following amounts of substances are brought together and allowed to react at this temperature: 1.00 mol CO, 1.00 mol H_2O, 2.00 mol CO_2, and 2.00 mol H_2. Compared with their initial amounts, which of the substances will be present in a greater amount and which in a lesser amount when equilibrium is established?

Analyze

Our task is to determine the direction of net change by evaluating Q_c and comparing it to K_c.

Solve

Write down the expression for Q_c.

$$Q_c = \frac{[CO_2][H_2]}{[CO][H_2O]}$$

Substitute concentrations into the expression for Q_c, by assuming an arbitrary volume V (which cancels out in the calculation).

$$Q_c = \frac{(2.00/V)(2.00/V)}{(1.00/V)(1.00/V)} = 4.00$$

Compare Q_c to K_c.

$$4.00 > 1.00$$

Because $Q_c > K_c$ (that is, $4.00 > 1.00$), a net change occurs to the *left*. When equilibrium is established, the amounts of CO and H_2O will be greater than the initial quantities and the amounts of CO_2 and H_2 will be less.

Assess

It is important to be able to determine the direction of reaction. As we will see in Section 6-7, this step must be completed before we attempt to determine what the equilibrium amounts will be.

PRACTICE EXAMPLE A: In Example 6-5, equal masses of CO, H_2O, CO_2, and H_2 are mixed at a temperature of about 1100 K. When equilibrium is established, which substance(s) will show an increase in quantity and which will show a decrease compared with the initial quantities?

PRACTICE EXAMPLE B: For the reaction $PCl_5(g) \rightleftharpoons PCl_3(g) + Cl_2(g)$, $K_c = 0.0454$ at 261 °C. If a vessel is filled with these gases such that the initial partial pressures are $P_{PCl_3} = 2.19$ atm, $P_{Cl_2} = 0.88$ atm, $P_{PCl_5} = 19.7$ atm, in which direction will a net change occur?

6-7 CONCEPT ASSESSMENT

A mixture of 1.00 mol each of $CO(g)$, $H_2O(g)$, and $CO_2(g)$ is placed in a 10.0 L flask at a temperature at which $K_p = 10.0$ in the reaction

$$CO(g) + H_2O(g) \rightleftharpoons CO_2(g) + H_2(g)$$

When equilibrium is established, **(a)** the amount of $H_2(g)$ will be 1.00 mol; **(b)** the amounts of all reactants and products will be greater than 1.00 mol; **(c)** the amounts of all reactants and products will be less than 1.00 mol; **(d)** the amount of $CO_2(g)$ will be greater than 1.00 mol and the amounts of $CO(g)$, $H_2O(g)$, and $H_2(g)$ will be less than 1.00 mol; **(e)** the amounts of reactants and products cannot be predicted and can only be determined by analyzing the equilibrium mixture.

KEEP IN MIND

that volumes cancel in a reaction quotient or equilibrium constant expression whenever the sum of the exponents in the numerator equals that in the denominator. This can simplify problem solving in some instances.

6-6 Altering Equilibrium Conditions: Le Châtelier's Principle

At times, we want only to make qualitative statements about a reversible reaction: the direction of a net change, whether the amount of a substance will have increased or decreased when equilibrium is reached, and so on. Also, we may not have the data needed for a quantitative calculation. In these cases, we can use a statement attributed to the French chemist Henri Le Châtelier (1884). **Le Châtelier's principle** is hard to state unambiguously, but its essential meaning is stated here.

> When an equilibrium system is subjected to a change in temperature, pressure, or concentration of a reacting species, the system responds by attaining a new equilibrium that *partially* offsets the impact of the change.

As we will see in the examples that follow, it is generally not difficult to predict the outcome of changing one or more variables in a system at equilibrium.

Effect of Changing the Amounts of Reacting Species on Equilibrium

Let's return to reaction (6.11)

$$2\,SO_2(g) + O_2(g) \rightleftharpoons 2\,SO_3(g) \qquad K_c = 2.8 \times 10^2 \text{ at } 1000\text{ K}$$

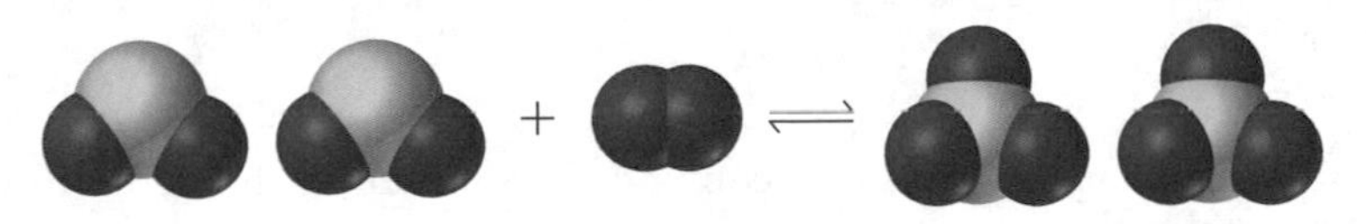

Suppose we start with certain equilibrium amounts of SO_2, O_2, and SO_3, as suggested by Figure 6-6(a). Now let's create a disturbance in the equilibrium mixture by forcing an additional 1.00 mol SO_3 into the 10.0 L flask (Fig. 6-6b). How will the amounts of the reacting species change to re-establish equilibrium?

According to Le Châtelier's principle, if the system is to partially offset an action that increases the equilibrium concentration of one of the reacting species, it must do so by favoring the reaction in which that species is consumed. In this case, this is the *reverse* reaction—conversion of some of the added SO_3 to SO_2 and O_2. In the new equilibrium, there are greater amounts of all the substances than in the original equilibrium, but the additional amount of SO_3 is less than the 1.00 mol that was added.

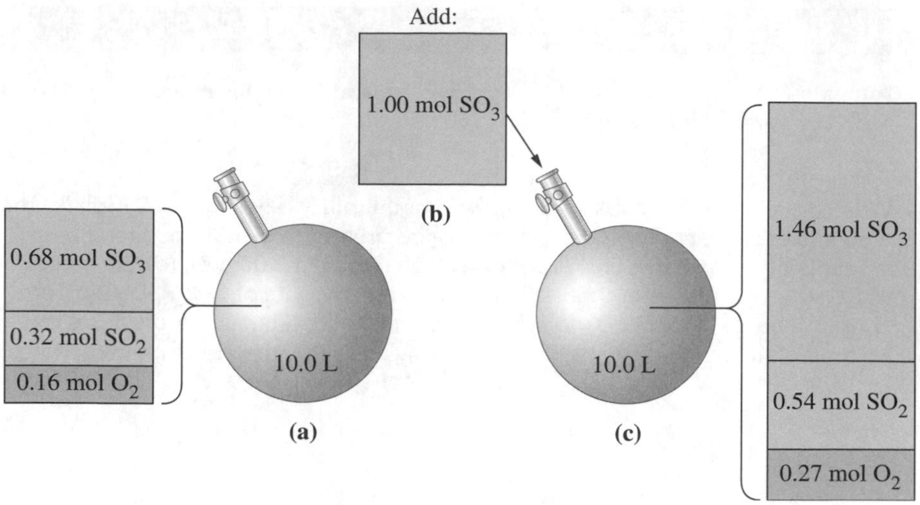

▲ FIGURE 6-6
Changing equilibrium conditions by changing the amount of a reactant

$$2\,SO_2(g) + O_2(g) \rightleftharpoons 2\,SO_3(g),\ K_c = 2.8 \times 10^2 \text{ at } 1000\text{ K}$$

(a) The original equilibrium condition. **(b)** Disturbance caused by adding 1.00 mol SO_3. **(c)** The new equilibrium condition. The amount of SO_3 in the new equilibrium mixture, 1.46 mol, is greater than the original 0.68 mol but it is not as great as immediately after the addition of 1.00 mol SO_3. The effect of adding SO_3 to an equilibrium mixture is *partially* offset when equilibrium is restored.

Another way to look at the matter is to evaluate the reaction quotient immediately after adding the SO_3.

Original equilibrium

$$Q_c = \frac{[SO_3]}{[SO_2]^2[O_2]} = K_c$$

Immediately following disturbance

$$Q_c = \frac{[SO_3]}{[SO_2]^2[O_2]} > K_c$$

EXAMPLE 6-6 Applying Le Châtelier's Principle: Effect of Adding More of a Reactant to an Equilibrium Mixture

Predict the effect of adding more $H_2(g)$ to a constant-volume equilibrium mixture of N_2, H_2, and NH_3.

$$N_2(g) + 3\,H_2(g) \rightleftharpoons 2\,NH_3(g)$$

Analyze

When a system at equilibrium is disturbed by adding more of one reactant, the system responds by using up (consuming) some of the added reactant.

Solve

Increasing $[H_2]$ stimulates the forward reaction and a shift in the equilibrium condition to the right. However, only a portion of the added H_2 is consumed in this reaction.

Assess

When equilibrium is re-established, there will be more H_2 than was present originally, and also more NH_3, but the amount of N_2 will be *smaller*. Some of the original N_2 must be consumed in converting some of the added H_2 to NH_3.

PRACTICE EXAMPLE A: Given the reaction $2\,CO(g) + O_2(g) \rightleftharpoons 2\,CO_2(g)$, what is the effect of adding $O_2(g)$ to a constant-volume equilibrium mixture?

PRACTICE EXAMPLE B: Calcination of limestone (decomposition by heating), $CaCO_3(s) \rightleftharpoons CaO(s) + CO_2(g)$, is the commercial source of quicklime, $CaO(s)$. After this equilibrium has been established in a constant-temperature, constant-volume container, what is the effect on the equilibrium amounts of materials caused by *adding* some **(a)** $CaO(s)$; **(b)** $CO_2(g)$; **(c)** $CaCO_3(s)$?

Adding any quantity of SO_3 to a constant-volume equilibrium mixture makes Q_c larger than K_c. A net change occurs in the direction that reduces $[SO_3]$, that is, to the left, or in the reverse direction. Notice that reaction in the reverse direction increases $[SO_2]$ and $[O_2]$, further decreasing the value of Q_c.

Effect of Changes in Pressure or Volume on Equilibrium

There are three ways to change the pressure of a constant-temperature equilibrium mixture.

1. **Add or remove a gaseous reactant or product.** The effect of these actions on the equilibrium condition is simply that caused by adding or removing a reaction component, as described previously.
2. **Add an inert gas to the constant-volume reaction mixture.** This has the effect of increasing the *total* pressure, but the partial pressures of the reacting species are all unchanged. An inert gas added to a constant-volume equilibrium mixture has no effect on the equilibrium condition.
3. **Change the pressure by changing the volume of the system.** Decreasing the volume of the system increases the pressure, and increasing the system volume decreases the pressure. Thus, the effect of this type of pressure change is simply that of a volume change.

Let's explore the third situation first. Consider, again, the formation of $SO_3(g)$ from $SO_2(g)$ and $O_2(g)$.

$$2\,SO_2(g) + O_2(g) \rightleftharpoons 2\,SO_3(g) \qquad K_c = 2.8 \times 10^2 \text{ at } 1000\text{ K}$$

The equilibrium mixture in Figure 6-7(a) has its volume reduced to one-tenth of its original value by increasing the external pressure. To see how the equilibrium amounts of the gases change, let's first rearrange the equilibrium constant expression to the form

$$K_c = \frac{[SO_3]^2}{[SO_2]^2[O_2]} = \frac{(n_{SO_3}/V)^2}{(n_{SO_2}/V)^2(n_{O_2}/V)} = \frac{(n_{SO_3})^2}{(n_{SO_2})^2(n_{O_2})} \times V = 2.8 \times 10^2 \qquad (6.23)$$

From equation (6.23), we see that if V is *reduced* by a factor of 10, the ratio

$$\frac{(n_{SO_3})^2}{(n_{SO_2})^2(n_{O_2})}$$

must *increase* by a factor of 10. In this way, the value of K_c is restored, as it must be to restore equilibrium. There is only one way in which the ratio of moles of gases will increase in value: The number of moles of SO_3 must increase, and

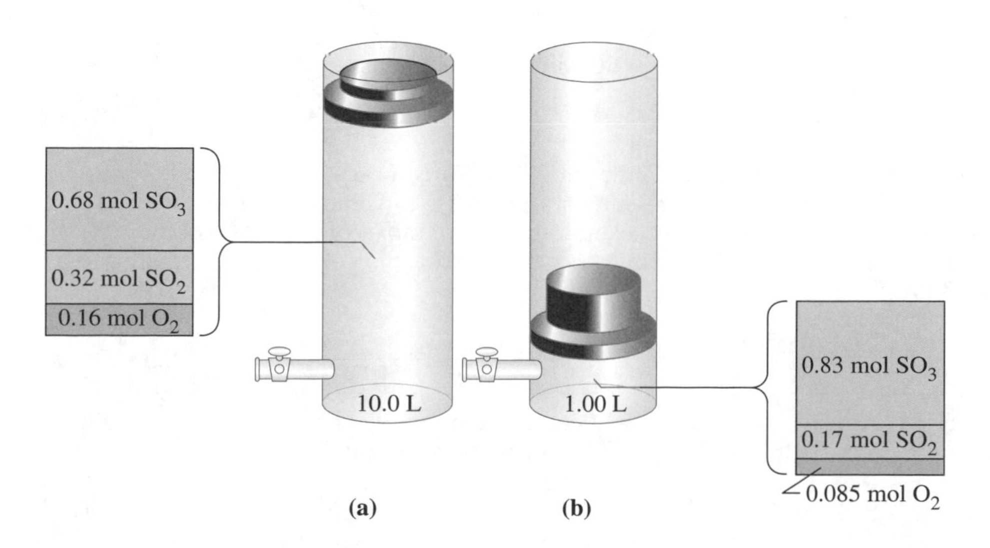

◀ FIGURE 6-7
Effect of pressure change on equilibrium in the reaction
$2SO_2(g) + O_2(g) \rightleftharpoons 2\,SO_3(g)$
An increase in external pressure causes a decrease in the reaction volume and a shift in equilibrium "to the right." (See Exercise 77 for a calculation of the new equilibrium amounts.)

the numbers of moles of SO_2 and O_2 must decrease. The equilibrium shifts in the direction producing more SO_3—to the right.

Notice that three moles of *gas* on the left produce two moles of *gas* on the right in reaction (6.11). When compared at the same temperature and pressure, two moles of $SO_3(g)$ occupy a smaller volume than does a mixture of two moles of $SO_2(g)$ and one mole of $O_2(g)$. Given this fact and the observation from equation (6.23) that a decrease in volume favors the production of additional SO_3, we can formulate a statement that is especially easy to apply.

When the volume of an equilibrium mixture of gases is *reduced*, a net change occurs in the direction that produces *fewer moles of gas*. When the volume is *increased*, a net change occurs in the direction that produces *more moles of gas*.

KEEP IN MIND

that an inert gas has no effect on an equilibrium condition if the gas is added to a system maintained at constant volume, but it can have an effect if added at constant pressure.

Figure 6-7 suggests a way of decreasing the volume of gaseous mixture at equilibrium—by increasing the external pressure. One way to increase the volume is to lower the external pressure. Another way is to transfer the equilibrium mixture from its original container to one of larger volume. A third method is to add an inert gas at *constant pressure*; the volume of the mixture must increase to make room for the added gas. The effect on the equilibrium, however, is the same for all three methods: Equilibrium shifts in the direction of the reaction producing the greater number of moles of gas.

Equilibria between condensed phases are not affected much by changes in external pressure because solids and liquids are not easily compressible. Also, we cannot assess whether the forward or reverse reaction is favored by these changes by examining only the chemical equation.

6-8 CONCEPT ASSESSMENT

To the hypothetical reaction $A(g) + B(g) \rightleftharpoons C(g)$ 0.100 mol of the inert gas argon is added. In addition, the volume of the container is decreased. According to Le Châtelier's principle, will the reaction shift to the right or left? Explain.

EXAMPLE 6-7 Applying Le Châtelier's Principle: The Effect of Changing Volume

An equilibrium mixture of $N_2(g)$, $H_2(g)$, and $NH_3(g)$ is transferred from a 1.50 L flask to a 5.00 L flask. In which direction does a net change occur to restore equilibrium?

$$N_2(g) + 3\,H_2(g) \rightleftharpoons 2\,NH_3(g)$$

Analyze

Because the volume has increased, the reaction will move in the direction that increases the number of moles of gas.

Solve

When the gaseous mixture is transferred to the larger flask, the partial pressure of each gas and the total pressure drop. Whether we think in terms of a decrease in pressure or an increase in volume, we reach the same conclusion. Equilibrium shifts in such a way as to produce a larger number of moles of gas. Some of the NH_3 originally present decomposes back to N_2 and H_2. A net change occurs in the direction of the reverse reaction—to the left—in restoring equilibrium.

Assess

Whether we think in terms of a decrease in pressure or an increase in volume, the conclusion is the same.

PRACTICE EXAMPLE A: The reaction $N_2O_4(g) \rightleftharpoons 2\,NO_2(g)$ is at equilibrium in a 3.00 L cylinder. What would be the effect on the concentrations of $N_2O_4(g)$ and $NO_2(g)$ if the pressure were doubled (that is, cylinder volume decreased to 1.50 L)?

PRACTICE EXAMPLE B: How is the equilibrium amount of $H_2(g)$ produced in the water–gas shift reaction affected by changing the total gas pressure or the system volume? Explain.

$$CO(g) + H_2O(g) \rightleftharpoons CO_2(g) + H_2(g)$$

6-9 CONCEPT ASSESSMENT

The following reaction is brought to equilibrium at 700 °C.

$$2\,H_2S(g) + CH_4(g) \rightleftharpoons CS_2(g) + 4\,H_2(g)$$

Indicate whether each of the following statements is true, false, or not possible to evaluate from the information given.

(a) If the equilibrium mixture is allowed to expand into an evacuated larger container, the mole fraction of H_2 will increase.

(b) If several moles of Ar(g) are forced into the reaction container, the amounts of H_2S and CH_4 will increase.

(c) If the equilibrium mixture is cooled to 100 °C, the mole fractions of the four gases will likely change.

(d) If the equilibrium mixture is forced into a slightly smaller container, the partial pressures of the four gases will all increase.

Effect of Temperature on Equilibrium

We can think of changing the temperature of an equilibrium mixture in terms of adding heat (raising the temperature) or removing heat (lowering the temperature). According to Le Châtelier's principle, adding heat favors the reaction in which heat is absorbed (*endothermic* reaction). Removing heat favors the reaction in which heat is evolved (*exothermic* reaction). Stated in terms of changing temperature,

> *Raising the temperature* of an equilibrium mixture shifts the equilibrium condition in the direction of the *endothermic* reaction. *Lowering the temperature* causes a shift in the direction of the *exothermic* reaction.

The principal effect of temperature on equilibrium is in changing the value of the equilibrium constant. For now, we will limit ourselves to making qualitative predictions.

EXAMPLE 6-8 Applying Le Châtelier's Principle: Effect of Temperature on Equilibrium

Consider the reaction

$$2\,SO_2(g) + O_2(g) \rightleftharpoons 2\,SO_3(g) \qquad \Delta H° = -197.8\ \text{kJ}$$

Will the amount of $SO_3(g)$ formed from given amounts of $SO_2(g)$ and $O_2(g)$ be greater at high or low temperatures?

Analyze

We must think of the impact made by changing the temperature. In general, an increase in temperature causes a shift in the direction of the endothermic reaction.

Solve

The sign of $\Delta H°$ tells us that the forward reaction is exothermic. Thus, the reverse reaction is endothermic. In this case, increasing the temperature will favor the reverse reaction and lowering the temperature will favor the forward reaction. The conversion of SO_2 to SO_3 is favored at *low* temperatures.

(continued)

Assess

Be sure not to confuse shifts in equilibrium with changes in reaction rates that result from temperature changes. That is, equilibria of exothermic and endothermic reactions will shift *differently* when temperatures are increased, but the rates of exothermic and endothermic reactions *both increase* with increasing temperature. Changing the temperature is somewhat different than other changes we have discussed in this section. Changing the temperature causes a shift in the equilibrium position and changes the value of the equilibrium constant.

PRACTICE EXAMPLE A: The reaction $N_2O_4(g) \rightleftharpoons 2\,NO_2(g)$ has $\Delta H° = +57.2$ kJ. Will the amount of $NO_2(g)$ formed from $N_2O_4(g)$ be greater at high or low temperatures?

PRACTICE EXAMPLE B: The enthalpy of formation of NH_3 is $\Delta H_f^\circ[NH_3(g)] = -46.11$ kJ/mol NH_3. Will the concentration of NH_3 in an equilibrium mixture with its elements be greater at 100 or at 300 °C? Explain.

▲ **Sulfuric acid is produced from SO_3**

$$SO_3(g) + H_2O(l) \rightleftharpoons H_2SO_4(aq)$$

The catalyst used to speed up the conversion of SO_2 to SO_3 in the commercial production of sulfuric acid is $V_2O_5(s)$. What appears to be smoke coming from the cooling tower (in the rear) is in fact just water vapor.

Effect of a Catalyst on Equilibrium

Adding a catalyst to a reaction mixture speeds up both the forward and reverse reactions. Equilibrium is achieved more rapidly, but the equilibrium amounts are unchanged by the catalyst. Consider again reaction (6.11)

$$2\,SO_2(g) + O_2(g) \rightleftharpoons 2\,SO_3(g) \qquad K_c = 2.8 \times 10^2 \text{ at } 1000\text{ K}$$

For a given set of reaction conditions, the equilibrium amounts of SO_2, O_2, and SO_3 have fixed values. This is true whether the reaction is carried out by a slow homogeneous reaction, catalyzed in the gas phase, or conducted as a heterogeneous reaction on the surface of a catalyst. Stated another way, the presence of a catalyst does not change the numerical value of the equilibrium constant.

We now have two thoughts about a catalyst to reconcile: one from the preceding chapter and one from this discussion.

- A catalyst changes the mechanism of a reaction to one with a lower activation energy.
- A catalyst has no effect on the condition of equilibrium in a reversible reaction.

Taken together, these two statements must mean that an equilibrium condition is *independent* of the reaction mechanism. Thus, even though equilibrium has been described in terms of opposing reactions occurring at equal rates, we do not have to be concerned with the kinetics of chemical reactions to work with the equilibrium concept. This observation is still another indication that the equilibrium constant is a thermodynamic quantity.

6-10 CONCEPT ASSESSMENT

Two students are performing the same experiment in which an endothermic reaction rapidly attains a condition of equilibrium. Student A does the reaction in a beaker resting on the surface of the lab bench while student B holds the beaker in which the reaction occurs. Assuming that all other environmental variables are the same, which student should end up with more product? Explain.

6-7 Equilibrium Calculations: Some Illustrative Examples

We are now ready to tackle the problem of describing, in quantitative terms, the condition of equilibrium in a reversible reaction. Part of the approach we use may seem unfamiliar at first—it has an algebraic look to it. But as you adjust to this "new look," do not lose sight of the fact that we continue to use some familiar and important ideas—molar masses, molarities, and stoichiometric factors from the balanced equation, for example.

The five numerical examples that follow apply the general equilibrium principles described earlier in the chapter. The first four involve gases, while the fifth deals with equilibrium in an aqueous solution. (The study of equilibria in aqueous solutions is the principal topic of the next three chapters.) Each example includes an assessment that summarizes the essential features of equilibrium calculations exemplified by that type of problem. You may find it helpful to return to these assessments from time to time as you encounter new equilibrium situations in later chapters.

Example 6-9 is relatively straightforward. It demonstrates how to determine the equilibrium constant of a reaction when the equilibrium concentrations of the reactants and products are known.

Example 6-10 is somewhat more involved than Example 6-9. We are still interested in determining the equilibrium constant for a reaction, but we do not have the same sort of information as in Example 6-9. We are given the initial concentrations of all the reactants and products, but the equilibrium concentration of only one substance. This case requires a little algebra and some careful bookkeeping. We will introduce a tabular system, sometimes called an **ICE table**, for keeping track of changing concentrations of reactants and products. The table contains the *initial, change in*, and *equilibrium concentration* of each species. It is a helpful device that we will use throughout Chapters 8 and 9.

EXAMPLE 6-9 Determining a Value of K_c from the Equilibrium Quantities of Substances

Dinitrogen tetroxide, $N_2O_4(l)$, is an important component of rocket fuels—for example, as an oxidizer of liquid hydrazine in the Titan rocket. At 25 °C, N_2O_4 is a colorless gas that partially dissociates into NO_2, a red-brown gas. The color of an equilibrium mixture of these two gases depends on their relative proportions, which in turn depends on the temperature (Fig. 6-8).

(continued)

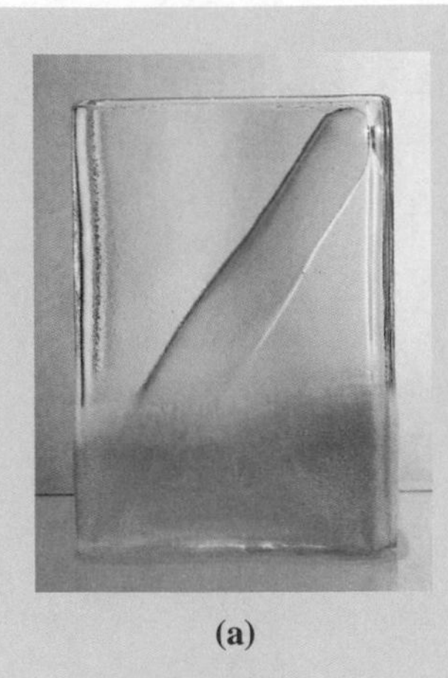

(a)

(b)

▲ FIGURE 6-8
The equilibrium $N_2O_4(g) \rightleftharpoons 2\ NO_2(g)$
(a) At dry ice temperatures, N_2O_4 exists as a solid. The gas in equilibrium with the solid is mostly colorless N_2O_4, with only a trace of brown NO_2.
(b) When warmed to room temperature and above, the N_2O_4 melts and vaporizes. The proportion of $NO_2(g)$ at equilibrium increases over that at low temperatures, and the equilibrium mixture of $N_2O_4(g)$ and $NO_2(g)$ has a red-brown color.

▲ **The Lewis structures of N_2O_4 and $NO_2(g)$**
Nitrogen dioxide is a free radical that combines exothermically to form dinitrogen tetroxide.

Equilibrium is established in the reaction $N_2O_4(g) \rightleftharpoons 2\ NO_2(g)$ at 25 °C. The quantities of the two gases present in a 3.00 L vessel are 7.64 g N_2O_4 and 1.56 g NO_2. What is the value of K_c for this reaction?

Analyze

We are given the equilibrium amounts (in terms of mass) of the reactants and products, along with the volume of the reaction vessel. We use these values to determine the equilibrium concentrations and plug them into the equilibrium constant expression.

Solve

Convert the mass of N_2O_4 to moles.

$$\text{mol } N_2O_4 = 7.64\ \text{g } N_2O_4 \times \frac{1\ \text{mol } N_2O_4}{92.01\ \text{g } N_2O_4} = 8.303 \times 10^{-2}\ \text{mol}$$

Convert moles of N_2O_4 to mol/L.

$$[N_2O_4] = \frac{8.303 \times 10^{2}\ \text{mol}}{3.00\ \text{L}} = 0.0277\ \text{M}$$

Convert the mass of NO_2 to moles.

$$\text{mol } NO_2 = 1.56\ \text{g } NO_2 \times \frac{1\ \text{mol } NO_2}{46.01\ \text{g } NO_2} = 3.391 \times 10^{-2}\ \text{mol}$$

Convert moles of NO_2 to mol/L.

$$[NO_2] = \frac{3.391 \times 10^{-2}}{3.00\ \text{L}} = 0.0113\ \text{M}$$

Write the equilibrium constant expression, substitute the equilibrium concentrations, and solve for K_c.

$$K_c = \frac{[NO_2]^2}{[N_2O_4]} = \frac{(0.0113)^2}{(0.0277)} = 4.61 \times 10^{-3}$$

Assess

The quantities required in an equilibrium constant expression, K_c, are equilibrium *concentrations in moles per liter*, not simply equilibrium amounts in moles or masses in grams. It is helpful to organize all the equilibrium data and carefully label each item.

PRACTICE EXAMPLE A: Equilibrium is established in a 3.00 L flask at 1405 K for the reaction $2\ H_2S(g) \rightleftharpoons 2\ H_2(g) + S_2(g)$. At equilibrium, there is 0.11 mol $S_2(g)$, 0.22 mol $H_2(g)$, and 2.78 mol $H_2S(g)$. What is the value of K_c for this reaction?

PRACTICE EXAMPLE B: Equilibrium is established at 25 °C in the reaction $N_2O_4(g) \rightleftharpoons 2\ NO_2(g)$, $K_c = 4.61 \times 10^{-3}$. If $[NO_2] = 0.0236$ M in a 2.26 L flask, how many grams of N_2O_4 are also present?

EXAMPLE 6-10 Determining a Value of K_p from Initial and Equilibrium Amounts of Substances: Relating K_c and K_p

The equilibrium condition for $SO_2(g)$, $O_2(g)$, and $SO_3(g)$ is important in sulfuric acid production. When a 0.0200 mol sample of SO_3 is introduced into an evacuated 1.52 L vessel at 900 K, 0.0142 mol SO_3 is present at equilibrium. What is the value of K_p for the dissociation of $SO_3(g)$ at 900 K?

$$2\,SO_3(g) \rightleftharpoons 2\,SO_2(g) + O_2(g) \qquad K_p = ?$$

Analyze

Let's first determine K_c and then convert to K_p by using equation (6.16). In the ICE table below, the key term leading to the other data is the change in amount of SO_3: In progressing from 0.0200 mol SO_3 to 0.0142 mol SO_3, 0.0058 mol SO_3 is dissociated. The *negative sign* (−0.0058 mol) indicates that this amount of SO_3 is consumed in establishing equilibrium. In the row labeled "changes," the changes in amounts of SO_2 and O_2 must be related to the change in amount of SO_3. For this, we use the stoichiometric coefficients from the balanced equation: 2, 2, and 1. That is, *two* moles of SO_2 and *one* mole of O_2 are produced for every *two* moles of SO_3 that dissociate.

Solve

The reaction:	$2\,SO_3(g)$	$\rightleftharpoons$	$2\,SO_2(g)$	+	$O_2(g)$
initial amounts:	0.0200 mol		0.00 mol		0.00 mol
changes:	−0.0058 mol		+0.0058 mol		+0.0029 mol
equil amounts:	0.0142 mol		0.0058 mol		0.0029 mol
equil concns:	$[SO_3] = \dfrac{0.0142\text{ mol}}{1.52\text{ L}}$;		$[SO_2] = \dfrac{0.0058\text{ mol}}{1.52\text{ L}}$;		$[O_2] = \dfrac{0.0029\text{ mol}}{1.52\text{ L}}$
	$[SO_3] = 9.34 \times 10^{-3}$ M;		$[SO_2] = 3.8 \times 10^{-3}$ M;		$[O_2] = 1.9 \times 10^{-3}$ M

$$K_c = \frac{[SO_2]^2[O_2]}{[SO_3]^2} = \frac{(3.8 \times 10^{-3})^2(1.9 \times 10^{-3})}{(9.34 \times 10^{-3})^2} = 3.1 \times 10^{-4}$$

$$K_p = K_c(RT)^{\Delta n_{gas}} = 3.1 \times 10^{-4}\,(0.0821 \times 900)^{(2+1)-2}$$
$$= 3.1 \times 10^{-4}\,(0.0821 \times 900)^1 = 2.3 \times 10^{-2}$$

Assess

The chemical equation for a reversible reaction serves both to establish the form of the equilibrium constant expression and to provide the conversion factors (stoichiometric factors) to relate the equilibrium quantity of one species to equilibrium quantities of the others.

For equilibria involving gases, we can use either K_c or K_p. In general, if the data given involve amounts of substances and volumes, it is easier to work with K_c. If data are given as partial pressures, then work with K_p. Whether working with K_c or K_p or the relationship between them, we must always base these expressions on the given chemical equation, not on equations we may have used in other situations.

PRACTICE EXAMPLE A: A 5.00 L evacuated flask is filled with 1.86 mol NOBr. At equilibrium at 25 °C, there is 0.082 mol of Br_2 present. Determine K_c and K_p for the reaction $2\,NOBr(g) \rightleftharpoons 2\,NO(g) + Br_2(g)$.

PRACTICE EXAMPLE B: 0.100 mol SO_2 and 0.100 mol O_2 are introduced into an evacuated 1.52 L flask at 900 K. When equilibrium is reached, the amount of SO_3 found is 0.0916 mol. Use these data to determine K_p for the reaction $2\,SO_3(g) \rightleftharpoons 2\,SO_2(g) + O_2(g)$.

The methods used in Examples 6-9 and 6-10 are summarized in Figure 6-9. Example 6-11 demonstrates that we can often determine several pieces of useful information about an equilibrium system from just the equilibrium constant and the reaction equation.

Example 6-12 brings back the ICE format, but with a twist. This time the known values include the equilibrium constant and an initial amount of the reactant, but no information is given about the equilibrium amount of the reactant or the product. That means that we do not know how much the initial value will change. We show this by using an "x" in that part of the table. The setup will be quite algebraic; in fact, we must use the quadratic formula to obtain a solution.

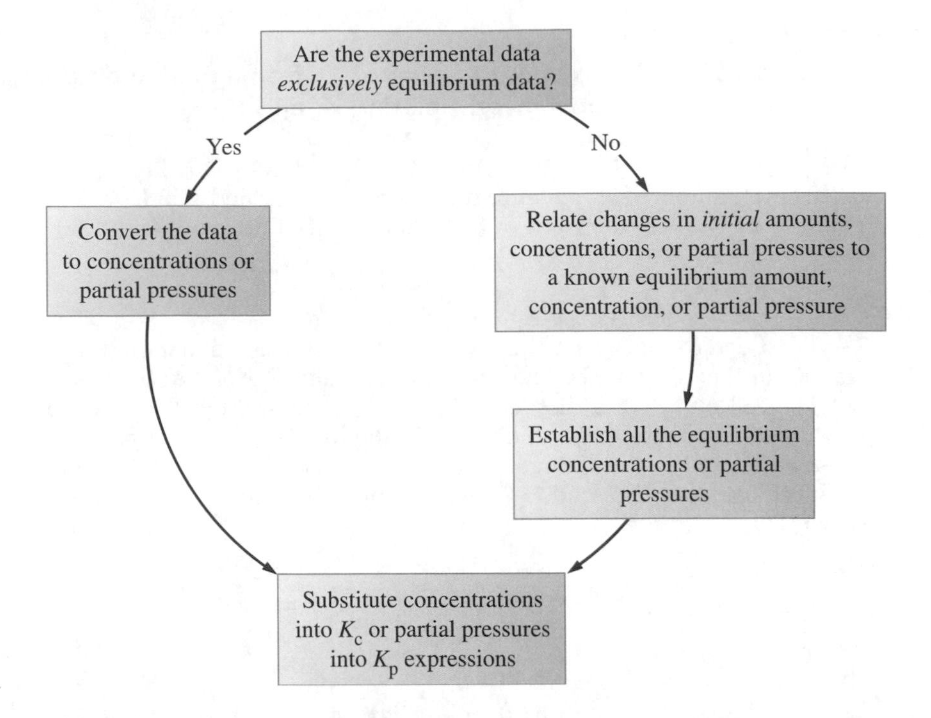

▲ FIGURE 6-9
Determining K_c or K_p from experimental data

EXAMPLE 6-11 Determining Equilibrium Partial and Total Pressures from a Value of K_p

Ammonium hydrogen sulfide, $NH_4HS(s)$, used as a photographic developer, is unstable and dissociates at room temperature.

$$NH_4HS(s) \rightleftharpoons NH_3(g) + H_2S(g) \qquad K_p = 0.108 \text{ at } 25\ °C$$

A sample of $NH_4HS(s)$ is introduced into an evacuated flask at 25 °C. What is the total gas pressure at equilibrium?

Analyze

We begin by writing the equilibrium constant expression in terms of pressure. The key step is to recognize that the pressure of ammonia is equal to the pressure of hydrogen sulfide. This will then allow us to determine the pressure of ammonia and hydrogen sulfide.

Solve

K_p for this reaction is just the product of the equilibrium partial pressures of $NH_3(g)$ and $H_2S(g)$, each stated in atmospheres. (There is no term for NH_4HS because it is a solid.) Because these gases are produced in equimolar amounts, $P_{NH_3} = P_{H_2S}$.

$$K_p = (P_{NH_3})(P_{H_2S}) = 0.108$$
$$K_p = (P_{NH_3})(P_{H_2S}) = (P_{NH_3})(P_{NH_3}) = (P_{NH_3})^2 = 0.108$$

Find P_{NH_3}. (Note that the unit atm appears because in the equilibrium expression the reference pressure $P°$ was implicitly included.)

$$P_{NH_3} = \sqrt{0.108} = 0.329 \text{ atm} \qquad P_{H_2S} = P_{NH_3} = 0.329 \text{ atm}$$

The total pressure is

$$P_{tot} = P_{NH_3} + P_{H_2S} = 0.329 \text{ atm} + 0.329 \text{ atm} = 0.658 \text{ atm}$$

Assess

When using K_p expressions, look for relationships among partial pressures of the reactants. If we need to relate the total pressure to the partial pressures of the reactants, we should be able to do this with some equations presented in Chapter 2 (for example, equations 2.15, 2.16, and 2.17).

PRACTICE EXAMPLE A: Sodium hydrogen carbonate (baking soda) decomposes at elevated temperatures and is one of the sources of $CO_2(g)$ when this compound is used in baking.

$$2\ NaHCO_3(s) \rightleftharpoons Na_2CO_3(s) + H_2O(g) + CO_2(g) \qquad K_p = 0.231 \text{ at } 100\ °C$$

What is the partial pressure of $CO_2(g)$ when this equilibrium is established starting with $NaHCO_3(s)$?

PRACTICE EXAMPLE B: If enough additional $NH_3(g)$ is added to the flask in Example 6-11 to raise its partial pressure to 0.500 atm at equilibrium, what will be the *total* gas pressure when equilibrium is re-established?

EXAMPLE 6-12 Calculating Equilibrium Concentrations from Initial Conditions

A 0.0240 mol sample of $N_2O_4(g)$ is allowed to come to equilibrium with $NO_2(g)$ in a 0.372 L flask at 25 °C. Calculate the amount of N_2O_4 present at equilibrium (Fig. 6-10).

$$N_2O_4(g) \rightleftharpoons 2\,NO_2(g) \qquad K_c = 4.61 \times 10^{-3} \text{ at } 25\text{ °C}$$

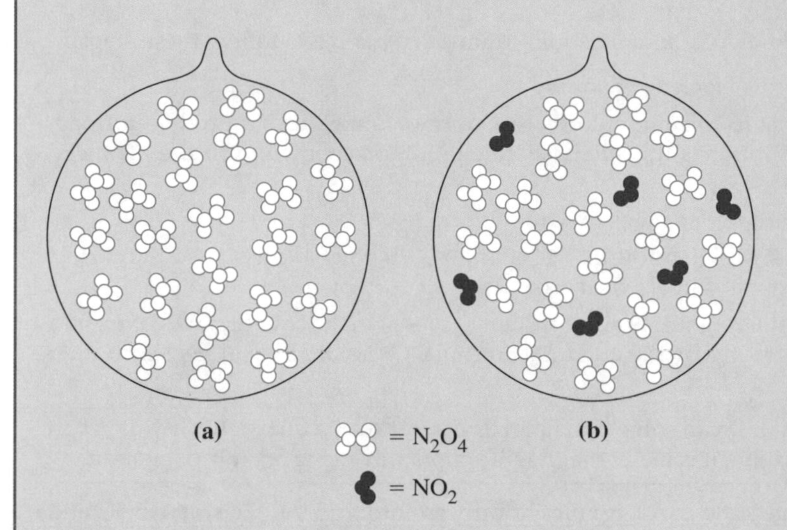

◀ FIGURE 6-10
Equilibrium in the reaction

$$N_2O_4(g) \rightleftharpoons 2\,NO_2(g)$$

at 25 °C—Example 6-12 illustrated
Each "molecule" illustrated represents 0.001 mol. **(a)** Initially, the bulb contains 0.024 mol N_2O_4, represented by 24 "molecules." **(b)** At equilibrium, some "molecules" of N_2O_4 have dissociated to NO_2. The 21 "molecules" of N_2O_4 and 6 of NO_2 correspond to 0.021 mol N_2O_4 and 0.006 mol NO_2 at equilibrium.

Analyze

We need to determine the amount of N_2O_4 that dissociates to establish equilibrium. For the first time, we introduce an algebraic unknown, x. Suppose we let x = the number of moles of N_2O_4 that dissociate. In the following ICE table, we enter the value $-x$ into the row labeled "changes." The amount of NO_2 produced is $+2x$ because the stoichiometric coefficient of NO_2 is 2 and that of N_2O_4 is *1*.

Solve

The reaction:	$N_2O_4(g)$	$\rightleftharpoons$	$2\,NO_2(g)$
initial amounts:	0.0240 mol		0.00 mol
changes:	$-x$ mol		$+2x$ mol
equil amounts:	$(0.0240 - x)$ mol		$2x$ mol
equil concns:	$[N_2O_4] = (0.0240 - x)$ mol/0.372 L		$[NO_2] = 2x$ mol/0.372 L

$$K_c = \frac{[NO_2]^2}{[N_2O_4]} = \frac{\left(\dfrac{2x}{0.372}\right)^2}{\left(\dfrac{0.0240 - x}{0.372}\right)} = \frac{4x^2}{0.372(0.0240 - x)} = 4.61 \times 10^{-3}$$

$$4x^2 = 4.12 \times 10^{-5} - (1.71 \times 10^{-3})x$$

$$x^2 + (4.28 \times 10^{-4})x - 1.03 \times 10^{-5} = 0$$

$$x = \frac{-4.28 \times 10^{-4} \pm \sqrt{(4.28 \times 10^{-4})^2 + 4 \times 1.03 \times 10^{-5}}}{2}$$

$$= \frac{-4.28 \times 10^{-4} \pm \sqrt{(1.83 \times 10^{-7}) + 4.12 \times 10^{-5}}}{2}$$

$$x = \frac{-4.28 \times 10^{-4} \pm \sqrt{4.14 \times 10^{-5}}}{2}$$

$$= \frac{-4.28 \times 10^{-4} \pm 6.43 \times 10^{-3}}{2}$$

$$= \frac{-4.28 \times 10^{-4} + 6.43 \times 10^{-3}}{2} = \frac{6.00 \times 10^{-3}}{2}$$

$$= 3.00 \times 10^{-3} \text{ mol } N_2O_4$$

The amount of N_2O_4 at equilibrium is $(0.0240 - x) = (0.0240 - 0.0030) = 0.0210$ mol N_2O_4.

Assess

When we need to introduce an algebraic unknown, x, into an equilibrium calculation, we follow these steps.

- Introduce x into the ICE setup in the row labeled "changes."
- Decide which change to label as x, that is, the amount of a reactant consumed or of a product formed. Usually, we base this on the species that has the smallest stoichiometric coefficient in the balanced chemical equation.
- Use stoichiometric factors to relate the other changes to x (that is, $2x, 3x, \ldots$).
- Consider that equilibrium amounts = initial amounts + "changes." (If you have assigned the correct signs to the changes, equilibrium amounts will also be correct.)
- After substitutions have been made into the equilibrium constant expression, the equation will often be a quadratic equation in x, which you can solve by the quadratic formula. Occasionally you may encounter a higher-degree equation.

Most of us can solve quadratic equations, but few can solve polynomials greater than a quadratic. If you get an equation that is a cubic or higher degree equation, it is likely that it will simplify by using an approximation.

PRACTICE EXAMPLE A: If 0.150 mol $H_2(g)$ and 0.200 mol $I_2(g)$ are introduced into a 15.0 L flask at 445 °C and allowed to come to equilibrium, how many moles of HI(g) will be present?

$$H_2(g) + I_2(g) \rightleftharpoons 2\,HI(g) \qquad K_c = 50.2 \text{ at } 445\text{ °C}$$

PRACTICE EXAMPLE B: Suppose the equilibrium mixture of Example 6-12 is transferred to a 10.0 L flask. **(a)** Will the equilibrium amount of N_2O_4 increase or decrease? Explain. **(b)** Calculate the number of moles of N_2O_4 in the new equilibrium condition.

Our final example is similar to the previous one, but with this slight complication: Initially, we don't know whether a net change occurs to the right or to the left to establish equilibrium. We can find out, though, by using the reaction quotient, Q_c, and proceeding in the manner suggested in Figure 6-11. Also, because the reactants and products are in solution, we can work exclusively with concentrations in formulating the K_c expression.

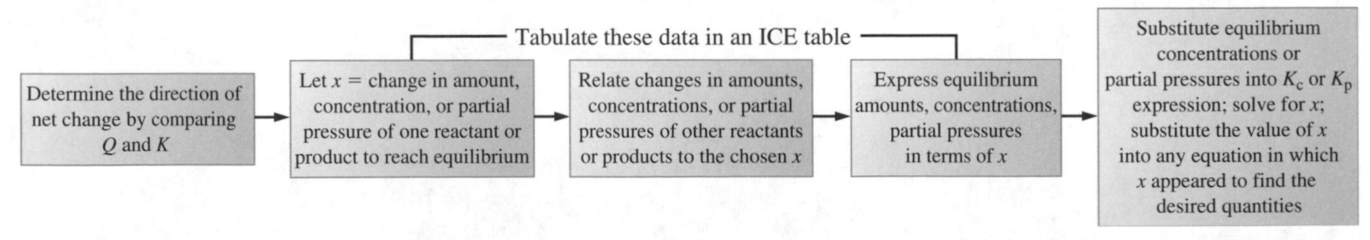

▲ FIGURE 6-11
Determining equilibrium concentrations and partial pressures

EXAMPLE 6-13 Using the Reaction Quotient, Q_c, in an Equilibrium Calculation

Solid silver is added to a solution with these initial concentrations: $[Ag^+] = 0.200$ M, $[Fe^{2+}] = 0.100$ M, and $[Fe^{3+}] = 0.300$ M. The following reversible reaction occurs.

$$Ag^+(aq) + Fe^{2+}(aq) \rightleftharpoons Ag(s) + Fe^{3+}(aq) \qquad K_c = 2.98$$

What are the ion concentrations when equilibrium is established?

(continued)

Analyze

Because all reactants and products are present initially, we need to use the reaction quotient Q_c to determine the direction in which a net change occurs.

$$Q_c = \frac{[Fe^{3+}]}{[Ag^+][Fe^{2+}]} = \frac{0.300}{(0.200)(0.100)} = 15.0$$

Because Q_c (15.0) is larger than K_c (2.98), a net change must occur in the direction of the reverse reaction, *to the left*. Let's define x as the change in molarity of Fe^{3+}. Because the net change occurs *to the left*, we designate the changes for the species on the left side of the equation as positive and those on the right side as negative.

Solve

The reaction:	$Ag^+(aq)$	+	$Fe^{2+}(aq)$	$\rightleftharpoons$ $Ag(s)$ + $Fe^{3+}(aq)$
initial concns:	0.200 M		0.100 M	0.300 M
changes:	$+x$ M		$+x$ M	$-x$ M
equil concns:	$(0.200 + x)$ M		$(0.100 + x)$ M	$(0.300 - x)$ M

$$K_c = \frac{[Fe^{3+}]}{[Ag^+][Fe^{2+}]} = \frac{(0.300 - x)}{(0.200 + x)(0.100 + x)} = 2.98$$

This equation is a quadratic equation for which the acceptable root is $x = 0.11$. To obtain the equilibrium concentrations, we substitute this value of x into the terms shown in the table of data.

$$[Ag^+]_{equil} = 0.200 + 0.11 = 0.31\ M$$
$$[Fe^{2+}]_{equil} = 0.100 + 0.11 = 0.21\ M$$
$$[Fe^{3+}]_{equil} = 0.300 - 0.11 = 0.19\ M$$

Assess

If we have done the calculation correctly, we should obtain a value very close to that given for K_c when we substitute the *calculated* equilibrium concentrations into the reaction quotient, Q_c. We do.

$$Q_c = \frac{[Fe^{3+}]}{[Ag^+][Fe^{2+}]} = \frac{(0.19)}{(0.31)(0.21)} = 2.9 \qquad (K_c = 2.98)$$

PRACTICE EXAMPLE A: Excess Ag(s) is added to 1.20 M $Fe^{3+}(aq)$. Given that

$$Ag^+(aq) + Fe^{2+}(aq) \rightleftharpoons Ag(s) + Fe^{3+}(aq) \qquad K_c = 2.98$$

what are the equilibrium concentrations of the species in solution?

PRACTICE EXAMPLE B: A solution is prepared with $[V^{3+}] = [Cr^{2+}] = 0.0100$ M and $[V^{2+}] = [Cr^{3+}] = 0.150$ M. The following reaction occurs.

$$V^{3+}(aq) + Cr^{2+}(aq) \rightleftharpoons V^{2+}(aq) + Cr^{3+}(aq) \qquad K_c = 7.2 \times 10^2$$

What are the ion concentrations when equilibrium is established? [*Hint*: The algebra can be greatly simplified by extracting the square root of both sides of an equation at the appropriate point.]

Summary

6-1 Dynamic Equilibrium—**Equilibrium** is the condition in which the forward and reverse reaction rates of reversible processes are equal. Chemical and physical processes in equilibrium are dynamic by nature.

6-2 The Equilibrium Constant Expression—This condition of dynamic equilibrium is described through an **equilibrium constant expression**. The form of the equilibrium constant expression is established from the balanced chemical equation using activities to express the "effective" concentrations (equation 6.7). The numerical value obtained from the equilibrium constant expression is referred to as the **equilibrium constant**, K. Equilibrium constants are unitless.

6-3 Relationships Involving Equilibrium Constants—When the equation for a reversible reaction is written in the reverse order, the equilibrium constant expression and the value of K are both inverted from their original form. When two or more reactions are coupled together, the equilibrium constant for the overall reaction is the product of the K values of the individual reactions. The equilibrium constant of a reaction can have different values depending on the reference state used. For K_c a concentration reference state is used, while for K_p, a pressure reference state is used. The relationship between K_c and K_p is given by equation (6.16).

6-4 The Magnitude of an Equilibrium Constant—The magnitude of the equilibrium constant can be used to determine the outcome of a reaction. For large values of K the reaction goes to completion, with all reactants converted to products. A very small equilibrium constant, for example, a large negative power of ten, indicates that practically none of the reactants have been converted to products. Finally, equilibrium constants of an intermediate value, for example, between 10^{-10} and 10^{10}, indicate that some of the reactants have been converted to products.

6-5 The Reaction Quotient, Q: Predicting the Direction of Net Change—The **reaction quotient**, Q (equation 6.20), has the same form as the equilibrium constant expression; however, its numerical value is determined using the initial reaction activities. A comparison of the reaction quotient with the equilibrium constant makes it possible to predict the direction of net change leading to equilibrium (Fig. 6-5). If $Q < K$, the forward reaction is favored, meaning that when equilibrium is established the amounts of products will have increased and the amounts of reactants will have decreased. If $Q > K$, the reverse reaction is favored until equilibrium is established. If $Q = K$, neither the forward nor reverse reaction is favored. The initial conditions are in fact equilibrium conditions.

6-6 Altering Equilibrium Conditions: Le Châtelier's Principle—**Le Châtelier's principle** is used to make qualitative predictions of the effects of different variables on an equilibrium condition. This principle describes how an equilibrium condition is modified, or "shifts," in response to the addition or removal of reactants or changes in reaction volume, external pressure, or temperature. Catalysts, by speeding up the forward and reverse reactions equally, have no effect on an equilibrium condition.

6-7 Equilibrium Calculations Some Illustrative Examples—For quantitative equilibrium calculations, a few basic principles and algebraic techniques are required. A useful method employs a tabular system, called an **ICE table**, for keeping track of the *initial* concentrations of the reactants and products, *changes* in these concentrations, and the *equilibrium* concentrations.

Integrative Example

In the manufacture of ammonia, the chief source of hydrogen gas is the following reaction for the reforming of methane at high temperatures.

$$CH_4(g) + 2\,H_2O(g) \rightleftharpoons CO_2(g) + 4\,H_2(g) \qquad \textbf{(6.24)}$$

The following data are also given.

(a) $CO(g) + H_2O(g) \rightleftharpoons CO_2(g) + H_2(g) \qquad \Delta H° = -40\text{ kJ};\ K_c = 1.4 \text{ at } 1000\text{ K}$

(b) $CO(g) + 3\,H_2(g) \rightleftharpoons H_2O(g) + CH_4(g) \qquad \Delta H° = -230\text{ kJ};\ K_c = 190 \text{ at } 1000\text{ K}$

At 1000 K, 1.00 mol each of CH_4 and H_2O are allowed to come to equilibrium in a 10.0 L vessel. Calculate the number of moles of H_2 present at equilibrium. Would the yield of H_2 increase if the temperature were raised above 1000 K?

Analyze

First, we should assemble the data needed to solve this problem. The amounts of substances and a reaction volume are given, so we should be able to work with a K_c expression. However, because the K_c value for the reaction of interest is not given, we will have to derive this value by combining the two equations for which data are given. This will yield values of both K_c and ΔH for the reaction of interest.

To calculate the number of moles of H_2 at equilibrium we can use the ICE method, and to assess the effect of temperature on the equilibrium yield of H_2 we can apply Le Châtelier's principle.

Solve

We combine equations (a) and (b) to obtain the data needed in this problem.

(a)	$CO(g) + H_2O(g) \rightleftharpoons CO_2(g) + H_2(g)$	$\Delta H = -40$ kJ	$K_c = 1.4$
(b)	$CH_4(g) + H_2O(g) \rightleftharpoons CO(g) + 3\,H_2(g)$	$\Delta H = 230$ kJ	$K_c = 1/190$
Overall:	$CH_4(g) + 2\,H_2O(g) \rightleftharpoons CO_2(g) + 4\,H_2(g)$	$\Delta H = 190$ kJ	$K_c = 1.4/190 = 7.4 \times 10^{-3}$

Next we set up an ICE table in which x represents the number of moles of CH_4 consumed in reaching equilibrium.

The reaction:	$CH_4(g)$	+	$2\,H_2O(g)$	$\rightleftharpoons$	$CO_2(g)$	+	$4\,H_2(g)$
initial amounts:	1.00 mol		1.00 mol		0.00 mol		0.00 mol
changes:	$-x$ mol		$-2x$ mol		x mol		$4x$ mol
equil amounts:	$(1.00 - x)$ mol		$(1.00 - 2x)$ mol		x mol		$4x$ mol
equil concns, M:	$(1.00 - x)/10.0$		$(1.00 - 2x)/10.0$		$x/10.0$		$4x/10.0$

Now we set up K_c and make substitutions into the expression.

$$K_c = \frac{[CO_2][H_2]^4}{[CH_4][H_2O]^2}$$

$$= \frac{(x/10.0)(4x/10.0)^4}{[(1.00 - x)/10.0][(1.00 - 2x)/10.0]^2}$$

$$= \frac{x(4x)^4}{100(1.00 - x)(1.00 - 2x)^2} = 7.4 \times 10^{-3}$$

The above equation reduces to

$$256x^5 = 0.74[(1.00 - x)(1.00 - 2x)^2]$$

and then to

$$256x^5 - 0.74[(1.00 - x)(1.00 - 2x)^2] = 0 \qquad \textbf{(6.25)}$$

The solution to this equation is $x = 0.23$ mol. The number of moles of $I I_2$ at equilibrium is $4x = 0.92$ mol.

Because the reaction is endothermic ($\Delta H = 190$ kJ), the forward reaction is favored at higher temperatures. The equilibrium yield of H_2 will increase if the temperature is raised above 1000 K.

Assess

Equation (6.25) looks impossibly difficult to solve, but it is not. It can be solved for x rather simply by the method of successive approximations. An important clue as to the possible range of values for x can be found in the ICE table. Note that the equilibrium amount of $H_2O(g)$ is $1.00 - 2x$, meaning that $x < 0.50$, or else all of the $H_2O(g)$ would be consumed. This marks a good place to start the approximations.

PRACTICE EXAMPLE A: Glycolysis involves ten biochemical reactions. The first two reactions of the glycolysis cycle are

$$C_6H_{12}O_6(aq) + ATP(aq) \rightleftharpoons G6P(aq) + ADP(aq) \qquad \Delta H^\circ = -19.74 \text{ kJ mol}^{-1}$$

$$G6P(aq) \rightleftharpoons F6P(aq) \qquad \Delta H^\circ = 2.84 \text{ kJ mol}^{-1}$$

Calculate the equilibrium concentration of F6P(aq) generated in the glycolysis cycle at normal body temperature, 37 °C, starting with $[C_6H_{12}O_6(aq)] = 1.20 \times 10^{-6}$ M; $[ATP(aq)] = 10^{-4}$ M; and $[ADP(aq)] = 10^{-2}$ M. The equilibrium constant for the first reaction is 4.630×10^3; for the second reaction it is 2.76×10^{-1}. During a fever body temperature increases. Will [G6P] increase or decrease with an increase with temperature?

PRACTICE EXAMPLE B: A procedure calls for adding 0.100 mol of $Br_2(g)$ at 25 °C to a reaction. The only source of bromine in the laboratory is a bottle of liquid bromine. **(a)** Given the following data, what size container (in liters) must be used to extract enough $Br_2(g)$ for this reaction? The equilibrium constant at 298 K for the reaction $Br_2(g) \rightleftharpoons 2Br(g)$ is $K = 3.30 \times 10^{-29}$. The vapor pressure of liquid bromine is 0.289 atm. **(b)** At 1000 K the equilibrium constant for the reaction $Br_2(g) \rightleftharpoons 2Br(g)$ is 3.4×10^{-5}. What size vessel (in liters) will be needed if the temperature of the vapor is raised to 1000 K?

Exercises

Writing Equilibrium Constants Expressions

1. Based on these descriptions, write a balanced equation and the corresponding K_c expression for each reversible reaction.
(a) Carbonyl fluoride, $COF_2(g)$, decomposes into gaseous carbon dioxide and gaseous carbon tetrafluoride.
(b) Copper metal displaces silver(I) ion from aqueous solution, producing silver metal and an aqueous solution of copper(II) ion.
(c) Peroxodisulfate ion, $S_2O_8^{2-}$, oxidizes iron(II) ion to iron(III) ion in aqueous solution and is itself reduced to sulfate ion.
2. Based on these descriptions, write a balanced equation and the corresponding K_p expression for each reversible reaction.
(a) Oxygen gas oxidizes gaseous ammonia to gaseous nitrogen and water vapor.
(b) Hydrogen gas reduces gaseous nitrogen dioxide to gaseous ammonia and water vapor.
(c) Nitrogen gas reacts with the solid sodium carbonate and carbon to produce solid sodium cyanide and carbon monoxide gas.
3. Write equilibrium constant expressions, K_c, for the reactions
(a) $2\,NO(g) + O_2(g) \rightleftharpoons 2\,NO_2(g)$
(b) $Zn(s) + 2\,Ag^+(aq) \rightleftharpoons Zn^{2+}(aq) + 2\,Ag(s)$
(c) $Mg(OH)_2(s) + CO_3^{2-}(aq) \rightleftharpoons MgCO_3(s) + 2\,OH^-(aq)$
4. Write equilibrium constant expressions, K_p, for the reactions
(a) $CS_2(g) + 4\,H_2(g) \rightleftharpoons CH_4(g) + 2\,H_2S(g)$
(b) $Ag_2O(s) \rightleftharpoons 2\,Ag(s) + \frac{1}{2}O_2(g)$
(c) $2\,NaHCO_3(s) \rightleftharpoons Na_2CO_3(s) + CO_2(g) + H_2O(g)$
5. Write an equilibrium constant, K_c, for the formation from its gaseous elements of **(a)** 1 mol $HF(g)$; **(b)** 2 mol $NH_3(g)$; **(c)** 2 mol $N_2O(g)$; **(d)** 1 mol $ClF_3(l)$.
6. Write an equilibrium constant, K_p, for the formation from its gaseous elements of **(a)** 1 mol $NOCl(g)$; **(b)** 2 mol $ClNO_2(g)$; **(c)** 1 mol $N_2H_4(g)$; **(d)** 1 mol $NH_4Cl(s)$.
7. Determine values of K_c from the K_p values given.
(a) $SO_2Cl_2(g) \rightleftharpoons SO_2(g) + Cl_2(g)$ $\quad K_p = 2.9 \times 10^{-2}$ at 303 K
(b) $2\,NO(g) + O_2(g) \rightleftharpoons 2\,NO_2(g)$ $\quad K_p = 1.48 \times 10^4$ at 184 °C
(c) $Sb_2S_3(s) + 3\,H_2(g) \rightleftharpoons 2\,Sb(s) + 3\,H_2S(g)$ $\quad K_p = 0.429$ at 713 K
8. Determine the values of K_p from the K_c values given.
(a) $N_2O_4(g) \rightleftharpoons 2\,NO_2(g)$ $\quad K_c = 4.61 \times 10^{-3}$ at 25 °C
(b) $2\,CH_4(g) \rightleftharpoons C_2H_2(g) + 3\,H_2(g)$ $\quad K_c = 0.154$ at 2000 K
(c) $2\,H_2S(g) + CH_4(g) \rightleftharpoons 4\,H_2(g) + CS_2(g)$ $\quad K_c = 5.27 \times 10^{-8}$ at 973 K
9. The vapor pressure of water at 25 °C is 23.8 mmHg. Write K_p for the vaporization of water, with pressures in atmospheres. What is the value of K_c for the vaporization process?
10. If $K_c = 5.12 \times 10^{-3}$ for the equilibrium established between liquid benzene and its vapor at 25 °C, what is the vapor pressure of C_6H_6 at 25 °C, expressed in millimeters of mercury?
11. Determine K_c for the reaction

$$\frac{1}{2}N_2(g) + \frac{1}{2}O_2(g) + \frac{1}{2}Br_2(g) \rightleftharpoons NOBr(g)$$

from the following information (at 298 K).

$$2\,NO(g) \rightleftharpoons N_2(g) + O_2(g) \quad K_c = 2.1 \times 10^{30}$$

$$NO(g) + \frac{1}{2}Br_2(g) \rightleftharpoons NOBr(g) \quad K_c = 1.4$$

12. Given the equilibrium constant values

$$N_2(g) + \frac{1}{2}O_2(g) \rightleftharpoons N_2O(g) \quad K_c = 2.7 \times 10^{-18}$$

$$N_2O_4(g) \rightleftharpoons 2\,NO_2(g) \quad K_c = 4.6 \times 10^{-3}$$

$$\frac{1}{2}N_2(g) + O_2(g) \rightleftharpoons NO_2(g) \quad K_c = 4.1 \times 10^{-9}$$

Determine a value of K_c for the reaction

$$2\,N_2O(g) + 3\,O_2(g) \rightleftharpoons 2\,N_2O_4(g)$$

13. Use the following data to estimate a value of K_p at 1200 K for the reaction $2\,H_2(g) + O_2(g) \rightleftharpoons 2\,H_2O(g)$

$$C(graphite) + CO_2(g) \rightleftharpoons 2\,CO(g) \quad K_c = 0.64$$

$$CO_2(g) + H_2(g) \rightleftharpoons CO(g) + H_2O(g) \quad K_c = 1.4$$

$$C(graphite) + \frac{1}{2}O_2(g) \rightleftharpoons CO(g) \quad K_c = 1 \times 10^8$$

14. Determine K_c for the reaction $N_2(g) + O_2(g) + Cl_2(g) \rightleftharpoons 2\,NOCl(g)$, given the following data at 298 K.

$$\frac{1}{2}N_2(g) + O_2(g) \rightleftharpoons NO_2(g) \quad K_p = 1.0 \times 10^{-9}$$

$$NOCl(g) + \frac{1}{2}O_2(g) \rightleftharpoons NO_2Cl(g) \qquad K_p = 1.1 \times 10^2$$

$$NO_2(g) + \frac{1}{2}Cl_2(g) \rightleftharpoons NO_2Cl(g) \qquad K_p = 0.3$$

15. An important environmental and physiological reaction is the formation of carbonic acid, $H_2CO_3(aq)$, from carbon dioxide and water. Write the equilibrium constant expression for this reaction in terms of activities. Convert that expression into an equilibrium constant expression containing concentrations and pressures.

16. Rust, $Fe_2O_3(s)$, is caused by the oxidation of iron by oxygen. Write the equilibrium constant expression first in terms of activities, and then in terms of concentration and pressure.

Experimental Determination of Equilibrium Constants

17. 1.00×10^{-3} mol PCl_5 is introduced into a 250.0 mL flask, and equilibrium is established at 284 °C: $PCl_5(g) \rightleftharpoons PCl_3(g) + Cl_2(g)$. The quantity of $Cl_2(g)$ present at equilibrium is found to be 9.65×10^{-4} mol. What is the value of K_c for the dissociation reaction at 284 °C?

18. A mixture of 1.00 g H_2 and 1.06 g H_2S in a 0.500 L flask comes to equilibrium at 1670 K: $2\,H_2(g) + S_2(g) \rightleftharpoons 2\,H_2S(g)$. The equilibrium amount of $S_2(g)$ found is 8.00×10^{-6} mol. Determine the value of K_p at 1670 K.

19. The two common chlorides of phosphorus, PCl_3 and PCl_5, both important in the production of other phosphorus compounds, coexist in equilibrium through the reaction

$$PCl_3(g) + Cl_2(g) \rightleftharpoons PCl_5(g)$$

At 250 °C, an equilibrium mixture in a 2.50 L flask contains 0.105 g PCl_5, 0.220 g PCl_3, and 2.12 g Cl_2. What are the values of **(a)** K_c and **(b)** K_p for this reaction at 250 °C?

20. A 0.682 g sample of ICl(g) is placed in a 625 mL reaction vessel at 682 K. When equilibrium is reached between the ICl(g) and $I_2(g)$ and $Cl_2(g)$ formed by its dissociation, 0.0383 g I_2 is present. What is K_c for this reaction?

21. Write the equilibrium constant expression for the following reaction,

$$Fe(OH)_3 + 3H^+(aq) \rightleftharpoons Fe^{3+}(aq) + 3H_2O(l) \qquad K = 9.1 \times 10^3$$

and compute the equilibrium concentration for $[Fe^{3+}]$ at pH = 7 (i.e., $[H^+] = 1.0 \times 10^{-7}$).

22. Write the equilibrium constant expression for the dissolution of ammonia in water:

$$NH_3(g) \rightleftharpoons NH_3(aq) \qquad K = 57.5$$

Use this equilibrium constant expression to estimate the partial pressure of $NH_3(g)$ over a solution containing 5×10^{-9} M $NH_3(aq)$. These are conditions similar to that found for acid rains with a high ammonium ion concentration.

Equilibrium Relationships

23. Equilibrium is established at 1000 K, where $K_c = 281$ for the reaction $2\,SO_2(g) + O_2(g) \rightleftharpoons 2\,SO_3(g)$. The equilibrium amount of $O_2(g)$ in a 0.185 L flask is 0.00247 mol. What is the ratio of $[SO_2]$ to $[SO_3]$ in this equilibrium mixture?

24. For the dissociation of $I_2(g)$ at about 1200 °C, $I_2(g) \rightleftharpoons 2\,I(g)$, $K_c = 1.1 \times 10^{-2}$. What volume flask should we use if we want 0.37 mol I to be present for every 1.00 mol I_2 at equilibrium?

25. In the Ostwald process for oxidizing ammonia, a variety of products is possible—N_2, N_2O, NO, and NO_2—depending on the conditions. One possibility is

$$NH_3(g) + \frac{5}{4}O_2(g) \rightleftharpoons NO(g) + \frac{3}{2}H_2O(g)$$

$$K_p = 2.11 \times 10^{19} \text{ at } 700\text{ K}$$

For the decomposition of NO_2 at 700 K,

$$NO_2(g) \rightleftharpoons NO(g) + \frac{1}{2}O_2(g) \qquad K_p = 0.524$$

(a) Write a chemical equation for the oxidation of $NH_3(g)$ to $NO_2(g)$.
(b) Determine K_p for the chemical equation you have written.

26. At 2000 K, $K_c = 0.154$ for the reaction $2\,CH_4(g) \rightleftharpoons C_2H_2(g) + 3\,H_2(g)$. If a 1.00 L equilibrium mixture at 2000 K contains 0.10 mol each of $CH_4(g)$ and $H_2(g)$,
(a) what is the mole fraction of $C_2H_2(g)$ present?
(b) Is the conversion of $CH_4(g)$ to $C_2H_2(g)$ favored at high or low pressures?
(c) If the equilibrium mixture at 2000 K is transferred from a 1.00 L flask to a 2.00 L flask, will the number of moles of $C_2H_2(g)$ increase, decrease, or remain unchanged?

27. An equilibrium mixture at 1000 K contains 0.276 mol H_2, 0.276 mol CO_2, 0.224 mol CO, and 0.224 mol H_2O.

$$CO_2(g) + H_2(g) \rightleftharpoons CO(g) + H_2O(g)$$

(a) Show that for this reaction, K_c is independent of the reaction volume, V.
(b) Determine the value of K_c and K_p.

28. For the reaction $CO(g) + H_2O(g) \rightleftharpoons CO_2(g) + H_2(g)$, $K_p = 23.2$ at 600 K. Explain which of the following situations might be found at equilibrium: **(a)** $P_{CO} = P_{H_2O} = P_{CO_2} = P_{H_2}$; **(b)** $P_{H_2}/P_{H_2O} = P_{CO_2}/P_{CO}$; **(c)** $(P_{CO_2})(P_{H_2}) = (P_{CO})(P_{H_2O})$; **(d)** $P_{CO_2}/P_{H_2O} = P_{H_2}/P_{CO}$.

Direction and Extent of Chemical Change

29. Can a mixture of 2.2 mol O_2, 3.6 mol SO_2, and 1.8 mol SO_3 be maintained indefinitely in a 7.2 L flask at a temperature at which $K_c = 100$ in this reaction? Explain.

$$2\,SO_2(g) + O_2(g) \rightleftharpoons 2\,SO_3(g)$$

30. Is a mixture of 0.0205 mol $NO_2(g)$ and 0.750 mol $N_2O_4(g)$ in a 5.25 L flask at 25 °C, at equilibrium? If not, in which direction will the reaction proceed—toward products or reactants?

$$N_2O_4(g) \rightleftharpoons 2\,NO_2(g) \qquad K_c = 4.61 \times 10^{-3} \text{ at } 25\text{ °C}$$

31. In the reaction $2\,SO_2(g) + O_2(g) \rightleftharpoons 2\,SO_3(g)$, 0.455 mol SO_2, 0.183 mol O_2, and 0.568 mol SO_3 are introduced simultaneously into a 1.90 L vessel at 1000 K.
(a) If $K_c = 2.8 \times 10^2$, is this mixture at equilibrium?
(b) If not, in which direction will a net change occur?

32. In the reaction $CO(g) + H_2O(g) \rightleftharpoons CO_2(g) + H_2(g)$, $K = 31.4$ at 588 K. Equal masses of each reactant and product are brought together in a reaction vessel at 588 K.
(a) Can this mixture be at equilibrium?
(b) If not, in which direction will a net change occur?

33. A mixture consisting of 0.150 mol H_2 and 0.150 mol I_2 is brought to equilibrium at 445 °C, in a 3.25 L flask. What are the equilibrium amounts of H_2, I_2, and HI?

$$H_2(g) + I_2(g) \rightleftharpoons 2\,HI\,(g) \qquad K_c = 50.2 \text{ at } 445\text{ °C}$$

34. Starting with 0.280 mol $SbCl_3$ and 0.160 mol Cl_2, how many moles of $SbCl_5$, $SbCl_3$, and Cl_2 are present when equilibrium is established at 248 °C in a 2.50 L flask?

$$SbCl_5(g) \rightleftharpoons SbCl_3(g) + Cl_2(g)$$
$$K_c = 2.5 \times 10^{-2} \text{ at } 248\text{ °C}$$

35. Starting with 0.3500 mol CO(g) and 0.05500 mol $COCl_2(g)$ in a 3.050 L flask at 668 K, how many moles of $Cl_2(g)$ will be present at equilibrium?

$$CO(g) + Cl_2(g) \rightleftharpoons COCl_2(g)$$
$$K_c = 1.2 \times 10^3 \text{ at } 668\text{ K}$$

36. 1.00 g *each* of CO, H_2O, and H_2 are sealed in a 1.41 L vessel and brought to equilibrium at 600 K. How many grams of CO_2 will be present in the equilibrium mixture?

$$CO(g) + H_2O(g) \rightleftharpoons CO_2(g) + H_2(g) \qquad K_c = 23.2$$

37. Equilibrium is established in a 2.50 L flask at 250 °C for the reaction

$$PCl_5(g) \rightleftharpoons PCl_3(g) + Cl_2(g) \qquad K_c = 3.8 \times 10^{-2}$$

How many moles of PCl_5, PCl_3, and Cl_2 are present at equilibrium, if
(a) 0.550 mol each of PCl_5 and PCl_3 are initially introduced into the flask?
(b) 0.610 mol PCl_5 alone is introduced into the flask?

38. For the following reaction, $K_c = 2.00$ at 1000 °C.

$$2\,COF_2(g) \rightleftharpoons CO_2(g) + CF_4(g)$$

If a 5.00 L mixture contains 0.145 mol COF_2, 0.262 mol CO_2, and 0.074 mol CF_4 at a temperature of 1000 °C,
(a) Will the mixture be at equilibrium?
(b) If the gases are not at equilibrium, in what direction will a net change occur?
(c) How many moles of each gas will be present at equilibrium?

39. In the following reaction, $K_c = 4.0$.

$$C_2H_5OH + CH_3COOH \rightleftharpoons CH_3COOC_2H_5 + H_2O$$

A reaction is allowed to occur in a mixture of 17.2 g C_2H_5OH, 23.8 g CH_3COOH, 48.6 g $CH_3COOC_2H_5$, and 71.2 g H_2O.
(a) In what direction will a net change occur?
(b) How many grams of each substance will be present at equilibrium?

40. The N_2O_4–NO_2 equilibrium mixture in the flask on the left in the figure is allowed to expand into the evacuated flask on the right. What is the composition of the gaseous mixture when equilibrium is re-established in the system consisting of the two flasks?

$$N_2O_4(g) \rightleftharpoons 2\,NO_2(g) \qquad K_c = 4.61 \times 10^{-3} \text{ at } 25\text{ °C}$$

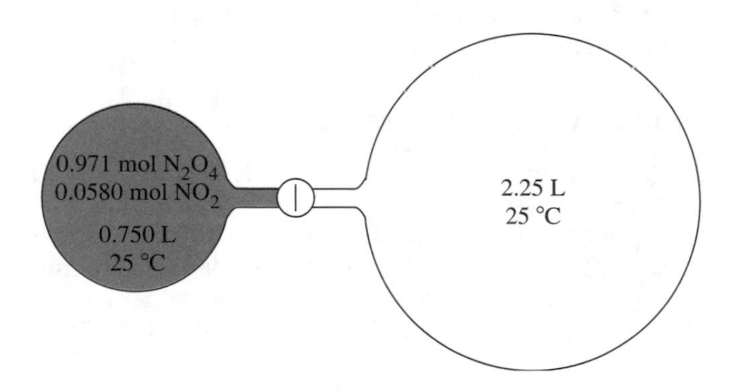

41. Formamide, used in the manufacture of pharmaceuticals, dyes, and agricultural chemicals, decomposes at high temperatures.

$$HCONH_2(g) \rightleftharpoons NH_3(g) + CO(g)$$
$$K_c = 4.84 \text{ at } 400\text{ K}$$

If 0.186 mol $HCONH_2(g)$ dissociates in a 2.16 L flask at 400 K, what will be the *total* pressure at equilibrium?

42. A mixture of 1.00 mol $NaHCO_3(s)$ and 1.00 mol $Na_2CO_3(s)$ is introduced into a 2.50 L flask in which the partial pressure of CO_2 is 2.10 atm and that of $H_2O(g)$ is 715 mmHg. When equilibrium is established at 100 °C, will the partial pressures of $CO_2(g)$ and $H_2O(g)$ be greater or less than their initial partial pressures? Explain.

$$2\,NaHCO_3(s) \rightleftharpoons Na_2CO_3(s) + CO_2(g) + H_2O(g)$$
$$K_p = 0.23 \text{ at } 100\text{ °C}$$

43. Cadmium metal is added to 0.350 L of an aqueous solution in which $[Cr^{3+}] = 1.00$ M. What are the concentrations of the different ionic species at equilibrium? What is the minimum mass of cadmium metal required to establish this equilibrium?

$$2\,Cr^{3+}(aq) + Cd(s) \rightleftharpoons 2\,Cr^{2+}(aq) + Cd^{2+}(aq) \qquad K_c = 0.288$$

44. Lead metal is added to 0.100 M Cr^{3+}(aq). What are $[Pb^{2+}]$, $[Cr^{2+}]$, and $[Cr^{3+}]$ when equilibrium is established in the reaction?

$$Pb(s) + 2\,Cr^{3+}(aq) \rightleftharpoons Pb^{2+}(aq) + 2\,Cr^{2+}(aq) \qquad K_c = 3.2 \times 10^{-10}$$

45. One sketch below represents an initial nonequilibrium mixture in the reversible reaction

$$SO_2(g) + Cl_2(g) \rightleftharpoons SO_2Cl_2(g) \qquad K_c = 4.0$$

Which of the other three sketches best represents an equilibrium mixture? Explain.

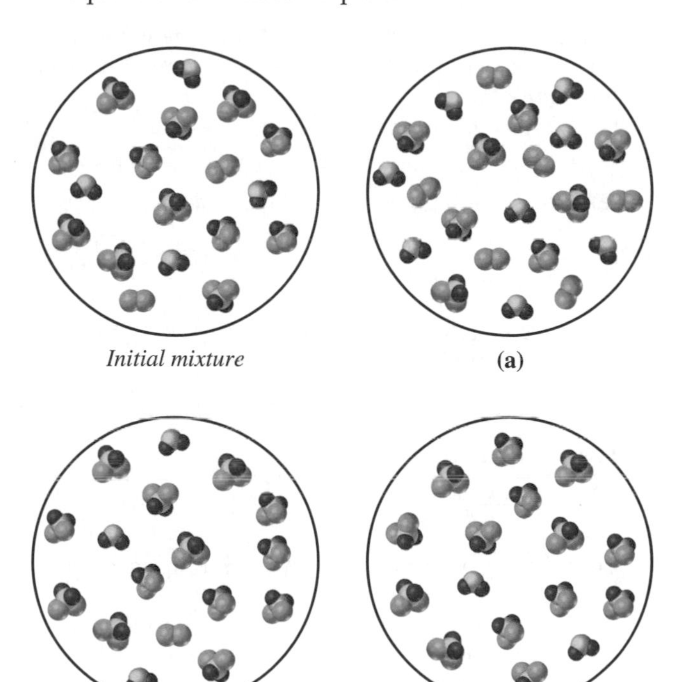

46. One sketch below represents an initial nonequilibrium mixture in the reversible reaction

$$2\,NO(g) + Br_2(g) \rightleftharpoons 2\,NOBr(g) \qquad K_c = 3.0$$

Which of the other three sketches best represents an equilibrium mixture? Explain.

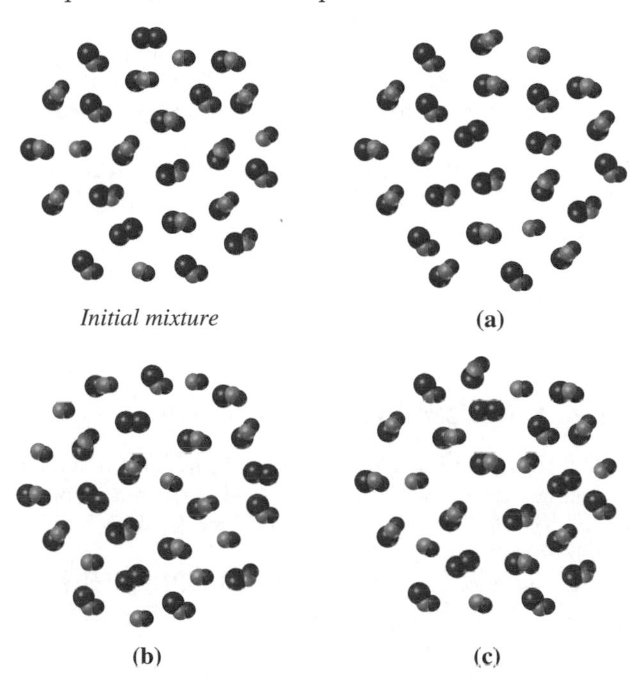

47. One important reaction in the citric acid cycle is

$$\text{citrate(aq)} \rightleftharpoons \text{aconitate(aq)} + H_2O(l) \qquad K = 0.031$$

Write the equilibrium constant expression for the above reaction. Given that the concentrations of [citrate(aq)] = 0.00128 M, [aconitate(aq)] = 4.0×10^{-5} M, and $[H_2O] = 55.5$ M, calculate the reaction quotient. Is this reaction at equilibrium? If not, in which direction will it proceed?

48. The following reaction is an important reaction in the citric acid cycle:

$$\text{citrate(aq)} + NAD_{ox}(aq) + H_2O(l) \rightleftharpoons CO_2(aq) + NAD_{red} + \text{oxoglutarate(aq)} \qquad K = 0.387$$

Write the equilibrium constant expression for the above reaction. Given the following data for this reaction, [citrate] = 0.00128 M, $[NAD_{ox}] = 0.00868$, $[H_2O] = 55.5$ M, $[CO_2] = 0.00868$ M, $[NAD_{red}] = 0.00132$ M, and [oxoglutarate] = 0.00868 M, calculate the reaction quotient. Is this reaction at equilibrium? If not, in which direction will it proceed?

Partial Pressure Equilibrium Constant, K_p

49. Refer to Example 6-4. H_2S(g) at 747.6 mmHg pressure and a 1.85 g sample of I_2(s) are introduced into a 725 mL flask at 60 °C. What will be the total pressure in the flask at equilibrium?

$$H_2S(g) + I_2(s) \rightleftharpoons 2\,HI(g) + S(s) \qquad K_p = 1.34 \times 10^{-5} \text{ at } 60\,°C$$

50. A sample of NH_4HS(s) is placed in a 2.58 L flask containing 0.100 mol NH_3(g). What will be the total gas pressure when equilibrium is established at 25 °C?

$$NH_4HS(s) \rightleftharpoons NH_3(g) + H_2S(g) \qquad K_p = 0.108 \text{ at } 25\,°C$$

51. The following reaction is used in some self-contained breathing devices as a source of $O_2(g)$.

$$4\,KO_2(s) + 2\,CO_2(g) \rightleftharpoons 2\,K_2CO_3(s) + 3\,O_2(g) \qquad K_p = 28.5 \text{ at } 25\,°C$$

Suppose that a sample of $CO_2(g)$ is added to an evacuated flask containing $KO_2(s)$ and equilibrium is established. If the equilibrium partial pressure of $CO_2(g)$ is found to be 0.0721 atm, what are the equilibrium partial pressure of $O_2(g)$ and the total gas pressure?

52. Concerning the reaction in Exercise 51, if $KO_2(s)$ and $K_2CO_3(s)$ are maintained in contact with air at 1.00 atm and 25 °C, in which direction will a net change occur to establish equilibrium? Explain. [*Hint:* Recall equation (6.17). Air is 20.946% O_2 and 0.0379% CO_2 by volume.]

53. 1.00 mol *each* of CO and Cl_2 are introduced into an evacuated 1.75 L flask, and the following equilibrium is established at 668 K.

$$CO(g) + Cl_2(g) \longrightarrow COCl_2(g) \qquad K_p = 22.5$$

For this equilibrium, calculate **(a)** the partial pressure of $COCl_2(g)$; **(b)** the total gas pressure.

54. For the reaction $2\,NO_2(g) \rightleftharpoons 2\,NO(g) + O_2(g)$, $K_c = 1.8 \times 10^{-6}$ at 184 °C. What is the value of K_p for this reaction at 184 °C?

$$NO(g) + \frac{1}{2}O_2(g) \rightleftharpoons NO_2(g)$$

Le Châtelier's Principle

55. Continuous removal of one of the products of a chemical reaction has the effect of causing the reaction to go to completion. Explain this fact in terms of Le Châtelier's principle.

56. We can represent the freezing of $H_2O(l)$ at 0 °C as $H_2O(l, d = 1.00\ g/cm^3) \rightleftharpoons H_2O(s, d = 0.92\ g/cm^3)$. Explain why increasing the pressure on ice causes it to melt. Is this the behavior you expect for solids in general? Explain.

57. Explain how each of the following affects the amount of H_2 present in an equilibrium mixture in the reaction

$$3\,Fe(s) + 4\,H_2O(g) \rightleftharpoons Fe_3O_4(s) + 4\,H_2(g) \qquad \Delta H° = -150\ kJ$$

(a) Raising the temperature of the mixture; **(b)** introducing more $H_2O(g)$; **(c)** doubling the volume of the container holding the mixture; **(d)** adding an appropriate catalyst.

58. In the gas phase, iodine reacts with cyclopentene (C_5H_8) by a free radical mechanism to produce cyclopentadiene (C_5H_6) and hydrogen iodide. Explain how each of the following affects the amount of HI(g) present in the equilibrium mixture in the reaction

$$I_2(g) + C_5H_8(g) \rightleftharpoons C_5H_6(g) + 2\,HI(g) \qquad \Delta H° = 92.5\ kJ$$

(a) Raising the temperature of the mixture; **(b)** introducing more $C_5H_6(g)$; **(c)** doubling the volume of the container holding the mixture; **(d)** adding an appropriate catalyst; **(e)** adding an inert gas such as He to a constant-volume reaction mixture.

59. The reaction $N_2(g) + O_2(g) \rightleftharpoons 2\,NO(g)$, $\Delta H° = +181\ kJ$, occurs in high-temperature combustion processes carried out in air. Oxides of nitrogen produced from the nitrogen and oxygen in air are intimately involved in the production of photochemical smog. What effect does increasing the temperature have on **(a)** the equilibrium production of NO(g); **(b)** the rate of this reaction?

60. Use data from Appendix A to determine whether the forward reaction is favored by high temperatures or low temperatures.

(a) $PCl_3(g) + Cl_2(g) \rightleftharpoons PCl_5(g)$

(b) $SO_2(g) + 2\,H_2S(g) \rightleftharpoons 2\,H_2O(g) + 3\,S(s)$

(c) $2\,N_2(g) + 3\,O_2(g) + 4\,HCl(g) \rightleftharpoons 4\,NOCl(g) + 2\,H_2O(g)$

61. If the volume of an equilibrium mixture of $N_2(g)$, $H_2(g)$, and $NH_3(g)$ is reduced by doubling the pressure, will P_{N_2} have increased, decreased, or remained the same when equilibrium is re established? Explain.

$$N_2(g) + 3\,H_2(g) \rightleftharpoons 2\,NH_3(g)$$

62. For the reaction

$$A(s) \rightleftharpoons B(s) + 2\,C(g) + \frac{1}{2}D(g) \qquad \Delta H° = 0$$

(a) Will K_p increase, decrease, or remain constant with temperature? Explain.
(b) If a *constant-volume* mixture at equilibrium at 298 K is heated to 400 K and equilibrium re-established, will the number of moles of D(g) increase, decrease, or remain constant? Explain.

63. What effect does increasing the volume of the system have on the equilibrium condition in each of the following reactions?

(a) $C(s) + H_2O(g) \rightleftharpoons CO(g) + H_2(g)$

(b) $Ca(OH)_2(s) + CO_2(g) \rightleftharpoons CaCO_3(s) + H_2O(g)$

(c) $4\,NH_3(g) + 5\,O_2(g) \rightleftharpoons 4\,NO(g) + 6\,H_2O(g)$

64. For which of the following reactions would you expect the extent of the forward reaction to increase with increasing temperatures? Explain.

(a) $NO(g) \rightleftharpoons \frac{1}{2}N_2(g) + \frac{1}{2}O_2(g) \qquad \Delta H° = -90.2\ kJ$

(b) $SO_3(g) \rightleftharpoons SO_2(g) + \frac{1}{2}O_2(g) \qquad \Delta H° = +98.9\ kJ$

(c) $N_2H_4(g) \rightleftharpoons N_2(g) + 2\,H_2(g) \qquad \Delta H° = -95.4\ kJ$

(d) $COCl_2(g) \rightleftharpoons CO(g) + Cl_2(g) \qquad \Delta H° = +108.3\ kJ$

65. The following reaction represents the binding of oxygen by the protein hemoglobin (Hb):

$$Hb(aq) + O_2(aq) \rightleftharpoons Hb{:}O_2(aq) \qquad \Delta H < 0$$

Explain how each of the following affects the amount of $Hb:O_2$: **(a)** increasing the temperature; **(b)** decreasing the pressure of O_2; **(c)** increasing the amount of hemoglobin.

66. In the human body, the enzyme carbonic anahydrase catalyzes the interconversion of CO_2 and HCO_3^- by either adding or removing the hydroxide anion. The overall reaction is endothermic. Explain how the following affect the amount of carbon dioxide: **(a)** increasing the amount of bicarbonate anion; **(b)** increasing the pressure of carbon dioxide; **(c)** increasing the amount of carbonic anhydrase; **(d)** decreasing the temperature.

67. A crystal of dinitrogen tetroxide (melting point, −9.3 °C; boiling point, 21.3 °C) is added to an equilibrium mixture of dintrogen tetroxide and nitrogen dioxide that is at 20.0 °C. Will the pressure of nitrogen dioxide increase, decrease, or remain the same? Explain.

68. When hydrogen iodide is heated, the degree of dissociation increases. Is the dissociation reaction exothermic or endothermic? Explain.

69. The standard enthalpy of reaction for the decomposition of calcium carbonate is $\Delta H° = 813.5\ kJ\ mol^{-1}$. As temperature increases, does the concentration of calcium carbonate increase, decrease, or remain the same? Explain.

70. Would you expect that the amount of N_2 to increase, decrease, or remain the same in a scuba diver's body as he or she descends below the water surface?

Integrative and Advanced Exercises

71. Explain why the percent of molecules that dissociate into atoms in reactions of the type $I_2(g) \rightleftharpoons 2\,I(g)$ *always* increases with an increase in temperature.

72. A 1.100 L flask at 25 °C and 1.00 atm pressure contains $CO_2(g)$ in contact with 100.0 mL of a saturated aqueous solution in which $[CO_2(aq)] = 3.29 \times 10^{-2}$ M.
(a) What is the value of K_c at 25 °C for the equilibrium $CO_2(g) \rightleftharpoons CO_2(aq)$?
(b) If 0.01000 mol of radioactive $^{14}CO_2$ is added to the flask, how many moles of the $^{14}CO_2$ will be found in the gas phase and in the aqueous solution when equilibrium is re-established? [*Hint:* The radioactive $^{14}CO_2$ distributes itself between the two phases in exactly the same manner as the nonradioactive $^{12}CO_2$.]

73. Refer to Example 6-13. Suppose that 0.100 L of the equilibrium mixture is diluted to 0.250 L with water. What will be the new concentrations when equilibrium is re-established?

74. In the equilibrium described in Example 6-12, the percent dissociation of N_2O_4 can be expressed as

$$\frac{3.00 \times 10^{-3}\ \text{mol}\ N_2O_4}{0.0240\ \text{mol}\ N_2O_4\ \text{initially}} \times 100\% = 12.5\%$$

What must be the total pressure of the gaseous mixture if $N_2O_4(g)$ is to be 10.0% dissociated at 298 K?

$$N_2O_4 \rightleftharpoons 2\,NO_2(g) \qquad K_p = 0.113 \text{ at } 298\ K$$

75. Starting with $SO_3(g)$ at 1.00 atm, what will be the total pressure when equilibrium is reached in the following reaction at 700 K?

$$2\,SO_3(g) \rightleftharpoons 2\,SO_2(g) + O_2(g) \qquad K_p = 1.6 \times 10^{-5}$$

76. A sample of air with a mole ratio of N_2 to O_2 of 79:21 is heated to 2500 K. When equilibrium is established in a closed container with air initially at 1.00 atm, the mole percent of NO is found to be 1.8%. Calculate K_p for the reaction.

$$N_2(g) + O_2(g) \rightleftharpoons 2\,NO(g)$$

77. Derive, by calculation, the equilibrium amounts of SO_2, O_2, and SO_3 listed in **(a)** Figure 6-6(c); **(b)** Figure 6-7(b).

78. The decomposition of salicylic acid to phenol and carbon dioxide was carried out at 200.0 °C, a temperature at which the reactant and products are all gaseous. A 0.300 g sample of salicylic acid was introduced into a 50.0 mL reaction vessel, and equilibrium was established. The equilibrium mixture was rapidly cooled to condense salicylic acid and phenol as solids; the $CO_2(g)$ was collected over mercury and its volume was measured at 20.0 °C and 730 mmHg. In two identical experiments, the volumes of $CO_2(g)$ obtained were 48.2 and 48.5 mL, respectively. Calculate K_p for this reaction.

OH ⇌ OH + CO_2

COOH

79. One of the key reactions in the gasification of coal is the methanation reaction, in which methane is produced from synthesis gas—a mixture of CO and H_2.

$$CO(g) + 3\,H_2(g) \rightleftharpoons CH_4(g) + H_2O(g)$$
$$\Delta H = -230\ kJ;\ K_c = 190 \text{ at } 1000\ K$$

(a) Is the equilibrium conversion of synthesis gas to methane favored at higher or lower temperatures? Higher or lower pressures?
(b) Assume you have 4.00 mol of synthesis gas with a 3:1 mol ratio of $H_2(g)$ to $CO(g)$ in a 15.0 L flask. What will be the mole fraction of $CH_4(g)$ at equilibrium at 1000 K?

80. A sample of pure $PCl_5(g)$ is introduced into an evacuated flask and allowed to dissociate.

$$PCl_5(g) \rightleftharpoons PCl_3(g) + Cl_2(g)$$

If the fraction of PCl_5 molecules that dissociate is denoted by α, and if the total gas pressure is P, show that

$$K_p = \frac{\alpha^2 P}{1 - \alpha^2}$$

81. Nitrogen dioxide obtained as a cylinder gas is always a mixture of $NO_2(g)$ and $N_2O_4(g)$. A 5.00 g sample obtained from such a cylinder is sealed in a 0.500 L flask at 298 K. What is the mole fraction of NO_2 in this mixture?

$$N_2O_4(g) \rightleftharpoons 2\,NO_2(g) \qquad K_c = 4.61 \times 10^{-3}$$

82. What is the apparent molar mass of the gaseous mixture that results when $COCl_2(g)$ is allowed to dissociate at 395 °C and a total pressure of 3.00 atm?

$$COCl_2(g) \rightleftharpoons CO(g) + Cl_2(g)$$
$$K_p = 4.44 \times 10^{-2} \text{ at } 395\text{ °C}$$

Think of the apparent molar mass as the molar mass of a hypothetical single gas that is equivalent to the gaseous mixture.

83. Show that in terms of mole fractions of gases and *total* gas pressure the equilibrium constant expression for

$$N_2(g) + 3\,H_2(g) \rightleftharpoons 2\,NH_3(g)$$

is

$$K_p = \frac{(x_{NH_3})^2}{(x_{N_2})(x_{H_2})^2} \times \frac{1}{(P_{tot})^2}$$

84. For the synthesis of ammonia at 500 K, $N_2(g) + 3\,H_2(g) \rightleftharpoons 2\,NH_3(g)$, $K_p = 9.06 \times 10^{-2}$. Assume that N_2 and H_2 are mixed in the mole ratio 1:3 and that the total pressure is maintained at 1.00 atm. What is the mole percent NH_3 at equilibrium? [*Hint*: Use the equation from Exercise 83.]

85. A mixture of $H_2S(g)$ and $CH_4(g)$ in the mole ratio 2:1 was brought to equilibrium at 700 °C and a total pressure of 1 atm. On analysis, the equilibrium mixture was found to contain 9.54×10^{-3} mol H_2S. The CS_2 present at equilibrium was converted successively to H_2SO_4 and then to $BaSO_4$; 1.42×10^{-3} mol $BaSO_4$ was obtained. Use these data to determine K_p at 700 °C for the reaction

$$2\,H_2S(g) + CH_4(g) \rightleftharpoons CS_2(g) + 4\,H_2(g)$$
$$K_p \text{ at } 700\text{ °C} = ?$$

86. A solution is prepared having these initial concentrations: $[Fe^{3+}] = [Hg_2^{2+}] = 0.5000$ M; $[Fe^{2+}] = [Hg^{2+}] = 0.03000$ M. The following reaction occurs among the ions at 25 °C.

$$2\,Fe^{3+}(aq) + Hg_2^{2+}(aq) \rightleftharpoons 2\,Fe^{2+}(aq) + 2\,Hg^{2+}(aq)$$
$$K_c = 9.14 \times 10^{-6}$$

What will be the ion concentrations at equilibrium?

87. Refer to the Integrative Example. A gaseous mixture is prepared containing 0.100 mol each of $CH_4(g)$, $H_2O(g)$, $CO_2(g)$, and $H_2(g)$ in a 5.00 L flask. Then the mixture is allowed to come to equilibrium at 1000 K in reaction (6.24). What will be the equilibrium amount, in moles, of each gas?

88. Concerning the reaction in Exercise 26 and the situation described in part (c) of that exercise, will the mole fraction of $C_2H_2(g)$ increase, decrease, or remain unchanged when equilibrium is re-established? Explain.

89. The formation of nitrosyl chloride is given by the following equation: $2\,NO(g) + Cl_2(g) \rightleftharpoons 2\,NOCl(g)$; $K_c = 4.6 \times 10^4$ at 298 K. In a 1.50 L flask, there are 4.125 mol of NOCl and 0.1125 mol of Cl_2 present at equilibrium (298 K).
(a) Determine the partial pressure of NO at equilibrium.
(b) What is the total pressure of the system at equilibrium?

90. At 500 K, a 10.0 L equilibrium mixture contains 0.424 mol N_2, 1.272 mol H_2, and 1.152 mol NH_3. The mixture is quickly chilled to a temperature at which the NH_3 liquefies, and the $NH_3(l)$ is completely removed. The 10.0 L gaseous mixture is then returned to 500 K, and equilibrium is re-established. How many moles of $NH_3(g)$ will be present in the new equilibrium mixture?

$$N_2(g) + 3\,H_2(g) \rightleftharpoons 2\,NH_3 \qquad K_c = 152 \text{ at } 500\text{ K}$$

91. Recall the formation of methanol from synthesis gas, the reversible reaction at the heart of a process with great potential for the future production of automotive fuels (page 219).

$$CO(g) + 2\,H_2(g) \rightleftharpoons CH_3OH(g)$$
$$K_c = 14.5 \text{ at } 483\text{ K}$$

A particular synthesis gas consisting of 35.0 mole percent $CO(g)$ and 65.0 mole percent $H_2(g)$ at a total pressure of 100.0 atm at 483 K is allowed to come to equilibrium. Determine the partial pressure of $CH_3OH(g)$ in the equilibrium mixture.

Feature Problems

92. A classic experiment in equilibrium studies dating from 1862 involved the reaction in solution of ethanol (C_2H_5OH) and acetic acid (CH_3COOH) to produce ethyl acetate and water.

$$C_2H_5OH + CH_3COOH \rightleftharpoons CH_3COOC_2H_5 + H_2O$$

The reaction can be followed by analyzing the equilibrium mixture for its acetic acid content.

$$2\,CH_3COOH(aq) + Ba(OH)_2(aq) \rightleftharpoons Ba(CH_3COO)_2(aq) + 2\,H_2O(l)$$

In one experiment, a mixture of 1.000 mol acetic acid and 0.5000 mol ethanol is brought to equilibrium. A sample containing exactly one-hundredth of the equilibrium mixture requires 28.85 mL 0.1000 M $Ba(OH)_2$ for its titration. Calculate the equilibrium constant, K_c, for the ethanol-acetic acid reaction based on this experiment.

93. The decomposition of HI(g) is represented by the equation

$$2\,HI(g) \rightleftharpoons H_2(g) + I_2(g)$$

HI(g) is introduced into five identical 400 cm^3 glass bulbs, and the five bulbs are maintained at 623 K. Each bulb is opened after a period of time and analyzed for I_2 by titration with 0.0150 M $Na_2S_2O_3(aq)$.

$$I_2(aq) + 2\,Na_2S_2O_3(aq) \longrightarrow Na_2S_4O_6(aq) + 2\,NaI(aq)$$

Data for this experiment are provided in the table below. What is the value of K_c at 623 K?

Bulb Number	Initial Mass of HI(g), g	Time Bulb Opened, h	Volume 0.0150 M $Na_2S_2O_3$ Required for Titration, in mL
1	0.300	2	20.96
2	0.320	4	27.90
3	0.315	12	32.31
4	0.406	20	41.50
5	0.280	40	28.68

94. In one of Fritz Haber's experiments to establish the conditions required for the ammonia synthesis reaction, pure $NH_3(g)$ was passed over an iron catalyst at 901 °C and 30.0 atm. The gas leaving the reactor was bubbled through 20.00 mL of a HCl(aq) solution. In this way, the $NH_3(g)$ present was removed by reaction with HCl. The remaining gas occupied a volume of 1.82 L at STP. The 20.00 mL of HCl(aq) through which the gas had been bubbled required 15.42 mL of 0.0523 M KOH for its titration. Another 20.00 mL sample of the same HCl(aq) through which no gas had been bubbled required 18.72 mL of 0.0523 M KOH for its titration. Use these data to obtain a value of K_p at 901 °C for the reaction $N_2(g) + 3\,H_2(g) \rightleftharpoons 2\,NH_3(g)$.

95. The following is an approach to establishing a relationship between the equilibrium constant and rate constants mentioned in the section on page 216.

- Work with the detailed mechanism for the reaction.
- Use the principle of microscopic reversibility, the idea that every step in a reaction mechanism is reversible. (In the presentation of elementary reactions we treated some reaction steps as reversible and others as going to completion. However, as noted in Table 6.3, every reaction has an equilibrium constant even though a reaction is generally considered to go to completion if its equilibrium constant is very large.)
- Use the idea that when equilibrium is attained in an overall reaction, it is also attained in each step of its mechanism. Moreover, we can write an equilibrium constant expression for each step in the mechanism, similar to what we did with the steady-state assumption in describing reaction mechanisms.
- Combine the K_c expressions for the elementary steps into a K_c expression for the overall reaction. The numerical value of the overall K_c can thereby be expressed as a ratio of rate constants, k.

Use this approach to establish the equilibrium constant expression for the overall reaction,

$$H_2(g) + I_2(g) \rightleftharpoons 2\,HI(g)$$

The mechanism of the reaction appears to be the following:

Fast: $I_2(g) \rightleftharpoons 2\,I(g)$

Slow: $2\,I(g) + H_2(g) \rightleftharpoons 2\,HI(g)$

96. The following two equilibrium reactions can be written for aqueous carbonic acid, $H_2CO_3(aq)$:

$$H_2CO_3(aq) \rightleftharpoons H^+(aq) + HCO_3^-(aq) \qquad K_1$$
$$HCO_3^-(aq) \rightleftharpoons H^+(aq) + CO_3^{2-}(aq) \qquad K_2$$

For each reaction write the equilibrium constant expression. By using Le Châtelier's principle we may naively predict that by adding H_2CO_3 to the system, the concentration of CO_3^{2-} would increase. What we observe is that after adding H_2CO_3 to the equilibrium mixture, an increase in the concentration of CO_3^{2-} occurs when $[CO_3^{2-}] \ll K_2$ however, the concentration of CO_3^{2-} will decrease when $[CO_3^{2-}] \gg K_2$. Show that this is true by considering the ratio of $[H^+]/[HCO_3^-]$ before and after adding a small amount of H_2CO_3 to the solution, and by using that ratio to calculate the $[CO_3^{2-}]$.

97. In organic synthesis many reactions produce very little yield, that is $K \ll 1$. Consider the following hypothetical reaction: $A(aq) + B(aq) \longrightarrow C(aq)$, $K = 1 \times 10^{-2}$. We can extract product, C, from the aqueous layer by adding an organic layer in which $C(aq) \longrightarrow C(or)$, $K = 15$. Given initial concentrations of $[A] = 0.1$ M, $[B] = 0.1$, and $[C] = 0.1$, calculate how much C will be found in the organic layer. If the organic layer was not present, how much C would be produced?

Self-Assessment Exercises

98. In your own words, define or explain the following terms or symbols: **(a)** K_p; **(b)** Q_c; **(c)** Δn_{gas}.

99. Briefly describe each of the following ideas or phenomena: **(a)** dynamic equilibrium; **(b)** direction of a net chemical change; **(c)** Le Châtelier's principle; **(d)** effect of a catalyst on equilibrium.

100. Explain the important distinctions between each pair of terms: **(a)** reaction that goes to completion and reversible reaction; **(b)** K_c and K_p; **(c)** reaction quotient (Q) and equilibrium constant expression (K); **(d)** homogeneous and heterogeneous reaction.

101. In the reversible reaction $H_2(g) + I_2(g) \rightleftharpoons 2\,HI(g)$, an initial mixture contains 2 mol H_2 and 1 mol I_2. The amount of HI expected at equilibrium is **(a)** 1 mol; **(b)** 2 mol; **(c)** less than 2 mol; **(d)** more than 2 mol but less than 4 mol.

102. Equilibrium is established in the reaction $2\,SO_2(g) + O_2(g) \rightleftharpoons 2\,SO_3(g)$ at a temperature where $K_c = 100$. If the number of moles of $SO_3(g)$ in the equilibrium mixture is the same as the number of moles of $SO_2(g)$, **(a)** the number of moles of $O_2(g)$ is also equal to the number of moles of $SO_2(g)$; **(b)** the number of moles of $O_2(g)$ is half the number of moles of SO_2; **(c)** $[O_2]$ may have any of several values; **(d)** $[O_2] = 0.010$ M.

103. The volume of the reaction vessel containing an equilibrium mixture in the reaction $SO_2Cl_2(g) \rightleftharpoons SO_2(g) + Cl_2(g)$ is increased. When equilibrium is re-established, **(a)** the amount of Cl_2 will have increased; **(b)** the amount of SO_2 will have decreased; **(c)** the amounts of SO_2 and Cl_2 will have remained the same; **(d)** the amount of SO_2Cl_2 will have increased.

104. For the reaction $2\,NO_2(g) \rightleftharpoons 2\,NO(g) + O_2(g)$, $K_c = 1.8 \times 10^{-6}$ at 184 °C. At 184 °C, the value of K_c for the reaction $NO(g) + \frac{1}{2}O_2(g) \rightleftharpoons NO_2(g)$ is **(a)** 0.9×10^6; **(b)** 7.5×10^2; **(c)** 5.6×10^5; **(d)** 2.8×10^5.

105. For the dissociation reaction $2\,H_2S(g) \rightleftharpoons 2\,H_2(g) + S_2(g)$, $K_p = 1.2 \times 10^{-2}$ at 1065 °C. For this same reaction at 1000 K, **(a)** K_c is less than K_p; **(b)** K_c is greater than K_p; **(c)** $K_c = K_p$; **(d)** whether K_c is less than, equal to, or greater than K_p depends on the total gas pressure.

106. The following data are given at 1000 K: $CO(g) + H_2O(g) \rightleftharpoons CO_2(g) + H_2(g)$; $\Delta H° = -42$ kJ; $K_c = 0.66$. After an initial equilibrium is established in a 1.00 L container, the equilibrium amount of H_2 can be increased by **(a)** adding a catalyst; **(b)** increasing the temperature; **(c)** transferring the mixture to a 10.0 L container; **(d)** in some way other than (a), (b), or (c).

107. Equilibrium is established in the reversible reaction $2\,A + B \rightleftharpoons 2\,C$. The equilibrium concentrations are $[A] = 0.55$ M, $[B] = 0.33$ M, $[C] = 0.43$ M. What is the value of K_c for this reaction?

108. The Deacon process for producing chlorine gas from hydrogen chloride is used in situations where HCl is available as a by-product from other chemical processes.

$$4\,HCl(g) + O_2(g) \rightleftharpoons 2\,H_2O(g) + 2\,Cl_2(g) \qquad \Delta H° = -114 \text{ kJ}$$

A mixture of HCl, O_2, H_2O, and Cl_2 is brought to equilibrium at 400 °C. What is the effect on the equilibrium amount of $Cl_2(g)$ if

(a) additional $O_2(g)$ is added to the mixture at constant volume?

(b) HCl(g) is removed from the mixture at constant volume?

(c) the mixture is transferred to a vessel of twice the volume?

(d) a catalyst is added to the reaction mixture?

(e) the temperature is raised to 500 °C?

109. For the reaction $SO_2(g) \rightleftharpoons SO_2(aq)$, $K = 1.25$ at 25 °C. Will the amount of $SO_2(g)$ be greater than or less than the amount of $SO_2(aq)$?

110. In the reaction $H_2O_2(g) \rightleftharpoons H_2O_2(aq)$, $K = 1.0 \times 10^5$ at 25 °C. Would you expect a greater amount of product or reactant?

111. An equilibrium mixture of SO_2, SO_3, and O_2 gases is maintained in a 2.05 L flask at a temperature at which $K_c = 35.5$ for the reaction

$$2\,SO_2(g) + O_2(g) \rightleftharpoons 2\,SO_3(g)$$

(a) If the numbers of moles of SO_2 and SO_3 in the flask are equal, how many moles of O_2 are present?
(b) If the number of moles of SO_3 in the flask is twice the number of moles of SO_2, how many moles of O_2 are present?

7

Electrochemistry

A transit bus fitted with hydrogen–oxygen fuel cells. The use of fuel cells could dramatically reduce urban air pollution. The conversion of chemical energy into electrical energy is one of the main subjects of this chapter.

CONTENTS

A conventional gasoline-powered automobile is only about 25% efficient in converting chemical energy into kinetic energy (energy of motion). An electric-powered auto is about three times as efficient. Unfortunately, when automotive technology was first being developed, devices for converting chemical energy to electrical energy did not perform at their intrinsic efficiencies. This fact, together with the availability of high-quality gasoline at a low cost, resulted in the preeminence of the internal combustion automobile. Now, with concern about long-term energy supplies and environmental pollution, there is a renewed interest in electric-powered buses and automobiles.

In this chapter, we will see how chemical reactions can be used to produce electricity and how electricity can be used to cause chemical reactions. The practical applications of electrochemistry are countless, ranging from batteries and fuel cells as electric power sources to the manufacture of key chemicals, the refining of metals, and methods for controlling corrosion. Also important, however, are the theoretical implications. Because electricity involves a flow of electric charge, a study of the relationship between chemistry and electricity gives us additional insight into reactions in which electrons are transferred—*oxidation–reduction reactions*.

7-1 Electrode Potentials and Their Measurement

The criteria for spontaneous change apply to reactions of all types—precipitation, acid–base, and oxidation–reduction (redox). We can devise an additional useful criterion for redox reactions, however.

Figure 7-1 shows that a redox reaction occurs between Cu(s) and $Ag^+(aq)$, but not between Cu(s) and $Zn^{2+}(aq)$. Specifically, we see that silver ions are reduced to silver atoms on a copper surface, whereas zinc ions are *not* reduced to zinc atoms on a copper surface. We can say that Ag^+ is more readily reduced than is Zn^{2+}. In this section, we will introduce the *electrode potential*, a property related to these reduction tendencies.

▶ The term *electrode* is sometimes used for the entire half-cell assembly.

When used in electrochemical studies, a strip of metal, M, is called an **electrode**. An electrode immersed in a solution containing ions of the same metal, M^{n+}, is called a **half-cell**. Two kinds of interactions are possible between metal atoms on the electrode and metal ions in solution (Fig. 7-2):

1. A metal ion M^{n+} from solution may collide with the electrode, gain n electrons from it, and be converted to a metal atom M. *The ion is reduced.*
2. A metal atom M on the surface may lose n electrons to the electrode and enter the solution as the ion M^{n+}. *The metal atom is oxidized.*

An equilibrium is quickly established between the metal and the solution, which can be represented as

$$M(s) \underset{\text{reduction}}{\overset{\text{oxidation}}{\rightleftharpoons}} M^{n+}(aq) + ne^- \quad (7.1)$$

KEEP IN MIND

that although $M^{n+}(aq)$ and ne^- appear together on the right-hand side of this expression, only the ion M^{n+} enters the solution. The electrons remain on the electrode, M(s). Free electrons are never found in an aqueous solution.

However, any changes produced at the electrode or in the solution as a consequence of this equilibrium are too slight to measure. Instead, measurements must be based on a combination of *two different* half-cells. Specifically, we must measure the tendency for electrons to flow from the electrode of one half-cell to the electrode of the other. Electrodes are classified according to whether oxidation or reduction takes place there. If oxidation takes place, the electrode is called the **anode**. If reduction takes place, the electrode is called the **cathode**.

▶ FIGURE 7-1
Behavior of $Ag^+(aq)$ and $Zn^+(aq)$ in the presence of copper
(a) Copper metal displaces silver ions from colorless $AgNO_3(aq)$ as a deposit of silver metal; the copper enters the solution as blue $Cu^{2+}(aq)$.

$$Cu(s) + 2\,Ag^+(aq) \longrightarrow Cu^{2+}(aq) + 2\,Ag(s)$$

(b) Cu(s) *does not* displace colorless Zn^{2+} from $Zn(NO_3)_2(aq)$.

$$Cu(s) + Zn^{2+}(aq) \longrightarrow \text{no reaction}$$

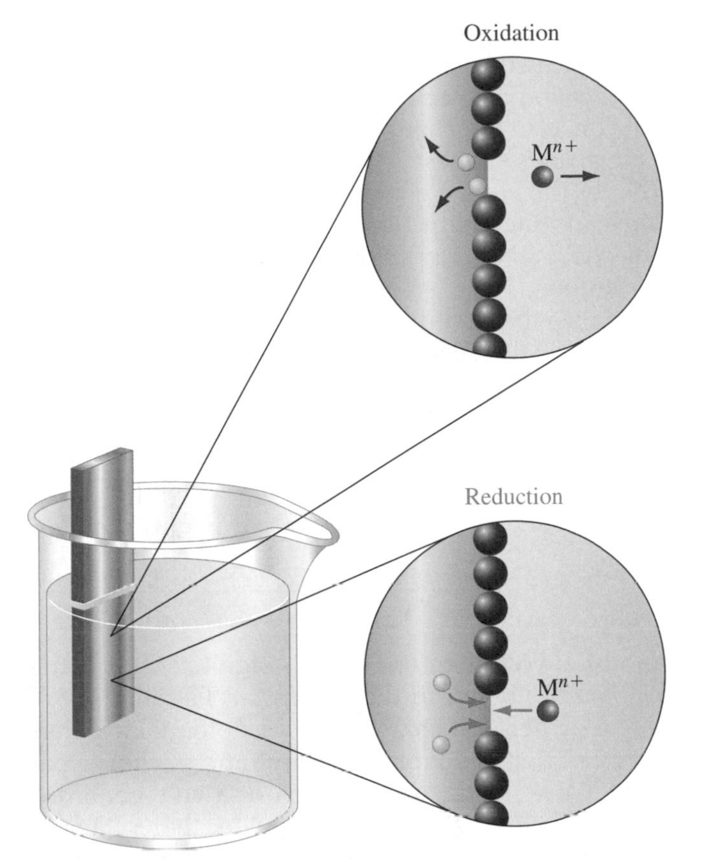

◀ FIGURE 7-2
An electrochemical half-cell
The half-cell consists of a metal electrode, M, partially immersed in an aqueous solution of its ions, M^{n+}. (The anions required to maintain electrical neutrality in the solution are not shown.) The situation illustrated here is limited to metals that do not react with water.

Figure 7-3 depicts a combination of two half-cells, one with a Cu electrode in contact with $Cu^{2+}(aq)$, and the other with an Ag electrode in contact with $Ag^{+}(aq)$. The two electrodes are joined by wires to an electric meter—here, a *voltmeter*. To complete the electric circuit, the two solutions must also be connected electrically. However, because charge is carried through solutions by the migration of *ions*, a wire cannot be used for this connection. The solutions

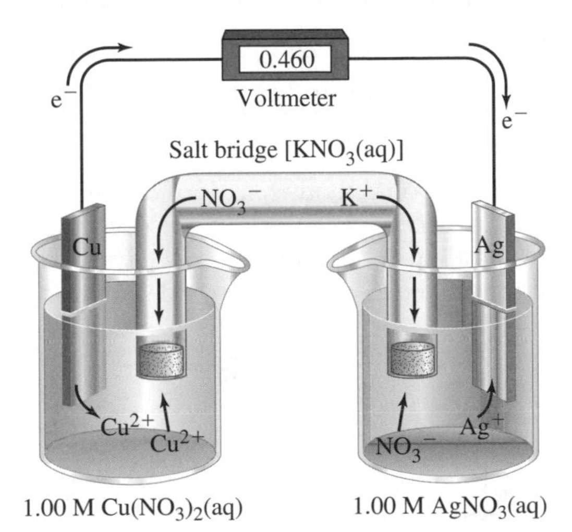

▲ FIGURE 7-3
Measurement of the electromotive force of an electrochemical cell
An electrochemical cell consists of two half-cells with electrodes joined by a wire and solutions joined by a salt bridge. (The ends of the salt bridge are plugged with a porous material that allows ions to migrate but prevents the bulk flow of liquid.) Electrons flow from the Cu electrode, the anode, where oxidation occurs to the Ag electrode, the cathode, where reduction occurs. For precise measurements, the amount of electric current drawn from the cell must be kept very small by means of either a specially designed voltmeter or a device called a potentiometer.

◀ Anions migrate toward the anode, and cations toward the cathode.

must either be in direct contact through a porous barrier or joined by a third solution in a U-tube called a **salt bridge**. The properly connected combination of two half-cells is called an **electrochemical cell**.

Now, we will consider the changes that occur in the electrochemical cell in Figure 7-3. As the arrows suggest, Cu atoms release electrons at the anode and enter the $Cu(NO_3)_2(aq)$ as Cu^{2+} ions. Electrons lost by the Cu atoms pass through the wires and the voltmeter to the cathode, where they are gained by Ag^+ ions from the $AgNO_3(aq)$, producing a deposit of metallic silver. Simultaneously, anions (NO_3^-) from the salt bridge migrate into the copper half-cell and neutralize the positive charge of the excess Cu^{2+} ions; cations (K^+) migrate into the silver half-cell and neutralize the negative charge of the excess NO_3^- ions. Each copper atom loses two electrons to produce Cu^{2+}; each Ag^+ ion requires one electron to produce Ag(s); consequently, two silver atoms are produced for every Cu^{2+} ion formed. The overall reaction that occurs as the electrochemical cell spontaneously produces electric current is

$$\begin{array}{lrcl} \textit{Oxidation:} & Cu(s) & \longrightarrow & Cu^{2+}(aq) + 2\,e^- \\ \textit{Reduction:} & 2\,\{Ag^+(aq) + e^- & \longrightarrow & Ag(s)\} \\ \hline \textit{Overall:} & Cu(s) + 2\,Ag^+(aq) & \longrightarrow & Cu^{2+}(aq) + 2\,Ag(s) \end{array} \qquad (7.2)$$

KEEP IN MIND

that the overall reaction occurring in the electrochemical cell is identical to what happens in the direct addition of Cu(s) to $Ag^+(aq)$ pictured in Figure 7-1(a).

The reading on the voltmeter (0.460 V) is significant. It is the **cell voltage**, or the *potential difference* between the two half-cells. The unit of cell voltage, **volt (V)**, is the energy per unit charge. Thus, a potential difference of one volt signifies an energy of one joule for every coulomb of charge passing through an electric circuit: $1\ V = 1\ J/C$. We can think of a voltage, or potential difference, as the driving force for electrons; the greater the voltage, the greater the driving force. The flow of water from a higher to a lower level is analogous to this situation. The greater the difference in water levels, the greater the force behind the flow of water. Cell voltage is also called **electromotive force (emf)**, or **cell potential**, and represented by the symbol E_{cell}.

▶ Such formulations as $Zn(s)/Zn^{2+}(aq)$ are called *couples* and are often used as abbreviations for half-cells.

Now let's return to the question raised by Figure 7-1: Why does copper *not* displace Zn^{2+} from solution? In an electrochemical cell consisting of a $Zn(s)/Zn^{2+}(aq)$ half-cell and a $Cu^{2+}(aq)/Cu(s)$ half-cell, electrons flow *from the Zn to the Cu*. The spontaneous reaction in the electrochemical cell in Figure 7-4 is

$$\begin{array}{lrcl} \textit{Oxidation:} & Zn(s) & \longrightarrow & Zn^{2+}(aq) + 2\,e^- \\ \textit{Reduction:} & Cu^{2+}(aq) + 2\,e^- & \longrightarrow & Cu(s) \\ \hline \textit{Overall:} & Zn(s) + Cu^{2+}(aq) & \longrightarrow & Zn^{2+}(aq) + Cu(s) \end{array} \qquad (7.3)$$

Because reaction (7.3) is a spontaneous reaction, the displacement of $Zn^{2+}(aq)$ by Cu(s)—the *reverse* of reaction (7.3)—does *not* occur spontaneously. This is the observation made in Figure 7-1. In Section 7-3, we will discuss how to predict the direction of spontaneous change for oxidation–reduction reactions:

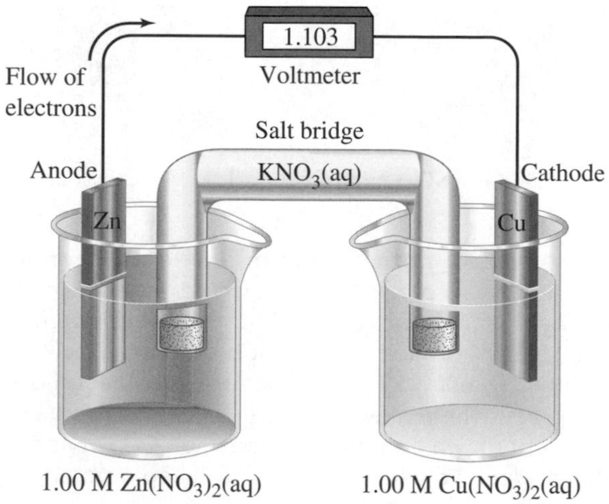

▶ FIGURE 7-4
The reaction $Zn(s) + Cu^{2+}(aq) \longrightarrow Zn^{2+}(aq) + Cu(s)$ in an electrochemical cell

Cell Diagrams and Terminology

Drawing sketches of electrochemical cells, as in Figures 7-3 and 7-4, is helpful, but more often a simpler representation is used. A **cell diagram** shows the components of an electrochemical cell in a symbolic way. We will use the following, generally accepted conventions in writing cell diagrams.

◀ Several memory devices have been proposed for the oxidation/anode and reduction/cathode relationships. Perhaps the simplest is that in the oxidation/anode relationship, both terms begin with a vowel: *o*/*a*; in the reduction/cathode relationship, both begin with a consonant: *r*/*c*.

- The anode, the electrode at which *oxidation* occurs, is placed at the *left* side of the diagram.
- The cathode, the electrode at which *reduction* occurs, is placed at the *right* side of the diagram.
- A boundary between different phases (for example, an electrode and a solution) is represented by a *single vertical line* (|).
- The boundary between half-cell compartments, commonly a salt bridge, is represented by a *double vertical line* (||). Species in aqueous solution are placed on either side of the double vertical line. Different species within the same solution are separated from each other by a comma. Although IUPAC recommends the use of double dashed vertical lines to represent the salt bridge, the recommendation has not yet been universally adopted by chemists. In this text, we will continue to use the double vertical line (||) for a salt bridge.

The cell diagram corresponding to both Figure 7-4 and reaction (7.3) is customarily written as

$$\text{anode} \longrightarrow \underset{\text{(oxidation)}}{\underset{\text{Half-cell}}{Zn(s)|Zn^{2+}(aq)}} \quad \underset{\text{bridge}}{\underset{\text{Salt}}{||}} \quad \underset{\text{(reduction)}}{\underset{\text{Half-cell}}{Cu^{2+}(aq)|Cu(s)}} \longleftarrow \text{cathode} \quad \underset{\text{Cell voltage}}{E_{cell} = 1.103\text{ V}} \qquad (7.4)$$

KEEP IN MIND

that the spectator ions are not shown in a cell diagram, but they are present. They pass through the salt bridge to maintain electrical neutrality.

The electrochemical cells of Figures 7-3 and 7-4 produce electricity as a result of spontaneous chemical reactions; as such, they are called **voltaic**, or **galvanic**, **cells**. In Section 7-7 we will consider *electrolytic cells*—electrochemical cells in which electricity is used to accomplish a nonspontaneous chemical change.

EXAMPLE 7-1 Representing a Redox Reaction by Means of a Cell Diagram

Aluminum metal displaces zinc(II) ion from aqueous solution.

(a) Write oxidation and reduction half-equations and an overall equation for this redox reaction.

(b) Write a cell diagram for a voltaic cell in which this reaction occurs.

Analyze

The term *displaces* means that aluminum goes into solution as $Al^{3+}(aq)$, forcing $Zn^{2+}(aq)$ out of solution as zinc metal. Al is oxidized to Al^{3+}, and Zn^{2+} is reduced to Zn. In combining the half-equations to produce the overall equation, we must take care to ensure that the *number of electrons involved in reduction equals the number involved in oxidation.* (This is the half-reaction method of balancing redox equations discussed in Section 1-5.) The cell diagram is written with the reduction half-equation as the right-hand electrode.

Solve

(a) The two half equations are

$$\textit{Oxidation:} \quad Al(s) \longrightarrow Al^{3+}(aq) + 3\,e^-$$

$$\textit{Reduction:} \quad Zn^{2+}(aq) + 2\,e^- \longrightarrow Zn(s)$$

On inspecting these half-equations, we see that the number of electrons involved in oxidation and reduction are different. In writing the overall equation, the coefficients must be adjusted so that equal numbers of electrons are involved in oxidation and in reduction.

$$\textit{Oxidation:} \quad 2\,\{Al(s) \longrightarrow Al^{3+}(aq) + 3\,e^-\}$$

$$\textit{Reduction:} \quad 3\,\{Zn^{2+}(aq) + 2\,e^- \longrightarrow Zn(s)\}$$

$$\textit{Overall:} \quad 2\,Al(s) + 3\,Zn^{2+}(aq) \longrightarrow 2\,Al^{3+}(aq) + 3\,Zn(s)$$

(continued)

(b) Al(s) is oxidized to $Al^{3+}(aq)$ in the anode half-cell (written on the left of the cell diagram), and $Zn^{2+}(aq)$ is reduced to Zn(s) in the cathode half-cell (written on the right of the cell diagram).

$$Al(s)|Al^{3+}(aq)||Zn^{2+}(aq)|Zn(s)$$

Assess

Whenever balancing redox equations, it is important to ensure that the number of electrons in the oxidation step equals the number of electrons in the reduction step. This is achieved by multiplying the entire half-reaction(s) by the appropriate factor(s).

PRACTICE EXAMPLE A: Write the overall equation for the redox reaction that occurs in the voltaic cell $Sc(s)|Sc^{3+}(aq)||Ag^{+}(aq)|Ag(s)$.

PRACTICE EXAMPLE B: Draw a voltaic cell in which silver ion is displaced from solution by aluminum metal. Label the cathode, the anode, and other features of the cell. Show the direction of flow of electrons. Also, indicate the direction of flow of cations and anions from a $KNO_3(aq)$ salt bridge. Write an equation for the half-reaction occurring at each electrode, write a balanced equation for the overall cell reaction, and write a cell diagram.

EXAMPLE 7-2 Deducing the Balanced Redox Reaction from a Cell Diagram

The cell diagram for an electrochemical cell is written as

$$Ni(s)|NiCl_2(aq)||Ce(ClO_4)_4(aq), Ce(ClO_4)_3(aq)|Pt(s)$$

Write the equations for the half-reactions that occur at the electrodes. Balance the overall cell reaction.

Analyze

When inspecting a cell diagram, we first need to identify the species involved in oxidation and in reduction. Then we can write balanced half-cell equations. Finally, we can combine the half-cell equations to give the overall cell reaction. The new part to this example is the Ce^{4+}/Ce^{3+} couple in the presence of the inert platinum electrode at which the reduction takes place. Again, when balancing redox equations, it is important to ensure that the number of electrons in the oxidation step equals the number of electrons in the reduction step.

Solve

The cerium reduction reaction is

$$Ce^{4+}(aq) + e^- \longrightarrow Ce^{3+}(aq)$$

The nickel oxidation reaction is

$$Ni(s) \longrightarrow Ni^{2+}(aq) + 2\,e^-$$

In these half-equations the number of electrons involved in oxidation and reduction are different. In writing the overall equation, the coefficients must be adjusted so that equal numbers of electrons are involved in oxidation and in reduction.

$$\begin{array}{ll} \textit{Oxidation:} & Ni(s) \longrightarrow Ni^{2+}(aq) + 2\,e^- \\ \textit{Reduction:} & 2\,\{Ce^{4+}(aq) + e^- \longrightarrow Ce^{3+}(aq)\} \\ \hline \textit{Overall:} & Ni(s) + 2\,Ce^{4+}(aq) \longrightarrow Ni^{2+}(aq) + 2\,Ce^{3+}(aq) \end{array}$$

Assess

We can see the importance of balancing each half-equation with respect to charge and mass.

PRACTICE EXAMPLE A: The cell diagram for an electrochemical cell is written as

$$Sn(s)|SnCl_2(aq)||AgNO_3(aq)|Ag(s)$$

Write the equations for the half-reactions that occur at the electrodes. Balance the overall cell reaction.

PRACTICE EXAMPLE B: The cell diagram for an electrochemical cell is written as

$$In(s)|In(ClO_4)_3(aq)||CdCl_2(aq)|Cd(s)$$

Write the equations for the half-reactions that occur at the electrodes. Balance the overall cell reaction.

7-1 CONCEPT ASSESSMENT

Add appropriate arrows to Figure 7-4 to show the direction of migration of ions through the electrochemical cell.

7-2 Standard Electrode Potentials

Cell voltages—*potential differences* between electrodes—are among the most precise scientific measurements possible. Potentials of individual electrodes, however, cannot be precisely established. If we could make such measurements, cell voltages could be obtained just by subtracting one electrode potential from another. The same result can be achieved by *arbitrarily* choosing a particular half-cell that is assigned an electrode potential of *zero*. Other half-cells can then be compared with this reference. The commonly accepted reference is the standard hydrogen electrode.

◀ This method is comparable to establishing standard enthalpies or Gibbs energies of formation on the basis of an arbitrary zero value.

The **standard hydrogen electrode (SHE)** is depicted in Figure 7-5. The SHE involves equilibrium established on the surface of an inert metal (such as platinum) between H_3O^+ ions from a solution in which they are at unit activity (that is, $a_{H_3O^+} = 1$) and H_2molecules from the gaseous state at a pressure of 1 bar. The equilibrium reaction produces a particular potential on the metal surface, but this potential is arbitrarily taken to be *zero*.

$$2\,H^+(a = 1) + 2\,e^- \xrightleftharpoons{\text{on Pt}} H_2(g, 1\,\text{bar}) \qquad E^\circ = 0\ \text{volt (V)} \qquad \textbf{(7.5)}$$

The diagram for this half-cell is

$$Pt|H_2(g, 1\,\text{bar})|H^+(a = 1)$$

The two vertical lines signify that three phases are present: solid platinum, gaseous hydrogen, and aqueous hydrogen ion. For simplicity, we will usually write H^+ for H_3O^+, assume that unit activity ($a = 1$) exists at roughly $[H^+] = 1$ M, and replace a pressure of 1 bar by 1 atm.

◀ In this chapter, we shall use the units bar and atm interchangeably. The reason is that, although the current standard pressure is defined as 1 bar, the most extensive and authoritative tabulations of E° values are based on the old standard of 1 atm. Fortunately, the difference between 1 bar and 1 atm is small and so too are the differences between E° values based on the old and new standards.

By international agreement, a **standard electrode potential, E°**, measures the tendency for a *reduction* process to occur at an electrode. In all cases, the

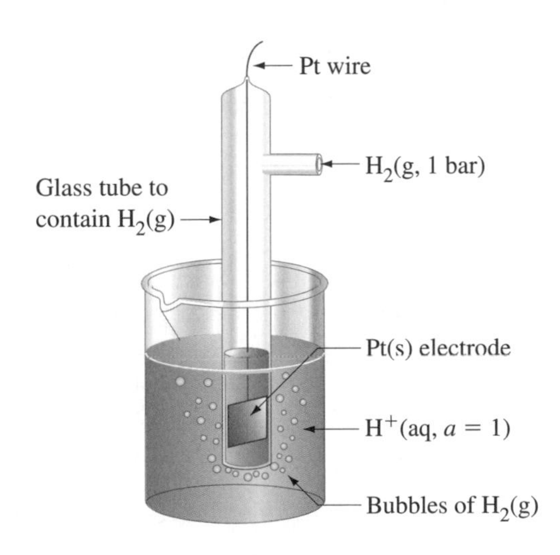

▲ FIGURE 7-5
The standard hydrogen electrode (SHE)
Because hydrogen is a gas at room temperature, electrodes cannot be constructed from it. The standard hydrogen electrode consists of a piece of platinum dipped into a solution containing 1 M $H^+(aq)$ with a stream of hydrogen passing over its surface. The platinum does not react but provides a surface for the reduction of $H_3O(aq)^+$ to $H_2(g)$ as well as the reverse oxidation half-reaction.

ionic species are present in aqueous solution at unit activity (approximately 1 M), and gases are at 1 bar pressure (approximately 1 atm). Where no metallic substance is indicated, the potential is established on an inert metallic electrode, such as platinum.

To emphasize that $E°$ refers to a reduction, we will write a reduction couple as a subscript to $E°$, as shown in half-reaction (7.6). The substance being reduced is written on the left of the slash sign (/), and the chief reduction product on the right.

$$Cu^{2+}(1\text{ M}) + 2\,e^- \longrightarrow Cu(s) \qquad E°_{Cu^{2+}/Cu} = ? \tag{7.6}$$

To determine the value of $E°$ for a standard electrode such as that to which half-reaction (7.6) applies, we compare it with a standard hydrogen electrode (SHE). In this comparison, the SHE is always taken as the electrode on the *left* of the cell diagram—the anode—and the compared electrode is the electrode on the *right*—the cathode. In the following voltaic cell, the measured potential difference is 0.340 V, with electrons flowing from the H_2 to the Cu electrode.

$$\underset{\text{anode}}{Pt|H_2(g, 1\text{ atm})|H^+(1\text{ M})}\|\underset{\text{cathode}}{Cu^{2+}(1\text{ M})|Cu(s)} \qquad E°_{cell} = 0.340\text{ V} \tag{7.7}$$

A **standard cell potential, $E°_{cell}$**, is the potential difference, or voltage, of a cell formed from two *standard* electrodes. The *difference* is always taken in the following way:

$$E°_{cell} = \underset{\text{(cathode)}}{E°(\text{right})} - \underset{\text{(anode)}}{E°(\text{left})}$$

Applied to the cell diagram (7.7), we get

$$\begin{aligned} E°_{cell} &= E°_{Cu^{2+}/Cu} - E°_{H^+/H_2} = 0.340\text{ V} \\ &= E°_{Cu^{2+}/Cu} - 0\text{ V} = 0.340\text{ V} \\ E°_{Cu^{2+}/Cu} &= 0.340\text{ V} \end{aligned}$$

Thus, the standard *reduction* half-reaction can be written as

$$Cu^{2+}(1\text{ M}) + 2\,e^- \longrightarrow Cu(s) \qquad E°_{Cu^{2+}/Cu} = +0.340\text{ V} \tag{7.8}$$

The overall reaction occurring in the voltaic cell diagrammed in (7.7) can be represented as

$$H_2(g, 1\text{ atm}) + Cu^{2+}(1\text{ M}) \longrightarrow 2\,H^+(1\text{ M}) + Cu(s) \qquad E°_{cell} = 0.340\text{ V} \tag{7.9}$$

Cell reaction (7.9) indicates that $Cu^{2+}(1\text{ M})$ is more easily reduced than is $H^+(1\text{ M})$.

Suppose the standard copper electrode in cell diagram (7.7) is replaced by a standard zinc electrode, and the potential difference between the standard hydrogen and zinc electrodes is measured by using the same voltmeter connections as in (7.7). In this case, the voltage is found to be −0.763 V. The negative sign indicates that electrons flow in the direction *opposite* that in (7.7)—that is, *from* the zinc electrode to the hydrogen electrode. Here $H^+(1\text{ M})$ is more easily reduced than is $Zn^{2+}(1\text{ M})$. These findings are represented in the following cell diagram, in which the zinc electrode appears on the *right*.

$$Pt|H_2(g, 1\text{ atm})|H^+(1\text{ M})\|Zn^{2+}(1\text{ M})|Zn(s) \qquad E°_{cell} = -0.763\text{ V} \tag{7.10}$$

The standard electrode potential for the Zn^{2+}/Zn couple can be written as

$$\begin{aligned} E°_{cell} &= E°(\text{right}) - E°(\text{left}) \\ &= E°_{Zn^{2+}/Zn} - 0\text{ V} = -0.763\text{ V} \\ E°_{Zn^{2+}/Zn} &= -0.763\text{ V} \end{aligned}$$

Thus, the standard *reduction* half-reaction is

$$Zn^{2+}(1\text{ M}) + 2\,e^- \longrightarrow Zn(s) \qquad E°_{Zn^{2+}/Zn} = -0.763\text{ V} \tag{7.11}$$

In summary, the potential of the standard hydrogen electrode is set at exactly 0 V. Any electrode at which a reduction half-reaction shows a *greater* tendency to occur than does the reduction of H^+ (1 M) to H_2 (g, 1 atm) has a *positive* value for its standard electrode potential, $E°$. Any electrode at which a reduction half-reaction shows a *lesser* tendency to occur than does the reduction of H^+(1 M) to H_2 (g, 1 atm) has a *negative* value for its standard reduction potential, $E°$. Comparisons of the standard copper and zinc electrodes to the standard hydrogen electrode are illustrated in Figure 7-6. Table 7.1 on the next page lists some common reduction half-reactions and their standard electrode potentials at 25 °C.

7-2 CONCEPT ASSESSMENT

For Figure 7-6, describe any changes in mass that might be detected at the Pt, Cu, and Zn electrodes as electric current passes through the electrochemical cells.

Standard reduction potentials are used throughout this chapter for many purposes. Our first objective will be to calculate standard cell potentials for redox reactions—$E°_{cell}$ values—from standard electrode potentials for half-cell reactions—$E°$ values. The procedure used is illustrated here for reaction (7.3) and cell diagram (7.4). Note that the first three equations are alternative ways of stating the same thing; we will generally not write all of them.

◀ Reaction (7.3) is shown on page 256 and diagram (7.4) on page 257.

$$\begin{aligned} E°_{cell} &= E°(\text{right}) - E°(\text{left}) \\ &= E°(\text{cathode}) - E°(\text{anode}) \\ &= E°(\text{reduction half-cell}) - E°(\text{oxidation half-cell}) \\ &= E°_{Cu^{2+}/Cu} - E°_{Zn^{2+}/Zn} \\ &= 0.340 \text{ V} - (-0.763 \text{ V}) = 1.103 \text{ V} \end{aligned}$$

KEEP IN MIND

that the $E°$ values in this formulation are for a reduction half-reaction, regardless of whether oxidation or reduction occurs in the half-cell.

Example 7-3 predicts $E°_{cell}$ for a new battery system. Example 7-4 uses one known electrode potential and a measured $E°_{cell}$ value to determine an unknown $E°$.

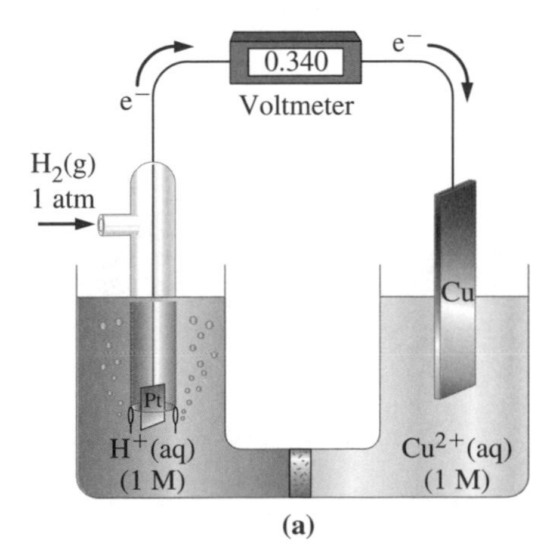

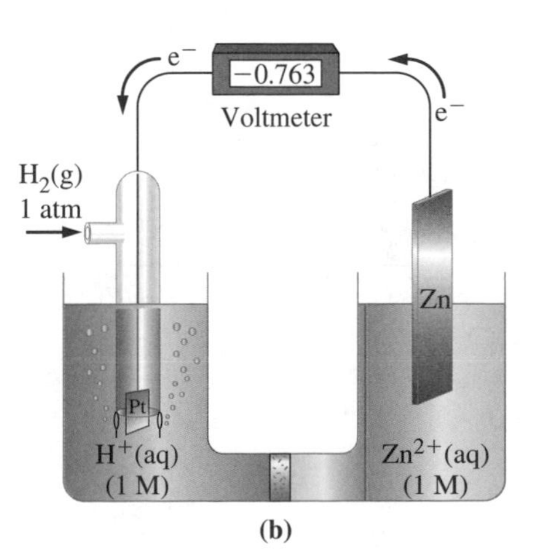

▲ FIGURE 7-6
Measuring standard electrode potentials
(a) A standard hydrogen electrode is the anode, and copper is the cathode. Contact between the half-cells occurs through a porous plate that prevents bulk flow of the solutions while allowing ions to pass. **(b)** This cell has the same connections as that in part (a), but with zinc substituting for copper. However, the electron flow is opposite that in (a), as noted by the *negative* voltage. (Zinc is the anode.)

▶ A more extensive listing of reduction half-reactions and their potentials is given in Appendix A.

▶ The placement of *oxidizing agents* is as follows: strongest oxidizing agents ($F_2, O_3, \ldots$), *left* sides, *top* of the list; weakest oxidizing agents ($Li^+, K^+, \ldots$), *left* sides, *bottom* of list. The placement of *reducing agents* is as follows: strongest reducing agents ($Li, K, \ldots$), *right* sides, *bottom* of list; weakest reducing agents ($F^-, O_2, \ldots$), *right* sides, *top* of list.

TABLE 7.1 Some Selected Standard Electrode (Reduction) Potentials at 25 °C

Reduction Half-Reaction	$E°$, V
Acidic solution	
$F_2(g) + 2\,e^- \longrightarrow 2\,F^-(aq)$	+2.866
$O_3(g) + 2\,H^+(aq) + 2\,e^- \longrightarrow O_2(g) + H_2O(l)$	+2.075
$S_2O_8^{2-}(aq) + 2\,e^- \longrightarrow 2\,SO_4^{2-}(aq)$	+2.01
$H_2O_2(aq) + 2\,H^+(aq) + 2\,e^- \longrightarrow 2\,H_2O(l)$	+1.763
$MnO_4^-(aq) + 8\,H^+(aq) + 5\,e^- \longrightarrow Mn^{2+}(aq) + 4\,H_2O(l)$	+1.51
$PbO_2(s) + 4\,H^+(aq) + 2\,e^- \longrightarrow Pb^{2+}(aq) + 2\,H_2O(l)$	+1.455
$Cl_2(g) + 2\,e^- \longrightarrow 2\,Cl^-(aq)$	+1.358
$Cr_2O_7^{2-}(aq) + 14\,H^+(aq) + 6\,e^- \longrightarrow 2\,Cr^{3+}(aq) + 7\,H_2O(l)$	+1.33
$MnO_2(s) + 4\,H^+(aq) + 2\,e^- \longrightarrow Mn^{2+}(aq) + 2\,H_2O(l)$	+1.23
$O_2(g) + 4\,H^+(aq) + 4\,e^- \longrightarrow 2\,H_2O(l)$	+1.229
$2\,IO_3^-(aq) + 12\,H^+(aq) + 10\,e^- \longrightarrow I_2(s) + 6\,H_2O(l)$	+1.20
$Br_2(l) + 2\,e^- \longrightarrow 2\,Br^-(aq)$	+1.065
$NO_3^-(aq) + 4\,H^+(aq) + 3\,e^- \longrightarrow NO(g) + 2\,H_2O(l)$	+0.956
$Ag^+(aq) + e^- \longrightarrow Ag(s)$	+0.800
$Fe^{3+}(aq) + e^- \longrightarrow Fe^{2+}(aq)$	+0.771
$O_2(g) + 2\,H^+(aq) + 2\,e^- \longrightarrow H_2O_2(aq)$	+0.695
$I_2(s) + 2\,e^- \longrightarrow 2\,I^-(aq)$	+0.535
$Cu^{2+}(aq) + 2\,e^- \longrightarrow Cu(s)$	+0.340
$SO_4^{2-}(aq) + 4\,H^+(aq) + 2\,e^- \longrightarrow 2\,H_2O(l) + SO_2(g)$	+0.17
$Sn^{4+}(aq) + 2\,e^- \longrightarrow Sn^{2+}(aq)$	+0.154
$S(s) + 2\,H^+(aq) + 2\,e^- \longrightarrow H_2S(g)$	+0.14
$2\,H^+(aq) + 2\,e^- \longrightarrow H_2(g)$	0
$Pb^{2+}(aq) + 2\,e^- \longrightarrow Pb(s)$	−0.125
$Sn^{2+}(aq) + 2\,e^- \longrightarrow Sn(s)$	−0.137
$Fe^{2+}(aq) + 2\,e^- \longrightarrow Fe(s)$	−0.440
$Zn^{2+}(aq) + 2\,e^- \longrightarrow Zn(s)$	−0.763
$Al^{3+}(aq) + 3\,e^- \longrightarrow Al(s)$	−1.676
$Mg^{2+}(aq) + 2\,e^- \longrightarrow Mg(s)$	−2.356
$Na^+(aq) + e^- \longrightarrow Na(s)$	−2.713
$Ca^{2+}(aq) + 2\,e^- \longrightarrow Ca(s)$	−2.84
$K^+(aq) + e^- \longrightarrow K(s)$	−2.924
$Li^+(aq) + e^- \longrightarrow Li(s)$	−3.040
Basic solution	
$O_3(g) + H_2O(l) + 2\,e^- \longrightarrow O_2(g) + 2\,OH^-(aq)$	+1.246
$OCl^-(aq) + H_2O(l) + 2\,e^- \longrightarrow Cl^-(aq) + 2\,OH^-(aq)$	+0.890
$O_2(g) + 2\,H_2O(l) + 4\,e^- \longrightarrow 4\,OH^-(aq)$	+0.401
$2\,H_2O(l) + 2\,e^- \longrightarrow H_2(g) + 2\,OH^-(aq)$	−0.828

EXAMPLE 7-3 Combining $E°$ Values into $E°_{cell}$ for a Reaction

A new battery system currently under study for possible use in electric vehicles is the zinc–chlorine battery. The overall reaction producing electricity in this cell is $Zn(s) + Cl_2(g) \longrightarrow ZnCl_2(aq)$. What is $E°_{cell}$ of this voltaic cell?

Analyze

First we identify the species that are oxidized and reduced. Then we obtain the standard reduction potentials for the cathode and anode from Table 7.1 and calculate E°_{cell}.

Solve

The oxidation state of zinc changes from 0 to +2 and therefore is oxidized; consequently, the chlorine is reduced. The half-reactions are indicated below and are combined into the overall equation (7.12).

$$\begin{array}{ll} \textit{Oxidation:} & Zn(s) \longrightarrow Zn^{2+}(aq) + 2\,e^- \\ \textit{Reduction:} & Cl_2(g) + 2\,e^- \longrightarrow 2\,Cl^-(aq) \\ \hline \textit{Overall:} & Zn(s) + Cl_2(g) \longrightarrow Zn^{2+}(aq) + 2\,Cl^-(aq) \end{array} \tag{7.12}$$

$$\begin{aligned} E^\circ_{cell} &= E^\circ(\text{reduction half-cell}) - E^\circ(\text{oxidation half-cell}) \\ &= 1.358\text{ V} - (-0.763\text{ V}) = 2.121\text{ V} \end{aligned}$$

Assess

Once the oxidized and reduced species are identified, we can establish E°_{cell}.

PRACTICE EXAMPLE A: What is E°_{cell} for the reaction in which $Cl_2(g)$ oxidizes $Fe^{2+}(aq)$ to $Fe^{3+}(aq)$?

$$2\,Fe^{2+}(aq) + Cl_2(g) \longrightarrow 2\,Fe^{3+}(aq) + 2\,Cl^-(aq) \qquad E^\circ_{cell} = ?$$

PRACTICE EXAMPLE B: Use data from Table 7.1 to determine E°_{cell} for the redox reaction in which $Fe^{2+}(aq)$ is oxidized to $Fe^{3+}(aq)$ by $MnO_4^-(aq)$ in acidic solution.

EXAMPLE 7-4 Determining an Unknown E° from an E°_{cell} Measurement

Cadmium is found in small quantities wherever zinc is found. Unlike zinc, which in trace amounts is an essential element, cadmium is an environmental poison. To determine cadmium ion concentrations by electrical measurements, we need the standard electrode potential for the Cd^{2+}/Cd electrode. The voltage of the following voltaic cell is measured.

$$Cd(s)|Cd^{2+}(1\text{ M})||Cu^{2+}(1\text{ M})|Cu(s) \qquad E^\circ_{cell} = 0.743\text{ V}$$

What is the standard electrode potential for the Cd^{2+}/Cd electrode?

Analyze

We know one half-cell potential and E°_{cell} for the overall redox reaction. We can solve for the unknown standard electrode potential, $E^\circ_{Cd^{2+}/Cd}$.

Solve

$$\begin{aligned} E^\circ_{cell} &= E^\circ(\text{right}) - E^\circ(\text{left}) \\ 0.743\text{ V} &= E^\circ_{Cu^{2+}/Cu} - E^\circ_{Cd^{2+}/Cd} \\ &= 0.340\text{ V} - E^\circ_{Cd^{2+}/Cd} \\ E^\circ_{Cd^{2+}/Cd} &= 0.340\text{ V} - 0.743\text{ V} = -0.403\text{ V} \end{aligned}$$

Assess

Based on the entries in Table 7.1 we see that Cd(s) is a stronger reducing agent than Sn(s), but weaker than Fe(s). $Cd^{2+}(aq)$ is a weaker oxidizing agent than $Sn^{2+}(aq)$.

PRACTICE EXAMPLE A: In acidic solution, dichromate ion oxidizes oxalic acid, $H_2C_2O_4(aq)$, to $CO_2(g)$ in a reaction with $E^\circ_{cell} = 1.81$ V.

$$Cr_2O_7^{2-}(aq) + 3\,H_2C_2O_4(aq) + 8\,H^+(aq) \longrightarrow 2\,Cr^{3+}(aq) + 7\,H_2O + 6\,CO_2(g)$$

Use the value of E°_{cell} for this reaction, together with appropriate data from Table 7.1, to determine E° for the $CO_2(g)/H_2C_2O_4(aq)$ electrode.

PRACTICE EXAMPLE B: In an acidic solution, $O_2(g)$ oxidizes $Cr^{2+}(aq)$ to $Cr^{3+}(aq)$. The $O_2(g)$ is reduced to $H_2O(l)$. E°_{cell} for the reaction is 1.653 V. What is the standard electrode potential for the couple Cr^{3+}/Cr^{2+}?

7-3 CONCEPT ASSESSMENT

For the half-cell reaction $ClO_4^-(aq) + 8\,H^+(aq) + 7\,e^- \longrightarrow \frac{1}{2}Cl_2(g) + 4\,H_2O(l)$, what are the standard-state conditions for the reactants and products?

7-3 E_{cell}, ΔG, and K

▶ It is quite common to see the symbol n used for the number of electrons; however, IUPAC recommends z to avoid confusion with the use of n as the amount of substance, such as the number of moles of gas in the ideal gas equation.

When a reaction occurs in a voltaic cell, the cell does work—electrical work. Think of this as the work of moving electric charges. The total work done is the product of three terms: (a) E_{cell}; (b) z, the number of electrons transferred between the electrodes; and (c) the electric charge per mole of electrons, called the **Faraday constant *(F)***. The Faraday constant is equal to 96,485 coulombs per mole of electrons (96,485 C/mol). Because the product volt × coulomb = joule, the unit of w_{elec} is joules (J).

$$w_{elec} = zFE_{cell} \qquad \textbf{(7.13)}$$

Expression (7.13) applies only if the cell operates reversibly. Thus,

$$\Delta G = -zFE_{cell} \qquad \textbf{(7.14)}$$

In the special case in which the reactants and products are in their standard states,

$$\Delta G° = -zFE°_{cell} \qquad \textbf{(7.15)}$$

At this point we should clear up some issues of units and definitions. The symbol z in equations (7.14) and (7.15) is properly called the *electron number* of an electrochemical reaction and is occasionally referred to as the *charge number*. The electron number has no units; that is, it is simply a number. For any given cell reaction we can write the reaction with a charge number of one or two. Thus, the hydrogen electrode reaction can be written as either

$$2\,H^+(aq) + 2\,e^- \longrightarrow H_2(g) \quad \text{or} \quad H^+(aq) + e^- \longrightarrow \frac{1}{2}H_2(g)$$

However, in considering an overall cell reaction, we must balance the electrons. Thus for the cell

$$Pt(s)|H_2(g)|H^+(aq, 1\,M)||Cu^{2+}(aq)|Cu(s)$$

the half-cell reactions can be written as

$$2\,H^+(aq) + 2\,e^- \longrightarrow H_2(g) \quad \text{and} \quad 2\,e^- + Cu^{2+}(aq) \longrightarrow Cu(s)$$

Thus, the electron number is two and the overall electrochemical reaction is

$$H_2(g) + Cu^{2+}(aq) \longrightarrow 2\,H^+(aq) + Cu(s)$$

The standard reduction potential for this reaction is

$$E°_{cell} = E°(\text{right}) - E°(\text{left})$$
$$= E°_{Cu^{2+}/Cu} - 0\text{ V} = 0.340\text{ V}$$

The standard Gibbs energy is given by

$$\Delta G°_{rxn} = -zFE°_{cell} = 2 \times \frac{96485\text{ C}}{\text{mol}} \times 0.340\text{ V}$$
$$= -6.5610\times10^4\text{ J mol}^{-1} = -65.6\text{ kJ mol}^{-1}$$

▲ **Michael Faraday (1791–1867)**
Faraday, an assistant to Humphry Davy and often called "Davy's greatest discovery," made many contributions to both physics and chemistry, including systematic studies of electrolysis.

That is, 65.6 kJ of energy is generated when 1 mole of Cu^{2+} ions is reduced or 2 moles of H^+ are produced. The process is accompanied by the passage of two moles of electrons around the outer circuit. We could also have written the reactions as

$$\textit{Oxidation:} \quad \frac{1}{2}H_2(g) \longrightarrow H^+(aq) + e^-$$

$$\textit{Reduction:} \quad \frac{1}{2}Cu^{2+}(aq) + e^- \longrightarrow \frac{1}{2}Cu(s)$$

$$\textit{Overall:} \quad \frac{1}{2}H_2(g) + \frac{1}{2}Cu^{2+}(aq) \longrightarrow \frac{1}{2}Cu(s) + H^+(aq)$$

This reaction is represented by the same cell diagram given above, but the electron number is one; consequently, the Gibbs energy is one-half of that previously calculated, but the value of E°_{cell} is the same. This result supports the fact that the standard reduction potential is an intensive property but the Gibbs energy is an extensive property. Finally, the reaction tells us that when 0.5 mole of Cu^{2+} is reduced, 32.8 kJ of energy is released and one mole of electrons passes from the anode to the cathode.

Our primary interest is not in calculating quantities of work but in using expression (7.15) as a means of evaluating Gibbs energy changes from measured cell potentials, as illustrated in Example 7-5.

EXAMPLE 7-5 Determining a Gibbs Energy Change from a Cell Potential

Use E° data to determine ΔG° for the reaction

$$Zn(s) + Cl_2(g, 1\ atm) \longrightarrow ZnCl_2(aq, 1\ M)$$

Solution

This reaction is cell reaction (7.12) occurring in the voltaic cell described in Example 7-3. In this type of problem, the overall equation generally needs to be separated into two half-equations. Then the value of E°_{cell} and the number of moles of electrons (n) involved in the cell reaction can be determined. Refer to Example 7-3 to see that $E^\circ_{cell} = 2.121$ V and $z = 2$ mol e^-. Now use equation (7.15).

$$\Delta G^\circ = -zFE^\circ_{cell} = -¢2\ mol\ e^- \times \frac{96{,}485\ C}{1\ mol\ e^-} \times 2.121\ V\dagger$$

$$= -4.093 \times 10^5\ J = -409.3\ kJ\ mol^{-1}$$

PRACTICE EXAMPLE A: Use electrode potential data to determine ΔG° for the reaction

$$2\ Al(s) + 3\ Br_2(l) \longrightarrow 2\ Al^{3+}(aq, 1\ M) + 6\ Br^-(aq, 1\ M) \qquad \Delta G^\circ = ?$$

PRACTICE EXAMPLE B: The hydrogen–oxygen fuel cell is a voltaic cell with a cell reaction of $2\ H_2(g) + O_2(g) \longrightarrow 2\ H_2O(l)$. Calculate E°_{cell} for this reaction. [*Hint:* Use thermodynamic data from Appendix A.]

Combining Reduction Half-Equations

Not only can equation (7.15) be used to determine ΔG° from E°_{cell}, as in Example 7-5, but the calculation can be reversed and an E°_{cell} value determined from ΔG°. Moreover, equation (7.15) can be applied to half-cell reactions and half-cell potentials—that is, to standard electrode potentials, E°. That is what we must do, for example, to determine E° for the half-reaction

$$Fe^{3+}(aq) + 3\ e^- \longrightarrow Fe(s)$$

Both in Table 7.1 and in Appendix A, the only entries that deal with Fe(s) and its ions are

$$Fe^{2+}(aq) + 2\ e^- \longrightarrow Fe(s), E^\circ = -0.440\ V \quad \text{and} \quad Fe^{3+}(aq) + e^- \longrightarrow Fe^{2+}(aq), E^\circ = 0.771\ V$$

The half-equation we are seeking is simply the sum of these two half-equations, but the $E°$ value we are seeking is *not* the sum of -0.440 V and 0.771 V. What we *can* add together, though, are the $\Delta G°$ values for the two known half-reactions.

KEEP IN MIND

that Gibbs energy changes are functions of state and therefore ΔG values can be combined to determine Gibbs energy changes for new reactions.

$$Fe^{2+}(aq) + 2\,e^- \longrightarrow Fe(s); \qquad \Delta G° = -2 \times F \times (-0.440\ V)$$
$$Fe^{3+}(aq) + e^- \longrightarrow Fe^{2+}(aq); \qquad \Delta G° = -1 \times F \times (0.771\ V)$$
$$Fe^{3+}(aq) + 3\,e^- \longrightarrow Fe(s); \qquad \Delta G° = (0.880F)\ V - (0.771F)\ V = (0.109F)\ V$$

Now, to get $E°_{Fe^{3+}/Fe}$, we can again use equation (7.15) and solve for $E°_{Fe^{3+}/Fe}$.

$$\Delta G° = -zFE°_{Fe^{3+}/Fe} = -3FE°_{Fe^{3+}/Fe} = (0.109F)\ V$$
$$E°_{Fe^{3+}/Fe} = (-0.109F/3F)\ V = -0.0363\ V$$

7-1 ARE YOU WONDERING...

How the procedure for combining two $E°$ values to obtain an unknown $E°_{cell}$ relates to combining two $E°$ values to obtain an unknown $E°$?

We have just seen how to obtain an unknown $E°$ from two known values of $E°$ by working through the expression $\Delta G = -zFE°$. As shown below for a hypothetical displacement reaction, we can similarly calculate an unknown $E°_{cell}$ through the expression $\Delta G° = -zFE°_{cell}$. (Note that for the oxidation half-reaction, $\Delta G°_{ox}$ is simply the negative of the value for the reverse half-reaction, $\Delta G°_{red}$.)

Reduction: $M^{z+}(aq) + z\,e^- \longrightarrow M(s)$ $\qquad \Delta G°_{red} = -zFE°_{M^{2+}/M}$

Oxidation: $N(s) \longrightarrow N^{z+}(aq) + z\,e^-$

$$\Delta G°_{ox} = -(\Delta G°_{red}) = -(-zFE°_{N^{z+}/N}) = zFE°_{N^{2+}/N}$$

Overall: $M^{z+}(aq) + N(s) \longrightarrow M(s) + N^{z+}(aq)$

$$\Delta G° = \Delta G°_{red} + \Delta G°_{ox} = -zFE°_{cell} = -zFE°_{M^{2+}/M} + zFE°_{N^{2+}/N}$$

Dividing through the above equation by the term $-zF$, we obtain $E°_{cell}$ as the familiar difference in two electrode potentials.

$$E°_{cell} = E°_{M^{z+}/M} - E°_{N^{z+}/N}$$

We have been able to skip this calculation based on $\Delta G°$ values and proceed straight to the expression

$$E°_{cell} = E°(\text{reduction}) - E°(\text{oxidation})$$

because the term $-zF$ always cancels out. That is, z, the number of electrons, must have the same value for the oxidation and reduction half-reactions and the overall reaction. By contrast, when obtaining an unknown $E°$ from the known $E°$ values, the value for z will not be the same in all three places where it appears, and so we do have to work through the $\Delta G°$ expressions.

Spontaneous Change in Oxidation–Reduction Reactions

Our main criterion for spontaneous change is that $\Delta G < 0$. According to equation (7.14), however, redox reactions have the property that, if $\Delta G < 0$, then $E_{cell} > 0$. That is, E_{cell} must be *positive* if ΔG is to be negative. Predicting the direction of spontaneous change in a redox reaction is a relatively simple matter by using the following ideas:

- If E_{cell} is *positive*, a reaction occurs spontaneously in the *forward* direction for the stated conditions. If E_{cell} is *negative*, the reaction occurs spontaneously in the *reverse* direction for the stated conditions. If $E_{cell} = 0$, the reaction is at equilibrium for the stated conditions.
- If a cell reaction is *reversed*, E_{cell} changes sign.

EXAMPLE 7-6 Applying the Criterion for Spontaneous Change in a Redox Reaction

Will aluminum metal displace Cu^{2+} ion from aqueous solution? That is, will a spontaneous reaction occur in the forward direction for the following reaction?

$$2\,Al(s) + 3\,Cu^{2+}(1\,M) \longrightarrow 3\,Cu(s) + 2\,Al^{3+}(1\,M)$$

Analyze

We need to identify the species reduced in the reaction as it is written. We then calculate E°_{cell}. If E°_{cell} is positive, then the reaction will occur spontaneously.

Solve

The cell diagram corresponding to the reaction is $Al(s)|Al^{3+}(aq)||Cu^{2+}(aq)|Cu(s)$, and E°_{cell} is

$$\begin{aligned} E^\circ_{cell} &= E^\circ(\text{cathode}) - E^\circ(\text{anode}) \\ &= E^\circ_{Cu^{2+}/Cu} - E^\circ_{Al^{3+}/Al} \\ &= 0.340\text{ V} - (-1.676\text{ V}) = 2.016\text{ V} \end{aligned}$$

Because E°_{cell} is positive, the direction of spontaneous change is that of the forward reaction. Al(s) will displace Cu^{2+} from aqueous solution under standard-state conditions.

Assess

The positive value of E°_{cell} means that the Gibbs energy change for the reaction is negative; hence, the reaction as written is spontaneous. Keep in mind that both E° and E°_{cell} are *intensive* properties. They do not depend on the quantities of materials involved, which means that their values are not affected by the choice of coefficients used to balance the equation for the cell reaction. We could just as well have written:

$$Al(s) + \frac{3}{2}Cu^{2+}(1\,M) \longrightarrow \frac{3}{2}Cu(s) + Al^{3+}(1\,M) \text{ or}$$

$$\frac{2}{3}Al(s) + Cu^{2+}(1\,M) \longrightarrow Cu(s) + \frac{2}{3}Al^{3+}(1\,M)$$

PRACTICE EXAMPLE A: Name one metal ion that Cu(s) will displace from aqueous solution, and determine E°_{cell} for the reaction.

PRACTICE EXAMPLE B: When sodium metal is added to seawater, which has $[Mg^{2+}] = 0.0512$ M, no magnesium metal is obtained. According to E° values, should this displacement reaction occur? What reaction does occur?

In the special case in which reactants and products are in their standard states, we work with ΔG° and E°_{cell} values, as illustrated in Examples 7-6 and 7-7.

Even though we used electrode potentials and cell voltage to predict a spontaneous reaction in Example 7-6, we do not have to carry out the reaction in a voltaic cell. This is an important point to keep in mind. Thus, Cu^{2+} is displaced from aqueous solution simply by adding aluminum metal, as shown in Figure 7-7. Another point, illustrated by Example 7-7, is that qualitative answers to questions concerning redox reactions can be found without going through a complete calculation of E°_{cell}.

▲ FIGURE 7-7
Reaction of Al(s) and Cu^{2+}(aq)
Notice the holes in the foil where Al(s) has dissolved. Notice also the dark deposit of Cu(s) at the bottom of the beaker.

The Behavior of Metals Toward Acids

In the discussion of redox reactions, it was noted that most metals react with an acid, such as HCl, but that a few do not. This observation can now be explained. When a metal, M, reacts with an acid, such as HCl, the metal is oxidized to the metal ion, such as M^{2+}. The reduction involves H^+ being reduced to $H_2(g)$. These ideas can be expressed as

$$\begin{aligned} &\textit{Oxidation:} & M(s) &\longrightarrow M^{2+}(aq) + 2\,e^- \\ &\textit{Reduction:} & 2\,H^+(aq) + 2\,e^- &\longrightarrow H_2(g) \\ &\textit{Overall:} & M(s) + 2\,H^+(aq) &\longrightarrow M^{2+}(aq) + H_2(g) \end{aligned}$$

$$E^\circ_{cell} = E^\circ_{H^+/H_2} - E^\circ_{M^{2+}/M} = 0\text{ V} - E^\circ_{M^{2+}/M} = -E^\circ_{M^{2+}/M}$$

EXAMPLE 7-7 Making Qualitative Predictions with Electrode Potential Data

Peroxodisulfate salts, such as $Na_2S_2O_8$, are oxidizing agents used in bleaching. Dichromates such as $K_2Cr_2O_7$ have been used as laboratory oxidizing agents. Which is the better oxidizing agent in acidic solution under standard conditions, $S_2O_8^{2-}$ or $Cr_2O_7^{2-}$?

Analyze

In a redox reaction, the oxidizing agent is reduced; the greater the tendency for this reduction to occur, the better the oxidizing agent. The reduction tendency, in turn, is measured by the $E°$ value.

Solve

Because the $E°$ value for the reduction of $S_2O_8^{2-}(aq)$ to $SO_4^{2-}(aq)$ (2.01 V) is larger than that for the reduction of $Cr_2O_7^{2-}(aq)$ to $Cr^{3+}(aq)$ (1.33 V), $S_2O_8^{2-}(aq)$ should be the better oxidizing agent.

Assess

Inspection of standard reduction potentials enables us to qualitatively assess the spontaneity of a particular redox reaction.

PRACTICE EXAMPLE A: An inexpensive way to produce peroxodisulfates would be to pass $O_2(g)$ through an acidic solution containing sulfate ion. Is this method feasible under standard conditions? [*Hint:* What would be the reduction half-reaction?]

PRACTICE EXAMPLE B: Consider the following observations: (1) Aqueous solutions of Sn^{2+} are difficult to maintain because atmospheric oxygen easily oxidizes Sn^{2+} to Sn^{4+}. (2) One way to preserve the $Sn^{2+}(aq)$ solutions is to add some metallic tin. *Without doing detailed calculations,* explain these two statements by using $E°$ data.

Metals with *negative* standard electrode potentials yield *positive* values of $E°_{cell}$ in the above expression. These are the metals that should displace $H_2(g)$ from acidic solutions. Thus, all the metals listed *below* hydrogen in Table 7.1 (Pb through Li) should react with acids.

In acids, such as HCl, HBr, and HI, the oxidizing agent is H^+ (that is, H_3O^+). Certain metals that will not react with HCl will react with an acid in the presence of an *anion* that is a better oxidizing agent than H^+. Nitrate ion is a good oxidizing agent in acidic solution, and silver metal, which does not react with HCl(aq), readily reacts with nitric acid, $HNO_3(aq)$.

$$3\,Ag(s) + NO_3^-(aq) + 4\,H^+(aq) \longrightarrow 3\,Ag^+(aq) + NO(g) + 2\,H_2O \quad E°_{cell} = 0.156\text{ V}$$

The Relationship Between $E°_{cell}$ and K

▶ Note that any electrochemical cell, if left in a completed circuit, will eventually die as the redox reaction goes to completion. This means that the cell potential will eventually drop to zero. The relationship between Gibbs energy and equilibrium was established in a similar way.

$\Delta G°$ and $E°_{cell}$ were related through equation (7.15). $\Delta G°$ and K were related. The three quantities are thus related in this way.

$$\Delta G° = -RT \ln K = -zFE°_{cell}$$

and therefore,

$$E°_{cell} = \frac{RT}{zF} \ln K \qquad \textbf{(7.16)}$$

▶ Equation 7.16 gives the expected result that reactions with equilibrium constants larger than one have a positive standard cell potential.

In equation (7.16), R has a value of 8.3145 J mol^{-1} K^{-1} and z represents the number of electrons involved in the reaction. If we then specify a temperature of 25 °C = 298.15 K (the temperature at which electrode potentials are generally determined), the combined terms "RT/F" in equation (7.16) can be replaced by a single constant. This constant has the value 0.025693 J/C = 0.025693 V.

$$E°_{cell} = \frac{RT}{zF} \ln K = \frac{8.3145\text{ J }\cancel{mol^{-1}}\ \cancel{K^{-1}} \times 298.15\ \cancel{K}}{z \times 96485\text{ C }\cancel{mol^{-1}}} \ln K$$

$$E^\circ_{cell} = \frac{0.025693\text{ V}}{z}\ln K \qquad \textbf{(7.17)}$$

The relationship between E°_{cell} and K is illustrated in Example 7-8. Also, Figure 7-8 summarizes several important relationships from thermodynamics, equilibrium, and electrochemistry.

EXAMPLE 7-8 Relating K to E°_{cell} for a Redox Reaction

What is the value of the equilibrium constant K for the reaction between copper metal and iron(III) ions in aqueous solution at 25 °C?

$$Cu(s) + 2\,Fe^{3+}(aq) \longrightarrow Cu^{2+}(aq) + 2\,Fe^{2+}(aq) \qquad K = ?$$

Analyze

We first identify the reactant that is reduced and the reactant that is oxidized. We then use the data in Table 7.1 to obtain the standard reduction potentials and hence the cell potential. Finally, we use equation (7.17) to obtain K from E°_{cell}.

Solve

First, we use data from Table 7.1 to determine E°_{cell}.

$$\begin{aligned} E^\circ_{cell} &= E^\circ(\text{reduction half-cell}) - E^\circ(\text{oxidation half-cell}) \\ &= E^\circ_{Fe^{3+}/Fe^{2+}} - E^\circ_{Cu^{2+}/Cu} \\ &= 0.771\text{ V} - 0.340\text{ V} = 0.431\text{ V} \end{aligned}$$

The charge number (z) for the cell reaction is 2.

$$E^\circ_{cell} = 0.431\text{ V} = \frac{0.02569\text{ V}}{2}\ln K$$

$$\ln K = \frac{2 \times 0.431\text{ V}}{0.02569\text{ V}} = 33.6$$

$$K = e^{33.6} = 4 \times 10^{14}$$

Assess

The positive value of the cell potential means that the equilibrium constant is greater than one. The value of the equilibrium constant is very large, and so we can expect this reaction to go to completion.

PRACTICE EXAMPLE A: Should the displacement of Cu^{2+} from aqueous solution by Al(s) go to completion? [*Hint:* Base your assessment on the value of K for the displacement reaction. We determined E°_{cell} for this reaction in Example 7-6.]

PRACTICE EXAMPLE B: Should the reaction of Sn(s) and Pb^{2+}(aq) go to completion? Explain.

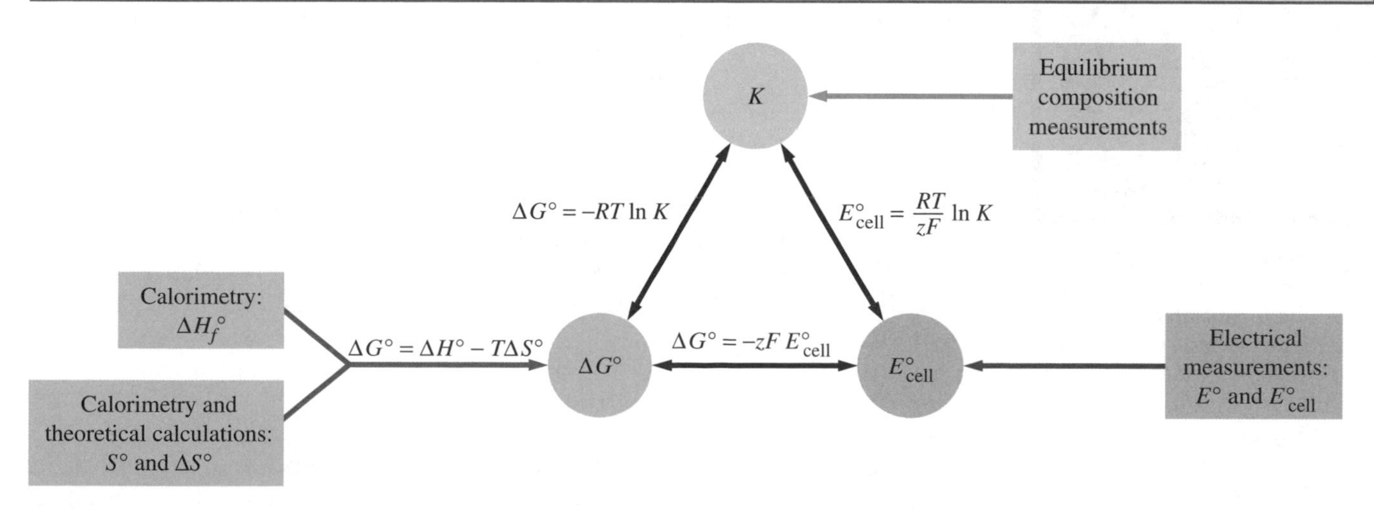

▲ FIGURE 7-8
A summary of important thermodynamic, equilibrium, and electrochemical relationships under standard conditions

7-4 CONCEPT ASSESSMENT

When two cell reactions with reactants and products in their standard states are compared, one is found to have a negative value of E°_{cell} and the other a positive value. Which cell reaction will proceed toward the formation of more products to establish equilibrium? Will a net cell reaction occur in the other case? If so, how will the equilibrium concentrations compare with the initial concentrations?

7-4 E_{cell} as a Function of Concentrations

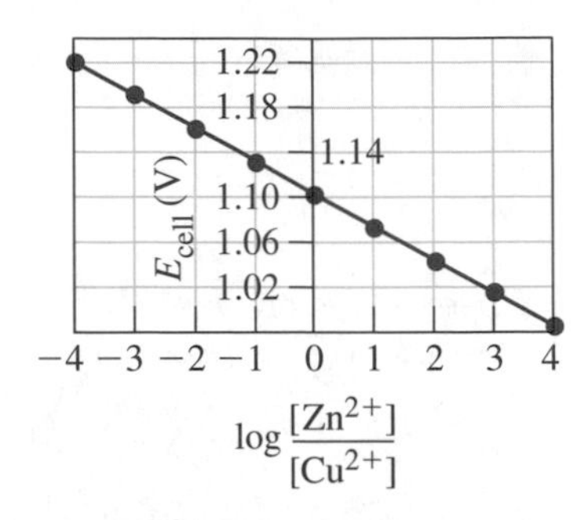

▲ FIGURE 7-9
Variation of E_{cell} with ion concentrations
The cell reaction is $Zn(s) + Cu^{2+}(aq) \longrightarrow Zn^{2+}(aq) + Cu(s)$ and has $E^\circ_{cell} = 1.103$ V.

When we combine standard electrode potentials, we obtain a standard E°_{cell}, such as $E^\circ_{cell} = 1.103$ V for the voltaic cell of Figure 7-4. For the following cell reaction at *nonstandard* conditions, however, the measured E_{cell} is not 1.103 V.

$$Zn(s) + Cu^{2+}(2.0\text{ M}) \longrightarrow Zn^{2+}(0.10\text{ M}) + Cu(s) \qquad E_{cell} = 1.142\text{ V}$$

Experimental measurements of cell potentials are often made for nonstandard conditions; these measurements have great significance, especially for performing chemical analyses.

From Le Châtelier's principle, it would seem that *increasing* the concentration of a reactant (Cu^{2+}) while *decreasing* the concentration of a product (Zn^{2+}) should favor the forward reaction. Zn(s) should displace $Cu^{2+}(aq)$ even more readily than for standard-state conditions and $E_{cell} > 1.103$ V. E_{cell} is found to vary linearly with $\log([Zn^{2+}]/[Cu^{2+}])$, as illustrated in Figure 7-9.

It is not difficult to establish the relationship between the cell potential, E_{cell}, and the concentrations of reactants and products. From Chapter 5 we can write equation (5.11).

$$\Delta G = \Delta G^\circ + RT \ln Q$$

For ΔG and ΔG°, we can substitute $-zFE_{cell}$ and $-zFE^\circ_{cell}$, respectively.

$$-zFE_{cell} = -zFE^\circ_{cell} + RT \ln Q$$

Dividing through by $-zF$ gives

$$E_{cell} = E^\circ_{cell} - \frac{RT}{zF} \ln Q \qquad (7.18)$$

▲ **Walther Nernst (1864–1941)**
Nernst was only 25 years old when he formulated his equation relating cell voltages and concentrations. He is also credited with proposing the solubility product concept in the same year. In 1906, he announced his "heat theorem," which we now know as the third law of thermodynamics.

This equation was first proposed by Walther Nernst in 1889. By specifying a temperature of 298.15 K and replacing RT/F by 0.025693 V, as in the development of equation (7.17), we can write the **Nernst equation** in the form

$$E_{cell} = E^\circ_{cell} - \frac{0.025693\text{ V}}{z} \ln Q \qquad (7.19)$$

The equation can be written in another form by switching from natural to common logarithms ($\ln Q = 2.3026 \log Q$).

At 298.15 K, the term $2.3026\, RT/F = 2.3026 \times 0.025693\text{ V} = 0.05916$ V, which is usually rounded off to 0.0592 V. Thus, the Nernst equation can also be written in the form

$$E_{cell} = E^\circ_{cell} - \frac{0.0592\text{ V}}{z} \log Q \qquad (7.20)$$

In the Nernst equation, we make the usual substitutions into Q: $a = 1$ for the activities of pure solids and liquids, partial pressures (atm) for the activities of gases, and molarities for the activities of solution components. Example 7-9 demonstrates that the Nernst equation makes it possible to calculate E_{cell} for any chosen concentrations, not just for standard conditions.

EXAMPLE 7-9 Applying the Nernst Equation for Determining E_{cell}

What is the value of E_{cell} for the voltaic cell pictured in Figure 7-10 and diagrammed as follows? Assume $T = 298.15$ K.

$$Pt|Fe^{2+}(0.10\ M), Fe^{3+}(0.20\ M)||Ag^{+}(1.0\ M)|Ag(s) \qquad E_{cell} = ?$$

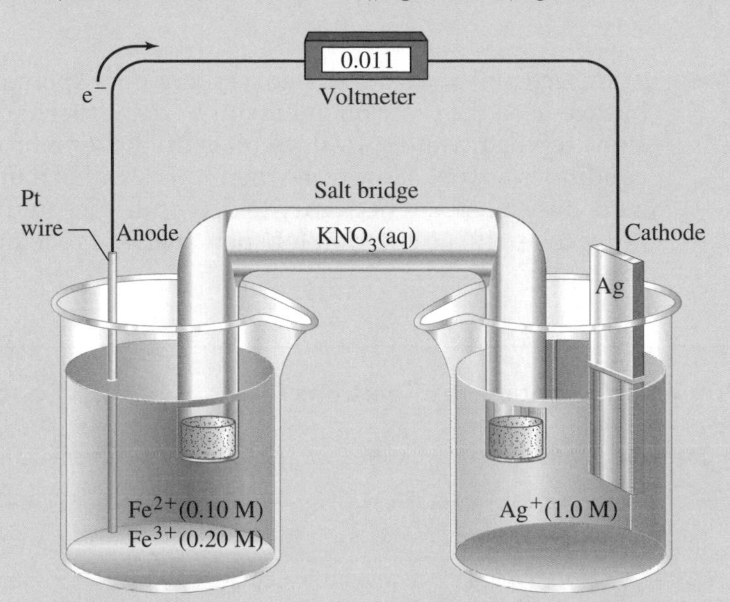

▲ FIGURE 7-10
A voltaic cell with nonstandard conditions—Example 7-9 illustrated

Analyze

To use the Nernst equation we need to establish E°_{cell} and the reaction to which the cell diagram corresponds so that the form of the reaction quotient (Q) can be revealed (see Example 7-2). Once we have determined the form of the Nernst equation, we can insert the concentration of the species.

Solve

Two steps are required when using the Nernst equation. First, to determine E°_{cell}, use data from Table 7.1 to write

$$E^{\circ}_{cell} = E^{\circ}(\text{cathode}) - E^{\circ}(\text{anode}) = E^{\circ}_{Ag^{+}/Ag} - E^{\circ}_{Fe^{3+}/Fe^{2+}} = 0.800\ V - 0.771\ V = 0.029\ V$$

Now, to determine E_{cell} for the reaction

$$Fe^{2+}(0.10\ M) + Ag^{+}(1.0\ M) \longrightarrow Fe^{3+}(0.20\ M) + Ag(s) \quad E_{cell} = ?$$

substitute appropriate values into the Nernst equation (7.18), starting with $E^{\circ}_{cell} = 0.029$ V and $z = 1$,

$$E_{cell} = 0.029\ V - \frac{8.3145\ J\ mol^{-1}\ K^{-1} \times 298.15\ K}{1 \times 96485\ C\ mol^{-1}} \ln \frac{[Fe^{3+}]}{[Fe^{2+}][Ag^{+}]}$$

and for concentrations $[Fe^{2+}] = 0.10$ M; $[Fe^{3+}] = 0.20$ M; $[Ag^{+}] = 1.0$ M.

$$E_{cell} = 0.029\ V - 0.0257\ V \times \ln \frac{0.20}{0.10 \times 1.0} = 0.029\ V - 0.0257\ V \times \ln 2 = 0.029\ V - 0.018\ V = 0.011\ V$$

Assess

The E_{cell} is positive so that the reaction is spontaneous in the direction of the reduction of silver.

PRACTICE EXAMPLE A: Calculate E_{cell} for the following voltaic cell.

$$Al(s)|Al^{3+}(0.36\ M)||Sn^{4+}(0.086\ M), Sn^{2+}(0.54\ M)|Pt$$

PRACTICE EXAMPLE B: Calculate E_{cell} for the following voltaic cell.

$$Pt(s)|Cl_2(1\ atm)|Cl^{-}(1.0\ M)||Pb^{2+}(0.050\ M), H^{+}(0.10\ M)|PbO_2(s)$$

7-5 CONCEPT ASSESSMENT

Describe *two* sets of conditions under which the measured E_{cell} for a reaction is equal to E°_{cell}.

In Section 7-3, we developed a criterion for spontaneous change ($E_{cell} > 0$), but we used the criterion only with E° data from Table 7.1 Qualitative conclusions reached with E°_{cell} values often hold over a broad range of nonstandard conditions as well. However, when E°_{cell} is within a few hundredths of a volt of zero, it is sometimes necessary to determine E_{cell} for nonstandard conditions in order to apply the criterion for spontaneity of redox reactions, as illustrated in Example 7-10.

EXAMPLE 7-10 Predicting Spontaneous Reactions for Nonstandard Conditions

Will the cell reaction proceed spontaneously as written for the following cell? Assume $T = 298.15$ K.

$$Ag(s)|Ag^{+}(0.075\ M)||Hg^{2+}(0.85\ M)|Hg(l)$$

Analyze

To decide whether a reaction is spontaneous, we need to calculate E_{cell} by using equation (7.18) with the concentrations given. We must first identify the oxidized and reduced species and look up the appropriate standard half-cell potentials. Then we construct the chemical equation that corresponds to the cell diagram, choosing an appropriate electron number (z).

Solve

To determine E°_{cell} from E° data we write

$$\begin{array}{lrcl} \textit{Oxidation:} & 2\,Ag(s) & \longrightarrow & 2\,Ag^{+}(aq) + 2\,e^{-} \\ \textit{Reduction:} & Hg^{2+}(aq) + 2\,e^{-} & \longrightarrow & Hg(l) \\ \hline \textit{Overall:} & 2\,Ag(s) + Hg^{2+}(aq) & \longrightarrow & 2\,Ag^{+}(aq) + Hg(l) \end{array}$$

$$\begin{aligned} E^{\circ}_{cell} &= E^{\circ}(\text{reduction half-cell}) - E^{\circ}(\text{oxidation half-cell}) \\ &= 0.854\ V - (0.800\ V) = 0.054\ V \end{aligned}$$

The overall reaction that we have written has an electron number, $z = 2$, so that the Nernst equation is

$$E_{cell} = 0.054\ V - \frac{8.3145\ J\ mol^{-1}\ K^{-1} \times 298.15\ K}{2 \times 96485\ C\ mol^{-1}} \ln \frac{[Ag^{+}]^2}{[Hg^{2+}]}$$

By using the concentrations $[Ag^{+}] = 0.075$ M and $[Hg^{2+}] = 0.85$ M provided, we obtain

$$\begin{aligned} E_{cell} &= 0.054\ V - 0.0128\ V \ln \frac{[0.075]^2}{[0.85]} \\ &= 0.054\ V - 0.0128\ V \ln(0.0066) = 0.054\ V - 0.0128\ V \times (-5.021) \\ &= 0.054\ V + 0.064\ V = -0.118\ V \end{aligned}$$

Because $E_{cell} > 0$, we conclude that the reaction as written is spontaneous.

Assess

If we had used an electron number of $z = 1$, the overall reaction would have been

$$\textit{Overall } (z = 1)\text{:}\ Ag(s) + \frac{1}{2} Hg^{2+}(aq) \longrightarrow Ag^{+}(aq) + \frac{1}{2} Hg(l)$$

The corresponding Nernst equation is

$$E_{cell} = 0.054\ V - \frac{0.0257\ V}{1} \ln \frac{[Ag^{+}]}{[Hg^{2+}]^{1/2}}$$

By rearranging slightly and using a property of logarithms,

$$E_{cell} = 0.054\text{ V} - \frac{0.0257\text{ V}}{1}\ln\left(\frac{[Ag^+]^2}{[Hg^{2+}]}\right)^{1/2} = 0.054\text{ V} - \frac{0.0257\text{ V}}{2}\ln\frac{[Ag^+]^2}{[Hg^{2+}]}$$

we have recovered the Nernst equation for the cell reaction by using an electron number (z) of 2. We conclude that as long as we balance charge and the electron number correctly, we will always get the correct result.

PRACTICE EXAMPLE A: Will the cell reaction proceed spontaneously as written for the following cell?

$$Cu(s)|Cu^{2+}(0.15\text{ M})||Fe^{3+}(0.35\text{ M}), Fe^{2+}(0.25\text{ M})|Pt(s)$$

PRACTICE EXAMPLE B: For what ratio of $[Ag^+]^2/[Hg^{2+}]$ will the cell reaction in Example 7-10 not be spontaneous in either direction?

7-6 CONCEPT ASSESSMENT

The following cell is set up under standard-state conditions.

$$Pb(s)|Pb^{2+}||Cu^{2+}|Cu(s) \qquad E^\circ_{cell} = 0.47\text{ V}$$

When sodium sulfate is added to the anode half-cell, formation of a white precipitate is observed, accompanied by a change in the value of E_{cell}. Explain these observations, and predict whether the new E_{cell} is greater or less than E°_{cell}.

Concentration Cells

The voltaic cell in Figure 7-11 consists of two hydrogen electrodes. One is a standard hydrogen electrode (SHE), and the other is a hydrogen electrode immersed in a solution of unknown $[H^+]$, less than 1 M. The cell diagram is

$$Pt|H_2(g, 1\text{ atm})|H^+(x\text{ M})||H^+(1\text{ M})|H_2(g, 1\text{ atm})|Pt$$

The reaction occurring in this cell is

$$\begin{aligned}
&\textit{Reduction:} && 2\,H^+(1\text{ M}) + \cancel{2e^-} \longrightarrow \cancel{H_2(g, 1\text{ atm})} \\
&\textit{Oxidation:} && \cancel{H_2(g, 1\text{ atm})} \longrightarrow 2\,H^+(x\text{ M}) + \cancel{2e^-} \\
&\textit{Overall:} && 2\,H^+(1\text{ M}) \longrightarrow 2\,H^+(x\text{ M}) \qquad \textbf{(7.21)}
\end{aligned}$$

$$E^\circ_{cell} = E^\circ_{H^+/H_2} - E^\circ_{H^+/H_2} = 0\text{ V}$$

The voltaic cell in Figure 7-11 is called a concentration cell. A **concentration cell** consists of two half-cells with *identical electrodes* but different ion concentrations. Because the electrodes are identical, the standard electrode potentials are numerically equal and subtracting one from the other leads to the value $E^\circ_{cell} = 0$. However, because the ion concentrations differ, there is a potential

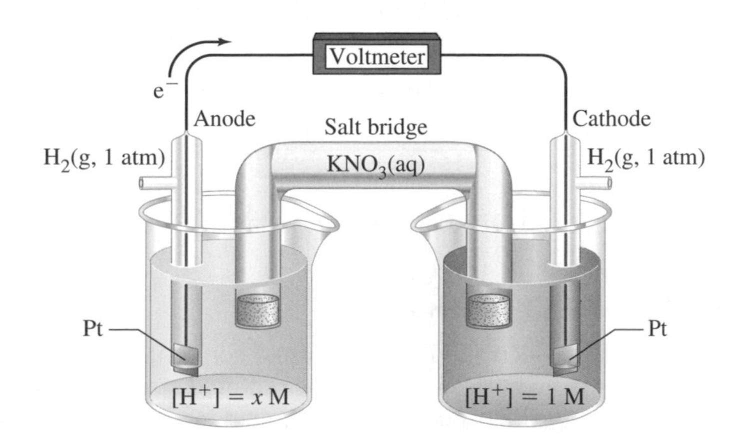

◄ FIGURE 7-11
A concentration cell
The cell consists of two hydrogen electrodes. The electrode on the right is a SHE. Oxidation occurs at the anode on the left, where $[H^+]$ is less than 1 M. The reading on the voltmeter is directly proportional to the pH of the solution in the anode compartment.

difference between the two half-cells. The spontaneous change in a concentration cell always occurs such that the concentrated solution becomes more dilute, and the dilute solution becomes more concentrated. The final result is as if the solutions were simply mixed. In a concentration cell, however, the natural tendency for entropy to increase in a mixing process is used as a means of producing electricity.

The Nernst equation for reaction (7.21) may be expressed in the form

$$E_{cell} = E^{\circ}_{cell} - \frac{0.0592\ V}{2}\log\frac{x^2}{1^2}$$

which simplifies to

$$E_{cell} = 0 - \frac{0.0592\ V}{2} \times 2\log\frac{x}{1} = -0.0592\ V \log x$$

Because x is $[H^+]$ in the unknown solution and $-\log x = -\log[H^+] = \text{pH}$, the final result is

$$E_{cell} = (0.0592\ \text{pH})\ V \quad \textbf{(7.22)}$$

where the pH is that of the unknown solution. If an unknown solution has a pH of 3.50, for example, the measured cell voltage in Figure 7-11 will be $E_{cell} = (0.0592 \times 3.50)\ V = 0.207\ V$.

Constructing and using a hydrogen electrode is difficult. The Pt metal surface must be specially prepared and maintained, gas pressure must be controlled, and the electrode cannot be used in the presence of strong oxidizing or reducing agents. The solution to these problems is discussed later in this chapter.

7-7 CONCEPT ASSESSMENT

Write a cell diagram for a possible voltaic cell in which the cell reaction is $Cl^-(0.50\ M) \longrightarrow Cl^-(0.10\ M)$. What would be E_{cell} for this reaction?

Measurement of K_{sp}

The difference in concentration of ions in the two half-cells of a concentration cell accounts for the observed E_{cell}. It also provides a basis for determining K_{sp} values for sparingly soluble ionic compounds. Consider the following concentration cell.

$$Ag(s)|Ag^+(\text{satd AgI})||Ag^+(0.100\ M)|Ag \qquad E_{cell} = 0.417\ V$$

At the anode, a silver electrode is placed in a saturated aqueous solution of silver iodide. At the cathode, a second silver electrode is placed in a solution with $[Ag^+] = 0.100$ M. The two half-cells are connected by a salt bridge, and the measured cell voltage is 0.417 V (Fig. 7-12). The cell reaction occurring in this *concentration cell* is

$$\begin{array}{lrl} \textit{Reduction:} & Ag^+(0.100\ M) + e^- & \longrightarrow Ag(s) \\ \textit{Oxidation:} & Ag(s) & \longrightarrow Ag^+(\text{satd AgI}) \\ \hline \textit{Overall:} & Ag^+(0.100\ M) & \longrightarrow Ag^+(\text{satd AgI}) \end{array} \quad \textbf{(7.23)}$$

The calculation of K_{sp} of silver iodide is completed in Example 7-11.

Alternative Standard Electrodes

The standard hydrogen electrode is not the most convenient to use because it requires highly flammable hydrogen gas to be bubbled over the platinum electrode. Other electrodes can be used as secondary standard electrodes, such as the

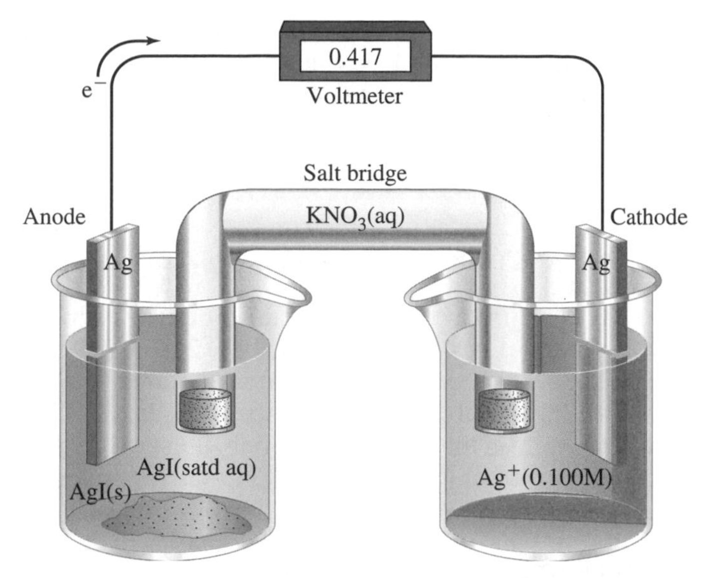

▲ FIGURE 7-12
A concentration cell for determining K_{sp} of AgI
The silver electrode in the anode compartment is in contact with a saturated solution of AgI. In the cathode compartment, $[Ag^+] = 0.100$ M.

EXAMPLE 7-11 Using a Voltaic Cell to Determine K_{sp} of a Slightly Soluble Solute

With the data given for reaction (7.23), calculate K_{sp} for AgI.

$$AgI(s) \rightleftharpoons Ag^+(aq) + I^-(aq) \qquad K_{sp} = ?$$

Analyze

Once we have determined the concentration of Ag^+ ions from the Nernst equation for the cell, we can calculate the equilibrium constant by using the expression for the solubility product.

Solve

$[Ag^+]$ in saturated silver iodide solution can be represented as x. The Nernst equation is then applied to reaction (7.23). (To simplify the equations that follow, we have dropped the unit V, which would otherwise appear in several places.)

$$E_{cell} = E^\circ_{cell} - \frac{0.0257}{z}\ln\frac{[Ag^+]_{satd\ AgI}}{[Ag^+]_{0.100\ M\ soln}}$$

$$= E^\circ_{cell} - \frac{0.0257}{1}\ln\frac{x}{0.100}$$

$$0.417 = 0 - 0.0257(\ln x - \ln 0.100)$$

Divide both sides of the equation by 0.0257.

$$\frac{0.417}{0.0257} = -\ln x + \ln 0.100$$

$$\ln x = \ln 0.100 - \frac{0.417}{0.0257} = -2.30 - 16.2 = -18.5$$

$$x = [Ag^+] = e^{-18.5} = 9 \times 10^{-9}\ M$$

Because in saturated AgI the concentrations of Ag^+ and I^- are equal,

$$K_{sp} = [Ag^+][I^-] = (9 \times 10^{-9})(9 \times 10^{-9}) = 8 \times 10^{-17}$$

Assess

Apart from the use of the Nernst equation, the other essential aspect is the realization that the only source of Ag^+ and I^- is from the AgI present; the saturated AgI(s) electrode has $[Ag^+] = [I^-]$.

PRACTICE EXAMPLE A: K_{sp} for AgCl $= 1.8 \times 10^{-10}$. What would be the measured E_{cell} for the voltaic cell in Example 7-11 if the contents of the anode half-cell were saturated AgCl(aq) and AgCl(s)?

PRACTICE EXAMPLE B: Calculate the K_{sp} for PbI_2 given the following concentration cell information.

$$Pb(s)|Pb^{2+}(satd\ PbI_2)||Pb^{2+}(0.100\ M)|Pb(s) \qquad E_{cell} = 0.0567\ V$$

silver–silver chloride electrode, in which a silver wire is covered with a layer of insoluble solid silver chloride. The silver-chloride-coated silver wire is immersed in a 1 M potassium chloride solution (see Fig. 7-13a), giving the electrode

$$Ag(s)|AgCl(s)|Cl^-(1.0\ M)$$

with a half-cell reaction of

$$AgCl(s) + e^- \longrightarrow Ag(s) + Cl^-(aq)$$

This electrode has been measured against the standard hydrogen electrode, and the electrode potential has been found to be 0.22233 V at 25 °C. Since all components of this electrode are in their standard states, the standard electrode potential of the silver–silver chloride electrode is 0.22233 V at 25 °C.

An alternative electrode is the calomel electrode, illustrated in Figure 7-13(b). In this electrode, mercurous chloride (calomel, Hg_2Cl_2) is mixed with mercury to form a paste, which is in contact with liquid mercury, Hg(l), and the whole setup is immersed in either a 1.0 M solution of potassium chloride or a saturated solution of potassium chloride. The electrode is

$$Hg(l)|Hg_2Cl_2(s)|Cl^-(1.0\ M)$$

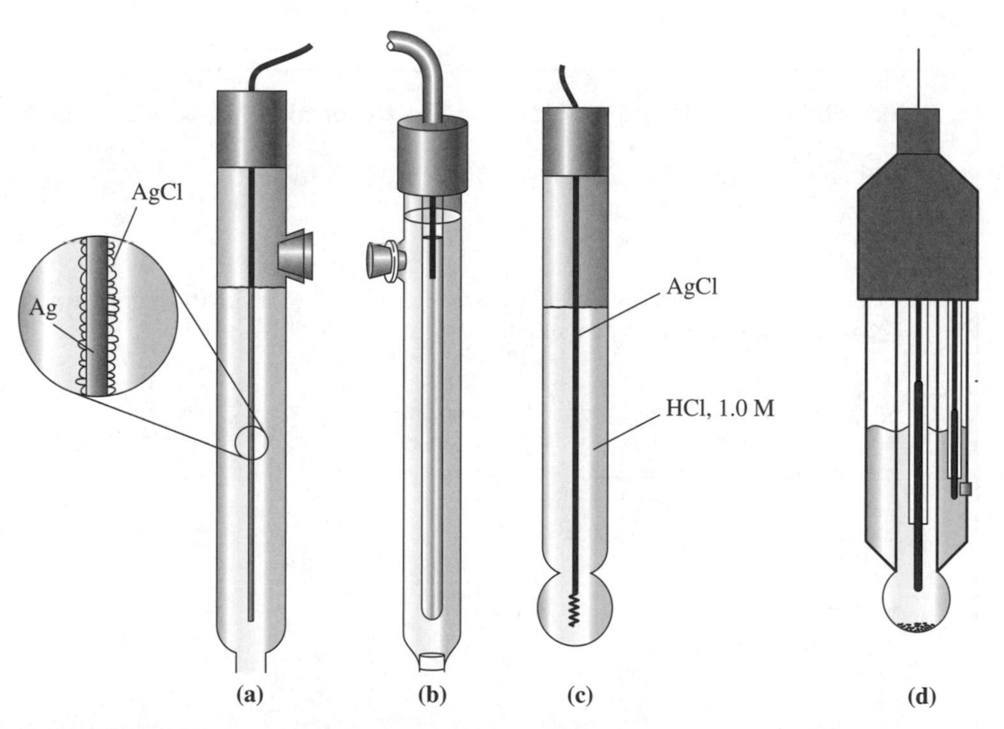

▲ FIGURE 7-13
Schematic diagrams of some common electrodes
(a) The silver–silver chloride electrode. Silver wire is coated with silver chloride and immersed in a 1 M aqueous solution of KCl. At the bottom of the tube is a fritted (porous) disc to allow contact with a solution of interest. **(b)** The standard calomel electrode is a tube containing a paste of calomel and mercury, immersed in a 1.0 M solution of KCl. Contact with an external circuit is made with a Pt wire inserted in the inner tube; the inner tube makes contact with the outer 1.0 M solution of KCl through a small hole in the bottom of the inner tube. **(c)** A glass electrode consists of tube with a very thin glass bulb at the end and a Ag–AgCl electrode immersed in a 1.0 M HCl solution. When the glass electrode is dipped into a solution, ions interact with the membrane. The potential established on the silver wire depends on the solution being tested. **(d)** A modern pH electrode consists of a glass electrode and an internal Ag–AgCl reference electrode. There is a small sintered disc in the side of the outer tube that acts as a salt bridge between the electrode and the unknown solution.

and the half-cell reaction is

$$\frac{1}{2}Hg_2Cl_2(s) + e^- \longrightarrow Hg(l) + Cl^-(aq)$$

The standard electrode potential at 25 °C is 0.2680 V. If, however, a saturated solution of KCl is used, as opposed to one of 1 M, the reduction potential is 0.2412 V. This electrode is known as the saturated calomel electrode (SCE) and is often used as a reference.

In practice a variety of reference electrodes are used; therefore, it is necessary to quote reduction potentials with respect to a specific reference.

7-8 CONCEPT ASSESSMENT

Why do the calomel standard reduction potential and the saturated calomel electrode have different potentials?

The Glass Electrode and the Electrochemical Measurement of pH

To measure the pH of a solution electrochemically, we need an electrode that responds to changes in $[H^+(aq)]$. We noted that the standard hydrogen electrode is difficult to use for this purpose, and so, for routine use, a simpler and safer electrode is needed. Such an electrode is the *glass electrode*, which consists of a very thin walled glass bulb (see Fig. 7-13c) at the end of a tube that contains a silver–silver chloride electrode and a HCl solution of known composition (e.g., 1 M). When the bulb is placed in a solution of unknown pH, a potential develops because of the concentration difference across the membrane, analogous to a concentration cell. To measure this potential difference, a reference electrode is used, which can be either a saturated calomel electrode or a second silver–silver chloride electrode, as in the combination electrode shown in Figure 7-13(d). The overall cell can be represented as

$$Ag(s)|AgCl(s)|Cl^-(1.0\ M), H^+(1.0\ M)|\text{glass membrane}|H^+(\text{unknown})||Cl^-(1.0\ M)|AgCl(s)|Ag(s)$$

where the two electrodes are connected by a salt bridge. The half-reactions are

$$\begin{aligned} Ag(s) + Cl^-(aq) &\longrightarrow AgCl(s) + e^- \\ H^+(1.0\ M) &\longrightarrow H^+(\text{unknown}) \\ AgCl(s) + e^- &\longrightarrow Ag(s) + Cl^-(aq) \end{aligned}$$

The half-cell potentials of the two half-reactions for the silver–silver chloride electrodes cancel each other out and make no contribution to the cell potential. The Gibbs energy change corresponding to the dilution of protons from a known concentration of 1.0 M to the unknown solution is the source of the potential difference across the glass membrane. The Gibbs energy difference across the membrane, using $G = G° + RT \ln[H^+]$, is

$$\begin{aligned} \Delta G &= G(\text{unknown}) - G(1.0\ M) \\ &= G° + RT \ln[\text{unknown}] - G° - RT \ln 1.0 \\ &= RT \ln[\text{unknown}] \end{aligned}$$

Converting this to a potential by dividing by $-zF$, $z = 1$, and assuming $T = 25$ °C, we obtain

$$E_{cell} = 0.0592\ \text{pH}$$

after converting the logarithm to base 10 and using the definition of $\text{pH} = -\log_{10}[\text{unknown}]$. The cell potential is measured with a pH meter, a voltage measuring device that electronically converts E_{cell} to pH and displays the result in pH units.

The glass electrode was devised in 1906 by German biologist Max Cremer, and it was the prototype for a large number of membrane electrodes that are selective for a particular ion, such as the ions K^+, NH_4^+, Cl^-, and many others. Such electrodes are known collectively as *ion-selective electrodes*, and they have many applications in environmental chemistry and biochemistry.

7-5 Batteries: Producing Electricity Through Chemical Reactions

▶ Batteries are vitally important to modern society. Annual production in developed nations has been estimated at more than 10 batteries per person per year.

A **battery** is a device that stores chemical energy for later release as electricity. Some batteries consist of a single voltaic cell with two electrodes and the appropriate electrolyte(s); an example is a flashlight cell. Other batteries consist of two or more voltaic cells joined in series fashion—plus to minus—to increase the total voltage; an example is an automobile battery. In this section, we will consider three types of voltaic cells and the batteries based on them.

▶ Cell phones, laptop computers, and many other devices rely heavily on rechargeable batteries. Advances in electrochemistry and engineering are leading to the development of batteries that weigh less, last longer, and provide more power for portable electronic devices.

- **Primary cells.** The cell reaction in a primary cell is not reversible. When the reactants have been mostly converted to products, no more electricity is produced and a battery employing a primary cell(s) is dead.
- **Secondary cells.** The cell reaction in a secondary cell *can* be reversed by passing electricity through the cell (charging). A battery employing secondary cells can be used through several hundred or more cycles of discharging followed by charging.
- **Flow batteries** and **fuel cells.** Materials (reactants, products, and electrolytes) pass through the battery, which is simply a converter of chemical energy to electric energy. These types of batteries can be run indefinitely as long as they are supplied by electrolytes.

The Leclanché (Dry) Cell

The most common form of voltaic cell is the *Leclanché cell*, invented by the French chemist Georges Leclanché (1839–1882) in the 1860s. Popularly called a *dry cell*, because no free liquid is present, or *flashlight battery*, the Leclanché cell is diagrammed in Figure 7-14. In this cell, oxidation occurs at a zinc anode and reduction at an inert carbon (graphite) cathode. The electrolyte is a moist paste of MnO_2, $ZnCl_2$, NH_4Cl, and carbon black (soot). The maximum cell voltage is 1.55 V. The anode (oxidation) half-reaction is simple.

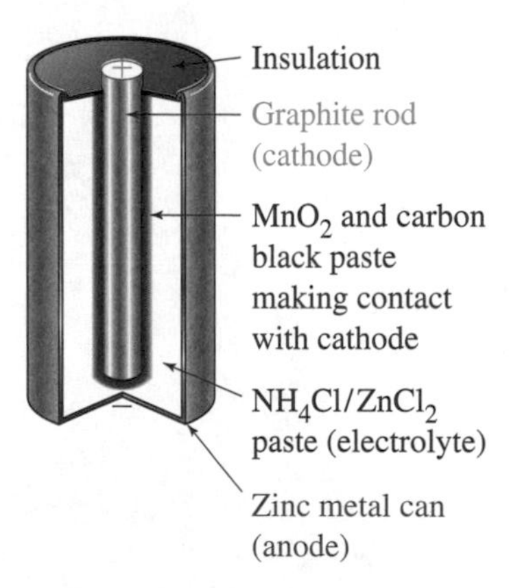

▲ FIGURE 7-14
The Leclanché (dry) cell
The chief components of the cell are a graphite (carbon) rod serving as the cathode, a zinc container serving as the anode, and an electrolyte.

$$\textit{Oxidation:}\quad Zn(s) \longrightarrow Zn^{2+}(aq) + 2\,e^-$$

The reduction is more complex. Essentially, it involves the reduction of MnO_2 to compounds having Mn in a +3 oxidation state, for example,

$$\textit{Reduction:}\quad 2\,MnO_2(s) + H_2O(l) + 2\,e^- \longrightarrow Mn_2O_3(s) + 2\,OH^-(aq)$$

An acid–base reaction occurs between NH_4^+ (from NH_4Cl) and OH^-.

$$NH_4^+(aq) + OH^-(aq) \longrightarrow NH_3(g) + H_2O(l)$$

A buildup of $NH_3(g)$ around the cathode would disrupt the current because the $NH_3(g)$ adheres to the cathode. That buildup is prevented by a reaction between Zn^{2+} and $NH_3(g)$ to form the complex ion $[Zn(NH_3)_2]^{2+}$, which crystallizes as the chloride salt.

$$Zn^{2+}(aq) + 2\,NH_3(g) + 2\,Cl^-(aq) \longrightarrow [Zn(NH_3)_2]Cl_2(s)$$

The Leclanché cell is a *primary cell*; it cannot be recharged. This cell is cheap to make, but it has some drawbacks. When current is drawn rapidly from the cell, products, such as NH_3, build up on the electrodes, causing the voltage to drop. Also, because the electrolyte medium is acidic, zinc metal slowly dissolves.

A superior form of the Leclanché cell is the *alkaline cell,* which uses NaOH or KOH in place of NH_4Cl as the electrolyte. The reduction half-reaction is the same as that shown above, but the oxidation half-reaction involves the formation of $Zn(OH)_2(s)$, which can be thought of as occurring in two steps.

$$\begin{array}{rcl} Zn(s) & \longrightarrow & Zn^{2+}(aq) + 2\,e^- \\ Zn^{2+}(aq) + 2\,OH^-(aq) & \longrightarrow & Zn(OH)_2(s) \\ \hline Zn(s) + 2\,OH^-(aq) & \longrightarrow & Zn(OH)_2(s) + 2\,e^- \end{array}$$

The advantages of the alkaline cell are that zinc does not dissolve as readily in a basic (alkaline) medium as in an acidic medium, and the cell does a better job of maintaining its voltage as current is drawn from it.

▲ **E°_{cell} is an intensive property** The voltage of a dry cell battery does not depend on the size of the battery—all of those pictured here are 1.5 V batteries. Although these batteries deliver the same voltage, the total energy output of each battery is different.

The Lead–Acid (Storage) Battery

Secondary cells are commonly encountered joined together in series in the *lead–acid battery,* or *storage battery,* which has been used in automobiles since about 1915 (Fig. 7-15). A storage battery is capable of repeated use because its chemical reactions are reversible. That is, the discharged energy can be restored by supplying electric current to recharge the cells in the battery.

The reactants in a lead–acid cell are spongy lead packed into a lead grid at the anode, red-brown lead(IV) oxide packed into a lead grid at the cathode, and an electrolyte solution consisting of dilute sulfuric acid (about 35% H_2SO_4, by mass). In this strongly acidic medium, the ionization of H_2SO_4 does not go to completion. Both $HSO_4^-(aq)$ and $SO_4^{2-}(aq)$ are present, but $HSO_4^-(aq)$ predominates. The half-reactions and overall reaction are

$$\begin{array}{ll} \textit{Reduction:} & PbO_2(s) + 3\,H^+(aq) + HSO_4^-(aq) + 2\,e^- \longrightarrow PbSO_4(s) + 2\,H_2O(l) \\ \textit{Oxidation:} & Pb(s) + HSO_4^-(aq) \longrightarrow PbSO_4(s) + H^+(aq) + 2\,e^- \\ \hline \textit{Overall:} & PbO_2(s) + Pb(s) + 2\,H^+(aq) + 2\,HSO_4^-(aq) \longrightarrow 2\,PbSO_4(s) + 2\,H_2O(l) \end{array}$$

$$E_{cell} = E_{PbO_2/PbSO_4} - E_{PbSO_4/Pb} = 1.74\text{ V} - (-0.28\text{ V}) = 2.02\text{ V} \qquad \textbf{(7.24)}$$

◀ You can think of the half-reactions as occurring in two steps: (1) oxidation of Pb(s) to $Pb^{2+}(aq)$ and reduction of $PbO_2(s)$ to $Pb^{2+}(aq)$, followed by (2) precipitation of $PbSO_4(s)$ at each electrode.

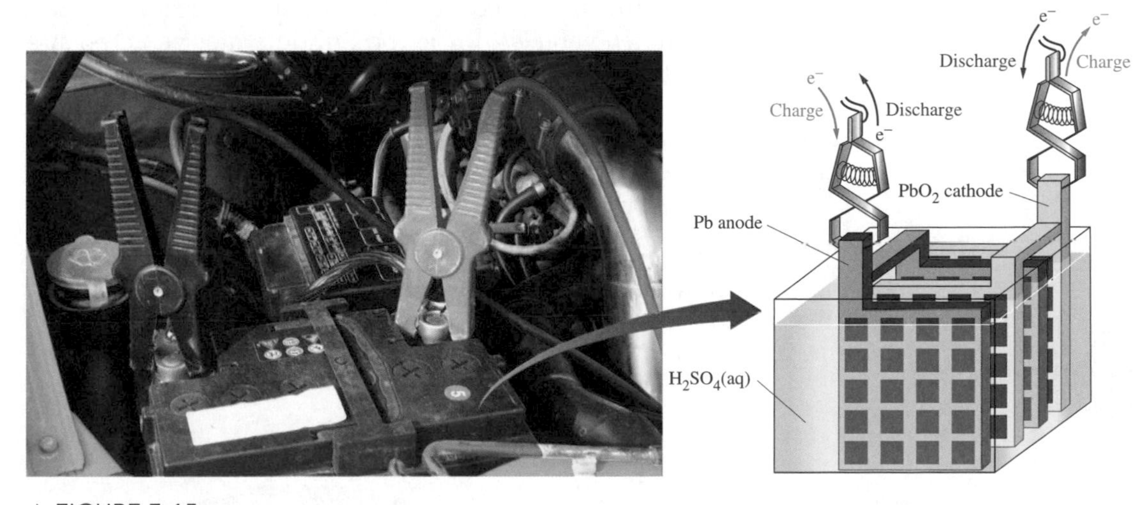

▲ FIGURE 7-15
A lead–acid (storage) cell
The composition of the electrodes is described in the text. The cell reaction that occurs as the cell is discharged is given in equation (7.24). The voltage of the cell is 2.02 V. In this figure, two anode plates are connected in parallel fashion, as are two cathode plates. The battery shown in this figure is the good battery used to charge a dead battery.

▶ In spite of its usefulness and ability to deliver a strong current, the lead storage battery is also a pollution hazard. All batteries should be disposed of properly and should not be dumped in land fills or garbage disposal sites.

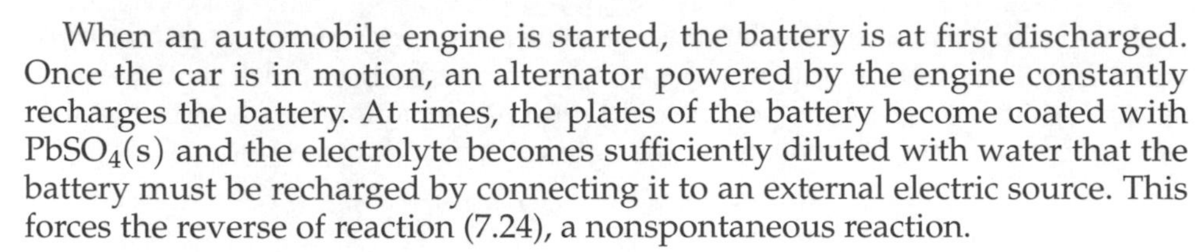

When an automobile engine is started, the battery is at first discharged. Once the car is in motion, an alternator powered by the engine constantly recharges the battery. At times, the plates of the battery become coated with $PbSO_4(s)$ and the electrolyte becomes sufficiently diluted with water that the battery must be recharged by connecting it to an external electric source. This forces the reverse of reaction (7.24), a nonspontaneous reaction.

$$2\,PbSO_4(s) + 2\,H_2O(l) \longrightarrow Pb(s) + PbO_2(s) + 2\,H^+(aq) + 2\,HSO_4^-(aq) \qquad E_{cell} = -2.02\text{ V}$$

▶ Lead-acid storage batteries are also used to power golf carts, wheelchairs, and passenger carts in airport terminals.

To prevent the anode and cathode from coming into contact with each other, causing a *short circuit*, sheets of an insulating material are used to separate alternating anode and cathode plates. A group of anodes is connected together electrically, as is a group of cathodes. This parallel connection increases the electrode area in contact with the electrolyte solution and increases the current-delivering capacity of the cell. Cells are then joined in a series fashion, positive to negative, to produce a battery. The typical 12 V battery consists of six cells, each cell with a potential of about 2 V.

The Silver–Zinc Cell: A Button Battery

▶ Rechargeable silver oxide batteries have been developed and provide alternatives to lithium-ion batteries.

The cell diagram of a *silver–zinc cell* (Fig. 7-16) is

$$Zn(s), ZnO(s)|KOH(satd)|Ag_2O(s), Ag(s)$$

The half-reactions on discharging are

$$\begin{aligned} &\textit{Reduction:} && Ag_2O(s) + H_2O(l) + 2\,e^- \longrightarrow 2\,Ag(s) + 2\,OH^-(aq) \\ &\textit{Oxidation:} && Zn(s) + 2\,OH^-(aq) \longrightarrow ZnO(s) + H_2O(l) + 2\,e^- \\ &\textit{Overall:} && Zn(s) + Ag_2O(s) \longrightarrow ZnO(s) + 2\,Ag(s) \end{aligned} \qquad \textbf{(7.25)}$$

Because no solution species is involved in the cell reaction, the quantity of electrolyte is very small and the electrodes can be maintained very close together. The cell voltage is 1.8 V, and its storage capacity is six times greater than that of a lead–acid battery of the same size. These characteristics make batteries, such as the silver–zinc cell, useful in button batteries. These miniature batteries are used in watches, hearing aids, and cameras. In addition, silver–zinc batteries fulfill the requirements of spacecraft, satellites, missiles, rockets, space launch vehicles, torpedoes, underwater vehicles, and life-support systems. On the Mars *Pathfinder* mission, the rover and the cruise system were powered by solar cells. The energy storage requirements of the lander were met by modified silver–zinc batteries with about three times the storage capacity of the standard nickel–cadmium rechargeable battery.

The Nickel–Cadmium Cell: A Rechargeable Battery

The *nickel–cadmium cell* (or *nicad battery*) is commonly used in cordless electric devices, such as electric shavers and handheld calculators. The anode in this cell is cadmium metal, and the cathode is the Ni(III) compound NiO(OH)

▲ A rechargeable nickel–cadmium cell, or nicad battery.

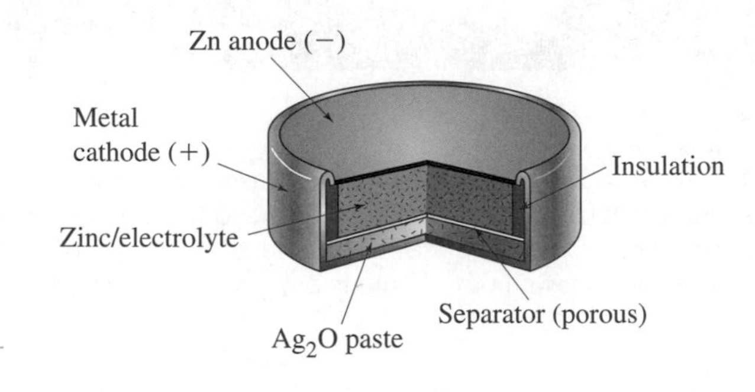

▶ FIGURE 7-16
A silver–zinc button (miniature) cell

supported on nickel metal. The half-cell reactions for a nickel–cadmium battery during discharge are

$$\begin{array}{ll} \textit{Reduction:} & 2\,NiO(OH)(s) + 2\,H_2O(l) + 2\,e^- \longrightarrow 2\,Ni(OH)_2(s) + 2\,OH^-(aq) \\ \textit{Oxidation:} & Cd(s) + 2\,OH^-(aq) \longrightarrow Cd(OH)_2(s) + 2\,e^- \\ \hline \textit{Overall:} & Cd(s) + 2\,NiO(OH)(s) + 2\,H_2O(l) \longrightarrow 2\,Ni(OH)_2(s) + Cd(OH)_2(s) \end{array}$$

This cell gives a fairly constant voltage of 1.4 V. When the cell is recharged by connection to an external voltage source, the reactions above are reversed. Nickel–cadmium batteries can be recharged many times because the solid products adhere to the surface of the electrodes.

In primary cells the positive and negative electrodes are known as the cathode, where reduction takes place, and the anode, where oxidation takes place. In rechargeable systems, however, we have either a charging mode or a discharging mode, and so depending whether electrons are flowing out of the cell or flowing into the cell, the notion of the anode and the cathode changes. On the discharge of a nicad battery, the NiO(OH) electrode is the cathode because reduction is taking place, but on the charge, it is the anode because oxidation is taking place (the reverse reaction). In discharge mode the NiO(OH) electrode electrons are removed from the electrode because of the reduction process, and so this electrode is positively charged. In the charging mode electrons are being removed from this electrode by the oxidation process; this is the anode and it is positively charged. Therefore, regardless of charging or discharging, the NiO(OH) electrode is positive.

The negative electrode, the cadmium electrode in a nicad battery, is the anode on discharging (oxidation) and the cathode (reduction) on charging. In both charging and discharging, the anode is the electrode from which electrons exit the battery, and the cathode is the electrode at which electrons enter the battery.

In summary, when dealing with rechargeable batteries, it is better to speak of the positive and negative electrodes and avoid the terms *cathode* and *anode*.

The Lithium-Ion Battery

Lithium-ion batteries are a type of rechargeable battery now commonly used in consumer electronics, such as cell phones, laptop computers, and MP3 players. In a lithium-ion battery, the lithium ion moves between the positive and negative electrodes. The positive electrode consists of lithium cobalt(III) oxide, $LiCoO_2$, and the negative electrode is highly crystallized graphite. To complete the battery an electrolyte is needed, which can consist of an organic solvent and ions, such as $LiPF_6$. The structure of $LiCoO_2$ and graphite electrodes is illustrated in Figure 7-17. In the charging cycle at the positive electrode, lithium ions are released into the electrolyte solution as electrons are removed from the electrode. To maintain a charge balance, one cobalt(III) ion is oxidized to cobalt(IV) for each lithium ion released:

$$LiCoO_2(s) \longrightarrow Li_{(1-x)}CoO_2(s) + xLi^+(\text{solvent}) + x\,e^-$$

At the negative electrode, lithium ions enter between the graphite layers and are reduced to lithium metal. This insertion of a guest atom into a host solid is called *intercalation*, and the resulting product is called an *intercalation compound*:

$$C(s) + xLi^+(\text{solvent}) + x\,e^- \longrightarrow Li_xC(s)$$

In the operation of a lithium-ion battery the source of the electrons is the oxidation of the Co(III) to Co(IV). The lithium ion takes these electrons to the graphite electrode during charging and returns them to the positive electrode during discharge.

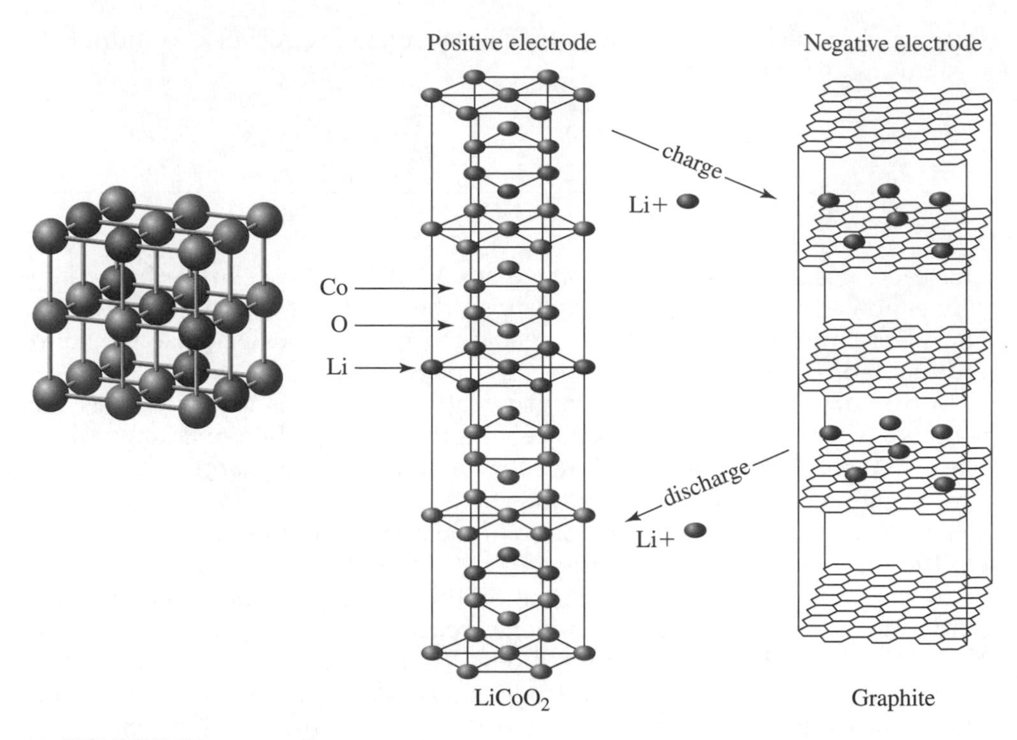

▲ FIGURE 7-17
The electrodes of a lithium-ion battery
The layered graphite electrode is shown with lithium ions (violet) intercalated. The $LiCoO_2$ is shown as a face-centered cubic lattice, with the oxygen atoms (red) occupying the corners and the faces, the cobalt atoms (pink) occupying half of the edges, and the lithium atoms occupying half of the edges and the central octahedral hole. This arrangement leads to planes of oxygen, cobalt, oxygen, lithium, oxygen, cobalt, and oxygen atoms, as indicated in the figure.

Many other lithium batteries exist that use many different materials for the positive electrode, while graphite is the most common negative electrode. A major development is in the use of conducting polymers as the electrolyte, which has led to a whole range of *lithium-ion polymer batteries*. The development of new batteries based on lithium ions is currently an area of great interest.

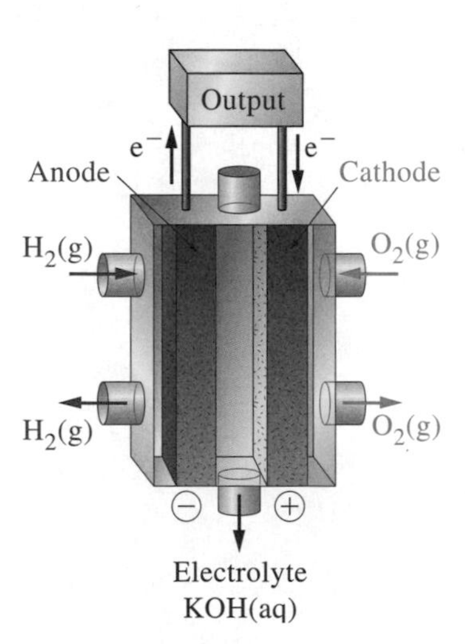

▲ FIGURE 7-18
A hydrogen–oxygen fuel cell
A key requirement in fuel cells is porous electrodes that allow for easy access of the gaseous reactants to the electrolyte. The electrodes chosen should also catalyze the electrode reactions.

Fuel Cells

The three types of cells considered in the remainder of this section fall into the third category mentioned on page 888; they are found in flow batteries.

For most of the twentieth century, scientists explored the possibility of converting the chemical energy of fuels directly to electricity. The essential process in a fuel cell is *fuel + oxygen* $\longrightarrow$ *oxidation products*. The first fuel cells were based on the reaction of hydrogen and oxygen. Figure 7-18 represents such a fuel cell. The overall change is that $H_2(g)$ and $O_2(g)$ in an alkaline medium produce $H_2O(l)$.

$$\begin{aligned}
&\textit{Reduction:} && O_2(g) + 2\,H_2O(l) + 4\,e^- \longrightarrow 4\,OH^-(aq) \\
&\textit{Oxidation:} && 2\,\{H_2(g) + 2\,OH^-(aq) \longrightarrow 2\,H_2O(l) + 2\,e^-\} \\
&\textit{Overall:} && 2\,H_2(g) + O_2(g) \longrightarrow 2\,H_2O(l) \qquad (7.26)
\end{aligned}$$

$$E^\circ_{cell} = E^\circ_{O_2/OH^-} - E^\circ_{H_2O/H_2} = 0.401\text{ V} - (-0.828\text{ V}) = 1.229\text{ V}$$

The theoretical maximum energy available as electric energy in any electrochemical cell is the Gibbs energy change for the cell reaction, ΔG°. The maximum energy release when a fuel is burned is the enthalpy change, ΔH°. One of the measures used to evaluate a fuel cell is the *efficiency value*, $e = \Delta G^\circ/\Delta H^\circ$. For the hydrogen–oxygen fuel cell, $e = -474.4\text{ kJ}/-571.6\text{ kJ} = 0.83$.

The day is fast approaching when fuel cells based on the direct oxidation of common fuels will become a reality. For example, the half-reaction and cell reaction for a fuel cell using methane (natural gas) are

$$\begin{array}{ll} \textit{Reduction:} & 2\,\{O_2(g) + 4\,H^+ + 4\,e^- \longrightarrow 2\,H_2O(l)\} \\ \textit{Oxidation:} & CH_4(g) + 2\,H_2O(l) \longrightarrow CO_2(g) + 8\,H^+ + 8\,e^- \\ \hline \textit{Overall:} & CH_4(g) + 2\,O_2(g) \longrightarrow CO_2(g) + 2\,H_2O(l) \end{array}$$

$$\Delta H^\circ = -890\text{ kJ} \qquad \Delta G^\circ = -818\text{ kJ} \qquad e = 0.92 \qquad \textbf{(7.27)}$$

▲ This Toyota prototype is a fuel-cell-powered electric car producing hydrogen from gasoline.

Although methane fuel cells are still in the research stage, an automobile engine is currently under development in which (1) a liquid hydrocarbon is vaporized; (2) the vaporized fuel is partially oxidized to CO(g); (3) in the presence of a catalyst, steam converts the CO(g) to $CO_2(g)$ and $H_2(g)$; and (4) $H_2(g)$ and air are fed through a fuel cell, producing electric energy.

A fuel cell should actually be called an *energy converter* rather than a battery. As long as fuel and $O_2(g)$ are available, the cell will produce electricity. It does not have the limited capacity of a primary battery or the fixed storage capacity of a secondary battery. Fuel cells based on reaction (7.26) have had their most notable successes as energy sources in space vehicles. (Water produced in the cell reaction is also a valuable product of the fuel cell.)

◀ Fuel cells are environmentally friendly. Oxygen and hydrogen are readily available. Hydrogen, although dangerous, can now be transported safely by the use of special materials that can adsorb large volumes.

Air Batteries

In a fuel cell, $O_2(g)$ is the oxidizing agent that oxidizes a fuel such as $H_2(g)$ or $CH_4(g)$. Another kind of flow battery, because it uses $O_2(g)$ from air, is known as an *air battery*. The substance that is oxidized in an air battery is typically a metal.

One heavily studied battery system is the aluminum–air battery in which oxidation occurs at an aluminum anode and reduction at a carbon–air cathode. The electrolyte circulated through the battery is NaOH(aq). Because it is in the presence of a high concentration of OH^-, Al^{3+} produced at the anode forms the complex ion $[Al(OH)_4]^-$. The operation of the battery is suggested by Figure 7-19. The half-reactions and the overall cell reaction are

$$\begin{array}{ll} \textit{Reduction:} & 3\,\{O_2(g) + 2\,H_2O(l) + 4\,e^- \longrightarrow 4\,OH^-(aq)\} \\ \textit{Oxidation:} & 4\,\{Al(s) + 4\,OH^-(aq) \longrightarrow [Al(OH)_4]^-(aq) + 3\,e^-\} \\ \hline \textit{Overall:} & 4\,Al(s) + 3\,O_2(g) + 6\,H_2O(l) + 4\,OH^-(aq) \longrightarrow 4[Al(OH)_4]^-(aq) \qquad \textbf{(7.28)} \end{array}$$

The battery is kept charged by feeding chunks of Al and water into it. A typical air battery can power an automobile several hundred miles before refueling is necessary. The electrolyte is circulated outside the battery, where $Al(OH)_3(s)$ is precipitated from the $[Al(OH)_4]^-(aq)$. This $Al(OH)_3(s)$ is collected and can then be converted back to aluminum metal at an aluminum manufacturing facility.

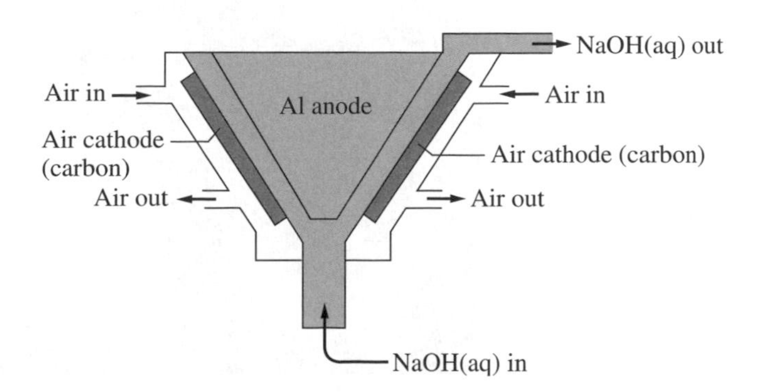

◀ FIGURE 7-19
A simplified aluminum–air battery

7-9 CONCEPT ASSESSMENT

Why do dry cells and lead-acid cells "run down" during use? Do you think a fuel cell runs down? Explain.

7-6 Corrosion: Unwanted Voltaic Cells

The reactions occurring in voltaic cells (batteries) are important sources of electricity, but similar reactions also underlie corrosion processes. First, we will consider the electrochemical basis of corrosion, and then we will see how electrochemical principles can be applied to control corrosion.

Figure 7-20(a) demonstrates the basic processes in the corrosion of an iron nail. The nail is embedded in an agar gel in water. The gel contains the common acid–base indicator phenolphthalein and potassium ferricyanide, $K_3[Fe(CN)_6]$. Within hours of starting the experiment, a deep blue precipitate forms at the head and tip of the nail. Along the body of the nail, the agar gel turns pink. The blue precipitate, Turnbull's blue, establishes the presence of iron(II). The pink color is that of phenolphthalein in basic solution. From these observations, we write two simple half-equations.

$$\textit{Reduction:} \quad O_2(g) + 2\,H_2O(l) + 4\,e^- \longrightarrow 4\,OH^-(aq)$$
$$\textit{Oxidation:} \quad 2\,Fe(s) \longrightarrow 2\,Fe^{2+}(aq) + 4\,e^-$$

The potential difference for these two half-reactions is

$$E^\circ_{cell} = E^\circ_{O_2/OH^-} - E^\circ_{Fe^{2+}/Fe} = 0.401\text{ V} - (-0.440\text{ V}) = 0.841\text{ V}$$

indicating that the corrosion process should be spontaneous when reactants and products are in their standard states. Typically, the corrosion medium has $[OH^-] \ll 1$ M, the reduction half-reaction is even more favorable, and E_{cell} is even greater than 0.841 V. Corrosion is especially significant in acidic solutions, in which the reduction half-reaction is

$$O_2(g) + 4\,H^+(aq) + 4\,e^- \longrightarrow 2\,H_2O(l) \qquad E^\circ_{O_2/H_2O} = 1.229\text{ V}$$

In the corroding nail of Figure 7-20(a), oxidation occurs at the head and tip. Electrons given up in the oxidation move along the nail and are used to reduce dissolved O_2. The reduction product, OH^-, is detected by the phenolphthalein. In the bent nail in Figure 7-20(b), oxidation occurs at *three* points: the head and tip and also the bend. The nail is preferentially oxidized

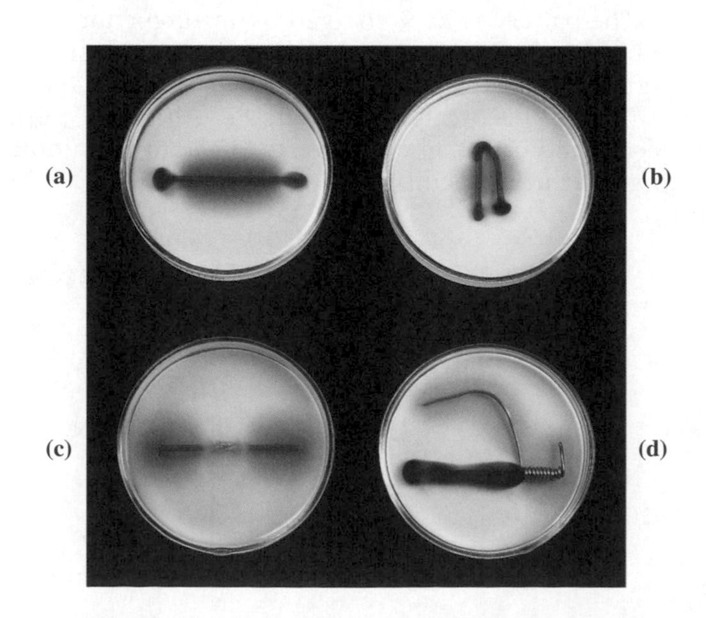

▶ FIGURE 7-20
Demonstration of corrosion and methods of corrosion protection
The pink color results from the indicator phenolphthalein in the presence of base; the dark blue color results from the formation of Turnbull's blue $KFe[Fe(CN)_6]$. Corrosion (oxidation) of the nail occurs at strained regions: **(a)** the head and tip and **(b)** a bend in the nail. **(c)** Contact with zinc protects the nail from corrosion. Zinc is oxidized instead of the iron (forming the faint white precipitate of zinc ferricyanide). **(d)** Copper does not protect the nail from corrosion. Electrons lost in the oxidation half-reaction distribute themselves along the copper wire, as seen by the pink color that extends the full length of the wire.

at these points because the strained metal is more active (more anodic) than the unstrained metal. This situation is similar to the preferential rusting of a dented automobile fender.

Some metals, such as aluminum, form corrosion products that adhere tightly to the underlying metal and protect it from further corrosion. Iron oxide (rust), however, flakes off and constantly exposes fresh surface. This difference in corrosion behavior explains why cans made of iron deteriorate rapidly in the environment, whereas aluminum cans have an almost unlimited lifetime. The simplest method of protecting a metal from corrosion is to cover it with paint or some other protective coating impervious to water, an important reactant and solvent in corrosion processes.

▲ **Galvanized nails**

Another method of protecting an iron surface is to plate it with a thin layer of a second metal. Iron can be plated with copper by electroplating or with tin by dipping the iron into molten tin. In either case, the underlying metal is protected as long as the coating remains intact. If the coating is cracked, as when a "tin" can is dented, the underlying iron is exposed and begins to corrode. Iron, being more active than copper and tin, undergoes oxidation; the reduction half-reaction occurs on the plating (Figs. 7-20d and 7-21).

When iron is coated with zinc (galvanized iron), the situation is different. Zinc is more active than iron. If a break occurs in the zinc plating, the iron is still protected because the zinc is oxidized instead of the iron, and corrosion products protect the zinc from further corrosion (Figs. 7-20c and 7-21).

▲ **Magnesium sacrificial anodes**
The small cylindrical bars of magnesium attached to the steel ship provide cathodic protection against corrosion.

Still another method is used to protect large iron and steel objects in contact with water or moist soils—ships, storage tanks, pipelines, plumbing systems. This method involves connecting a chunk of magnesium or some other active metal to the object, either directly or through a wire. Oxidation occurs at the active metal, which slowly dissolves. The iron surface acquires electrons from the oxidation of the active metal; the iron acts as a cathode and supports a *reduction* half-reaction. As long as some of the active metal remains, the iron is protected. This type of protection is called **cathodic protection**, and the active metal is called, appropriately, a *sacrificial anode*. Millions of pounds of magnesium are used annually in the United States in sacrificial anodes.

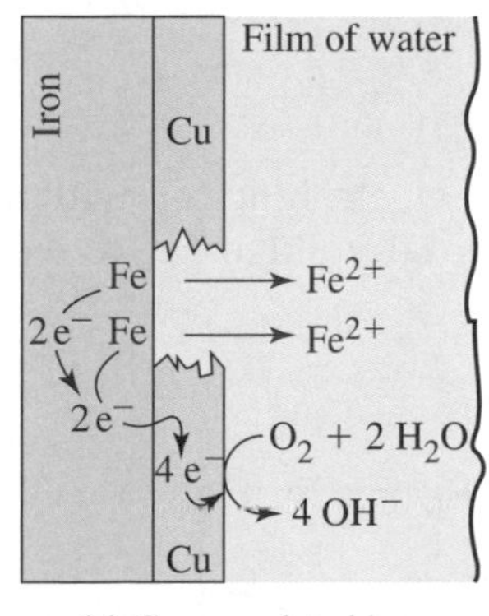

(a) Copper-plated iron **(b)** Galvanized iron

▲ FIGURE 7-21
Protection of iron against electrolytic corrosion
In the *anodic* reaction, the metal that is more easily oxidized loses electrons to produce metal ions. In **(a)**, this is iron; in **(b)**, it is zinc. In the *cathodic* reaction, oxygen gas, which is dissolved in a thin film of water on the metal, is reduced to OH^-. Rusting of iron occurs in (a), but it does not in (b). When iron corrodes, Fe^{2+} and OH^- ions from the half-reactions initiate these further reactions.

$$Fe^{2+} + 2\,OH^- \longrightarrow Fe(OH)_2(s)$$

$$4\,Fe(OH)_2(s) + O_2 + 2\,H_2O \longrightarrow 4\,Fe(OH)_3(s)$$

$$2\,Fe(OH)_3(s) \longrightarrow \underset{\text{rust}}{Fe_2O_3 \cdot H_2O(s)} + H_2O(l)$$

7-10 CONCEPT ASSESSMENT

Of the metals Al, Cu, Ni, and Zn, which could act as a sacrificial anode for iron?

7-7 Electrolysis: Causing Nonspontaneous Reactions to Occur

KEEP IN MIND

that voltaic (galvanic) and electrolytic cells are the two categories subsumed under the more general term *electrochemical cell.*

Until now, the emphasis has been on voltaic (galvanic) cells, electrochemical cells in which chemical change is used to produce electricity. Another type of electrochemical cell—the **electrolytic cell**—uses electricity to produce a *nonspontaneous* reaction. The process in which a nonspontaneous reaction is driven by the application of electric energy is called **electrolysis**.

Let's explore the relationship between voltaic and electrolytic cells by returning briefly to the cell shown in Figure 7-4. When the cell functions spontaneously, electrons flow from the zinc to the copper and the overall chemical change in the voltaic cell is

$$\mathrm{Zn(s) + Cu^{2+}(aq) \longrightarrow Zn^{2+}(aq) + Cu(s)} \qquad E^\circ_{\text{cell}} = 1.103\ \mathrm{V}$$

Now suppose the same cell is connected to an external electric source of voltage greater than 1.103 V (Fig. 7-22). That is, the connection is made so that electrons are forced into the zinc electrode (now the cathode) and removed from the copper electrode (now the anode). The overall reaction in this case is the *reverse* of the voltaic cell reaction, and E°_{cell} is *negative.*

$$\begin{aligned}
&\textit{Reduction:} && \mathrm{Zn^{2+}(aq) + 2\,e^- \longrightarrow Zn(s)}\\
&\textit{Oxidation:} && \mathrm{Cu(s) \longrightarrow Cu^{2+}(aq) + 2\,e^-}\\
&\textit{Overall:} && \mathrm{Cu(s) + Zn^{2+}(aq) \longrightarrow Cu^{2+}(aq) + Zn(s)}
\end{aligned}$$

$$E^\circ_{\text{cell}} = E^\circ_{\mathrm{Zn^{2+}/Zn}} - E^\circ_{\mathrm{Cu^{2+}/Cu}} = -0.763\ \mathrm{V} - 0.340\ \mathrm{V} = -1.103\ \mathrm{V}$$

Thus, reversing the direction of the electron flow changes the voltaic cell into an electrolytic cell.

Predicting Electrolysis Reactions

For the cell in Figure 7-22 to function as an electrolytic cell with reactants and products in their standard states, the external voltage has to exceed 1.103 V.

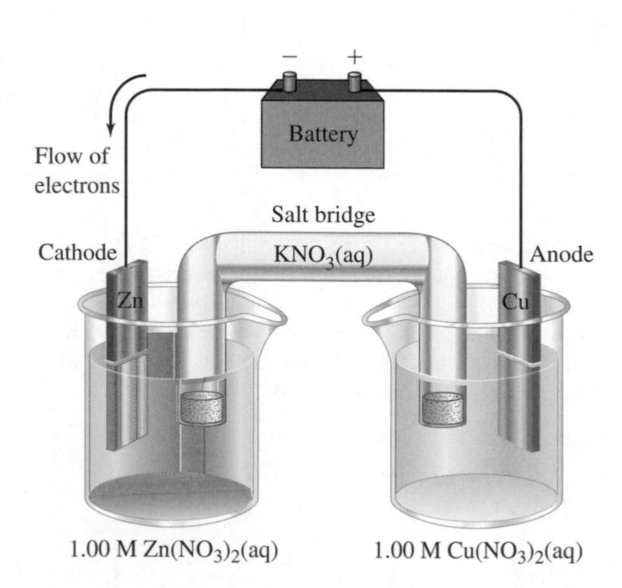

▶ FIGURE 7-22
An electrolytic cell
The direction of electron flow is the reverse of that in the voltaic cell of Figure 7-4, and so is the cell reaction. Now the zinc electrode is the *cathode* and the copper electrode, the *anode*. The battery must have a voltage in excess of 1.103 V in order to force electrons to flow in the reverse (nonspontaneous) direction.

7-2 ARE YOU WONDERING...

Why the anode is (+) in an electrolytic cell but (−) in a voltaic cell?

Assigning the terms *anode* and *cathode* is not based on the electrode charges; it is based on the half-reactions at the electrode surfaces. Specifically,

- *Oxidation* always occurs at the *anode* of an electrochemical cell. Because of the buildup of electrons freed in the oxidation half-reaction, the anode of a *voltaic* cell is (−). Because electrons are withdrawn from it, the anode in an *electrolytic* cell is (+). For both cell types, the anode is the electrode from which electrons *exit* the cell.
- *Reduction* always occurs at the cathode of an electrochemical cell. Because of the *removal* of electrons by the reduction half-reaction, the cathode of a *voltaic* cell is (+). Because of the electrons forced onto it, the cathode of an *electrolytic* cell is (−). For both cell types, the cathode is the electrode at which electrons *enter* the cell.

The following table summarizes the relationship between a voltaic cell and an electrolytic cell.

	Voltaic Cell			Electrolytic Cell	
Oxidation:	$A \longrightarrow A^+ + e^-$	Anode (negative)	*Oxidation:*	$B \longrightarrow B^+ + e^-$	Anode (positive)
Reduction:	$B^+ + e^- \longrightarrow B$	Cathode (positive)	*Reduction:*	$A^+ + e^- \longrightarrow A$	Cathode (negative)
Overall:	$A + B^+ \longrightarrow A^+ + B$ $\Delta G < 0$ Spontaneous redox reaction releases energy		*Overall:*	$A^+ + B \longrightarrow A + B^+$ $\Delta G > 0$ Nonspontaneous redox reaction absorbs energy to drive it	
	The system (the cell) does work on the surroundings			The surroundings (the source of energy) do work on the system	

Note that the sign of each electrode in an electrolytic cell is the same as the sign of the battery electrode to which it is attached.

We can make similar calculations for other electrolyses. What actually happens, however, does not always correspond to these calculations. Four complicating factors must be considered:

1. A voltage significantly in excess of the calculated value, an **overpotential**, may be necessary to cause a particular electrode reaction to occur. Overpotentials are needed to overcome interactions at the electrode surface and are particularly common when gases are involved. For example, the overpotential for the discharge of $H_2(g)$ at a mercury cathode is approximately 1.5 V; the overpotential on a platinum cathode is practically zero.
2. Competing electrode reactions may occur. In the electrolysis of *molten* sodium chloride with inert electrodes, only one oxidation and one reduction are possible.

   Reduction: $2\,Na^+ + 2\,e^- \longrightarrow 2\,Na(l)$

   Oxidation: $2\,Cl^- \longrightarrow Cl_2(g) + 2\,e^-$

   In the electrolysis of *aqueous* sodium chloride with inert electrodes, there are *two* possible reduction half-reactions and *two* possible oxidation half-reactions.

$$\text{Reduction: } 2\,Na^+(aq) + 2\,e^- \longrightarrow Na(s) \qquad E^\circ_{Na^+/Na} = -2.71\ V \qquad (7.29)$$

$$2\,H_2O(l) + 2\,e^- \longrightarrow H_2(g) + 2\,OH^-(aq) \qquad E^\circ_{H_2O/H_2} = (-0.83\ V) \qquad (7.30)$$

$$\text{Oxidation: } 2\,Cl^-(aq) \longrightarrow Cl_2(g) + 2\,e^- \qquad -E^\circ_{Cl_2/Cl^-} = -(1.36\ V) \qquad (7.31)$$

$$2\,H_2O(l) \longrightarrow O_2(g) + 4\,H^+(aq) + 4\,e^- \qquad -E^\circ_{O_2/H_2O} = -(1.23\ V) \qquad (7.32)$$

▶ We have written a *minus* sign in front of the electrode potentials in (7.31) and (7.32) as a way of emphasizing the *oxidation* rather than the reduction tendency.

Reaction (7.29) can be eliminated as a possible reduction half-reaction: Unless the overpotential for $H_2(g)$ is unusually high, the reduction of Na^+ is far more difficult to accomplish than that of H_2O. This leaves two possibilities for the cell reaction.

Half-reaction (7.30) + half-reaction (7.31):

$$\text{Reduction: } 2\,H_2O(l) + 2\,e^- \longrightarrow H_2(g) + 2\,OH^-(aq)$$

$$\text{Oxidation: } 2\,Cl^-(aq) \longrightarrow Cl_2(g) + 2\,e^-$$

$$\text{Overall: } 2\,Cl^-(aq) + 2\,H_2O(l) \longrightarrow Cl_2(g) + H_2(g) + 2\,OH^-(aq) \qquad (7.33)$$

$$E^\circ_{cell} = E^\circ_{H_2O/H_2} - E^\circ_{Cl_2/Cl^-} = -0.83\ V - (1.36\ V) = -2.19\ V$$

Half-reaction (7.30) + half-reaction (7.32):

$$\text{Reduction: } 2\,\{2\,H_2O(l) + 2\,e^- \longrightarrow H_2(g) + 2\,OH^-(aq)\}$$

$$\text{Oxidation: } 2\,H_2O(l) \longrightarrow O_2(g) + 4\,H^+(aq) + 4\,e^-$$

$$\text{Overall: } 2\,H_2O(l) \longrightarrow 2\,H_2(g) + O_2(g) \qquad (7.34)$$

$$E^\circ_{cell} = E^\circ_{H_2O/H_2} - E^\circ_{O_2/H_2O} = -0.83\ V - (1.23\ V) = -2.06\ V$$

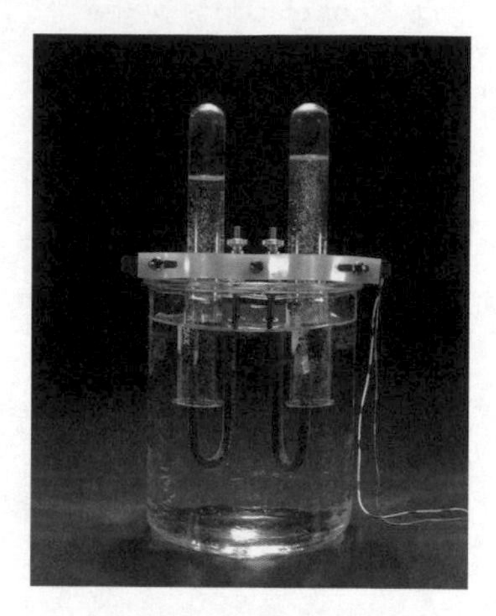

▲ The electrolysis of water into $H_2(g)$ and $O_2(g)$, shown by bubbles at the electrodes and the gases collecting in the test tubes—twice the volume of $H_2(g)$ as $O_2(g)$.

In the electrolysis of NaCl(aq), $H_2(g)$ is the product expected at the *cathode*. Because cell reactions (7.33) and (7.34) have E°_{cell} values that are so similar, a mixture of $Cl_2(g)$ and $O_2(g)$ would be the expected product at the *anode*. Actually, because of the high overpotential of $O_2(g)$ compared to $Cl_2(g)$, cell reaction (7.33) predominates; $Cl_2(g)$ is essentially the only product at the anode.

3. The reactants very often are in *nonstandard* states. In the industrial electrolysis of NaCl(aq), $[Cl^-] \approx 5.5$ M, not the unit activity ($[Cl^-] \approx 1$ M) implied in half-reaction (7.31); therefore $E_{Cl_2/Cl^-} = 1.31$ V (*not* 1.36 V). Also, the pH in the anode half-cell is adjusted to 4, not the unit activity ($[H_3O^+] \approx 1$ M) implied in half-reaction (7.32); hence $E_{O_2/H_2O} = 0.99$ V (*not* 1.23 V). The net effect of these nonstandard conditions is to favor the production of O_2 at the anode. In practice, however, the $Cl_2(g)$ obtained contains less than 1% $O_2(g)$, indicating the overpowering effect of the high overpotential of $O_2(g)$. Not surprisingly, the proportion of $O_2(g)$ increases significantly in the electrolysis of very dilute NaCl(aq).
4. The nature of the electrodes matters. An *inert electrode*, such as platinum, provides a surface on which an electrolysis half-reaction occurs, but the reactants themselves must come from the electrolyte solution. An *active electrode* is one that can itself participate in the oxidation or reduction half-reaction. The distinction between inert and active electrodes is explored in Figure 7-23 and Example 7-12.

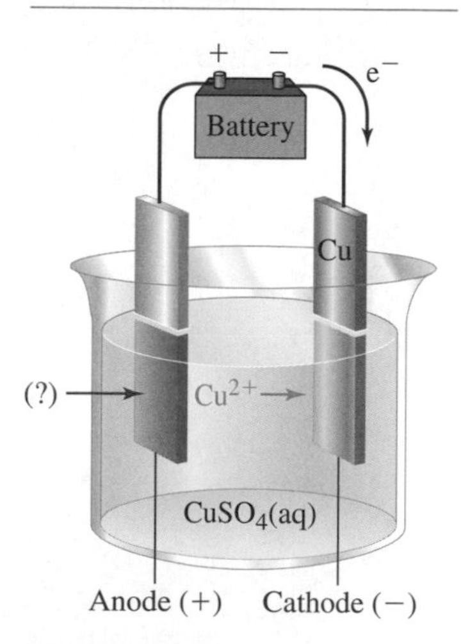

▲ FIGURE 7-23
Predicting electrode reactions in electrolysis—Example 7-11 illustrated
Electrons are forced onto the copper cathode by the external source (battery). Cu^{2+} ions are attracted to the cathode and are reduced to Cu(s). The oxidation half-reaction depends on the metal used for the anode.

Quantitative Aspects of Electrolysis

We have seen how to calculate the theoretical voltage required for electrolysis. Equally important are calculations of the quantities of reactants consumed and products formed in an electrolysis. For these calculations, we will continue to use stoichiometric factors from the chemical equation, but another

EXAMPLE 7-12 Predicting Electrode Half-Reactions and Overall Reactions in Electrolysis

Refer to Figure 7-23. Predict the electrode reactions and the overall reaction when the anode is made of **(a)** copper and **(b)** platinum.

Analyze

In both cases we have to decide on the likely oxidation and reduction processes. The low reduction potential of $Cu^{2+}(aq)$ makes this the likely reduction process in both cases. What about oxidation processes? The possibilities are in **(a)** oxidation of the copper electrode (anode) ($E° = 0.340$ V), oxidation of sulfate anion (2.01 V), and oxidation of water (1.23 V). Thus, the most easily oxidized is the copper at the anode. In **(b)**, the platinum electrode is inert and is not easily oxidized. Of the other two candidates, sulfate anion and water, water has the lower oxidation potential.

Solve

$$\textit{Reduction:} \quad Cu^{2+}(aq) + 2\,e^- \longrightarrow Cu(s) \qquad E°_{Cu^{2+}/Cu} = 0.340\text{ V}$$

(a) At the cathode we have the reduction of $Cu^{2+}(aq)$. At the anode, Cu(s) can be oxidized to $Cu^{2+}(aq)$, as represented by

$$\textit{Oxidation:} \quad Cu(s) \longrightarrow Cu^{2+}(aq) + 2\,e^-$$

If the oxidation and reduction half-equations are added, $Cu^{2+}(aq)$ cancels out. The electrolysis reaction is simply

$$Cu(s)[\text{anode}] \longrightarrow Cu(s)[\text{cathode}] \qquad \textbf{(7.35)}$$

$$E°_{cell} = E°_{Cu^{2+}/Cu} - E°_{Cu^{2+}/Cu} = 0.340\text{ V} - 0.340\text{ V} = 0$$

(b) The oxidation that occurs most readily is that of H_2O, shown in reaction (7.32).

$$\textit{Oxidation:} \quad 2\,H_2O(l) \longrightarrow O_2(g) + 4\,H^+(aq) + 4\,e^-$$

$$-E°_{O_2/H_2O} = -1.23\text{ V}$$

The electrolysis reaction and its $E°_{cell}$ are

$$2\,Cu^{2+}(aq) + 2\,H_2O(l) \longrightarrow 2\,Cu(s) + 4\,H^+(aq) + O_2(g) \qquad \textbf{(7.36)}$$

$$\begin{aligned} E°_{cell} &= E°(\text{reduction half-cell}) - E°(\text{oxidation half-cell}) \\ &= E°_{Cu^{2+}/Cu} - E°_{O_2/H_2O} \\ &= 0.340\text{ V} - 1.23\text{ V} = -0.89\text{ V} \end{aligned}$$

Assess

(a) Only a very small voltage is needed to overcome the resistance in the electric circuit for this electrolysis. For every Cu atom that enters the solution at the anode, an active electrode, one Cu^{2+} ion, deposits as a Cu atom at the cathode. Copper is transferred from the anode to the cathode through the solution as Cu^{2+} and the concentration of $CuSO_4(aq)$ remains unchanged.

(b) A potential greater than 0.89 V is required to electrolyze water and deposit copper. Keep in mind that when calculating $E°_{cell}$ as a *difference* between two $E°$ values, the $E°$ values are reduction potentials. Because $-E°$ corresponds to the half-cell potential for the oxidation process, the *difference* between two reduction potentials is equivalent to the *sum* of a reduction potential and an oxidation potential.

PRACTICE EXAMPLE A: Use data from Table 7.1 to predict the probable products when Pt electrodes are used in the electrolysis of KI(aq).

PRACTICE EXAMPLE B: In the electrolysis of $AgNO_3(aq)$, what are the expected electrolysis products if the anode is silver metal and the cathode is platinum?

factor enters in as well: the quantity of electric charge associated with one mole of electrons. This factor is provided by the Faraday constant, which we can write as

$$1\text{ mol }e^- = 96{,}485\text{ C}$$

Generally, electric charge is not measured directly; instead, it is the electric current that is measured. One *ampere* (A) of electric current represents the passage of 1 coulomb of charge per second (C/s). The product of current and time yields the total quantity of charge transferred.

$$\text{charge (C)} = \text{current (C/s)} \times \text{time (s)}$$

To determine the number of moles of electrons involved in an electrolysis reaction, we can write

$$\text{number of mol } e^- = \text{current}\left(\frac{\text{C}}{\text{s}}\right) \times \text{time (s)} \times \frac{1 \text{ mol } e^-}{96{,}485 \text{ C}}$$

As illustrated in Example 7-13, to determine the mass of a product in an electrolysis reaction, follow this conversion pathway.

$$\text{C/s} \longrightarrow \text{C} \longrightarrow \text{mol } e^- \longrightarrow \text{mol product} \longrightarrow \text{g product}$$

EXAMPLE 7-13 Calculating Quantities Associated with Electrolysis Reactions

The electrodeposition of copper can be used to determine the copper content of a sample. The sample is dissolved to produce $Cu^{2+}(aq)$, which is electrolyzed. At the cathode, the reduction half-reaction is $Cu^{2+}(aq) + 2\,e^- \longrightarrow Cu(s)$. What mass of copper can be deposited in 1.00 hour by a current of 1.62 A?

Analyze

To find the mass of copper deposited, we first need to determine the number of moles of electrons generated in the given time. Because we know that for each copper(II) ion we need two electrons, we can calculate the mass by using the number of moles of electrons.

Solve

First, we determine the number of moles of electrons involved in the electrolysis in the manner outlined above:

$$1.00 \text{ h} \times \frac{60 \text{ min}}{1 \text{ h}} \times \frac{60 \text{ s}}{1 \text{ min}} \times \frac{1.62 \text{ C}}{1 \text{ s}} \times \frac{1 \text{ mol } e^-}{96{,}485 \text{ C}} = 0.0604 \text{ mol } e^-$$

The mass of Cu(s) produced at the cathode by this number of moles of electrons is calculated as follows:

$$\text{mass of Cu} = 0.0604 \text{ mol } e^- \times \frac{1 \text{ mol Cu}}{2 \text{ mol } e^-} \times \frac{63.5 \text{ g Cu}}{1 \text{ mol Cu}} = 1.92 \text{ g Cu}$$

Assess

The key factor in this calculation, relating moles of copper to moles of electrons, is printed in blue. This type of conversion is very similar to the one you learned when doing stoichiometric problems.

PRACTICE EXAMPLE A: If 12.3 g of Cu is deposited at the cathode of an electrolytic cell after 5.50 h, what was the current used?

PRACTICE EXAMPLE B: For how long would the electrolysis in Example 7-13 have to be carried out, using Pt electrodes and a current of 2.13 A, to produce 2.62 L $O_2(g)$ at 26.2 °C and 738 mmHg pressure at the anode?

7-8 Industrial Electrolysis Processes

Modern industry could not function in its present form without electrolysis reactions. A number of elements are produced almost exclusively by electrolysis—for example, aluminum, magnesium, chlorine, and fluorine. Among chemical compounds produced industrially by electrolysis are NaOH, $K_2Cr_2O_7$, $KMnO_4$, $Na_2S_2O_8$, and a number of organic compounds.

◀ The refining of copper by electrolysis.

Electrorefining

The *electrorefining* of metals involves the deposition of pure metal at a cathode, from a solution containing the metal ion. Copper produced by the smelting of copper ores is of sufficient purity for some uses, such as plumbing, but it is not pure enough for applications in which high electrical conductivity is required. For these applications, the copper must be more than 99.5% pure. The electrolysis reaction (7.35) on page 289 is used to obtain such high-purity copper. A chunk of impure copper is the anode and a thin sheet of pure copper is the cathode. During the electrolysis, Cu^{2+} produced at the anode migrates through an aqueous sulfuric acid–copper(II) sulfate solution to the cathode, where it is reduced to Cu(s). The pure copper cathode increases in size as the impure chunk of copper is consumed. As noted in Example 7-12a, the electrolysis is carried out at a low voltage—from 0.15 to 0.30 V. Under these conditions, Ag, Au, and Pt impurities are not oxidized at the anode, and they drop to the bottom of the tank as a sludge called *anode mud*. Sn, Bi, and Sb are oxidized, but they precipitate as oxides or hydroxides; Pb is oxidized but precipitates as $PbSO_4(s)$. As, Fe, Ni, Co, and Zn are oxidized but form water-soluble species. Recovery of Ag, Au, and Pt from the anode mud helps offset the cost of the electrolysis.

Electroplating

In *electroplating*, one metal is plated onto another, often less expensive, metal by electrolysis. This procedure is done for decorative purposes or to protect the underlying metal from corrosion. Silver-plated flatware, for example, consists of a thin coating of metallic silver on an underlying base of iron. In electroplating, the item to be plated is the cathode in an electrolytic cell. The electrolyte contains ions of the metal to be plated, which are attracted to the cathode, where they are reduced to metal atoms.

In copper plating, the electrolyte is usually copper sulfate. In silver plating, it is commonly $K[Ag(CN)_2](aq)$. The concentration of free silver ion in a solution of the complex ion $[Ag(CN)_2]^-(aq)$ is very low, and electroplating under these conditions promotes a strongly adherent microcrystalline deposit of the metal. Chromium plating is useful for its resistance to corrosion as well as its appearance. Steel can be chromium-plated from an aqueous solution of CrO_3 and H_2SO_4. The plating obtained, however, is thin and porous and tends to develop cracks. In practice, the steel is first plated with a thin coat of copper or nickel, and then the chromium plating is applied. Chromium plating or cadmium plating is used to weatherproof machine parts. Metal plating can even be applied to some plastics. The plastic must first be made electrically conductive—for example, by coating it with graphite powder. Copper plating of plastics has been used to improve the quality of some microelectronic circuit boards. Electroplating is even used, quite literally, to make money. The U.S. penny is no longer copper throughout. A zinc plug is electroplated with a thin coat of copper, and the copper-plated plug is stamped to create a penny.

▲ A rack of metal parts being lifted from the electrolyte solution after electroplating.

Electrosynthesis

Electrosynthesis is a method of producing substances through electrolysis reactions. It is useful for certain syntheses in which reaction conditions must be carefully controlled. Manganese dioxide occurs naturally as the mineral *pyrolusite,* but small crystal size and lattice imperfections make this material inadequate for certain modern applications, such as alkaline batteries. The electrosynthesis of MnO_2 is carried out in a solution of $MnSO_4$ in $H_2SO_4(aq)$ Pure $MnO_2(s)$ is formed by the oxidation of Mn^{2+} at an inert anode, such as graphite.

$$\textit{Oxidation:} \quad Mn^{2+}(aq) + 2\,H_2O(l) \longrightarrow MnO_2(s) + 4\,H^+(aq) + 2\,e^-$$

The reaction at the cathode is the reduction of H^+ to $H_2(g)$, and the overall electrolysis reaction is

$$Mn^{2+}(aq) + 2\,H_2O(l) \longrightarrow MnO_2(s) + 2\,H^+(aq) + H_2(g)$$

An example of electrosynthesis in organic chemistry is the reduction of acrylonitrile, $CH_2{=}CH{-}C{\equiv}N$, to adiponitrile, $N{\equiv}C(CH_2)_4C{\equiv}N$, at a lead cathode (chosen because of the high overpotential of H_2 on lead). Oxygen is released at the anode.

$$\textit{Reduction:} \quad 2\,CH_2{=}CH{-}C{\equiv}N + 2\,H_2O + 2\,e^- \longrightarrow N{\equiv}C(CH_2)_4C{\equiv}N + 2\,OH^-$$

The commercial importance of this electrolysis is that adiponitrile can be readily converted to two other compounds: hexamethylenediamine, $H_2NCH_2(CH_2)_4CH_2NH_2$, and adipic acid, $HOOCCH_2(CH_2)_2CH_2COOH$. These two compounds are the monomers used to make the polymer *Nylon-66.*

The Chlor–Alkali Process

We described the electrolysis of NaCl(aq) through the reduction half-reaction (7.30) and the oxidation half-reaction (7.31).

$$2\,Cl^-(aq) + 2\,H_2O(l) \longrightarrow 2\,OH^-(aq) + H_2(g) + Cl_2(g) \qquad E^\circ_{cell} = -2.19\text{ V}$$

When conducted on an industrial scale, this electrolysis is called the *chlor–alkali process,* named after the two principal products: *chlorine* and the *alkali* NaOH(aq). The chlor–alkali process is one of the most important of all electrolytic processes because of the high value of these products.

In the *diaphragm cell* depicted in Figure 7-24, $Cl_2(g)$ is produced in the anode compartment, and $H_2(g)$ and NaOH(aq) in the cathode compartment. If $Cl_2(g)$ comes in contact with NaOH(aq), the Cl_2 disproportionates into $ClO^-(aq)$, $ClO_3^-(aq)$, and $Cl^-(aq)$. The purpose of the diaphragm is to prevent this contact. The NaCl(aq) in the anode compartment is kept at a slightly higher level than that in the cathode compartment. This disparity creates a gradual flow of NaCl(aq) between the compartments and reduces the backflow of NaOH(aq) into the anode compartment. The solution in the cathode compartment, about 10%–12% NaOH(aq) and 14%–16% NaCl(aq), is concentrated and purified by evaporating some water and crystallizing the NaCl(s). The final product is 50% NaOH(aq), with up to 1% NaCl(aq).

The theoretical voltage required for this electrolysis is 2.19 V. However, as a result of the internal resistance of the cell and overpotentials at the electrodes, a voltage of about 3.5 V is used. The current is kept very high, typically about 1×10^5 A.

The NaOH(aq) produced in a diaphragm cell is not pure enough for certain uses, such as rayon manufacture. A higher purity is achieved if electrolysis is carried out in a mercury cell, illustrated in Figure 7-25. This cell takes advantage of the high overpotential for the reduction of $H_2O(l)$ to $H_2(g)$ and $OH^-(aq)$ at a mercury cathode. The reduction that occurs instead is that of $Na^+(aq)$ to Na,

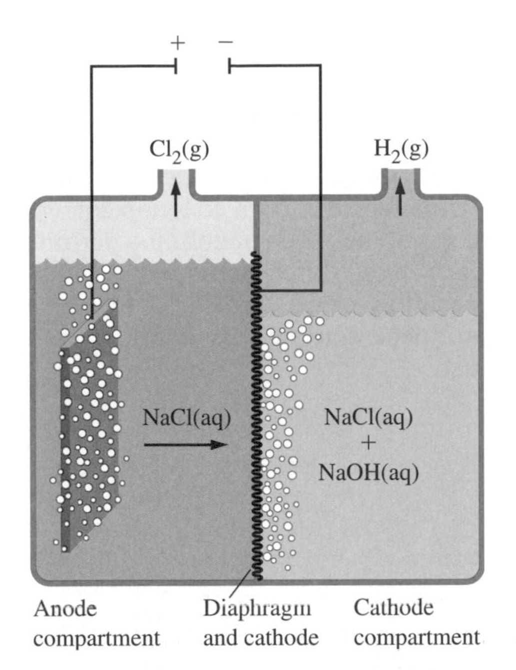

◀ FIGURE 7-24
A diaphragm chlor–alkali cell
The anode may be made of graphite or, in more modern technology, specially treated titanium metal. The diaphragm and cathode are generally fabricated as a composite unit consisting of asbestos or an asbestos–polymer mixture deposited on a steel wire mesh. To avoid the use of asbestos, a more modern development substitutes a fluorocarbon mesh for the asbestos.

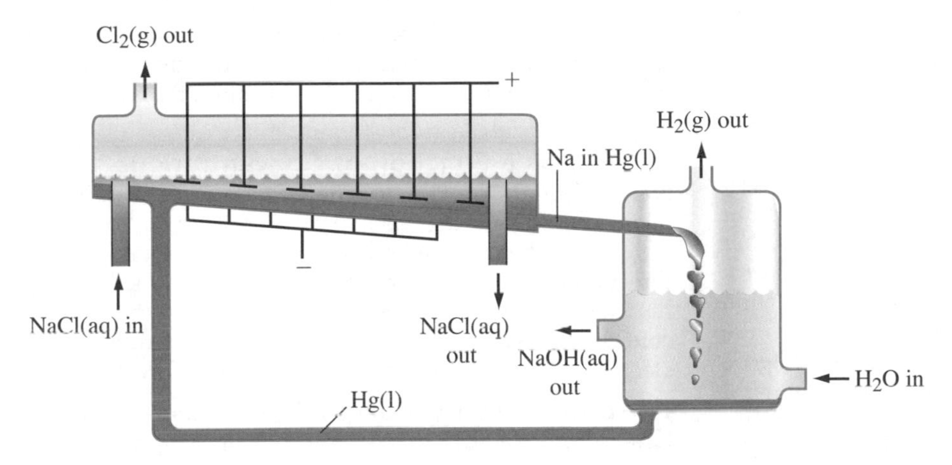

▲ FIGURE 7-25
The mercury-cell chlor–alkali process
The cathode is a layer of Hg(l) that flows along the bottom of the tank. Anodes, at which $Cl_2(g)$ forms, are situated in the NaCl(aq) just above the Hg(l). Sodium formed at the cathode dissolves in the Hg(l), and the sodium amalgam is decomposed with water to produce NaOH(aq) and $H_2(g)$. The regenerated Hg(l) is recycled.

which dissolves in Hg(l) to form an amalgam (Na–Hg alloy) with about 0.5% Na by mass.

$$2\,Na^+(aq) + 2\,Cl^-(aq) \longrightarrow 2\,Na(in\ Hg) + Cl_2(g) \qquad E^\circ_{cell} = -3.20\ V$$

When the Na amalgam is removed from the cell and treated with water, NaOH(aq) forms,

$$2\,Na(in\ Hg) + 2\,H_2O(l) \longrightarrow 2\,Na^+(aq) + 2\,OH^-(aq) + H_2(g) + Hg(l)$$

and the liquid mercury is recycled back to the electrolytic cell.

Although the mercury cell has the advantage of producing concentrated high-purity NaOH(aq), it has some disadvantages. The mercury cell requires a higher voltage (about 4.5 V) than does the diaphragm cell (3.5 V) and consumes more electrical energy, about 3400 kWh/ton Cl_2 in a mercury cell, compared with 2500 kWh/ton Cl_2 in a diaphragm cell. Another serious drawback is the need to control mercury effluents to the environment. Mercury losses, which at one time were as high as 200 g Hg per ton Cl_2, have been reduced to about 0.25 g Hg per ton of Cl_2 in older plants and half this amount in new plants.

The ideal chlor–alkali process is one that is energy-efficient and does not use mercury. A type of cell offering these advantages is the *membrane cell,* in which the porous diaphragm of Figure 7-24 is replaced by a cation-exchange membrane, normally made of a fluorocarbon polymer. The membrane permits hydrated cations (Na^+ and H_3O^+) to pass between the anode and cathode compartments but severely restricts the backflow of Cl^- and OH^- ions. As a result, the sodium hydroxide solution produced contains less than 50 ppm chloride ion contaminant.

Summary

7-1 Electrode Potentials and Their Measurement—In an **electrochemical cell** electrons in an oxidation–reduction reaction are transferred at metal strips called **electrodes** and conducted through an external circuit. The oxidation and reduction half-reactions occur in separate regions called **half-cells.** In a half-cell, an electrode is immersed in a solution. The electrodes of the two half-cells are joined by a wire, and an electrical connection between the solutions is also made, as through a **salt bridge** (Fig. 7-3). The cell reaction involves oxidation at one electrode called the **anode** and reduction at the other electrode called the **cathode.** A **voltaic (galvanic) cell** produces electricity from a spontaneous oxidation–reduction reaction. The difference in electric potential between the two electrodes is the **cell voltage**; the unit of cell voltage is the **volt** (**V**). The cell voltage is also called the **cell potential** or **electromotive force (emf)** and designated as $\mathbf{E_{cell}}$. A **cell diagram** displays the components of a cell in a symbolic way (expression 7-4).

7-2 Standard Electrode Potentials—The reduction occurring at a **standard hydrogen electrode (SHE),** $2\,H^+(a = 1) + 2\,e^- \xrightarrow{\text{on Pt}} H_2(g, 1\text{ bar})$, is arbitrarily assigned a potential of zero. A half-cell has a **standard electrode potential,** $E°$, in which all reactants and products are at unit activity. A half-cell reaction with a *positive* standard electrode potential ($E°$) occurs more readily than does reduction of H^+ ions at the SHE. A *negative* standard electrode potential signifies a lesser tendency to undergo reduction. The **standard cell potential** ($\mathbf{E°_{cell}}$) of a voltaic cell is the *difference* between $E°$, of the cathode and $E°$, of the anode; that is, $E°_{cell} = E°(\text{cathode}) - E°(\text{anode})$.

7-3 E_{cell}, ΔG, and K—Cell voltages based on standard electrode potentials are $E°_{cell}$ values. The electrical work that can be obtained from a cell depends on the number of electrons involved in the cell reaction, the cell potential, and the **Faraday constant (*F*)**, which is the number of coulombs of charge per mole of electrons—96,485 C/mol e^-. An important relationship exists between $E°_{cell}$ and $\Delta G°$, namely, $\Delta G° = -zFE°_{cell}$. The equilibrium constant of the cell reaction K is related to $E°_{cell}$ through the expression $\Delta G° = -RT \ln K = -zFE°_{cell}$.

7-4 E_{cell} as a Function of Concentrations—In the **Nernst equation,** E_{cell} for nonstandard conditions is related to $E°_{cell}$ and the reaction quotient Q (equation 7.18). If $E_{cell} > 0$, the cell reaction is spontaneous in the forward direction for the stated conditions; if $E_{cell} < 0$, the forward reaction is *nonspontaneous* for those conditions. A **concentration cell** consists of two half-cells with identical electrodes but different solution concentrations.

7-5 Batteries: Producing Electricity Through Chemical Reactions—An important application of voltaic cells is found in various battery systems. A **battery** stores chemical energy so that it can be released as energy. Batteries consist of one or more voltaic cells and are divided into three major classes: **primary** (Leclanché), **secondary** (lead–acid, silver–zinc nicad, and lithium-ion), and **flow batteries** or **fuel cells** in which reactants, such as hydrogen and oxygen, are continuously fed into the battery and chemical energy is converted to electric energy.

7-6 Corrosion: Unwanted Voltaic Cells—Electrochemistry plays a key role in corrosion and its control. Oxidation half-reactions produce anodic regions and reduction half-reactions, cathodic regions. **Cathodic protection** is achieved when a more active metal is attached to the metal being protected from corrosion. The more active metal, a "sacrificial" anode, is preferentially oxidized while the protected metal is a cathode at which a harmless reduction half-reaction occurs.

7-7 Electrolysis: Causing Nonspontaneous Reactions to Occur—In **electrolysis**, a nonspontaneous chemical reaction occurs as electrons from an external source are forced to flow in a direction opposite that in which they would flow spontaneously. The electrochemical cell in which electrolysis is conducted is called an **electrolytic cell**. $E°$, values are used to establish the theoretical voltage requirements for an electrolysis. Sometimes, particularly when a gas is liberated at an electrode, the voltage requirement for the electrode reaction exceeds the value of $E°$. The additional voltage requirement is called the **overpotential**. The amounts of reactants and products involved in an electrolysis can be calculated from the amount of electric charge passing through the electrolytic cell. The Faraday constant is featured in these calculations.

7-8 Industrial Electrolysis Processes—Electrolysis has many industrial applications, including electroplating, refining of metals, and production of substances such as $NaOH(aq)$, $H_2(g)$, and $Cl_2(g)$.

Integrative Example

Two electrochemical cells are connected as shown.

Cell A
$Zn(s)|Zn^{2+}(0.85\ M)||Cu^{2+}(1.10\ M)|Cu(s)$

$Zn(s)|Zn^{2+}(1.05\ M)||Cu^{2+}(0.75\ M)|Cu(s)$
Cell B

(a) Do electrons flow in the direction of the red arrows or the blue arrows?

(b) What are the ion concentrations in the half-cells at the point at which current ceases to flow?

Analyze

The two cells differ only in their ion concentrations, which means that they have the same $E°_{cell}$ value but different E_{cell} values. In part **(a)**, use the Nernst equation (7.19) to determine which cell has the greater E_{cell} value when functioning as a voltaic cell. This will establish the direction that electrons flow. In part **(b)**, write and solve an equation relating ion concentrations to the condition where the two cells have the same voltage but, being connected in opposition to each other, produce no net electric current.

Solve

(a) In each voltaic cell zinc is the anode, copper is the cathode, and the cell reaction is

$$Zn(s) + Cu^{2+}(aq) \longrightarrow Zn^{2+}(aq) + Cu(s)$$

The E_{cell} values are given by the Nernst equation.

$$E_{cell} = E°_{cell} - (0.025693/2)\ \ln[Zn^{2+}]/[Cu^{2}] \qquad \textbf{(7.37)}$$

Note that for Cell A,

$$[Zn^{2+}]/[Cu^{2+}] = 0.85\ M/1.10\ M < 1$$
$$\ln[Zn^{2+}]/[Cu^{2+}] < 0, \quad \text{and} \quad E_{cell} > E°_{cell}$$

For Cell B,

$$[Zn^{2+}]/[Cu^{2+}] = 1.05\ M/0.75\ M > 1$$
$$\ln[Zn^{2+}]/[Cu^{2+}] > 0, \text{ and } E_{cell} < E°_{cell}$$

The voltage of Cell A is greater than that of Cell B.

In the connection of the two cells shown in the diagram, Cell A is a *voltaic cell* and Cell B is an *electrolytic cell*. There is an emf from Cell B that resists that of Cell A, but on balance, the electron flow is in the direction of the red arrows.

(b) As electrons flow between the two cells, the overall reaction in Cell A causes $[Zn^{2+}]$ to increase, $[Cu^{2+}]$ to decrease, and E_{cell} to decrease. The overall reaction in Cell B causes $[Zn^{2+}]$ to decrease, $[Cu^{2+}]$ to increase, and the back emf to increase. When the back emf from Cell B equals E_{cell} of Cell A, electrons cease to flow.

The cell diagrams when this condition is reached, with x representing *changes* in concentrations, are

Cell A: $Zn(s)|Zn^{2+}(0.85 + x)\ M||Cu^{2+}(1.10 - x)\ M|Cu(s)$
Cell B: $Zn(s)|Zn^{2+}(1.05 - x)\ M||Cu^{2+}(0.75 + x)\ M|Cu(s)$

Use equation (7.37) to obtain E_{cell} for each cell.

$$\textit{Cell A:} \quad E_{cell} = E^{\circ}_{cell} - \frac{0.025693\ V}{2} \ln \frac{(0.85 + x)}{(1.10 - x)}$$

$$\textit{Cell B:} \quad E_{cell} = E^{\circ}_{cell} - \frac{0.025693\ V}{2} \ln \frac{(1.05 - x)}{(0.75 + x)}$$

Set the two expressions equal to one another, cancel the terms E°_{cell} and $(0.0592\ V)/2$, to obtain

$$\ln \frac{(0.85 + x)}{(1.10 - x)} = \ln \frac{(1.05 - x)}{(0.75 + x)}$$

Because the logarithms of the quantities on the two sides are equal, so too are the quantities themselves.

$$\frac{(0.85 + x)}{(1.10 - x)} = \frac{(1.05 - x)}{(0.75 + x)}$$

The expression to be solved is a quadratic equation

$$(0.85 + x)(0.75 + x) = (1.10 - x)(1.05 - x)$$

Cancel x^2 on each side

$$0.64 + 1.60x + \cancel{x^2} = 1.16 - 2.15x + \cancel{x^2}$$

$$0.64 + 1.60x = 1.16 - 2.15x$$

Solve to obtain

$$3.75x = 0.52 \quad \text{and} \quad x = 0.14$$

When electrons no longer flow, the ion concentrations are as follows:

Cell A: $[Zn^{2+}] = 0.99\ M$; $[Cu^{2+}] = 0.96\ M$.
Cell B: $[Zn^{2+}] = 0.91\ M$; $[Cu^{2+}] = 0.89\ M$.

Assess

Once the direction of electron flow had been established, it was possible to decide in which cell $[Zn^{2+}]$ would increase and in which cell it would decrease. At equilibrium the two cell potentials became equal. That the calculated equilibrium concentrations are correct can be seen in $0.99/0.96 \approx 0.91/0.89$.

PRACTICE EXAMPLE A: Current fuel cells use the reaction of $H_2(g)$ and $O_2(g)$ to form $H_2O(l)$. Often, the $H_2(g)$ is obtained by the steam reforming of a hydrocarbon, such as $C_3H_8(g) + 3\,H_2O(g) \longrightarrow 3\,CO(g) + 7\,H_2(g)$. A future possibility is a fuel cell that converts a hydrocarbon, such as propane, directly to $CO_2(g)$ and $H_2O(l)$:

$$C_3H_8(g) + 5\,O_2(g) \longrightarrow 3\,CO_2(g) + 4\,H_2O(l)$$

Based on this reaction, use data from Table 7.1 and Appendix A to determine E° for the reduction of $CO_2(g)$ to $C_3H_8(g)$ in an acidic solution.

PRACTICE EXAMPLE B: A battery system that may be used to power automobiles in the future is the aluminum–air battery. This is a *flow battery* in which oxidation occurs at an aluminum anode and reduction at a carbon–air cathode. The electrolyte circulated through the battery is NaOH(aq); the ultimate reaction product is $Al(OH)_3(s)$, which is removed from the battery as it is formed. In operation the battery can be kept charged by feeding Al anode slugs and water into it; oxygen is drawn from the air (see Fig. 7-18). The battery can power an automobile several hundred miles between charges. The $Al(OH)_3(s)$ removed from the battery can be converted back to aluminum in an aluminum manufacturing facility.

(a) In actual practice Al^{3+} produced at the anode does not precipitate as $Al(OH)_3(s)$ but is obtained as the complex ion $[Al(OH)_4]^-$ in the presence of NaOH(aq). $Al(OH)_3$ is precipitated from the circulating NaOH(aq) electrolyte *outside* the battery. Write plausible equations for oxidation and reduction half-reactions, and for the net reaction that occurs in the battery.

(b) The theoretical voltage of the aluminum–air cell is +2.73 V. Use this information and data from Table 7.1 to obtain E° for the reduction

$$[Al(OH)_4]^- + 3\,e^- \longrightarrow Al(s) + 4\,OH^- \quad E^{\circ} = ?$$

(c) Given that E°_{cell} for the reaction is +2.73 V, that $\Delta G^{\circ}_f[OH^-(aq)] = -157\ kJ\ mol^{-1}$, and that $\Delta G^{\circ}_f[H_2O(l)] = -237.2\ kJ\ mol^{-1}$, determine the Gibbs energy of formation, ΔG°_f, of the aluminate ion, $[Al(OH)_4]^-$.

(d) What mass of aluminum is consumed if 10.0 A of electric current is drawn from the battery for 4.00 h?

Exercises

(Use data from Table 7.1 and Appendix A as necessary.)

Standard Electrode Potentials

1. From the observations listed, estimate the value of $E°$ for the half-reaction $M^{2+}(aq) + 2\,e^- \longrightarrow M(s)$.
(a) The metal M reacts with $HNO_3(aq)$, but not with HCl(aq); M displaces $Ag^+(aq)$, but not $Cu^{2+}(aq)$.
(b) The metal M reacts with HCl(aq), producing $H_2(g)$, but displaces neither $Zn^{2+}(aq)$ nor $Fe^{2+}(aq)$.
2. You must estimate $E°$ for the half-reaction $In^{3+}(aq) + 3\,e^- \longrightarrow In(s)$. You have no electrical equipment, but you do have all of the metals listed in Table 7.1 and aqueous solutions of their ions, as well as In(s) and $In^{3+}(aq)$. Describe the experiments you would perform and the accuracy you would expect in your result.
3. $E°_{cell} = 0.201$ V for the reaction

$$3\,Pt(s) + 12\,Cl^-(aq) + 2\,NO_3^-(aq) + 8\,H^+(aq) \longrightarrow 3[PtCl_4]^{2-}(aq) + 2\,NO(g) + 4\,H_2O(l)$$

What is $E°$ for the reduction of $[PtCl_4]^{2-}$ to Pt in acidic solution?
4. Given that $E°_{cell} = 3.20$ V for the reaction

$$2\,Na(in\ Hg) + Cl_2(g) \longrightarrow 2\,Na^+(aq) + 2\,Cl^-(aq)$$

What is $E°$ for the reduction $2\,Na^+(aq) + 2\,e^- \longrightarrow 2\,Na(in\ Hg)$?
5. Given that $E°_{cell}$ for the aluminum-air battery is 2.71 V, what is $E°$ for the reduction half-reaction $[Al(OH)_4]^-(aq) + 3\,e^- \longrightarrow Al(s) + 4\,OH^-(aq)$? [*Hint:* Refer to cell reaction (7.28).]
6. The theoretical $E°_{cell}$ for the methane–oxygen fuel cell is 1.06 V. What is $E°$ for the reduction half-reaction $CO_2(g) + 8\,H^+(aq) + 8\,e^- \longrightarrow CH_4(g) + 2\,H_2O(l)$? [*Hint:* Refer to cell reaction (7.27).]
7. The following sketch is of a voltaic cell consisting of two standard electrodes for two metals, M and N:

$$M^{z+}(aq) + z\,e^- \longrightarrow M(s) \qquad E°_{M^{z+}/M}$$
$$N^{z+}(aq) + z\,e^- \longrightarrow N(s) \qquad E°_{N^{z+}/N}$$

Use the standard reduction potentials of these half-reactions to answer the questions that follow:

$$Ag^+(aq) + e^- \longrightarrow Ag(s)$$
$$Zn^{2+}(aq) + 2\,e^- \longrightarrow Zn(s)$$
$$Cu^{2+}(aq) + 2\,e^- \longrightarrow Cu(s)$$
$$Al^{3+}(aq) + 3\,e^- \longrightarrow Al(s)$$

(a) Determine which pair of these half-cell reactions leads to a cell reaction with the largest positive cell potential, and calculate its value. Which couple is at the anode and which at the cathode?
(b) Determine which pair of these half-cell reactions leads to the cell with the smallest positive cell potential, and calculate its value. Which couple is at the anode and which is at the cathode?

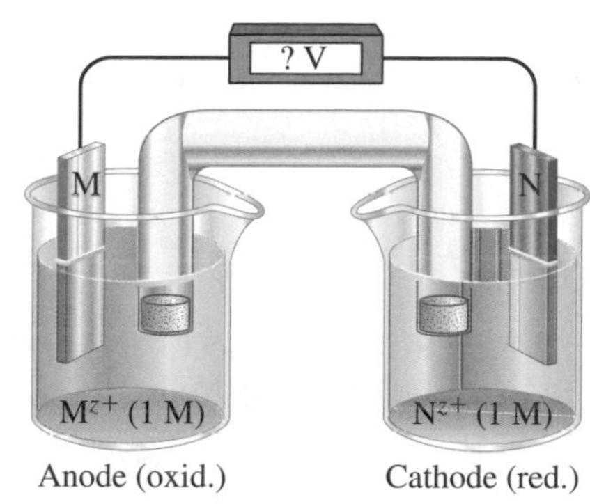

8. Given these half-reactions and associated standard reduction potentials, answer the questions that follow:

$$[Zn(NH_3)_4]^{2+}(aq) + 2\,e^- \longrightarrow Zn(s) + 4\,NH_3(aq) \qquad E° = -1.015\ V$$
$$Ti^{3+}(aq) + e^- \longrightarrow Ti^{2+}(aq) \qquad E° = -0.37\ V$$
$$VO^{2+}(aq) + 2\,H^+(aq) + e^- \longrightarrow V^{3+}(aq) + H_2O(l) \qquad E° = 0.340\ V$$
$$Sn^{2+}(aq) + 2\,e^- \longrightarrow Sn(aq) \qquad E° = -0.14\ V$$

(a) Determine which pair of half-cell reactions leads to a cell reaction with the largest positive cell potential, and calculate its value. Which couple is at the anode and which is at the cathode?
(b) Determine which pair of these half-cell reactions leads to the cell with the smallest positive cell potential, and calculate its value. Which couple is at the anode and which is at the cathode?

Predicting Oxidation–Reduction Reactions

9. Ni^{2+} has a more positive reduction potential than Cd^{2+}.
(a) Which ion is more easily reduced to the metal?
(b) Which metal, Ni or Cd, is more easily oxidized?
10. Refer to standard reduction potentials, and predict which metal in each of the following pairs is the stronger reducing agent:
(a) sodium or potassium
(b) magnesium or barium
11. Assume that all reactants and products are in their standard states, and use data from Table 7.1 to predict whether a spontaneous reaction will occur in the forward direction in each case.
(a) $Sn(s) + Pb^{2+}(aq) \longrightarrow Sn^{2+}(aq) + Pb(s)$
(b) $Cu^{2+}(aq) + 2\,I^-(aq) \longrightarrow Cu(s) + I_2(s)$
(c) $4\,NO_3^-(aq) + 4\,H^+(aq) \longrightarrow 3\,O_2(g) + 4\,NO(g) + 2\,H_2O(l)$
(d) $O_3(g) + Cl^-(aq) \longrightarrow OCl^-(aq) + O_2(g)$ (basic solution)
12. For the reduction half-reaction $Hg_2^{2+}(aq) + 2\,e^- \longrightarrow 2\,Hg(l)$, $E° = 0.797$ V. Will Hg(l) react with and dissolve in HCl(aq)? in $HNO_3(aq)$? Explain.
13. Use data from Table 7.1 to predict whether, to any significant extent,
(a) Mg(s) will displace Pb^{2+} from aqueous solution;
(b) Sn(s) will react with and dissolve in 1 M HCl;

(c) SO_4^{2-} will oxidize Sn^{2+} to Sn^{4+} in acidic solution;
(d) $MnO_4^-(aq)$ will oxidize $H_2O_2(aq)$ to $O_2(g)$ in acidic solution;
(e) $I_2(s)$ will displace $Br^-(aq)$ to produce $Br_2(l)$.

14. Consider the reaction $Co(s) + Ni^{2+}(aq) \longrightarrow Co^{2+}(aq) + Ni(s)$, with $E^\circ_{cell} = 0.02$ V. If Co(s) is added to a solution with $[Ni^{2+}] = 1$ M, should the reaction go to completion? Explain.

15. Dichromate ion ($Cr_2O_7^{2-}$) in acidic solution is a good oxidizing agent. Which of the following oxidations can be accomplished with dichromate ion in acidic solution? Explain.
(a) $Sn^{2+}(aq)$ to $Sn^{4+}(aq)$
(b) $I_2(s)$ to $IO_3^-(aq)$
(c) $Mn^{2+}(aq)$ to $MnO_4^-(aq)$

16. The standard electrode potential for the reduction of $Eu^{3+}(aq)$ to $Eu^{2+}(aq)$ is -0.43 V. Use the data in Appendix A to determine which of the following is capable of reducing $Eu^{3+}(aq)$ to $Eu^{2+}(aq)$ under standard-state conditions: Al(s), Co(s), $H_2O_2(aq)$, Ag(s), $H_2C_2O_4(aq)$.

17. Predict whether the following metals will react with the acid indicated. If a reaction does occur, write the net ionic equation for the reaction. Assume that reactants and products are in their standard states. **(a)** Ag in $HNO_3(aq)$; **(b)** Zn in HI(aq); **(c)** Au in HNO_3 (for the couple Au^{3+}/Au, $E^\circ = 1.52$ V).

18. Predict whether, to any significant extent,
(a) Fe(s) will displace $Zn^{2+}(aq)$;
(b) $MnO_4^-(aq)$ will oxidize $Cl^-(aq)$ to $Cl_2(g)$ in acidic solution;
(c) Ag(s) will react with 1 M HCl(aq);
(d) $O_2(g)$ will oxidize $Cl^-(aq)$ to $Cl_2(g)$ in acidic solution.

Galvanic Cells

19. Write cell reactions for the electrochemical cells diagrammed here, and use data from Table 7.1 to calculate E°_{cell} for each reaction.
(a) $Al(s)|Al^{3+}(aq)||Sn^{2+}(aq)|Sn(s)$
(b) $Pt(s)|Fe^{2+}(aq), Fe^{3+}(aq)||Ag^+(aq)|Ag(s)$
(c) $Cr(s)|Cr^{2+}(aq)||Au^{3+}(aq)|Au(s)$
(d) $Pt(s)|O_2(g)|H^+(aq)||OH^-(aq)|O_2(g)|Pt(s)$

20. Write the half-reactions and the balanced chemical equation for the electrochemical cells diagrammed here. Use data from Table 7.1 and Appendix A to calculate E°_{cell} for each reaction.
(a) $Cu(s)|Cu^{2+}(aq)||Cu^+(aq)|Cu(s)$
(b) $Ag(s)|AgI(s)|I^-(aq)||Cl^-(aq)|AgCl(s)|Ag(s)$
(c) $Pt|Ce^{4+}(aq), Ce^{3+}(aq)||I^-(aq), I_2(s)|C(s)$
(d) $U(s)|U^{3+}(aq)||V^{2+}(aq)|V(s)$

21. Use the data in Appendix A to calculate the standard cell potential for each of the following reactions. Which reactions will occur spontaneously?
(a) $H_2(g) + F_2(g) \longrightarrow 2\,H^+(aq) + 2\,F^-(aq)$
(b) $Cu(s) + Ba^{2+}(aq) \longrightarrow Cu^{2+}(aq) + Ba(s)$
(c) $3\,Fe^{2+}(aq) \longrightarrow Fe(s) + 2\,Fe^{3+}(aq)$
(d) $Hg(l) + HgCl_2(aq) \longrightarrow Hg_2Cl_2(s)$

22. In each of the following examples, sketch a voltaic cell that uses the given reaction. Label the anode and cathode; indicate the direction of electron flow; write a balanced equation for the cell reaction; and calculate E°_{cell}.
(a) $Cu(s) + Fe^{3+}(aq) \longrightarrow Cu^{2+}(aq) + Fe^{2+}(aq)$
(b) $Pb^{2+}(aq)$ is displaced from solution by Al(s)
(c) $Cl_2(g) + H_2O(l) \longrightarrow Cl^-(aq) + O_2(g) + H^+(aq)$
(d) $Zn(s) + H^+ + NO_3^- \longrightarrow Zn^{2+} + H_2O(l) + NO(g)$

23. Use the data in Appendix A to calculate the standard cell potential for each of the following reactions. Which reactions will occur spontaneously?
(a) $Fe^{3+}(aq) + Ag(s) \longrightarrow Fe^{2+}(aq) + Ag^+(aq)$
(b) $Sn(s) + Sn^{4+}(aq) \longrightarrow 2\,Sn^{2+}(aq)$
(c) $2\,Hg^{2+}(aq) + 2\,Br^-(aq) \longrightarrow Hg_2^{2+}(aq) + Br_2(l)$
(d) $2\,NO_3^-(aq) + 4\,H^+(aq) + Zn(s) \longrightarrow Zn^{2+}(aq) + 2\,NO_2(g) + 2\,H_2O(l)$

24. Write a cell diagram and calculate the value of E°_{cell} for a voltaic cell in which
(a) $Cl_2(g)$ is reduced to $Cl^-(aq)$ and Fe(s) is oxidized to $Fe^{2+}(aq)$;
(b) $Ag^+(aq)$ is displaced from solution by Zn(s);
(c) The cell reaction is $2\,Cu^+(aq) \longrightarrow Cu^{2+}(aq) + Cu(s)$;
(d) $MgBr_2(aq)$ is produced from Mg(s) and $Br_2(l)$.

ΔG°, E°_{cell}, and K

25. Determine the values of ΔG° for the following reactions carried out in voltaic cells.
(a) $2\,Al(s) + 3\,Cu^{2+}(aq) \longrightarrow 2\,Al^{3+}(aq) + 3\,Cu(s)$
(b) $O_2(g) + 4\,I^-(aq) + 4\,H^+(aq) \longrightarrow 2\,H_2O(l) + 2\,I_2(s)$
(c) $Cr_2O_7^{2-}(aq) + 14\,H^+(aq) + 6\,Ag(s) \longrightarrow 2\,Cr^{3+}(aq) + 6\,Ag^+(aq) + 7\,H_2O(l)$

26. Write the equilibrium constant expression for each of the following reactions, and determine the value of K at 25 °C. Use data from Table 7.1.
(a) $2\,V^{3+}(aq) + Ni(s) \longrightarrow 2\,V^{2+}(aq) + Ni^{2+}(aq)$
(b) $MnO_2(s) + 4\,H^+(aq) + 2\,Cl^-(aq) \longrightarrow Mn^{2+}(aq) + 2\,H_2O(l) + Cl_2(g)$
(c) $2\,OCl^-(aq) \longrightarrow 2\,Cl^-(aq) + O_2(g)$ (basic solution)

27. For the reaction

$$MnO_4^-(aq) + 8\,H^+(aq) + 5\,Ce^{3+}(aq) \longrightarrow 5\,Ce^{4+}(aq) + Mn^{2+}(aq) + 4\,H_2O(l)$$

use data from Table 7.1 to determine **(a)** E°_{cell}; **(b)** ΔG°; **(c)** K; **(d)** whether the reaction goes substantially to completion when the reactants and products are initially in their standard states.

28. For the reaction that occurs in the voltaic cell

$$Pt|Pb^{4+}(aq), Pb^{2+}(aq)||Sn^{4+}(aq), Sn^{2+}(aq)|C(s)$$

use data from Appendix A to determine **(a)** the equation for the cell reaction; **(b)** E°_{cell}; **(c)** ΔG°; **(d)** K; **(e)** whether the reaction goes substantially to completion when the reactants and products are initially in their standard states.

29. For the reaction $2\,Cu^+(aq) + Sn^{4+}(aq) \longrightarrow 2\,Cu^{2+}(aq) + Sn^{2+}(aq)$, $E^\circ_{cell} = -0.0050$ V,
(a) can a solution be prepared at 298 K that is 0.500 M in each of the four ions?
(b) If not, in which direction will a reaction occur?

30. For the reaction $2\,H^+(aq) + BrO_4^-(aq) + 2\,Ce^{3+}(aq) \longrightarrow BrO_3^-(aq) + 2\,Ce^{4+}(aq) + H_2O(l)$, $E^\circ_{cell} = -0.017$ V, answer the following questions:
(a) Can a solution be prepared at 298 K that has $[BrO_4^-] = [Ce^{4+}] = 0.675$ M, $[BrO_3^-] = [Ce^{3+}] = 0.600$ M and pH = 1?
(b) If not, in which direction will a reaction occur?

31. Use thermodynamic data from Appendix A to calculate a theoretical voltage of the silver–zinc button cell described on page 280.

32. The theoretical voltage of the aluminum–air battery is $E^\circ_{cell} = 2.71$ V. Use data from Appendix A and equation (7.28) to determine ΔG°_f for $Al[(OH)_4]^-$.

33. By the method of combining reduction half-equations illustrated on page 265, determine $E^\circ_{IrO_2/Ir}$, given that $E^\circ_{Ir^{3+}/Ir} = 1.156$ V and $E^\circ_{IrO_2/Ir^{3+}} = 0.223$ V.

34. Determine $E^\circ_{MoO_2/Mo^{3+}}$, given that $E^\circ_{H_2MoO_4/MoO_2} = 0.646$ V and $E^\circ_{H_2MoO_4/Mo^{3+}} = 0.428$ V. (See page 265).

Concentration Dependence of E_{cell}—The Nernst Equation

35. A voltaic cell represented by the following cell diagram has $E_{cell} = 1.250$ V. What must be $[Ag^+]$ in the cell?

$$Zn(s)|Zn^{2+}(1.00\text{ M})||Ag^+(x\text{ M})|Ag(s)$$

36. For the cell pictured in Figure 7-11, what is E_{cell} if the unknown solution in the half-cell on the left **(a)** has pH = 5.25; **(b)** is 0.0103 M HCl; **(c)** is 0.158 M $HC_2H_3O_2$ ($K_a = 1.8 \times 10^{-5}$)?

37. Use the Nernst equation and Table 7.1 to calculate E_{cell} for each of the following cells.
(a) $Al(s)|Al^{3+}(0.18\text{ M})||Fe^{2+}(0.85\text{ M})|Fe(s)$
(b) $Ag(s)|Ag^+(0.34\text{ M})||Cl^-(0.098\text{ M}), Cl_2(g, 0.55\text{ atm})|Pt(s)$

38. Use the Nernst equation and data from Appendix A to calculate E_{cell} for each of the following cells.
(a) $Mn(s)|Mn^{2+}(0.40\text{ M})||Cr^{3+}(0.35\text{ M}), Cr^{2+}(0.25\text{ M})|Pt(s)$
(b) $Mg(s)|Mg^{2+}(0.016\text{ M})||[Al(OH)_4]^-(0.25\text{ M}), OH^-(0.042\text{ M})|Al(s)$

39. Consider the reduction half-reactions listed in Appendix A, and give plausible explanations for the following observations:
(a) For some half-reactions, E depends on pH; for others, it does not.
(b) Whenever H^+ appears in a half-equation, it is on the *left* side.
(c) Whenever OH^- appears in a half-equation, it is on the *right* side.

40. Write an equation to represent the oxidation of $Cl^-(aq)$ to $Cl_2(g)$ by $PbO_2(s)$ in an acidic solution. Will this reaction occur spontaneously in the forward direction if all other reactants and products are in their standard states and **(a)** $[H^+] = 6.0$ M; **(b)** $[H^+] = 1.2$ M; **(c)** pH = 4.25? Explain.

41. If $[Zn^{2+}]$ is maintained at 1.0 M,
(a) what is the minimum $[Cu^{2+}]$ for which reaction (7.3) is spontaneous in the forward direction?
(b) Should the displacement of $Cu^{2+}(aq)$ by Zn(s) go to completion? Explain.

42. Can the displacement of Pb(s) from 1.0 M $Pb(NO_3)_2$ be carried to completion by tin metal? Explain.

43. A concentration cell is constructed of two hydrogen electrodes: one immersed in a solution with $[H^+] = 1.0$ M and the other in 0.65 M KOH.
(a) Determine E_{cell} for the reaction that occurs.
(b) Compare this value of E_{cell} with E° for the reduction of H_2O to $H_2(g)$ in basic solution, and explain the relationship between them.

44. If the 0.65 M KOH of Exercise 43 is replaced by 0.65 M NH_3,
(a) will E_{cell} be higher or lower than in the cell with 0.65 M KOH?
(b) What will be the value of E_{cell}?

45. A voltaic cell is constructed as follows:

$$Ag(s)|Ag^+(\text{satd } Ag_2CrO_4)||Ag^+(0.125\text{ M})|Ag(s)$$

What is the value of E_{cell}? For Ag_2CrO_4, $K_{sp} = 1.1 \times 10^{-12}$.

46. A voltaic cell, with $E_{cell} = 0.180$ V, is constructed as follows:

$$Ag(s)|Ag^+(\text{satd } Ag_3PO_4)||Ag^+(0.140\text{ M})|Ag(s)$$

What is the K_{sp} of Ag_3PO_4?

47. For the voltaic cell,

$$Sn(s)|Sn^{2+}(0.075\text{ M})||Pb^{2+}(0.600\text{ M})|Pb(s)$$

(a) what is E_{cell} initially?
(b) If the cell is allowed to operate spontaneously, will E_{cell} increase, decrease, or remain constant with time? Explain.
(c) What will be E_{cell} when $[Pb^{2+}]$ has fallen to 0.500 M?
(d) What will be $[Sn^{2+}]$ at the point at which $E_{cell} = 0.020$ V?
(e) What are the ion concentrations when $E_{cell} = 0$?

48. For the voltaic cell,

$$Ag(s)|Ag^{+}(0.015\ M)||Fe^{3+}(0.055\ M), Fe^{2+}(0.045\ M)|Pt(s)$$

(a) what is E_{cell} initially?
(b) As the cell operates, will E_{cell} increase, decrease, or remain constant with time? Explain.
(c) What will be E_{cell} when $[Ag^{+}]$ has increased to 0.020 M?
(d) What will be $[Ag^{+}]$ when $E_{cell} = 0.010$ V?
(e) What are the ion concentrations when $E_{cell} = 0$?

49. Show that the oxidation of $Cl^{-}(aq)$ to $Cl_2(g)$ by $Cr_2O_7^{2-}(aq)$ in acidic solution, with reactants and products in their standard states, does not occur spontaneously. Explain why it is still possible to use this method to produce $Cl_2(g)$ in the laboratory. What experimental conditions would you use?

50. Derive a balanced equation for the reaction occurring in the cell:

$$Fe(s)|Fe^{2+}(aq)||Fe^{3+}(aq), Fe^{2+}(aq)|Pt(s)$$

(a) If $E^{\circ}_{cell} = 1.21$ V, calculate ΔG° and the equilibrium constant for the reaction.
(b) Use the Nernst equation to determine the potential for the cell:

$$Fe(s)|Fe^{2+}(aq, 1.0 \times 10^{-3}\ M)||Fe^{3+}(aq, 1.0 \times 10^{-3}\ M), Fe^{2+}(aq, 0.10\ M)|Pt(s)$$

(c) In light of **(a)** and **(b)**, what is the likelihood of being able to observe the disproportionation of Fe^{2+} into Fe^{3+} and Fe under standard conditions?

Batteries and Fuel Cells

51. The iron–chromium redox battery makes use of the reaction

$$Cr^{2+}(aq) + Fe^{3+}(aq) \longrightarrow Cr^{3+}(aq) + Fe^{2+}(aq)$$

occurring at a chromium anode and an iron cathode.
(a) Write a cell diagram for this battery.
(b) Calculate the theoretical voltage of the battery.

52. Refer to the discussion of the Leclanché cell (page 278).
(a) Combine the several equations written for the operation of the Leclanché cell into a single overall equation.
(b) Given that the voltage of the Leclanché cell is 1.55 V, estimate the electrode potentials, E, for each of the half-reactions. Why are your values only estimates?

53. What is the theoretical standard cell voltage, E°_{cell}, of each of the following voltaic cells: **(a)** the hydrogen–oxygen fuel cell described by equation (7.26); **(b)** the zinc–air battery; **(c)** a magnesium–iodine battery?

54. For the alkaline Leclanché cell (page 278)
(a) write the overall cell reaction.
(b) Determine E°_{cell} for that cell reaction.

55. One of the advantages of the aluminum-air battery over the iron–air and zinc–air batteries is the greater quantity of charge transferred per unit mass of metal consumed. Show that this is indeed the case. Assume that zinc and iron are oxidized to oxidation state +2 in air batteries.

56. Describe how you might construct batteries with each of the following voltages: **(a)** 0.10 V; **(b)** 2.5 V; **(c)** 10.0 V. Be as specific as you can about the electrodes and solution concentrations you would use, and indicate whether the battery would consist of a single cell or two or more cells connected in series.

57. A lithium battery, which is different from a lithium-ion battery, uses lithium metal as one electrode and carbon in contact with MnO_2 in a paste of KOH as the other electrode. The electrolyte is lithium perchlorate in a nonaqueous solvent, and the construction is similar to the silver battery. The half-cell reactions involve the oxidation of lithium and the reaction

$$MnO_2(s) + 2\,H_2O(l) + e^{-} \longrightarrow Mn(OH)_3(s) + OH^{-}(aq) \qquad E^{\circ} = -0.20\ V$$

Draw a cell diagram for the lithium battery, identify the negative and positive electrodes, and estimate the cell potential under standard conditions.

58. For each of the following potential battery systems, describe the electrode reactions and the net cell reaction you would expect. Determine the theoretical voltage of the battery.
(a) $Zn-Br_2$
(b) $Li-F_2$

Electrochemical Mechanism of Corrosion

59. Refer to Figure 7-20, and describe in words or with a sketch what you would expect to happen in each of the following cases.
(a) Several turns of copper wire are wrapped around the head and tip of an iron nail.
(b) A deep scratch is filed at the center of an iron nail.
(c) A galvanized nail is substituted for the iron nail.

60. When an iron pipe is partly submerged in water, the iron dissolves more readily below the waterline than at the waterline. Explain this observation by relating it to the description of corrosion given in Figure 7-21.

61. Natural gas transmission pipes are sometimes protected against corrosion by the maintenance of a small potential difference between the pipe and an inert electrode buried in the ground. Describe how the method works.

62. In the construction of the Statue of Liberty, a framework of iron ribs was covered with thin sheets of copper less than 2.5 mm thick. A layer of asbestos separated the copper skin and iron framework. Over time, the asbestos wore away and the iron ribs corroded. Some of the ribs lost more than half their mass in the 100 years before the statue was restored. At the same time, the copper skin lost only about 4% of its thickness. Use electrochemical principles to explain these observations.

Electrolysis Reactions

63. How many grams of metal are deposited at the cathode by the passage of 2.15 A of current for 75 min in the electrolysis of an aqueous solution containing **(a)** Zn^{2+}; **(b)** Al^{3+}; **(c)** Ag^{+}; **(d)** Ni^{2+}?

64. A quantity of electric charge brings about the deposition of 3.28 g Cu at a cathode during the electrolysis of a solution containing $Cu^{2+}(aq)$. What volume of $H_2(g)$, measured at 28.2 °C and 763 mmHg, would be produced by this same quantity of electric charge in the reduction of $H^{+}(aq)$ at a cathode?

65. Which of the following reactions occur spontaneously, and which can be brought about only through electrolysis, assuming that all reactants and products are in their standard states? For those requiring electrolysis, what is the *minimum* voltage required?

(a) $2\,H_2O(l) \longrightarrow 2\,H_2(g) + O_2(g)$ [in 1 M $H^{+}(aq)$]
(b) $Zn(s) + Fe^{2+}(aq) \longrightarrow Zn^{2+}(aq) + Fe(s)$
(c) $2\,Fe^{2+}(aq) + I_2(s) \longrightarrow 2\,Fe^{3+}(aq) + 2\,I^{-}(aq)$
(d) $Cu(s) + Sn^{4+}(aq) \longrightarrow Cu^{2+}(aq) + Sn^{2+}(aq)$

66. An aqueous solution of K_2SO_4 is electrolyzed by means of Pt electrodes.
(a) Which of the following gases should form at the *anode:* O_2, H_2, SO_2, SO_3? Explain.
(b) What product should form at the *cathode*? Explain.
(c) What is the *minimum* voltage required? Why is the actual voltage needed likely to be higher than this value?

67. If a lead storage battery is charged at too high a voltage, gases are produced at each electrode. (It is possible to recharge a lead-storage battery only because of the high overpotential for gas formation on the electrodes.)
(a) What are these gases?
(b) Write a cell reaction to describe their formation.

68. A dilute aqueous solution of Na_2SO_4 is electrolyzed between Pt electrodes for 3.75 h with a current of 2.83 A. What volume of gas, saturated with water vapor at 25 °C and at a total pressure of 742 mmHg, would be collected at the *anode*? Use data from Table 3.4, as required.

69. Calculate the quantity indicated for each of the following electrolyses.
(a) the mass of Zn deposited at the cathode in 42.5 min when 1.87 A of current is passed through an aqueous solution of Zn^{2+}
(b) the time required to produce 2.79 g I_2 at the anode if a current of 1.75 A is passed through KI(aq)

70. Calculate the quantity indicated for each of the following electrolyses.
(a) $[Cu^{2+}]$ *remaining* in 425 mL of a solution that was originally 0.366 M $CuSO_4$, after passage of 2.68 A for 282 s and the deposition of Cu at the cathode
(b) the time required to reduce $[Ag^{+}]$ in 255 mL of $AgNO_3(aq)$ from 0.196 to 0.175 M by electrolyzing the solution between Pt electrodes with a current of 1.84 A

71. A *coulometer* is a device for measuring a quantity of electric charge. In a silver coulometer, $Ag^{+}(aq)$ is reduced to Ag(s) at a Pt cathode. If 1.206 g Ag is deposited in 1412 s by a certain quantity of electricity, **(a)** how much electric charge (in C) must have passed, and **(b)** what was the magnitude (in A) of the electric current?

72. Electrolysis is carried out for 2.00 h in the following cell. The platinum *cathode*, which has a mass of 25.0782 g, weighs 25.8639 g after the electrolysis. The platinum *anode* weighs the same before and after the electrolysis.
(a) Write plausible equations for the half-reactions that occur at the two electrodes.
(b) What must have been the magnitude of the current used in the electrolysis (assuming a constant current throughout)?
(c) A gas is collected at the anode. What is this gas, and what volume should it occupy if (when dry) it is measured at 23 °C and 755 mmHg pressure?

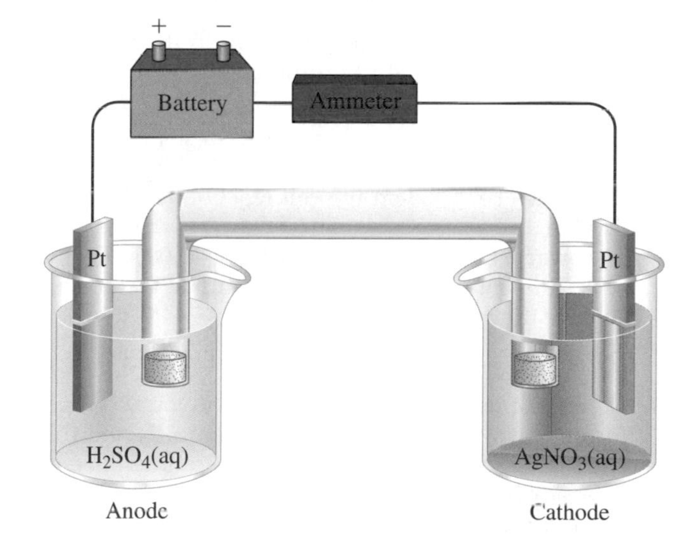

73. A solution containing both Ag^{+} and Cu^{2+} ions is subjected to electrolysis. **(a)** Which metal should plate out first? **(b)** Plating out is finished after a current of 0.75 A is passed through the solution for 2.50 hours. If the total mass of metal is 3.50 g, what is the mass percent of silver in the product?

74. A solution containing a mixture of a platinum(II) salt contaminated by approximately 10 mole % of another oxidation state is electrolyzed at 1.20 A for 32.0 minutes, at which point no more platinum is deposited. **(a)** What is the oxidation state of the contaminant? **(b)** What is the composition of the mixture?

Integrative and Advanced Exercises

75. Two voltaic cells are assembled in which the following reactions occur.

$$V^{2+}(aq) + VO^{2+}(aq) + 2\,H^+(aq) \longrightarrow 2\,V^{3+}(aq) + H_2O(l) \quad E^\circ_{cell} = 0.616\ V$$

$$V^{3+}(aq) + Ag^+(aq) + H_2O(l) \longrightarrow VO^{2+}(aq) + 2\,H^+(aq) + Ag(s) \quad E^\circ_{cell} = 0.439\ V$$

Use these data and other values from Table 7.1 to calculate E° for the half-reaction $V^{3+} + e^- \longrightarrow V^{2+}$.

76. Suppose that a fully charged lead–acid battery contains 1.50 L of 5.00 M H_2SO_4. What will be the concentration of H_2SO_4 in the battery after 2.50 A of current is drawn from the battery for 6.0 h?

77. The energy consumption in electrolysis depends on the product of the charge and the voltage [volt × coulomb = V·C = J(joules)]. Determine the theoretical energy consumption per 1000 kg Cl_2 produced in a diaphragm chlor–alkali cell (page 902) that operates at 3.45 V. Express this energy in **(a)** kJ; **(b)** kilowatt-hours, kWh.

78. For the half-reaction $Cr^{3+} + e^- \longrightarrow Cr^{2+}$, $E^\circ = -0.424$ V. If excess Fe(s) is added to a solution in which $[Cr^{3+}] = 1.00$ M, what will be $[Fe^{2+}]$ when equilibrium is reached at 298 K?

$$Fe(s) + 2\,Cr^{3+} \rightleftharpoons Fe^{2+} + 2\,Cr^{2+}$$

79. A voltaic cell is constructed based on the following reaction and initial concentrations:

$$Fe^{2+}(0.0050\ M) + Ag^+(2.0\ M) \rightleftharpoons Fe^{3+}(0.0050\ M) + Ag(s)$$

Calculate $[Fe^{2+}]$ when the cell reaction reaches equilibrium.

80. To construct a voltaic cell with $E_{cell} = 0.0860$ V, what $[Cl^-]$ must be present in the cathode half-cell to achieve this result?

$$Ag(s)|Ag^+(\text{satd AgI})||Ag^+(\text{satd AgCl}, x\ M\ Cl^-)|Ag(s)$$

81. Describe a laboratory experiment that you could perform to evaluate the Faraday constant, *F*, and then show how you could use this value to determine the Avogadro constant.

82. The hydrazine fuel cell is based on the reaction

$$N_2H_4(aq) + O_2(g) \longrightarrow N_2(g) + 2\,H_2O(l)$$

The theoretical E°_{cell} of this fuel cell is 1.559 V. Use this information and data from Appendix A to calculate a value of ΔG°_f for $[N_2H_4(aq)]$.

83. It is sometimes possible to separate two metal ions through electrolysis. One ion is reduced to the free metal at the cathode, and the other remains in solution. In which of these cases would you expect complete or nearly complete separation: **(a)** Cu^{2+} and K^+; **(b)** Cu^{2+} and Ag^+; **(c)** Pb^{2+} and Sn^{2+}? Explain.

84. Show that for some fuel cells the efficiency value, $e = \Delta G^\circ/\Delta H^\circ$, can have a value greater than 1.00. Can you identify one such reaction? [*Hint:* Use data from Appendix A.]

85. In one type of Breathalyzer (alcohol meter), the quantity of ethanol in a sample is related to the amount of electric current produced by an ethanol–oxygen fuel cell. Use data from Table 7.1 and Appendix A to determine **(a)** E°_{cell} and **(b)** E° for the reduction of $CO_2(g)$ to $CH_3CH_2OH(g)$.

86. You prepare 1.00 L of a buffer solution that is 1.00 M NaH_2PO_4 and 1.00 M Na_2HPO_4. The solution is divided in half between the two compartments of an electrolytic cell. Both electrodes used are Pt. Assume that the only electrolysis is that of water. If 1.25 A of current is passed for 212 min, what will be the pH in each cell compartment at the end of the electrolysis?

87. Assume that the volume of each solution in Figure 7-22 is 100.0 mL. The cell is operated as an electrolytic cell, using a current of 0.500 A. Electrolysis is stopped after 10.00 h, and the cell is allowed to function as a voltaic cell. What is E_{cell} at this point?

88. A common reference electrode consists of a silver wire coated with AgCl(s) and immersed in 1 M KCl.

$$AgCl(s) + e^- \longrightarrow Ag(s) + Cl^-(1\ M) \quad E^\circ = 0.2223\ V$$

(a) What is E°_{cell} when this electrode is a cathode in combination with a standard zinc electrode as an anode?
(b) Cite several reasons why this electrode should be easier to use than a standard hydrogen electrode.
(c) By comparing the potential of this silver–silver chloride electrode with that of the silver–silver ion electrode, determine K_{sp} for AgCl.

89. The electrodes in the following electrochemical cell are connected to a voltmeter as shown. The half-cell on the right contains a standard silver–silver chloride electrode (see Exercise 88). The half-cell on the left contains a silver electrode immersed in 100.0 mL of 1.00×10^{-3} M $AgNO_3(aq)$. A porous plug through which ions can migrate separates the half-cells.
(a) What is the initial reading on the voltmeter?
(b) What is the voltmeter reading after 10.00 mL of 0.0100 M K_2CrO_4 has been added to the half-cell on the left and the mixture has been thoroughly stirred?
(c) What is the voltmeter reading after 10.00 mL of 10.0 M NH_3 has been added to the half-cell described in part (b) and the mixture has been thoroughly stirred?

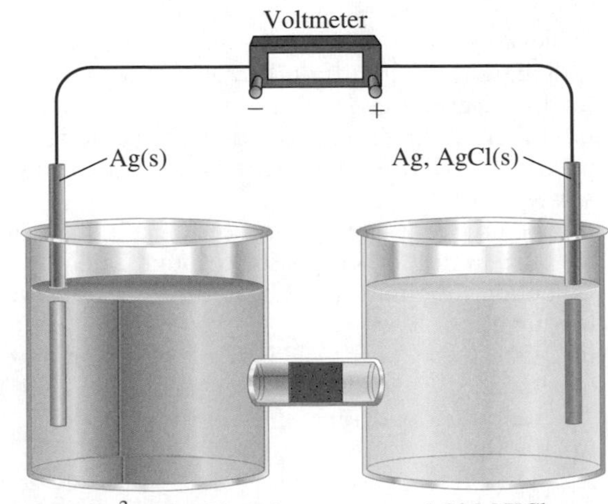

90. An important source of Ag is recovery as a by-product in the metallurgy of lead. The percentage of Ag in lead was determined as follows. A 1.050-g sample was dissolved in nitric acid to produce $Pb^{2+}(aq)$ and $Ag^{+}(aq)$. The solution was then diluted to 500.0 mL with water, a Ag electrode was immersed in the solution, and the potential difference between this electrode and a SHE was found to be 0.503 V. What was the percent Ag by mass in the lead metal?

91. A test for completeness of electrodeposition of Cu from a solution of $Cu^{2+}(aq)$ is to add $NH_3(aq)$. A blue color signifies the formation of the complex ion $[Cu(NH_3)_4]^{2+}$ ($K_f = 1.1 \times 10^{13}$). Let 250.0 mL of 0.1000 M $CuSO_4(aq)$ be electrolyzed with a 3.512 A current for 1368 s. At this time, add a sufficient quantity of $NH_3(aq)$ to complex any remaining Cu^{2+} and to maintain a free $[NH_3] = 0.10$ M. If $[Cu(NH_3)_4]^{2+}$ is detectable at concentrations as low as 1×10^{-5} M, should the blue color appear?

92. A solution is prepared by saturating 100.0 mL of 1.00 M $NH_3(aq)$ with AgBr. A silver electrode is immersed in this solution, which is joined by a salt bridge to a standard hydrogen electrode. What will be the measured E_{cell}? Is the standard hydrogen electrode the anode or the cathode?

93. The electrolysis of $Na_2SO_4(aq)$ is conducted in two separate half-cells joined by a salt bridge, as suggested by the cell diagram $Pt|Na_2SO_4(aq)||Na_2SO_4(aq)|Pt$.

(a) In one experiment, the solution in the anode compartment becomes more acidic and that in the cathode compartment, more basic during the electrolysis. When the electrolysis is discontinued and the two solutions are mixed, the resulting solution has pH = 7. Write half-equations and the overall electrolysis equation.

(b) In a second experiment, a 10.00-mL sample of an unknown concentration of $H_2SO_4(aq)$ and a few drops of phenolphthalein indicator are added to the $Na_2SO_4(aq)$ in the cathode compartment. Electrolysis is carried out with a current of 21.5 mA (milliamperes) for 683 s, at which point, the solution in the cathode compartment acquires a lasting pink color. What is the molarity of the unknown $H_2SO_4(aq)$?

94. A Ni anode and an Fe cathode are placed in a solution with $[Ni^{2+}] = 1.0$ M and then connected to a battery. The Fe cathode has the shape shown. How long must electrolysis be continued with a current of 1.50 A to build a 0.050-mm-thick deposit of nickel on the iron? (Density of nickel = 8.90 g/cm^3.)

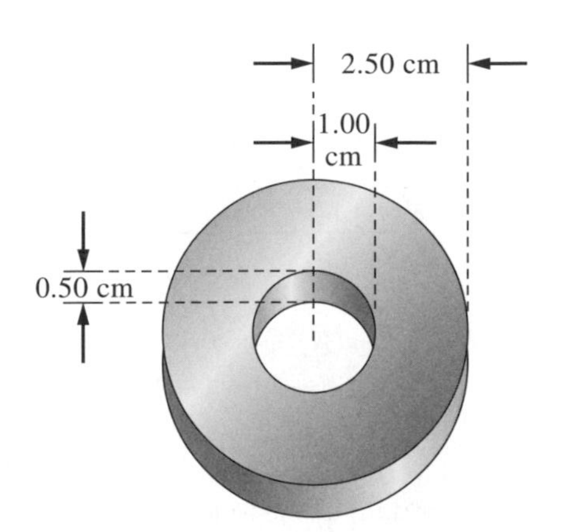

95. Initially, each of the half-cells in Figure 7-21 contained a 100.0-mL sample of solution with an ion concentration of 1.000 M. The cell was operated as an electrolytic cell, with copper as the anode and zinc as the cathode. A current of 0.500 A was used. Assume that the only electrode reactions occurring were those involving Cu/Cu^{2+} and Zn/Zn^{2+}. Electrolysis was stopped after 10.00 h, and the cell was allowed to function as a voltaic cell. What was E_{cell} at that point?

96. Silver tarnish is mainly Ag_2S:

$$Ag_2S(s) + 2\,e^- \longrightarrow 2\,Ag(s) + S^{2-}(aq) \qquad E^\circ = -0.691\text{ V}$$

A tarnished silver spoon is placed in contact with a commercially available metallic product in a glass baking dish. Boiling water, to which some $NaHCO_3$ has been added, is poured into the dish, and the product and spoon are completely covered. Within a short time, the removal of tarnish from the spoon begins.

(a) What metal or metals are in the product?

(b) What is the probable reaction that occurs?

(c) What do you suppose is the function of the $NaHCO_3$?

(d) An advertisement for the product appears to make two claims: (1) No chemicals are involved, and (2) the product will never need to be replaced. How valid are these claims? Explain.

97. Your task is to determine E° for the reduction of $CO_2(g)$ to $C_3H_8(g)$ in two different ways and to explain why each gives the same result. **(a)** Consider a fuel cell in which the cell reaction corresponds to the complete combustion of propane gas. Write the half-cell reactions and the overall reaction. Determine ΔG° and E°_{cell} for the reaction, then obtain $E^\circ_{CO_2/C_3H_8}$. **(b)** Without considering the oxidation that occurs simultaneously, obtain $E^\circ_{CO_2/C_3H_8}$ directly from tabulated thermodynamic data for the reduction half-reaction.

98. Equation (7.15) gives the relationship between the standard Gibbs energy of a reaction and the standard cell potential. We know how the Gibbs energy varies with temperature.

(a) Making the assumption that ΔH° and ΔS° do not vary significantly over a small temperature range, derive an equation for the temperature variation of E°_{cell}.

(b) Calculate the cell potential of a Daniell cell at 50 °C under standard conditions. The overall cell reaction for a Daniell cell is $Zn(s) + Cu^{2+}(aq) \rightarrow Zn^{2+}(aq) + Cu(s)$.

99. Show that for nonstandard conditions the temperature variation of a cell potential is

$$E(T_1) - E(T_2) = (T_1 - T_2)\frac{(\Delta S^\circ - R\ln Q)}{zF}$$

where $E(T_1)$ and $E(T_2)$ are the cell potentials at T_1 and T_2, respectively. We have assumed that the value of Q is maintained at a constant value. For the nonstandard cell below, the potential drops from 0.394 V at 50.0 °C to 0.370 V at 25.0 °C. Calculate Q, $\Delta H°$, and $\Delta S°$ for the reaction, and calculate K for the two temperatures.

$$Cu(s)|Cu^{2+}(aq)||Fe^{3+}(aq), Fe^{2+}(aq)|Pt(s)$$

Choose concentrations of the species involved in the cell reaction that give the value of Q that you have calculated, and then determine the equilibrium concentrations of the species at 50.0 °C.

100. Show that for a combination of half-cell reactions that produce a standard reduction potential for a half-cell that is not directly observable, the standard reduction potential is

$$E° = \frac{\Sigma n_i E_i°}{\Sigma n_i}$$

where n_i is the number of electrons in each half-reaction of potential $E_i°$. Use the following half-reactions:

$$H_5IO_6(aq) + H^+(aq) + 2\,e^- \longrightarrow IO_3^-(aq) + 3H_2O(l) \quad E° = 1.60\text{ V}$$

$$IO_3^-(aq) + 6\,H^+(aq) + 5\,e^- \longrightarrow \frac{1}{2}I_2(s) + 3\,H_2O(l) \quad E° = 1.19\text{ V}$$

$$2\,HIO(aq) + 2\,H^+(aq) + 2\,e^- \longrightarrow I_2(s) + 2\,H_2O(l) \quad E° = 1.45\text{ V}$$

$$I_2(s) + 2\,e^- \longrightarrow 2\,I^-(aq) \quad E° = 0.535\text{ V}$$

Calculate the standard reduction potential for

$$H_6IO_6 + 5\,H^+ + 2\,I^- + 3\,e^- \longrightarrow \frac{1}{2}I_2 + 4\,H_2O + 2\,HIO$$

Feature Problems

101. Consider the following electrochemical cell:

$$Pt(s)|H_2(g, 1\text{ atm})|H^+(1\text{ M})||Ag^+(x\text{ M})|Ag(s)$$

(a) What is $E°_{cell}$—that is, the cell potential when $[Ag^+] = 1$ M?
(b) Use the Nernst equation to write an equation for E_{cell} when $[Ag^+] = x$.
(c) Now imagine titrating 50.0 mL of 0.0100 M $AgNO_3$ in the cathode half-cell compartment with 0.0100 M KI. The titration reaction is

$$Ag^+(aq) + I^-(aq) \longrightarrow AgI(s)$$

Calculate $[Ag^+]$ and then E_{cell} after addition of the following volumes of 0.0100 M KI: (i) 0.0 mL; (ii) 20.0 mL; (iii) 49.0 mL; (iv) 50.0 mL; (v) 51.0 mL; (vi) 60.0 mL.
(d) Use the results of part (c) to sketch the titration curve of E_{cell} versus volume of titrant.

102. Ultimately, $\Delta G_f°$ values must be based on experimental results; in many cases, these experimental results are themselves obtained from $E°$ values. Early in the twentieth century, G. N. Lewis conceived of an experimental approach for obtaining standard potentials of the alkali metals. This approach involved using a solvent with which the alkali metals do not react. Ethylamine was the solvent chosen. In the following cell diagram, Na(amalg, 0.206%) represents a solution of 0.206% Na in liquid mercury.

1. $Na(s)|Na^+(\text{in ethylamine})|Na(\text{amalg}, 0.206\%)$ $\quad E_{cell} = 0.8453$ V

Although Na(s) reacts violently with water to produce $H_2(g)$, at least for a short time, a sodium amalgam electrode does not react with water. This makes it possible to determine E_{cell} for the following voltaic cell.

2. $Na(\text{amalg}, 0.206\%)|Na^+(1\text{ M})||H^+(1\text{ M})|H_2(g, 1\text{ atm})$ $\quad E_{cell} = 1.8673$ V

(a) Write equations for the cell reactions that occur in the voltaic cells (1) and (2).
(b) Use equation (7.14) to establish ΔG for the cell reactions written in part (a).
(c) Write the overall equation obtained by combining the equations of part (a), and establish $\Delta G°$ for this overall reaction.
(d) Use the $\Delta G°$ value from part (c) to obtain $E°_{cell}$ for the overall reaction. From this result, obtain $E°_{Na^+/Na}$. Compare your result with the value listed in Appendix A.

103. The following sketch is called an electrode potential diagram. Such diagrams summarize electrode potential data more efficiently than do listings such as that in Appendix A. In this diagram for bromine and its ions in basic solution,

$$BrO_4^- \xrightarrow{1.025\text{ V}} BrO_3^-$$

signifies

$$BrO_4^-(aq) + H_2O(l) + 2\,e^- \longrightarrow BrO_3^-(aq) + 2\,OH^-(aq), \quad E°_{BrO_4^-/BrO_3^-} = 1.025\text{ V}$$

Similarly,

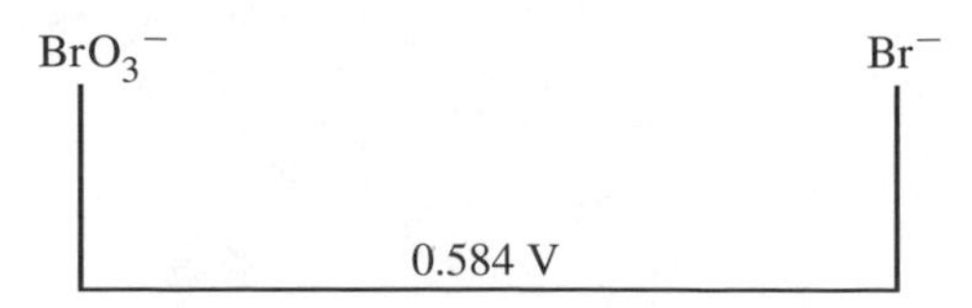

signifies

$$BrO_3^-(aq) + 3\,H_2O(l) + 6\,e^- \longrightarrow Br^-(aq) + 6\,OH^-(aq), \quad E°_{BrO_3^-/Br^-} = 0.584\text{ V}$$

With reference to Appendix A and to the method of determining $E°$ values outlined on page 265, supply the missing data in the following diagram.

Basic solution ($[OH^-] = 1$ M):

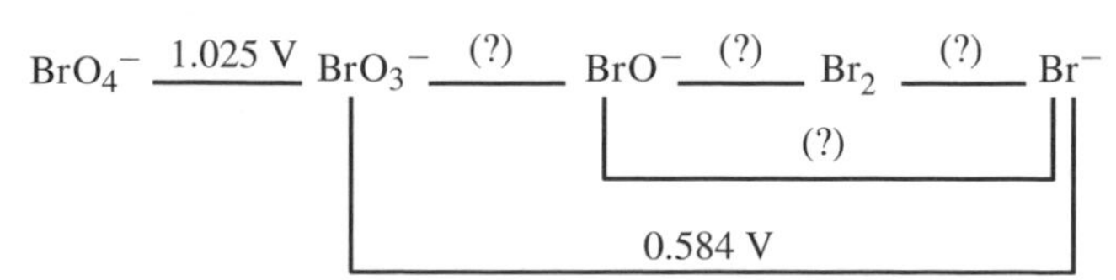

104. Only a tiny fraction of the diffusible ions move across a cell membrane in establishing a Nernst potential, so there is no detectable concentration change. Consider a typical cell with a volume of 10^{-8} cm^3, a surface area (A) of 10^{-6} cm^2, and a membrane thickness (l) of 10^{-6} cm. Suppose that $[K^+] =$ 155 mM inside the cell and $[K^+] = 4$ mM outside the cell and that the observed Nernst potential across the cell wall is 0.085 V. The membrane acts as a charge-storing device called a *capacitor*, with a *capacitance*, C, given by

$$C = \frac{\varepsilon_0 \varepsilon A}{l}$$

where ε_0 is the *dielectric constant* of a vacuum and the product $\varepsilon_0 \varepsilon$ is the dielectric constant of the membrane, having a typical value of $3 \times 8.854 \times 10^{-12}$ $C^2\,N^{-1}m^{-2}$ for a biological membrane. The SI unit of capacitance is the *farad*, $1\text{ F} = 1$ coulomb per volt $= 1\,C\,V^{-1} = 1 \times C^2\,N^{-1}\,m^{-1}$.

(a) Determine the capacitance of the membrane for the typical cell described.
(b) What is the net charge required to maintain the observed membrane potential?
(c) How many K^+ ions must flow through the cell membrane to produce the membrane potential?
(d) How many K^+ ions are in the typical cell?
(e) Show that the fraction of the intracellular K^+ ions transferred through the cell membrane to produce the membrane potential is so small that it does not change $[K^+]$ within the cell.

105. When deciding whether a particular reaction corresponds to a cell with a positive standard cell potential, which of the following thermodynamic properties would you use to get your answer without performing any calculations? Which would you not use? Explain. **(a)** $\Delta G°$; **(b)** $\Delta S°$; **(c)** $\Delta H°$; **(d)** $\Delta U°$; **(e)** K.

106. Consider two cells involving two metals X and Y

$$X(s)|X^+(aq)||H^+(aq), H_2(g, 1\text{ bar})|Pt(s)$$
$$X(s)|X^+(aq)||Y^{2+}(aq)|Y(s)$$

In the first cell electrons flow from the metal X to the standard hydrogen electrode. In the second cell electrons flow from metal X to metal Y. Is $E°_{X^+/X}$ greater or less than zero? Is $E°_{X^+/X} > E_{Y^{2+}/Y}$? Explain.

107. Describe in words how you would calculate the standard potential of the $Fe^{2+}/Fe(s)$ couple from those of Fe^{3+}/Fe^{2+} and $Fe^{3+}/Fe(s)$.

Self-Assessment Exercises

108. In your own words, define the following symbols or terms: **(a)** $E°$; **(b)** F; **(c)** anode; **(d)** cathode.

109. Briefly describe each of the following ideas, methods, or devices: **(a)** salt bridge; **(b)** standard hydrogen electrode (SHE); **(c)** cathodic protection; **(d)** fuel cell.

110. Explain the important distinctions between each pair of terms: **(a)** half-reaction and overall cell reaction; **(b)** voltaic cell and electrolytic cell; **(c)** primary battery and secondary battery; **(d)** E_{cell} and $E°_{cell}$.

111. Of the following statements concerning electrochemical cells, the correct ones are: **(a)** The cathode is the negative electrode in both voltaic and electrolytic cells. **(b)** The function of a salt bridge is to permit the migration of electrons between the half-cell compartments of an electrochemical cell. **(c)** The anode is the negative electrode in a voltaic cell. **(d)** Electrons leave the cell from either the cathode or the anode, depending on what electrodes are used. **(e)** Reduction occurs at the cathode in both voltaic and electrolytic cells. **(f)** If electric current is drawn from a voltaic cell long enough, the cell becomes an electrolytic cell. **(g)** The cell reaction is an oxidation-reduction reaction.

112. For the half-reaction $Hg^{2+}(aq) + 2\,e^- \longrightarrow Hg(l)$, $E° = 0.854$ V. This means that **(a)** Hg(l) is more readily oxidized than $H_2(g)$; **(b)** $Hg^{2+}(aq)$ is more readily reduced than $H^+(aq)$; **(c)** Hg(l) will dissolve in 1 M HCl; **(d)** Hg(l) will displace Zn(s) from an aqueous solution of Zn^{2+} ion.

113. The value of $E°_{cell}$ for the reaction $Zn(s) + Pb^{2+}(aq) \longrightarrow Zn^{2+}(aq) + Pb(s)$ is 0.66 V. This means that for the reaction $Zn(s) + Pb^{2+}(0.01\text{ M}) \longrightarrow Zn^{2+}(0.10\text{ M}) + Pb(s)$, E_{cell} equals **(a)** 0.72 V; **(b)** 0.69 V; **(c)** 0.66 V; **(d)** 0.63 V.

114. For the reaction $Co(s) + Ni^{2+}(aq) \longrightarrow Co^{2+}(aq) + Ni(s)$, $E°_{cell} = 0.03$ V. If cobalt metal is added to an aqueous solution in which $[Ni^{2+}] = 1.0$ M, **(a)** the reaction will not proceed in the forward direction at all; **(b)** the displacement of Ni(s) from the $Ni^{2+}(aq)$ will go to completion; **(c)** the displacement of Ni(s) from the solution will proceed to a considerable extent, but the reaction will not go to completion; **(d)** there is no way to predict how far the reaction will proceed.

115. The gas evolved at the *anode* when $K_2SO_4(aq)$ is electrolyzed between Pt electrodes is most likely to be **(a)** O_2; **(b)** H_2; **(c)** SO_2; **(d)** SO_3; **(e)** a mixture of sulfur oxides.

116. The quantity of electric charge that will deposit 4.5 g Al at a cathode will also produce the following volume at STP of $H_2(g)$ from $H^+(aq)$ at a cathode: **(a)** 44.8 L; **(b)** 22.4 L; **(c)** 11.2 L; **(d)** 5.6 L.

117. If a chemical reaction is carried out in a fuel cell, the maximum amount of useful work that can be obtained is **(a)** ΔG; **(b)** ΔH; **(c)** $\Delta G/\Delta H$; **(d)** $T\,\Delta S$.

118. For the reaction $Zn(s) + H^+(aq) + NO_3^-(aq) \longrightarrow Zn^{2+}(aq) + H_2O(l) + NO(g)$, describe the voltaic cell in which it occurs, label the anode and cathode, use a table of standard electrode potentials to evaluate E°_{cell}, and balance the equation for the cell reaction.

119. The following voltaic cell registers an $E_{cell} = 0.108$ V. What is the pH of the unknown solution?

$$\text{Pt}|\text{H}_2(\text{g}, 1\text{ atm})|\text{H}^+(x\text{ M})||\text{H}^+(1.00\text{ M})|\text{H}_2(\text{g}, 1\text{ atm})|\text{Pt}$$

120. $E^\circ_{cell} = -0.0050$ V for the reaction, $2\,Cu^+(aq) + Sn^{4+}(aq) \longrightarrow 2\,Cu^{2+}(aq) + Sn^{2+}(aq)$.
(a) Can a solution be prepared that is 0.500 M in each of the four ions at 298 K?
(b) If not, in what direction must a net reaction occur?

121. For each of the following combinations of electrodes (A and B) and solutions, indicate
- the overall cell reaction
- the direction in which electrons flow spontaneously (from A to B, or from B to A)
- the magnitude of the voltage read on the voltmeter, V

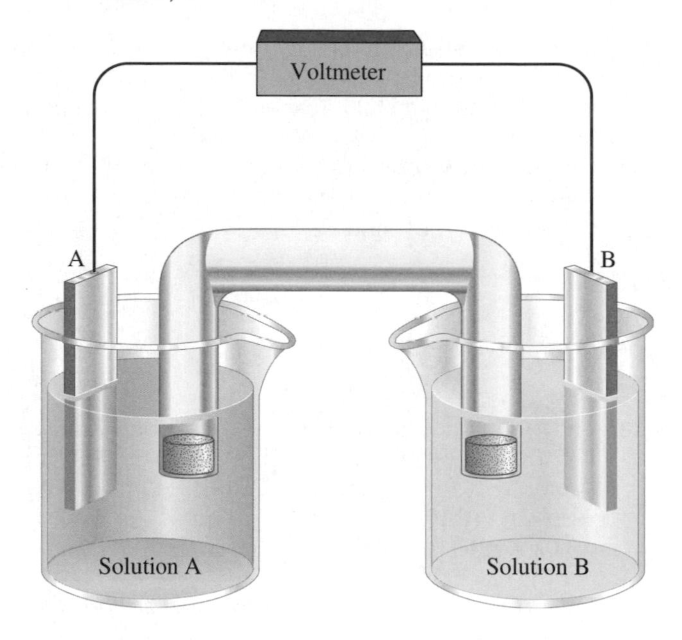

	A	Solution A	B	Solution B
(a)	Cu	1.0 M Cu^{2+}	Fe	1.0 M Fe^{2+}
(b)	Pt	1.0 M Sn^{2+}/1.0 M Sn^{4+}	Ag	1.0 M Ag^+
(c)	Zn	0.10 M Zn^{2+}	Fe	1.0×10^{-3} M Fe^{2+}

122. Use data from Table 7.1, as necessary, to predict the probable products when Pt electrodes are used in the electrolysis of **(a)** $CuCl_2(aq)$; **(b)** $Na_2SO_4(aq)$; **(c)** $BaCl_2(l)$; **(d)** KOH(aq).

123. Construct a concept map showing the relationship between electrochemical cells and thermodynamic properties.

124. Construct a concept map illustrating the relationship between batteries and electrochemical ideas.

125. Construct a concept map illustrating the principles of electrolysis and its industrial applications.

8

Acids and Bases

Citrus fruit derives its acidic qualities from citric acid, $H_3C_6H_5O_7$, a type of acid (polyprotic) discussed in Section 8-6. Another important constituent of citrus fruit is ascorbic acid, or vitamin C, a dietary requirement to prevent scurvy.

CONTENTS

The general public is familiar with the concepts of acids and bases. The environmental problem of acid rain is a popular topic in newspapers and magazines, and television commercials mention pH in relation to such products as deodorants, shampoos, and antacids.

Chemists have been classifying substances as acids and bases for a long time. Antoine Lavoisier thought that the common element in all acids was oxygen, a fact conveyed by its name. (*Oxygen* means "acid former" in Greek). In 1810, Humphry Davy showed that hydrogen instead is the element that acids have in common. In 1884, Svante Arrhenius developed the theory of acids and bases. There we emphasized the stoichiometry of acid–base reactions.

Some of the topics we will study in this chapter are modern acid–base theories, factors affecting the strengths of acids and bases, the pH scale, and the calculation of ion concentrations in solutions of weak acids and bases.

▶ Descriptions of acids and bases become more general, less restrictive, as we move from the Arrhenius theory, to the Brønsted–Lowry theory, to the Lewis theory.

8-1 Arrhenius Theory: A Brief Review

Some aspects of the behavior of acids and bases can be explained adequately with the theory developed by Arrhenius as part of his studies of electrolytic dissociation. Arrhenius proposed that in aqueous solutions, strong electrolytes exist only in the form of ions, whereas weak electrolytes exist partly as ions and partly as molecules. When the acid HCl dissolves in water, the HCl molecules ionize completely, yielding hydrogen ions, H^+, as one of the products.

$$\text{HCl} \xrightarrow{\text{H}_2\text{O}} \text{HCl(aq)} \rightarrow \text{H}^+\text{(aq)} + \text{Cl}^-\text{(aq)}$$

When the base NaOH dissolves in water, the Na^+ and OH^- ions in the solid become dissociated from one another through the action of H_2O molecules.

$$\text{NaOH(s)} \xrightarrow{\text{H}_2\text{O}} \text{Na}^+\text{(aq)} + \text{OH}^-\text{(aq)}$$

The neutralization reaction of HCl and NaOH can be represented with the ionic equation

$$\underset{\text{An acid}}{\text{H}^+\text{(aq)} + \text{Cl}^-\text{(aq)}} + \underset{\text{A base}}{\text{Na}^+\text{(aq)} + \text{OH}^-\text{(aq)}} \longrightarrow \underset{\text{A salt}}{\text{Na}^+\text{(aq)} + \text{Cl}^-\text{(aq)}} + \underset{\text{Water}}{\text{H}_2\text{O(l)}}$$

or, perhaps better still, with the net ionic equation

$$\underset{\text{An acid}}{\text{H}^+\text{(aq)}} + \underset{\text{A base}}{\text{OH}^-\text{(aq)}} \longrightarrow \underset{\text{Water}}{\text{H}_2\text{O(l)}} \tag{8.1}$$

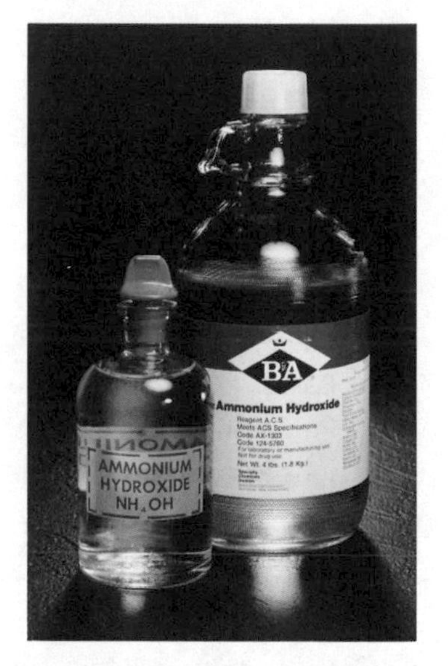

▲ A holdover of the Arrhenius theory. Although there is no compelling evidence that NH_4OH molecules exist in NH_3(aq), solutions are commonly labeled as if they do.

Equation (8.1) illustrates an essential idea of the Arrhenius theory: *A neutralization reaction involves the combination of hydrogen ions and hydroxide ions to form water.*

Despite its early successes and continued usefulness, the Arrhenius theory does have limitations. One of the most glaring is in its treatment of the weak base ammonia, NH_3. The Arrhenius theory suggests that all bases contain OH^-. Where is the OH^- in NH_3? To get around this difficulty, chemists began to think of aqueous solutions of NH_3 as containing the compound ammonium hydroxide, NH_4OH, which as a weak base is partially ionized into $NH_4{}^+$ and OH^- ions:

$$\text{NH}_3\text{(g)} + \text{H}_2\text{O(l)} \longrightarrow \text{NH}_4\text{OH(aq)}$$
$$\text{NH}_4\text{OH(aq)} \rightleftharpoons \text{NH}_4{}^+\text{(aq)} + \text{OH}^-\text{(aq)}$$

The problem with this formulation is that there is no compelling evidence that NH_4OH exists in aqueous solutions. We should always question a hypothesis or theory that postulates the existence of hypothetical substances. As we will see in Section 8-2, the essential failure of the Arrhenius theory is in not recognizing the key role of the *solvent* in the ionization of a solute.

8-2 Brønsted–Lowry Theory of Acids and Bases

KEEP IN MIND

that a "proton donor" is a donor of H^+ ions. That is, a hydrogen atom consists of one proton and one electron, and the hydrogen ion, H^+, is simply a proton.

In 1923, J. N. Brønsted in Denmark and T. M. Lowry in Great Britain independently proposed a new acid–base theory. According to their theory, an acid is a **proton donor** and a base is a **proton acceptor**. To describe the behavior of ammonia as a base, which we found difficult to do with the Arrhenius theory, we can write

$$\underset{\text{Base}}{\text{NH}_3} + \underset{\text{Acid}}{\text{H}_2\text{O}} \longrightarrow \text{NH}_4{}^+ + \text{OH}^- \tag{8.2}$$

In reaction (8.2), H_2O acts as an *acid*. It gives up a proton, H^+, which is taken up by NH_3, a *base*. As a result of this transfer, the polyatomic ions $NH_4{}^+$ and OH^- are formed—the same ions produced by the ionization of the hypothetical

NH_4OH of the Arrhenius theory. Because NH_3 is a weak base, we need also to consider the reverse of reaction (8.2). In the reverse reaction, NH_4^+ is an acid and OH^- is a base.

$$\underset{\text{Acid}}{NH_4^+} + \underset{\text{Base}}{OH^-} \longrightarrow NH_3 + H_2O \qquad (8.3)$$

◀ Brønsted–Lowry theory is not restricted to the dissociation of acids and bases in water, but is valid for any solvent.

The conventional way to represent a reversible reaction is to use the double arrow notation. In identifying the species in this reversible ionization reaction, we have used the number "1" for the related pair NH_3 and NH_4^+ and the number "2" for the related pair H_2O and OH^-.

$$\underset{\text{Base(1)}}{NH_3} + \underset{\text{Acid(2)}}{H_2O} \rightleftharpoons \underset{\text{Acid(1)}}{NH_4^+} + \underset{\text{Base(2)}}{OH^-} \qquad (8.4)$$

An acid and a base that are related to each other as the pair NH_3/NH_4^+ or the pair H_2O/OH^- in reaction (8.4) are referred to as a *conjugate pair*. Thus, when considering an NH_3 molecule as a base, an NH_4^+ ion is the **conjugate acid** of NH_3. Similarly, in reaction (8.4) H_2O is an acid and OH^- is its **conjugate base**. Figure 8-1 illustrates the proton transfer involved in the forward and reverse reactions of (8.4).

KEEP IN MIND

that in designating conjugate pairs, it does not matter which conjugate pair we call (1) and which we call (2). Nor does it matter in what order the acid and base are written on each side of the equation.

We might write as the equilibrium constant expression for reaction (8.4)

$$K = \frac{a_{NH_4^+} a_{OH^-}}{a_{NH_3} a_{H_2O}}$$

In an aqueous solution the activities of NH_4^+, OH^-, and NH_3 are approximately equal to $[NH_4^+]$, $[OH^-]$, and $[NH_3]$, respectively. The expression above can be written as

$$K = \frac{[NH_4^+][OH^-]}{[NH_3]} = 1.8 \times 10^{-5} = K_b$$

The equilibrium constant K_b is called the **base ionization constant**.

The ionization of acetic acid can be expressed as

$$\underset{\text{Acid(1)}}{CH_3COOH} + \underset{\text{Base(2)}}{H_2O} \rightleftharpoons \underset{\text{Base(1)}}{CH_3COO^-} + \underset{\text{Acid(2)}}{H_3O^+}$$

Here, acetate ion, CH_3COO^-, is the conjugate base of the acid CH_3COOH. This time, H_2O acts as a base. Its conjugate acid is the **hydronium ion, H_3O^+**. We first

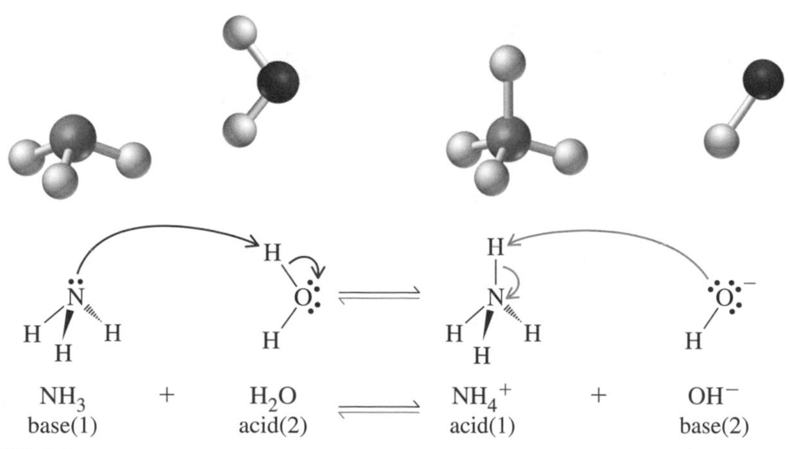

▲ FIGURE 8-1
Brønsted–Lowry acid–base reaction: weak base
The curved arrows summarize our visualization of how electrons flow to form and break bonds. The red arrows represent the forward reaction; the blue arrows, the reverse reaction. Because NH_4^+ is a stronger acid than H_2O and OH^- is a stronger base than NH_3, the reverse reaction proceeds to a greater extent than does the forward reaction. Hence, NH_3 is only slightly ionized.

discussed the formation of the hydronium ion in Chapter 1. Because the simple H^+ ion is tiny, the positive charge of this ion is concentrated in a very small region; the ion has a high positive charge density. We should expect H^+ ions (protons) to seek out centers of negative charge with which to bond. When a H^+ ion attaches to a lone pair of electrons in an O atom in H_2O, the resulting hydronium ion forms hydrogen bonds with several water molecules (Fig. 8-2). Figure 8-3 illustrates the proton transfer involved in the forward and reverse reactions of the ionization of acetic acid.

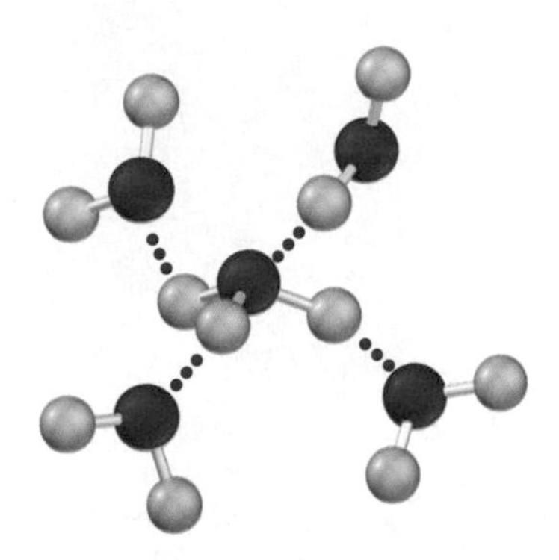

▲ FIGURE 8-2
A hydrated hydronium ion
This species, $H_{11}O_5^+$, consists of a central H_3O^+ ion hydrogen-bonded to four H_2O molecules.

Using the same approach as for $NH_3(aq)$, the ionization of acetic acid can be described in the following way.

$$K_a = \frac{[CH_3COO^-][H_3O^+]}{[CH_3COOH]} = 1.8 \times 10^{-5}$$

The equilibrium constant K_a is called the **acid ionization constant**. (The fact that K_a of acetic acid and K_b of ammonia have the same value is just a coincidence.)

We can represent the ionization of HCl in the same way that we did for acetic acid. In this case, however, because K_a is so large (about 10^6), we can treat the ionization of HCl as a reaction that goes to completion. We denote this by writing the ionization equation with a single arrow.

$$HCl + H_2O \longrightarrow Cl^- + H_3O^+ \quad \textbf{(8.5)}$$

Figure 8-4 illustrates the proton transfer involved in the complete ionization of hydrochloric acid.

In Example 8-1, we identify acids and bases in some typical acid–base reactions. In working through this example, notice the following additional features: (1) Any species that is an acid according to the Arrhenius theory is also an acid according to the Brønsted–Lowry theory; the same is true of bases. (2) Certain species, even though they do not contain the OH group, produce OH^- in aqueous solution—for example, OCl^-. As such, they are Brønsted–Lowry bases. (3) The Brønsted–Lowry theory accounts for substances that can act either as an acid or a base; such substances are said to be **amphiprotic**. The Arrhenius theory does not account for the behavior of amphiprotic substances.

▶ The term *amphiprotic* is similar to the term *amphoteric,* which indicates the ability of a substance to behave as both an acid and a base. Amphiprotic conveys the notion of proton transfer embodied in the Brønsted–Lowry theory of acids and bases.

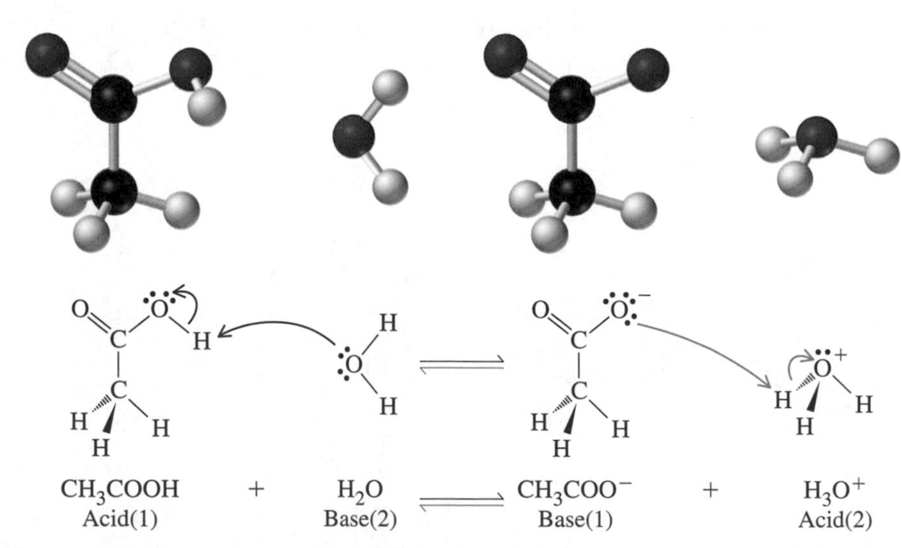

▲ FIGURE 8-3
Brønsted–Lowry acid–base reaction: weak acid
The arrows represent the proton transfer in the ionization of acetic acid. The red arrows represent the forward reaction; the blue arrows, the reverse reaction. Because H_3O^+ is a stronger acid than CH_3COOH and CH_3COO^- is a stronger base than H_2O, the reverse reaction proceeds to a greater extent than does the forward reaction. Hence, CH_3COOH is only slightly ionized.

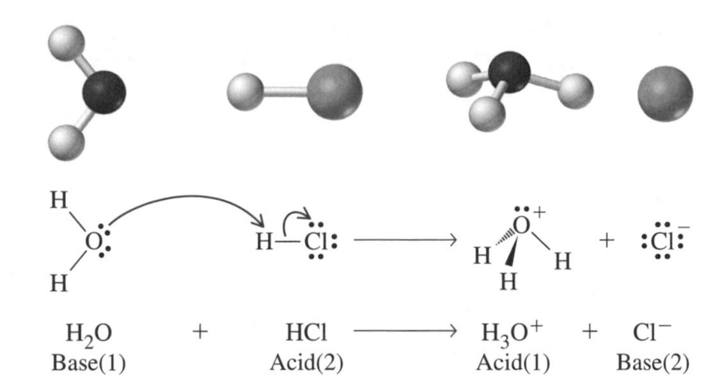

◀ FIGURE 8-4
Brønsted–Lowry acid–base reaction: strong acid
The red arrows represent the proton transfer in the ionization of hydrochloric acid. Because H_3O^+ is a weaker acid than HCl and Cl^- is a much weaker base than H_2O, the forward reaction proceeds almost to completion. Hence, HCl is essentially completely ionized.

EXAMPLE 8-1 Identifying Brønsted–Lowry Acids and Bases and Their Conjugates

For each of the following, identify the acids and bases in both the forward and reverse reactions in the manner shown in equation (8.4).

(a) $HClO_2 + H_2O \rightleftharpoons ClO_2^- + H_3O^+$
(b) $OCl^- + H_2O \rightleftharpoons HOCl + OH^-$
(c) $NH_3 + H_2PO_4^- \rightleftharpoons NH_4^+ + HPO_4^{2-}$
(d) $HCl + H_2PO_4^- \rightleftharpoons Cl^- + H_3PO_4$

Analyze

Recall that a Brønsted–Lowry acid is one that gives up a proton and a Brønsted–Lowry base is one that takes a proton. Consider $HClO_2$ in reaction (a). It gives up a proton, H^+, to become ClO_2^-. Therefore, $HClO_2$ is an acid, and ClO_2^- is its conjugate base. Now consider H_2O. It takes the proton from $HClO_2$ and becomes H_3O^+. Thus, H_2O is a base, and H_3O^+ is its conjugate acid. In reaction (b), OCl^- is a base and gains a proton from water. OH^- produced in this reaction is the conjugate base of H_2O.

Solve

(a) $HClO_2 + H_2O \rightleftharpoons ClO_2^- + H_3O^+$
Acid(1) Base(2) Base(1) Acid(2)

(b) $OCl^- + H_2O \rightleftharpoons HOCl + OH^-$
Base(1) Acid(2) Acid(1) Base(2)

(c) $NH_3 + H_2PO_4^- \rightleftharpoons NH_4^+ + HPO_4^{2-}$
Base(1) Acid(2) Acid(1) Base(2)

(d) $HCl + H_2PO_4^- \rightleftharpoons Cl^- + H_3PO_4$
Acid(1) Base(2) Base(1) Acid(2)

Assess

Notice that in (c), $H_2PO_4^-$ is acting as an acid but in (d), it is acting as a base. The conjugate base of $H_2PO_4^-$ is HPO_4^{2-} (the deprotonated form of $H_2PO_4^-$), and the conjugate acid of $H_2PO_4^-$ is H_3PO_4 (the protonated form of $H_2PO_4^-$). This is an example of the general rule that in a conjugate pair, the acid is the protonated form and the base is the deprotonated form.

PRACTICE EXAMPLE A: For each of the following reactions, identify the acids and bases in both the forward and reverse directions.

(a) $HF + H_2O \rightleftharpoons F^- + H_3O^+$
(b) $HSO_4^- + NH_3 \rightleftharpoons SO_4^{2-} + NH_4^+$
(c) $CH_3COO^- + HCl \rightleftharpoons CH_3COOH + Cl^-$

PRACTICE EXAMPLE B: Of the following species, one is acidic, one is basic, and one is amphiprotic in their reactions with water: HNO_2, PO_4^{3-}, HCO_3^-. Write the *four* equations needed to represent these facts.

8-1 CONCEPT ASSESSMENT

Is it appropriate to describe each of the following as a conjugate acid–base pair? Explain. **(a)** HCO_3^-–CO_3^{2-}; **(b)** HSO_3^-–SO_4^{2-}; **(c)** H_2CO_3–$H_2C_2O_4$; **(d)** HClO–ClO^-; **(e)** H_2S–S^{2-}.

The ionization of HCl in aqueous solution (reaction 8.5) goes to completion because HCl is a strong acid; it readily gives up protons to H_2O. At the same time, Cl^- ion, the conjugate base of HCl, has very little tendency to take a proton from H_3O^+; Cl^- is a very weak base. This observation suggests the generalization that follows.

> In an acid–base reaction, the favored direction of the reaction is from the stronger to the weaker member of a conjugate acid–base pair.

With this generalization, we can predict that the neutralization of HCl by OH^- should go to completion.

$$\underset{\substack{\text{Acid(1)}\\\text{strong}}}{HCl} + \underset{\substack{\text{Base(2)}\\\text{strong}}}{OH^-} \longrightarrow \underset{\substack{\text{Base(1)}\\\text{weak}}}{Cl^-} + \underset{\substack{\text{Acid(2)}\\\text{weak}}}{H_2O}$$

And we would predict that the following reaction should occur almost exclusively in the *reverse* direction.

$$\underset{\substack{\text{Acid(1)}\\\text{weak}}}{H_2O} + \underset{\substack{\text{Base(2)}\\\text{weak}}}{I^-} \longleftarrow \underset{\substack{\text{Base(1)}\\\text{strong}}}{OH^-} + \underset{\substack{\text{Acid(2)}\\\text{strong}}}{HI}$$

▶ The acid–base strengths listed in Table 8.1 are the result of experiments carried out by many chemists.

To be able to apply the generalization more broadly, though, we need a tabulation of acid and base strengths, such as that in Table 8.1. The strongest acids are at the top of the column on the left, and the strongest bases are at the

TABLE 8.1 Relative Strengths of Some Common Brønsted–Lowry Acids and Bases

Acid		Conjugate Base	
Perchloric acid	$HClO_4$	Perchlorate ion	ClO_4^-
Hydroiodic acid	HI	Iodide ion	I^-
Hydrobromic acid	HBr	Bromide ion	Br^-
Hydrochloric acid	HCl	Chloride ion	Cl^-
Sulfuric acid	H_2SO_4	Hydrogen sulfate ion	HSO_4^-
Nitric acid	HNO_3	Nitrate ion	NO_3^-
Hydronium ion[a]	H_3O^+	Water[a]	H_2O
Hydrogen sulfate ion	HSO_4^-	Sulfate ion	SO_4^{2-}
Nitrous acid	HNO_2	Nitrite ion	NO_2^-
Acetic acid	CH_3COOH	Acetate ion	CH_3COO^-
Carbonic acid	H_2CO_3	Hydrogen carbonate ion	HCO_3^-
Ammonium ion	NH_4^+	Ammonia	NH_3
Hydrogen carbonate ion	HCO_3^-	Carbonate ion	CO_3^{2-}
Water	H_2O	Hydroxide ion	OH^-
Methanol	CH_3OH	Methoxide ion	CH_3O^-
Ammonia	NH_3	Amide ion	NH_2^-

(Arrow on acids: Increasing acid strength, upward. Arrow on bases: Increasing base strength, downward.)

[a]The hydronium ion–water combination refers to the ease with which a proton is passed from one water molecule to another; that is, $H_3O^+ + H_2O \rightleftharpoons H_2O + H_3O^+$.

bottom of the column on the right. It is important to note that *the stronger an acid, the weaker its conjugate base.*

Both HCl and $HClO_4$ are strong acids because H_2O is a sufficiently strong base to take protons from either acid in a reaction that goes to completion. Because both HCl and $HClO_4$ react to completion with water, yielding H_3O^+ (the strongest acid possible in water), the solvent water is said to have a *leveling effect* on these two acids. How can we ascertain that $HClO_4$ is a stronger acid than HCl as we indicate in Table 8.1?

To determine whether $HClO_4$ or HCl is the stronger acid, we need to use a solvent that is a weaker base than water—a solvent that will take protons from the stronger of the two acids more readily than from the weaker one. In the solvent $(C_2H_5)_2O$, diethyl ether, $HClO_4$ is completely ionized, but HCl is only partially ionized. Thus, $HClO_4$ is a stronger acid than is HCl, and ClO_4^- is a weaker base than Cl^-.

$$HClO_4 + C_2H_5-\ddot{\underset{\cdot\cdot}{O}}-C_2H_5 \longrightarrow ClO_4^- + C_2H_5-\underset{\cdot\cdot}{\overset{H}{\overset{|}{O^+}}}-C_2H_5$$

$$HCl + C_2H_5-\ddot{\underset{\cdot\cdot}{O}}-C_2H_5 \rightleftharpoons Cl^- + C_2H_5-\underset{\cdot\cdot}{\overset{H}{\overset{|}{O^+}}}-C_2H_5$$

8-3 Self-Ionization of Water and the pH Scale

Even when it is pure, water contains a very low concentration of ions that can be detected in precise electrical conductivity measurements. The ions form as a result of the amphiprotic nature of water; some water molecules donate protons and others accept protons. In the **self-ionization** (or *autoionization*) of water, for each H_2O molecule that acts as an acid, another H_2O molecule acts as a base, and hydronium (H_3O^+) and hydroxide (OH^-) ions are formed. The reaction is reversible, and in the reverse reaction, H_3O^+ releases a proton to OH^-. The reverse reaction is far more significant than the forward reaction. *Equilibrium is displaced far to the left*. In reaction (8.6), acid(1) and base(2) are *much* stronger than are acid(2) and base(1).

$$\underset{\text{Base(1)}}{H-\ddot{\underset{\cdot\cdot}{O}}:} + \underset{\text{Acid(2)}}{H-\ddot{\underset{\cdot\cdot}{O}}-H} \rightleftharpoons \underset{\text{Acid(1)}}{H_3O^+} + \underset{\text{Base(2)}}{:\ddot{\underset{\cdot\cdot}{O}}-H^-} \quad (8.6)$$

Again, we follow the approach we used in writing equilibrium constants for the ionization of NH_3 and CH_3COOH, namely we assume an activity of one for H_2O molecules and replace activities of other species by their molarities. For the self-ionization of water

$$H_2O + H_2O \rightleftharpoons H_3O^+ + OH^-$$

we can write

$$K = [H_3O^+][OH^-]$$

Equation (8.6) indicates that $[H_3O^+]$ and $[OH^-]$ are equal in pure water. There are several experimental methods of determining these concentrations. All lead to this result.

$$\textit{At 25 °C in pure water:} \quad [H_3O^+] = [OH^-] = 1.0 \times 10^{-7}\,M$$

◀ A common misconception is that K_w is K_c for the self-ionization reaction. Strictly speaking, it is the ionic product. The equilibrium constant $K_c = [H_3O^+][OH^-]/[H_2O]$ has the value of $10^{-14}/55.55 = 1.8 \times 10^{-16}$ at 25 °C. We see that

$$K = (a_{H_3O^+})(a_{OH^-})/(a_{H_2O})^2 = 1.0 \times 10^{-14}$$

The equilibrium condition for the self-ionization of water is called the **ion product of water**. It is symbolized as K_w. At 25 °C,

$$K_w = [H_3O^+][OH^-] = 1.0 \times 10^{-14} \qquad (8.7)$$

Since K_w is an equilibrium constant, the product of the concentrations of the hydronium and hydroxide ions must always equal 10^{-14}. If the concentration of H_3O^+ is increased by the addition of an acid, then the concentration of OH^- must decrease to maintain the value of K_w. If the concentration of OH^- is increased by the addition of a base, then the concentration of H_3O^+ must decrease. Equation (8.7) connects the concentrations of H_3O^+ and OH^- and applies to *all* aqueous solutions, not just to pure water, as we shall see shortly.

pH and pOH

Because their product in an aqueous solution is only 1.0×10^{-14}, we expect $[H_3O^+]$ and $[OH^-]$ also to be small. Typically, they are less than 1 M—often very much less. Exponential notation is useful in these situations; for example, $[H_3O^+] = 2.2 \times 10^{-13}$ M. But we now want to consider an even more convenient way to describe hydronium and hydroxide ion concentrations.

In 1909, the Danish biochemist Søren Sørensen proposed the term **pH** to refer to the "potential of hydrogen ion." He defined pH as the *negative of the logarithm of* $[H^+]$. Restated in terms of $[H_3O^+]$,*

KEEP IN MIND

that this definition of pH is one of the few scientific expressions that uses logarithms to the base 10 (log) rather than natural logarithms (ln).

$$pH = -\log[H_3O^+] \qquad (8.8)$$

Thus, in a solution that is 0.0025 M HCl,

$$[H_3O^+] = 2.5 \times 10^{-3}\ M \quad \text{and} \quad pH = -\log(2.5 \times 10^{-3}) = 2.60$$

To determine the $[H_3O^+]$ that corresponds to a particular pH value, we do an inverse calculation. In a solution with pH = 4.50,

$$\log[H_3O^+] = -4.50 \quad \text{and} \quad [H_3O^+] = 10^{-4.50} = 3.2 \times 10^{-5}\ M$$

The quantity **pOH** can be defined as

$$pOH = -\log[OH^-] \qquad (8.9)$$

Still another useful expression can be derived by taking the *negative logarithm* of the K_w expression (written for 25 °C) and introducing the symbol pK_w.

$$\begin{aligned} K_w &= [H_3O^+][OH^-] = 1.0 \times 10^{-14} \\ -\log K_w &= -(\log[H_3O^+][OH^-]) = -\log(1.0 \times 10^{-14}) \\ pK_w &= -(\log[H_3O^+] + \log[OH^-]) = -(-14.00) \\ &= -\log[H_3O^+] - \log[OH^-] = 14.00 \end{aligned}$$

$$pK_w = pH + pOH = 14.00 \qquad (8.10)$$

*Strictly speaking, we should use the *activity* of H_3O^+, $a_{H_3O^+}$, a dimensionless quantity. But we will not use activities here. We will substitute the numerical value of the molarity of H_3O^+ for its activity and recognize that some pH calculations may be only approximations.

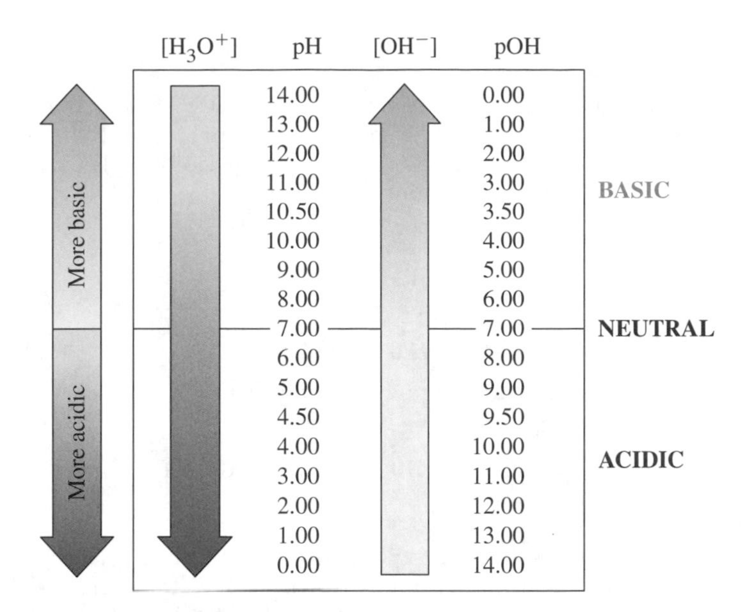

▲ FIGURE 8-5
Relating $[H_3O^+]$, pH, $[OH^-]$, and pOH
In aqueous solutions, the sum of the pH and pOH values always gives $pK_w = 14$ because of the self-ionization equilibrium of water.

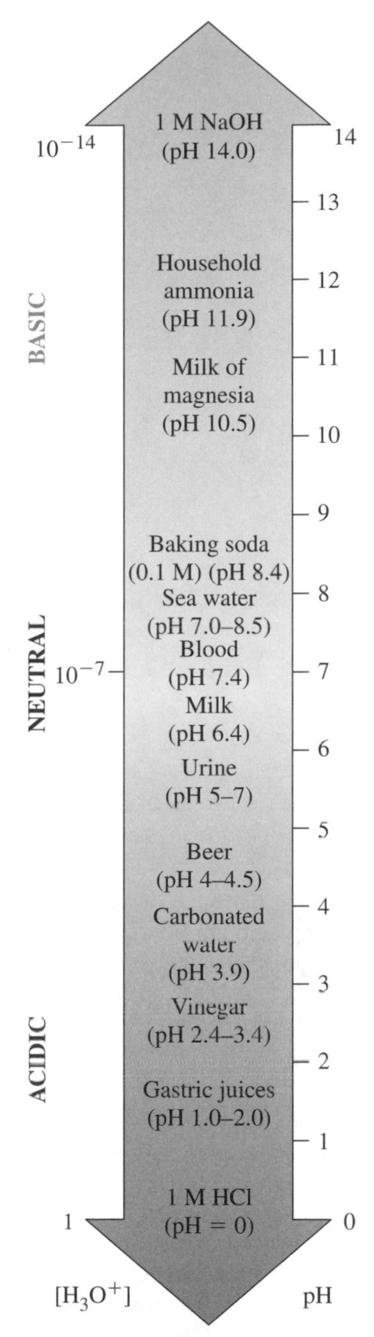

▲ FIGURE 8-6
The pH scale and pH values of some common materials
The scale shown here ranges from pH 0 to pH 14. Slightly negative pH values, perhaps to about −1 (corresponding to $[H_3O^+] \approx 10$ M), are possible. Also possible are pH values up to about 15 (corresponding to $[OH^-] \approx 10$ M). For practical purposes, however, the pH scale is useful only in the range $2 < \text{pH} < 12$, because the molarities of H_3O^+ and OH^- in concentrated acids and bases may differ significantly from their true activities.

An aqueous solution with $[H_3O^+] = [OH^-]$ is said to be *neutral*. In pure water at 25 °C, $[H_3O^+] = [OH^-] = 1.0 \times 10^{-7}$ M and pH = 7.00. Thus at 25 °C, all aqueous solutions with pH = 7.00 are neutral. If the pH is less than 7.00, the solution is *acidic*; if the pH is greater than 7.00, the solution is *basic*, or alkaline. Equation 8.10 is a restatement of the interrelationship between $[H_3O^+]$, $[OH^-]$, and K_w in terms of pH, pOH, and pK_w. If we know the value of either $[H_3O^+]$ or $[OH^-]$, we can calculate the value of the other (Fig. 8-5).

8-2 CONCEPT ASSESSMENT

Figure 8-5 indicates that pH and pOH *decrease* as $[H^+]$ and $[OH^-]$ increase. If pH and pOH were defined as $\text{pH} = \log[H_3O^+]$ and $\text{pOH} = \log[OH^-]$, pH and pOH would *increase* as $[H^+]$ and $[OH^-]$ increase. Why do you suppose that this alternate definition was not adopted? Logarithmic functions appear frequently in chemistry (for example, in chemical kinetics and thermodynamics), but these are based on natural logarithms, ln. Why do you suppose that the definitions $\text{pH} = -\ln[H_3O^+]$ and $\text{pOH} = -\ln[OH^-]$ were not adopted?

The pH values of a number of materials are depicted in Figure 8-6. These values and the many examples in this chapter and the next should familiarize you with the pH concept. Later, we will consider two methods for measuring pH: by means of acid–base indicators and electrical measurements.

EXAMPLE 8-2 Relating $[H_3O^+]$, $[OH^-]$, pH, and pOH

In a laboratory experiment, students measured the pH of samples of rainwater and household ammonia. Determine **(a)** $[H_3O^+]$ in the rainwater, with pH measured at 4.35; **(b)** $[OH^-]$ in the ammonia, with pH measured at 11.28.

(continued)

Analyze

In this example we use the definition $pH = -\log[H_3O^+]$. For pOH we first determine pOH by using $pOH = 14 - pH$, and then by using $pOH = -\log[OH^-]$. To calculate concentration from a pH, we take the antilogarithm by raising 10 to minus the pH.

Solve

(a) $\log[H_3O^+] = -pH = -4.35$

$[H_3O^+] = 10^{-4.35} = 4.5 \times 10^{-5}\ M$

(b) $pOH = 14.00 - pH = 14.00 - 11.28 = 2.72$

Now, use the definition $pOH = -\log[OH^-]$.

$\log[OH^-] = -pOH = -2.72$

$[OH^-] = 10^{-2.72} = 1.9 \times 10^{-3}\ M$

Assess

The process of calculating hydronium ion concentration, $[H_3O^+]$, from pH is simply the antilogarithm of minus the pH value. To determine the concentration of $[OH^-]$ from a pH, we first calculated pOH, which is $14 - pH$, and then calculated $[OH^-]$. Be careful when working these types of problems, and keep straight what you have to determine.

PRACTICE EXAMPLE A: Students found that a yogurt sample had a pH of 2.85. What are the $[H^+]$ and $[OH^-]$ of the yogurt?

PRACTICE EXAMPLE B: The pH of a solution of HCl in water is found to be 2.50. What volume of water would you add to 1.00 L of this solution to raise the pH to 3.10?

▶ Most people consider strong acids to be more dangerous than strong bases, but strong bases can cause serious burns and should be treated with as much care as acids.

▶ The dilution of strong acids and bases is usually exothermic. Never add water to concentrated strong acids and bases (particularly sulfuric acid) as the heat of dilution will boil the water and spatter concentrated acid.

8-4 Strong Acids and Strong Bases

As equation (8.5) indicated, the ionization of HCl in dilute aqueous solutions

$$HCl + H_2O \longrightarrow Cl^- + H_3O^+$$

goes essentially to completion.* In contrast, equation (8.6) suggested that the self-ionization of water occurs only to a very slight extent. As a result, we conclude that in calculating $[H_3O^+]$ in an aqueous solution of a strong acid, the strong acid is the only significant source of H_3O^+. The contribution due to the self-ionization of water can generally be ignored *unless the solution is extremely dilute.*

EXAMPLE 8-3 Calculating Ion Concentrations in an Aqueous Solution of a Strong Acid

Calculate $[H_3O^+]$, $[Cl^-]$, and $[OH^-]$ in 0.015 M HCl(aq).

Analyze

Because HCl is a strong acid, all the HCl dissociates. The hydronium ion concentration is equal to the molarity of the solution. The hydroxide concentration is determined by using the water equilibrium because the product of the hydronium ion concentration and hydroxide concentration must equal $K_w = 1.0 \times 10^{-14}$.

*In very concentrated aqueous solutions, HCl does not exist exclusively as the separated ions H_3O^+ and Cl^-. One indication of this is that we can smell HCl in the vapor above such solutions.

Solve

Therefore,

$$[H_3O^+] = 0.015\,M$$

Because one Cl^- ion is produced for every H_3O^+ ion,

$$[Cl^-] = [H_3O^+] = 0.015\,M$$

To calculate $[OH^-]$, we must use the following facts.

1. All the OH^- is derived from the self-ionization of water, by reaction (8.6).
2. $[OH^-]$ and $[H_3O^+]$ must have values consistent with K_w for water.

$$K_w = [H_3O^+][OH^-] = 1.0 \times 10^{-14}$$

So we have

$$[OH^-] = \frac{1.0 \times 10^{-14}}{1.5 \times 10^{-2}} = 6.7 \times 10^{-13}\,M$$

Assess

The self-ionization of water contributes equal amounts of OH^- and H_3O^+ to the solution. The results of this example show that the self-ionization of water contributes only a small amount (6.7×10^{-13} M) of OH^- and H_3O^+. The self-ionization of water usually, but not always, plays a very minor role in determining the pH of a solution.

PRACTICE EXAMPLE A: A 0.0025 M solution of HI(aq) has $[H_3O^+] = 0.0025$ M. Calculate $[I^-]$, $[OH^-]$, and the pH of the solution.

PRACTICE EXAMPLE B: If 535 mL of *gaseous* HCl, at 26.5 °C and 747 mmHg, is dissolved in enough water to prepare 625 mL of solution, what is the pH of this solution?

The common strong bases are ionic hydroxides. When these bases dissolve in water, H_2O molecules completely dissociate the cations and anions (OH^-) of the base from each other. The self-ionization of water, because it occurs to so very limited an extent, is an inconsequential source of OH^-. This means that in calculating $[OH^-]$ in an aqueous solution of a strong base, the strong base is the only significant source of OH^- *unless the solution is extremely dilute.*

The number of common strong acids and strong bases is quite small. Memorize the listing in Table 8.2.

EXAMPLE 8-4 Calculating the pH of an Aqueous Solution of a Strong Base

Calcium hydroxide (slaked lime), $Ca(OH)_2$, is the cheapest strong base available. It is generally used for industrial operations in which a high concentration of OH^- is not required. $Ca(OH)_2(s)$ is soluble in water only to the extent of 0.16 g $Ca(OH)_2$/100.0 mL solution at 25 °C. What is the pH of saturated $Ca(OH)_2(aq)$ at 25 °C?

Analyze

Because the volume of solution is not specified, let's assume it is 100.0 mL = 0.1000 L. The resulting solution will be basic, so we should focus on the hydroxide ion. To solve this problem, we first calculate the molarity of the solution, and then determine the concentration of hydroxide ion in this solution. Finally, we calculate pOH and then pH.

Solve

Express the solubility of $Ca(OH)_2$ on a molar basis.

$$\text{molarity} = \frac{0.16\,g\,Ca(OH)_2 \times \dfrac{1\,mol\,Ca(OH)_2}{74.1\,g\,Ca(OH)_2}}{0.1000\,L} = 0.022\,M\,Ca(OH)_2$$

(continued)

Relate the molarity of OH^- to the molarity of $Ca(OH)_2$.

$$[OH^-] = \frac{0.022 \text{ mol } Ca(OH)_2}{1 \text{ L}} \times \frac{2 \text{ mol } OH^-}{1 \text{ mol } Ca(OH)_2} = 0.044 \text{ M } OH^-$$

Calculate the pOH and, from it, the pH.

$$pOH = -\log[OH^-] = -\log 0.044 = 1.36$$
$$pH = 14.00 - pOH = 14.00 - 1.36 = 12.64$$

Assess

A common error is to neglect the factor 2 mol OH^-/1 mol $Ca(OH)_2$ in determining $[OH^-]$. When solving problems involving basic solutions, we often solve first for pOH. We must remember to finish the problem and convert from pOH to pH. Finally, although $Ca(OH)_2$ is a slightly soluble hydroxide salt, we observe that the pH of the solution is quite high.

PRACTICE EXAMPLE A: Milk of magnesia is a saturated solution of $Mg(OH)_2$. Its solubility is 9.63 mg $Mg(OH)_2$/100.0 mL solution at 20 °C. What is the pH of saturated $Mg(OH)_2$ at 20 °C?

PRACTICE EXAMPLE B: Calculate the pH of an aqueous solution that is 3.00% KOH, by mass, and has a density of 1.0242 g/mL.

TABLE 8.2 The Common Strong Acids and Strong Bases

Acids	Bases
HCl	LiOH
HBr	NaOH
HI	KOH
$HClO_4$	RbOH
HNO_3	CsOH
H_2SO_4[a]	$Mg(OH)_2$
	$Ca(OH)_2$
	$Sr(OH)_2$
	$Ba(OH)_2$

[a]H_2SO_4 ionizes in two distinct steps. It is a strong acid only in its first ionization (see page 330).

8-1 ARE YOU WONDERING...

How to calculate $[H_3O^+]$ in an extremely dilute solution of a strong acid?

The method of Example 8-3 won't work for calculating the pH of a solution as dilute as 1.0×10^{-8} M HCl. We would write $[H_3O^+] = 1.0 \times 10^{-8}$ M, and pH = 8.00. But how can a solution of a strong acid, no matter how dilute, have a pH greater than 7? The difficulty is that at this extreme dilution, we must consider two sources of H_3O^+. The sources of H_3O^+ and the ion concentrations from both sources are indicated as follows:

$$H_2O + H_2O \rightleftharpoons H_3O^+ + OH^-$$

Molarity: $\quad x \quad x$

$$HCl + H_2O \longrightarrow H_3O^+ + Cl^-$$

Molarity: $\quad 1.0 \times 10^{-8} \quad 1.0 \times 10^{-8}$

To satisfy the K_w expression for water in this solution, we use equation (8.7) to get

$$[H_3O^+][OH^-] = (x + 1.0 \times 10^{-8})x = 1.0 \times 10^{-14}$$

This expression rearranges to the quadratic form

$$x^2 + (1.0 \times 10^{-8}x) - (1.0 \times 10^{-14}) = 0$$

The solution to this equation is $x = 9.5 \times 10^{-8}$ M. Therefore, we combine $[H_3O^+]$ from both sources to get $[H_3O^+] = (9.5 \times 10^{-8}) + (1.0 \times 10^{-8}) = 1.05 \times 10^{-7}$ M, and pH = 6.98.

From this result, we conclude that the pH is slightly less than 7, as expected for a very dilute acid, and that the self-ionization of water contributes nearly ten times as much hydronium ion to the solution as does the strong acid.

8-5 Weak Acids and Weak Bases

Figure 8-7 illustrates two ways of showing that ionization has occurred in an aqueous solution of an acid: One is by the color of an acid–base indicator; the other, the response of a pH meter. The pink color of the solution in Figure 8-7 tells us the pH of 0.1 M HCl is *less than 1.2*. The pH meter registers a value of 1.20, about what we expect for a strong acid solution with $[H_3O^+]$ approximately equal to 0.1 M. The yellow color of the solution in Figure 8-7 indicates that the pH of 0.1 M CH_3COOH (acetic acid) is *2.8 or greater*. The pH meter registers 2.80.

So we see that two acids can have the same molarity but different pH values. The acid's molarity simply indicates what was put into the solution, but $[H_3O^+]$ and pH depend on what *happens* in the solution. In both solutions, some self-ionization of water occurs, but this reaction is negligible. Ionization of HCl, a strong acid, can be assumed to go to completion, as indicated in equation (8.5). As we previously noted, ionization of CH_3COOH, a weak acid, is a reversible reaction that reaches a condition of equilibrium.*

$$CH_3COOH + H_2O \rightleftharpoons H_3O^+ + CH_3COO^- \qquad \textbf{(8.11)}$$

The equilibrium constant expression for reaction (8.11) is

$$K_a = \frac{[H_3O^+][CH_3COO^-]}{[CH_3COOH]} = 1.8 \times 10^{-5} \qquad \textbf{(8.12)}$$

Just as pH is a convenient shorthand designation related to $[H_3O^+]$, pK is related to an equilibrium constant. That is, **p*K*** $= -\log K$. Thus, for acetic acid,

$$pK_a = -\log K_a = -\log(1.8 \times 10^{-5}) = -(-4.74) = 4.74$$

◀ Equilibrium constants (and therefore pK_a and pK_b values) vary with temperature.

As with other equilibrium constants, the larger the value of K_a (or K_b for a base), the farther the equilibrium condition lies in the direction of the forward reaction. And the more extensive the ionization, the greater are the concentrations of the ions produced. Ionization constants must be determined *by experiment*.

◀ The p$K = -\log K$ is introduced so that very large and very small numbers that arise for K can be more easily handled.

◀ Most laboratory pH meters can be read to the nearest 0.01 unit. Some pH meters for research work can be read to 0.001 unit, but unless unusual precautions are taken, the reading of the meter may not correspond to the true pH.

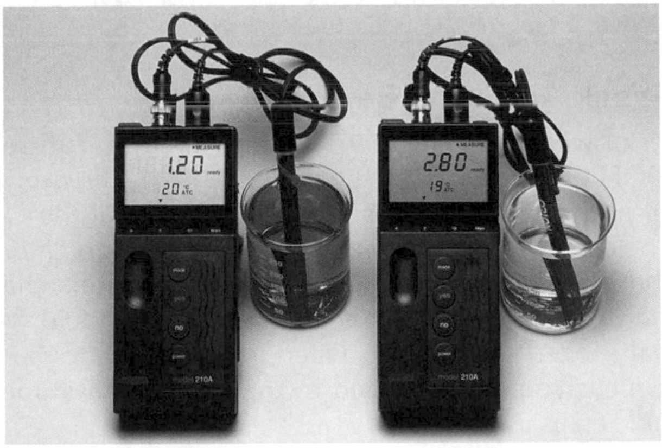

▲ FIGURE 8-7
Strong and weak acids compared
The color of thymol blue indicator, which is present in both solutions, depends on the pH of the solution.

$$\underset{\text{Red}}{\text{pH} < 1.2} < \underset{\text{Orange}}{\text{pH} < 2.8} < \underset{\text{Yellow}}{\text{pH}}$$

The principle of the pH meter is discussed in Section 20-4. (Left) 0.1 M HCl has pH ≈ 1. The pH meter shows a value of 1.20 rather than 1.00 because the molarity of the HCl solution is, in fact, slightly less than 0.1 M. (Right) 0.1 M CH_3COOH has pH ≈ 2.8.

*We have been writing ionization equations in the form: acid(1) + base(2) $\rightleftharpoons$ base(1) + acid(2). Here we have written acid(1) + base(2) $\rightleftharpoons$ acid(2) + base(1) to highlight H_3O^+, the species that is usually the subject of a calculation.

TABLE 8.3 Ionization Constants of Some Weak Acids and Weak Bases in Water at 25 °C

	Ionization Equilibrium	Ionization Constant *K*	p*K*	
Acid		$K_a =$	$pK_a =$	Acid strength (↑)
Iodic acid	$HIO_3 + H_2O \rightleftharpoons H_3O^+ + IO_3^-$	1.6×10^{-1}	0.80	
Chlorous acid	$HClO_2 + H_2O \rightleftharpoons H_3O^+ + ClO_2^-$	1.1×10^{-2}	1.96	
Chloroacetic acid	$ClCH_2COOH + H_2O \rightleftharpoons H_3O^+ + ClCH_2COO^-$	1.4×10^{-3}	2.85	
Nitrous acid	$HNO_2 + H_2O \rightleftharpoons H_3O^+ + NO_2^-$	7.2×10^{-4}	3.14	
Hydrofluoric acid	$HF + H_2O \rightleftharpoons H_3O^+ + F^-$	6.6×10^{-4}	3.18	
Formic acid	$HCOOH + H_2O \rightleftharpoons H_3O^+ + HCOO^-$	1.8×10^{-4}	3.74	
Benzoic acid	$C_6H_5COOH + H_2O \rightleftharpoons H_3O^+ + C_6H_5COO^-$	6.3×10^{-5}	4.20	
Hydrazoic acid	$HN_3 + H_2O \rightleftharpoons H_3O^+ + N_3^-$	1.9×10^{-5}	4.72	
Acetic acid	$CH_3COOH + H_2O \rightleftharpoons H_3O^+ + CH_3COO^-$	1.8×10^{-5}	4.74	
Hypochlorous acid	$HOCl + H_2O \rightleftharpoons H_3O^+ + OCl^-$	2.9×10^{-8}	7.54	
Hydrocyanic acid	$HCN + H_2O \rightleftharpoons H_3O^+ + CN^-$	6.2×10^{-10}	9.21	
Phenol	$HOC_6H_5 + H_2O \rightleftharpoons H_3O^+ + C_6H_5O^-$	1.0×10^{-10}	10.00	
Hydrogen peroxide	$H_2O_2 + H_2O \rightleftharpoons H_3O^+ + HO_2^-$	1.8×10^{-12}	11.74	
Base		$K_b =$	$pK_b =$	Base strength (↑)
Diethylamine	$(C_2H_5)_2NH + H_2O \rightleftharpoons (C_2H_5)_2NH_2^+ + OH^-$	6.9×10^{-4}	3.16	
Ethylamine	$C_2H_5NH_2 + H_2O \rightleftharpoons C_2H_5NH_3^+ + OH^-$	4.3×10^{-4}	3.37	
Ammonia	$NH_3 + H_2O \rightleftharpoons NH_4^+ + OH^-$	1.8×10^{-5}	4.74	
Hydroxylamine	$HONH_2 + H_2O \rightleftharpoons HONH_3^+ + OH^-$	9.1×10^{-9}	8.04	
Pyridine	$C_5H_5N + H_2O \rightleftharpoons C_5H_5NH^+ + OH^-$	1.5×10^{-9}	8.82	
Aniline	$C_6H_5NH_2 + H_2O \rightleftharpoons C_6H_5NH_3^+ + OH^-$	7.4×10^{-10}	9.13	

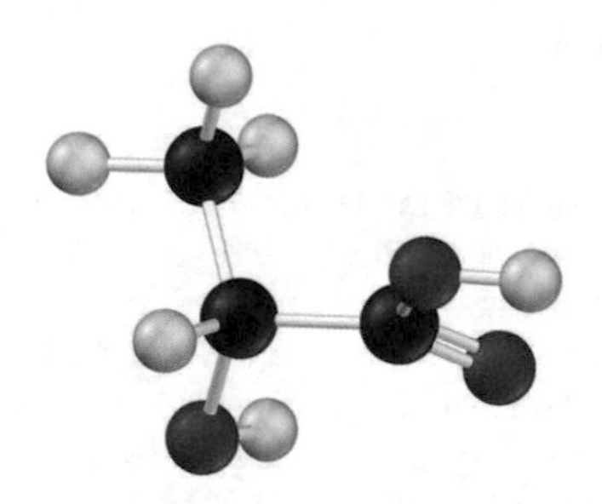

▲ Lactic acid, $CH_3CH(OH)COOH$.

A few ionization constants for weak acids and weak bases are listed in Table 8.3.

Identifying Weak Acids and Bases

A large number of weak acids have the same structural feature as acetic acid: that is, a $-COOH$ group as part of the molecule. This *carboxyl group* is a common feature of many organic acids, including such biologically important acids as lactic acid and all the amino acids, including glycine. We will use a number of carboxylic acids as examples in this and the next chapter.

In general, to distinguish a weak acid from a strong acid, you need recall only that the half-dozen strong acids listed in Table 8.2 are the most common strong acids. Unless you are informed to the contrary, assume that any acid not listed in Table 8.2 is a weak acid.

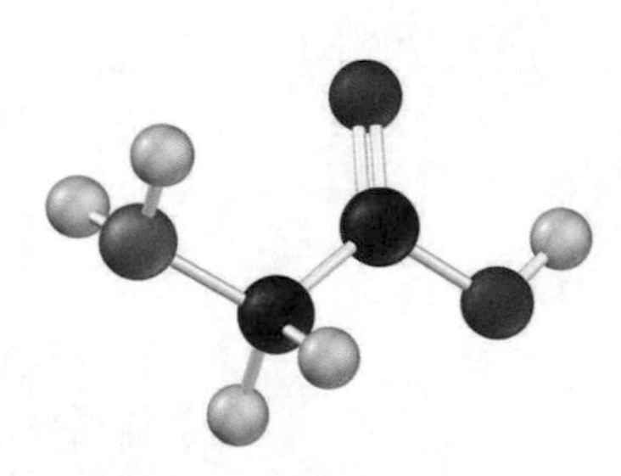

▲ Glycine, NH_2CH_2COOH.

At first glance, weak bases seem more difficult to identify than weak acids: There is no distinctive element, such as H written first in the formula. Yet, if you study the bases in Table 8.3, you will see that all but one of them (pyridine) can be viewed as an ammonia molecule in which some other group ($-C_6H_5$, $-C_2H_5$, $-OH$, or $-CH_3$) has been substituted for one of the H atoms. The substitution of a methyl group, $-CH_3$, for a H atom is suggested in the following structural formulas.

```
                       H
                       |
H—N—H              H—C—N—H
  |                    |  |
  H                    H  H
Ammonia             Methylamine
```

We can represent the ionization of methylamine in this way.

$$\underset{\text{Base}}{H_3C{-}\ddot{N}H{-}H} + \underset{\text{Acid}}{H{-}\ddot{O}{-}H} \rightleftharpoons \underset{\text{Acid}}{H_3C{-}NH_2^{+}{-}H} + \underset{\text{Base}}{H{-}\ddot{O}^{-}}$$

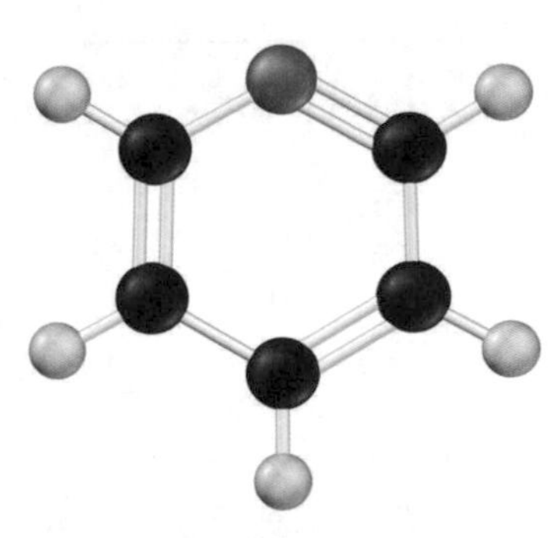
▲ Pyridine, C_5H_5N.

The ionization constant expression is

$$K_b = \frac{[CH_3NH_3^+][OH^-]}{[CH_3NH_2]} = 4.2 \times 10^{-4} \qquad \textbf{(8.13)}$$

Not all weak bases contain N. Yet, so many of them do that the similarity to NH_3 outlined here is well worth remembering. These weak bases derived from ammonia are known as *amines*.

8-3 CONCEPT ASSESSMENT

Is it possible for a weak acid solution to have a lower pH than a strong acid solution? If not, why not? If it is possible, under what conditions?

Illustrative Examples

For some students, solution equilibrium calculations are among the most challenging in general chemistry. At times, the difficulty is in sorting out what is relevant to a given problem. The number of types of calculations seems very large, although in fact it is quite limited. The key to solving solution equilibrium problems is to be able to imagine what is going on. Here are some questions to ask yourself.

- Which are the principal species in solution?
- What are the chemical reactions that produce them?
- Can some reactions (for example, the self-ionization of water) be ignored?
- Can you make any assumptions that allow you to simplify the equilibrium calculations?
- What is a reasonable answer to the problem? For instance, should the final solution be acidic ($pH < 7$) or basic ($pH > 7$)?

In short, first think through a problem *qualitatively*. At times, you may not even have to do a calculation. Next, organize the relevant data in a clear, logical manner. In this way, many problems that at first appear new to you will take on a familiar pattern. Look for other helpful hints as you proceed through this chapter and the following chapter.

Example 8-6 presents a common problem involving weak acids and weak bases: calculating the pH of a solution of known molarity. The calculation invariably involves a quadratic equation, but very often we can make a simplifying assumption that leads to a shortcut that saves both time and effort.

EXAMPLE 8-5 Determining a Value of K_a from the pH of a Solution of a Weak Acid

Butyric acid, $CH_3(CH_2)_2COOH$, is used to make compounds employed in artificial flavorings and syrups. A 0.250 M aqueous solution of butyric acid is found to have a pH of 2.72. Determine K_a for butyric acid.

$$CH_3(CH_2)_2COOH + H_2O \rightleftharpoons H_3O^+ + CH_3(CH_2)_2COO^- \qquad K_a = ?$$

▲ Butyric acid, $CH_3CH_2CH_2COOH$.

Analyze

For $CH_3(CH_2)_2COOH$, K_a is likely to be much larger than K_w. Therefore, we can assume that self-ionization of water is unimportant and that ionization of the butyric acid is the only source of H_3O^+. Let's treat the situation as if $CH_3(CH_2)_2COOH$ first dissolves in molecular form, and then the molecules ionize until equilibrium is reached. That is, we write the balanced chemical equation and use it as the basis for an ICE table, as discussed in Chapter 6. We will represent the concentrations of H_3O^+ and $CH_3(CH_2)_2COO^-$ at equilibrium as x M.

Solve

	$CH_3(CH_2)_2COOH$ + H_2O $\rightleftharpoons$	H_3O^+ +	$CH_3(CH_2)_2COO^-$
initial concns:	0.250 M	—	—
changes:	$-x$ M	$+x$ M	$+x$ M
equil concns:	$(0.250 - x)$ M	x M	x M

But x is known. It is the $[H_3O^+]$ in solution, which we can determine from the pH.

$$\log[H_3O^+] = -pH = -2.72$$
$$[H_3O^+] = 10^{-2.72} = 1.9 \times 10^{-3} = x$$

Now we can solve the following expression for K_a, substituting in the known value for x.

$$K_a = \frac{[H_3O^+][CH_3(CH_2)_2COO^-]}{[CH_3(CH_2)_2COOH]} = \frac{x \cdot x}{0.250 - x}$$
$$= \frac{(1.9 \times 10^{-3})(1.9 \times 10^{-3})}{0.250 - (1.9 \times 10^{-3})} = 1.5 \times 10^{-5}$$

Assess

Notice that our original assumption was correct: K_a is much larger than K_w.

PRACTICE EXAMPLE A: Hypochlorous acid, HOCl, is used in water treatment and as a disinfectant in swimming pools. A 0.150 M solution of HOCl has a pH of 4.18. Determine K_a for hypochlorous acid.

PRACTICE EXAMPLE B: The much-abused drug cocaine is an alkaloid. Alkaloids are noted for their bitter taste, an indication of their basic properties. Cocaine, $C_{17}H_{21}O_4N$, is soluble in water to the extent of 0.17 g/100 mL solution, and a saturated solution has a pH = 10.08. What is the value of K_b for cocaine?

$$C_{17}H_{21}O_4N + H_2O \rightleftharpoons C_{17}H_{21}O_4NH^+ + OH^- \qquad K_b = ?$$

EXAMPLE 8-6 Calculating the pH of a Weak Acid Solution

Show by calculation that the pH of 0.100 M CH_3COOH should be about the value shown on the pH meter in Figure 8-7; that is, pH $\approx$ 2.8.

Analyze

Here, we know that K_a is much larger than K_w. Let's again treat the situation as if CH_3COOH first dissolves in molecular form and then ionizes until equilibrium is reached. In this case, the quantity x is an unknown that must be obtained by an algebraic solution.

Solve

$$CH_3COOH + H_2O \rightleftharpoons H_3O^+ + CH_3COO^-$$

	CH_3COOH	H_3O^+	CH_3COO^-
initial concns:	0.100 M	—	—
changes:	$-x$ M	$+x$ M	$+x$ M
equil concns:	$(0.100 - x)$ M	x M	x M

$$K_a = \frac{[H_3O^+][CH_3COO^-]}{[CH_3COOH]} = \frac{x \cdot x}{0.100 - x} = 1.8 \times 10^{-5}$$

We could solve this equation by using the quadratic formula, but let's instead make a simplifying assumption that is often valid. Assume that x is very small compared with 0.100. That is, assume that $(0.100 - x) \approx 0.100$.

$$x^2 = 0.100 \times 1.8 \times 10^{-5} = 1.8 \times 10^{-6}$$

$$x = [H_3O^+] = \sqrt{1.8 \times 10^{-6}} = 1.3 \times 10^{-3}\,M$$

Now, we must check our assumption: $0.100 - 0.0013 = 0.099 \approx 0.100$. Our assumption is good to about 1 part per 100 (1%) and is valid for a calculation involving two or three significant figures.

Finally,

$$pH = -\log[H_3O^+] = -\log(1.3 \times 10^{-3}) = -(-2.89) = 2.89$$

Assess

We observe that our answer is very close to the number on the pH meter. Therefore, our assumption to simplify the calculation was reasonable. This type of assumption may not always work and so we need to check the final answer until we are comfortable with knowing when and when not to apply the assumption to simplify the calculations.

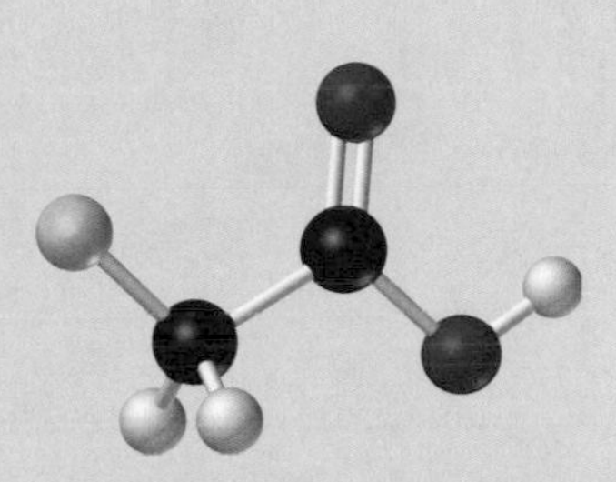

▲ Fluoroacetic acid, CH_2FCOOH.

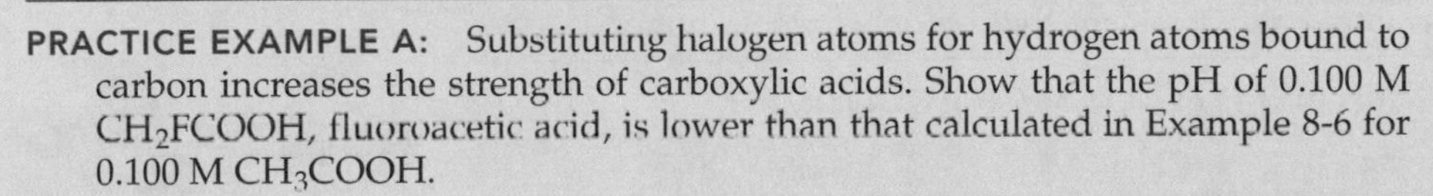

PRACTICE EXAMPLE A: Substituting halogen atoms for hydrogen atoms bound to carbon increases the strength of carboxylic acids. Show that the pH of 0.100 M CH_2FCOOH, fluoroacetic acid, is lower than that calculated in Example 8-6 for 0.100 M CH_3COOH.

$$CH_2FCOOH + H_2O \rightleftharpoons H_3O^+ + CH_2FCOO^- \qquad K_a = 2.6 \times 10^{-3}$$

PRACTICE EXAMPLE B: Acetylsalicylic acid, $HC_9H_7O_4$, is the active component in aspirin. This acid is the cause of the stomach upset some people get when taking aspirin. Two extra-strength aspirin tablets, each containing 500 mg of acetylsalicylic acid, are dissolved in 325 mL of water. What is the pH of this solution?

$$HC_9H_7O_4 + H_2O \rightleftharpoons H_3O^+ + C_9H_7O_4^- \qquad K_a = 3.3 \times 10^{-4}$$

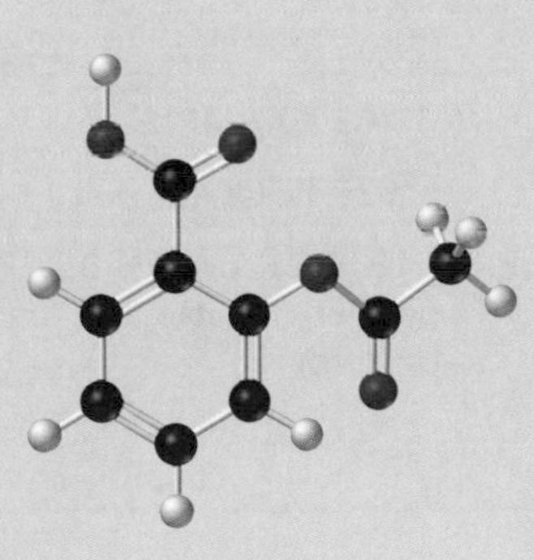

▲ Acetylsalicylic acid, $C_6H_4(OOCCH_3)COOH$.

EXAMPLE 8-7 Dealing with the Failure of a Simplifying Assumption

What is the pH of a solution that is 0.00250 M $CH_3NH_2(aq)$? For methylamine, $K_b = 4.2 \times 10^{-4}$.

Analyze

In this example we will apply the same techniques as we did in Example 8-6. We will work the problem twice to see that the simplifying assumption breaks down for weak acids and weak bases at very low concentrations.

(continued)

Solve

$$CH_3NH_2 + H_2O \rightleftharpoons CH_3NH_3^+ + OH^-$$

	CH_3NH_2		$CH_3NH_3^+$	OH^-
initial concns:	0.00250 M		—	—
changes:	$-x$ M		$+x$ M	$+x$ M
equil concns:	$(0.00250 - x)$ M		x M	x M

$$K_b = \frac{[CH_3NH_3^+][OH^-]}{[CH_3NH_2]} = \frac{x \cdot x}{0.00250 - x} = 4.2 \times 10^{-4}$$

Now let's assume that x is very much less than 0.00250 and that $0.00250 - x \approx 0.00250$.

$$\frac{x^2}{0.00250} = 4.2 \times 10^{-4} \qquad x^2 = 1.1 \times 10^{-6} \qquad [OH^-] = x = 1.0 \times 10^{-3}\,M$$

The value of x is nearly half as large as 0.00250—too large to ignore. This means using the *quadratic* formula.

$$\frac{x^2}{0.00250 - x} = 4.2 \times 10^{-4}$$

$$x^2 + (4.2 \times 10^{-4}x) - (1.1 \times 10^{-6}) = 0$$

$$x = \frac{(-4.2 \times 10^{-4}) \pm \sqrt{(4.2 \times 10^{-4})^2 + 4 \times 1.1 \times 10^{-6}}}{2}$$

$$x = [OH^-] = \frac{(-4.2 \times 10^{-4}) \pm (2.1 \times 10^{-3})}{2} = 8.4 \times 10^{-4}\,M$$

$$pOH = -\log[OH^-] = -\log(8.4 \times 10^{-4}) = 3.08$$

$$pH = 14.00 - pOH = 14.00 - 3.08 = 10.92$$

Assess

After applying the simplifying assumption, if the value of x is a significant percentage of the initial concentration (for example, greater than 5%), then we should not use the simplifying assumption to obtain the hydronium concentration.

PRACTICE EXAMPLE A: What is the pH of 0.015 M $CH_2FCOOH(aq)$?

$$CH_2FCOOH + H_2O \rightleftharpoons H_3O^+ + CH_2FCOO^- \qquad K_a = 2.6 \times 10^{-3}$$

PRACTICE EXAMPLE B: Piperidine is a base found in small amounts in black pepper. What is the pH of 315 mL of an aqueous solution containing 114 mg piperidine?

$$C_5H_{11}N + H_2O \rightleftharpoons C_5H_{11}NH^+ + OH^- \qquad K_b = 1.6 \times 10^{-3}$$

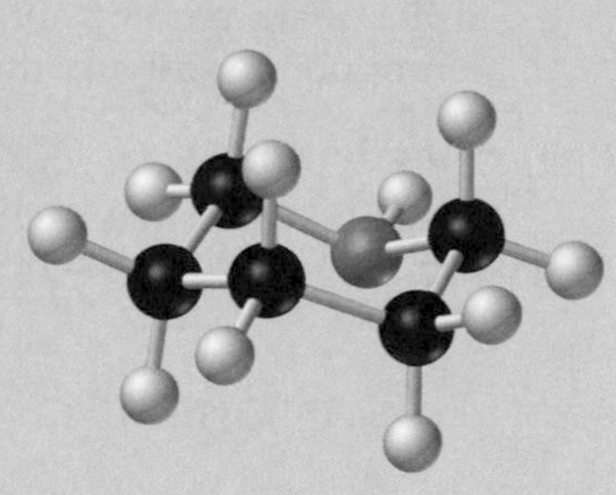

▲ Piperidine, $C_5H_{10}NH$.

8-2 ARE YOU WONDERING...

How to calculate the pH of a very dilute solution of a weak acid?

Think of this as a companion question to the one posed in Are You Wondering 8-1, except here the acid in question is weak (represented as HA) rather than strong. The initial approach is similar: Write two equations representing the sources of H_3O^+, and indicate the concentrations of various species in the solution.

	$H_2O + H_2O$	$\rightleftharpoons$	H_3O^+	+	OH^-
Molarity:			x		x
	$HA + H_2O$	$\rightleftharpoons$	H_3O^+	+	A^-
Molarity:	$M - y$		y		y

Our ultimate objective is to determine $[H_3O^+]$ in the solution, and this is $x + y$. From $[H_3O^+]$, we can easily get the pH.

Our principal task is to solve a pair of equations simultaneously for x and y. The two equations are

$$K_w = [H_3O^+][OH^-] = (x + y) \times x = 1.0 \times 10^{-14}$$
$$K_a = \frac{[H_3O^+][A^-]}{[HA]} = \frac{(x + y) \times y}{(M - y)}$$

Note the following three points in these equations. (1) There can be only one value of $[H_3O^+]$ in the solution, and it is this value $(x + y)$ that appears in each equation. (2) The stoichiometric concentration of the acid is M (its molarity), and its *equilibrium* concentration is $[HA] = M - y$. The numerical value of M depends on the particular case considered. (3) Similarly, the numerical value of K_a depends on the particular case. When we solve the K_a expression for x, we obtain

$$x = \frac{K_a(M - y)}{y} - y \quad \text{and} \quad x + y = \frac{K_a(M - y)}{y}$$

And when we substitute these values of x and $x + y$ into the K_w equation, we get

$$K_w = \frac{K_a(M - y)}{y} \times \left(\frac{K_a(M - y)}{y} - y\right) = 1.0 \times 10^{-14}$$

The value of y satisfying this equation is not difficult to obtain by the method of successive approximations.

The solution of this problem is left for you to do (see Exercise 89), but you will find that for 1.0×10^{-5} M HCN ($K_a = 6.2 \times 10^{-10}$), $y \cong 4.8 \times 10^{-8}$, $(x + y) \cong 1.3 \times 10^{-7}$, and pH $\cong$ 6.90. This certainly seems like a reasonable pH for a very dilute solution of a weak acid in water—just below the neutral pH of 7.00.

Finally, we can use the results of the previous discussion to establish a criterion for ignoring the self-ionization of water in calculations. When we do this, we are assuming that $y \gg x$, so that $y \approx x + y$, and $yx \approx (x + y)x = [H_3O^+][OH^-] = K_w$. Also, if $y \gg x$, then $y^2 \gg K_w$. For what values of y can we say that $y \gg x$? Let's take the maximum value of x consistent with ignoring the self-ionization of water to be 1/100 of y which, as shown below, means that $[H_3O^+]$ must be greater than 10^{-6} M.

$$y^2 > y \times x = y \times \frac{y}{100} = K_w = 1 \times 10^{-14}$$
$$y^2 > 1 \times 10^{-12} \quad \text{and} \quad y > 1 \times 10^{-6}$$

In acid–base calculations, we should first use the simplifying assumptions (ignore K_w and assume that [HA] can be replaced by the molarity of the acid). Then check the answer to see whether $[H_3O^+]$ is greater than 1×10^{-6} M and the 5% criterion presented below is also met.

More on Simplifying Assumptions

The usual simplifying assumption is that of treating a weak acid or weak base as though it remains essentially nonionized (so that $M - x \approx M$). In general, this assumption will work if the molarity of the weak acid, M_A, or that of the weak base, M_B, exceeds the value of K_a or K_b by a factor of at least 100. That is,

$$\frac{M_A \text{ (or } M_B)}{K_a \text{ (or } K_b)} > 100$$

◀ Be sure to maintain a clear distinction between the *property* (molarity, M) and the *unit* in which it is expressed, M = mol/L.

In any case, it is important to test the validity of any assumption that you make. If the assumption is good to within a few percent (say, less than 5%), then it is generally valid. In Example 8-6, the simplifying assumption was good to about 1%, but in Example 8-7 it was off by 40%.

Percent Ionization

The extent of ionization of a weak acid or weak base can be described in terms of the degree of ionization or percent ionization. It is convenient to introduce the generic symbol HA for any weak acid, and A^- as the conjugate base of the acid HA.

For the ionization $HA + H_2O \rightleftharpoons H_3O^+ + A^-$, the degree of ionization is the fraction of the acid molecules that ionize. Thus, if in 1.00 M HA, ionization produces $[H_3O^+] = [A^-] = 0.05$ M, the degree of ionization = 0.05 M/1.00 M = 0.05. **Percent ionization** gives the proportion of ionized molecules on a percentage basis.

$$\text{percent ionization} = \frac{\text{molarity of } H_3O^+ \text{ derived from HA}}{\text{initial molarity of HA}} \times 100\% \tag{8.14}$$

If, for example, the degree of ionization is 0.05, then the percent of ionization is 5%.

Figure 8-8 compares percent ionization and solution molarity for a weak acid and a strong acid. Example 8-8 shows by calculation that the percent ionization of a weak acid or a weak base *increases* as the solution becomes *more dilute*, a fact that we can also demonstrate by a simple analysis of the ionization reaction

$$HA + H_2O \rightleftharpoons H_3O^+ + A^-$$

At equilibrium, n_{HA} moles of the acid HA, $n_{H_3O^+}$ moles of H_3O^+, and n_{A^-} moles of A^- are present in a volume of V liters. The K_a expression is

$$K_a = \frac{[H_3O^+][A^-]}{[HA]} = \frac{(n_{H_3O^+}/V)(n_{A^-}/V)}{n_{HA}/V} = \frac{(n_{H_3O^+})(n_{A^-})}{n_{HA}} \times \frac{1}{V}$$

When we dilute the solution, V increases, $1/V$ decreases, and the ratio $(n_{H_3O^+})(n_{A^-})/n_{HA}$ must increase to maintain the constant value of K_a. In turn, $n_{H_3O^+}$ and n_{A^-} must increase and n_{HA} must decrease, signifying an increase in the percent ionization.

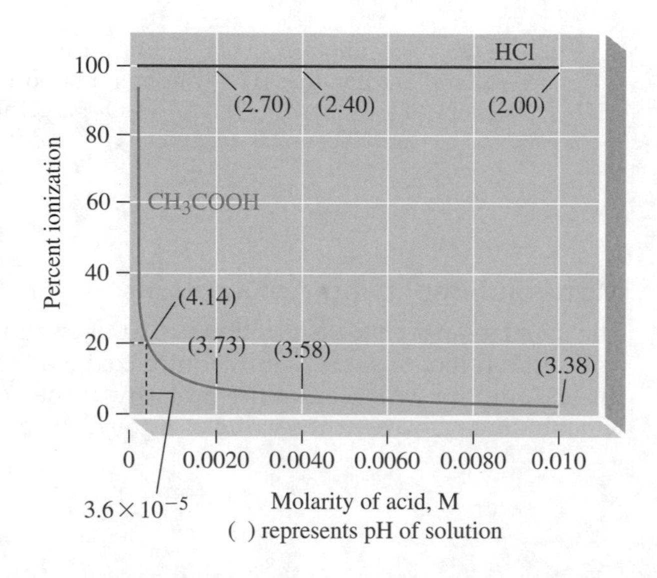

▶ FIGURE 8-8
Percent ionization of an acid as a function of concentration
Over the concentration range shown, HCl, a strong acid, is essentially 100% ionized. The percent ionization of CH_3COOH, a weak acid, increases from about 4% in 0.010 M to 20% in 3.6×10^{-5} M. For solutions of acetic acid more dilute than 3.6×10^{-5} M, the percent ionization rises sharply with increasing dilution. The pH of 1.0×10^{-7} M CH_3COOH is about 6.79, the same as for 1.0×10^{-7} M HCl.

EXAMPLE 8-8 Determining Percent Ionization as a Function of Weak Acid Concentration

What is the percent ionization of acetic acid in 1.0 M, 0.10 M, and 0.010 M CH_3COOH?

Analyze

The percent ionization is determined by dividing the amount of ionized acid by the initial acid concentration and multiplying by 100%.

Solve

Use the ICE format to describe 1.0 M CH_3COOH:

$$CH_3COOH + H_2O \rightleftharpoons H_3O^+ + CH_3COO^-$$

	CH_3COOH	H_3O^+	CH_3COO^-
initial concns:	1.0 M	—	—
changes:	$-x$ M	$+x$ M	$+x$ M
equil concns:	$(1.0 - x)$ M	x M	x M

We need to calculate $x = [H_3O^+] = [CH_3COO^-]$. In doing so, let's make the usual assumption: $1.0 - x \approx 1.0$.

$$K_a = \frac{[H_3O^+][CH_3COO^-]}{[CH_3COOH]} = \frac{x \cdot x}{1.0 - x} = \frac{x^2}{1.0} = 1.8 \times 10^{\ 5}$$

$$x = [H_3O^+] = [C_2H_3O_2^-] = \sqrt{1.8 \times 10^{-5}} = 4.2 \times 10^{-3}\,M$$

The percent ionization of 1.0 M $HC_2H_3O_2$ is

$$\%\ ionization = \frac{[H_3O^+]}{[CH_3COOH]} \times 100\% = \frac{4.2 \times 10^{-3}\,M}{1.0\,M} \times 100\% = 0.42\%$$

The assumption that x is small compared to 1.0 is clearly valid: x is only 0.42% of 1.0 M. The calculations for 0.10 M CH_3COOH and 0.010 M CH_3COOH are very similar. In 0.10 M CH_3COOH, 1.3% of the acetic acid molecules are ionized and in 0.010 M CH_3COOH, 4.2% are ionized.

Assess

The purpose of calculating the percent ionization for three acetic acid solutions was to confirm the very important point made on page 326: For a weak acid, percent ionization increases with increasing dilution (Fig. 8-8). For very dilute solutions, the calculation of percent ionization is more complicated. (See Are You Wondering 8-2 on page 324.)

PRACTICE EXAMPLE A: What is the percent ionization of hydrofluoric acid in 0.20 M HF and in 0.020 M HF?

PRACTICE EXAMPLE B: An 0.0284 M aqueous solution of lactic acid, a carboxylic acid that accumulates in the blood and muscles during physical activity, is found to be 6.7% ionized. Determine K_a for lactic acid.

$$CH_3CH(OH)COOH + H_2O \rightleftharpoons H_3O^+ + CH_3CH(OH)COO^- \qquad K_a = ?$$

8-4 CONCEPT ASSESSMENT

You are given two bottles, each of which contains a 0.1 M solution of an unidentified acid. One bottle is labeled $K_a = 7.2 \times 10^{-4}$, and the other is labeled $K_a = 1.9 \times 10^{-5}$. Which bottle contains the more acidic solution? Which bottle has the acid with the larger pK_a?

▲ Phosphoric acid, H_3PO_4.

8-6 Polyprotic Acids

All the acids listed in Table 8.3 are weak *monoprotic acids*, meaning that their molecules have only one ionizable H atom, even though several of these acids contain more than one H atom. But some acids have more than one ionizable H atom per molecule. These are **polyprotic acids**. Table 8.4 lists ionization constants for several polyprotic acids. We will focus on phosphoric acid, H_3PO_4.

◀ Phosphoric acid ranks second only to sulfuric acid among the important commercial acids. It is used in the manufacture of phosphate fertilizers. Various sodium, potassium, and calcium phosphates are used in the food industry.

TABLE 8.4 Ionization Constants of Some Polyprotic Acids

Acid	Ionization Equilibria	Ionization Constants, K	pK
Hydrosulfuric[a]	$H_2S + H_2O \rightleftharpoons H_3O^+ + HS^-$	$K_{a_1} = 1.0 \times 10^{-7}$	$pK_{a_1} = 7.00$
	$HS^- + H_2O \rightleftharpoons H_3O^+ + S^{2-}$	$K_{a_2} = 1 \times 10^{-19}$	$pK_{a_2} = 19.0$
Carbonic[b]	$H_2CO_3 + H_2O \rightleftharpoons H_3O^+ + HCO_3^-$	$K_{a_1} = 4.4 \times 10^{-7}$	$pK_{a_1} = 6.36$
	$HCO_3^- + H_2O \rightleftharpoons H_3O^+ + CO_3^{2-}$	$K_{a_2} = 4.7 \times 10^{-11}$	$pK_{a_2} = 10.33$
Citric	$H_3C_6H_5O_7 + H_2O \rightleftharpoons H_3O^+ + H_2C_6H_5O_7^-$	$K_{a_1} = 7.5 \times 10^{-4}$	$pK_{a_1} = 3.12$
	$H_2C_6H_5O_7^- + H_2O \rightleftharpoons H_3O^+ + HC_6H_5O_7^{2-}$	$K_{a_2} = 1.7 \times 10^{-5}$	$pK_{a_2} = 4.77$
	$HC_6H_5O_7^{2-} + H_2O \rightleftharpoons H_3O^+ + C_6H_5O_7^{3-}$	$K_{a_3} = 4.0 \times 10^{-7}$	$pK_{a_3} = 6.40$
Phosphoric	$H_3PO_4 + H_2O \rightleftharpoons H_3O^+ + H_2PO_4^-$	$K_{a_1} = 7.1 \times 10^{-3}$	$pK_{a_1} = 2.15$
	$H_2PO_4^- + H_2O \rightleftharpoons H_3O^+ + HPO_4^{2-}$	$K_{a_2} = 6.3 \times 10^{-8}$	$pK_{a_2} = 7.20$
	$HPO_4^{2-} + H_2O \rightleftharpoons H_3O^+ + PO_4^{3-}$	$K_{a_3} = 4.2 \times 10^{-13}$	$pK_{a_3} = 12.38$
Oxalic	$H_2C_2O_4 + H_2O \rightleftharpoons H_3O^+ + HC_2O_4^-$	$K_{a_1} = 5.6 \times 10^{-2}$	$pK_{a_1} = 1.25$
	$HC_2O_4^- + H_2O \rightleftharpoons H_3O^+ + C_2O_4^{2-}$	$K_{a_2} = 5.4 \times 10^{-5}$	$pK_{a_2} = 4.27$
Sulfurous[c]	$H_2SO_3 + H_2O \rightleftharpoons H_3O^+ + HSO_3^-$	$K_{a_1} = 1.3 \times 10^{-2}$	$pK_{a_1} = 1.89$
	$HSO_3^- + H_2O \rightleftharpoons H_3O^+ + SO_3^{2-}$	$K_{a_2} = 6.2 \times 10^{-8}$	$pK_{a_2} = 7.21$
Sulfuric[d]	$H_2SO_4 + H_2O \rightleftharpoons H_3O^+ + HSO_4^-$	K_{a_1} = very large	$pK_{a_1} < 0$
	$HSO_4^- + H_2O \rightleftharpoons H_3O^+ + SO_4^{2-}$	$K_{a_2} = 1.1 \times 10^{-2}$	$pK_{a_2} = 1.96$

Acid strength

[a]The value for K_{a_2} of H_2S most commonly found in older literature is about 1×10^{-14}, but current evidence suggests that the value is considerably smaller.

[b]H_2CO_3 cannot be isolated. It is in equilibrium with H_2O and dissolved CO_2. The value given for K_{a_1} is actually for the reaction

$$CO_2(aq) + 2\,H_2O \rightleftharpoons H_3O^+ + HCO_3^-$$

Generally, aqueous solutions of CO_2 are treated *as if* the $CO_2(aq)$ were first converted to H_2CO_3, followed by ionization of the H_2CO_3.

[c]H_2SO_3 is a hypothetical, nonisolatable species. The value listed for K_{a_1} is actually for the reaction

$$SO_2(aq) + 2\,H_2O \rightleftharpoons H_3O^+ + HSO_3^-$$

[d]H_2SO_4 is completely ionized in the first step.

The H_3PO_4 molecule has *three* ionizable H atoms; it is a *triprotic acid*. It ionizes in three steps. For each step, we can write an ionization equation and an acid ionization constant expression with a distinctive value of K_a.

▶ A common error is to assume that the $[H_3O^+]$ is the same for all three ionizations. In fact, the pH is dominated by only the first ionization as seen from the different K_a values here. This is only true, of course, for weak acids. The examples here illustrate the points well.

$$\textbf{(1)}\quad H_3PO_4 + H_2O \rightleftharpoons H_3O^+ + H_2PO_4^- \qquad K_{a_1} = \frac{[H_3O^+][H_2PO_4^-]}{[H_3PO_4]} = 7.1 \times 10^{-3}$$

$$\textbf{(2)}\quad H_2PO_4^- + H_2O \rightleftharpoons H_3O^+ + HPO_4^{2-} \qquad K_{a_2} = \frac{[H_3O^+][HPO_4^{2-}]}{[H_2PO_4^-]} = 6.3 \times 10^{-8}$$

$$\textbf{(3)}\quad HPO_4^{2-} + H_2O \rightleftharpoons H_3O^+ + PO_4^{3-} \qquad K_{a_3} = \frac{[H_3O^+][PO_4^{3-}]}{[HPO_4^{2-}]} = 4.2 \times 10^{-13}$$

There is a ready explanation for the relative magnitudes of the ionization constants—that is, for the fact that $K_{a_1} > K_{a_2} > K_{a_3}$. When ionization occurs in step (1), a proton (H^+) moves away from an ion with a 1− charge ($H_2PO_4^-$). In step (2), the proton moves away from an ion with a 2− charge (HPO_4^{2-}), a more difficult separation. As a result, the ionization constant in the second step is smaller than that in the first. Ionization is more difficult still in step (3).

We can make three key statements about the ionization of phosphoric acid, as illustrated in Example 8-9.

Phosphoric acid

1. K_{a_1} is so much larger than K_{a_2} and K_{a_3} that essentially all the H_3O^+ is produced in the first ionization step.
2. So little of the $H_2PO_4^-$ forming in the first ionization step ionizes any further that we can assume $[H_2PO_4^-] = [H_3O^+]$ in the solution.
3. $[HPO_4^{2-}] \approx K_{a_2}$, regardless of the molarity of the acid.*

Although statement (1) seems essential if statements (2) and (3) are to be valid, it is not as crucial as might first appear. Even for polyprotic acids whose K_a values do not differ greatly between successive ionizations, H_3O^+ is often still determined almost exclusively by the K_{a_1} expression, and statements (2) and (3) remain valid. As long as the polyprotic acid is weak in its first ionization step, the concentration of the anion produced in this step will be so much less than the molarity of the acid that additional $[H_3O^+]$ produced in the second ionization remains negligible.

EXAMPLE 8-9 Calculating Ion Concentrations in a Polyprotic Acid Solution

For a 3.0 M H_3PO_4 solution, calculate **(a)** $[H_3O^+]$; **(b)** $[H_2PO_4^-]$; **(c)** $[HPO_4^{2-}]$; and **(d)** $[PO_4^{3-}]$.

Analyze

For a solution of a *weak* polyprotic acid, the first ionization step produces essentially all the H_3O^+ in solution, so we begin as we would for a weak monoprotic acid solution. The concentrations of the other species are obtained by using the expressions for K_{a2} and K_{a3}.

Solve

(a) For the reasons discussed above, let's assume that all the H_3O^+ forms in the *first* ionization step. This is equivalent to thinking of H_3PO_4 as though it were a monoprotic acid, ionizing only in the first step.

	$H_3PO_4 + H_2O \rightleftharpoons$	H_3O^+	$+\ H_2PO_4^-$
initial concns:	3.0 M	—	—
changes:	$-x$ M	$+x$ M	$+x$ M
after first ionization:	$(3.0 - x)$ M	x M	x M

Following the usual assumption that x is much smaller than 3.0 and that $3.0 - x \approx 3.0$, we obtain

$$K_{a_1} = \frac{[H_3O^+][H_2PO_4^-]}{[H_3PO_4]} = \frac{x \cdot x}{(3.0 - x)} = \frac{x^2}{3.0} = 7.1 \times 10^{-3}$$

$$x^2 = 0.021 \qquad x = [H_3O^+] = 0.14\ \text{M}$$

In the assumption $3.0 - x \approx 3.0$, $x = 0.14$, which is 4.7% of 3.0. This is about the maximum error that can be tolerated for an acceptable assumption.

(b) From part (a), $x = [H_2PO_4^-] = [H_3O^+] = 0.14$ M.

(c) To determine $[H_3O^+]$ and $[H_2PO_4^-]$, we assumed that the second ionization is insignificant. Here we must consider the second ionization, no matter how slight; otherwise we would have no source of the ion HPO_4^{2-}. We can represent the second ionization, as shown in the following table. *Note especially how the results of the first ionization enter in.* We start with a solution in which $[H_2PO_4^-] = [H_3O^+] = 0.14$ M.

	$H_2PO_4^- + H_2O \rightleftharpoons$	H_3O^+	$+\ HPO_4^{2-}$
from first ionization:	0.14 M	0.14 M	—
changes:	$-y$ M	$+y$ M	$+y$ M
after second ionization:	$(0.14 - y)$ M	$(0.14 + y)$ M	y M

If we assume that y is much smaller than 0.14, then $(0.14 + y) \approx (0.14 - y) \approx 0.14$.

(continued)

*If we assume that $[H_2PO_4^-] = [H_3O^+]$, the second ionization expression reduces to

$$\frac{\cancel{[H_3O^+]}[HPO_4^{2-}]}{\cancel{[H_2PO_4^-]}} = K_{a_2}$$

We then get

$$K_{a_2} = \frac{[H_3O^+][HPO_4^{2-}]}{[H_2PO_4^-]} = \frac{(0.14 + y)(y)}{(0.14 - y)} = \frac{\cancel{(0.14)}(y)}{\cancel{(0.14)}} = 6.3 \times 10^{-8}$$

$$y = [HPO_4^{2-}] = 6.3 \times 10^{-8}\,M$$

Note that the assumption is valid.

(d) The PO_4^{3-} ion forms only in the third ionization step. When we write this acid ionization constant expression, we see that we have already calculated the ion concentrations other than $[PO_4^{3-}]$. We can simply solve the K_{a_3} expression for $[PO_4^{3-}]$.

$$K_{a_3} = \frac{[H_3O^+][PO_4^{3-}]}{[HPO_4^{2-}]} = \frac{0.14 \times [PO_4^{3-}]}{6.3 \times 10^{-8}} = 4.2 \times 10^{-13}$$

$$[PO_4^{3-}] = \frac{4.2 \times 10^{-13} \times 6.3 \times 10^{-8}}{0.14} = 1.9 \times 10^{-19}\,M$$

Assess

In this example the major source of hydronium ions is from the first ionization step. In the second step the amount of hydronium ions is around 10^{-8} M, which is negligible compared with 0.14 M.

PRACTICE EXAMPLE A: Malonic acid, $HOOCCH_2COOH$, is a diprotic acid used in the manufacture of barbiturates.

$$HOOCCH_2COOH + H_2O \rightleftharpoons H_3O^+ + HOOCCH_2COO^- \qquad K_{a_1} = 1.4 \times 10^{-3}$$
$$HOOCCH_2COO^- + H_2O \rightleftharpoons H_3O^+ + {}^-OOCCH_2COO^- \qquad K_{a_2} = 2.0 \times 10^{-6}$$

Calculate $[H_3O^+]$, $[HOOCCH_2COO^-]$, and $[{}^-OOCCH_2COO^-]$ in a 1.00 M solution of malonic acid.

PRACTICE EXAMPLE B: Oxalic acid, found in the leaves of rhubarb and other plants, is a diprotic acid.

$$H_2C_2O_4 + H_2O \rightleftharpoons H_3O^+ + HC_2O_4^- \qquad K_{a_1} = ?$$
$$HC_2O_4^- + H_2O \rightleftharpoons H_3O^+ + C_2O_4^{2-} \qquad K_{a_2} = ?$$

An aqueous solution that is 1.05 M $H_2C_2O_4$ has pH = 0.67. The free oxalate ion concentration in this solution is $[C_2O_4^{2-}] = 5.3 \times 10^{-5}$ M. Determine K_{a_1} and K_{a_2} for oxalic acid.

▲ Sulfuric acid, H_2SO_4.

A Somewhat Different Case: H_2SO_4

Sulfuric acid differs from most polyprotic acids in this important respect: It is a *strong* acid in its first ionization and a *weak* acid in its second. Ionization is complete in the first step, which means that in most $H_2SO_4(aq)$ solutions, $[H_2SO_4] \approx 0$ M. Thus, if a solution is 0.50 M H_2SO_4, we can treat it as though it were 0.50 M H_3O^+ and 0.50 M HSO_4^- initially. Then we can determine the extent to which ionization of HSO_4^- produces additional H_3O^+ and SO_4^{2-}, as illustrated in Example 8-10.

EXAMPLE 8-10 Calculating Ion Concentrations in Sulfuric Acid Solutions: Strong Acid Ionization Followed by Weak Acid Ionization

Calculate $[H_3O^+]$, $[HSO_4^-]$, and $[SO_4^{2-}]$ in 0.50 M H_2SO_4.

Analyze

We will modify the approach we used in Example 8-9 to incorporate the fact that for H_2SO_4 the first ionization step goes to completion.

Solve

	$H_2SO_4 + H_2O \longrightarrow$	H_3O^+	$+ HSO_4^-$
initial concn:	0.50 M	—	—
changes:	−0.50 M	+0.50 M	+0.50 M
after first ionization:	≈ 0	0.50 M	0.50 M

	$HSO_4^- + H_2O \rightleftharpoons$	H_3O^+	$+ SO_4^{2-}$
from first ionization:	0.50 M	0.50 M	—
changes:	$-x$ M	$+x$ M	$+x$ M
after second ionization:	$(0.50 - x)$ M	$(0.50 + x)$ M	x M

We need to deal only with the ionization constant expression for K_{a_2}. If we assume that x is much smaller than 0.50, then $(0.50 + x) \approx (0.50 - x) \approx 0.50$ and

$$K_{a_2} = \frac{[H_3O^+][SO_4^{2-}]}{[HSO_4^-]} = \frac{(0.50 + x) \cdot x}{(0.50 - x)} = \frac{\cancel{0.50} \cdot x}{\cancel{0.50}} = 1.1 \times 10^{-2}$$

Our results, then, are

$$[H_3O^+] = 0.50 + x = 0.51\ M; \qquad [HSO_4^-] = 0.50 - x = 0.49\ M$$

$$[SO_4^{2-}] = x = K_{a_2} = 0.011\ M$$

Assess

In obtaining these results, we assumed that x was much smaller than 0.50. This assumption is appropriate because $x = 0.011$ is only 2.2% of 0.50. Had x been greater than 5% of 0.50, then the assumption would not have been appropriate. Such a situation arises when dealing with more dilute solutions of H_2SO_4.

PRACTICE EXAMPLE A: Calculate $[H_3O^+]$, $[HSO_4^-]$, and $[SO_4^{2-}]$ in 0.20 M H_2SO_4.

PRACTICE EXAMPLE B: Calculate $[H_3O^+]$, $[HSO_4^-]$, and $[SO_4^{2-}]$ in 0.020 M H_2SO_4. [*Hint:* Is the assumption that $[HSO_4^-] = [H_3O^+]$ valid?]

A General Approach to Solution Equilibrium Calculations

Suppose we were required to determine the stoichiometric molarity of the $H_2SO_4(aq)$ that is required to produce a solution with pH = 2.15. We could start by determining the hydronium ion concentration in the solution: $[H_3O^+] = 10^{-pH} = 10^{-2.15} = 7.1 \times 10^{-3}$ M. What next? We cannot follow the approach used in Example 8-6 because H_2SO_4 is not a monoprotic acid. Instead, we have to use a method like that outlined in Are You Wondering 8-1 and 8-2. An alternative approach worth considering has the appeal of getting us on the right track for all kinds of solution equilibrium calculations. That method has the following format.

1. Identify the species present in any significant amount in the solution (excluding H_2O molecules). Consider the concentrations of these species as unknowns.
2. Write equations that include these species. The number of equations involving these species should match the number of unknowns. The equations are of three types.
   (a) equilibrium constant expressions
   (b) material balance equations
   (c) an electroneutrality condition
3. Solve the system of equations for the unknowns.

Let's apply this approach to the $H_2SO_4(aq)$ solution mentioned in the first sentence of this section.

Possible Species:

$$\cancel{H_2SO_4}, H_3O^+, HSO_4^-, SO_4^{2-}, \cancel{OH^-}$$

We can eliminate H_2SO_4 because its ionization goes to completion in the first step. We can also eliminate OH^- because $[OH^-]$ is exceedingly small in an *acidic* solution that has a pH = 2.15.

Unknowns:

$$\cancel{[H_3O^+]}, [HSO_4^-], [SO_4^{2-}], \text{and } M\,[\text{the molarity of the } H_2SO_4(aq)]$$

We can eliminate $[H_3O^+]$ because we essentially know its value from the outset. A pH = 2.15 corresponds to $[H_3O^+] = 0.0071$ M. Thus, we are left with three unknowns, and we need three equations.

▶ Calculations like this are not as complicated when performed for other polyprotic acids (phosphoric acid, carbonic acid, etc.) because essentially all the hydronium ions are produced in the first ionization step.

Equations:

(a) The K_a expression for the ionization $HSO_4^- + H_2O \rightleftharpoons H_3O^+ + SO_4^{2-}$ is

$$K_{a_2} = \frac{[H_3O^+][SO_4^{2-}]}{[HSO_4^-]} = 1.1 \times 10^{-2}$$

(b) The following material balance equation accounts for the fact that the sum of the concentrations of the sulfur-containing species must equal the stoichiometric molarity of the $H_2SO_4(aq)$.

$$[HSO_4^-] + [SO_4^{2-}] = M$$

(c) The electroneutrality condition simply verifies that the solution carries no net charge. The sum of the positive charges must equal the sum of the negative charges. We can sum these charges on a mol/liter basis. For example, because there is one positive charge for every H_3O^+ ion, the number of moles per liter of positive charge is the same as the number of moles per liter of H_3O^+, 0.0071 M. We multiply $[SO_4^{2-}]$ by *two* because each SO_4^{2-} ion carries two units of negative charge.

$$[H_3O^+] = [HSO_4^-] + (2 \times [SO_4^{2-}]) = 0.0071$$

Solving the Equations:

Solve equation (c) for $[HSO_4^-]$: $[HSO_4^-] = 0.0071 - 2[SO_4^{2-}]$. Substitute this result, together with $[H_3O^+] = 0.0071$, into equation (a) and obtain the expression

$$\frac{0.0071 \times [SO_4^{2-}]}{0.0071 - 2[SO_4^{2-}]} = 1.1 \times 10^{-2}$$

Solve this equation to find that $[SO_4^{2-}] = 0.0027$ M. Then substitute this result into equation (c) to obtain $[HSO_4^-] = 0.0017$ M. Finally, according to equation (b), $[HSO_4^-] + [SO_4^{2-}] = 0.0044$ M. The required molarity is 0.0044 M H_2SO_4.

KEEP IN MIND

that although this method gives you a quick way to set up a solution equilibrium calculation, more information may be needed for you to arrive at an answer without undue effort. For example, answers to the general questions posed on page 321 may point the way to simplifying the algebraic solution.

Check:

There are usually ways to check the reasonableness of an answer obtained by this method. In this case, we can easily determine the possible pH range for 0.0044 M H_2SO_4. If the acid ionized only in the first step, $[H_3O^+] = 0.0044$ M (pH = 2.36); if the second ionization step also went to completion, $[H_3O^+] = 0.0088$ M (pH = 2.06). The observed pH, 2.15, falls squarely in this range.

The alternative method outlined here is ideal for computerized calculation. Moreover, because the additional manipulations required to convert stoichiometric concentrations to activities can be incorporated into the calculations, the solutions obtained are generally both more accurate and more readily obtained than are those derived by traditional methods.

8-7 Ions as Acids and Bases

In our discussion to this point, we have emphasized the behavior of electrically neutral molecules as acids (for example, HCl, CH_3COOH, H_3PO_4) or as bases (for example, NH_3, CH_3NH_2). We have also seen, however, that ions can act as acids or bases. For instance, in the second ionization step of H_3PO_4 (part c of Example 8-9), the $H_2PO_4^-$ ion acts as an acid.

Let's think about how each of the following can be described as an acid–base reaction.

$$\underset{\text{Acid(1)}}{NH_4^+} + \underset{\text{Base(2)}}{H_2O} \rightleftharpoons \underset{\text{Base(1)}}{NH_3} + \underset{\text{Acid(2)}}{H_3O^+} \quad (8.15)$$

$$\underset{\text{Base(1)}}{CH_3COO^-} + \underset{\text{Acid(2)}}{H_2O} \rightleftharpoons \underset{\text{Acid(1)}}{CH_3COOH} + \underset{\text{Base(2)}}{OH^-} \quad (8.16)$$

In reaction (8.15), NH_4^+ is an *acid*, giving up a proton to water, a *base*. Equilibrium in this reaction is described by means of the *acid ionization constant* of the ammonium ion, NH_4^+.

$$K_a = \frac{[NH_3][H_3O^+]}{[NH_4^+]} = ? \quad (8.17)$$

Two of the concentrations in equation (8.17)—$[NH_3]$ and $[NH_4^+]$—are the same as in the K_b expression for NH_3, the conjugate base of NH_4^+. It seems that K_a for NH_4^+ and K_b for NH_3 should bear some relationship to each other, and they do. The easiest way to see this is to multiply both the numerator and the denominator of (8.17) by $[OH^-]$. The product $[H_3O^+] \times [OH^-]$ is the ion product of water, K_w, shown in red. The other concentrations, shown in blue, represent the *inverse* of K_b for NH_3. The value obtained, 5.6×10^{-10}, is the missing value of K_a in expression (8.17).

$$K_a = \frac{[NH_3][H_3O^+][OH^-]}{[NH_4^+][OH^-]} = \frac{K_w}{K_b} = \frac{1.0 \times 10^{-14}}{1.8 \times 10^{-5}} = 5.6 \times 10^{-10}$$

This result is an important consequence of the Brønsted–Lowry theory.

The product of the ionization constants of an acid and its conjugate base equals the ion product of water.

$$\begin{aligned} K_a\,(\text{acid}) \times K_b\,(\text{its conjugate base}) &= K_w \\ K_b\,(\text{base}) \times K_a\,(\text{its conjugate acid}) &= K_w \end{aligned} \quad (8.18)$$

◀ In many tabulations of ionization constants, only K_a values are listed, whether for neutral molecules or for ions. Equation (8.18) can be used to obtain the values of their conjugates.

In reaction (8.16), CH_3COO^- acts as a *base* by taking a proton from water, an *acid*. Here, equilibrium is described by means of the *base ionization constant* of the acetate ion, CH_3COO^-. With expression (8.18) we can evaluate K_b.

$$K_b = \frac{[CH_3COOH][OH^-]}{[CH_3COO^-]} = \frac{K_w}{K_a(CH_3COOH)} = \frac{1.0 \times 10^{-14}}{1.8 \times 10^{-5}} = 5.6 \times 10^{-10}$$

From equation (8.18), we deduce that (1) the stronger the acid, the weaker its conjugate base; and (2) the weaker the acid, the stronger its conjugate base. It is easy to misinterpret the second statement. It does *not* mean that the conjugate base of a weak acid is a strong base. When we compare the values of the ionization constants for CH_3COOH and CH_3COO^-, it is clear that *the conjugate base of a weak acid is a weak base*. It is also true that the conjugate acid of a weak base is a weak acid. The following statement summarizes these relationships.

The conjugate of *weak* is *weak*.

8-5 CONCEPT ASSESSMENT

A handbook that lists only pK_a values for weak electrolytes has the following entry for 1,2-ethanediamine, $NH_2CH_2CH_2NH_2$: $pK_1 = 6.85(+2)$; $pK_2 = 9.92(+1)$, and 2-aminopropanoic acid, $NH_2CH(CH_3)COOH$: $pK_1 = 2.34(+1)$; $pK_2 = 9.87(0)$. Interpret these handbook entries by writing equations for the ionization reactions to which these pK values apply. What are the corresponding values of the base ionization constants K_{b_1} and K_{b_2}?

Hydrolysis

In pure water at 25 °C, $[H_3O^+] = [OH^-] = 1.0 \times 10^{-7}$ M and pH = 7.00. *Pure water is pH neutral.* When NaCl dissolves in water at 25 °C, complete dissociation into Na^+ and Cl^- ions occurs, and the pH of the solution remains 7.00. We can represent this fact with the equation

$$Na^+ + Cl^- + H_2O \longrightarrow \text{no reaction}$$

As shown in Figure 8-9, when NH_4Cl is added to water, the pH falls below 7. This means that $[H_3O^+] > [OH^-]$ in the solution. A reaction producing H_3O^+ must occur.

$$Cl^- + H_2O \longrightarrow \text{no reaction}$$
$$NH_4^+ + H_2O \rightleftharpoons NH_3 + H_3O^+$$

KEEP IN MIND

that many students find hydrolysis problems challenging. The equilibrium calculations are actually quite straightforward. The challenging aspect of these problems is recognizing *when* a hydrolysis reaction is the one on which to base the calculations.

The reaction between NH_4^+ and H_2O is fundamentally no different from other acid–base reactions. A reaction between an ion and water, however, is often called a **hydrolysis** reaction. We say that ammonium ion *hydrolyzes* (and chloride ion does not).

When sodium acetate is dissolved in water, the pH rises above 7 (see Figure 8-9). This means that $[OH^-] > [H_3O^+]$ in the solution. Here, acetate ion hydrolyzes.

$$Na^+ + H_2O \longrightarrow \text{no reaction}$$
$$CH_3COO^- + H_2O \rightleftharpoons CH_3COOH + OH^-$$

▲ FIGURE 8-9
Ions as acids and bases
Each of these 1 M solutions contains bromthymol blue indicator, which has the following colors:

pH < 7	pH = 7	pH > 7
Yellow	Green	Blue

(Left) $NH_4Cl(aq)$ is acidic. (Center) NaCl(aq) is neutral. (Right) $NaCH_3COO(aq)$ is basic.

The pH of Salt Solutions

We are now in a position to make both qualitative predictions and quantitative calculations concerning the pH values of aqueous solutions of salts. Whichever of these tasks is called for, note that hydrolysis takes place only if there is a chemical reaction producing a weak acid or weak base. The following generalizations are useful.

- Salts of strong bases and strong acids (for example, NaCl) *do not hydrolyze*: for the solution, pH = 7.
- Salts of strong bases and *weak* acids (for example, $NaCH_3COO$) *hydrolyze*: pH > 7. (The *anion* acts as a *base*.)
- Salts of *weak* bases and strong acids (for example, NH_4Cl) *hydrolyze*: pH < 7. (The *cation* acts as an *acid*.)
- Salts of *weak* bases and *weak* acids (for example, NH_4CH_3COO) *hydrolyze*. (The cations are acids, and the anions are bases. Whether the solution is acidic or basic, however, depends on the relative values of K_a and K_b for the ions.)

EXAMPLE 8-11 Making Qualitative Predictions About Hydrolysis Reactions

Predict whether each of the following solutions is acidic, basic, or pH neutral: **(a)** NaOCl(aq); **(b)** KCl(aq); **(c)** NH_4NO_3(aq).

Analyze

We need to recognize that all three salts are strong electrolytes and completely dissociate in water. Then, we can consider the ions separately and ask which will react (either as an acid or as a base) with water. Recall that the anions from strong acids (e.g., Cl^-) and the cations from strong bases (e.g., Na^+) do not participate in hydrolysis.

Solve

(a) The ions present are Na^+, which does not hydrolyze, and OCl^-, which does. OCl^- is the conjugate base of HOCl and forms a basic solution.

$$OCl^- + H_2O \rightleftharpoons HOCl + OH^-$$

(b) Neither K^+ nor Cl^- hydrolyzes. KCl(aq) is neutral—that is, pH = 7.

(c) NH_4^+ hydrolyzes, but NO_3^- does not (HNO_3 is a strong acid).

$$NH_4^+ + H_2O \rightleftharpoons NH_3 + H_3O^+$$

In this case, $[H_3O^+] > [OH^-]$, and the solution is acidic.

Assess

Recognizing that certain ions in solution can undergo hydrolysis in water will be an important concept in the next chapter. It is important to learn and understand here how this concept works.

PRACTICE EXAMPLE A: Predict whether each of the following 1.0 M solutions is acidic, basic, or pH neutral: **(a)** $CH_3NH_3^+NO_3^-$(aq); **(b)** NaI(aq); **(c)** $NaNO_2$(aq).

PRACTICE EXAMPLE B: An aqueous solution containing $H_2PO_4^-$ has a pH of about 4.7. Write equations for *two* reactions of $H_2PO_4^-$ with water, and explain which reaction occurs to the greater extent.

8-6 CONCEPT ASSESSMENT

Write a chemical equation showing how an HPO_4^{2-} ion can act as both an acid and a base in aqueous solution. Without doing any pH calculations, determine whether 0.10 M Na_2HPO_4 is acidic, basic, or pH neutral. What about 0.10 M NaH_2PO_4?

EXAMPLE 8-12 Evaluating Ionization Constants for Hydrolysis Reactions

Both sodium nitrite, $NaNO_2$, and sodium benzoate, NaC_6H_5COO, are used as food preservatives. If separate solutions of these two salts have the same molarity, which solution will have the *higher* pH?

Analyze

Each of these substances is the salt of a strong base (NaOH) and a *weak acid*. The anions should ionize as *bases*, making their solutions somewhat basic. The hydrolysis will lead to a weak acid species, for which we know the K_a value; however, the expression we write will be for K_b.

$$NO_2^- + H_2O \rightleftharpoons HNO_2 + OH^- \qquad K_b(NO_2^-) = ?$$

$$C_6H_5COO^- + H_2O \rightleftharpoons C_6H_5COOH + OH^- \qquad K_b(C_6H_5COO^-) = ?$$

Therefore, we will need to recall the relationship between K_a and K_b.

Solve

Our task is to determine the K_b values, neither of which is listed in a table in this chapter. Table 8.3 does list K_a for the conjugate acids, however. Equation (8.18) can be used to write

$$K_b \text{ of } NO_2^- = \frac{K_w}{K_a(HNO_2)} = \frac{1.0 \times 10^{-14}}{7.2 \times 10^{-4}} = 1.4 \times 10^{-11}$$

$$K_b \text{ of } C_6H_5COO^- = \frac{K_w}{K_a(C_6H_5COOH)} = \frac{1.0 \times 10^{-14}}{6.3 \times 10^{-5}} = 1.6 \times 10^{-10}$$

Because the K_b of $C_6H_5COO^-$ is larger than that of NO_2^-, the benzoate ion will hydrolyze to a greater extent than the nitrite ion and will give a solution with a higher $[OH^-]$. A sodium benzoate solution is more basic and has a higher pH than a sodium nitrite solution of the same concentration.

Assess

We could have reasoned out the answer without performing any calculations by focusing instead on the conjugate acids. Because HNO_2 is a stronger acid than C_6H_5COOH, the NO_2^- ion must be a weaker base than the $C_6H_5COO^-$ ion. This is all the information we need to decide which of the two solutions is more basic.

PRACTICE EXAMPLE A: The organic bases cocaine ($pK_b = 8.41$) and codeine ($pK_b = 7.95$) react with hydrochloric acid to form salts (similar to the formation of NH_4Cl by the reaction of NH_3 and HCl). If solutions of the following salts have the same molarity, which solution would have the higher pH: cocaine hydrochloride, $C_{17}H_{21}O_4NH^+Cl^-$, or codeine hydrochloride, $C_{18}H_{21}ClO_3NH^+Cl^-$?

PRACTICE EXAMPLE B: Predict whether the solution $NH_4CN(aq)$ is acidic, basic, or neutral; and explain the basis of your prediction.

EXAMPLE 8-13 Calculating the pH of a Solution in Which Hydrolysis Occurs

Sodium cyanide, NaCN, is extremely poisonous, but it has very useful applications in gold and silver metallurgy and in the electroplating of metals. Aqueous solutions of cyanides are especially hazardous if they become acidified, because toxic hydrogen cyanide gas, HCN(g), is released. Are NaCN(aq) solutions normally acidic, basic, or pH neutral? What is the pH of 0.50 M NaCN(aq)? Note that solutions containing cyanide ion must be handled with extreme caution. They should be handled only in a fume hood by an operator wearing protective clothing.

Analyze

Na^+ does not hydrolyze, but as represented below, CN^- does hydrolyze, producing a basic solution. The question now becomes a hydrolysis equilibrium problem.

Solve

In the tabulation of the concentrations of the species involved in the hydrolysis reaction, let $[OH^-] = x$.

	CN^- + H_2O ⇌	HCN +	OH^-
initial concns:	0.50 M	—	—
changes:	$-x$ M	$+x$ M	$+x$ M
equil concns:	$(0.50 - x)$ M	x M	x M

Use equation (8.18) to obtain a value of K_b.

$$K_b = \frac{K_w}{K_a(HCN)} = \frac{1.0 \times 10^{-14}}{6.2 \times 10^{-10}} = 1.6 \times 10^{-5}$$

Now return to the tabulated data.

$$K_b = \frac{[HCN][OH^-]}{[CN^-]} = \frac{x \cdot x}{0.50 - x} = \frac{x^2}{0.50 - x} = 1.6 \times 10^{-5}$$

Assume: $x \ll 0.50$ and $0.50 - x \approx 0.50$.

$$x^2 = 0.50 \times 1.6 \times 10^{-5} = 0.80 \times 10^{-5} = 8.0 \times 10^{-6}$$

$$x = [OH^-] = (8.0 \times 10^{-6})^{1/2} = 2.8 \times 10^{-3}$$

$$pOH = -\log[OH^-] = -\log(2.8 \times 10^{-3}) = 2.55$$

$$pH = 14.00 - pOH = 14.00 - 2.55 = 11.45$$

Assess

We see that in this example, the simplifying assumption works. We also note that the solution is fairly basic for a relatively dilute solution of a salt of a weak acid and a strong base.

PRACTICE EXAMPLE A: Sodium fluoride, NaF, is found in some toothpaste formulations as an anticavity agent. What is the pH of 0.10 M NaF(aq)?

PRACTICE EXAMPLE B: The pH of an aqueous solution of NaCN is 10.38. What is $[CN^-]$ in this solution?

8-8 Molecular Structure and Acid–Base Behavior

We have now dealt with a number of aspects of acid–base chemistry, both qualitatively and quantitatively. Yet some very fundamental questions still remain to be answered, such as these: Why is HCl a strong acid, whereas HF is a weak acid? Why is acetic acid (CH_3COOH) a stronger acid than ethanol (CH_3CH_2OH) but a weaker acid than chloroacetic acid ($ClCH_2COOH$)?

These questions involve relative acid strengths. In this section, we will examine the relationship between molecular structure and the strengths of acids and bases.

Strengths of Binary Acids

Because the behavior of acids requires the loss of a proton through bond breakage, acid strength and bond strength appear to be related. In general, the stronger the H—X bond, the *weaker* the acid is. Stronger bonds are characterized by short bond lengths and high bond dissociation energies. The appropriate bond dissociation energy to use is the ionization of the H—X bond in the gas phase in equation (8.19):

$$HX(g) \longrightarrow H^+(g) + X^-(g) \qquad \textbf{(8.19)}$$

The bond dissociation energy for the gas phase ionization reaction (equation 8.19) can be obtained by using the following thermodynamic cycle:

$$\begin{array}{ccccc} HX(g) & \xrightarrow{D(H-X)} & H(g) & + & X(g) \\ & & \downarrow IE(H),\ -e^- & & \downarrow \Delta H_{ea},\ +e^- \\ & \xrightarrow{D(H^+X^-)} & H^+(g) & + & X^-(g) \end{array}$$

We can write $D(H^+X^-) = D(H—X) + IE(H) + \Delta H_{ea}$, where $D(C_6H_5O_7$ is the bond dissociation energy for $HX(g) \rightarrow H(g) + X(g)$, $IE(H)$ is the ionization energy of the hydrogen atom, and ΔH_{ea} is the electron affinity of X. $D(H^+X^-)$ is called the *heterolytic bond dissociation energy.*

▶ The dissociation of a gas-phase molecule, AB, into A^+ and B^- is called *heterolysis* and the energy change for this process is called the *heterolytic bond dissociation energy*. The dissociation of a gas-phase molecule, AB, into A and B is called *homolysis*. Thus, the bond dissociation energy (*D*) is more precisely called the *homolytic bond dissociation energy*.

Figure 8-10 shows $D(H^+X^-)$ values of binary acids formed by several elements. For binary acids, acid strength increases as the heterolytic bond dissociation energy decreases. Intuitively, this makes a lot of sense. The lower the energy requirement for converting an H—X molecule into H^+ and X^- ions, the greater the acid strength. Can we explain the trend in acid strengths in terms of (homolytic) bond dissociation energies, *D*(H—X)? Not really. For example, *D*(H—X) values tend to increase from left to right in Figure 8-10, suggesting that the acid strength should decrease across the row. But they don't. The energy requirements for converting an H—X molecule into H and X atoms are not reliable for predicting trends in acid strengths.

Trends in the strengths of binary acids are often explained by considering variations in bond length and bond polarity. Such rationalizations are possible but a little tricky. Intuitively, we expect the acid strength of H—X to increase as the length and polarity of the bond increase. Longer bonds are weaker and easier to break. Polar H—X bonds more readily produce H^+ and X^- ions because such bonds already have partial ionic charges on the H and X atoms. As we move from left to right across a row in Figure 8-10, the H—X bond length decreases whereas the polarity of the bond increases. Because the acid strength (K_a value) increases across the row, we arrive at the following conclusion.

KEEP IN MIND

that electronegativity increases as we move from left to right across a period and decreases from top to bottom in a given group. Thus, the polarity of the H—X bond increases from left to right across a row in Figure 8-10 and decreases as we move from top to bottom down a column. Atomic radii show the opposite trend (decrease from left to right and increase from top to bottom) and so H—X bond lengths decrease from left to right and increase from top to bottom in Figure 8-10.

When comparing binary acids of elements *in the same row* of the periodic table, acid strength increases as the polarity of the bond increases.

We arrive at a different conclusion if we compare binary acids from the same column in Figure 8-10. As we move from top to bottom in a column, both the bond length and acid strength of H—X increase whereas the polarity of the H—X bond decreases. The following statement summarizes the situation.

When comparing binary acids of elements *in the same group* of the periodic table, acid strength increases as the length of the bond increases.

That HF is a weaker acid than the other hydrogen halides is expected, but that it should be so much weaker has always seemed an anomaly. Explanations

increasing acid strength →

	H—CH_3	H—NH_2	H—OH	H—F
K_a	1×10^{-60}	1×10^{-34}	1.8×10^{-16}	6.6×10^{-4}
D(H—X)	414	389	464	565
$D(H^+X^-)$	**1717**	**1630**	**1598**	**1549**

	H—SH	H—Cl
K_a	1.0×10^{-7}	1×10^{6}
D(H—X)	368	431
$D(H^+X^-)$	**1458**	**1394**
	H—SeH	**H—Br**
K_a	1.3×10^{-4}	1×10^{8}
D(H—X)	335	364
$D(H^+X^-)$	**1434**	**1351**
	H—TeH	**H—I**
K_a	2.3×10^{-3}	1×10^{9}
D(H—X)	277	297
$D(H^+X^-)$	**1386**	**1314**

(increasing acid strength ↓ down each column)

▶ FIGURE 8-10
Bond dissociation energies (kJ mol^{-1}) and K_a values for some binary acids
Homolytic bond dissociation energies, D(X—H), tend to increase from left to right and decrease from top to bottom in this table. Heterolytic bond dissociation energies, $D(H^+X^-)$, decrease from left to right and from top to bottom in this table. The arrows indicate that acid strengths (K_a values) increase from left to right and from top to bottom. The K_a values for NH_3 and CH_4 are very small. These molecules do not behave as acids in water.

of this behavior center on the tendency for hydrogen bonding in HF. For example, in HF(aq), ion pairs are held together by strong hydrogen bonds, which keeps the concentration of free H_3O^+ from being as large as otherwise expected.

$$HF + H_2O \longrightarrow \underset{\text{Ion pair}}{(^{-}F \cdots H_3O^+)} \rightleftharpoons H_3O^+ + F^-$$

CH_4 and NH_3 do not have acidic properties in water, but HF is an acid of moderate strength ($K_a = 6.6 \times 10^{-4}$).

Strengths of Oxoacids

To describe the relative strengths of oxoacids, we must focus on the attraction of electrons from the O—H bond toward the central atom. The following factors promote this electron withdrawal from O—H bonds: (1) a high electronegativity (EN) of the central atom and (2) a large number of terminal O atoms in the acid molecule.

Neither HOCl nor HOBr has a terminal O atom. The major difference between the two acids is one of electronegativity—Cl is slightly more electronegative than Br. As expected, HOCl is more acidic than HOBr.

H—O—Cl:
$EN_{Cl} = 3.0$
$K_a = 2.9 \times 10^{-8}$

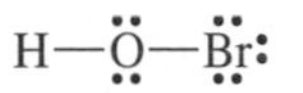

H—O—Br:
$EN_{Br} = 2.8$
$K_a = 2.1 \times 10^{-9}$

To compare the acid strengths of H_2SO_4 and H_2SO_3, we must look beyond the central atom, which is S in each acid.

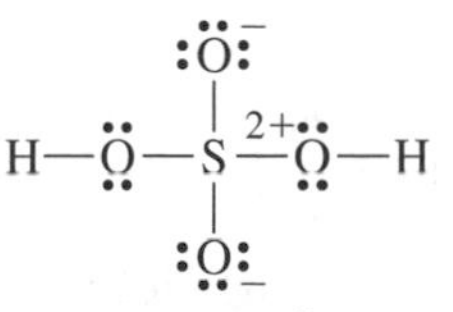

:O:⁻ | H—O—S(2+)—O—H | :O:⁻
$K_{a_1} \approx 10^3$

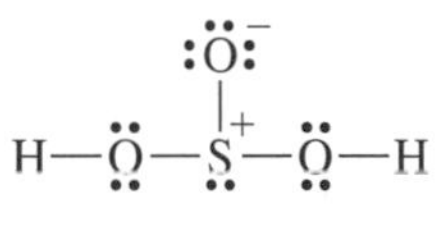

:O:⁻ | H—O—S(+)—O—H
$K_{a_1} = 1.3 \times 10^{-2}$

A highly electronegative terminal O atom tends to withdraw electrons from the O—H bonds, weakening the bonds and increasing the acidity of the molecule. Because H_2SO_4 has *two* terminal O atoms to only one in H_2SO_3, the electron-withdrawing effect is greater in H_2SO_4. As a result, H_2SO_4 is a stronger acid than H_2SO_3.

Strengths of Organic Acids

This discussion of the relationship between molecular structure and acid strength concludes with a brief consideration of some organic compounds. Consider first the case of acetic acid and ethanol. Both have an O—H group bonded to a carbon atom, but acetic acid is a much stronger acid than ethanol.

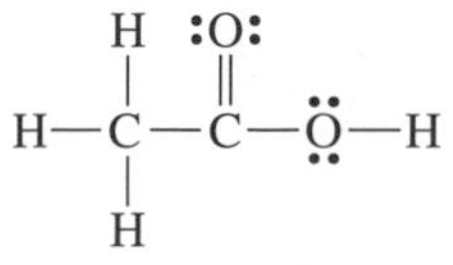

H—C(H)(H)—C(=O)—O—H
Acetic acid
$K_a = 1.8 \times 10^{-5}$

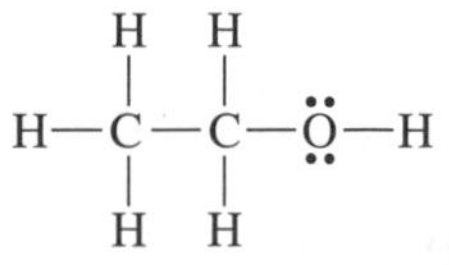

H—C(H)(H)—C(H)(H)—O—H
Ethanol
$K_a = 1.3 \times 10^{-16}$

◀ Review the concept of resonance. Compounds or ions with more resonance structures are more stable.

One possible explanation for the large difference in acidity of these two compounds is that the highly electronegative terminal O atom in acetic acid withdraws electrons from the O—H bond. The bond is weakened, and a proton (H^+) is more readily taken from a molecule of the acid by a base. A more satisfactory explanation focuses on the anions formed in the ionization.

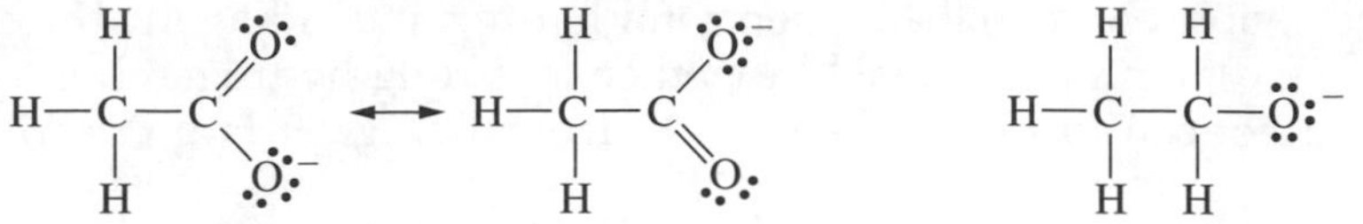

Acetate ion

Ethoxide ion

There are two plausible structures for the acetate ion. These structures suggest that each carbon-to-oxygen bond is a "$\frac{3}{2}$" bond and that each O atom carries "$\frac{1}{2}$" unit of negative charge. In short, the excess unit of negative charge in CH_3COO^- is spread out. This arrangement reduces the ability of either O atom to attach a proton and makes acetate ion only a weak Brønsted–Lowry base. In ethoxide ion, conversely, the unit of negative charge is localized on the single O atom. Ethoxide ion is a much stronger base than is acetate ion. The stronger the conjugate base, the weaker the corresponding acid.

The length of the carbon chain in a carboxylic acid has little effect on the acid strength, as in a comparison of acetic acid and octanoic acid.

CH_3COOH	$CH_3(CH_2)_6COOH$
Acetic acid	Octanoic acid
$K_a = 1.8 \times 10^{-5}$	$K_a = 1.3 \times 10^{-5}$

Yet, other atoms or groups of atoms substituted onto the carbon chain may strongly affect acid strength. If a Cl atom is substituted for one of the H atoms that is bonded to carbon in acetic acid, the result is chloroacetic acid.

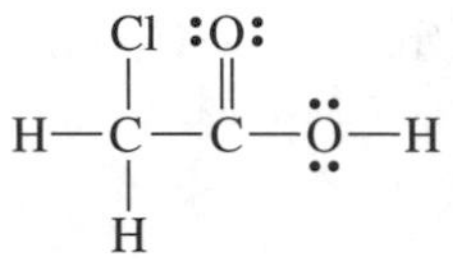

Chloroacetic acid
$K_a = 1.4 \times 10^{-3}$

The highly electronegative Cl atom helps draw electrons away from the O—H bond. The O—H bond is weakened, the proton is lost more readily, and the acid is a stronger acid than acetic acid. This effect falls off rapidly as the distance increases between the substituted atom or group and the O—H bond in an organic acid.

Example 8-14 illustrates some of the factors affecting acid strength that are discussed in this section.

EXAMPLE 8-14 Identifying Factors That Affect the Strengths of Acids

Explain which member of each of the following pairs is the stronger acid.

(a) (I) 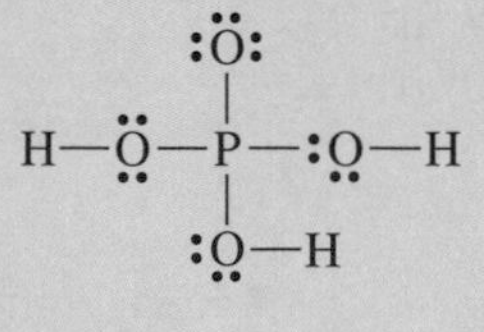 or (II)

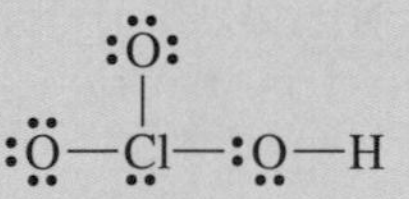

(b) (I) 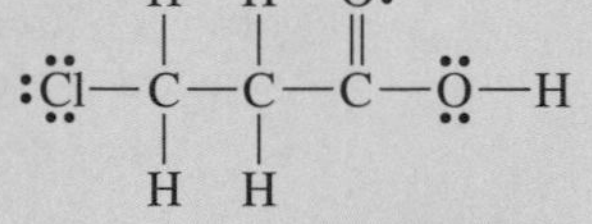 or (II)

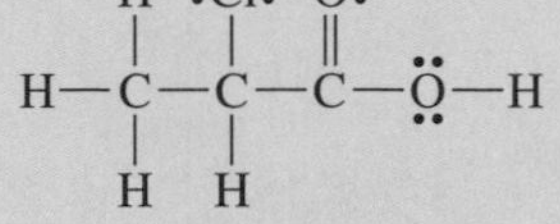

Analyze

In these types of questions we first identify the acidic proton(s), and then look for electronegative atoms or groups that pull electron density away from the acidic proton(s). The more electron density that is pulled away from the proton, the more acidic it is.

(a) Phosphoric acid, H_3PO_4, has four O atoms to the three in $HClO_3$, but it is the number of *terminal* O atoms that we must consider, not just the total number of O atoms in the molecule. $HClO_3$ has *two* terminal O atoms and H_3PO_4 has *one*. Also, the Cl atom (EN = 3.0) is considerably more electronegative than the P atom (EN = 2.1). These facts point to chloric acid (II) as being the stronger of the two acids. ($K_a \approx 5 \times 10^2$ for $HClO_3$ and $K_{a_1} = 7.1 \times 10^{-3}$ for H_3PO_4.)

(b) The Cl atom withdraws electrons more strongly when it is directly adjacent to the carboxyl group. Compound (II), 2-chloropropanoic acid ($K_a = 1.4 \times 10^{-3}$), is a stronger acid than compound (I), 3-chloropropanoic acid ($K_a = 1.0 \times 10^{-4}$).

Assess

This type of analysis is important in organic chemistry. To successfully solve these types of problems, we must know how to draw Lewis structures and we must understand the concept of electronegativity.

PRACTICE EXAMPLE A: Explain which is the stronger acid, HNO_3 or $HClO_4$; CH_2FCOOH or $CH_2BrCOOH$. [*Hint:* Draw plausible Lewis structures.]

PRACTICE EXAMPLE B: Explain which is the stronger acid, H_3PO_4 or H_2SO_3; CCl_3CH_2COOH or CCl_2FCH_2COOH. [*Hint:* Draw plausible Lewis structures.]

Strengths of Amines as Bases

The fundamental factor affecting the strength of an amine as a base concerns the ability of the lone pair of electrons on the N atom to bind a proton taken from an acid. When an atom or group of atoms more electronegative than H replaces one of the H atoms of NH_3, the electronegative group withdraws electron density from the N atom. The lone-pair electrons cannot bind a proton as strongly, and the base is weaker. Thus, bromamine, in which the electronegative Br atom is attached to the amine group (NH_2), is a *weaker* base than ammonia.

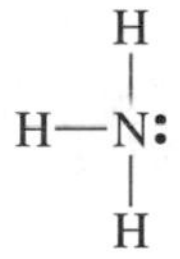

```
     H              H
     |              |
   H—N:          Br—N:
     |              |
     H              H
```

Ammonia
$pK_b = 4.74$

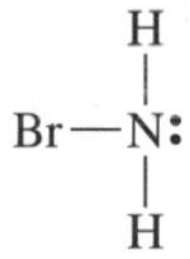

Bromamine
NH_2Br, $pK_b = 7.61$

Hydrocarbon chains have no electron-withdrawing ability. When they are attached to the amine group, the pK_b values are lower than for ammonia due to the electron-donating ability of CH_3 and CH_2CH_3.

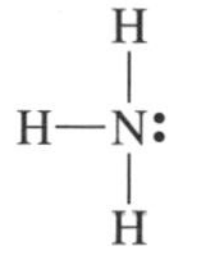

```
     H           H  H            H  H  H
     |           |  |            |  |  |
   H—N:        H—C—N:          H—C—C—N:
     |           |  |            |  |  |
     H           H  H            H  H  H
```

Ammonia
$pK_b = 4.74$

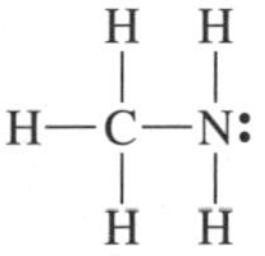

Methylamine
CH_3NH_2, $pK_b = 3.38$

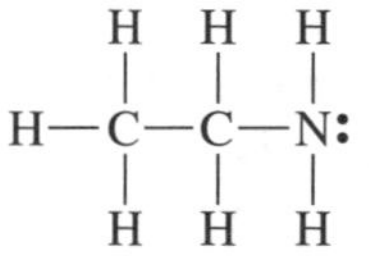

Ethylamine
$CH_3CH_2NH_2$, $pK_b = 3.37$

An additional electron-withdrawing effect is seen in amines that are based on the benzene ring or related structures. Such amines are called *aromatic* amines. Aniline, $C_6H_5NH_2$, is based on benzene, C_6H_6, which is a six-carbon ring molecule with unsaturation in the carbon-to-carbon bonds. The electrons associated with this unsaturation are said to be *delocalized*. As suggested by the following structures, to some extent even the lone-pair electrons of the NH_2 group participate in the "spreading out" of delocalized electrons. (The curved arrows suggest the progressive movement of electrons around the ring.)

◀ Note that these are actually resonance Lewis structures.

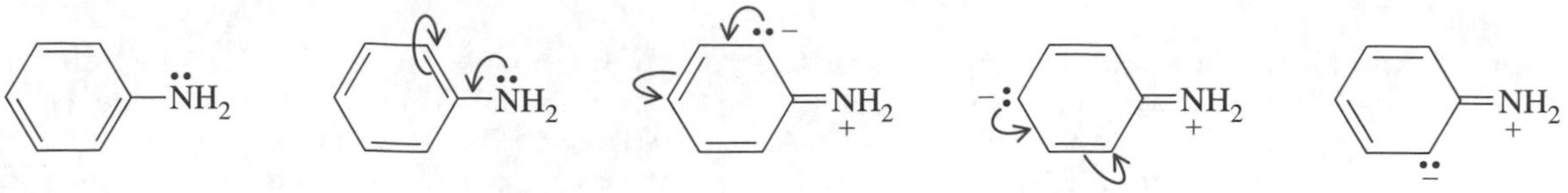

The withdrawal of electron charge density from the NH_2 group causes aniline to be a much weaker base than is cyclohexylamine. (H atoms bonded to ring carbon atoms are not shown in the following structures.)

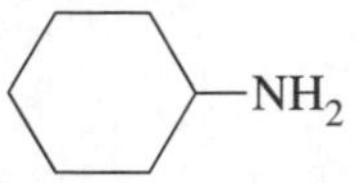

Cyclohexylamine, $pK_b = 3.36$ 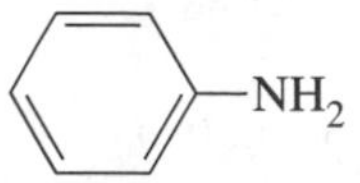 Aniline, $pK_b = 9.13$

▶ The pK_b for *meta*-chloroaniline is 10.66.

Replacement of a ring-bound H atom in aniline with an atom or group that has a high electronegativity causes even more electron density to be drawn away from the NH_2 group, further reducing the base strength. Also, the closer this ring substituent is to the NH_2 group, the greater is the effect.

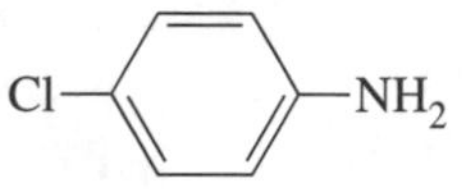

para-Chloroaniline, $pK_b = 10.01$ 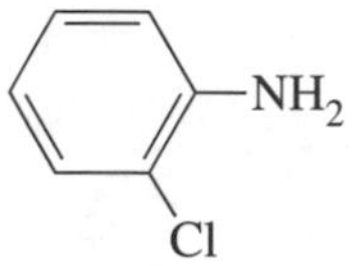 *ortho*-Chloroaniline, $pK_b = 11.36$

8-7 CONCEPT ASSESSMENT

Would you expect pK_a of *ortho*-chlorophenol to be greater than, less than, or nearly the same as that of phenol? Explain.

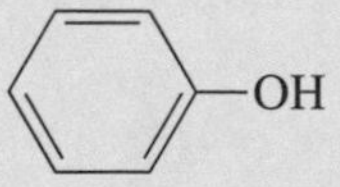

Phenol, $pK_a = 10.00$ 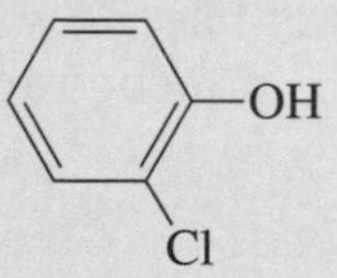 *ortho*-Chlorophenol, $pK_a = ?$

8-9 Lewis Acids and Bases

In the previous section, we presented ideas about the molecular structures of acids and bases. In 1923, G. N. Lewis proposed an acid–base theory closely related to bonding and structure. The Lewis acid–base theory is not limited to reactions involving H^+ and OH^-: It extends acid–base concepts to reactions in gases and in solids. It is especially important in describing certain reactions between organic molecules.

A **Lewis acid** is a species (an atom, ion, or molecule) that is an *electron-pair acceptor*, and a **Lewis base** is a species that is an *electron-pair donor*. A reaction between a Lewis acid (A) and a Lewis base (B:) results in the formation of a covalent bond between them. The product of a Lewis acid–base reaction is called an **adduct** (or *addition compound*). The reaction can be represented as

$$B\colon + A \longrightarrow B - A$$

where B:A is the adduct. The formation of a covalent chemical bond by one species donating a pair of electrons to another is called *coordination*, and the bond joining the Lewis acid and Lewis base is called a *coordinate covalent bond. Lewis acids* are species with vacant orbitals that can accommodate electron pairs; *Lewis bases* are species that have lone-pair electrons available for sharing.

By these definitions, OH^-, a Brønsted–Lowry base, is also a Lewis base because lone-pair electrons are present on the O atom. So too is NH_3 a Lewis base. HCl, conversely, is not a Lewis acid: It is not an electron-pair acceptor. We can think of HCl as producing H^+, however, and H^+ is a Lewis acid. H^+ forms a coordinate covalent bond with an available electron pair.

Species with an incomplete valence shell are Lewis acids. When the Lewis acid forms a coordinate covalent bond with a Lewis base, the octet is completed. A good example of octet completion is the reaction of BF_3 and NH_3.

$$H_3N: + BF_3 \longrightarrow H_3N—BF_3$$

◀ Bonding in the $H_3N—BF_3$ adduct can be described by the overlap of sp^3 orbitals on the N and B atoms, with the two electrons donated by the N atom.

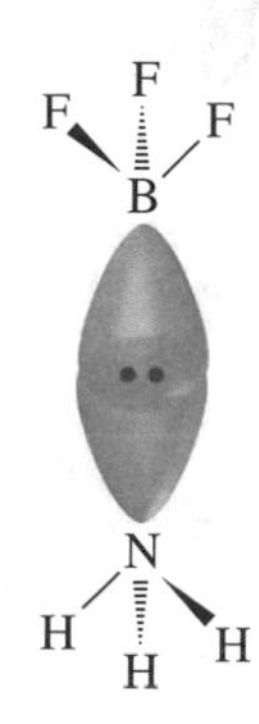

The reaction of lime (CaO) with sulfur dioxide is an important reaction for reducing SO_2 emissions from coal-fired power plants. This reaction between a solid and a gas underscores that Lewis acid–base reactions can occur in all states of matter. The smaller curved red arrow in reaction (8.20) suggests that an electron pair in the Lewis structure is rearranged.

$$Ca^{2+}:\ddot{O}:^{2-} + SO_2 \longrightarrow Ca^{2+}[:\ddot{O}—SO_2]^{2-} \qquad (8.20)$$

An important application of the Lewis acid–base theory involves the formation of *complex ions.* Complex ions are polyatomic ions that contain a central metal ion to which other ions or small molecules are attached. *Hydrated metal ions* form in aqueous solution because the water acts as a Lewis base and the metal ion as a Lewis acid. The water molecules attach themselves to the metal ion by means of coordinate covalent bonds. Thus, for example, when anhydrous $AlCl_3$ is added to water, the resultant solution becomes hot because of the heat evolved in the formation of the hydrated metal ion $[Al(H_2O)_6]^{3+}(aq)$ (Fig. 8-11).

The interaction between the metal ion and the water molecules is so strong that when the salt is crystallized from the solution, the water molecules crystallize along with the metal ion, forming the hydrated metal salt $AlCl_3 \cdot 6\,H_2O$. In aqueous solution, the hydrated metal ions can act as Brønsted acids. For instance, the hydrolysis of hydrated Al^{3+} is given by

$$[Al(H_2O)_6]^{3+} + H_2O \rightleftharpoons [Al(OH)(H_2O)_5]^{2+} + H_3O^+$$

In the hydrated metal ion, the OH bond in a water molecule becomes weakened. This happens because, in forming the coordinate covalent bond with the O atom of the water, the metal ion causes electron density to be drawn toward it; hence, electron density is drawn away from the OH bond. As a consequence, the coordinated H_2O molecule can donate a H^+ to a solvent H_2O molecule (Fig. 8-12). The H_2O molecule that has ionized is converted to OH^-, which remains attached to the Al^{3+}; the charge on the complex ion is reduced from 3+ to 2+. The extent of ionization of $[Al(H_2O)_6]^{3+}$, measured by its K_a value and as pictured in Figure 8-13, is essentially the same as that of acetic acid ($K_a = 1.8 \times 10^{-5}$). Many other metal ions hydrolyze, especially the transition metal ions. These and other hydrated metal ions acting as acids are discussed in later chapters.

$$[Al(H_2O)_6]^{3+}$$

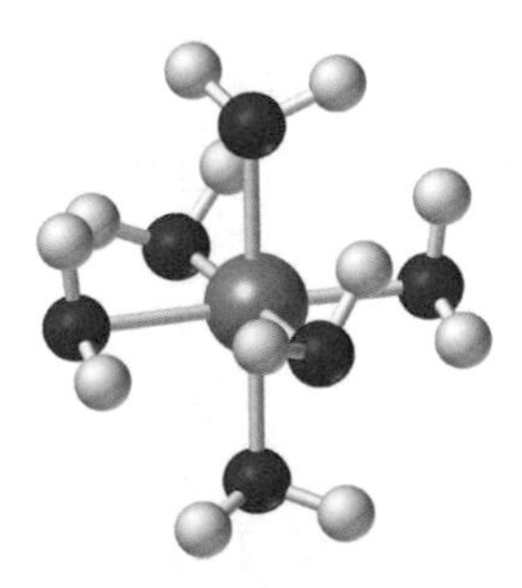

▲ FIGURE 8-11
The Lewis structure of $[Al(H_2O)_6]^{3+}$ and a ball-and-stick representation

$$[Al(H_2O)_6]^{3+} + H_2O \rightleftharpoons [Al(OH)(H_2O)_5]^{2+} + H_3O^+$$

◀ FIGURE 8-12
Hydrolysis of $[Al(H_2O)_6]^{3+}$ to produce H_3O^+
An uncoordinated water molecule removes a proton from a coordinated water molecule.

▲ FIGURE 8-13
Acidic properties of hydrated metal ions
The yellow color of bromthymol blue indicator in $Al_2(SO_4)_3$(aq) denotes that the solution is acidic. The pH meter gives a more precise indication of the pH.

Complex ions can also form between transition metal ions and other Lewis bases, such as NH_3. For instance, Zn^{2+} combines with NH_3 to form the complex ion $[Zn(NH_3)_4]^{2+}$. The central Zn^{2+} ion accepts electrons from the Lewis base NH_3. to form coordinate covalent bonds; it is a Lewis acid.

8-3 ARE YOU WONDERING...

Why Na^+(aq) does not act as an acid in aqueous solution?

Whether an aqueous solution of a metal ion is acidic depends on two principal factors. The first is the amount of charge on the cation; the second is the size of the ion. The greater the charge on the cation, the greater is the ability of the metal ion to draw electron density away from the O—H bond in a H_2O molecule in its hydration sphere, favoring the release of a H^+ ion. The smaller the cation, the more highly concentrated is the positive charge. Hence, for a given positive charge, the smaller the cation, the more acidic the solution.

The ratio of the charge on the cation to the volume of the cation is called the *charge density*.

$$\rho = \text{charge density} = \frac{\text{ionic charge}}{\text{ionic volume}}$$

The greater its charge density, the more effective a metal ion is at pulling electron density from the O—H bond and the more acidic is the hydrated cation (see the table and plot below). A highly concentrated positive charge on a small cation is better able to pull electron density from the O—H bond than is a less concentrated positive charge on a larger cation.

Thus the small, highly charged Al^{3+} ion produces acidic solutions, but the larger Na^+ cation, with a charge of just 1+, does not increase the concentration of H_3O^+. In fact, none of the group 1 cations produces appreciably acidic solutions, and only Be^{2+} of the group 2 elements is small enough to do so ($pK_a = 5.4$).

Metal Cation	Ionic Radius, pm	$\rho \times 10^7$, Charge pm^{-3}	pK_a
Li^+	76	3.27	13.6
Na^+	102	1.53	14.2
K^+	138	0.680	14.5
Be^{2+}	45	23.2	5.4
Cu^{2+}	66	9.33	8.0
Ni^{2+}	69	8.35	9.9
Mg^{2+}	72	7.51	11.4
Zn^{2+}	74	7.00	9.0
Co^{2+}	74	7.00	9.7
Mn^{2+}	83	5.23	10.6
Ca^{2+}	100	3.22	12.8
Al^{3+}	53	23.8	5.0
Cr^{3+}	61	17.0	4.0
Ti^{3+}	67	13.5	2.2
Fe^{3+}	78	9.19	2.2

The pK_a of H_3O^+ is −1.7, and the pK_a of water is 15.7.

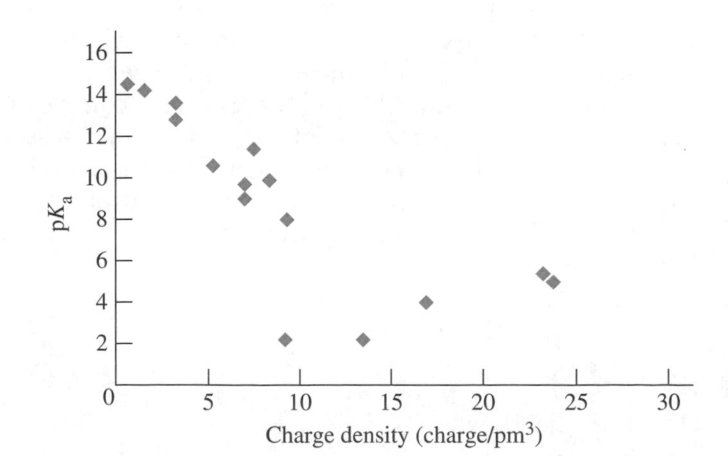

EXAMPLE 8-15 Identifying Lewis Acids and Bases

According to the Lewis theory, each of the following is an acid–base reaction. Which species is the acid and which is the base?

(a) $BF_3 + F^- \longrightarrow BF_4^-$

(b) $OH^-(aq) + CO_2(aq) \longrightarrow HCO_3^-(aq)$

Analyze

Recall that in Lewis theory an acid–base reaction involves the movement of electrons. The Lewis acid accepts electrons and the Lewis base donates electrons. In this example, we need to identify the species that is accepting the electrons and the one that is donating electrons.

Solve

(a) In BF_3, the B atom has a vacant orbital and an incomplete octet. The fluoride ion has an outer-shell octet of electrons. BF_3 is the electron-pair acceptor—the acid. F^- is the electron-pair donor—the base.

(b) We have already identified OH^- as a Lewis base, so we might suspect that it is the base and that $CO_2(aq)$ is the Lewis acid. The following Lewis structures show this to be so. As in reaction (8.20), a rearrangement of an electron pair at one of the double bonds is also required, as indicated by the smaller red arrow.

$$H{-}\ddot{\underset{\cdot\cdot}{O}}{:}^- + O{=}C{=}O \longrightarrow \left[H{-}\ddot{\underset{\cdot\cdot}{O}}{-}C(\text{:}\ddot{O}\text{:})({=}\ddot{O}\text{:})\right]^-$$

Assess

Typically, those species that have filled orbitals are Lewis bases, and those with vacant orbitals are Lewis acids. The transfer of electron density from a Lewis base to a vacant orbital on a Lewis acid is a recurring concept in chemistry. We will make use of this concept in the later chapters, as well as in organic chemistry. To describe the reaction in (b) in this way requires us to consider the electronic structure of CO_2 in terms of molecular orbital theory. Some of the 2*p* orbitals on the carbon and oxygen atoms in CO_2 combine to give bonding and antibonding π-type molecular orbitals. The vacant orbital in CO_2 that accepts the lone pair from OH^- is an antibonding π-type orbital.

PRACTICE EXAMPLE A: Identify the Lewis acids and bases in these reactions.

(a) $BF_3 + NH_3 \longrightarrow F_3BNH_3$

(b) $Cr^{3+} + 6\,H_2O \longrightarrow [Cr(H_2O)_6]^{3+}$

PRACTICE EXAMPLE B: Identify the Lewis acids and bases in these reactions.

(a) $Al(OH)_3 + OH^- \longrightarrow [Al(OH)_4]^-$

(b) $SnCl_4 + 2\,Cl^- \longrightarrow [SnCl_6]^{2-}$

8-8 CONCEPT ASSESSMENT

Liquid bromine in the presence of iron(III) tribromide forms a bromonium:iron(III) tribromide adduct. Propose a plausible mechanism for adduct formation and identify the Lewis acid and Lewis base. [*Hint*: What is the iron(III) electron configuration?]

Summary

8-1 Arrhenius Theory—The central concept in Arrhenius theory describes a neutralization reaction as the combination of hydrogen ions and hydroxide ions to form water (expression 8.1). A major failing of this theory is that it does not account for the key role of the solvent in the ionization of a solute.

8-2 Brønsted–Lowry Theory of Acids and Bases—The Brønsted–Lowry theory describes an acid as a **proton donor** and a base as a **proton acceptor**. In an acid–base reaction, a base takes a proton (H^+) from an acid. In general, acid–base reactions are reversible, but equilibrium is displaced in the direction from the *stronger* acids and bases to their *weaker* conjugates. The **conjugate base** (A^-) is derived from the acid HA while the **conjugate acid** (HB^+) is derived from the base (B). The combinations of HA/A^- and B/HB^+ are known as conjugate acid–base pairs. The conjugate acid of the base H_2O is the **hydronium ion**, H_3O^+. The equilibrium constants representing the ionization of an acid or a base in water are commonly referred to as the **acid ionization constant** and **base ionization constant**, respectively. Certain substances, for example water, are said to be **amphiprotic**. They can act as an acid or base.

8-3 Self-Ionization of Water and the pH Scale—In pure water and in aqueous solutions, **self-ionization** of the water occurs to a very slight extent, producing H_3O^+ and OH^-, as described by the equilibrium constant K_w, known as the **ion product of water** (expression 8.7). The designations **pH** (expression 8.8) and **pOH** (expression 8.9) are often used to describe the concentrations of H_3O^+ and OH in aqueous solutions.

8-4 Strong Acids and Strong Bases—In aqueous solutions, strong acids ionize completely to produce H_3O^+, and strong bases dissociate completely to produce OH^-. Common strong acids and bases are given in Table 8.2 and can be easily memorized.

8-5 Weak Acids and Weak Bases—The ionizations of weak acids and weak bases are reversible reactions, and the extent of their ionization can be related to the ionization constants K_a and K_b or their logarithmic equivalents $pK_a = -\log K_a$ and $pK_b = -\log K_b$ (Table 8.3). Another method used to indicate the degree of ionization is **percent ionization** (expression 8.14). The acidity of many weak acids is associated with the carboxylic acid group, —COOH. Weak bases typically contain one or more nitrogen atoms. Calculations involving ionization equilibria are in many ways similar to those introduced in Chapter 6, although some additional considerations are necessary for polyprotic acids.

8-6 Polyprotic Acids—**Polyprotic acids** are acids with more than one ionizable H atom that undergo a stepwise ionization and have a different ionization constant, $K_{a_1}, K_{a_2}, \ldots$, for each ionization step.

8-7 Ions as Acids and Bases—In reactions between ions and water—**hydrolysis** reactions—the ions react as weak acids or weak bases. The pH of salt solutions depends on the anions and/or cations present. Anions from weak acids lead to solutions with $pH > 7$ while cations from weak bases lead to $pH < 7$.

8-8 Molecular Structure and Acid–Base Behavior—Molecular composition and structure are the keys to determining whether a substance is acidic, basic, or amphiprotic. In addition, molecular structure affects whether an acid or base is strong or weak. In assessing acid strength, for example, factors that affect the strength of the bond that must be broken to release H^+ must be considered. In assessing base strength, factors that affect the ability of lone-pair electrons to bind a proton are of primary concern.

8-9 Lewis Acids and Bases—The Lewis acid–base theory views an electron-pair acceptor as a **Lewis acid** and an electron-pair donor as a **Lewis base**. The addition compound of a Lewis acid–base reaction is referred to as an **adduct**. The theory is most useful in situations that cannot be described by means of proton transfers, for example, in reactions involving gases and solids and in reactions between organic compounds.

Integrative Example

Bromoacetic acid, $BrCH_2COOH$, has $pK_a = 2.902$. Calculate the expected values of **(a)** the freezing point of 0.0500 M $BrCH_2COOH(aq)$ and **(b)** the osmotic pressure at 25 °C of 0.00500 M $BrCH_2COOH(aq)$.

Analyze

Freezing point and osmotic pressure are both colligative properties. The values of these properties depend on the total concentrations of particles (molecules and ions) in a solution, but not on the identity of those particles. We can use the ICE method for equilibrium calculations to determine the total concentrations of particles (molecules and ions) in a weak electrolyte solution, as we learned to do in this chapter.

Solve

A good place to begin is to convert the pK_a for bromoacetic acid to K_a.

$$pK_a = 2.902 = -\log K_a$$

$$K_a = 10^{-2.902} = 1.25 \times 10^{-3}$$

Next, write the equation for the reversible ionization reaction and the equilibrium constant expression.

$$BrCH_2COOH + H_2O \rightleftharpoons H_3O^+ + BrCH_2COO^-$$

$$K_a = \frac{[H_3O^+][BrCH_2COO^-]}{[BrCH_2COOH]} = 1.25 \times 10^{-3}$$

(a) Enter the relevant data into the ICE format under the equation for the ionization reaction.

	$BrCH_2COOH + H_2O \rightleftharpoons$	$H_3O^+ +$	$BrCH_2COO^-$
initial concns:	0.0500 M	—	—
changes:	$-x$ M	$+x$ M	$+x$ M
equil concns:	$(0.0500 - x)$ M	x M	x M

The equilibrium constant expression based on these data is

$$K_a = \frac{[H_3O^+][BrCH_2COO^-]}{[BrCH_2COOH]} = \frac{x \cdot x}{0.0500 - x} = 1.25 \times 10^{-3}$$

Solve for x.

$$x^2 + 1.25 \times 10^{-3}x - 6.25 \times 10^{-5} = 0$$

$$x = \frac{-1.25 \times 10^{-3} \pm \sqrt{(1.25 \times 10^{-3})^2 + 4 \times 6.25 \times 10^{-5}}}{2}$$

$$x = \frac{-1.25 \times 10^{-3} \pm 1.59 \times 10^{-2}}{2} = 7.3 \times 10^{-3}\,\text{M}$$

The total concentration of molecules and ions at equilibrium is

$$(0.0500 - x)\,\text{M} + x\,\text{M} + x\,\text{M} = (0.0500 + x)\,\text{M} = 0.0573\,\text{M}$$

Assuming that 0.0573 M = 0.0573 m, the freezing point depression of water caused by 0.0573 mol/L of particles is

$$\Delta T_f = -K_f \times m = -1.86\,°\text{C}\,m^{-1} \times 0.0573\,m = -0.107\,°\text{C}$$

The freezing point of 0.0500 M $BrCH_2COOH(aq)$ is 0.107 °C below the freezing point of water (0.000 °C), that is, −0.107 °C.

(b) Enter the relevant data into the ICE format under the equation for the ionization reaction.

	$BrCH_2COOH + H_2O \rightleftharpoons$	$H_3O^+ +$	$BrCH_2COO^-$
initial concns:	0.00500 M	—	—
changes:	$-x$ M	$+x$ M	$+x$ M
equil concns:	$(0.00500 - x)$ M	x M	x M

The equilibrium constant expression based on these data is

$$K_a = \frac{[H_3O^+][BrCH_2COO^-]}{[BrCH_2COOH]} = \frac{x \cdot x}{0.00500 - x} = 1.25 \times 10^{-3}$$

Solve for x.

$$x^2 + 1.25 \times 10^{-3}x - 6.25 \times 10^{-6} = 0$$

$$x = \frac{-1.25 \times 10^{-3} \pm \sqrt{(1.25 \times 10^{-3})^2 + 4 \times 6.25 \times 10^{-6}}}{2}$$

$$x = \frac{-1.25 \times 10^{-3} \pm 5.15 \times 10^{-3}}{2} = 1.95 \times 10^{-3}\,\text{M}$$

The total concentration of molecules and ions at equilibrium is

$$(0.00500 - x)\,\text{M} + x\,\text{M} + x\,\text{M} = (0.00500 + x)\,\text{M} = 0.00695\,\text{M}$$

At 25.00 °C, the osmotic pressure of an aqueous solution with 0.00695 mol/L of particles (molecules and ions) is

$$\pi = \text{M} \times RT = 0.00695\,\text{mol L}^{-1} \times 0.08206\,\text{L atm mol}^{-1}\,\text{K}^{-1} \times 298.15\,\text{K} = 0.170\,\text{atm}$$

Assess

The pK_a is stated more precisely than in most previous equilibrium calculations, and this permitted us to carry three significant figures rather than the usual two in most of the calculations. The assumption in part (a) that 0.0573 M = 0.0573 *m* is reasonable for a dilute aqueous solution with a density of essentially 1.00 g/mL. The mass of solvent (water) in one liter of solution is very close to one kilogram, so that molarity (mol solute/L solution) and molality (mol solute/kg solvent) are essentially the same. The calculation in part (b) could have been done more easily by assuming that the concentration of solute particles would be just 10% of that in part (a), that is, 0.00573 M compared to 0.0573 M. However, this would have been a false assumption. Because the percent ionization of the acid is a function of its concentration, the total particle concentration in part (b) was about 12% of that found in part (a), not 10%.

PRACTICE EXAMPLE A: The solubility of $CO_2(g)$ in H_2O at 25 °C and under a $CO_2(g)$ pressure of 1 atm is 1.45 g CO_2/L. Air contains 0.037% CO_2 by volume. Use this information, together with data from Table 8.4, to show that rainwater saturated with CO_2 has a pH ≈ 5.6 (the normal pH for rainwater). [*Hint:* Recall Henry's law. What is the partial pressure of $CO_2(g)$ in air?]

PRACTICE EXAMPLE B: Often the following generalization applies to oxoacids with the formula $EO_m(OH)_n$ (where E is the central atom): If $m = 0$, $K_a \approx 10^{-7}$; if $m = 1$, $K_a \approx 10^{-2}$; if $m = 2$, K_a is large; and if $m = 3$, K_a is very large.

(a) Show that this generalization works well for the oxoacids of chlorine: HOCl, $pK_a = 7.52$; HOClO, $pK_a = 1.92$; $HOClO_2$, $pK_a = -3$; $HOClO_3$, $pK_a = -8$.

(b) Estimate the value of K_{a_1} for H_3AsO_4.

(c) Write a Lewis structure for hypophosphorous acid, H_3PO_2, for which $pK_a = 1.1$.

Exercises

Brønsted–Lowry Theory of Acids and Bases

1. According to the Brønsted–Lowry theory, label each of the following as an acid or a base. **(a)** HNO_2; **(b)** OCl^-; **(c)** NH_2^-; **(d)** NH_4^+; **(e)** $CH_3NH_3^+$
2. Write the formula of the conjugate base in the reaction of each acid with water. **(a)** HIO_3; **(b)** C_6H_5COOH; **(c)** HPO_4^{2-}; **(d)** $C_2H_5NH_3^+$
3. For each of the following, identify the acids and bases involved in both the forward and reverse directions.
   (a) $HOBr + H_2O \rightleftharpoons OBr^- + H_3O^+$
   (b) $HSO_4^- + H_2O \rightleftharpoons SO_4^{2-} + H_3O^+$
   (c) $HS^- + H_2O \rightleftharpoons H_2S + OH^-$
   (d) $C_6H_5NH_3^+ + OH^- \rightleftharpoons C_6H_5NH_2 + H_2O$
4. Which of the following species are *amphiprotic* in aqueous solution? For such a species, write one equation showing it acting as an acid, and another equation showing it acting as a base. OH^-, NH_4^+, H_2O, HS^-, NO_2^-, HCO_3^-, HBr.
5. With which of the following bases will the ionization of acetic acid, CH_3COOH, proceed furthest toward completion (to the right): **(a)** H_2O; **(b)** NH_3; **(c)** Cl^-; **(d)** NO_3^-? Explain your answer.
6. In a manner similar to equation (8.6), represent the self-ionization of the following liquid solvents: **(a)** NH_3; **(b)** HF; **(c)** CH_3OH; **(d)** CH_3COOH; **(e)** H_2SO_4.
7. With the aid of Table 8.1, predict the direction (forward or reverse) favored in each of the following acid–base reactions.
   (a) $NH_4^+ + OH^- \rightleftharpoons H_2O + NH_3$
   (b) $HSO_4^- + NO_3^- \rightleftharpoons HNO_3 + SO_4^{2-}$
   (c) $CH_3OH + CH_3COO \rightleftharpoons CH_3COOH + CH_3O^-$
8. With the aid of Table 8.1, predict the direction (forward or reverse) favored in each of the following acid–base reactions.
   (a) $CH_3COOH + CO_3^{2-} \rightleftharpoons HCO_3^- + CH_3COO$
   (b) $HNO_2 + ClO_4^- \rightleftharpoons HClO_4 + NO_2^-$
   (c) $H_2CO_3 + CO_3^{2-} \rightleftharpoons HCO_3^- + HCO_3^-$

Strong Acids, Strong Bases, and pH

9. Calculate $[H_3O^+]$ and $[OH^-]$ for each solution: **(a)** 0.00165 M HNO_3; **(b)** 0.0087 M KOH; **(c)** 0.00213 M $Sr(OH)_2$; **(d)** 5.8×10^{-4} M HI.
10. What is the pH of each of the following solutions? **(a)** 0.0045 M HCl; **(b)** 6.14×10^{-4} M HNO_3; **(c)** 0.00683 M NaOH; **(d)** 4.8×10^{-3} M $Ba(OH)_2$.

11. Calculate $[H_3O^+]$ and pH in saturated $Ba(OH)_2(aq)$, which contains 3.9 g $Ba(OH)_2 \cdot 8\,H_2O$ per 100 mL of solution.

12. A saturated aqueous solution of $Ca(OH)_2$ has a pH of 12.35. What is the solubility of $Ca(OH)_2$, expressed in milligrams per 100 mL of solution?

13. What is $[H_3O^+]$ in a solution obtained by dissolving 205 mL HCl(g), measured at 23 °C and 751 mmHg, in 4.25 L of aqueous solution?

14. What is the pH of the solution obtained when 125 mL of 0.606 M NaOH is diluted to 15.0 L with water?

15. How many milliliters of concentrated HCl(aq) (36.0% HCl by mass, d = 1.18 g/mL) are required to produce 12.5 L of a solution with pH = 2.10?

16. How many milliliters of a 15.0%, by mass solution of KOH(aq) (d = 1.14 g/mL) are required to produce 25.0 L of a solution with pH = 11.55?

17. What volume of 6.15 M HCl(aq) is required to exactly neutralize 1.25 L of 0.265 M $NH_3(aq)$?

$$NH_3(aq) + H_3O^+(aq) \longrightarrow NH_4^+(aq) + H_2O$$

18. A 28.2 L volume of HCl(g), measured at 742 mmHg and 25.0 °C, is dissolved in water. What volume of $NH_3(g)$, measured at 762 mmHg and 21.0 °C, must be absorbed by the same solution to neutralize the HCl?

19. 50.00 mL of 0.0155 M HI(aq) is mixed with 75.00 mL of 0.0106 M KOH(aq). What is the pH of the final solution?

20. 25.00 mL of a $HNO_3(aq)$ solution with a pH of 2.12 is mixed with 25.00 mL of a KOH(aq) solution with a pH of 12.65. What is the pH of the final solution?

Weak Acids, Weak Bases, and pH

(Use data from Table 8.3 as necessary.)

21. What are the $[H_3O^+]$ and pH of 0.143 M HNO_2?

22. What are the $[H_3O^+]$ and pH of 0.085 M $C_2H_5NH_2$?

23. For the ionization of phenylacetic acid,

$$C_6H_5CH_2CO_2H + H_2O \rightleftharpoons H_3O^+ + C_6H_5CH_2CO_2^- \qquad K_a = 4.9 \times 10^{-5}$$

(a) What is $[C_6H_5CH_2CO_2^-]$ in 0.186 M $C_6H_5CH_2CO_2H$?

(b) What is the pH of 0.121 M $C_6H_5CH_2CO_2H$?

24. A 625 mL sample of an aqueous solution containing 0.275 mol propionic acid, $CH_3CH_2CO_2H$, has $[H_3O^+]$ = 0.00239 M. What is the value of K_a for propionic acid?

$$CH_3CH_2CO_2H + H_2O \rightleftharpoons H_3O^+ + CH_3CH_2CO_2^- \qquad K_a = ?$$

25. Fluoroacetic acid occurs in gifblaar, one of the most poisonous of all plants. A 0.318 M solution of the acid is found to have a pH = 1.56. Calculate K_a of fluoroacetic acid.

$$CH_2FCOOH(aq) + H_2O \rightleftharpoons H_3O^+(aq) + CH_2FCOO^-(aq) \qquad K_a = ?$$

26. Caproic acid, $HC_6H_{11}O_2$, found in small amounts in coconut and palm oils, is used in making artificial flavors. A saturated aqueous solution of the acid contains 11 g/L and has pH = 2.94. Calculate K_a for the acid.

$$HC_6H_{11}O_2 + H_2O \rightleftharpoons H_3O^+ + C_6H_{11}O_2^- \qquad K_a = ?$$

27. What mass of benzoic acid, C_6H_5COOH, would you dissolve in 350.0 mL of water to produce a solution with a pH = 2.85?

$$C_6H_5COOH + H_2O \rightleftharpoons H_3O^+ + C_6H_5COO^- \qquad K_a = 6.3 \times 10^{-5}$$

28. What must be the molarity of an aqueous solution of trimethylamine, $(CH_3)_3N$, if it has a pH = 11.12?

$$(CH_3)_3N + H_2O \rightleftharpoons (CH_3)_3NH^+ + OH^- \qquad K_b = 6.3 \times 10^{-5}$$

29. What are $[H_3O^+]$, $[OH^-]$, pH, and pOH of 0.55 M M $HClO_2$?

30. What are $[H_3O^+]$, $[OH^-]$, pH, and pOH of 0.386 M CH_3NH_2?

31. The solubility of 1-naphthylamine, $C_{10}H_7NH_2$, a substance used in the manufacture of dyes, is given in a handbook as 1 g per 590 g H_2O. What is the approximate pH of a saturated aqueous solution of 1-naphthylamine?

$$C_{10}H_7NH_2 + H_2O \rightleftharpoons C_{10}H_7NH_3^+ + OH^- \qquad pK_b = 3.92$$

32. A saturated aqueous solution of *o*-nitrophenol, $HOC_6H_4NO_2$, has pH = 4.53. What is the solubility of *o*-nitrophenol in water, in grams per liter?

$$HOC_6H_4NO_2 + H_2O \rightleftharpoons H_3O^+ + {}^-OC_6H_4NO_2 \qquad pK_a = 7.23$$

33. A particular vinegar is found to contain 5.7% acetic acid, CH_3COOH, by mass. What mass of this vinegar should be diluted with water to produce 0.750 L of a solution with pH = 4.52?

34. A particular household ammonia solution (d = 0.97 g/mL) is 6.8% NH_3 by mass. How many milliliters of this solution should be diluted with water to produce 625 mL of a solution with pH = 11.55?

35. A 275 mL sample of vapor in equilibrium with 1-propylamine at 25.0 °C is removed and dissolved in 0.500 L H_2O. For 1-propylamine, pK_b = 3.43 and v.p. = 316 Torr.

(a) What should be the pH of the aqueous solution?

(b) How many mg of NaOH dissolved in 0.500 L of water give the same pH?

36. One handbook lists a value of 9.5 for pK_b of quinoline, C_9H_7N, a weak base used as a preservative for anatomical specimens and to make dyes. Another handbook lists the solubility of quinoline in water at 25 °C as 0.6 g/100 mL. Use this information to calculate the pH of a saturated solution of quinoline in water.

37. The sketch on the far left represents the $[H_3O^+]$ present in an acetic acid solution of molarity M. If the molarity of the solution is doubled, which of the sketches below best represents the resulting solution?

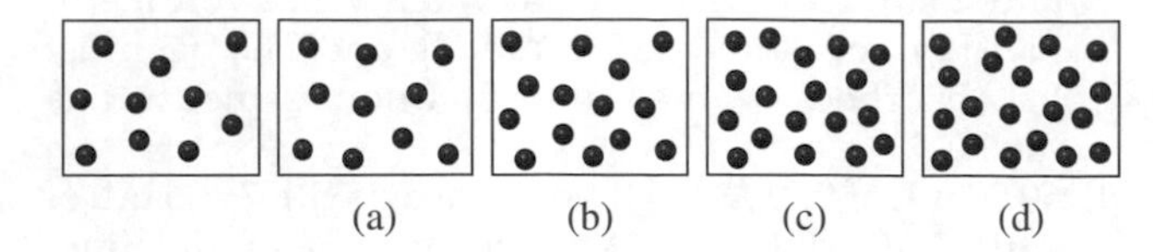

38. The sketch on the far left represents the $[OH^-]$ present in an ammonia solution of molarity M. If the solution is diluted to half its original molarity, which of the sketches below best represents the resulting solution?

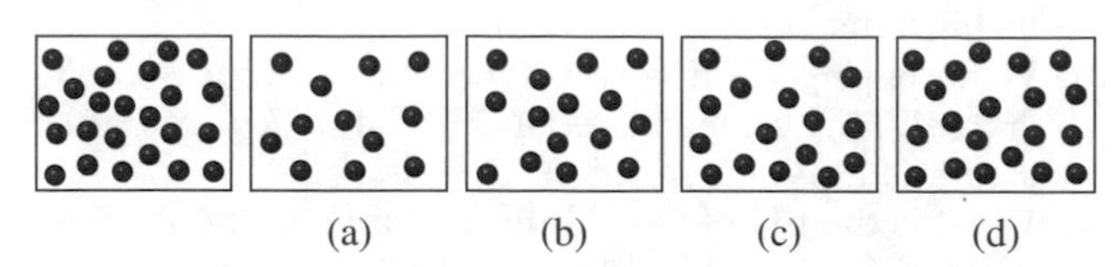

Percent Ionization

39. What is the **(a)** degree of ionization and **(b)** percent ionization of propionic acid in a solution that is 0.45 M $CH_3CH_2CO_2H$?

$$CH_3CH_2CO_2H + H_2O \rightleftharpoons H_3O^+ + CH_3CH_2CO_2^- \qquad pK_a = 4.89$$

40. What is the **(a)** degree of ionization and **(b)** percent ionization of ethylamine, $C_2H_5NH_2$, in an 0.85 M aqueous solution?

41. What must be the molarity of an aqueous solution of NH_3 if it is 4.2% ionized?

42. What must be the molarity of an acetic acid solution if it has the same percent ionization as 0.100 M $CH_3CH_2CO_2H$ (propionic acid, $K_a = 1.3 \times 10^{-5}$)?

43. Continuing the dilutions described in Example 8-8, should we expect the percent ionization to be 13% in 0.0010 M CH_3COOH and 42% in 0.00010 M CH_3COOH? Explain.

44. What is the **(a)** degree of ionization and **(b)** percent ionization of trichloroacetic acid in a 0.035 M CCl_3COOH solution?

$$CCl_3COOH + H_2O \rightleftharpoons H_3O^+ + CCl_3COO^- \qquad pK_a = 0.52$$

Polyprotic Acids

(Use data from Table 8.4 as necessary.)

45. Explain why $[PO_4^{3-}]$ in 1.00 M H_3PO_4 is *not* simply $\frac{1}{3}[H_3O^+]$, but much, much less than $\frac{1}{3}[H_3O^+]$.

46. Cola drinks have a phosphoric acid content that is described as "from 0.057 to 0.084% of 75% phosphoric acid, by mass." Estimate the pH range of cola drinks corresponding to this range of H_3PO_4 content.

47. Determine $[H_3O^+]$, $[HS^-]$, and $[S^{2-}]$ for the following $H_2S(aq)$ solutions: **(a)** 0.075 M H_2S; **(b)** 0.0050 M H_2S; **(c)** 1.0×10^{-5} M H_2S.

48. For 0.045 M H_2CO_3, a weak diprotic acid, calculate **(a)** $[H_3O^+]$, **(b)** $[HCO_3^-]$, and **(c)** $[CO_3^{2-}]$. Use data from Table 8.4 as necessary.

49. Calculate $[H_3O^+]$, $[HSO_4^-]$, and $[SO_4^{2-}]$ in **(a)** 0.75 M H_2SO_4; **(b)** 0.075 M H_2SO_4; **(c)** 7.5×10^{-4} M H_2SO_4. [*Hint:* Check any assumptions that you make.]

50. Adipic acid, $HOOC(CH_2)_4COOH$, is among the top 50 manufactured chemicals in the United States (nearly 1 million metric tons annually). Its chief use is in the manufacture of nylon. It is a *diprotic* acid having $K_{a_1} = 3.9 \times 10^{-5}$ and $K_{a_2} = 3.9 \times 10^{-6}$. A saturated solution of adipic acid is about 0.10 M $HOOC(CH_2)_4COOH$. Calculate the concentration of each ionic species in this solution.

51. The antimalarial drug quinine, $C_{20}H_{24}O_2N_2$, is a *diprotic base* with a water solubility of 1.00 g/1900 mL of solution.
(a) Write equations for the ionization equilibria corresponding to $pK_{b_1} = 6.0$ and $pK_{b_2} = 9.8$.
(b) What is the pH of saturated aqueous quinine?

52. For hydrazine, N_2H_4, $pK_{b_1} = 6.07$ and $pK_{b_2} = 15.05$. Draw a structural formula for hydrazine, and write equations to show the ionization of hydrazine in two distinctive steps. Calculate the pH of 0.245 M $N_2H_4(aq)$.

Ions as Acids and Bases (Hydrolysis)

53. Codeine, $C_{18}H_{21}O_3N$, is an opiate, has analgesic and antidiarrheal properties, and is widely used. In water, codeine is a weak base. A handbook gives $pK_a = 6.05$ for protonated codeine, $C_{18}H_{21}O_3NH^+$. Write the reaction for $C_{18}H_{21}O_3NH^+$ and calculate pK_b for codeine.

Codeine

54. Approximately 4 metric tons of quinoline, C_9H_7N, is produced annually. The principal source of quinoline is coal tar. Quinoline is a weak base in water. A handbook gives $K_a = 6.3 \times 10^{-10}$ for protonated quinoline, $C_9H_7NH^+$. Write the ionization reaction for $C_9H_7NH^+$ and calculate pK_b for quinoline.

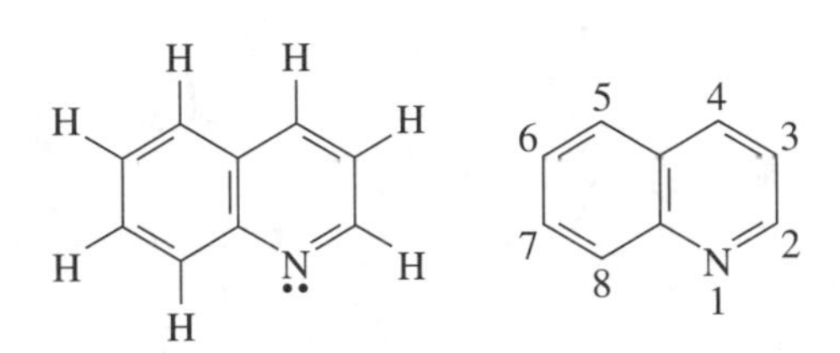

Quinoline

55. Complete the following equations in those instances in which a reaction (hydrolysis) will occur. If no reaction occurs, so state.
(a) $NH_4^+(aq) + NO_3^-(aq) + H_2O \longrightarrow$
(b) $Na^+(aq) + NO_2^-(aq) + H_2O \longrightarrow$
(c) $K^+(aq) + C_6H_5COO^-(aq) + H_2O \longrightarrow$
(d) $K^+(aq) + Cl^-(aq) + Na^+(aq) + I^-(aq) + H_2O \longrightarrow$
(e) $C_6H_5NH_3^+(aq) + Cl^-(aq) + H_2O \longrightarrow$

56. From data in Table 8.3, determine **(a)** K_a for $C_5H_5NH^+$; **(b)** K_b for $HCOO^-$; **(c)** K_b for $C_6H_5O^-$.

57. Predict whether a solution of each of the following salts is acidic, basic, or pH neutral: **(a)** KCl; **(b)** KF; **(c)** $NaNO_3$; **(d)** $Ca(OCl)_2$; **(e)** NH_4NO_2.

58. Arrange the following 0.010 M solutions in order of *increasing* pH: $NH_3(aq)$, $HNO_3(aq)$, $NaNO_2(aq)$, $CH_3COOH(aq)$, $NaOH(aq)$, $NH_4CH_3COO(aq)$, $NH_4ClO_4(aq)$.

59. What is the pH of an aqueous solution that is 0.089 M NaOCl?

60. What is the pH of an aqueous solution that is 0.123 M NH_4Cl?

61. Sorbic acid, $CH_2CH{=}CH{=}CHCH_2CO_2H$ (pK_a = 4.77), is widely used in the food industry as a preservative. For example, its potassium salt (potassium sorbate) is added to cheese to inhibit the formation of mold. What is the pH of 0.37 M potassium sorbate solution?

62. Pyridine, C_5H_5N (pK_b = 8.82), forms a salt, pyridinium chloride, as a result of a reaction with HCl. Write an ionic equation to represent the hydrolysis of the pyridinium ion, and calculate the pH of 0.0482 M $C_5H_5NH^+Cl^-(aq)$.

63. For each of the following ions, write two equations—one showing its ionization as an acid and the other as a base: **(a)** HSO_3^-; **(b)** HS^-; **(c)** HPO_4^-. Then use data from Table 8.4 to predict whether each ion makes the solution acidic or basic.

64. Suppose you wanted to produce an aqueous solution of pH = 8.65 by dissolving one of the following salts in water. Which salt would you use, and at what molarity? **(a)** NH_4Cl; **(b)** $KHSO_4$; **(c)** KNO_2; **(d)** $NaNO_3$.

Molecular Structure and Acid–Base Behavior

65. Predict which is the stronger acid: **(a)** $HClO_2$ or $HClO_3$; **(b)** H_2CO_3 or HNO_2; **(c)** H_2SiO_3 or H_3PO_4. Explain.

66. Explain why trichloroacetic acid, CCl_3COOH, is a stronger acid than acetic acid, CH_3COOH.

67. Which is the stronger acid of each of the following pairs of acids? Explain your reasoning. **(a)** HBr or HI; **(b)** HOClO or HOBr; **(c)** $I_3CCH_2CH_2COOH$ or $CH_3CH_2CCl_2COOH$.

68. Indicate which of the following is the *weakest* acid, and give reasons for your choice: HBr; $CH_2ClCOOH$; CH_3CH_2COOH; CH_2FCH_2COOH; Cl_3COOH.

69. From the following bases, select the one with the *smallest* K_b and the one with the *largest* K_b, and give reasons for your choices.
(a) $-NH_2$, Cl **(b)** H_3C- $-NH_2$
(c) $CH_3CH_2CH_2NH_2$ **(d)** $N{\equiv}CCH_2NH_2$

70. For the molecular models shown, write the formula of the species that is the most acidic and the one that is most basic, and give reasons for your choices.

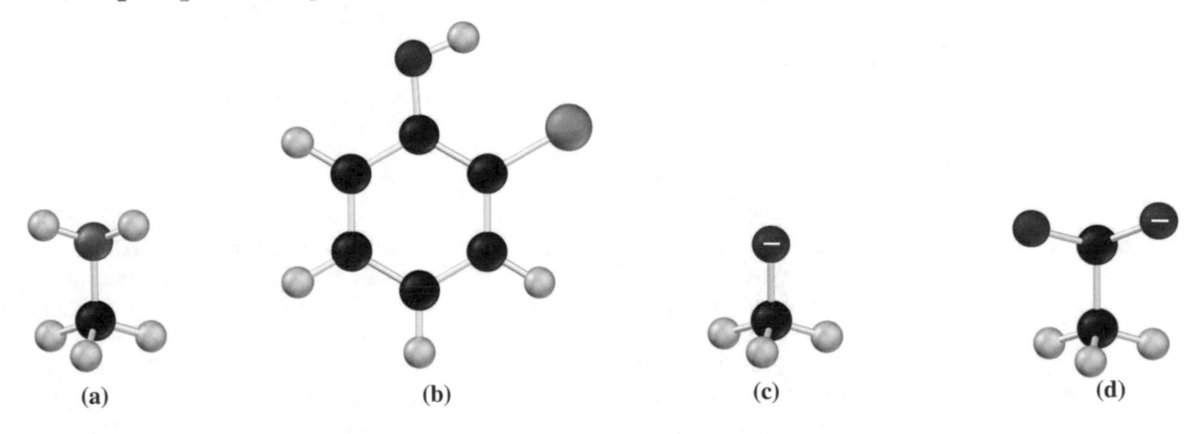

(a) (b) (c) (d)

Lewis Theory of Acids and Bases

71. For each reaction draw a Lewis structure for each species and indicate which is the acid and which is the base:
(a) $CO_2 + H_2O \longrightarrow H_2CO_3$
(b) $H_2O + BF_3 \longrightarrow H_2OBF_3$
(c) $O^{2-} + H_2O \longrightarrow 2\,OH^-$
(d) $S^{2-} + SO_3 \longrightarrow S_2O_3^{2-}$

72. In the following reactions indicate which is the Lewis acid and which is the Lewis base:
(a) $SOI_2 + BaSO_3 \longrightarrow Ba^{2+} + 2\,I^- + 2\,SO_2$
(b) $HgCl_3^- + Cl^- \longrightarrow HgCl_4^{2-}$

73. Indicate whether each of the following is a Lewis acid or base. **(a)** OH^-; **(b)** $(C_2H_5)_3B$; **(c)** CH_3NH_2.

74. Each of the following is a Lewis acid–base reaction. Which reactant is the acid, and which is the base? Explain.
(a) $SO_3 + H_2O \longrightarrow H_2SO_4$
(b) $Zn(OH)_2(s) + 2\,OH^-(aq) \longrightarrow [Zn(OH)_4]^{2-}(aq)$

75. The three following reactions are acid–base reactions according to the Lewis theory. Draw Lewis structures, and identify the Lewis acid and Lewis base in each reaction.
(a) $B(OH)_3 + OH^- \longrightarrow [B(OH)_4]^-$
(b) $N_2H_4 + H_3O^+ \longrightarrow N_2H_5^+ + H_2O$
(c) $(C_2H_5)_2O + BF_3 \longrightarrow (C_2H_5)_2OBF_3$

76. $CO_2(g)$ can be removed from confined quarters (such as a spacecraft) by allowing it to react with an alkali metal hydroxide. Show that this is a Lewis acid–base reaction. For example,

$$CO_2(g) + LiOH(s) \longrightarrow LiHCO_3(s)$$

77. The molecular solid $I_2(s)$ is only slightly soluble in water but will dissolve to a much greater extent in an aqueous solution of KI, because the I_3^- anion forms. Write an equation for the formation of the I_3^- anion, and indicate the Lewis acid and Lewis base.

78. The following very strong acids are formed by the reactions indicated:

$$HF + SbF_5 \longrightarrow HSbF_6$$

(called "super acid," hexafluoroantimonic acid)

$$HF + BF_3 \longrightarrow HBF_4$$

(tetrafluoroboric acid)

(a) Identify the Lewis acids and bases.
(b) To which atom is the H atom bonded in each acid?

79. Use Lewis structures to diagram the following reaction in the manner of reaction (8.20).

$$H_2O + SO_2 \longrightarrow H_2SO_3$$

Identify the Lewis acid and Lewis base.

80. Use Lewis structures to diagram the following reaction in the manner of reaction (8.19).

$$2\,NH_3 + Ag^+ \longrightarrow [Ag(NH_3)_2]^+$$

Identify the Lewis acid and Lewis base.

Integrative and Advanced Exercises

81. The Brønsted–Lowry theory can be applied to acid–base reactions in nonaqueous solvents, where the relative strengths of acids and bases can differ from what they are in aqueous solutions. Indicate whether each of the following would be an acid, a base, or amphiprotic in pure liquid acetic acid, CH_3COOH, as a solvent. **(a)** CH_3COO^-; **(b)** H_2O; **(c)** CH_3COOH; **(d)** $HClO_4$. [*Hint:* Refer to Table 8.1.]

82. The pH of saturated $Sr(OH)_2(aq)$ is found to be 13.12. A 10.0 mL sample of saturated $Sr(OH)_2(aq)$ is diluted to 250.0 mL in a volumetric flask. A 10.0 mL sample of the diluted $Sr(OH)_2(aq)$ is transferred to a beaker, and some water is added. The resulting solution requires 25.1 mL of a HCl solution for its titration. What is the molarity of this HCl solution?

83. Several approximate pH values are marked on the following pH scale.

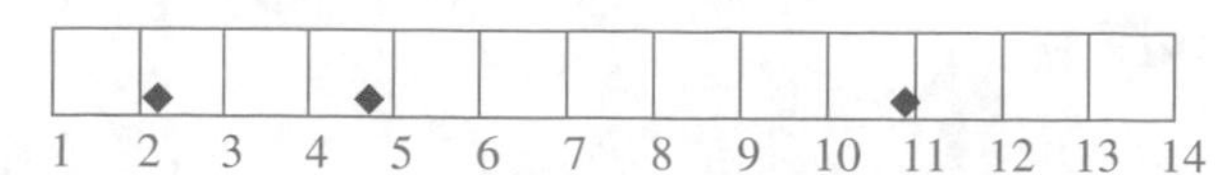

Some of the following solutions can be matched to one of the approximate pH values marked on the scale; others cannot. For solutions that can be matched to a pH value, identify each solution and its pH value. Identify the solutions that cannot be matched, and give reasons why matches are not possible. **(a)** 0.010 M H_2SO_4; **(b)** 1.0 M NH_4Cl; **(c)** 0.050 M KI; **(d)** 0.0020 M CH_3NH_2; **(e)** 1.0 M NaOCl; **(f)** 0.10 M C_6H_5OH; **(g)** 0.10 M HOCl; **(h)** 0.050 M $ClCH_2COOH$; **(i)** 0.050 M HCOOH.

84. Show that when $[H_3O^+]$ is reduced to half its original value, the pH of a solution increases by 0.30 unit, *regardless of the initial pH.* Is it also true that when any solution is diluted to half its original concentration, the pH increases by 0.30 unit? Explain.

85. Explain why $[H_3O^+]$ in a strong acid solution *doubles* as the total acid concentration doubles, whereas in a weak acid solution, $[H_3O^+]$ increases only by about a factor of $\sqrt{2}$.

86. Use data from Appendix A to determine whether the ion product of water, K_w, increases, decreases, or remains unchanged with increasing temperature.

87. From the observation that 0.0500 M vinylacetic acid has a freezing point of $-0.096\ °C$, determine K_a for this acid.

$$CH_2{=}CHCH_2CO_2H + H_2O \rightleftharpoons H_3O^+ + CH_2{=}CHCH_2CO_2^-$$

88. You are asked to prepare a 100.0 mL sample of a solution with a pH of 5.50 by dissolving the appropriate amount of a solute in water with pH = 7.00. Which of these solutes would you use, and in what quantity? Explain your choice. **(a)** 15 M $NH_3(aq)$; **(b)** 12 M $HCl(aq)$; **(c)** $NH_4Cl(s)$; **(d)** glacial (pure) acetic acid, CH_3COOH.

89. Determine the pH of **(a)** 1.0×10^{-5} M HCN and **(b)** 1.0×10^{-5} M $C_6H_5NH_2$ (aniline).

90. It is possible to write simple equations to relate pH, p*K*, and molarities (M) of various solutions. Three such equations are shown here.

Weak acid: $pH = \frac{1}{2}pK_a - \frac{1}{2}\log M$

Weak base: $pH = 14.00 - \frac{1}{2}pK_b + \frac{1}{2}\log M$

Salt of weak acid (pK_a) *and strong base:* $pH = 14.00 - \frac{1}{2}pK_w + \frac{1}{2}pK_a + \frac{1}{2}\log M$

(a) Derive these three equations, and point out the assumptions involved in the derivations.
(b) Use these equations to determine the pH of 0.10 M $CH_3COOH(aq)$, 0.10 M $NH_3(aq)$, and 0.10 M $NaCH_3COO$. Verify that the equations give correct results by determining these pH values in the usual way.

91. A handbook lists the following formula for the percent ionization of a weak acid.

$$\% \text{ ionized} = \frac{100}{1 + 10^{(pK-pH)}}$$

(a) Derive this equation. What assumptions must you make in this derivation?
(b) Use the equation to determine the percent ionization of a formic acid solution, HCOOH(aq), with a pH of 2.50.
(c) A 0.150 M solution of propionic acid, CH_3CH_2COOH, has a pH of 2.85. What is K_a for propionic acid?

$$CH_3CH_2CO_2H + H_2O \rightleftharpoons H_3O^+ + CH_3CH_2CO_2^-$$

92. Oxalic acid, HOOCCOOH, a weak diprotic acid, has $pK_{a_1} = 1.25$ and $pK_{a_2} = 3.81$. A related diprotic acid, suberic acid, $HOOC(CH_2)_8COOH$ has $pK_{a_1} = 4.21$ and $pK_{a_2} = 5.40$. Offer a plausible reason as to why the *difference* between pK_{a_1} and pK_{a_2} is so much greater for oxalic acid than for suberic acid.

93. Here is a way to test the validity of the statement made on page 329 in conjunction with the three key ideas governing the ionization of polyprotic acids. Determine the pH of 0.100 M succinic acid in two ways: first by assuming that H_3O^+ is produced only in the first ionization step, and then by allowing for the possibility that some H_3O^+ is also produced in the second ionization step. Compare the results, and discuss the significance of your finding.

$$H_2C_4H_4O_4 + H_2O \rightleftharpoons H_3O^+ + HC_4H_4O_4^- \qquad K_{a_1} = 6.2 \times 10^{-5}$$

$$HC_4H_4O_4^- + H_2O \rightleftharpoons H_3O^+ + C_4H_4O_4^{2-} \qquad K_{a_2} = 2.3 \times 10^{-6}$$

94. What mass of acetic acid, CH_3COOH, must be dissolved per liter of aqueous solution if the solution is to have the same freezing point as 0.150 M $ClCH_2COOH$ (chloroacetic acid)?

95. What is the pH of a solution that is 0.68 M H_2SO_4 and 1.5 M HCOOH (formic acid)?

96. An aqueous solution of two weak acids has a stoichiometric molarity, M, in each acid. If one acid has a K_a value twice as large as the other, show that the pH of the solution is given by the equation $pH = -\frac{1}{2}\log 3\,M\,K_a$. Assume that the criteria for the simplifying assumption on page 325 are met.

97. Use the concept of hybrid orbitals to describe the bonding in the strong acids given in Exercise 78.

98. Phosphorous acid is listed in Appendix A as a *diprotic* acid. Propose a Lewis structure for phosphorous acid that is consistent with this fact.

99. The following four equilibria lie to the right: $N_2H_5^+ + CH_3NH_2 \longrightarrow N_2H_4 + CH_3NH_3^+$; $H_2SO_3 + F^- \longrightarrow HSO_3^- + HF$; $CH_3NH_3^+ + OH^- \longrightarrow CH_3NH_2 + H_2O$; and $HF + N_2H_4 \longrightarrow F^- + N_2H_5^+$.
(a) Rank all the acids involved in order of decreasing acid strength.
(b) Rank all the bases involved in order of decreasing base strength.
(c) State whether each of the following two equilibria lies primarily to the right or to the left: **(i)** $HF + OH^- \longrightarrow F^- + H_2O$; **(ii)** $CH_3NH_3^+ + HSO_3^- \longrightarrow CH_3NH_2 + H_2SO_3$.

Feature Problems

100. Maleic acid is a carbon–hydrogen–oxygen compound used in dyeing and finishing fabrics and as a preservative of oils and fats. In a combustion analysis, a 1.054 g sample of maleic acid yields 1.599 g CO_2 and 0.327 g H_2O. In a freezing-point depression experiment, a 0.615 g sample of maleic acid dissolved in 25.10 g of glacial acetic acid, $CH_3COOH(l)$ (which has the freezing-point depression constant $K_f = 3.90\ °C\ m^{-1}$ and in which maleic acid does not ionize), lowers the freezing point by 0.82°C. In a titration experiment, a 0.4250 g sample of maleic acid is dissolved in water and requires 34.03 mL of 0.2152 M KOH for its complete neutralization. The pH of a 0.215 g sample of maleic acid dissolved in 50.00 mL of aqueous solution is found to be 1.80.
(a) Determine the empirical and molecular formulas of maleic acid. [*Hint:* Which experiment(s) provide the necessary data?]
(b) Use the results of part (a) and the titration data to rewrite the molecular formula to reflect the number of ionizable H atoms in the molecule.
(c) Given that the ionizable H atom(s) is(are) associated with the carboxyl group(s), write the plausible condensed structural formula of maleic acid.
(d) Determine the ionization constant(s) of maleic acid. If the data supplied are insufficient, indicate what additional data would be needed.

(e) Calculate the expected pH of a 0.0500 M aqueous solution of maleic acid. Indicate any assumptions required in this calculation.

101. In Example 8-7, rather than use the quadratic formula to solve the quadratic equation, we could have proceeded in the following way. Substitute the value yielded by our failed assumption—$x = 0.0010$—into the *denominator* of the quadratic equation; that is, use $(0.00250 - 0.0010)$ as the value of $[CH_3NH_2]$ and solve for a new value of x. Use this second value of x to re-evaluate $[CH_3NH_2]$: $[CH_3NH_2] = (0.00250 - \text{second value of } x)$. Solve the simple quadratic equation for a third value of x, and so on. After three or four trials, you will find that the value of x no longer changes. This is the answer you are seeking. **(a)** Complete the calculation of the pH of 0.00250 M CH_3NH_2 by this method, and show that the result is the same as that obtained by using the quadratic formula. **(b)** Use this method to determine the pH of 0.500 M $HClO_2$.

102. Apply the general method for solution equilibrium calculations outlined on page 330 to determine the pH values of the following solutions. In applying the method, look for valid assumptions that may simplify the numerical calculations.
(a) a solution that is 0.315 M CH_3COOH and 0.250 M $HCOOH$
(b) a solution that contains 1.55 g CH_3NH_2 and 12.5 g NH_3 in 375 mL
(c) 1.0 M $NH_4CN(aq)$

Self-Assessment Exercises

103. In your own words, define or explain the following terms or symbols: **(a)** K_w; **(b)** pH; **(c)** pK_a; **(d)** hydrolysis; **(e)** Lewis acid.

104. Briefly describe each of the following ideas or phenomena: **(a)** conjugate base; **(b)** percent ionization of an acid or base; **(c)** self-ionization; **(d)** amphiprotic behavior.

105. Explain the important distinctions between each pair of terms: **(a)** Brønsted–Lowry acid and base; **(b)** $[H_3O^+]$ and pH; **(c)** K_a for NH_4^+ and K_b for NH_3; **(d)** leveling effect and electron-withdrawing effect.

106. Of the following, the amphiprotic ion is **(a)** HCO_3^-; **(b)** CO_3^{2-}; **(c)** NH_4^+; **(d)** $CH_3NH_3^+$; **(e)** ClO_4^-.

107. The pH in 0.10 M $CH_3CH_2COOH(aq)$ must be **(a)** equal to $[H_3O^+]$ in 0.10 M $HNO_2(aq)$; **(b)** less than the pH in 0.10 M HI(aq); **(c)** greater than the pH in 0.10 M HBr(aq); **(d)** equal to 1.0.

108. In 0.10 M $CH_3NH_2(aq)$, **(a)** $[H_3O^+] = 0.10$ M; **(b)** $[OH^-] = 0.10$ M; **(c)** pH < 7; **(d)** pH < 13.

109. The reaction of $CH_3COOH(aq)$ proceeds furthest toward completion with a base when that base is **(a)** H_2O; **(b)** $CH_3NH_3^+$; **(c)** NH_4^+; **(d)** Cl^-; **(e)** CO_3^{2-}.

110. In 0.10 M $H_2SO_4(aq)$, $[H_3O^+]$ is equal to **(a)** 0.050 M; **(b)** 0.10 M; **(c)** 0.11 M; **(d)** 0.20 M.

111. For $H_2SO_3(aq)$, $K_{a_1} = 1.3 \times 10^{-2}$ and $K_{a_2} = 6.3 \times 10^{-8}$. In 0.10 M $H_2SO_3(aq)$, **(a)** $[HSO_3^-] = 0.013$ M; **(b)** $[SO_3^{2-}] = 6.3 \times 10^{-8}$ M; **(c)** $[H_3O^+] = 0.10$ M; **(d)** $[H_3O^+] = 0.013$ M; **(e)** $[SO_3^{2-}] = 0.036$ M.

112. What is the pH of the solution obtained by mixing 24.80 mL of 0.248 M HNO_3 and 15.40 mL of 0.394 M KOH?

113. How many milliliters of a concentrated acetic acid solution (35.0% CH_3COOH by mass; $d = 1.044$ g/mL) must be diluted with water to produce 12.5 L of solution with pH 3.25?

114. Determine the pH of 2.05 M $NaCH_2ClCOO$. (Use data from Table 8.3, as necessary.)

115. Several aqueous solutions are prepared. *Without consulting any tables in the text*, arrange these ten solutions in order of *increasing* pH: 1.0 M NaBr, 0.05 M CH_3COOH, 0.05 M NH_3, 0.02 M KCH_3COO, 0.05 M $Ba(OH)_2$, 0.05 M H_2SO_4, 0.10 M HI, 0.06 M NaOH, 0.05 M NH_4Cl, and 0.05 M $CH_2ClCOOH$.

116. A solution is found to have pH $= 5 \times$ pOH. Is this solution acidic or basic? What is $[H_3O^+]$ in the solution? Which of the following could be the solute in this solution: NH_3, CH_3COOH, or NH_4CH_3COO, and what would be its molarity?

117. Propionic acid, CH_3CH_2COOH, is 0.42% ionized in 0.80 M solution. The K_a for this acid is **(a)** 1.42×10^{-5}; **(b)** 1.42×10^{-7}; **(c)** 1.77×10^{-5}; **(d)** 6.15×10^4; **(e)** none of these.

118. The conjugate acid of HPO_4^{2-} is **(a)** PO_4^{3-}; **(b)** $H_2PO_4^-$; **(c)** H_3PO_4; **(d)** H_3O^+; **(e)** none of these.

119. The equilibria $OH^- + HClO \longrightarrow H_2O + ClO^-$ and $ClO^- + HNO_2 \longrightarrow HClO + NO_2^-$ both lie to the right. Which of the following is a list of acids ranked in order of decreasing strength?
(a) $HClO > HNO_2 > H_2O$
(b) $ClO^- > NO_2^- > OH^-$
(c) $NO_2^- > ClO^- > OH^-$
(d) $HNO_2 > HClO > H_2O$
(e) none of these

120. 3.00 mol of calcium chlorite is dissolved in enough water to produce 2.50 L of solution. $K_a = 2.9 \times 10^{-8}$ for HClO, and $K_a = 1.1 \times 10^{-2}$ for $HClO_2$. Compute the pH of the solution.

Additional Aspects of Acid–Base Equilibria

9

CONTENTS

NaOH(aq) is slowly added to an aqueous solution containing HCl(aq) and the indicator phenolphthalein. The indicator color changes from colorless to red as the pH changes from 8.0 to 10.0. The equivalence point of the neutralization is reached when the solution turns a lasting pink (the pink seen here disappears when the flask is swirled to mix the reactants). The selection of indicators for acid–base titrations is one of the topics considered in this chapter.

In our study of acid rain, we learned that a very small amount of atmospheric $CO_2(g)$ dissolves in rainwater. Yet this amount is sufficient to lower the pH of rainwater by nearly 2 units. And when acid-forming air pollutants, such as SO_2, SO_3, and NO_2, also dissolve in rainwater, it becomes even more acidic. A chemist would say that water has no "buffer capacity"—that is, its pH changes sharply when even small quantities of acids or bases are dissolved in it.

One of the main topics of this chapter is buffer solutions—solutions that can resist a change in pH when acids or bases are added to them. We will consider how such solutions are prepared, how they maintain a nearly constant pH, and how they are used. At the end of the chapter, we will consider perhaps the most important buffer system to humans: the buffer system that maintains the constant pH of blood.

▲ FIGURE 9-1
A weak acid–strong acid mixture
The solution pictured is 0.100 M CH_3COOH and 0.100 M HCl. The reading on the pH meter (1.0) indicates that essentially all the H_3O^+ comes from the strong acid HCl. The red color of the solution is that of thymol blue indicator. Compare this photo with Figure 8-7, in which the separate acids are shown.

▶ The common-ion effect is not restricted to weak acids and weak bases. Buffers are the most important examples of the common-ion effect in weak acids and weak bases.

A second topic that we will explore is acid–base titrations. Here, our aim will be to calculate how pH changes during a titration. We can use this information to select an appropriate indicator for a titration and to determine, in general, which acid–base titrations work well and which do not.

9-1 Common-Ion Effect in Acid–Base Equilibria

The questions answered in Chapter 8 were mostly of the type, "What is the pH of 0.10 M $HC_2H_3O_2$, of 0.10 M NH_3, of 0.10 M H_3PO_4, of 0.10 M NH_4Cl?" In each of these cases, we think of dissolving a *single* substance in aqueous solution and determining the concentrations of the species present at equilibrium. In most situations in this chapter, a solution of a weak acid or weak base initially contains a second source of one of the ions produced in the ionization of the acid or base. The added ions are said to be *common* to the weak acid or weak base. The presence of a common ion can have some important consequences.

Solutions of Weak Acids and Strong Acids

Consider a solution that is at the same time 0.100 M CH_3COOH and 0.100 M HCl. We can write separate equations for the ionizations of the acids, one weak and the other strong, and indicate the expected concentrations of molecules and ions in the solution.

$$\underset{(0.100-x)\,M}{CH_3COOH} + H_2O \rightleftharpoons \underset{x\,M}{H_3O^+} + \underset{x\,M}{CH_3COO^-} \qquad K_a = 1.8 \times 10^{-5}$$

$$HCl + H_2O \longrightarrow \underset{0.100\,M}{H_3O^+} + \underset{0.100\,M}{Cl^-}$$

Of course, there can be only a single concentration of H_3O^+ in the solution, and this must be $[H_3O^+] = (0.100 + x)$ M. Because H_3O^+ is formed in both ionization processes, we say that it is a *common ion*. The weak acid–strong acid mixture described here is pictured in Figure 9-1. Although it might seem that the pH would be lower than 1.0, the figure indicates that this is not the case.

Concentrations of the species present in this mixture of a weak acid and a strong acid are calculated in Example 9-1, followed by comments on the significance of the result.

EXAMPLE 9-1 Demonstrating the Common-Ion Effect: A Solution of a Weak Acid and a Strong Acid

(a) Determine $[H_3O^+]$ and $[CH_3COO^-]$ in 0.100 M CH_3COOH. **(b)** Then determine these same quantities in a solution that is 0.100 M in both CH_3COOH and HCl.

Analyze

In part (a) we must determine the species in a weak acid solution, and in part (b) we investigate the effects of the addition of a strong acid. The two acids have the common ion H_3O^+.

Solve

(a) This calculation was done in Example 8-6. We found that in 0.100 M CH_3COOH, $[H_3O^+] = [CH_3COO^-] = 1.3 \times 10^{-3}$ M.

(b) Instead of writing two separate ionization equations, as we did just prior to this example, let's write only the ionization equation for CH_3COOH and enter information about the common ion, H_3O^+, in the following format.

	CH_3COOH	+	H_2O	$\rightleftharpoons$	H_3O^+	+	CH_3COO^-
initial concns:							
weak acid:	0.100 M				—		—
strong acid:	—				0.100 M		—
changes:	$-x$ M				$+x$ M		$+x$ M
equil concns:	$(0.100 - x)$ M				$(0.100 + x)$ M		x M

As is customary, we begin with the assumption that x is very small compared with 0.100. Thus, $0.100 - x \approx 0.100 + x \approx 0.100$.

$$K_a = \frac{[H_3O^+][CH_3COO^-]}{[CH_3COOH]} = \frac{(0.100 + x) \cdot x}{0.100 - x} = \frac{\cancel{0.100} \cdot x}{\cancel{0.100}} = 1.8 \times 10^{-5}$$

$$x = [CH_3COO^-] = 1.8 \times 10^{-5}\text{ M} \quad 0.100 + x = [H_3O^+] = 0.100\text{ M}$$

Notice that x is only 0.018% of 0.100, and so the assumption that x is small compared with 0.100 is valid.

Assess

In this example the acetate ion concentration goes down after the addition of hydronium ion. In other words, ionization of acetic acid is suppressed by the addition of strong acid. The common-ion effect is not restricted to weak acids and weak bases. Buffers are the most important examples of the common-ion effect in weak acids and weak bases. This shift in equilibrium concentration because of the addition of a common ion is another illustration of Le Châtelier's principle.

PRACTICE EXAMPLE A: Determine $[H_3O^+]$ and $[HF]$ in 0.500 M HF. Then determine these concentrations in a solution that is 0.100 M HCl and 0.500 M HF.

PRACTICE EXAMPLE B: How many drops of 12 M HCl would you add to 1.00 L of 0.100 M CH_3COOH to make $[CH_3COO^-] = 1.0 \times 10^{-4}$ M? Assume that 1 drop = 0.050 mL and that the volume of solution remains 1.00 L after the 12 M HCl is diluted. [*Hint*: What must be the $[H_3O^+]$ in the solution?]

Now we see the consequence of adding a strong acid (HCl) to a weak acid (CH_3COOH): The concentration of the anion $[CH_3COO^-]$ is greatly reduced. Between parts (a) and (b) of Example 9-1, $[CH_3COO^-]$ is lowered from 10^{-3} M to 1.8×10^{-5} M—almost a 100-fold decrease. Another way to state this result is through Le Châtelier's principle. Increasing the concentration of one of the *products* of a reaction—the common ion—shifts the equilibrium condition in the *reverse* direction. The **common-ion effect** is the suppression of the ionization of a weak electrolyte caused by adding more of an ion that is a product of this ionization. The common-ion effect of H_3O^+ on the ionization of acetic acid is suggested as follows.

When a strong acid supplies the common ion H_3O^+, the equilibrium shifts to form more CH_3COOH.

Added H_3O^+

$$CH_3COOH + H_2O \rightleftharpoons H_3O^+ + CH_3COO^- \quad K_a = 1.8 \times 10^{-5}$$

Equilibrium shifts to form more CH_3COOH

(a) (b)

▲ FIGURE 9-2
A mixture of a weak acid and its salt
Bromphenol blue indicator is present in both solutions. Its color dependence on pH is

$pH < 3.0 < pH < 4.6 < pH$
Yellow Green Blue-Violet

(a) 0.100 M CH_3COOH has a calculated pH of 2.89, but **(b)** if the solution is also 0.100 M in $NaCH_3COO$, the calculated pH is 4.74. (The readability of the pH meters used here is 0.1 unit, and their accuracy is probably somewhat less than that. The discrepancy between 4.74 and the 4.9 value shown here is a result of their limited accuracy.)

The ionization of a weak base, such as NH_3, is suppressed when a strong base, such as NaOH, is added. Here, OH^- is the common ion, and its increased concentration shifts the equilibrium to the left.

When a strong base supplies the common ion OH^-, the equilibrium shifts to form more NH_3.

Added OH^-

$$NH_3 + H_2O \rightleftharpoons NH_4^+ + OH^- \qquad K_b = 1.8 \times 10^{-5}$$

Equilibrium shifts to form more NH_3

Solutions of Weak Acids and Their Salts

The salt of a weak acid is a strong electrolyte—its ions become completely dissociated from one another in aqueous solution. One of the ions, the *anion*, is an ion common to the ionization equilibrium of the weak acid. The presence of this common ion suppresses the ionization of the weak acid. For example, we can represent the effect of acetate salts on the acetic acid equilibrium as

When a salt supplies the common anion CH_3COO^-, the equilibrium shifts to form more CH_3COOH.

$$NaCH_3COO(aq) \longrightarrow Na^+ + CH_3COO^-$$

Added CH_3COO^-

$$CH_3COOH + H_2O \rightleftharpoons H_3O^+ + CH_3COO^- \qquad K_a = 1.8 \times 10^{-5}$$

Equilibrium shifts to form more CH_3COOH

▶ When concentrations of a weak acid and its conjugate base are the same, $K_a = [H_3O^+]$ and $pH = pK_a$.

The common-ion effect of acetate ion on the ionization of acetic acid is depicted in Figure 9-2 and demonstrated in Example 9-2. In solving common-ion problems, such as Example 9-2, assume that ionization of the weak acid (or base) does not begin until both the weak acid (or base) and its salt have been placed in solution. Then consider that ionization occurs until equilibrium is reached.

EXAMPLE 9-2 **Demonstrating the Common-Ion Effect: A Solution of a Weak Acid and a Salt of That Weak Acid**

Calculate $[H_3O^+]$ and $[CH_3COO^-]$ in a solution that is 0.100 M in both CH_3COOH and $NaCH_3COO$.

Analyze

This example is very similar to Example 9-1; however, in this case we will be adding a salt of a weak acid and observing the shift in equilibrium. The setup shown here is very similar to that in Example 9-1(b), except that $NaCH_3COO$ is the source of the common ion. This is another illustration of Le Châtelier's principle.

Solve

Begin by setting up the ICE table.

	CH_3COOH	+	H_2O	$\rightleftharpoons$	H_3O^+	+	CH_3COO^-
initial concns:							
weak acid:	0.100 M				—		—
salt:	—				—		0.100 M
changes:	$-x$ M				$+x$ M		$+x$ M
equil concns:	$(0.100 - x)$ M				x M		$(0.100 + x)$ M

Because the salt suppresses the ionization of $HC_2H_3O_2$, we expect $[H_3O^+] = x$ to be very small and $0.100 - x \approx 0.100 + x \approx 0.100$. This proves to be a valid assumption.

$$K_a = \frac{[H_3O^+][CH_3COO^-]}{[CH_3COOH]} = \frac{x \cdot (0.100 + x)}{0.100 - x} = \frac{x \cdot \cancel{0.100}}{\cancel{0.100}} = 1.8 \times 10^{-5}$$

$$x = [H_3O^+] = 1.8 \times 10^{-5}\ M \qquad 0.100 + x = [CH_3COO^-] = 0.100\ M$$

Assess

The ionization of CH_3COOH is reduced about 100-fold because of the salt that was added. The calculations we performed in this example are very similar to those we did in Example 9-1(b). An important difference, however, is that here we solved for $x = [H_3O^+]$. In Example 9-1(b), we solved for $x = [CH_3COO^-]$.Note that when the concentrations of a weak acid and its conjugate base are the same, $K_a = [H_3O^+]$ and $pH = pK_a$.

PRACTICE EXAMPLE A: Calculate $[H_3O^+]$ and $[HCOO^-]$ in a solution that is 0.100 M HCOOH and 0.150 M NaHCOO.

PRACTICE EXAMPLE B: What mass of $NaCH_3COO$ should be added to 1.00 L of 0.100 M CH_3COOH to produce a solution with pH = 5.00? Assume that the volume remains 1.00 L.

Solutions of Weak Bases and Their Salts

The common-ion effect of a salt of a weak base is similar to the weak acid–anion situation just described. The suppression of the ionization of NH_3 by the common *cation*, NH_4^+, is pictured in Figure 9-3 and represented as follows.

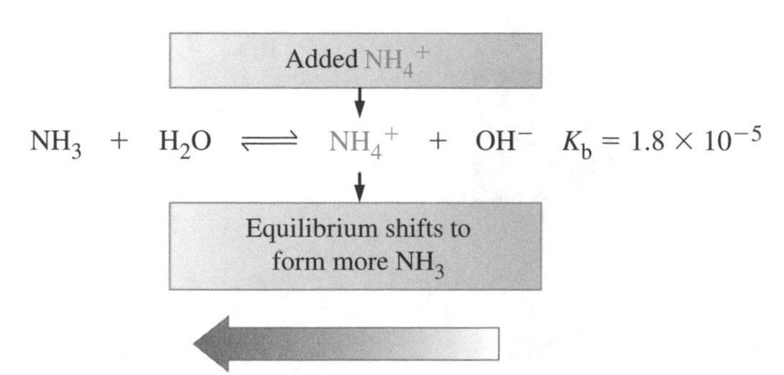
When a salt supplies the common cation NH_4^+,
the equilibrium shifts to form more NH_3.
$NH_4Cl(aq) \longrightarrow NH_4^+ + Cl^-$
Added NH_4^+
$NH_3 + H_2O \rightleftharpoons NH_4^+ + OH^- \quad K_b = 1.8 \times 10^{-5}$
Equilibrium shifts to form more NH_3

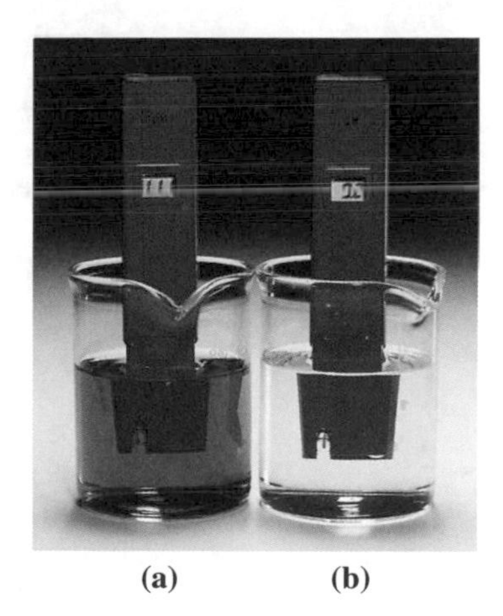
(a)
(b)

▲ FIGURE 9-3
A mixture of a weak base and its salt
Thymolphthalein indicator is blue if pH > 10 and colorless if pH < 10. **(a)** The pH of 0.100 M NH_3 is above 10 (calculated value: 11.11). **(b)** If the solution is also 0.100 M NH_4Cl, the pH drops below 10 (calculated value: 9.26). The ionization of NH_3 is suppressed in the presence of added NH_4^+. $[OH^-]$ decreases, $[H_3O^+]$ increases, and the pH is lowered.

9-1 CONCEPT ASSESSMENT

Without doing detailed calculations, determine which of the following will *raise* the pH when added to 1.00 L of 0.100 M $NH_3(aq)$: **(a)** 0.010 mol $NH_4Cl(s)$; **(b)** 0.010 mol $(CH_3CH_2)_2NH(l)$; **(c)** 0.010 mol HCl(g); **(d)** 1.00 L of 0.050 M $NH_3(aq)$; **(e)** 1.00 g $Ca(OH)_2(s)$. For NH_3, $pK_b = 4.74$; for $(CH_3CH_2)_2NH$, $pK_b = 3.16$.

9-2 Buffer Solutions

Figure 9-4 illustrates a statement made in the chapter introduction: Pure water has no buffer capacity. There are some aqueous solutions, however, called **buffer** (or buffered) **solutions**, whose pH values change only very slightly on the addition of small amounts of either an acid or a base.

What buffer solutions require are two components; one component is able to neutralize acids, and the other is able to neutralize bases. But the two components must not neutralize each other. This requirement rules out mixtures of a strong acid and a strong base. Instead, common buffer solutions are described as combinations of

▶ Recall the Brønsted–Lowry theory and the conjugate acid–base definitions.

- a weak acid and its conjugate base, or
- a weak base and its conjugate acid

To show that such mixtures function as buffer solutions, let's consider a solution that has the equilibrium concentrations $[CH_3COOH] = [CH_3COO^-]$. As summarized in expression (9.1), in this solution $[H_3O^+] = K_a = 1.8 \times 10^{-5}$ M.

$$K_a = \frac{[H_3O^+][CH_3COO^-]}{[CH_3COOH]} = 1.8 \times 10^{-5}$$

$$[H_3O^+] = K_a \times \frac{\cancel{[CH_3COOH]}}{\cancel{[CH_3COO^-]}} = 1.8 \times 10^{-5}\text{ M} \quad \textbf{(9.1)}$$

As a result, $pH = -\log[H_3O^+] = -\log K_a = -\log 1.8 \times 10^{-5} = 4.74$.

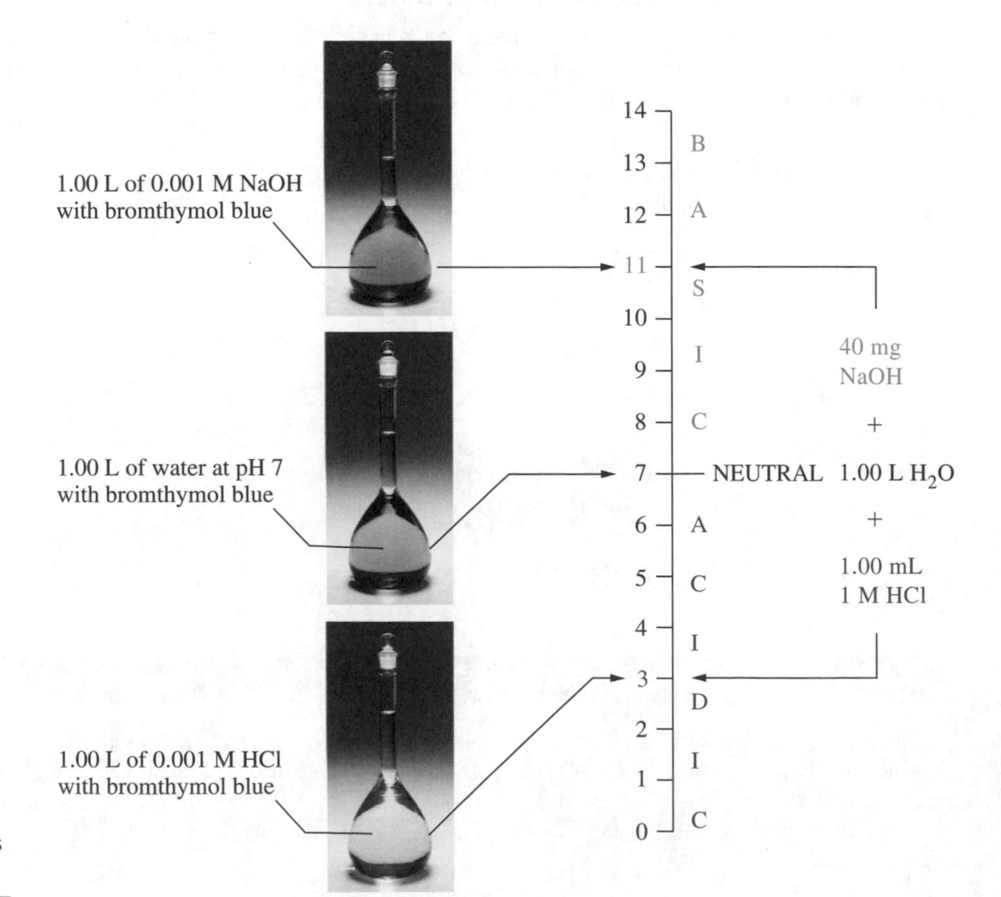

▶ FIGURE 9-4
Pure water has no buffering ability
Bromthymol blue indicator is blue at pH > 7, green at pH = 7, and yellow at pH < 7. Pure water has pH = 7.0. The addition of 0.001 mol H_3O^+ (1.00 mL of 1 M HCl) to 1.00 L water produces $[H_3O^+] =$ 0.001 M and pH = 3.0. The addition of 0.001 mol OH^- (40 mg NaOH) to 1.00 L of water produces $[OH^-] = 0.001$ M and pH = 11.0.

Now, imagine adding a *small* amount of a strong acid to this buffer solution. A reaction occurs in which a *small* amount of the base CH_3COO^- is converted to its conjugate acid CH_3COOH.

$$CH_3COO^- + H_3O^+ \longrightarrow CH_3COOH + H_2O$$

After the neutralization of the added H_3O^+, we find that in expression (9.1) $[CH_3COOH]$ has increased *slightly* and $[CH_3COO^-]$ has decreased *slightly*. The ratio $[CH_3COOH]/[CH_3COO^-]$ is only *slightly* greater than 1, and $[H_3O^+]$ has barely changed. The buffer solution has resisted a change in pH following the addition of a small amount of acid; the pH remains close to the original 4.74.

Next, imagine adding a *small* amount of a strong base to the original buffer solution with $[CH_3COOH] = [CH_3COO^-]$. A reaction occurs in which a *small* amount of the weak acid CH_3COOH is converted to its conjugate base CH_3COO^-.

$$CH_3COOH + OH^- \longrightarrow CH_3COO^- + H_2O$$

Here we find that $[CH_3COO^-]$ has increased *slightly*, and $[CH_3COOH]$ has decreased *slightly*. The ratio $[CH_3COOH]/[CH_3COO^-]$ is only *slightly* smaller than 1, and again $[H_3O^+]$ has barely changed. The buffer solution has resisted a change in pH following the addition of a small amount of base; again, the pH remains close to the original 4.74. The variation of the concentration of the weak acid and its conjugate base are illustrated in Figure 9-5.

Later in this section, we will be more specific about what constitutes *small* additions of an acid or a base and *slight* changes in the concentrations of the buffer components and pH. Also, we will discover that an acetic acid–sodium acetate buffer is good only for maintaining a nearly constant pH in a range of about 2 pH units centered on a pH $= pK_a = 4.74$. A buffer solution that maintains a nearly constant pH outside this range requires different buffer components, as suggested in Example 9-3.

We commonly need to calculate the pH of a buffer solution. At a minimum, such a calculation requires use of the ionization constant expression for a weak acid or weak base. Aspects of solution stoichiometry may also be required.

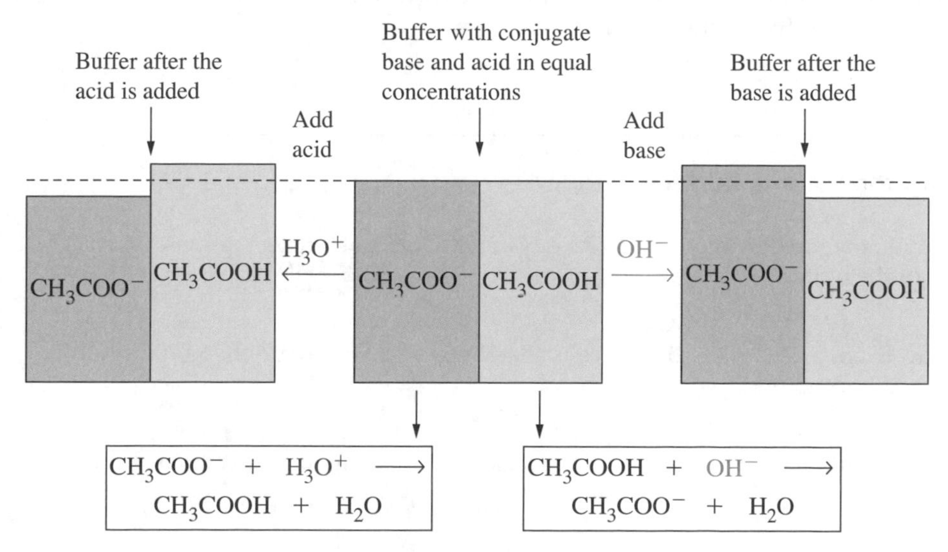

▲ FIGURE 9-5
How a buffer works
Acetate ion, the conjugate base of acetic acid, acts as a proton sink when strong acid is added. In this way, the ratio [conjugate base]/[acid] is kept approximately constant, so there is a minimal change in pH. Similarly, acetic acid acts as a proton donor when strong base is added, keeping the ratio [conjugate base]/[acid] approximately constant and minimizing the change in pH.

EXAMPLE 9-3 Predicting Whether a Solution Is a Buffer Solution

Show that an NH_3-NH_4Cl solution is a buffer solution. Over what pH range would you expect it to function?

Analyze

To show that a solution has buffer properties, first identify a component in the solution that neutralizes acids and a component that neutralizes bases.

Solve

In this example, these components are NH_3 and NH_4^+, respectively.

$$NH_3 + H_3O^+ \longrightarrow NH_4^+ + H_2O$$
$$NH_4^+ + OH^- \longrightarrow NH_3 + H_2O$$

In *all* aqueous solutions containing NH_3 and NH_4^+, we know that

$$NH_3 + H_2O \rightleftharpoons NH_4^+ + OH^- \quad \text{and}$$

$$K_b = \frac{[NH_4^+][OH^-]}{[NH_3]} = 1.8 \times 10^{-5}$$

If a solution has approximately equal concentrations of NH_4^+ and NH_3, then $[OH^-] \approx 1.8 \times 10^{-5}$ M; pOH $\approx$ 4.74; and pH $\approx$ 9.26. Ammonia–ammonium chloride solutions are *basic* buffer solutions that function over the approximate pH range of 8 to 10.

Assess

As we will soon see, not all NH_3-NH_4Cl buffer solutions will be effective buffers. The best buffers have large values for $[NH_3]$ and $[NH_4^+]$, with $[NH_3] \approx [NH_4^+]$.

PRACTICE EXAMPLE A: Describe how a mixture of a strong acid (such as HCl) and the salt of a weak acid (such as $NaCH_3COO$) can be a buffer solution. [*Hint:* What is the reaction that produces CH_3COOH?]

PRACTICE EXAMPLE B: Describe how a mixture of NH_3 and HCl can result in a buffer solution.

In Example 9-4, we first determine the stoichiometric concentrations of the buffer components. Then we perform an equilibrium calculation in the same fashion as in Examples 9-1 and 9-2.

EXAMPLE 9-4 Calculating the pH of a Buffer Solution

What is the pH of a buffer solution prepared by dissolving 25.5 g $NaCH_3COO$ in a sufficient volume of 0.550 M CH_3COOH to make 500.0 mL of the buffer?

Analyze

This example is very similar to Example 9-2. The difference is that we need to calculate the molarity of the acetate ion before solving the equilibrium part.

Solve

The molarity of CH_3COO^- corresponding to 25.5 g $NaCH_3COO$ in 500.0 mL of solution is calculated as follows.

$$\text{amount of } CH_3COO^- = 25.5 \text{ g } NaCH_3COO \times \frac{1 \text{ mol } NaCH_3COO}{82.04 \text{ g } NaCH_3COO}$$
$$\times \frac{1 \text{ mol } CH_3COO^-}{1 \text{ mol } NaCH_3COO}$$
$$= 0.311 \text{ mol } CH_3COO^-$$

$$[CH_3COO^-] = \frac{0.311 \text{ mol } CH_3COO^-}{0.500 \text{ L}} = 0.622 \text{ M } CH_3COO^-$$

Equilibrium Calculation:

	CH_3COOH	+	H_2O	$\rightleftharpoons$	H_3O^+	+	CH_3COO^-
initial concns:							
weak acid:	0.550 M				—		—
salt:	—				—		0.622 M
changes:	$-x$ M				$+x$ M		$+x$ M
equil concns:	$(0.550 - x)$ M				$+x$ M		$(0.622 + x)$ M

Let's assume that x is very small, so $0.550 - x \approx 0.550$ and $0.622 + x \approx 0.622$. We will find this assumption to be valid.

$$K_a = \frac{[H_3O^+][CH_3COO^-]}{[CH_3COOH]} = \frac{(x)(0.622)}{0.550} = 1.8 \times 10^{-5}$$

$$x = [H_3O^+] = \frac{0.550}{0.622} \times 1.8 \times 10^{-5} = 1.6 \times 10^{-5}$$

$$pH = -\log[H_3O^+] = -\log(1.6 \times 10^{-5}) = 4.80$$

Notice that $x = 1.6 \times 10^{-5}$ is only 0.003% of 0.550, and so the assumption that x is small was justified.

Assess

We have seen that $pH = pK_a = 4.74$ when acetic acid and acetate ion are present in equal concentrations. Here the concentration of the conjugate *base* (acetate ion) is greater than that of the acetic acid. The solution should be somewhat more basic (less acidic) than $pH = 4.74$. A pH of 4.80 is a reasonable answer.

PRACTICE EXAMPLE A: What is the pH of a buffer solution prepared by dissolving 23.1 g NaHCOO in a sufficient volume of 0.432 M HCOOH to make 500.0 mL of the buffer?

PRACTICE EXAMPLE B: A handbook states that to prepare 100.0 mL of a particular buffer solution, mix 63.0 mL of 0.200 M CH_3COOH with 37.0 mL of 0.200 M $NaCH_3COO$. What is the pH of this buffer?

An important point worth noting in Example 9-4 is that if a solution is to be an effective buffer, the assumptions $(c - x) \approx c$ and $(c + x) \approx c$ will always be valid (c represents the numerical part of an expression of molarity). That is, the *equilibrium* concentrations of the buffer components will be very nearly the same as their *stoichiometric* concentrations. As a result, in Example 9-4 we could have gone directly from the stoichiometric concentrations of the buffer components to the expression

KEEP IN MIND

that stoichiometric concentration is based on the amount of solute dissolved.

$$K_a = \frac{[H_3O^+][CH_3COO^-]}{[CH_3COOH]} = \frac{[H_3O^+](0.622)}{0.550} = 1.8 \times 10^{-5}$$

without setting up the ICE table. This procedure can be formalized through the special equation that is introduced next.

An Equation for Buffer Solutions: The Henderson–Hasselbalch Equation

Although we can continue to use the format demonstrated in Example 9-4 for buffer calculations, it is often useful to describe a buffer solution by means of an equation known as the **Henderson–Hasselbalch equation**. Biochemists and molecular biologists commonly use this equation. To derive this variation of the ionization constant expression, let's consider a mixture of a hypothetical weak acid, HA (such as CH_3COOH), and its salt, NaA (such as $NaCH_3COO$). We start with the familiar expressions

$$HA + H_2O \rightleftharpoons H_3O^+ + A^-$$

$$K_a = \frac{[H_3O^+][A^-]}{[HA]}$$

and rearrange the right side of the K_a expression to obtain

$$K_a = [H_3O^+] \times \frac{[A^-]}{[HA]}$$

Next, we take the *negative logarithm* of each side of this equation.

$$-\log K_a = -\log[H_3O^+] - \log\frac{[A^-]}{[HA]}$$

Now, recall that $pH = -\log[H_3O^+]$ and that $pK_a = -\log K_a$, which gives

$$pK_a = pH - \log\frac{[A^-]}{[HA]}$$

Solve for pH by rearranging the equation.

$$pH = pK_a + \log\frac{[A^-]}{[HA]}$$

A^- is the conjugate base of the weak acid HA, so we can write the more general equation (9.2), the Henderson–Hasselbalch equation.

▶ When the [conjugate base] = [acid], then $pH = pK_a$. When we get to titrations, an indicator is chosen to change color at $pH = pK_a$ of the indicator.

$$pH = pK_a + \log\frac{[\text{conjugate base}]}{[\text{acid}]} \qquad (9.2)$$

To apply this equation to an acetic acid–sodium acetate buffer, we use pK_a for CH_3COOH and these concentrations: $[CH_3COOH]$ for [acid] and $[CH_3COO^-]$ for [conjugate base]. To apply it to an ammonia–ammonium chloride buffer, we use pK_a for NH_4^+ and these concentrations: $[NH_4^+]$ for [acid] and $[NH_3]$ for [conjugate base].

KEEP IN MIND

that the Henderson–Hasselbalch equation is very useful but should probably not be committed to memory; it is easy to get the conjugate base and acid terms inverted. It is most important to understand the principles that lead to this equation, thereby avoiding the pitfalls of using the equation incorrectly or when it is not valid.

Equation (9.2) is useful only when we can substitute *stoichiometric* or initial concentrations for equilibrium concentrations to give

$$pH = pK_a + \log\frac{[\text{conjugate base}]_{\text{initial}}}{[\text{acid}]_{\text{initial}}}$$

thus avoiding the need to set up an ICE table. This constraint places important limitations on the equation's validity, however. Later, we will see that there are also conditions that must be met if a mixture is to be an effective buffer solution. Although the following rules may be overly restrictive in some cases, a reasonable approach to the twin concerns of effective buffer action and the validity of equation (9.2) is to ensure that

1. the ratio [conjugate base]/[acid] is within the limits

$$0.10 < \frac{[\text{conjugate base}]}{[\text{acid}]} < 10 \qquad (9.3)$$

2. the molarity of each buffer component exceeds the value of K_a by a factor of at least 100

Viewed another way, equation (9.2) works only for cases in which the assumption $c - x \approx c$ is valid. If a quadratic equation is required to solve the equilibrium constant expression, equation (9.2) will likely fail.

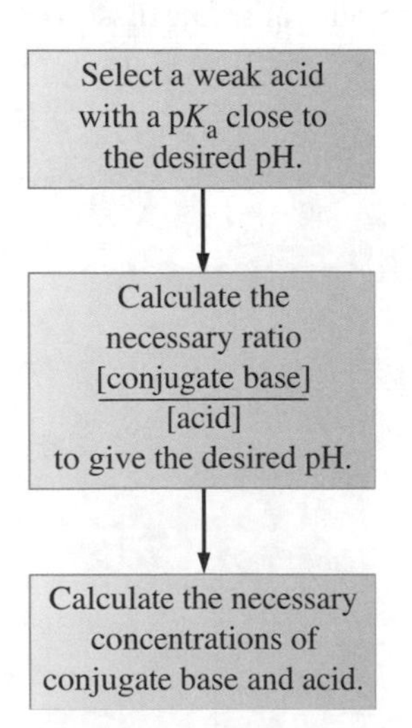

▲ One procedure to follow in making a buffer solution with a desired pH.

Preparing Buffer Solutions

Suppose we need a buffer solution with pH = 5.09. Equation (9.2) suggests two alternatives. One is to find a weak acid, HA, that has $pK_a = 5.09$ and prepare a solution with equal molarities of the acid and its salt.

$$pH = pK_a + \log\frac{\cancel{[A^-]}}{\cancel{[HA]}} = 5.09 + \log 1 = 5.09$$

Although this alternative is simple in concept, generally, it is not practical. We are not likely to find a readily available, water-soluble weak acid with exactly $pK_a = 5.09$. The second alternative, summarized in the margin, is to use a cheap, common weak acid such as acetic acid, CH_3COOH ($pK_a = 4.74$), and establish an appropriate ratio of $[CH_3COO^-]/[CH_3COOH]$ to obtain a pH of 5.09. Example 9-5 demonstrates this second alternative.

EXAMPLE 9-5 Preparing a Buffer Solution of a Desired pH

What mass of $NaCH_3COO$ must be dissolved in 0.300 L of 0.25 M CH_3COOH to produce a solution with pH = 5.09? (Assume that the solution volume remains constant at 0.300 L.)

Analyze

Equilibrium among the buffer components is expressed by the equation

$$CH_3COOH + H_2O \rightleftharpoons H_3O^+ + CH_3COO^- \qquad K_a = 1.8 \times 10^{-5}$$

and by the ionization constant expression for acetic acid.

$$K_a = \frac{[H_3O^+][CH_3COO^-]}{[CH_3COOH]} = 1.8 \times 10^{-5}$$

Each of the three concentration terms appearing in a K_a expression should be an equilibrium concentration. The $[H_3O^+]$ corresponding to a pH of 5.09 is the equilibrium concentration. For $[CH_3COOH]$, we will assume that the equilibrium concentration is equal to the stoichiometric or initial concentration. The value of $[CH_3COO^-]$ that we calculate with the K_a expression is the equilibrium concentration, and we will assume that it is also the same as the stoichiometric concentration. Thus, we assume that neither the ionization of CH_3COOH to form CH_3COO^- nor the hydrolysis of CH_3COO^- to form CH_3COOH produces much of a difference between the stoichiometric (initial) and equilibrium concentrations of the buffer components. These assumptions work well if the conditions stated in expression (9.3) are met.

Solve

The relevant concentration terms, then, are

$$[H_3O^+] = 10^{-pH} = 10^{-5.09} = 8.1 \times 10^{-6}\ M$$
$$[CH_3COOH] = 0.25\ M$$
$$[CH_3COO^-] = ?$$

The required acetate ion concentration in the buffer solution is

$$[CH_3COO^-] = K_a \times \frac{[CH_3COOH]}{[H_3O^+]} = 1.8 \times 10^{-5} \times \frac{0.25}{8.1 \times 10^{-6}} = 0.56\ M$$

We complete the calculation of the mass of sodium acetate with some familiar ideas of solution stoichiometry.

$$\text{mass} = 0.300\ L \times \frac{0.56\ \text{mol}\ CH_3COO^-}{1\ L} \times \frac{1\ \text{mol}\ NaCH_3COO}{1\ \text{mol}\ CH_3COO^-} \times \frac{82.0\ g\ NaCH_3COO}{1\ \text{mol}\ NaCH_3COO} = 14\ g\ NaCH_3COO$$

Assess

We check the answer by inserting the acetate ion and acetic acid concentrations, along with the pK_a of acetic acid, into equation (9.2) to obtain pH = 5.09. The method described in Example 9-5 is one way to obtain a buffer solution. Another approach involves adding an appropriate amount of strong base (e.g., 0.052 mol NaOH) to 0.300 L of 0.025 M $CH_3COOH(aq)$.

PRACTICE EXAMPLE A: How many grams of $(NH_4)_2SO_4$ must be dissolved in 0.500 L of 0.35 M NH_3 to produce a solution with pH = 9.00? (Assume that the solution volume remains at 0.500 L.)

PRACTICE EXAMPLE B: In Practice Example 9-3A, we established that an appropriate mixture of a strong acid and the salt of a weak acid is a buffer solution. Show that a solution made by adding 33.05 g $NaCH_3COO \cdot 3\,H_2O(s)$ to 300 mL of 0.250 M HCl should have pH $\approx$ 5.1.

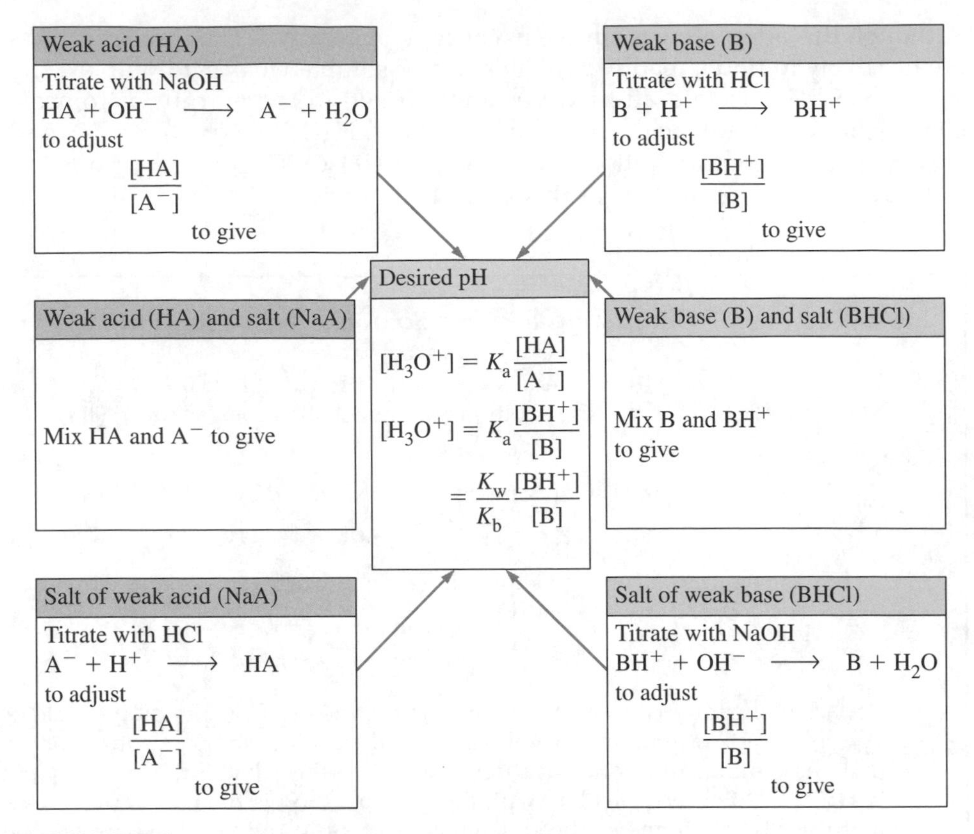

▲ FIGURE 9-6
Six methods for preparing buffer solutions
Depending on the pH range required and the type of experiment the buffer is to be used for, either a weak acid or a weak base can be used to prepare a buffer solution.

In Example 9-5, we achieved the desired ratio of $[CH_3COO^-]/[CH_3COOH]$ by adding 14 g of sodium acetate to the previously prepared 0.25 M CH_3COOH solution. This is a common method of obtaining a buffer solution. Other methods are sometimes useful as well. Sufficient NaOH(aq) could be added to $CH_3COOH(aq)$ to neutralize the acid partially, *producing* CH_3COO^- as a product. Or enough $NaCH_3COO(s)$ could be added to HCl(aq) to neutralize all the HCl, producing some CH_3COOH and leaving some CH_3COO^- in excess. As we saw in Chapter 8, amines are weak bases, so an aqueous mixture of an amine and its conjugate acid is a buffer solution. Buffer solutions based on amines can be prepared in ways analogous to those based on weak acids. The methods available for making buffer solutions are summarized in Figure 9-6.

Calculating pH Changes in Buffer Solutions

To calculate how the pH of a buffer solution changes when small amounts of a strong acid or base are added, we must first use *stoichiometric* principles to establish how much of one buffer component is consumed and how much of the other component is produced. Then the new concentrations of weak acid (or weak base) and its salt can be used to calculate the pH of the buffer solution. Essentially, this problem is solved in two steps. First, we assume that the neutralization reaction proceeds to *completion* and determine new stoichiometric concentrations. Then these new stoichiometric concentrations are substituted into the equilibrium constant expression and the expression is solved for $[H_3O^+]$, which is converted to pH. This method is applied in Example 9-6 and illustrated in Figure 9-7.

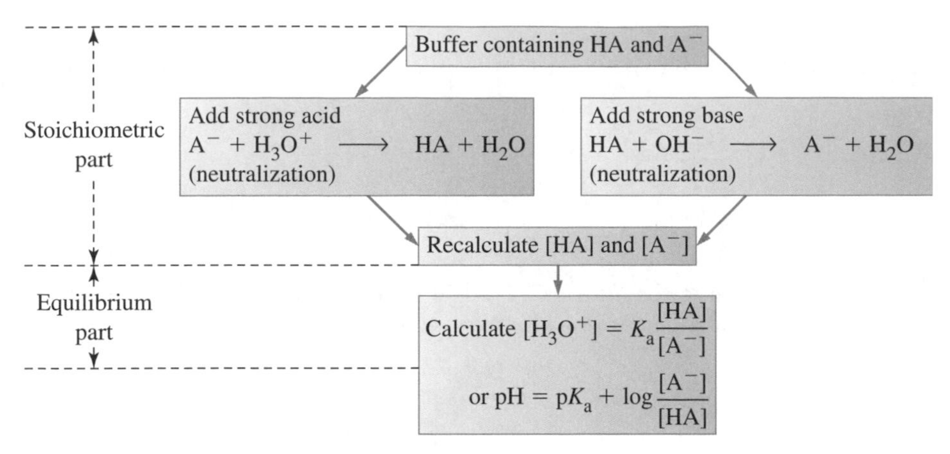

▲ FIGURE 9-7
Calculation of the new pH of a buffer after strong acid or base is added
The stoichiometric and equilibrium parts of the calculation are indicated. This scheme can also be applied to the conjugate acid–base pair BH^+/B, where B is a base.

EXAMPLE 9-6 Calculating pH Changes in a Buffer Solution

What are the effects on the pH of adding **(a)** 0.0060 mol HCl and **(b)** 0.0060 mol NaOH to 0.300 L of a buffer solution that is 0.250 M CH_3COOH and 0.560 M $NaCH_3COO$?

Analyze

In parts (a) and (b) we complete essentially the same calculations. We should recognize that we are adding a strong acid or a strong base to the buffer solution. To investigate this effect we make a stoichiometric calculation, followed by an equilibrium calculation. The stoichiometric calculation is necessary to account for the neutralization of the base or acid components of the buffer.

Solve

To judge the effect of adding either (a) acid or (b) base on the pH of the buffer, the value we must keep in mind is the pH of the original buffer. Because the initial (or stoichiometric) concentrations of CH_3COOH and CH_3COO^- are large and not too different, the initial pH of the buffer can be obtained by substituting the initial concentrations into equation (9.2). (See the discussion following equation (9.2).)

$$pH = pK_a + \log\frac{[CH_3COO^-]}{[CH_3COOH]}$$

$$= 4.74 + \log\frac{0.560}{0.250} = 4.74 + 0.35 = 5.09$$

(a) Stoichiometric Calculation: Let's calculate amounts in moles, and assume that the neutralization goes to completion. Essentially, this is a limiting reactant calculation. In neutralizing the added H_3O^+, 0.0060 mol CH_3COO^- is converted to 0.0060 mol CH_3COOH.

	CH_3COO^-	+	H_3O^+	$\longrightarrow$	CH_3COOH	+	H_2O
original buffer:	$\underbrace{0.300\ L \times 0.560\ M}$ 0.168 mol				$\underbrace{0.300\ L \times 0.250\ M}$ 0.0750 mol		
add:			0.0060 mol				
changes:	−0.0060 mol		−0.0060 mol		+0.0060 mol		
final buffer:							
amounts:	0.162 mol		≈ 0		0.0810 mol		
concns:	$\underbrace{0.162\ mol/0.300\ L}$ 0.540 M		≈ 0		$\underbrace{0.0810\ mol/0.300\ L}$ 0.270 M		

(continued)

Equilibrium Calculation: We can calculate the pH with equation (9.2), using the new equilibrium concentrations.

$$pH = pK_a + \log\frac{[CH_3COO^-]}{[CH_3COOH]}$$

$$= 4.74 + \log\frac{0.540}{0.270} = 4.74 + 0.30 = 5.04$$

(b) Stoichiometric Calculation: In neutralizing the added OH^-, 0.0060 mol CH_3COOH is converted to 0.0060 mol CH_3COO^-. The calculation of the new stoichiometric concentrations is shown on the last line of the following table.

	CH_3COOH	+	OH^-	$\longrightarrow$	CH_3COO^-	+	H_2O
original buffer:	0.300 L × 0.250 M = 0.0750 mol				0.300 L × 0.560 M = 0.168 mol		
add:			0.0060 mol				
changes:	−0.0060 mol		−0.0060 mol		+0.0060 mol		
final buffer:							
amounts:	0.0690 mol		≈0		0.174 mol		
concns:	0.0690 mol/0.300 L = 0.230 M		≈0		0.174 mol/0.300 L = 0.580 M		

Equilibrium Calculation: This is the same type of calculation as in part (a), but with slightly different concentrations.

$$pH = 4.74 + \log\frac{0.580}{0.230} = 4.74 + 0.40 = 5.14$$

Assess

The addition of 0.0060 mol HCl *lowers* the pH from 5.09 to 5.04, which is only a small change in pH. The addition of 0.0060 mol OH^- *raises* the pH from 5.09 to 5.14—another small change. Had we instead added 0.0060 mol HCl or 0.0060 mol NaOH to 0.300 L of water, the pH would have changed by more than 5 pH units. The most important factors to confirm in a calculation of this type are that the magnitude of the pH change is small and that the change occurs in the correct direction: *lowering* of the pH by an acid and *raising* of the pH by a base. The results are indeed reasonable.

PRACTICE EXAMPLE A: A 1.00 L volume of buffer is made with concentrations of 0.350 M NaHCOO (sodium formate) and 0.550 M HCOOH (formic acid). **(a)** What is the initial pH? **(b)** What is the pH after the addition of 0.0050 mol HCl(aq)? (Assume that the volume remains 1.00 L.) **(c)** What would be the pH after the addition of 0.0050 mol NaOH to the original buffer?

PRACTICE EXAMPLE B: How many milliliters of 6.0 M HNO_3 would you add to 300.0 mL of the buffer solution of Example 9-6 to change the pH from 5.09 to 5.03?

▶ Dilute and concentrated buffers will have the same pH, but as mentioned in the next section, a given volume of a dilute buffer will have a lower buffer capacity than the same volume of a more concentrated buffer.

Perhaps you have already noticed a way to simplify the calculation in Example 9-6. Because the buffer components are always present in the same solution of volume V, the numbers of moles can be substituted directly into equation (9.2) without regard for the particular value of V. Thus, in Example 9-6(b),

$$pH = 4.74 + \log\frac{[CH_3COO^-]}{[CH_3COOH]} = 4.74 + \log\frac{0.174\ \cancel{mol/V}}{0.0690\ \cancel{mol/V}} = 4.74 + 0.40 = 5.14$$

This expression is also consistent with the observation that, on dilution, buffer solutions resist pH changes. Diluting a buffer solution means increasing its volume V by adding water. This action produces the same change in the numerator and the denominator of the ratio [conjugate base]/[acid]. The ratio itself remains unchanged, as does the pH.

Buffer Capacity and Buffer Range

It is not difficult to see that if we add more than 0.0750 mol OH^- to the buffer solution described in Example 9-6, the 0.0750 mol CH_3COOH will be completely converted to 0.0750 mol CH_3COO^-. An excess of OH^- will remain, and the solution will become rather strongly basic.

Buffer capacity refers to the amount of acid or base that a buffer can neutralize before its pH changes appreciably. In general, the maximum buffer capacity exists when the concentrations of a weak acid and its conjugate base are kept *large* and *approximately equal to each other*. The **buffer range** is the pH range over which a buffer effectively neutralizes added acids and bases and maintains a fairly constant pH. As equation (9.2) suggests,

$$\text{pH} = \text{p}K_a + \log\frac{[\text{conjugate base}]}{[\text{acid}]}$$

when the ratio [conjugate base]/[acid] = 1, pH = $\text{p}K_a$. When the ratio falls to 0.10, the pH *decreases* by 1 pH unit from $\text{p}K_a$ because $\log 0.10 = -1$. If the ratio increases to a value of 10, the pH *increases* by 1 unit because $\log 10 = 1$. For practical purposes, this range of 2 pH units is the maximum range to which a buffer solution should be exposed. For acetic acid–sodium acetate buffers, the effective range is about pH 3.7–5.7; for ammonia–ammonium chloride buffers, it is about pH 8.3–10.3.

◀ Our eyes can see an indicator color change over a range of about 2 pH units.

KEEP IN MIND

that as a rule of thumb, the amounts of the buffer components should be at least ten times as great as the amount of acid or base to be neutralized.

◀ The buffer range for the ammonia–ammonium chloride solution is based on the $\text{p}K_a$ of NH_4^+, 9.26.

Applications of Buffer Solutions

An important example of a buffered system is that found in blood, which must be maintained at a pH of 7.4 in humans. But buffers have other important applications, too.

Protein studies often must be performed in buffered media because the structures of protein molecules, including the magnitude and kind of electric charges they carry, depend on the pH. The typical enzyme is a protein capable of catalyzing a biochemical reaction, so enzyme activity is closely linked to protein structure and hence to pH. Most enzymes in the body have their maximum activity between pH 6 and pH 8. Studying enzyme activity in the laboratory usually means working with media buffered in this pH range.

The control of pH is often important in industrial processes. For example, in the mashing of barley malt, the first step of making beer, the pH of the solution must be maintained at 5.0 to 5.2, so that the protease and peptidase enzymes can hydrolyze the proteins from the barley. The inventor of the pH scale, Søren Sørensen, was a research scientist in a brewery.

▲ A master brewer inspecting wort temperature and pH in the making of beer.

9-2 CONCEPT ASSESSMENT

You are asked to make a buffer with a pH value close to 4 that would best resist an increase in pH. You can select one of the following acid–conjugate base pairs: acetic acid–acetate, $K_a = 1.8 \times 10^{-5}$; ammonium ion–ammonia, $K_a = 5.6 \times 10^{-10}$; or benzoic acid–benzoate, $K_a = 6.3 \times 10^{-5}$; and you can mix them in the following acid–conjugate base ratios: 1:1, 2:1, or 1:2. What combination would make the best buffer?

9-3 Acid–Base Indicators

An **acid–base indicator** is a substance whose color depends on the pH of the solution to which it is added. Several of the photographs in this and the preceding chapter have shown acid–base indicators in use. The indicator chosen

◀ Two of the most important biological buffers are the phosphate and bicarbonate buffer systems. Proteins and nucleotides also function as buffers on the cellular level.

depended on just how acidic or basic the solution was. In this section, we will consider how an acid–base indicator works and how an appropriate indicator is selected for a pH measurement.

Acid–base indicators exist in two forms: (1) a weak acid, represented symbolically as HIn and having one color, and (2) its conjugate base, represented as In^- and having a different color. When just a small amount of indicator is added to a solution, the indicator does not affect the pH of the solution. Instead, the ionization equilibrium of the indicator is itself affected by the prevailing $[H_3O^+]$ in solution.

$$\underset{\text{Acid color}}{HIn} + H_2O \rightleftharpoons H_3O^+ + \underset{\text{Base color}}{In^-}$$

From Le Châtelier's principle, we see that *increasing* $[H_3O^+]$ in a solution displaces the equilibrium to the left, increasing the proportion of HIn and hence the acid color. *Decreasing* $[H_3O^+]$ in a solution displaces the equilibrium to the right, increasing the proportion of In^- and hence the base color. The color of the solution depends on the relative proportions of the acid and base. The pH of the solution can be related to these relative proportions and to the pK_a of the indicator by means of an equation similar to equation (9.2).

$$pH = pK_{HIn} + \log\frac{[In^-]}{[HIn]} \tag{9.4}$$

▶ The acid "color" of a few indicators is colorless.

In general, if 90% or more of an indicator is in the form HIn, the solution will take on the acid color. If 90% or more is in the form In^-, the solution takes on the base (or anion) color. If the concentrations of HIn and In^- are about equal, the indicator is in the process of changing from one form to the other and has an intermediate color. The complete change in color occurs over a range of about *2 pH units*, with $pH = pK_{HIn}$ at about the middle of the range. The colors and pH ranges of several acid–base indicators are shown in Figure 9-8. A summary of these ideas is presented in Table 9.1, and an example of their use is given below.

Bromthymol blue, $pK_{HIn} = 7.1$

$pH < 6.1$ (yellow) $pH \approx 7.1$ (green) $pH > 8.1$ (blue)

An acid–base indicator is usually prepared as a solution (in water, ethanol, or some other solvent). In acid–base titrations, a few drops of the indicator solution are added to the solution being titrated. In other applications, porous paper is impregnated with an indicator solution and dried. When this paper is moistened with the solution being tested, it acquires a color determined by the pH of the solution. This paper is usually called *pH test paper*.

TABLE 9.1 pH and the Colors of Acid–Base Indicators

Acid Color	Intermediate Color	Base Color
$[In^-]/[HIn] < 0.10$ $pH < pK_{HIn} + \log 0.10$ $pH < pK_{HIn} - 1$	$[In^-]/[HIn] \approx 1$ $pH \approx pK_{HIn} + \log 1$ $pH \approx pK_{HIn}$	$[In^-]/[HIn] > 10$ $pH > pK_{HIn} + \log 10$ $pH > pK_{HIn} + 1$

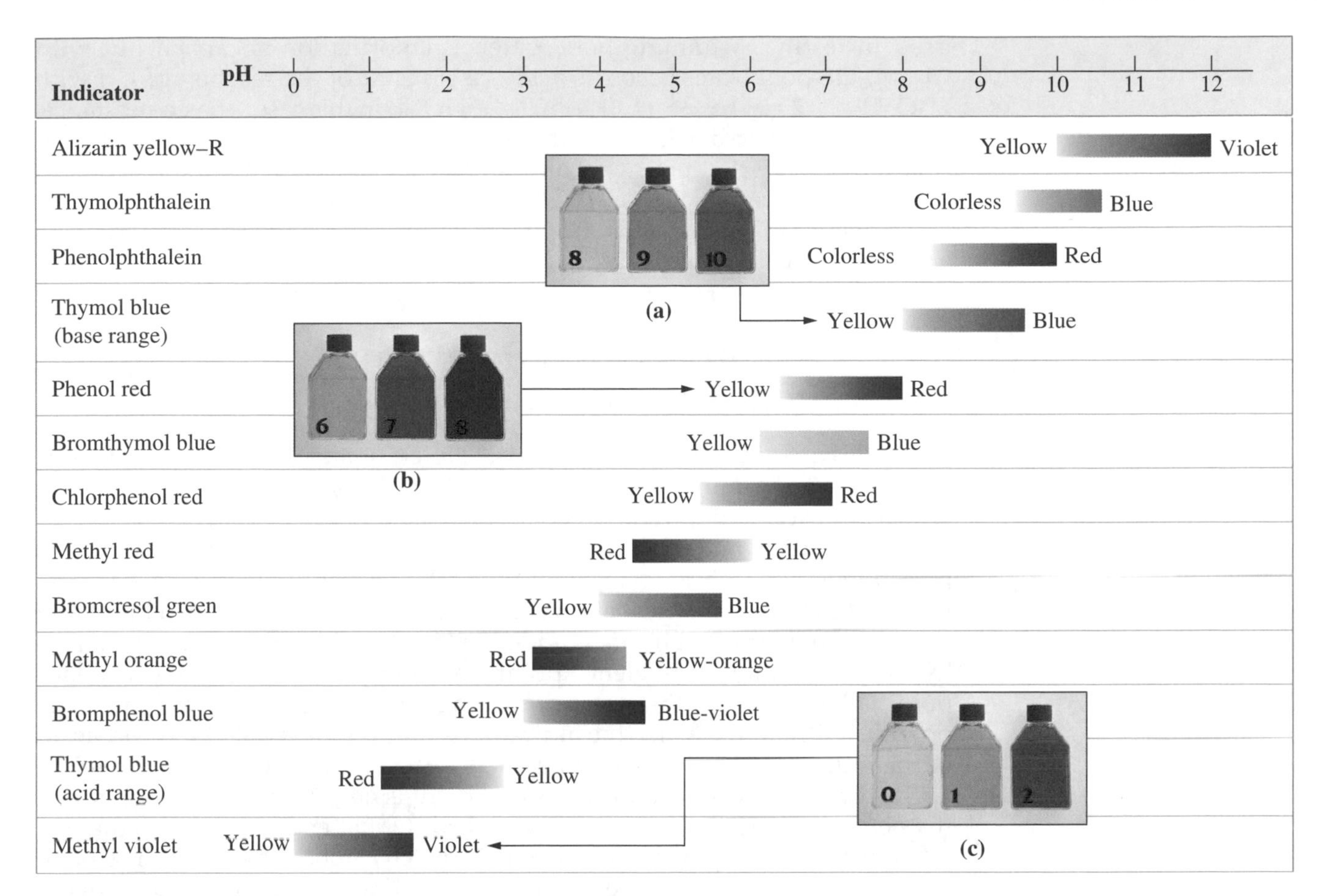

▲ FIGURE 9-8
pH and color changes for some common acid–base indicators
The indicators pictured and the pH values at which they change color are **(a)** thymol blue (pH 8–10); **(b)** phenol red (pH 6–8); and **(c)** methyl violet (pH 0–2).

9-3 CONCEPT ASSESSMENT

(1) Given that an indicator is itself a weak acid or base, why does adding it to a solution not change the nature of the equilibrium?

(2) Starting with about 10 mL of dilute NaCl(aq) containing a couple of drops of phenol red indicator, what color would the solution be for each of the following actions: **(a)** first 10 drops of 1.0 M HCl(aq) are added to the solution; **(b)** next 15 drops of 1.0 M $NaCH_3COO$(aq) are added to solution **(a)**; **(c)** then one drop of 1.0 M KOH(aq) is added to solution **(b)**; and **(d)** 10 more drops of 1.0 M KOH(aq) are added to solution **(c)**.

Applications

Acid–base indicators are most useful when only an approximate pH determination is needed. For example, they are used in soil-testing kits to establish the approximate pH of soils. Soils are usually acidic in regions of high rainfall and heavy vegetation, and they are alkaline in more arid regions. The pH can vary considerably with local conditions, however. If a soil is found to be too acidic for a certain crop, its pH can be raised by adding slaked lime [$Ca(OH)_2$]. To reduce the pH of a soil, organic matter might be added.

▲ Testing swimming pool water for its chlorine content and pH.

In swimming pools, chlorinating agents are most effective at a pH of about 7.4. At this pH, the growth of algae is avoided, and the corrosion of pool plumbing is minimized. Phenol red (see Figure 9-8) is a common indicator used in testing swimming pool water. If chlorination is carried out with $Cl_2(g)$, the pool water becomes acidic as a result of the reaction of Cl_2 with H_2O: $Cl_2 + 2\,H_2O \longrightarrow H_3O^+ + Cl^- + HOCl$. In this case, a basic substance, such as sodium carbonate, is used to raise the pH. Another widely used chlorinating agent is sodium hypochlorite, NaOCl(aq), made by the reaction of $Cl_2(g)$ with excess NaOH(aq): $Cl_2 + 2\,OH^- \longrightarrow Cl^- + OCl^- + H_2O$. The excess NaOH raises the pH of the pool water. The pH is adjusted by adding an acid, such as HCl or H_2SO_4.

9-4 Neutralization Reactions and Titration Curves

As we learned in the discussion of the stoichiometry of titration reactions (Section 1-7), the **equivalence point** of a neutralization reaction is the point at which both acid and base have been consumed and *neither* is in excess.

In a titration, one of the solutions to be neutralized—say, the acid—is placed in a flask or beaker, together with a few drops of an acid–base indicator. The other solution (the base) used in a titration is added from a buret and is called the **titrant**. The titrant is added to the acid, first rapidly and then drop by drop, up to the equivalence point (recall Figure 1-17). The equivalence point is located by noting the color change of the acid–base indicator. The point in a titration at which the indicator changes color is called the **end point** of the indicator. The end point must match the equivalence point of the neutralization. That is, if the indicator's end point is near the equivalence point of the neutralization, the color change marked by that end point will signal the attainment of the equivalence point. This match can be achieved by use of an indicator whose color change occurs over a pH range that includes the pH of the equivalence point.

A graph of pH versus volume of titrant (the solution in the buret) is called a **titration curve**. Titration curves are most easily constructed by measuring the pH during a titration with a pH meter and plotting the data with a recorder. In this section we will emphasize calculating the pH at various points in a titration. These calculations will serve as a review of aspects of acid–base equilibria considered earlier in this chapter and in the preceding chapter.

The Millimole

In a typical titration, the volume of solution delivered from a buret is less than 50 mL (usually about 20–25 mL). The molarity of the solution used for the titration is generally less than 1 M. The typical amount of OH^- (or H_3O^+) delivered from the buret during a titration is only a few thousandths of a mole—for example, 5.00×10^{-3} mol. In calculations it is often easier to work with millimoles instead of moles. The symbol **mmol** stands for a **millimole**, which is one thousandth of a mole, or 10^{-3} mol.

Molarity is defined as the number of moles per liter. We can use an alternative definition of molarity by converting from moles to millimoles and from liters to milliliters.

$$\text{M} = \frac{\text{mol}}{\text{L}} = \frac{\text{mol}/1000}{\text{L}/1000} = \frac{\text{mmol}}{\text{mL}}$$

Thus, the amount of solute is the product of molarity and solution volume and can be based either on mol/L × L = mol or on mmol/mL × mL = mmol.

Titration of a Strong Acid with a Strong Base

Suppose that 25.00 mL of 0.100 M HCl (a strong acid) is placed in a small flask or beaker and that 0.100 M NaOH (a strong base) is added to it from a buret.

The pH of the accumulated solution can be calculated at different points in the titration, and these pH values can be plotted against the volume of NaOH added. From this titration curve we can establish the pH at the equivalence point and identify an appropriate indicator for the titration. Some typical calculations are outlined in Example 9-7.

EXAMPLE 9-7 **Calculating Points on a Titration Curve: Strong Acid Titrated with a Strong Base**

What is the pH at each of the following points in the titration of 25.00 mL of 0.100 M HCl with 0.100 M NaOH?

(a) before the addition of any NaOH (*initial pH*)
(b) after the addition of 24.00 mL 0.100 M NaOH (*before the equivalence point*)
(c) after the addition of 25.00 mL 0.100 M NaOH (*the equivalence point*)
(d) after the addition of 26.00 mL 0.100 M NaOH (*beyond the equivalence point*)

Analyze

Parts (a) to (d) correspond to four different stages of the titration. In part (a) we calculate the initial pH of the HCl solution before the titration begins. In part (b) most but not all the acid has been neutralized. In part (c) all the acid is neutralized, which corresponds to the equivalence point. In part (d) we are past the equivalence point and are dealing with a solution containing an unreacted strong base.

Solve

First, let's write the titration equation in the ionic and net ionic form.

Ionic form: $H_3O^+(aq) + Cl^-(aq) + Na^+(aq) + OH^-(aq) \longrightarrow Na^+(aq) + Cl^-(aq) + 2\,H_2O(l)$

Net ionic form: $H_3O^+(aq) + OH^-(aq) \longrightarrow 2\,H_2O(l)$

(a) Before any NaOH is added, we are dealing with 0.100 M HCl. This solution has $[H_3O^+] = 0.100$ M and pH = 1.00.

(b) The number of millimoles of H_3O^+ to be titrated is

$$25.00\ \text{mL} \times \frac{0.100\ \text{mmol}\ H_3O^+}{1\ \text{mL}} = 2.50\ \text{mmol}\ H_3O^+$$

The number of millimoles of OH^- present in 24.00 mL of 0.100 M NaOH is

$$24.00\ \text{mL} \times \frac{0.100\ \text{mmol}}{1\ \text{mL}} = 2.40\ \text{mmol}\ OH^-$$

Now we can represent the net ionic equation of the neutralization reaction in a familiar format.

	H_3O^+	+	OH^-	$\longrightarrow$	$2\,H_2O$
initially present:	2.50 mmol		—		
add:			2.40 mmol		
changes:	−2.40 mmol		−2.40 mmol		
after reaction:	0.10 mmol		≈0		

The remaining 0.10 mmol of H_3O^+ is present in 49.00 mL of solution (25.00 mL original + 24.00 mL added base).

$$[H_3O^+] = \frac{0.10\ \text{mmol}\ H_3O^+}{49.00\ \text{mL}} = 2.0 \times 10^{-3}\ \text{M}$$

$$\text{pH} = -\log[H_3O^+] = -\log(2.0 \times 10^{-3}) = 2.70$$

(c) The equivalence point is the point at which the HCl is completely neutralized and no excess NaOH is present. As seen in the ionic form of the equation for the neutralization reaction, the solution at the equivalence point is simply NaCl(aq). And, because neither Na^+ nor Cl^- hydrolyzes in water, pH = 7.00.

(continued)

(d) To determine the pH of the solution beyond the equivalence point, we can return to the format in (b), except that now OH^- is in excess. The amount of OH^- added is 26.00 mL × 0.100 mmol/L = 2.60 mmol.

	H_3O^+	+ OH^-	$\longrightarrow$ $2\,H_2O$
initially present:	2.50 mmol	—	
add:		2.60 mmol	
changes:	−2.50 mmol	−2.50 mmol	
after reaction:	≈0	0.10 mmol	

The excess 0.10 mmol of NaOH is present in 51.00 mL of solution (25.00 mL original acid + 26.00 mL added base). The concentration of OH^- in this solution is

$$[OH^-] = \frac{0.10\text{ mmol }OH^-}{51.00\text{ mL}} = 2.0 \times 10^{-3}\text{ M}$$

$$pOH = -\log(2.0 \times 10^{-3}) = 2.70 \qquad pH = 14.00 - 2.70 = 11.30$$

Assess

In strong acid–strong base titrations, changes in pH are abrupt and occur mostly right before and right after the equivalence point. For a strong acid–strong base titration, the pH at the equivalence point is equal to 7.

PRACTICE EXAMPLE A: For the titration of 25.00 mL of 0.150 M HCl with 0.250 M NaOH, calculate **(a)** the initial pH; **(b)** the pH when neutralization is 50.0% complete; **(c)** the pH when neutralization is 100.0% complete; and **(d)** the pH when 1.00 mL of NaOH is added beyond the equivalence point.

PRACTICE EXAMPLE B: For the titration of 50.00 mL of 0.00812 M Ba(OH) with 0.0250 M HCl, calculate **(a)** the initial pH; **(b)** the pH when neutralization is 50.0% complete; **(c)** the pH when neutralization is 100.0% complete.

Figure 9-9 presents pH versus volume data and the titration curve for the HCl—NaOH titration. From this figure, we can establish these principal features of the titration curve for the titration of a *strong acid with a strong base*.

- The pH has a low value at the beginning of the titration.
- The pH changes slowly until just before the equivalence point.

Titration Data

mL NaOH(aq)	pH
0.00	1.00
10.00	1.37
20.00	1.95
22.00	2.19
24.00	2.70
25.00	7.00
26.00	11.30
28.00	11.75
30.00	11.96
40.00	12.36
50.00	12.52

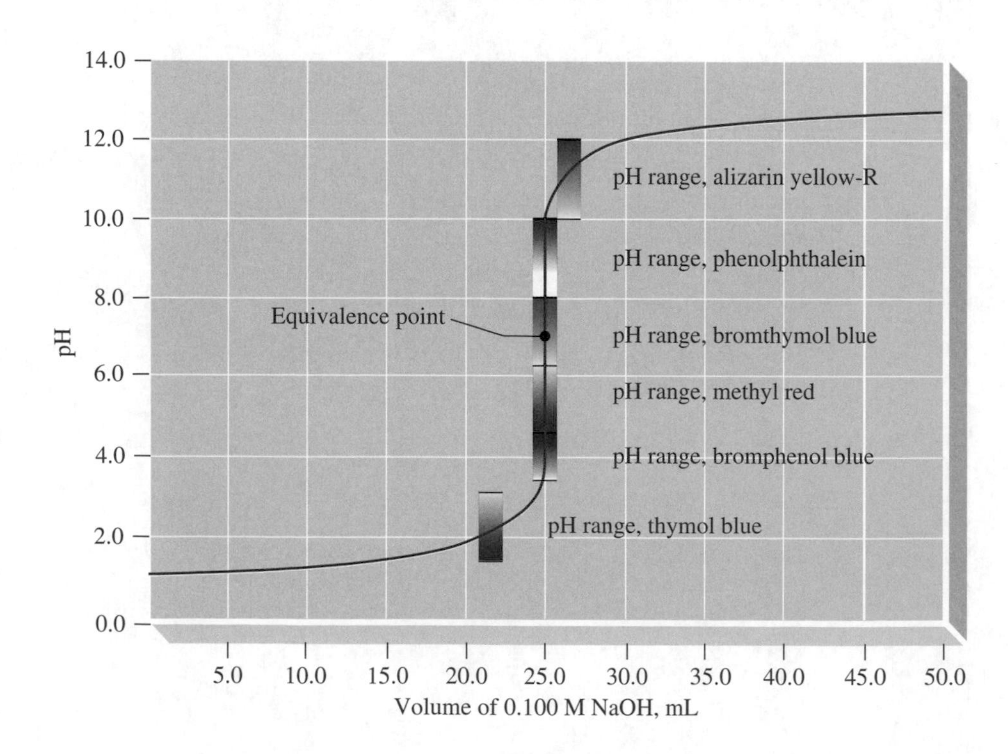

▶ FIGURE 9-9
Titration curve for the titration of a strong acid with a strong base—25.00 mL of 0.100 M HCl with 0.100 M NaOH
All indicators whose color ranges fall along the steep portion of the titration curve are suitable for this titration. Thymol blue changes color too soon; alizarin yellow-R, too late.

- At the equivalence point, the pH rises very sharply, perhaps by 6 units for an addition of only 0.10 mL (2 drops) of base.
- Beyond the equivalence point, the pH again rises only slowly.
- Any acid–base indicator whose color changes in the pH range from about 4 to 10 is suitable for this titration.

In the titration of a strong base with a strong acid, we can obtain a titration curve essentially identical to Figure 9-9 by plotting pOH against volume of titrant (the strong acid). Also, we can make a set of statements similar to those listed above, except that pOH would be substituted for pH. Alternatively, if pH is plotted against volume of titrant (the strong acid), the titration curve looks like Figure 9-9 flipped over from top to bottom, as shown in Figure 9-10.

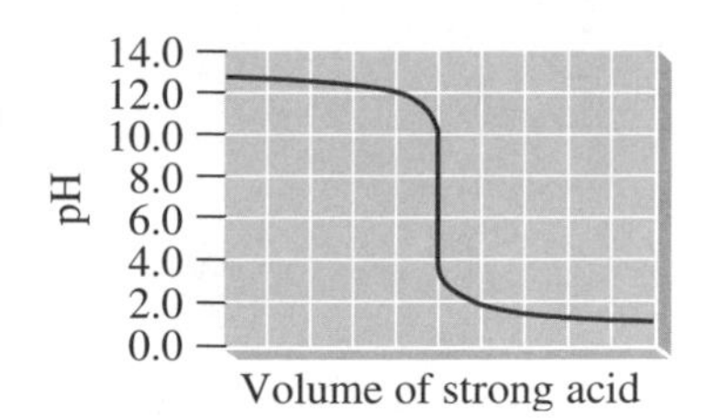

▲ FIGURE 9-10
Titration curve for the titration of a strong base with a strong acid

Titration of a Weak Acid with a Strong Base

Several important differences exist between the titration of a weak acid with a strong base and a strong acid with a strong base, but one feature is *unchanged* when we compare the two titrations.

> For equal volumes of acid solutions of the same molarity, the volume of base required to titrate to the equivalence point is independent of the strength of the acid.

We can think of the neutralization of a weak acid, such as CH_3COOH as involving the direct transfer of protons from CH_3COOH molecules to OH^- ions. In the neutralization of a strong acid, the protons are transferred from H_3O^+ ions. In either case, the acid and base react in a 1:1 mole ratio.

$$CH_3COOH + OH^- \longrightarrow H_2O + CH_3COO^-$$
$$H_3O^+ + OH^- \longrightarrow H_2O + H_2O$$

Calculations for the titration of a weak acid with a strong base can be divided into a stoichiometric part and an equilibrium part to take into account the partial ionization of the weak acid. The calculation strategy is analogous to that adopted when we considered the addition of a strong base to a buffer solution. In Example 9-8 and in Figure 9-11, we consider the titration of 25.00 mL of 0.100 M CH_3COOH with 0.100 M NaOH.

Titration Data

mL NaOH(aq)	pH
0.00	2.89
5.00	4.14
10.00	4.57
12.50	4.74
15.00	4.92
20.00	5.35
24.00	6.12
25.00	8.72
26.00	11.30
30.00	11.96
40.00	12.36
50.00	12.52

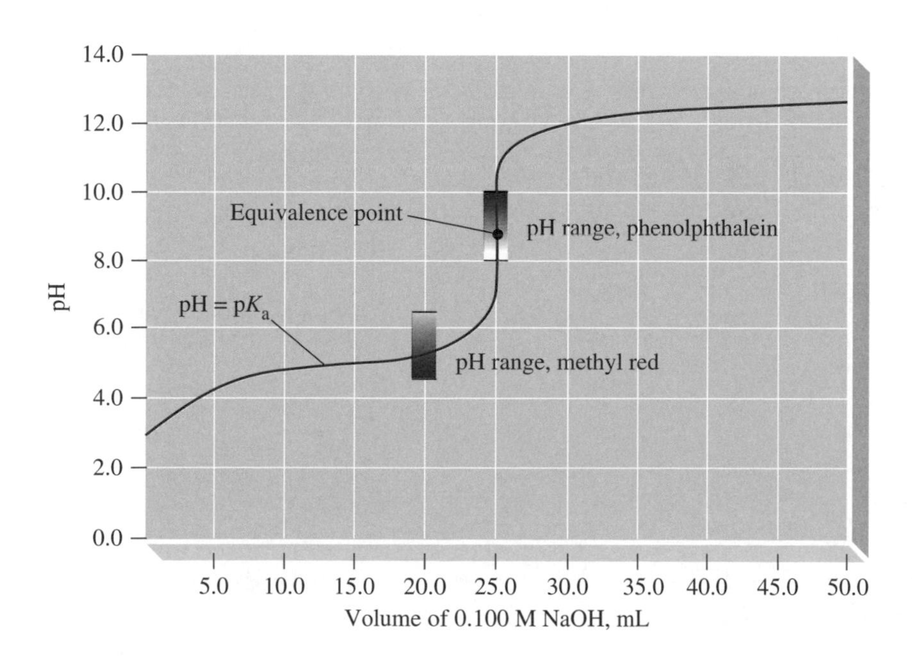

◀ FIGURE 9-11
Titration curve for the titration of a weak acid with a strong base—25.00 mL of 0.100 M CH_3COOH with 0.100 M NaOH
Phenolphthalein is a suitable indicator for this titration, but methyl red is not. When exactly half of the acid is neutralized, $[CH_3COOH] = [CH_3COO^-]$ and pH = pK_a 4.74.

EXAMPLE 9-8 Calculating Points on a Titration Curve: Weak Acid Titrated with a Strong Base

What is the pH at each of the following points in the titration of 25.00 mL of 0.100 M CH_3COOH with 0.100 M NaOH?

(a) before the addition of any NaOH (*initial pH*)
(b) after the addition of 10.00 mL 0.100 M NaOH (*before equivalence point*)
(c) after the addition of 12.50 mL 0.100 M NaOH (*half-neutralization*)
(d) after the addition of 25.00 mL 0.100 M NaOH (*equivalence point*)
(e) after the addition of 26.00 mL 0.100 M NaOH (*beyond equivalence point*)

Analyze

Titrations between weak acids and strong bases or strong acids and weak bases have four regions of interest. The first is the initial pH, which we calculate in the same way we would calculate the pH for a solution of a weak acid or weak base. The second is the buffer region; the third is the hydrolysis region; and the fourth is beyond the equivalence point.

Solve

(a) The initial $[H_3O^+]$ is obtained by the calculation in Example 8-6. $pH = -\log(1.3 \times 10^{-3}) = 2.89$.

(b) The number of millimoles of CH_3COOH to be neutralized is

$$25.00 \text{ mL} \times \frac{0.100 \text{ mmol } CH_3COOH}{1 \text{ mL}} = 2.50 \text{ mmol } CH_3COOH$$

At this point in the titration, the number of millimoles of OH^- added is

$$10.00 \text{ mL} \times \frac{0.100 \text{ mmol } OH^-}{1 \text{ mL}} = 1.00 \text{ mmol } OH^-$$

The total solution volume = 25.00 mL original acid + 10.00 mL added base = 35.00 mL. We enter this information at appropriate points into the following setup.

Stoichiometric Calculation:

	CH_3COOH +	OH^- ⟶	CH_3COO^- + H_2O
initially present:	2.50 mmol	—	—
add:		1.00 mmol	
changes:	−1.00 mmol	−1.00 mmol	+1.00 mmol
after reaction:			
mmol:	1.50 mmol		1.00 mmol
concns:	1.50 mmol/35.00 mL	≈0	1.00 mmol/35.00 mL
	0.0429 M		0.0286 M

Equilibrium Calculation: The most direct approach is to recognize that the acetic acid–sodium acetate solution is a buffer solution whose pH can be calculated with the Henderson–Hasselbalch equation. Use of that equation is justified for two reasons: (1) The ratio: $[CH_3COO^-]/[CH_3COOH] = 0.0286/0.0429 = 0.667$ (satisfying the requirement on page 364 that it be between 0.10 and 10), and (2) CH_3COO^- and CH_3COOH exceed $K_a(1.8 \times 10^{-5})$ by the factors 1.6×10^3 and 2.4×10^3, respectively (satisfying the requirement that the factor exceed 100). So

$$pH = pK_a + \log\frac{[A^-]}{[HA]} = 4.74 + \log\frac{0.0286}{0.0429} = 4.74 - 0.18 = 4.56$$

Simpler still would be to substitute the numbers of millimoles of CH_3COO^- and CH_3COOH directly into the Henderson–Hasselbalch equation, without converting to molarities. That is,

$$pH = pK_a + \log\frac{[A^-]}{[HA]}$$
$$= 4.74 + \log\frac{1.00 \cancel{\text{mmol}/V}}{1.50 \cancel{\text{mmol}/V}} = 4.74 - 0.18 = 4.56$$

(c) When we have added 12.50 mL of 0.100 M NaOH, we have added 12.50 × 0.100 = 1.25 mmol OH^-. As the following setup shows, this is enough base to neutralize exactly *half* of the acid.

	CH_3COOH	+	OH^-	⟶	CH_3COO^-	+	H_2O
initially present:	2.50 mmol		—		—		
add:			1.25 mmol				
changes:	−1.25 mmol		−1.25 mmol		+1.25 mmol		
after reaction:	1.25 mmol				1.25 mmol		

Again, applying the Henderson–Hasselbalch equation, we get

$$pH = pK_a + \log\frac{[CH_3COO^-]}{[CH_3COOH]}$$
$$= 4.74 + \log\frac{1.25\ \cancel{mmol/V}}{1.25\ \cancel{mmol/V}} = 4.74 + \log 1 = 4.74$$

(d) At the equivalence point, neutralization is complete and 2.50 mmol $NaCH_3COO$ has been produced in 50.00 mL of solution, leading to 0.0500 M $NaCH_3COO$ The question becomes, "What is the pH of 0.0500 M $NaCH_3COO$?" To answer this question, we must recognize that CH_3COO^- hydrolyzes (and Na^+ does not). The hydrolysis reaction and value of K_b are

$$CH_3COO^- + H_2O \rightleftharpoons CH_3COOH + OH^-$$
$$K_b = \frac{K_w}{K_a} = \frac{1.0 \times 10^{-14}}{1.8 \times 10^{-5}} = 5.6 \times 10^{-10}$$

With a format similar to that used in the hydrolysis calculation of Example 8-13, we obtain the following expression, where $x = [OH^-]$ and $x \ll 0.0500$.

$$K_b = \frac{[CH_3COOH]}{[CH_3COO^-]} = \frac{x \cdot x}{0.0500 - x} = 5.6 \times 10^{-10}$$
$$x^2 = 2.8 \times 10^{-11} \qquad x = [OH^-] = 5.3 \times 10^{-6}\ M$$
$$pOH = -\log(5.3 \times 10^{-6}) = 5.28$$
$$pH = 14.00 - pOH = 14.00 - 5.28 = 8.72$$

(e) The amount of OH^- added is 26.00 mL × 0.100 mmol/mL = 2.60 mmol. The volume of solution is 25.00 mL acid + 26.00 mL base = 51.00 mL. The 2.60 mmol OH^- neutralizes the 2.50 mmol of available acid, and 0.10 mmol OH^- remains in *excess*. Beyond the equivalence point, the pH of the solution is determined by the excess strong base.

$$[OH^-] = \frac{0.10\ mmol\ OH^-}{51.00\ mL} = 2.0 \times 10^{-3}\ M$$
$$pOH = -\log(2.0 \times 10^{-3}) = 2.70 \qquad pH = 14.00 - 2.70 = 11.30$$

Assess

In this example the pH at the equivalence point is *not* 7 as it was in the strong acid–strong base problem. We could have predicted this result before performing a single calculation. At the equivalence point, the principal species in solution is CH_3COO^-, the conjugate base of a weak acid (CH_3COOH). Recalling that the conjugate of weak is weak, we conclude that CH_3COO^- is a weak base and thus, the pH at the equivalence point must be greater than 7.

PRACTICE EXAMPLE A: A 20.00 mL sample of 0.150 M HF solution is titrated with 0.250 M NaOH. Calculate **(a)** the initial pH and the pH when neutralization is **(b)** 25.0%, **(c)** 50.0%, **(d)** 100.0% complete. [*Hint*: What is the initial amount of HF, and what amount remains unneutralized at the points in question?]

PRACTICE EXAMPLE B: For the titration of 50.00 mL of 0.106 M NH_3 with 0.225 M HCl, calculate **(a)** the initial pH and the pH when neutralization is **(b)** 25.0% complete; **(c)** 50.0% complete; **(d)** 100.0% complete.

▶ FIGURE 9-12
Constructing the titration curve for a weak acid with a strong base
The calculations needed to plot this graph, illustrated in Example 9-8, can be divided into *four* types.

1. pH of a pure weak acid (initial pH)
2. pH of a buffer solution of a weak acid and its salt (over a broad range before the equivalence point)
3. pH of a salt solution undergoing hydrolysis (equivalence point)
4. pH of a solution of a strong base (over a broad range beyond the equivalence point)

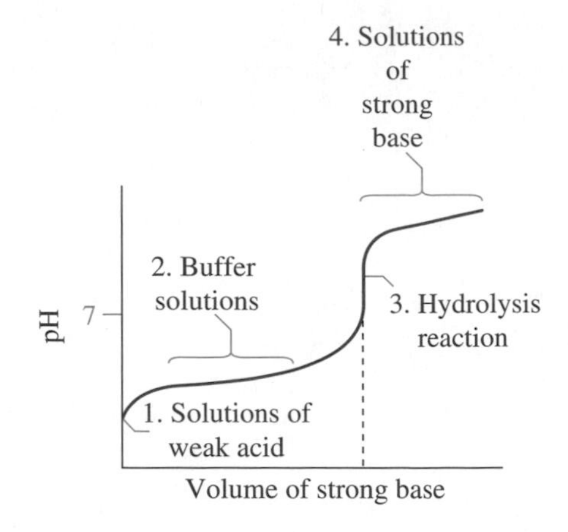

Here are the principal features of the titration curve for a weak acid titrated with a strong base (Fig. 9-11).

- The initial pH is higher (less acidic) than in the titration of a strong acid. (The weak acid is only partially ionized.)
- There is an initial rather sharp increase in pH at the start of the titration. (The anion produced by the neutralization of the weak acid is a common ion that reduces the extent of ionization of the acid.)
- Over a long section of the curve preceding the equivalence point, the pH changes only gradually. (Solutions corresponding to this portion of the curve are buffer solutions.)
- Because $[HA] = [A^-]$ at the point of half-neutralization, $pH = pK_a$.
- At the equivalence point, $pH > 7$. (The conjugate base of a weak acid hydrolyzes, producing OH^-.)
- Beyond the equivalence point, the titration curve is identical to that of a strong acid with a strong base. (In this portion of the titration, the pH is established entirely by the concentration of unreacted OH^-.)
- The steep portion of the titration curve at the equivalence point occurs over a relatively short pH range (from about pH 7 to pH 10).
- The selection of indicators available for the titration is more limited than in a strong acid–strong base titration. (Indicators that change color below pH 7 cannot be used.)

As illustrated in Example 9-8 and suggested by Figure 9-12, the necessary calculations for a weak acid–strong base titration curve are of four distinct types, depending on the portion of the titration curve being described. One type of titration that generally cannot be performed successfully is that of a weak acid with a weak base (or vice versa). The equivalence point cannot be located precisely because the change in pH with volume of titrant is too gradual.

9-4 CONCEPT ASSESSMENT

To raise the pH of 1.00 L of 0.50 M HCl(aq) *significantly*, which of the following would you add to the solution and why? **(a)** 0.50 mol CH_3COOH; **(b)** 1.00 mol NaCl; **(c)** 0.60 mol $NaCH_3COO$; **(d)** 0.40 mol NaOH.

▶ This stepwise neutralization is observed only if successive ionization constants ($K_{a_1}, K_{a_2}, \ldots$) differ significantly in magnitude (for example, by a factor of 10^3 or more). Otherwise, the second neutralization step begins before the first step is completed, and so on.

Titration of a Weak Polyprotic Acid

The most striking evidence that a polyprotic acid ionizes in distinct steps comes by way of its titration curve. For a polyprotic acid, we expect to see a separate equivalence point for each acidic hydrogen. Thus, we expect to see three equivalence points when H_3PO_4 is titrated with NaOH(aq). In the neutralization of phosphoric acid by sodium hydroxide, essentially all the H_3PO_4 molecules are

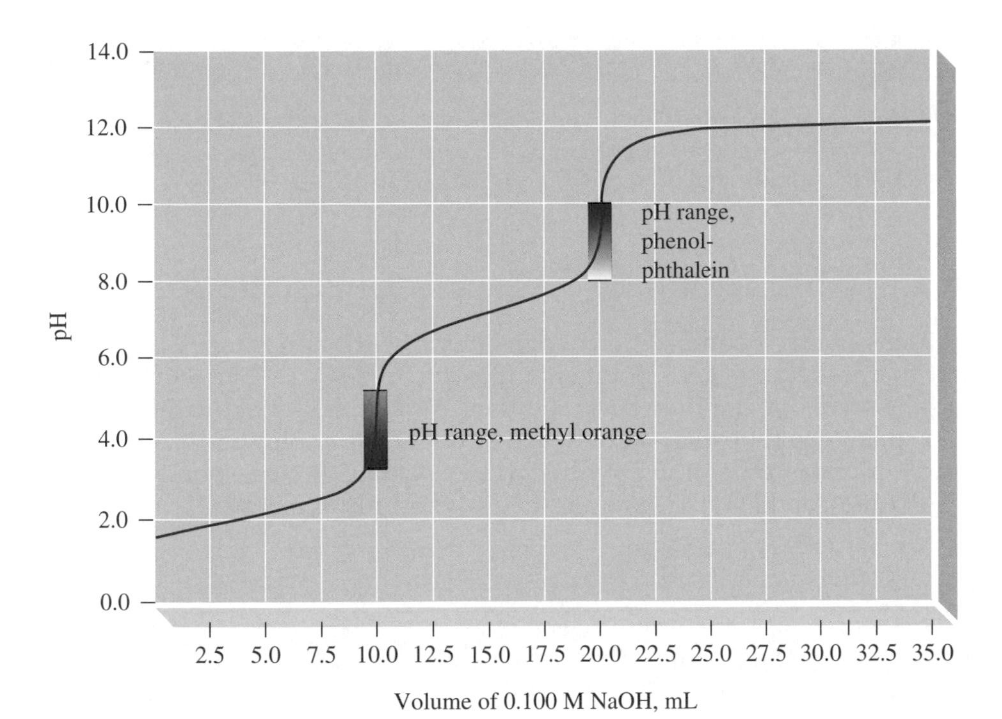

▲ FIGURE 9-13
Titration of a weak polyprotic acid—10.0 mL of 0.100 M H_3PO_4 with 0.100 M NaOH
A 10.0 mL volume of 0.100 M NaOH is required to reach the first equivalence point. The additional volume of 0.100 M NaOH required to reach the second equivalence point is also 10.0 mL. The pH does not increase sharply in the vicinity of the third equivalence point (30 mL).

first converted to the salt, NaH_2PO_4. Then all the NaH_2PO_4 is converted to Na_2HPO_4; and finally the Na_2HPO_4 is converted to Na_3PO_4.

The titration of 10.0 mL of 0.100 M H_3PO_4 with 0.100 M NaOH is pictured in Figure 9-13. Notice that the first two equivalence points come at equal intervals on the volume axis, at 10.0 mL and at 20.0 mL. Although we expect a third equivalence point at 30.0 mL, it is not realized in this titration. The pH of the strongly hydrolyzed Na_3PO_4 solution at the third equivalence point—approaching pH 13—is higher than can be reached by adding 0.100 M NaOH to water. Na_3PO_4(aq) is nearly as basic as the NaOH(aq) used in the titration (as we will see in Section 9-5).

Let's focus on a few details of this titration. For each mole of H_3PO_4, 1 mol NaOH is required to reach the first equivalence point. At this first equivalence point, the solution is essentially NaH_2PO_4(aq). This is an *acidic* solution because $K_{a_2} > K_b$ for $H_2PO_4^-$: the reaction that produces H_3O^+ predominates over the one that produces OH^-.

$$H_2PO_4^- + H_2O \rightleftharpoons H_3O^+ + HPO_4^{2-} \qquad K_{a_2} = 6.3 \times 10^{-8}$$
$$H_2PO_4^- + H_2O \rightleftharpoons H_3PO_4 + OH^- \qquad K_b = 1.4 \times 10^{-12}$$

The pH at the equivalence point falls within the pH range over which the color of methyl orange indicator changes from red to orange.

An additional mole of NaOH is required to convert 1 mol $H_2PO_4^-$ to 1 mol HPO_4^{2-}. At this second equivalence point in the titration of H_3PO_4, the solution is basic because $K_b > K_{a_3}$ for HPO_4^{2-}.

$$HPO_4^{2-} + H_2O \rightleftharpoons H_2PO_4^- + OH^- \qquad K_b = 1.6 \times 10^{-7}$$
$$HPO_4^{2-} + H_2O \rightleftharpoons H_3O^+ + PO_4^{3-} \qquad K_{a_3} = 4.2 \times 10^{-13}$$

Phenolphthalein is an appropriate indicator for this equivalence point; the color of this indicator changes from colorless to light pink.

9-5 CONCEPT ASSESSMENT

Sketch the titration curve for 1,2-ethanediamine, $NH_2CH_2CH_2NH_2(aq)$, with HCl(aq) and label all important points on the titration curve. For 1,2-ethanediamine, $pK_{b_1} = 4.08$; $pK_{b_2} = 7.15$.

9-5 Solutions of Salts of Polyprotic Acids

In discussing the neutralization of phosphoric acid by a strong base, we found that the first equivalence point should come in a somewhat acidic solution and the second in a mildly basic solution. We reasoned that the third equivalence point could be reached only in a strongly basic solution. The pH at this third equivalence point is not difficult to calculate. It corresponds to that of $Na_3PO_4(aq)$, and PO_4^{3-} can ionize (hydrolyze) only as a base.

$$PO_4^{3-} + H_2O \rightleftharpoons HPO_4^{2-} + OH^- \qquad K_b = K_w/K_{a_3} = 2.4 \times 10^{-2}$$

EXAMPLE 9-9 Determining the pH of a Solution Containing the Anion (A^{n-}) of a Polyprotic Acid

Sodium phosphate, Na_3PO_4, is an ingredient of some preparations used to clean painted walls before they are repainted. What is the pH of 0.025 M $Na_3PO_4(aq)$?

Analyze

PO_4^{3-} is a weak base that will react with water to form HPO_4^{2-} and OH^-, thereby making the solution basic. We don't have to consider additional reactions, such as the reaction of HPO_4^{2-} and H_2O to give $H_2PO_4^-$ and OH^-, because most of the OH^- in solution will come from the reaction of PO_4^{3-} and H_2O. The value of K_b for PO_4^{3-} is large enough, however, that we will *not* be able to make the usual simplifying approximation that $0.025 - x \approx 0.025$.

Solve

In the usual fashion, we can write

	PO_4^{3-} + H_2O ⇌	HPO_4^{2-} +	OH^-	$K_b = 2.4 \times 10^{-2}$
initial concns:	0.025 M	—	—	
changes:	$-x$ M	$+x$ M	$+x$ M	
equil concns:	$(0.025 - x)$ M	x M	x M	

$$K_b = \frac{[HPO_4^{2-}][OH^-]}{[PO_4^{3-}]} = \frac{x \cdot x}{0.025 - x} = 2.4 \times 10^{-2}$$

Solving the quadratic equation $x^2 + 0.024x - (0.025)(0.024) = 0$ yields $x = [OH^-] = 0.015$ M. Thus,

$$pOH = -\log[OH^-] = -\log(0.015) = 1.82$$
$$pH = 14.00 - 1.82 = 12.18$$

Assess

Notice that more than half (about 61%) of the PO_4^{3-} reacts. In solving this problem, we assumed that most of the OH^- in solution comes from the reaction of PO_4^{3-} and H_2O. That is, the subsequent reaction of HPO_4^{2-} and H_2O does not contribute a significant amount of OH^-. Can we test the validity of this approximation? Of course we can. We saw that

$$HPO_4^{2-} + H_2O \rightleftharpoons H_2PO_4^- + OH^- \qquad K_b = [H_2PO_4^-][OH^-]/[HPO_4^{2-}] = 1.6 \times 10^{-7}$$

Using $[HPO_4^{2-}] \approx [OH^-] \approx 0.015$ M (from above), we obtain $[H_2PO_4^-] \approx 1.6 \times 10^{-7}$. The amount of $H_2PO_4^-$ (and OH^-) generated from the reaction of HPO_4^{2-} and H_2O is, as predicted, very small. The approximation is valid.

PRACTICE EXAMPLE A: Using data from Table 8.4, calculate the pH of 1.0 M Na_2CO_3.

PRACTICE EXAMPLE B: Using data from Table 8.4, calculate the pH of 0.500 M Na_2SO_3.

It is more difficult to calculate the pH values of NaH_2PO_4(aq) and Na_2HPO_4(aq) than of Na_3PO_4(aq). This is because with both $H_2PO_4^-$ and HPO_4^{2-}, two equilibria must be considered *simultaneously*: ionization as an acid and ionization as a base (hydrolysis). For solutions that are reasonably concentrated (say, 0.10 M or greater), the pH values prove to be *independent* of the solution concentration. Shown here are general expressions, printed in blue, and their application to $H_2PO_4^-$(aq) and HPO_4^{2-}(aq):

$$\text{for } H_2PO_4^-: \quad \text{pH} = \frac{1}{2}(\text{p}K_{a_1} + \text{p}K_{a_2}) = \frac{1}{2}(2.15 + 7.20) = 4.68 \qquad (9.5)$$

$$\text{for } HPO_4^{2-}: \quad \text{pH} = \frac{1}{2}(\text{p}K_{a_2} + \text{p}K_{a_3}) = \frac{1}{2}(7.20 + 12.38) = 9.79 \qquad (9.6)$$

9-1 ARE YOU WONDERING...

How to derive equations (9.5) and (9.6)?

Here is good place to use the general problem-solving method. Consider a solution of NaH_2PO_4, of molarity M. The principal concentrations that we must account for are $[H_2PO_4^-]$, $[HPO_4^{2-}]$, and $[OH^-]$. Of these, two have very simple values: $[Na^+] = M$, and $[OH^-] = K_w/[H_3O^+]$. Additionally, we can write the following equations.

1. *Acid Ionization*: $H_2PO_4^- + H_2O \rightleftharpoons H_3O^+ + HPO_4^{2-}$

$$K_{a_2} = \frac{[H_3O^+][HPO_4^{2-}]}{[H_2PO_4^-]}$$

2. *Hydrolysis*: $H_2PO_4^- + H_2O \rightleftharpoons H_3PO_4 + OH^-$

$$K_b = K_w/K_{a_1} = \frac{[H_3PO_4][OH^-]}{[H_2PO_4^-]}$$

3. *Material Balance*: The total concentration of the phosphorus-containing species is the stoichiometric molarity, M. Also, $[Na^+] = M$. We can write $[H_3PO_4] + [H_2PO_4^-] + [HPO_4^{2-}] + [PO_4^{3-}] = M = [Na^+]$
4. *Electroneutrality Condition*: $[H_3O^+] + [Na^+] = [H_2PO_4^-] + 2 \times [HPO_4^{2-}] + 3 \times [PO_4^{3-}] + [OH^-]$.

The material balance equation and the electroneutrality condition can both be simplified by neglecting the terms involving $[PO_4^{3-}]$ and $[OH^-]$.

Solving the set of equations: Begin by substituting equation (3) into equation (4).

$$[H_3O^+] = [H_2PO_4^-] + 2 \times [HPO_4^{2-}] - [H_3PO_4] - [H_2PO_4^-] - [HPO_4^{2-}]$$
$$= [HPO_4^{2-}] - [H_3PO_4]$$

To continue from here, rearrange equation (1) to obtain $[HPO_4^{2-}]$ in terms of $[H_3O^+]$, $[H_2PO_4^-]$, and K_{a_2}; then rearrange equation (2) to obtain $[H_3PO_4]$ in terms of $[H_3O^+]$, $[H_2PO_4^-]$, and K_{a_1}. Next, substitute the results into the expression, $[H_3O^+] = [HPO_4^{2-}] - [H_3PO_4]$. At this point, you will have an equation in terms of $[H_3O^+]$, $[H_2PO_4^-]$, K_{a_1}, and K_{a_2} and both $[PO_4^{3-}]$ and $[OH^-]$. Assume that $K_{a1} + [H_2PO_4^-] \approx [H_2PO_4^-]$ and you will get an equation from which you can derive equation (9.5). The remainder of this derivation and the derivation of equation (9.6) are left for you to do (see Exercise 79).

◀ The K_a and K_b values for $H_2PO_4^-$ tell us that there is a greater tendency for $H_2PO_4^-$ to act as an acid. The solution will be acidic and $[OH^-]$ will be less than 10^{-7} M. Also, we expect $[PO_4^{3-}]$ to be very small. To obtain PO_4^{3-}, $H_2PO_4^-$ must ionize twice. However, because $H_2PO_4^-$ is a weak acid, only a small fraction will ionize to HPO_4^{2-} and an even smaller fraction will ionize further to PO_4^{3-}.

9-6 Acid–Base Equilibrium Calculations: A Summary

In this and the preceding chapter, we have considered a variety of acid–base equilibrium calculations. When you are faced with a new problem-solving situation, you might find it helpful to relate the new problem to a type that you have encountered before. It is best not to rely exclusively on "labeling" a problem, however. Some problems might not fit a recognizable category. Instead, keep in mind some principles that apply regardless of the particular problem, as suggested by these questions.

1. **Which species are potentially present in solution, and how large are their concentrations likely to be?**
   In a solution containing similar amounts of HCl and CH_3COOH, the only significant *ionic* species are H_3O^+ and Cl^-. HCl is a completely ionized strong acid, and in the presence of a strong acid, the weak acid $HC_2H_3O_2$ is only very slightly ionized because of the common-ion effect. In a mixture containing similar amounts of two *weak* acids of similar strengths, such as CH_3COOH and HNO_2, each acid partially ionizes. All of these concentrations would be significant: $[CH_3COOH]$, $[CH_3COO^-]$, $[HNO_2]$, $[NO_2^-]$, and $[H_3O^+]$. In a solution containing phosphoric acid or a phosphate salt (or both), H_3PO_4, $H_2PO_4^-$, HPO_4^{2-}, PO_4^{3-}, OH^-, H_3O^+, and possibly other cations might be present. If the solution is simply $H_3PO_4(aq)$, however, the only species present in significant concentrations are those associated with the first ionization: H_3PO_4, H_3O^+, and $H_2PO_4^-$. If the solution is instead described as $Na_3PO_4(aq)$, the significant species are Na^+, PO_4^{3-}, and the ions associated with the hydrolysis of PO_4^{3-}, that is, HPO_4^{2-} and OH^-.

▶ Body temperature is 37 °C and at that temperature K_w does not equal 1.0×10^{-14}. Refer to Exercise 83 on page 391.

2. **Are reactions possible among any of the solution components; if so, what is their stoichiometry?**
   Suppose that you are asked to calculate $[OH^-]$ in a solution that is prepared to be 0.10 M NaOH and 0.20 M NH_4Cl. Before you answer that $[OH^-] = 0.10$ M, consider whether a solution can be *simultaneously* 0.10 M in OH^- and 0.20 M in NH_4^+. It cannot; any solution containing both NH_4^+ and OH^- must also contain NH_3. The OH^- and NH_4^+ react in a 1:1 mole ratio until OH^- is almost totally consumed:

$$NH_4^+ + OH^- \longrightarrow NH_3 + H_2O$$

   You are now dealing with the buffer solution 0.10 M NH_3–0.10 M NH_4^+.

3. **Which equilibrium equations apply to the particular situation? Which are the most significant?**
   One equation that applies to all acids and bases in aqueous solutions is $K_w = [H_3O^+][OH^-] = 1.0 \times 10^{-14}$. In many calculations, however, this equation is not significant compared with others. One situation in which it is significant is in calculating $[OH^-]$ in an *acidic* solution or $[H_3O^+]$ in a *basic* solution. After all, an acid does not produce OH^-, and a base does not produce H_3O^+. Another situation in which K_w is likely to be significant is in a solution with a pH near 7.

Often you will find that the ionization equilibrium with the largest K value is the most significant, but this will not always be the case. The amounts of the various species in solution are also an important consideration. When one drop of 1.00 M H_3PO_4 ($K_{a_1} = 7.1 \times 10^{-3}$) is added to 1.00 L of 0.100 M CH_3COOH ($K_a = 1.8 \times 10^{-5}$), the acetic acid ionization is most important in establishing the pH of the solution. The solution contains far more acetic acid than it does phosphoric acid.

9-6 CONCEPT ASSESSMENT

A solution is formed by mixing 200.0 mL of 0.100 M KOH with 100.0 mL of a solution that is both 0.200 M in CH_3COOH and 0.050 M in HI. *Without doing detailed calculations*, identify in the final solution **(a)** all the solute species present, **(b)** the two most abundant solute species, and **(c)** the two least abundant species.

Summary

9-1 Common-Ion Effect in Acid–Base Equilibria—The ionization of a weak electrolyte is suppressed by the addition of an ion that is the product of the ionization and is known as the **common-ion effect**. This effect is a manifestation of Le Châtelier's principle, introduced in Chapter 6.

9-2 Buffer Solutions—Solutions that resist changes in pH upon the addition of small amounts of an acid or base are referred to as **buffer solutions**. The finite amount of acid or base that a buffer solution can neutralize is known as the **buffer capacity**, while the pH range over which the buffer solution neutralizes the added acid or base is referred to as **buffer range**. Pure water has no buffer capacity (Fig. 9-4). Key to the functioning of a buffer solution is the presence of either a weak acid and its conjugate base or a weak base and its conjugate acid (Fig. 9-5). Calculating the pH of a buffer solution can be accomplished by using the ICE method developed in Chapter 6 or by application of the **Henderson–Hasselbalch equation** (expression 9.2). Determination of the pH of a buffer solution after the addition of a strong acid or base requires a stoichiometric calculation followed by an equilibrium calculation (Fig. 9-7).

9-3 Acid-Base Indicators—Substances whose colors depend on the pH of a solution are known as **acid–base indicators**. Acid–base indicators exist in solution as a weak acid (HIn) and its conjugate base (In^-). Each form has a different color and the proportions of the two forms determine the color of the solution, which in turn depends on the pH of the solution. The pH range over which an acid–base indicator changes color is determined by the K_a of the specific indicator (Fig. 9-8).

9-4 Neutralization Reactions and Titration Curves—As described in Chapter 1, the concentration of an acidic or basic solution of unknown concentration can be determined by titration with a base or acid of precisely known concentration. In this process a precisely measured volume of the solution of known concentration, the **titrant**, is added through a buret into a precisely measured quantity of the "unknown" contained in a beaker or flask. Typically, the amounts of reactants in a titration are of the order of 10^{-3} mol, that is, **millimoles (mmol)**. A **titration curve** is a graph of a measured property of the reaction mixture as a function of the volume of titrant added—pH for an acid–base titration (Fig. 9-9). The point at which neither reactant is in excess in a titration is known as the **equivalence point**. The **end point** of an acid–base titration can be located through the change in color of an indicator. The indicator must be chosen such that its color change occurs as close to the equivalence point as possible. Strong acid-strong base titration curves (Figs. 9-9 and 9-10) are different from weak acid-strong base titration curves (Fig. 9-11). The two main differences are seen in the latter type, a buffer region and a hydrolysis reaction at the equivalence point (Fig. 9-12).

9-5 Solutions of Salts of Polyprotic Acids—Calculating the pH of solutions containing the salts of polyprotic acids is made difficult by the fact that two or more equilibria occur simultaneously. Yet for certain solutions, the calculations can be reduced to a simple form (expressions 9.5 and 9.6).

9-6 Acid–Base Equilibrium Calculations: A Summary—As a general summary of acid–base equilibrium calculations, the essential factors are identifying all the species in solution, their concentrations, the possible reactions between them, and the stoichiometry and equilibrium constants of those reactions.

Integrative Example

The structural formula shown is *para*-hydroxybenzoic acid, a weak diprotic acid used as a food preservative. Titration of 25.00 mL of a dilute aqueous solution of this acid requires 16.24 mL of 0.0200 M NaOH to reach the first equivalence point. The measured pH after the addition of 8.12 mL of the base is 4.57; after 16.24 mL, the pH is 7.02. Determine the values of pK_{a_1} and pK_{a_2} of *para*-hydroxybenzoic acid and the pH values for the two equivalence points in the titration.

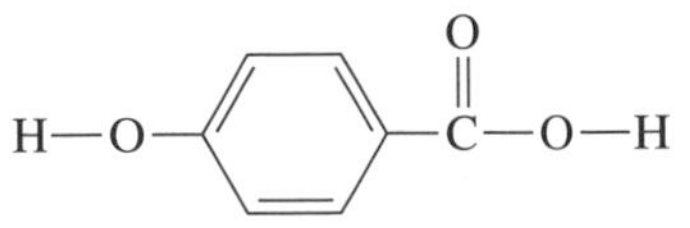

Analyze

This is a titration of a polyprotic weak acid with a strong base, and the titration curve for this problem should look very similar to Figure 9-13. In the titration of a weak acid by a strong base we know that at the point of half-neutralization, $pH = pK_a$ and therefore pK_{a_1} should be the pH at 8.12 mL. For pK_{a_2}, we will use expression 9.5 since at this point in the titration we will have an aqueous solution of HOC_6H_4COONa, which is a salt of a polyprotic acid. The pH of the first equivalence point is given and to find the pH of the second equivalence point we must perform an ICE calculation similar to the one in Example 8-13.

Solve

The volume of base needed to reach the first equivalence point is 16.24 mL; at this point, the pH = 7.02. A volume of 8.12 mL is needed to half-neutralize the acid in its first ionization step; at this point the pH = pK_{a_1}, that is, $pK_{a_1} = 4.57$.

At the first equivalence point, the solution is $HOC_6H_4COONa(aq)$ with pH = 7.02. Recognizing this as the salt produced in neutralizing a polyprotic acid in its first ionization, we use equation (9.5) to solve for pK_{a_2}. That is, the pH of an aqueous solution of the ion $HOC_6H_6COO^-$ is given by the expression

$$pH = \frac{1}{2}(pK_{a_1} + pK_{a_2}) = \frac{1}{2}(4.57 + pK_{a_2}) = 7.02$$
$$pK_{a_2} = (2 \times 7.02) - 4.57 = 9.47$$

Determining the pH at the second equivalence point involves additional calculations. We begin by noting that at the second equivalence point the solution is one of $NaOC_6H_4COONa$. The pH of the solution is established by the hydrolysis of $^-OC_6H_4COO^-$.

$$^-OC_6H_4COO^- + H_2O \rightleftharpoons HOC_6H_4COO^- + OH^-$$
$$K_b = K_w/K_{a_2}$$

To evaluate K_b, let's first obtain K_{a_2} from pK_{a_2}.

$$pK_{a_2} = -\log K_{a_2} = 9.47 \text{ and } K_{a_2} = 10^{-9.47} = 3.4 \times 10^{-10}$$
$$K_b = K_w/K_{a_2} = 1.0 \times 10^{-14}/3.4 \times 10^{-10} = 2.9 \times 10^{-5}$$

We can get the pH of this solution by first calculating $[OH^-]$ and pOH. However, to do this, we still need one more piece of data—the molarity of the $NaOC_6H_4COONa(aq)$. We can get this from data for titration to the first equivalence point.

$$? \text{ mmol } OH^- = 16.24 \text{ mL} \times 0.0200 \text{ mmol } OH^-/\text{mL}$$
$$= 0.325 \text{ mmol } OH^-$$
$$? \text{ mmol } HOC_6H_4COOH = 0.325 \text{ mmol } OH^- \times 1 \text{ mmol } HOC_6H_4COOH/\text{mmol } OH^- = 0.325 \text{ mmol } HOC_6H_4COOH$$

The amount of $^-OC_6H_4COO^-$ at the second equivalence point is the same as the amount of acid at the start of the titration.

$$0.325 \text{ mmol } ^-OC_6H_4COO^-$$

The volume of solution at the second equivalence point is

$$25.00 \text{ mL} + 16.24 \text{ mL} + 16.24 \text{ mL} = 57.48 \text{ mL}.$$

Thus,

$$[^-OC_6H_4COO^-] = 0.325 \text{ mmol } ^-OC_6H_4COO^-/57.48 \text{ mL}$$
$$= 5.65 \times 10^{-3} \text{ M}.$$

Now we can return to the hydrolysis equation and the expression for K_b, using the method of Example 8-13.

$$^{-}OC_6H_4COO^- + H_2O \rightleftharpoons HOC_6H_4COO^- + OH^-$$

	$^{-}OC_6H_4COO^-$	$HOC_6H_4COO^-$	OH^-
initial concns:	5.65×10^{-3} M	—	—
changes:	$-x$ M	$+x$ M	$+x$ M
equil concns:	$(5.65 \times 10^{-3} - x)$ M	x M	x M

$$K_b = \frac{x \cdot x}{(5.65 \times 10^{-3} - x)} = 2.9 \times 10^{-5}$$

The solution to this quadratic equation is $x = [OH^-] = 3.9 \times 10^{-4}$, corresponding to pOH = 3.41 and pH = 10.59.

Assess

The polyprotic acid, *para*-hydroxybenzoic acid, has two functional groups, a carboxylic acid and a phenolic group. Each group has an ionizable proton. Given just two basic pieces of titration data, we used concepts from this and the preceding chapter to determine the pK_a values for both ionizable groups as well as the pH at the two equivalence points. As a check, note that the pK_a values of these groups are comparable to the values for their parent compounds, acetic acid and phenol (see Table 8.3).

PRACTICE EXAMPLE A: 7.500 g of a weak acid HA is added to sufficient distilled water to produce 500.0 mL of solution with pH = 2.716. This solution is titrated with NaOH(aq). Halfway to the equivalence point, pH = 4.602. What is the freezing point of the solution?

PRACTICE EXAMPLE B: The following titration curve was obtained as part of a general chemistry laboratory experiment for an unknown that weighed 0.8 g. The titrant was either a 0.2 M strong base or 0.2 M strong acid. Estimate the molar mass of the unknown and its ionization constant.

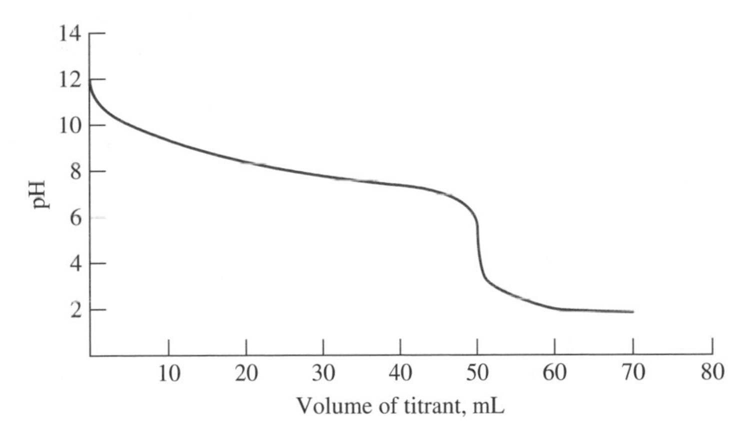

Exercises

The Common-Ion Effect

(Use data from Table 8.3 as necessary.)

1. For a solution that is 0.275 M CH_3CH_2COOH (propionic acid, $K_a = 1.3 \times 10^{-5}$) and 0.0892 M HI, calculate **(a)** $[H_3O^+]$; **(b)** $[OH^-]$; **(c)** CH_3CH_2COO; **(d)** $[I^-]$.
2. For a solution that is 0.164 M NH_3 and 0.102 M NH_4Cl, calculate **(a)** $[OH^-]$; **(b)** $[NH_4^+]$; **(c)** $[Cl^-]$; **(d)** $[H_3O^+]$.
3. Calculate the *change* in pH that results from adding **(a)** 0.100 mol $NaNO_2$ to 1.00 L of 0.100 M HNO_2(aq); **(b)** 0.100 mol $NaNO_3$ to 1.00 L of 0.100 M HNO_3(aq). Why are the changes not the same? Explain.
4. In Example 16-8, we calculated the percent ionization of CH_3COOH in **(a)** 1.0 M; **(b)** 0.10 M; and **(c)** 0.010 M CH_3COOH solutions. Recalculate those percent ionizations if each solution also contains 0.10 M $NaCH_3COO$. Explain why the results are different from those of Example 8-8.

5. Calculate $[H_3O^+]$ in a solution that is **(a)** 0.035 M HCl and 0.075 M HOCl; **(b)** 0.100 M $NaNO_2$ and 0.0550 M HNO_2; **(c)** 0.0525 M HCl and 0.0768 M $NaCH_3COO$.

6. Calculate $[OH^-]$ in a solution that is **(a)** 0.0062 M $Ba(OH)_2$ and 0.0105 M $BaCl_2$; **(b)** 0.315 M $(NH_4)_2SO_4$ and 0.486 M NH_3; **(c)** 0.196 M NaOH and 0.264 M NH_4Cl.

Buffer Solutions

(Use data from Tables 8.3 and 8.4 as necessary.)

7. What concentration of formate ion, $[HCOO^-]$, should be present in 0.366 M HCOOH to produce a buffer solution with pH = 4.06?

$$HCOOH + H_2O \rightleftharpoons H_3O^+ + HCOO^- \qquad K_a = 1.8 \times 10^{-4}$$

8. What concentration of ammonia, $[NH_3]$, should be present in a solution with $[NH_4^+] = 0.732$ M to produce a buffer solution with pH = 9.12? For NH_3, $K_b = 1.8 \times 10^{-5}$.
9. Calculate the pH of a buffer that is
(a) 0.012 M C_6H_5COOH($K_a = 6.3 \times 10^{-5}$) and 0.033 M NaC_6H_5COO;
(b) 0.408 M NH_3 and 0.153 M NH_4Cl.
10. Lactic acid, CH_3CH_2COOH, is found in sour milk. A solution containing 1.00 g $NaCH_3CH_2COO$ in 100.0 mL of 0.0500 M $HC_3H_5O_3$ has a pH = 4.11. What is K_a of lactic acid?
11. Indicate which of the following aqueous solutions are buffer solutions, and explain your reasoning. [*Hint:* Consider any reactions that might occur between solution components.]
(a) 0.100 M NaCl
(b) 0.100 M NaCl–0.100 M NH_4Cl
(c) 0.100 M CH_3NH_2–0.150 M $CH_3NH_3^+Cl^-$
(d) 0.100 M HCl–0.050 M $NaNO_2$
(e) 0.100 M HCl–0.200 M $NaCH_3COO$
(f) 0.100 M CH_3COOH–0.125 M $NaCH_3CH_2COO$
12. The $H_2PO_4^-$–HPO_4^{2-} combination plays a role in maintaining the pH of blood.
(a) Write equations to show how a solution containing these ions functions as a buffer.
(b) Verify that this buffer is most effective at pH 7.2.
(c) Calculate the pH of a buffer solution in which $[H_2PO_4^-] = 0.050$ M and $[HPO_4^{2-}] = 0.150$ M. [*Hint:* Focus on the second step of the phosphoric acid ionization.]
13. What is the pH of a solution obtained by adding 1.15 mg of aniline hydrochloride ($C_6H_5NH_3^+Cl^-$) to 3.18 L of 0.105 M aniline ($C_6H_5NH_2$)? [*Hint:* Check any assumptions that you make.]
14. What is the pH of a solution prepared by dissolving 8.50 g of aniline hydrochloride ($C_6H_5NH_3^+Cl^-$) in 750 mL of 0.215 M aniline, ($C_6H_5NH_2$)? Would this solution be an effective buffer? Explain.
15. You wish to prepare a buffer solution with pH = 9.45.
(a) How many grams of $(NH_4)_2SO_4$ would you add to 425 mL of 0.258 M NH_3 to do this? Assume that the solution's volume remains constant.
(b) Which buffer component, and how much (in grams), would you add to 0.100 L of the buffer in part (a) to change its pH to 9.30? Assume that the solution's volume remains constant.
16. You prepare a buffer solution by dissolving 2.00 g each of benzoic acid, C_6H_5COOH, and sodium benzoate, NaC_6H_5COO, in 750.0 mL of water.
(a) What is the pH of this buffer? Assume that the solution's volume is 750.0 mL.
(b) Which buffer component, and how much (in grams), would you add to the 750.0 mL of buffer solution to change its pH to 4.00?
17. If 0.55 mL of 12 M HCl is added to 0.100 L of the buffer solution in Exercise 15(a), what will be the pH of the resulting solution?
18. If 0.35 mL of 15 M NH_3 is added to 0.750 L of the buffer solution in Exercise 16(a), what will be the pH of the resulting solution?
19. You are asked to prepare a buffer solution with a pH of 3.50. The following solutions, all 0.100 M, are available to you: HCOOH, CH_3COOH, H_3PO_4, NaCHOO, $NaCH_3COO$, and NaH_2PO_4. Describe how you would prepare this buffer solution. [*Hint:* What volumes of which solutions would you use?]
20. You are asked to reduce the pH of the 0.300 L of buffer solution in Example 9-5 from 5.09 to 5.00. How many milliliters of which of these solutions would you use: 0.100 M NaCl, 0.150 M HCl, 0.100 M $NaCH_3COO$, 0.125 M NaOH? Explain your reasoning.
21. Given 1.00 L of a solution that is 0.100 M CH_3CH_2COOH and 0.100 M CH_3CH_2COO,
(a) Over what pH range will this solution be an effective buffer?
(b) What is the buffer capacity of the solution? That is, how many millimoles of strong acid or strong base can be added to the solution before any significant change in pH occurs?
22. Given 125 mL of a solution that is 0.0500 M CH_3NH_2 and 0.0500 M $CH_3NH_3^+Cl^-$,
(a) Over what pH range will this solution be an effective buffer?
(b) What is the buffer capacity of the solution? That is, how many millimoles of strong acid or strong base can be added to the solution before any significant change in pH occurs?
23. A solution of volume 75.0 mL contains 15.5 mmol $HCHO_2$ and 8.50 mmol NaHCOO.
(a) What is the pH of this solution?
(b) If 0.25 mmol $Ba(OH)_2$ is added to the solution, what will be the pH?
(c) If 1.05 mL of 12 M HCl is added to the original solution, what will be the pH?
24. A solution of volume 0.500 L contains 1.68 g NH_3 and 4.05 g $(NH_4)_2SO_4$.
(a) What is the pH of this solution?
(b) If 0.88 g NaOH is added to the solution, what will be the pH?
(c) How many milliliters of 12 M HCl must be added to 0.500 L of the original solution to change its pH to 9.00?

25. A handbook lists various procedures for preparing buffer solutions. To obtain a pH = 9.00, the handbook says to mix 36.00 mL of 0.200 M NH_3 with 64.00 mL of 0.200 M NH_4Cl.
(a) Show by calculation that the pH of this solution is 9.00.
(b) Would you expect the pH of this solution to remain at pH = 9.00 if the 100.00 mL of buffer solution were diluted to 1.00 L? To 1000 L? Explain.
(c) What will be the pH of the original 100.00 mL of buffer solution if 0.20 mL of 1.00 M HCl is added to it?
(d) What is the maximum volume of 1.00 M HCl that can be added to 100.00 mL of the original buffer solution so that the pH does not drop below 8.90?

26. An acetic acid–sodium acetate buffer can be prepared by the reaction

$$\underset{\text{(From NaCH}_3\text{COO)}}{CH_3COO^-} + \underset{\text{(From HCl)}}{H_3O^+} \longrightarrow CH_3COOH + H_2O$$

(a) If 12.0 g $NaCH_3COO$ is added to 0.300 L of 0.200 M HCl, what is the pH of the resulting solution?
(b) If 1.00 g $Ba(OH)_2$ is added to the solution in part (a), what is the new pH?
(c) What is the maximum mass of $Ba(OH)_2$ that can be neutralized by the buffer solution of part (a)?
(d) What is the pH of the solution in part (a) following the addition of 5.50 g $Ba(OH)_2$?

Acid–Base Indicators

(Use data from Tables 8.3 and 8.4 as necessary.)

27. A handbook lists the following data:

Indicator	K_{HIn}	Color Change Acid → Anion
Bromphenol blue	1.4×10^{-4}	yellow → blue
Bromcresol green	2.1×10^{-5}	yellow → blue
Bromthymol blue	7.9×10^{-8}	yellow → blue
2,4-Dinitrophenol	1.3×10^{-4}	colorless → yellow
Chlorphenol red	1.0×10^{-6}	yellow → red
Thymolphthalein	1.0×10^{-10}	colorless → blue

(a) Which of these indicators change color in acidic solution, which in basic solution, and which near the neutral point?
(b) What is the approximate pH of a solution if bromcresol green indicator turns green? if chlorphenol red turns orange?

28. With reference to the indicators listed in Exercise 27, what would be the color of each combination?
(a) 2,4-dinitrophenol in 0.100 M HCl(aq)
(b) chlorphenol red in 1.00 M NaCl(aq)
(c) thymolphthalein in 1.00 M NH_3(aq)
(d) bromcresol green in seawater (recall Figure 9-8)

29. In the use of acid–base indicators,
(a) Why is it generally sufficient to use a *single* indicator in an acid–base titration, but often necessary to use *several* indicators to establish the approximate pH of a solution?
(b) Why must the quantity of indicator used in a titration be kept as small as possible?

30. The indicator methyl red has a $pK_{HIn} = 4.95$. It changes from red to yellow over the pH range from 4.4 to 6.2.
(a) If the indicator is placed in a buffer solution of pH = 4.55, what percent of the indicator will be present in the acid form, HIn, and what percent will be present in the base or anion form, In^-?
(b) Which form of the indicator has the "stronger" (that is, more visible) color—the acid (red) form or base (yellow) form? Explain.

31. Phenol red indicator changes from yellow to red in the pH range from 6.6 to 8.0. *Without making detailed calculations*, state what color the indicator will assume in each of the following solutions: **(a)** 0.10 M KOH; **(b)** 0.10 M CH_3COOH; **(c)** 0.10 M NH_4NO_3; **(d)** 0.10 M HBr; **(e)** 0.10 M NaCN; **(f)** 0.10 M CH_3COOH–0.10 M $NaCH_3COO$.

32. Thymol blue indicator has *two* pH ranges. It changes color from red to yellow in the pH range from 1.2 to 2.8, and from yellow to blue in the pH range from 8.0 to 9.6. What is the color of the indicator in each of the following situations?
(a) The indicator is placed in 350.0 mL of 0.205 M HCl.
(b) To the solution in part (a) is added 250.0 mL of 0.500 M $NaNO_2$.
(c) To the solution in part (b) is added 150.0 mL of 0.100 M NaOH.
(d) To the solution in part (c) is added 5.00 g $Ba(OH)_2$.

33. In the titration of 10.00 mL of 0.04050 M HCl with 0.01120 M $Ba(OH)_2$ in the presence of the indicator 2,4-dinitrophenol, the solution changes from colorless to yellow when 17.90 mL of the base has been added. What is the approximate value of pK_{HIn} for 2,4-dinitrophenol? Is this a good indicator for the titration?

34. Solution **(a)** is 100.0 mL of 0.100 M HCl and solution **(b)** is 150.0 mL of 0.100 M $NaCH_3COO$. A few drops of thymol blue indicator are added to each solution. What is the color of each solution? What is the color of the solution obtained when these two solutions are mixed?

Neutralization Reactions

35. A 25.00 mL sample of H_3PO_4(aq) requires 31.15 mL of 0.2420 M KOH for titration to the second equivalence point. What is the molarity of the H_3PO_4(aq)?

36. A 20.00 mL sample of H_3PO_4(aq) requires 18.67 mL of 0.1885 M NaOH for titration from the first to the second equivalence point. What is the molarity of the H_3PO_4(aq)?

37. Two aqueous solutions are mixed: 50.0 mL of 0.0150 M H_2SO_4 and 50.0 mL of 0.0385 M NaOH. What is the pH of the resulting solution?

38. Two solutions are mixed: 100.0 mL of HCl(aq) with pH 2.50 and 100.0 mL of NaOH(aq) with pH 11.00. What is the pH of the resulting solution?

Titration Curves

39. Calculate the pH at the points in the titration of 25.00 mL of 0.160 M HCl when **(a)** 10.00 mL and **(b)** 15.00 mL of 0.242 M KOH have been added.

40. Calculate the pH at the points in the titration of 20.00 mL of 0.275 M KOH when **(a)** 15.00 mL and **(b)** 20.00 mL of 0.350 M HCl have been added.

41. Calculate the pH at the points in the titration of 25.00 mL of 0.132 M HNO_2 when **(a)** 10.00 mL and **(b)** 20.00 mL of 0.116 M NaOH have been added. For HNO_2, $K_a = 7.2 \times 10^{-4}$.

$$HNO_2 + OH^- \longrightarrow H_2O + NO_2^-$$

42. Calculate the pH at the points in the titration of 20.00 mL of 0.318 M NH_3 when **(a)** 10.00 mL and **(b)** 15.00 mL of 0.475 M HCl have been added. For NH_3, $K_b = 1.8 \times 10^{-5}$.

$$NH_3(aq) + HCl(aq) \longrightarrow NH_4^+(aq) + Cl^-(aq)$$

43. Explain why the volume of 0.100 M NaOH required to reach the equivalence point in the titration of 25.00 mL of 0.100 M HA is the same regardless of whether HA is a strong or a weak acid, yet the pH at the equivalence point is not the same.

44. Explain whether the equivalence point of each of the following titrations should be below, above, or at pH 7: **(a)** $NaHCO_3(aq)$ titrated with NaOH(aq); **(b)** HCl(aq) titrated with $NH_3(aq)$; **(c)** KOH(aq) titrated with HI(aq).

45. Sketch the titration curves of the following mixtures. Indicate the initial pH and the pH corresponding to the equivalence point. Indicate the volume of titrant required to reach the equivalence point, and select a suitable indicator from Figure 9-8.
    (a) 25.0 mL of 0.100 M KOH with 0.200 M HI
    (b) 10.0 mL of 1.00 M NH_3 with 0.250 M HCl

46. Determine the following characteristics of the titration curve for 20.0 mL of 0.275 M $NH_3(aq)$ titrated with 0.325 M HI(aq).
    (a) the initial pH
    (b) the volume of 0.325 M HI(aq) at the equivalence point
    (c) the pH at the half-neutralization point
    (d) the pH at the equivalence point

47. In the titration of 20.00 mL of 0.175 M NaOH, calculate the number of milliliters of 0.200 M HCl that must be added to reach a pH of **(a)** 12.55, **(b)** 10.80, **(c)** 4.25. [*Hint:* Solve an algebraic equation in which the number of milliliters is x. Which reactant is in excess at each pH?]

48. In the titration of 25.00 mL of 0.100 M CH_3COOH, calculate the number of milliliters of 0.200 M NaOH that must be added to reach a pH of **(a)** 3.85, **(b)** 5.25, **(c)** 11.10. [*Hint:* Solve an algebraic equation in which the number of milliliters is x. Which reactant is in excess at each pH?]

49. Sketch a titration curve (pH versus mL of titrant) for each of the following three hypothetical weak acids when titrated with 0.100 M NaOH. Select suitable indicators for the titrations from Figure 9-8. [*Hint:* Select a few key points at which to estimate the pH of the solution.]
    (a) 10.00 mL of 0.100 M HX; $K_a = 7.0 \times 10^{-3}$
    (b) 10.00 mL of 0.100 M HY; $K_a = 3.0 \times 10^{-4}$
    (c) 10.00 mL of 0.100 M HZ; $K_a = 2.0 \times 10^{-8}$

50. Sketch a titration curve (pH versus mL of titrant) for each of the following hypothetical weak bases when titrated with 0.100 M HCl. (Think of these bases as involving the substitution of organic groups, R, for one of the H atoms of NH_3.) Select suitable indicators for the titrations from Figure 9-8. [*Hint:* Select a few key points at which to estimate the pH of the solution.]
    (a) 10.00 mL of 0.100 M RNH_2; $K_b = 1 \times 10^{-3}$
    (b) 10.00 mL of 0.100 M $R'NH_2$; $K_b = 3 \times 10^{-6}$
    (c) 10.00 mL of 0.100 M $R''NH_2$; $K_b = 7 \times 10^{-8}$

51. For the titration of 25.00 mL of 0.100 M NaOH with 0.100 M HCl, calculate the pOH at a few representative points in the titration, sketch the titration curve of pOH versus volume of titrant, and show that it has exactly the same form as Figure 9-9. Then, using this curve and the simplest method possible, sketch the titration curve of pH versus volume of titrant.

52. For the titration of 25.00 mL 0.100 M NH_3 with 0.100 M HCl, calculate the pOH at a few representative points in the titration, sketch the titration curve of pOH versus volume of titrant, and show that it has exactly the same form as Figure 9-11. Then, using this curve and the simplest method possible, sketch the titration curve of pH versus volume of titrant.

Salts of Polyprotic Acids

(*Use data from Table 8.4 or Appendix A as necessary.*)

53. Is a solution that is 0.10 M $Na_2S(aq)$ likely to be acidic, basic, or pH neutral? Explain.

54. Is a solution of sodium dihydrogen citrate, NaH_2Cit, likely to be acidic, basic, or neutral? Explain. Citric acid, H_3Cit, is $H_3C_6H_5O_7$.

55. Sodium phosphate, Na_3PO_4, is made commercially by first neutralizing phosphoric acid with sodium carbonate to obtain Na_2HPO_4. The Na_2HPO_4 is further neutralized to Na_3PO_4 with NaOH.
    (a) Write net ionic equations for these reactions.
    (b) Na_2CO_3 is a much cheaper base than is NaOH. Why do you suppose that NaOH must be used as well as Na_2CO_3 to produce Na_3PO_4?

56. Both sodium hydrogen carbonate (sodium bicarbonate) and sodium hydroxide can be used to neutralize acid spills. What is the pH of 1.00 M $NaHCO_3(aq)$ and of 1.00 M NaOH(aq)? On a per-liter basis, do these two solutions have an equal capacity to neutralize acids? Explain. On a per-gram basis, do the two

solids, $NaHCO_3(s)$ and $NaOH(s)$, have an equal capacity to neutralize acids? Explain. Why do you suppose that $NaHCO_3$ is often preferred to NaOH in neutralizing acid spills?

57. The pH of a solution of 19.5 g of malonic acid in 0.250 L is 1.47. The pH of a 0.300 M solution of sodium hydrogen malonate is 4.26. What are the values of K_{a_1} and K_{a_2} for malonic acid?

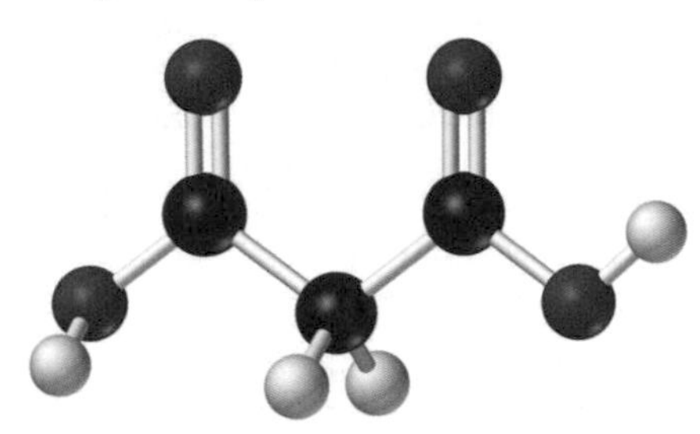

Malonic acid

58. The ionization constants of *ortho*-phthalic acid are $K_{a_1} = 1.1 \times 10^{-3}$ and $K_{a_2} = 3.9 \times 10^{-6}$.

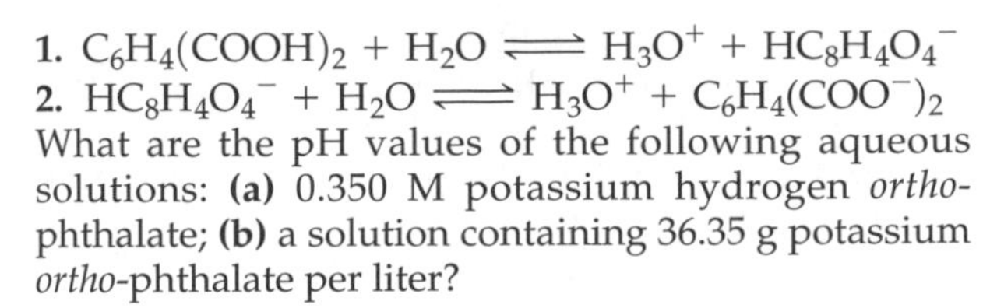

1. $C_6H_4(COOH)_2 + H_2O \rightleftharpoons H_3O^+ + HC_8H_4O_4^-$
2. $HC_8H_4O_4^- + H_2O \rightleftharpoons H_3O^+ + C_6H_4(COO^-)_2$

What are the pH values of the following aqueous solutions: **(a)** 0.350 M potassium hydrogen *ortho*-phthalate; **(b)** a solution containing 36.35 g potassium *ortho*-phthalate per liter?

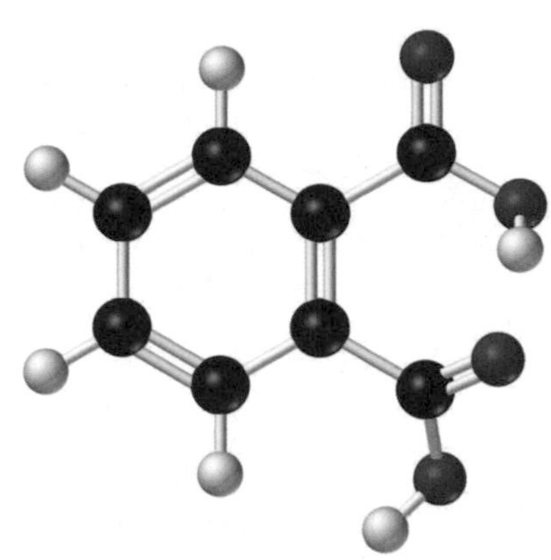

ortho Phthalic acid

General Acid–Base Equilibria

59. What stoichiometric concentration of the indicated substance is required to obtain an aqueous solution with the pH value shown: **(a)** $Ba(OH)_2$ for pH = 11.88; **(b)** CH_3COOH in 0.294 M $NaCH_3COO$ for pH = 4.52?

60. What stoichiometric concentration of the indicated substance is required to obtain an aqueous solution with the pH value shown: **(a)** aniline, $C_6H_5NH_2$, for pH = 8.95; **(b)** NH_4Cl for pH = 5.12?

61. Using appropriate equilibrium constants but *without doing detailed calculations*, determine whether a solution can be simultaneously:
(a) 0.10 M NH_3 and 0.10 M NH_4Cl, with pH = 6.07
(b) 0.10 M $NaC_2H_3O_2$ and 0.058 M HI
(c) 0.10 M KNO_2 and 0.25 M KNO_3
(d) 0.050 M $Ba(OH)_2$ and 0.65 M NH_4Cl
(e) 0.018 M C_6H_5COOH and 0.018 M NaC_6H_5COO, with pH = 4.20
(f) 0.68 M KCl, 0.42 M KNO_3, 1.2 M NaCl, and 0.55 M $NaCH_3COO$, with pH = 6.4

62. This single equilibrium equation applies to different phenomena described in this or the preceding chapter.

$$CH_3COOH + H_2O \rightleftharpoons H_3O^+ + CH_3COO^-$$

Of these four phenomena, ionization of pure acid, common-ion effect, buffer solution, and hydrolysis, indicate which occurs if
(a) $[H_3O^+]$ and $[CH_3COOH]$ are high, but $[CH_3COO^-]$ is very low.
(b) $[CH_3COO^-]$ is high, but $[CH_3COOH]$ and $[H_3O^+]$ are very low.
(c) $[CH_3COOH]$ is high, but $[H_3O^+]$ and $[CH_3COO^-]$ are low.
(d) $[CH_3COOH]$ and $[CH_3COO^-]$ are high, but $[H_3O^+]$ is low.

Integrative and Advanced Exercises

63. Sodium hydrogen sulfate, $NaHSO_4$, is an acidic salt with a number of uses, such as metal pickling (removal of surface deposits). $NaHSO_4$ is made by the reaction of H_2SO_4 with NaCl. To determine the percent NaCl impurity in $NaHSO_4$, a 1.016 g sample is titrated with NaOH(aq); 36.56 mL of 0.225 M NaOH is required.
(a) Write the net ionic equation for the neutralization reaction.
(b) Determine the percent NaCl in the sample titrated.
(c) Select a suitable indicator(s) from Figure 9-8.

64. You are given 250.0 mL of 0.100 M CH_3CH_2COOH (propionic acid, $K_a = 1.35 \times 10^{-5}$). You want to adjust its pH by adding an appropriate solution. What volume would you add of **(a)** 1.00 M HCl to lower the pH to 1.00; **(b)** 1.00 M $NaCH_3CH_2COO$ to raise the pH to 4.00; **(c)** water to raise the pH by 0.15 unit?

65. Even though the carbonic acid–hydrogen carbonate buffer system is crucial to the maintenance of the pH of blood, it has no practical use as a laboratory buffer solution. Can you think of a reason(s) for this? [*Hint:* Refer to data in Practice Example A of the Integrative Example in Chapter 8.]

66. Thymol blue in its acid range is not a suitable indicator for the titration of HCl by NaOH. Suppose that a

student uses thymol blue by mistake in the titration of Figure 9-9 and that the indicator end point is taken to be pH = 2.0.
(a) Would there be a sharp color change, produced by the addition of a single drop of NaOH(aq)?
(b) Approximately what percent of the HCl remains unneutralized at pH = 2.0?

67. Rather than calculate the pH for different volumes of titrant, a titration curve can be established by calculating the volume of titrant required to reach certain pH values. Determine the volumes of 0.100 M NaOH required to reach the following pH values in the titration of 20.00 mL of 0.150 M HCl: pH = **(a)** 2.00; **(b)** 3.50; **(c)** 5.00; **(d)** 10.50; **(e)** 12.00. Then plot the titration curve.

68. Use the method of Exercise 67 to determine the volume of titrant required to reach the indicated pH values in the following titrations.
(a) 25.00 mL of 0.250 M NaOH titrated with 0.300 M HCl; pH = 13.00, 12.00, 10.00, 4.00, 3.00
(b) 50.00 mL of 0.0100 M benzoic acid (C_6H_5COOH) titrated with 0.0500 M KOH: pH = 4.50, 5.50, 11.50 ($K_a = 6.3 \times 10^{-5}$)

69. A buffer solution can be prepared by starting with a weak acid, HA, and converting some of the weak acid to its salt (for example, NaA) by titration with a strong base. The *fraction* of the original acid that is converted to the salt is designated f.
(a) Derive an equation similar to equation (9.2) but expressed in terms of f rather than concentrations.
(b) What is the pH at the point in the titration of phenol, C_6H_5OH, at which $f = 0.27$ (pK_a of phenol = 10.00)?

70. You are asked to prepare a KH_2PO_4–Na_2HPO_4 solution that has the same pH as human blood, 7.40.
(a) What should be the ratio of concentrations $[HPO_4^{2-}]/[H_2PO_4^-]$ in this solution?
(b) Suppose you have to prepare 1.00 L of the solution described in part (a) and that this solution must be isotonic with blood (have the same osmotic pressure as blood). What masses of KH_2PO_4 and of $Na_2HPO_4 \cdot 12H_2O$ would you use? [*Hint:* Refer to the definition of isotonic. Recall that a solution of NaCl with 9.2 g NaCl/L solution is isotonic with blood, and assume that NaCl is completely ionized in aqueous solution.]

71. You are asked to bring the pH of 0.500 L of 0.500 M NH_4Cl(aq) to 7.00. How many drops (1 drop = 0.05 mL) of which of the following solutions would you use: 10.0 M HCl or 10.0 M NH_3?

72. Because an acid–base indicator is a weak acid, it can be titrated with a strong base. Suppose you titrate 25.00 mL of a 0.0100 M solution of the indicator *p*-nitrophenol, $HOC_6H_4NO_2$, with 0.0200 M NaOH. The pK_a of *p*-nitrophenol is 7.15, and it changes from colorless to yellow in the pH range from 5.6 to 7.6.
(a) Sketch the titration curve for this titration.
(b) Show the pH range over which *p*-nitrophenol changes color.
(c) Explain why *p*-nitrophenol cannot serve as its own indicator in this titration.

73. The neutralization of NaOH by HCl is represented in equation (1), and the neutralization of NH_3 by HCl in equation (2).

1. $OH^- + H_3O^+ \rightleftharpoons 2\,H_2O \qquad K = ?$
2. $NH_3 + H_3O^+ \rightleftharpoons NH_4^+ + H_2O \qquad K = ?$

(a) Determine the equilibrium constant K for each reaction.
(b) Explain why each neutralization reaction can be considered to go to completion.

74. The titration of a weak acid by a weak base is not a satisfactory procedure because the pH does not increase sharply at the equivalence point. Demonstrate this fact by sketching a titration curve for the neutralization of 10.00 mL of 0.100 M CH_3COOH with 0.100 M NH_3.

75. At times, a salt of a weak base can be titrated by a strong base. Use appropriate data from the text to sketch a titration curve for the titration of 10.00 mL of 0.0500 M $C_6H_5NH_3^+Cl^-$ with 0.100 M NaOH.

76. Sulfuric acid is a diprotic acid, strong in the first ionization step and weak in the second ($K_{a_2} = 1.1 \times 10^{-2}$). By using appropriate calculations, determine whether it is feasible to titrate 10.00 mL of 0.100 M H_2SO_4 to two distinct equivalence points with 0.100 M NaOH.

77. Carbonic acid is a weak diprotic acid (H_2CO_3) with $K_{a_1} = 4.43 \times 10^{-7}$ and $K_{a_2} = 4.73 \times 10^{-11}$. The equivalence points for the titration come at approximately pH 4 and 9. Suitable indicators for use in titrating carbonic acid or carbonate solutions are methyl orange and phenolphthalein.
(a) Sketch the titration curve that would be obtained in titrating a sample of $NaHCO_3$(aq) with 1.00 M HCl.
(b) Sketch the titration curve for Na_2CO_3(aq) with 1.00 M HCl.
(c) What volume of 0.100 M HCl is required for the complete neutralization of 1.00 g $NaHCO_3$(s)?
(d) What volume of 0.100 M HCl is required for the complete neutralization of 1.00 g Na_2CO_3(s)?
(e) A sample of NaOH contains a small amount of Na_2CO_3. For titration to the phenolphthalein end point, 0.1000 g of this sample requires 23.98 mL of 0.1000 M HCl. An additional 0.78 mL is required to reach the methyl orange end point. What is the percent Na_2CO_3, by mass, in the sample?

78. Piperazine is a diprotic weak base used as a corrosion inhibitor and an insecticide. Its ionization is described by the following equations.

$$HN(C_4H_8)\,NH + H_2O \rightleftharpoons [HN(C_4H_8)\,NH_2]^+ + OH^- \qquad pK_{b_1} = 4.22$$

$$[HN(C_4H_8)\,NH_2]^+ + H_2O \rightleftharpoons [H_2N(C_4H_8)\,NH_2]^{2+} + OH^- \qquad pK_{b_2} = 8.67$$

The piperazine used commercially is a hexahydrate, $C_4H_{10}N_2 \cdot 6H_2O$. A 1.00-g sample of this hexahydrate is dissolved in 100.0 mL of water and titrated with 0.500 M HCl. Sketch a titration curve for this titration, indicating **(a)** the initial pH; **(b)** the pH at the half-neutralization point of the first neutralization; **(c)** the volume of HCl(aq) required to reach the first equivalence point; **(d)** the pH at the first equivalence point; **(e)** the pH at the point at which the second step of the neutralization is half-completed; **(f)** the volume of 0.500 M HCl(aq) required to reach the second equivalence point of the titration; **(g)** the pH at the second equivalence point.

79. Complete the derivation of equation (9.5) outlined in Are You Wondering 9-1. Then derive equation (9.6).

80. Explain why equation (9.5) fails when applied to dilute solutions—for example, when you calculate the pH of 0.010 M NaH_2PO_4. [*Hint:* Refer also to Exercise 79.]

81. A solution is prepared that is 0.150 M CH_3COOH and 0.250 M $NaHCOO$.
(a) Show that this is a buffer solution.
(b) Calculate the pH of this buffer solution.
(c) What is the final pH if 1.00 L of 0.100 M HCl is added to 1.00 L of this buffer solution?

82. A series of titrations of lactic acid, $CH_3CH(OH)COOH$ ($pK_a = 3.86$) is planned. About 1.00 mmol of the acid will be titrated with NaOH(aq) to a final volume of about 100 mL at the equivalence point. **(a)** Which acid–base indicator from Figure 9-8 would you select for the titration? To assist in locating the equivalence point in the titration, a buffer solution is to be prepared having the same pH as that at the equivalence point. A few drops of the indicator in this buffer will produce the color to be matched in the titrations. **(b)** Which of the following combinations would be suitable for the buffer solutions: $CH_3COOH–CH_3COO^-$, $H_2PO_4^-–HPO_4^{2-}$, or $NH_4^+–NH_3$? **(c)** What ratio of conjugate base to acid is required in the buffer?

83. Hydrogen peroxide, H_2O_2, is a somewhat stronger acid than water. Its ionization is represented by the equation

$$H_2O_2 + H_2O \rightleftharpoons H_3O^+ + HO_2^-$$

In 1912, the following experiments were performed to obtain an approximate value of pK_a for this ionization at 0 °C. A sample of H_2O_2 was shaken together with a mixture of water and 1-pentanol. The mixture settled into two layers. At equilibrium, the hydrogen peroxide had distributed itself between the two layers such that the water layer contained 6.78 times as much H_2O_2 as the 1-pentanol layer. In a second experiment, a sample of H_2O_2 was shaken together with 0.250 M NaOH(aq) and 1-pentanol. At equilibrium, the concentration of H_2O_2 was 0.00357 M in the 1-pentanol layer and 0.259 M in the aqueous layer. In a third experiment, a sample of H_2O_2 was brought to equilibrium with a mixture of 1-pentanol and 0.125 M NaOH(aq); the concentrations of the hydrogen peroxide were 0.00198 M in the 1-pentanol and 0.123 M in the aqueous layer. For water at 0 °C, $pK_w = 14.94$. Find an approximate value of pK_a for H_2O_2 at 0 °C. [*Hint:* The hydrogen peroxide concentration in the aqueous layers is the total concentration of H_2O_2 and HO_2^-. Assume that the 1-pentanol solutions contain no ionic species.]

84. Sodium ammonium hydrogen phosphate, $NaNH_4HPO_4$, is a salt in which one of the ionizable H atoms of H_3PO_4 is replaced by Na^+, another is replaced by NH_4^+, and the third remains in the anion HPO_4^{2-}. Calculate the pH of 0.100 M $NaNH_4HPO_4$(aq). [*Hint:* You can use the general method introduced earlier. First, identify all the species that could be present and the equilibria involving these species. Then identify the two equilibrium expressions that will predominate and eliminate all the species whose concentrations are likely to be negligible. At that point, only a few algebraic manipulations are required.]

85. Consider a solution containing two weak monoprotic acids with dissociation constants K_{HA} and K_{HB}. Find the charge balance equation for this system, and use it to derive an expression that gives the concentration of H_3O^+ as a function of the concentrations of HA and HB and the various constants.

86. Calculate the pH of a solution that is 0.050 M acetic acid and 0.010 M phenylacetic acid.

87. A very common buffer agent used in the study of biochemical processes is the weak base TRIS, $(HOCH_2)_3CNH_2$, which has a pK_b of 5.91 at 25 °C. A student is given a sample of the hydrochloride of TRIS together with standard solutions of 10 M NaOH and HCl.
(a) Using TRIS, how might the student prepare 1 L of a buffer of pH = 7.79?
(b) In one experiment, 30 mmol of protons are released into 500 mL of the buffer prepared in part (a). Is the capacity of the buffer sufficient? What is the resulting pH?
(c) Another student accidentally adds 20 mL of 10 M HCl to 500 mL of the buffer solution prepared in part (a). Is the buffer ruined? If so, how could the buffer be regenerated?

88. The Henderson–Hasselbalch equation can be written as

$$pH = pK_a - \log\left(\frac{1}{\alpha} - 1\right) \text{ where } \alpha = \frac{[A^-]}{[A^-] + [HA]}.$$

Thus, the degree of ionization (α) of an acid can be determined if both the pH of the solution and the pK_a of the acid are known.
(a) Use this equation to plot the pH versus the degree of ionization for the second ionization constant of phosphoric acid ($K_a = 6.3 \times 10^{-8}$).
(b) If pH = pK_a what is the degree of ionization?
(c) If the solution had a pH of 6.0 what would the value of α be?

89. The pH of ocean water depends on the amount of atmospheric carbon dioxide. The dissolution of carbon dioxide in ocean water can be approximated by the following chemical reactions (Henry's Law constant for CO_2 is $K_H = [CO_2(aq)]/[CO_2(g)] = 0.8317$.):

$$CO_2(g) \rightleftharpoons CO_2(aq) \quad (1)$$
$$CaCO_3(s) \rightleftharpoons Ca^{2+}(aq) + CO_3^-(aq) \quad (2)$$
$$H_3O^+(aq) + CO_3^-(aq) \rightleftharpoons HCO_3^-(aq) + H_2O(l) \quad (3)$$
$$H_3O^+(aq) + HCO_3^-(aq) \rightleftharpoons CO_2(aq) + 2\,H_2O(l) \quad (4)$$

(a) Use the equations above to determine the hydronium ion concentration as a function of $[CO_2(g)]$ and $[Ca^{2+}]$.
(b) During preindustrial conditions, we will assume that the equilibrium concentration of $[CO_2(g)] = 280$ ppm and $[Ca^{2+}] = 10.24$ mM. Calculate the pH of a sample of ocean water.

90. A sample of water contains 23.0 g L^{-1} of Na^+(aq), 10.0 g L^{-1} of Ca^{2+}(aq), 40.2 g L^{-1} CO_3^{2-}(aq), and 9.6 g L^{-1} SO_4^{2-}(aq). What is the pH of the solution if the only other ions present are H_3O^+ and OH^-?

91. In 1922 Donald D. van Slyke (*J. Biol. Chem.*, **52**, 525) defined a quantity known as the buffer index: $\beta = dC_b/d(pH)$, where dC_b represents the increment of moles of strong base to one liter of the buffer. For the addition of a strong acid, he wrote $\beta = -dC_a/d(pH)$.

By applying this idea to a monoprotic acid and its conjugate base, we can derive the following expression:

$$\beta = 2.303\left(\frac{K_w}{[H_3O^+]} + [H_3O^+] + \frac{CK_a[H_3O^+]}{(K_a + [H_3O^+])^2}\right)$$

where C is the total concentration of monoprotic acid and conjugate base.

(a) Use the above expression to calculate the buffer index for the acetic acid buffer with a total acetic acid and acetate ion concentration of 2.0×10^{-2} and a pH = 5.0.

(b) Use the buffer index from part (a) and calculate the pH of the buffer after the addition of of a strong acid. (*Hint:* Let $dC_a/d(pH) \approx \Delta C_a/\Delta pH$.)

(c) Make a plot of β versus pH for a 0.1 M acetic acid buffer system. Locate the maximum buffer index as well as the minimum buffer indices.

Feature Problems

92. The graph below, which is related to a titration curve, shows the fraction (f) of the stoichiometric amount of acetic acid present as non-ionized CH_3COOH and as acetate ion, CH_3COO^-, as a function of the pH of the solution containing these species.

(a) Explain the significance of the point at which the two curves cross. What are the fractions and the pH at that point?

(b) Sketch a comparable set of curves for carbonic acid, H_2CO_3. [*Hint:* How many carbonate-containing species should appear in the graph? How many points of intersection should there be? at what pH values?]

(c) Sketch a comparable set of curves for phosphoric acid, H_3PO_4. [*Hint:* How many phosphate-containing species should appear in the graph? How many points of intersection should there be? at what pH values?]

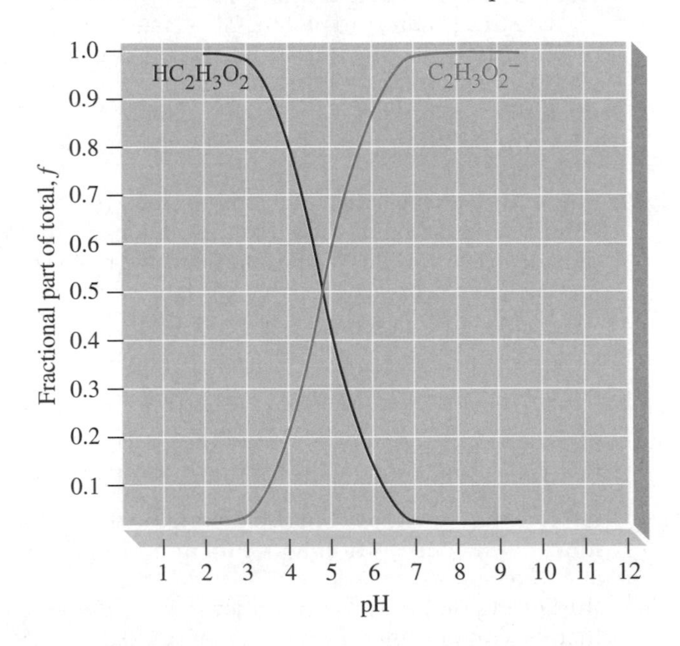

93. In some cases, the titration curve for a mixture of *two* acids has the same appearance as that for a single acid; in other cases it does not.

(a) Sketch the titration curve (pH versus volume of titrant) for the titration with 0.200 M NaOH of 25.00 mL of a solution that is 0.100 M in HCl and 0.100 M in HNO_3. Does this curve differ in any way from what would be obtained in the titration of 25.00 mL of 0.200 M HCl with 0.200 M NaOH? Explain.

(b) The titration curve shown was obtained when 10.00 mL of a solution containing both HCl and H_3PO_4 was titrated with 0.216 M NaOH. From this curve, determine the stoichiometric molarities of both the HCl and the H_3PO_4.

(c) A 10.00 mL solution that is 0.0400 M H_3PO_4 and 0.0150 M NaH_2PO_4 is titrated with 0.0200 M NaOH. Sketch the titration curve.

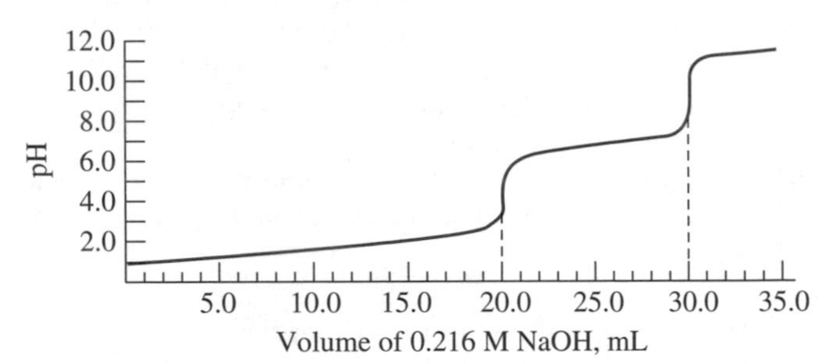

94. Amino acids contain both an acidic carboxylic acid group (—COOH) and a basic amino group (—NH_2). The amino group can be *protonated* (that is, it has an extra proton attached) in a strongly acidic solution. This produces a diprotic acid of the form H_2A^+, as exemplified by the protonated amino acid alanine.

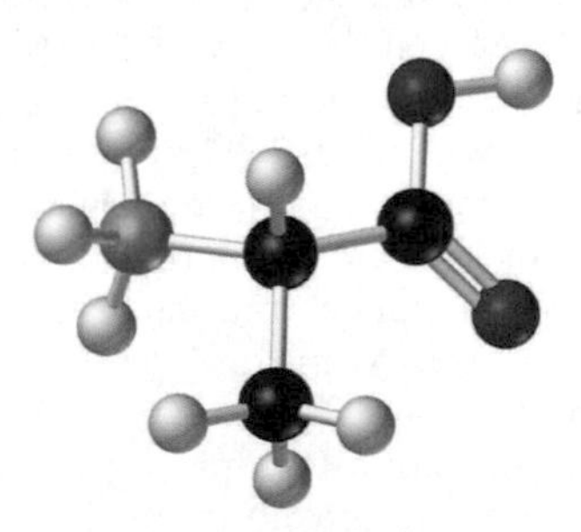

Protonated alanine

The protonated amino acid has two ionizable protons that can be titrated with OH^-.

$$\underset{\text{Protonated form of alanine } (H_2A^+)}{^+H_3NCH(CH_3)C(=O)OH} \xrightarrow{OH^-} \underset{\text{Neutral form of alanine (HA)}}{^+H_3NCH(CH_3)C(=O)O^-} \xrightarrow{OH^-} \underset{\text{Anionic form of alanine } (A^-)}{H_2NCH(CH_3)C(=O)O^-}$$

For the —COOH group, $pK_{a_1} = 2.34$; for the —NH_3^+ group, $pK_{a_2} = 9.69$. Consider the titration of a 0.500 M solution of alanine hydrochloride with

0.500 M NaOH solution. What is the pH of **(a)** the 0.500 M alanine hydrochloride; **(b)** the solution at the first half-neutralization point; **(c)** the solution at the first equivalence point?

The dominant form of alanine present at the first equivalence point is electrically neutral despite the positive charge and negative charge it possesses. The point at which the neutral form is produced is called the *isoelectric point*. Confirm that the pH at the isoelectric point is

$$pH = \frac{1}{2}(pK_{a_1} + pK_{a_2})$$

What is the pH of the solution **(d)** halfway between the first and second equivalence points? **(e)** at the second equivalence point?

(f) Calculate the pH values of the solutions when the following volumes of the 0.500 M NaOH have been added to 50 mL of the 0.500 M alanine hydrochloride solution: 10.0 mL, 20.0 mL, 30.0 mL, 40.0 mL, 50.0 mL, 60.0 mL, 70.0 mL, 80.0 mL, 90.0 mL, 100.0 mL, and 110.0 mL.

(g) Sketch the titration curve for the 0.500 M solution of alanine hydrochloride, and label significant points on the curve.

Self-Assessment Exercises

95. In your own words, define or explain the following terms or symbols: **(a)** mmol; **(b)** HIn; **(c)** equivalence point of a titration; **(d)** titration curve.

96. Briefly describe each of the following ideas, phenomena, or methods: **(a)** the common-ion effect; **(b)** the use of a buffer solution to maintain a constant pH; **(c)** the determination of pK_a of a weak acid from a titration curve; **(d)** the measurement of pH with an acid–base indicator.

97. Explain the important distinctions between each pair of terms: **(a)** buffer capacity and buffer range; **(b)** hydrolysis and neutralization; **(c)** first and second equivalence points in the titration of a weak diprotic acid; **(d)** equivalence point of a titration and end point of an indicator.

98. Write equations to show how each of the following buffer solutions reacts with a small added amount of a strong acid or a strong base: **(a)** $HCOOH-KHCOO$; **(b)** $C_6H_5NH_2-C_6H_5NH_3^+Cl^-$; **(c)** KH_2PO_4- Na_2HPO_4.

99. Sketch the titration curves that you would expect to obtain in the following titrations. Select a suitable indicator for each titration from Figure 9-8.
(a) $NaOH(aq)$ titrated with $HNO_3(aq)$
(b) $NH_3(aq)$ titrated with $HCl(aq)$
(c) $CH_3COOH(aq)$ titrated with $KOH(aq)$
(d) $NaH_2PO_4(aq)$ titrated with $KOH(aq)$

100. A 25.00-mL sample of 0.0100 M C_6H_5COOH ($K_a = 6.3 \times 10^{-5}$) is titrated with 0.0100 M $Ba(OH)_2$. Calculate the pH **(a)** of the initial acid solution; **(b)** after the addition of 6.25 mL of 0.0100 M $Ba(OH)_2$; **(c)** at the equivalence point; **(d)** after the addition of a total of 15.00 mL of 0.0100 M $Ba(OH)_2$.

101. To *repress* the ionization of formic acid, $HCOOH(aq)$, which of the following should be added to the solution? **(a)** NaCl; **(b)** NaOH; **(c)** NaHCOO; **(d)** $NaNO_3$

102. To *increase* the ionization of formic acid, $HCOOH(aq)$, which of the following should be added to the solution? **(a)** NaCl; **(b)** NaHCOO; **(c)** H_2SO_4; **(d)** $NaHCO_3$

103. To convert $NH_4^+(aq)$ to $NH_3(aq)$, **(a)** add H_3O^+; **(b)** raise the pH; **(c)** add $KNO_3(aq)$; **(d)** add NaCl.

104. During the titration of equal concentrations of a weak base and a strong acid, at what point would the $pH = pK_a$? **(a)** the initial pH; **(b)** halfway to the equivalence point; **(c)** at the equivalence point; **(d)** past the equivalence point.

105. Calculate the pH of the buffer formed by mixing equal volumes $[C_2H_5NH_2] = 1.49$ M with $[HClO_4] = 1.001$ M. $K_b = 4.3 \times 10^{-4}$.

106. Calculate the pH of a 0.5 M solution of $Ca(HSe)_2$, given that H_2Se has $K_{a_1} = 1.3 \times 10^{-4}$ and $K_{a_2} = 1 \times 10^{-11}$.

107. The effect of adding 0.001 mol KOH to 1.00 L of a solution that is 0.10 M NH_3–0.10 M NH_4Cl is to **(a)** raise the pH very slightly; **(b)** lower the pH very slightly; **(c)** raise the pH by several units; **(d)** lower the pH by several units.

108. The most acidic of the following 0.10 M salt solutions is **(a)** Na_2S; **(b)** $NaHSO_4$; **(c)** $NaHCO_3$; **(d)** Na_2HPO_4.

109. If an indicator is to be used in an acid–base titration having an equivalence point in the pH range 8 to 10, the indicator must **(a)** be a weak base; **(b)** have $K_a = 1 \times 10^{-9}$; **(c)** ionize in two steps; **(d)** be added to the solution only after the solution has become alkaline.

110. Indicate whether you would expect the equivalence point of each of the following titrations to be below, above, or at pH 7. Explain your reasoning. **(a)** $NaHCO_3(aq)$ is titrated with $NaOH(aq)$; **(b)** $HCl(aq)$ is titrated with $NH_3(aq)$; **(c)** $KOH(aq)$ is titrated with $HI(aq)$.

111. Construct a concept map relating the concepts in Sections 9-2, 9-3, and 9-4.

CHAPTER

10

Electronic Structure and Bonding • Acids and Bases

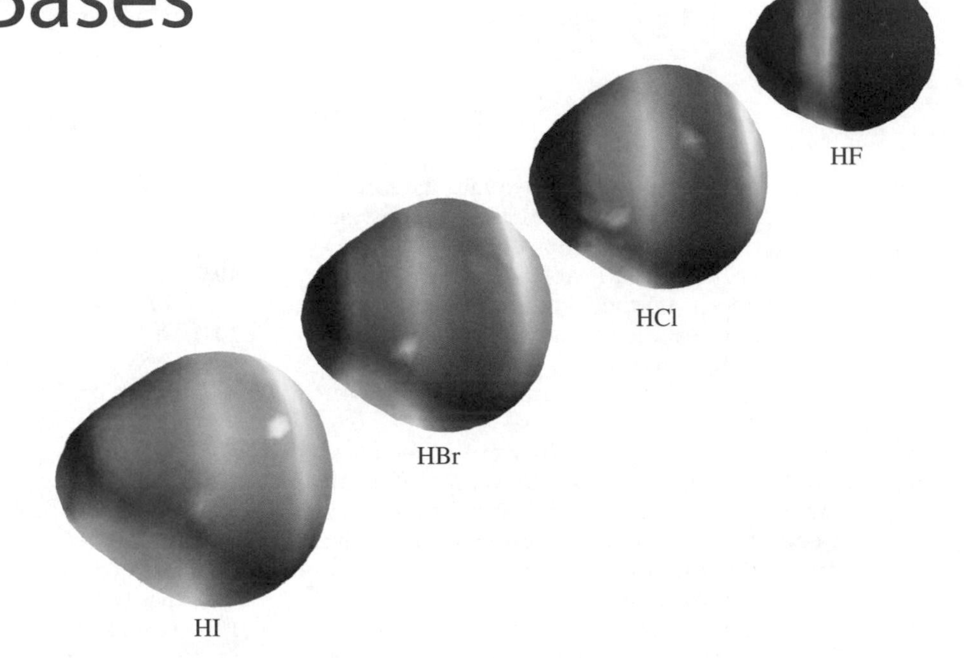

BIOGRAPHY

Jöns Jakob Berzelius (1779–1848), *an important figure in the development of modern chemistry, was born in Sweden. When Berzelius was two, his father died. His mother remarried, but died only two years after her first husband. Unhappy in his stepfather's home because his new stepmother treated the children poorly, Berzelius left when he was 14 and supported himself by working as a tutor for a wealthy landowner and laboring in his fields. Berzelius received a medical degree in 1802, but decided to pursue a career in research. He not only coined the terms organic and inorganic, but also invented the system of chemical symbols still used today. He published the first list of accurate atomic weights and proposed the idea that atoms carry an electric charge. He purified or discovered the elements cerium, selenium, silicon, thorium, titanium, and zirconium.*

TO STAY ALIVE, EARLY HUMANS MUST HAVE BEEN ABLE TO TELL THE DIFFERENCE between the kinds of materials in their world. "You can live on roots and berries," they might have said, "but you can't eat dirt. You can stay warm by burning tree branches, but you can't burn rocks."

By the early eighteenth century, scientists thought they had grasped the nature of that difference, and in 1807 Jöns Jakob Berzelius gave names to the two kinds of materials. Compounds derived from living organisms were believed to contain an unmeasurable vital force—the essence of life. These he called "organic." Compounds derived from minerals—those lacking that vital force—were "inorganic."

Because chemists could not create life in the laboratory, they assumed they could not create compounds that had a vital force. Since this was their mind-set, you can imagine how surprised chemists were in 1828 when Friedrich Wöhler produced urea—a compound known to be excreted by mammals—by heating ammonium cyanate, an inorganic mineral.

$$\overset{+}{N}H_4\ \overset{-}{O}CN \xrightarrow{\text{heat}} H_2N{-}C({=}O){-}NH_2$$

ammonium cyanate → urea

For the first time, an "organic" compound had been obtained from something other than a living organism and certainly without the aid of any kind of vital force. Clearly, chemists needed a new definition for "organic compounds." **Organic compounds** are now defined as *compounds that contain carbon*.

Why is an entire branch of chemistry devoted to the study of carbon-containing compounds? We study organic chemistry because just about all of the molecules that make life possible—proteins, enzymes, vitamins, lipids, carbohydrates, and nucleic acids—contain carbon. Thus the chemical reactions that take place in living systems, including our own bodies, are reactions of organic compounds. Most of the compounds found in nature—those we rely on for food, medicine, clothing (cotton, wool, silk), and energy (natural gas, petroleum)—are organic as well.

Organic compounds are not, however, limited to those found in nature. Chemists have learned to synthesize millions of organic compounds never found in nature, including synthetic fabrics, plastics, synthetic rubber, medicines, and even things like photographic film and Super Glue. Many of these synthetic compounds prevent shortages of naturally occurring products. For example, it has been estimated that if synthetic materials were not available for clothing, all of the arable land in the United States would have to be used for the production of cotton and wool just to provide enough material to clothe us. Currently, there are about 16 million known organic compounds, and many more are possible.

What makes carbon so special? Why are there so many carbon-containing compounds? The answer lies in carbon's position in the periodic table. Carbon is in the center of the second row of elements. We will see that the atoms to the left of carbon have a tendency to give up electrons, whereas the atoms to the right have a tendency to accept electrons.

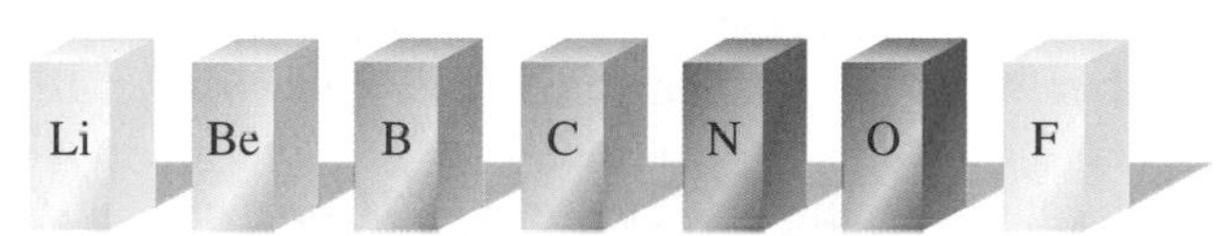

the second row of the periodic table

Because carbon is in the middle, it neither readily gives up nor readily accepts electrons. Instead, it shares electrons. Carbon can share electrons with several different kinds of atoms, and it can also share electrons with other carbon atoms. Consequently, carbon is able to form millions of stable compounds with a wide range of chemical properties simply by sharing electrons.

When we study organic chemistry, we study how organic compounds react. When an organic compound reacts, some bonds break and some new bonds form. Bonds form when two atoms share electrons, and bonds break when two atoms no longer share electrons. How readily a bond forms and how easily it breaks depend on the particular electrons that are shared, which, in turn, depend on the atoms to which the electrons belong. So if we are going to start our study of organic chemistry at the beginning, we must start with an understanding of the structure of an atom—what electrons an atom has and where they are located.

B I O G R A P H Y

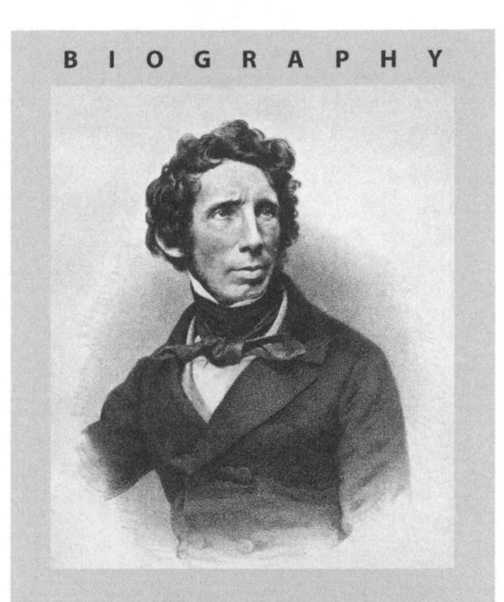

German chemist **Friedrich Wöhler (1800–1882)** *began his professional life as a physician and later became a professor of chemistry at the University of Göttingen. Wöhler codiscovered the fact that two different compounds could have the same molecular formula. He also developed methods of purifying aluminum—at the time, the most expensive metal on Earth—and beryllium.*

Natural Versus Synthetic

It is a popular belief that natural substances—those made in nature—are superior to synthetic ones—those made in the laboratory. Yet when a chemist synthesizes a compound, such as penicillin or estradiol, it is exactly the same in all respects as the compound synthesized in nature. Sometimes chemists can improve on nature. For example, chemists have synthesized analogs of morphine compounds with structures similar to but not identical to that of morphine—that have pain-killing effects like morphine but, unlike morphine, are not habit forming. Chemists have synthesized analogs of penicillin that do not produce the allergic responses that a significant fraction of the population experiences from naturally produced penicillin, or that do not have the bacterial resistance of the naturally produced antibiotic.

A field of poppies growing in Afghanistan. Commercial morphine is obtained from opium, the juice obtained from this species of poppy. Morphine is the starting material for the synthesis of heroin. Nearly three-quarters of the world's supply of heroin comes from the poppy fields of Afghanistan.

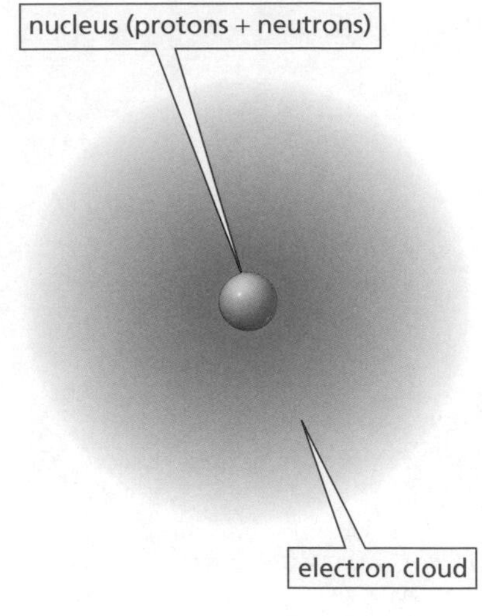
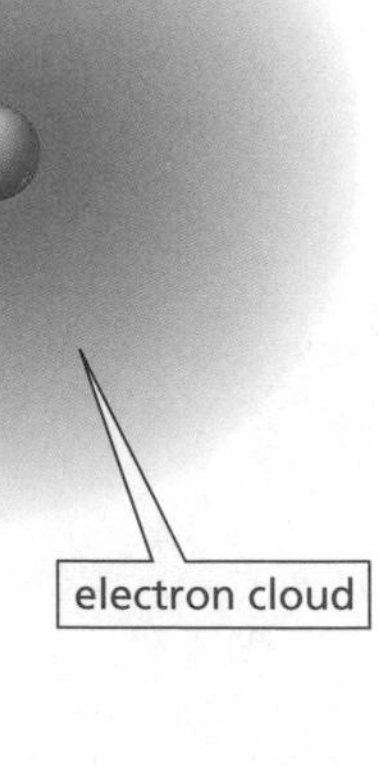

10.1 THE STRUCTURE OF AN ATOM

An atom consists of a tiny dense nucleus surrounded by electrons that are spread throughout a relatively large volume of space around the nucleus. The nucleus contains *positively charged protons* and *neutral neutrons*, so it is positively charged. The *electrons are negatively charged.* They are moving continuously. Like anything that moves, electrons have kinetic energy, and this energy is what counters the attractive force of the positively charged protons that would otherwise pull the negatively charged electrons into the nucleus.

Because the amount of positive charge on a proton equals the amount of negative charge on an electron, a neutral atom has an equal number of protons and electrons. Atoms can gain electrons and thereby become negatively charged, or they can lose electrons and become positively charged, but the number of protons in an atom does not change.

Protons and neutrons have approximately the same mass and are about 1800 times more massive than an electron. This means that most of the mass of an atom is in its nucleus. However, most of the *volume* of an atom is occupied by its electrons, and that is where our focus will be because it is the electrons that form chemical bonds.

The **atomic number** of an atom equals the *number of protons* in its nucleus. The atomic number is also the number of electrons that surround the nucleus of a neutral atom. For example, the atomic number of carbon is 6, which means that a neutral carbon atom has six protons and six electrons.

The **mass number** of an atom is the *sum of its protons and neutrons*. All carbon atoms have the same atomic number because they all have the same number of protons. They do not all have the same mass number because they do not all have the same number of neutrons. For example, 98.89% of naturally occurring carbon atoms have six neutrons—giving them a mass number of 12—and 1.11% have seven neutrons—giving them a mass number of 13. These two different kinds of carbon atoms (^{12}C and ^{13}C) are called isotopes. **Isotopes** have the same atomic number (that is, the same number of protons), but different mass numbers because they have different numbers of neutrons.

Naturally occurring carbon also contains a trace amount of ^{14}C, which has six protons and eight neutrons. This isotope of carbon is radioactive, decaying with a half-life of 5730 years. (The *half-life* is the time it takes for one-half of the nuclei to decay.) As long as a plant or animal is alive, it takes in as much ^{14}C as it excretes or exhales. When it dies, it no longer takes in ^{14}C, so the ^{14}C in the organism slowly decreases. Therefore, the age of a substance derived from a living organism can be determined by its ^{14}C content.

The bronze sculpture of Albert Einstein, on the grounds of the National Academy of Sciences in Washington, D.C., measures 21 feet from the top of the head to the tip of the feet and weighs 7000 pounds. In his left hand, Einstein holds the mathematical equations that represent his three most important contributions to science: the photoelectric effect, the equivalency of energy and matter, and the theory of relativity. At his feet is a map of the sky.

The **atomic weight** of a naturally occurring element is the *average mass of its atoms*. Because an *atomic mass unit (amu)* is defined as exactly 1/12 of the mass of ^{12}C, the atomic mass of ^{12}C is 12.0000 amu; the atomic mass of ^{13}C is 13.0034 amu. Therefore, the atomic weight of carbon is 12.011 amu because $(0.9889 \times 12.0000) + (0.0111 \times 13.0034) = 12.011$. The **molecular weight** of a compound is the *sum of the atomic weights* of all the atoms in the molecule.

PROBLEM 1 ♦

Oxygen has three isotopes with mass numbers of 16, 17, and 18. The atomic number of oxygen is eight. How many protons and neutrons does each of the isotopes have?

10.2 HOW THE ELECTRONS IN AN ATOM ARE DISTRIBUTED

For a long time, electrons were perceived to be particles—infinitesimal "planets" orbiting the nucleus of an atom. In 1924, however, a French physicist named Louis de Broglie showed that electrons also have wavelike properties. He did this by combining a formula developed by Albert Einstein that relates mass and energy with a formula developed by Max Planck that relates frequency and energy. The realization that electrons have wavelike properties spurred physicists to propose a mathematical concept known as quantum mechanics.

Quantum mechanics uses the same mathematical equations that describe the wave motion of a guitar string to characterize the motion of an electron around a nucleus. The version of quantum mechanics most useful to chemists was proposed by Erwin Schrödinger in 1926. According to Schrödinger, the behavior of each electron in an atom can be described by a **wave equation**. The solutions to the Schrödinger equation are called **wave functions** or **orbitals**. They tell us the *energy* of the electron and the *volume of space* around the nucleus where an electron is most likely to be found.

According to quantum mechanics, the electrons in an atom can be thought of as occupying a set of concentric shells that surround the nucleus. The first shell is the one closest to the nucleus. The second shell lies farther from the nucleus, and even farther out lie the third and higher numbered shells. Each shell contains subshells known as **atomic orbitals**. Each atomic orbital has a characteristic shape and energy and occupies a characteristic volume of space, which is predicted by the Schrödinger equation. An important point to remember is that *the closer the atomic orbital is to the nucleus, the lower is its energy*.

The first shell consists of only an *s* atomic orbital; the second shell consists of *s* and *p* atomic orbitals; the third shell consists of *s, p,* and *d* atomic orbitals; and the fourth and higher shells consist of *s, p, d,* and *f* atomic orbitals (Table 10.1).

Table 10.1 Distribution of Electrons in the First Four Shells That Surround the Nucleus

	First shell	Second shell	Third shell	Fourth shell
Atomic orbitals	*s*	*s, p*	*s, p, d*	*s, p, d, f*
Number of atomic orbitals	1	1, 3	1, 3, 5	1, 3, 5, 7
Maximum number of electrons	2	8	18	32

BIOGRAPHY

Louis Victor Pierre Raymond duc de Broglie (1892–1987) *was born in France and studied history at the Sorbonne. During World War I, he was stationed in the Eiffel Tower as a radio engineer. Intrigued by this exposure to radio communications, he returned to school after the war, earned a Ph.D. in physics, and became a professor of theoretical physics at the Faculté des Sciences at the Sorbonne. He received the Nobel Prize in Physics in 1929, five years after obtaining his degree, for his work that showed electrons to have properties of both particles and waves. In 1945, he became an adviser to the French Atomic Energy Commissariat.*

The closer the orbital is to the nucleus, the lower is its energy.

Degenerate orbitals are orbitals that have the same energy.

Each shell contains one *s* orbital. The second and higher shells—in addition to their *s* orbital—each contain three *degenerate p* orbitals. **Degenerate orbitals** are orbitals that have the same energy. The third and higher shells—in addition to their *s* and *p* orbitals—contain five degenerate *d* orbitals, and the fourth and higher shells also contain seven degenerate *f* orbitals. Because a maximum of two electrons can coexist in an atomic orbital (see the Pauli exclusion principle, below), the first shell, with only one atomic orbital, can contain no more than two electrons. The second shell, with four atomic orbitals—one *s* and three *p*—can have a total of eight electrons. Eighteen electrons can occupy the nine atomic orbitals—one *s*, three *p*, and five *d*—of the third shell, and 32 electrons can occupy the 16 atomic orbitals of the fourth shell. In studying organic chemistry, we will be concerned primarily with atoms that have electrons only in the first and second shells.

The **ground-state electronic configuration** of an atom describes the orbitals occupied by the atom's electrons when they are all in the available orbitals with the lowest energy. If energy is applied to an atom in the ground state, one or more electrons can jump into a higher energy orbital. The atom then would be in an **excited-state electronic configuration**. The ground-state electronic configurations of the 11 smallest atoms are shown in Table 10.2. (Each arrow—whether pointing up or down—represents one electron.) The following three rules specify which orbitals an atom's electrons occupy:

1. The **aufbau principle** (*aufbau* is German for "building up") tells us the first thing we need to know to be able to assign electrons to the various atomic orbitals. According to this principle, *an electron always goes into the available orbital with the lowest energy*.

An important point to remember is that *the closer the atomic orbital is to the nucleus, the lower is its energy*. Because a 1*s* orbital is closer to the nucleus, it is lower in energy than a 2*s* orbital, which is lower in energy—and closer to the nucleus—than a 3*s* orbital. Comparing atomic orbitals in the same shell, we see that an *s* orbital is lower in energy than a *p* orbital, and a *p* orbital is lower in energy than a *d* orbital.

Relative energies of atomic orbitals:

$$1s < 2s < 2p < 3s < 3p < 4s < 3d < 4p < 5s < 4d < 5p < 6s < 4f < 5d < 6p < 7s < 5f$$

2. The **Pauli exclusion principle** states that (a) *no more than two electrons can occupy each atomic orbital*, and (b) *the two electrons must be of opposite spin*.

BIOGRAPHY

Erwin Schrödinger (1887–1961) *was teaching physics at the University of Berlin when Hitler rose to power. Although not Jewish, Schrödinger left Germany to return to his native Austria, only to see it taken over later by the Nazis. He moved to the School for Advanced Studies in Dublin and then to Oxford University. In 1933, he shared the Nobel Prize in Physics with Paul Dirac, a professor of physics at Cambridge University, for mathematical work on quantum mechanics.*

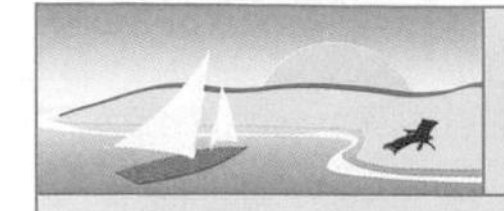

Albert Einstein

Albert Einstein (1879–1955) was born in Germany. When he was in high school, his father's business failed and his family moved to Milan, Italy. Although Einstein wanted to join his family in Italy, he had to stay behind because German law required military service after high school. To help him, his high school mathematics teacher wrote a letter saying that Einstein could have a nervous breakdown without his family and also that there was nothing left to teach him. Eventually, Einstein was asked to leave the school because of his disruptive behavior. Popular folklore says he left because of poor grades in Latin and Greek, but his grades in those subjects were fine. Einstein and his first wife, Mileva Maric, who was also a scientist, had a daughter and two sons. After their divorce, he married his cousin Elsa.

Einstein was visiting the United States when Hitler came to power, so he accepted a position at the Institute for Advanced Study in Princeton, New Jersey, becoming a U.S. citizen in 1940. Although a lifelong pacifist, he wrote a letter to President Roosevelt warning of ominous advances in German nuclear research. This led to the creation of the Manhattan Project, which developed the atomic bomb and tested it in New Mexico in 1945.

Max Karl Ernst Ludwig Planck

Max Planck (1858–1947) was born in Germany, the son of a professor of civil law. He himself was a professor at the Universities of Kiel (1885–1889) and Berlin (1889–1926). Two of his daughters died in childbirth, and one of his sons was killed in action in World War I. In 1918, Planck received the Nobel Prize in Physics for his development of quantum theory. He became president of the Kaiser Wilhelm Society of Berlin—later renamed the Max Planck Society—in 1930. Planck felt that it was his duty to remain in Germany during the Nazi era, but he never supported the Nazi regime. He unsuccessfully interceded with Hitler on behalf of his Jewish colleagues and, as a consequence, was forced to resign from the presidency of the Kaiser Wilhelm Society in 1937. A second son was accused of taking part in the plot to kill Hitler and was executed. Planck lost his home to Allied bombings. He was rescued by Allied forces during the final days of the war.

It is called an exclusion principle because it limits the number of electrons that can occupy any particular shell. (Notice in Table 10.2 that spin in one direction is designated by ↑, and spin in the opposite direction by ↓.)

From these first two rules, we can assign electrons to atomic orbitals for atoms that contain one, two, three, four, or five electrons. The single electron of a hydrogen atom occupies a 1*s* orbital, the second electron of a helium atom fills the 1*s* orbital, the third electron of a lithium atom occupies a 2*s* orbital, the fourth electron of a beryllium atom fills the 2*s* orbital, and the fifth electron of a boron atom occupies one of the 2*p* orbitals. (The subscripts *x*, *y*, and *z* distinguish the three 2*p* orbitals.) Because the three *p* orbitals are degenerate, the electron can be put into any one of them. Before we can discuss atoms containing six or more electrons, we need Hund's rule:

3. **Hund's rule** states that when there are degenerate orbitals—two or more orbitals with the same energy—an electron will occupy an empty orbital before it will pair up with another electron. In this way, electron repulsion is minimized.

Table 10.2 The Electronic Configurations of the Smallest Atoms

Atom	Name of element	Atomic number	1*s*	2*s*	$2p_x$	$2p_y$	$2p_z$	3*s*
H	Hydrogen	1	↑					
He	Helium	2	↑↓					
Li	Lithium	3	↑↓					
Be	Beryllium	4	↑↓	↑↓				
B	Boron	5	↑↓	↑↓	↑			
C	Carbon	6	↑↓	↑↓	↑	↑		
N	Nitrogen	7	↑↓	↑↓	↑	↑	↑	
O	Oxygen	8	↑↓	↑↓	↑↓	↑	↑	
F	Fluorine	9	↑↓	↑↓	↑↓	↑↓	↑	
Ne	Neon	10	↑↓	↑↓	↑↓	↑↓	↑↓	
Na	Sodium	11	↑↓	↑↓	↑↓	↑↓	↑↓	↑

The sixth electron of a carbon atom, therefore, goes into an empty 2*p* orbital, rather than pairing up with the electron already occupying a 2*p* orbital (see Table 10.2). There is one more empty 2*p* orbital, so that is where nitrogen's seventh electron goes. The eighth electron of an oxygen atom pairs up with an electron occupying a 2*p* orbital rather than going into the higher-energy 3*s* orbital.

The locations of the electrons in the remaining elements can be assigned using these three rules.

Electrons in inner shells (those below the outermost shell) are called **core electrons**. Core electrons do not participate in chemical bonding. Electrons in the outermost shell are called **valence electrons**. Carbon, for example, has two core electrons and four valence electrons (Table 10.2). Lithium and sodium each have one valence electron. If you examine the periodic table inside the front cover of this book, you will see that lithium and sodium are in the same column. Elements in the same column of the periodic table have the same number of valence electrons. Because the number of valence electrons is the major factor determining an element's chemical properties, elements in the same column of the periodic table have similar chemical properties. Thus, the chemical behavior of an element depends on its electronic configuration.

PROBLEM 2♦

How many valence electrons do the following atoms have?

a. boron **b.** nitrogen **c.** oxygen **d.** fluorine

PROBLEM 3♦

a. Write electronic configurations for chlorine (atomic number 17), bromine (atomic number 35), and iodine (atomic number 53).

b. How many valence electrons do chlorine, bromine, and iodine have?

PROBLEM 4

Look at the relative positions of each pair of atoms in the periodic table. How many core electrons does each have? How many valence electrons does each have?

a. carbon and silicon
b. oxygen and sulfur
c. nitrogen and phosphorus
d. magnesium and calcium

BIOGRAPHY

As a teenager, Austrian **Wolfgang Pauli (1900–1958)** *wrote articles on relativity that caught the attention of Albert Einstein. Pauli went on to teach physics at the University of Hamburg and at the Zurich Institute of Technology. When World War II broke out, he immigrated to the United States, where he joined the Institute for Advanced Study at Princeton.*

chem place Tutorial: Electrons in orbitals

BIOGRAPHY

Friedrich Hermann Hund (1896–1997) *was born in Germany. He was a professor of physics at several German universities, the last being the University of Göttingen. He spent a year as a visiting professor at Harvard University. In February 1996, the University of Göttingen held a symposium to honor Hund on his 100th birthday.*

BIOGRAPHY

American chemist **Gilbert Newton Lewis (1875–1946)** *was born in Weymouth, Massachusetts, and received a Ph.D. from Harvard in 1899. He was the first person to prepare "heavy water," which has deuterium atoms in place of the usual hydrogen atoms (D_2O versus H_2O). Because heavy water can be used as a moderator of neutrons, it became important in the development of the atomic bomb. Lewis started his career as a professor at the Massachusetts Institute of Technology and joined the faculty at the University of California, Berkeley, in 1912.*

10.3 IONIC AND COVALENT BONDS

In trying to explain why atoms form bonds, G. N. Lewis proposed that *an atom is most stable if its outer shell is either filled or contains eight electrons, and it has no electrons of higher energy*. According to Lewis's theory, an atom will give up, accept, or share electrons in order to achieve a filled outer shell or an outer shell that contains eight electrons. This theory has come to be called the **octet rule** (even though hydrogen has only two electrons in its filled outer shell).

Lithium (Li) has a single electron in its 2*s* orbital. If it loses this electron, the lithium atom ends up with a filled outer shell—a stable configuration. Lithium, therefore, loses an electron relatively easily. Sodium (Na) has a single electron in its 3*s* orbital, so it too loses an electron easily. Elements (such as lithium and sodium) that readily lose an electron and thereby become positively charged are said to be **electropositive**. The elements in the first column of the periodic table are all electropositive—each readily loses an electron because each has a single electron in its outermost shell.

When we draw the electrons around an atom, as in the following equations, core electrons are not shown; only valence electrons are shown because only valence electrons are used in bonding. Each valence electron is shown as a dot. Notice that when the single valence electron of lithium or sodium is removed, the species that is formed is called an ion because it carries a charge.

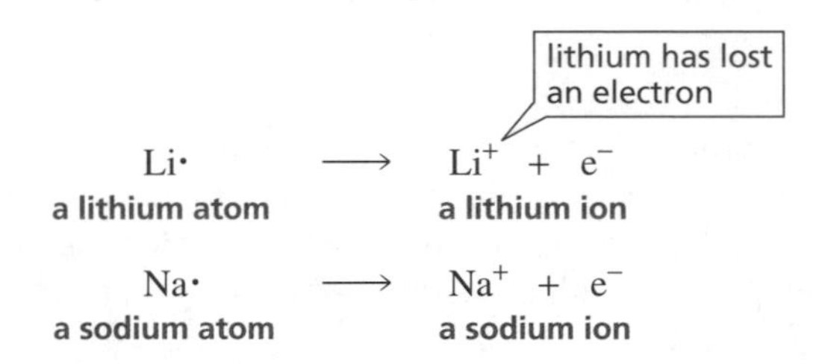

Fluorine has seven valence electrons (Table 10.2). Consequently, it readily acquires an electron in order to have an outer shell of eight electrons. Elements in the same column as fluorine (for example, chlorine, bromine, and iodine) also need only one electron to have an outer shell of eight, so they, too, readily acquire an electron. Elements that readily acquire an electron are said to be **electronegative**—they acquire an electron easily and thereby become negatively charged.

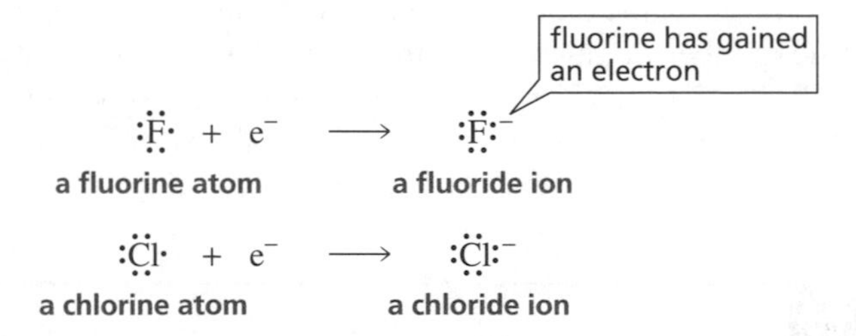

PROBLEM 5♦

a. Find potassium (K) in the periodic table and predict how many valence electrons it has.
b. What orbital does the unpaired electron occupy?

Ionic Bonds Are Formed by the Attraction Between Ions of Opposite Charge

We have just seen that sodium gives up an electron easily and chlorine readily acquires an electron. Therefore, when sodium metal and chlorine gas are mixed, each sodium atom transfers an electron to a chlorine atom, and crystalline sodium chloride (table salt) is formed as a result. The positively charged sodium ions and negatively charged chloride ions are independent species held together by the attraction of opposite charges (Figure 10.1).

A **bond** is an attractive force between two ions or between two atoms. Attractive forces between opposite charges are called **electrostatic attractions**. A bond that results from *the electrostatic attraction between ions of opposite charge* is called an **ionic bond**.

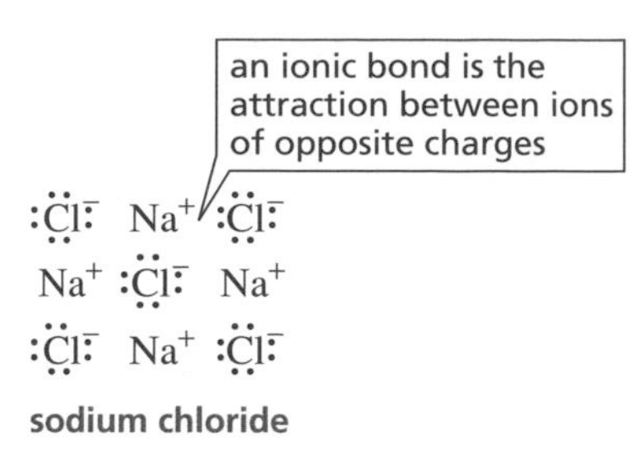

a.

b.
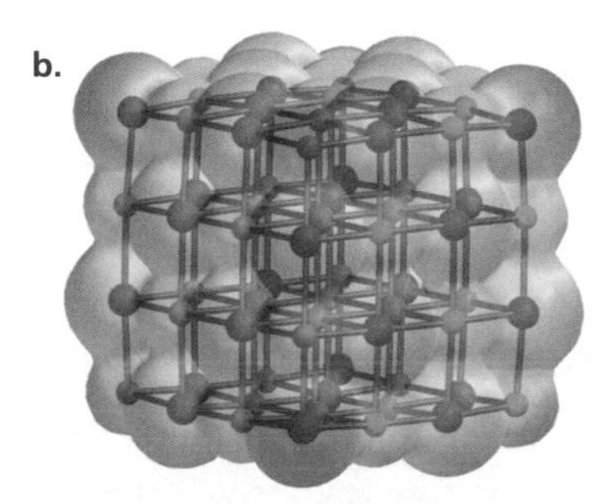

◀ **Figure 10.1**
(a) Crystalline sodium chloride.
(b) The electron-rich chloride ions are red, and the electron-poor sodium ions are blue. Each chloride ion is surrounded by six sodium ions, and each sodium ion is surrounded by six chloride ions. Ignore the sticks holding the balls together; they are there only to keep the model from falling apart.

Sodium chloride is an example of an ionic compound. **Ionic compounds** are formed when an element on the left side of the periodic table (an electropositive element) transfers one or more electrons to an element on the right side of the periodic table (an electronegative element).

Covalent Bonds Are Formed by Sharing Electrons

Instead of giving up or acquiring electrons, an atom can achieve a filled outer shell by sharing electrons. For example, two fluorine atoms can each attain a filled second shell by sharing their unpaired valence electrons. A bond formed as a result of *sharing electrons* is called a **covalent bond**.

a covalent bond is formed by sharing electrons

$$:\ddot{\underset{..}{F}}\cdot + \cdot\ddot{\underset{..}{F}}: \longrightarrow :\ddot{\underset{..}{F}}:\ddot{\underset{..}{F}}:$$

Two hydrogen atoms can form a covalent bond by sharing electrons. As a result of covalent bonding, each hydrogen acquires a stable, filled first shell.

$$H\cdot + \cdot H \longrightarrow H:H$$

Similarly, hydrogen and chlorine can form a covalent bond by sharing electrons. In doing so, hydrogen fills its only shell, and chlorine achieves an outer shell of eight electrons.

$$H\cdot + \cdot\ddot{\underset{..}{Cl}}: \longrightarrow H:\ddot{\underset{..}{Cl}}:$$

A hydrogen atom can achieve a completely empty shell by losing an electron. Loss of its sole electron results in a positively charged **hydrogen ion**. A positively charged hydrogen ion is called a **proton** because when a hydrogen atom loses its valence electron, only the hydrogen nucleus—which consists of a single proton—remains. A hydrogen atom can achieve a filled outer shell by gaining an electron, thereby forming a negatively charged hydrogen ion, called a **hydride ion**.

$$\underset{\text{a hydrogen atom}}{H\cdot} \longrightarrow \underset{\text{a proton}}{H^+} + e^-$$

$$\underset{\text{a hydrogen atom}}{H\cdot} + e^- \longrightarrow \underset{\text{a hydride ion}}{H:^-}$$

Because oxygen has six valence electrons, it needs to form two covalent bonds to achieve an outer shell of eight electrons. Nitrogen, with five valence electrons, must form three covalent bonds, and carbon, with four valence electrons, must form four covalent bonds to achieve a filled outer shell. Notice that all the atoms in water, ammonia, and methane have filled outer shells.

$$2\,H\cdot + \cdot\ddot{O}: \longrightarrow H:\ddot{O}:H$$

water — oxygen has formed 2 covalent bonds

$$3\,H\cdot + \cdot\dot{N}\cdot \longrightarrow H:\ddot{N}:H \;(\text{with a third } H)$$

ammonia — nitrogen has formed 3 covalent bonds

$$4\,H\cdot + \cdot\dot{C}\cdot \longrightarrow H:\ddot{C}:H \;(\text{with } H \text{ above and below})$$

methane — carbon has formed 4 covalent bonds

Polar Covalent Bonds

The atoms that share the bonding electrons in the F—F and H—H covalent bonds are identical. Therefore, they share the electrons equally; that is, each electron spends as much time in the vicinity of one atom as in the other. Such a bond is called a **nonpolar covalent bond**.

In contrast, the bonding electrons in hydrogen chloride, water, and ammonia are more attracted to one atom than to another because the atoms that share the electrons in these molecules are different and have different electronegativities. **Electronegativity** is a measure of the ability of an atom to pull the bonding electrons toward itself. The bonding electrons in hydrogen chloride, water, and ammonia are more attracted to the atom with the greater electronegativity. The bonds in these compounds are called polar covalent bonds. A **polar covalent bond** is a covalent bond between atoms of different electronegativities. The electronegativities of some of the elements are shown in Table 10.3. Notice that electronegativity increases from left to right across a row of the periodic table or going up any of the columns.

chem place Tutorial: Periodic trends in electronegativity

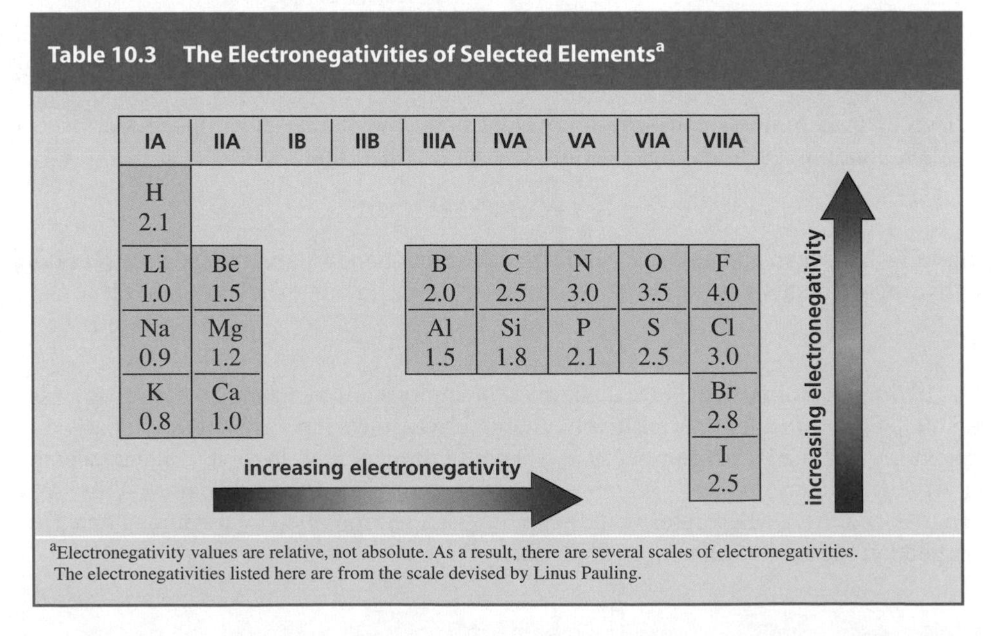
Table 10.3 The Electronegativities of Selected Elements[a]

IA	IIA	IB	IIB	IIIA	IVA	VA	VIA	VIIA
H 2.1								
Li 1.0	Be 1.5			B 2.0	C 2.5	N 3.0	O 3.5	F 4.0
Na 0.9	Mg 1.2			Al 1.5	Si 1.8	P 2.1	S 2.5	Cl 3.0
K 0.8	Ca 1.0							Br 2.8
								I 2.5

[a]Electronegativity values are relative, not absolute. As a result, there are several scales of electronegativities. The electronegativities listed here are from the scale devised by Linus Pauling.

A polar covalent bond has a slight positive charge on one end and a slight negative charge on the other. Polarity in a covalent bond is indicated by the symbols δ^+ and δ^-, which denote partial positive and partial negative charges, respectively. The negative end of the bond is the end that has the more electronegative atom. The greater the difference in electronegativity between the bonded atoms, the more polar the bond will be. (Notice that a pair of shared electrons can be shown as a line between two atoms.)

$\overset{\delta+}{H}—\overset{\delta-}{\ddot{Cl}}:$ $\overset{\delta+}{H}—\overset{\delta-}{\ddot{O}}:$ (with $\underset{\delta+}{H}$ below O) $\overset{\delta+}{H}—\overset{\delta-}{\ddot{N}}—\overset{\delta+}{H}$ (with $\underset{\delta+}{H}$ below N)

The direction of bond polarity can be indicated with an arrow. By convention, chemists draw the arrow so that it points in the direction in which the electrons are pulled. Thus, the head of the arrow is at the negative end of the bond; a short perpendicular line near the tail of the arrow marks the positive end of the bond. (Physicists draw the arrow in the opposite direction.)

$\overset{+\!\!\longrightarrow}{H—\ddot{Cl}:}$ the negative end of the bond

You can think of ionic bonds and nonpolar covalent bonds as being at the opposite ends of a continuum of bond types. All bonds fall somewhere on this line. At one end is an ionic bond, a bond in which there is no sharing of electrons. At the other end is a nonpolar covalent bond, a bond in which the electrons are shared equally. Polar covalent bonds fall somewhere in between. The greater the difference in electronegativity between the atoms forming the bond, the closer the bond is to the ionic end of the continuum.

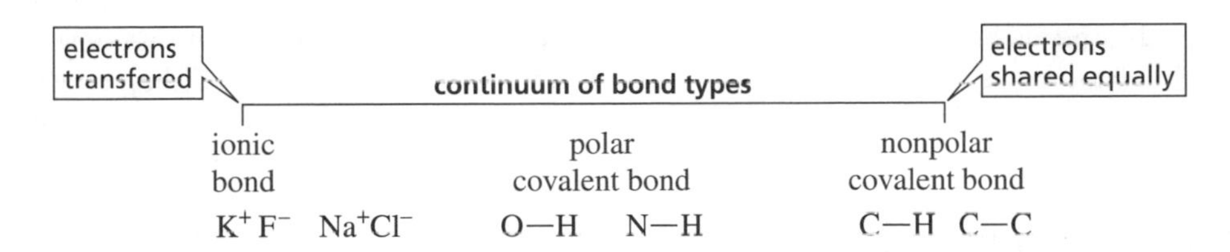

C—H bonds are relatively nonpolar, because carbon and hydrogen have similar electronegativities (electronegativity difference = 0.4; see Table 10.3); N—H bonds are more polar (electronegativity difference = 0.9), but not as polar as O—H bonds (electronegativity difference = 1.4). Even closer to the ionic end of the continuum is the bond between sodium and chloride ions (electronegativity difference = 2.1), but sodium chloride is not as ionic as potassium fluoride (electronegativity difference = 3.2).

PROBLEM 6♦

Which bond is more polar?

a. $H—CH_3$ or $Cl—CH_3$

b. H—OH or H—H

c. H—Cl or H—F

d. Cl—Cl or $Cl—CH_3$

PROBLEM 7♦

Which of the following has

a. the most polar bond?

b. the least polar bond?

NaI LiBr Cl_2 KCl

chem place Tutorial: Electronegativity differences and bond types

A polar bond has a **dipole**—it has a negative end and a positive end. The size of the dipole is indicated by the dipole moment, symbolized by the Greek letter μ. The **dipole moment** of a bond is equal to the magnitude of the charge (e) on the atom (either the partial positive charge or the partial negative charge, because they have the same magnitude) times the distance between the two charges (d):

$$\text{dipole moment} = \mu = e \times d$$

BIOGRAPHY

Peter Debye (1884–1966) *was born in the Netherlands. He taught at the Universities of Zürich (succeeding Einstein), Leipzig, and Berlin, but returned to his homeland in 1939 when the Nazis ordered him to become a German citizen. Upon visiting Cornell to give a lecture, he decided to stay in the United States, and he became a U.S. citizen in 1946. He received the Nobel Prize in chemistry in 1936 for his work on dipole moments and on the diffraction of X-rays and electrons in gases.*

A dipole moment is reported in a unit called a **debye (D)** (pronounced de-bye). Because the charge on an electron is 4.80×10^{-10} electrostatic units (esu) and the distance between charges in a polar bond will have units of 10^{-8} cm, the product of charge and distance will have units of 10^{-18} esu cm. Thus, $1.0\ D = 1.0 \times 10^{-18}$ esu cm, so a dipole moment of 1.5×10^{-18} esu cm can be more simply stated as 1.5 D. The dipole moments of some bonds commonly found in organic compounds are listed in Table 10.4.

Table 10.4 The Dipole Moments of Some Commonly Encountered Bonds

Bond	Dipole moment (D)	Bond	Dipole moment (D)
H—C	0.4	C—C	0
H—N	1.3	C—N	0.2
H—O	1.5	C—O	0.7
H—F	1.7	C—F	1.6
H—Cl	1.1	C—Cl	1.5
H—Br	0.8	C—Br	1.4
H—I	0.4	C—I	1.2

When a molecule has only one covalent bond and the bond is polar, the molecule has a dipole moment that is identical to the dipole moment of the bond. For example, the dipole moment of hydrogen chloride (HCl) is 1.1 D because the dipole moment of the H—Cl bond is 1.1 D. The dipole moment of a molecule with more than one covalent bond depends on the dipole moments of all the bonds in the molecule and the geometry of the molecule. We will examine the dipole moments of molecules with more than one covalent bond in Section 10.15 after you learn about the geometry of molecules.

PROBLEM 8 SOLVED

Determine the partial negative charge on the fluorine atom in a C—F bond. The bond length is 1.39 Å* and the bond dipole moment is 1.60 D.

Solution If there were a full negative charge on the fluorine atom, the dipole moment would be

$$(4.80 \times 10^{-10}\ \text{esu})\,(1.39 \times 10^{-8}\ \text{cm}) = 6.97\ \text{esu cm} = 6.97\ \text{D}$$

Knowing that the dipole moment is 1.60 D, we calculate that the partial negative charge on the fluorine atom is about 0.23 of a full charge:

$$\frac{1.60}{6.97} = 0.23$$

PROBLEM 9

Explain why HCl has a smaller dipole moment than HF, even though the H—Cl bond is longer than the H—F bond.

PROBLEM 10◆

Use the symbols δ^+ and δ^- to show the direction of polarity of the indicated bond in each of the following compounds, for example,

$$\overset{\delta+}{H_3C}—\overset{\delta-}{OH}$$

a. HO—H
b. F—Br
c. $H_3C—NH_2$
d. $H_3C—Cl$
e. HO—Br
f. $H_3C—MgBr$
g. I—Cl
h. $H_2N—OH$

*The angstrom (Å) is not a Système International unit. Those who opt to adhere strictly to SI units can convert it into picometers: 1 picometer (pm) = 10^{-12} m; 1 Å = 10^{-10} m = 100 pm. Because the angstrom continues to be used by many organic chemists, we will use angstroms in this book.

Understanding bond polarity is critical to understanding how organic reactions occur, because a central rule governing the reactivity of organic compounds is that *electron-rich atoms or molecules are attracted to electron-deficient atoms or molecules*. **Electrostatic potential maps** (often called simply potential maps) are models that show how charge is distributed in the molecule under the map. They, therefore, show the kind of electrostatic attraction an atom or molecule has for another atom or molecule. The potential maps for LiH, H_2, and HF are shown below.

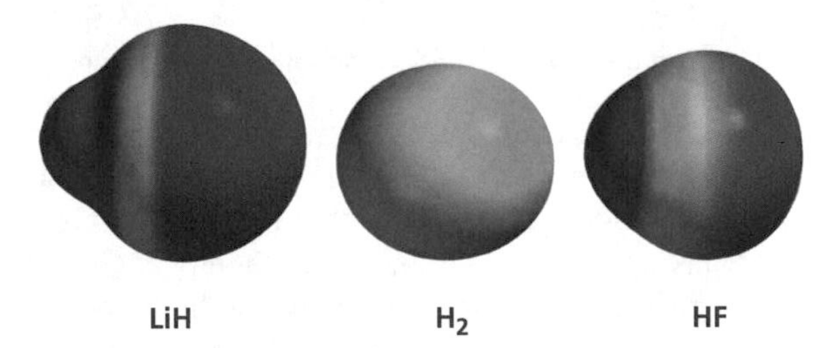

The colors on a potential map indicate the degree to which a molecule or an atom in a molecule attracts charged particles. Red, signifying the most negative electrostatic potential, is used for regions that attract positively charged molecules most strongly. Blue is used for areas with the most positive electrostatic potential, regions that attract negatively charged molecules most strongly. Other colors indicate intermediate levels of attraction.

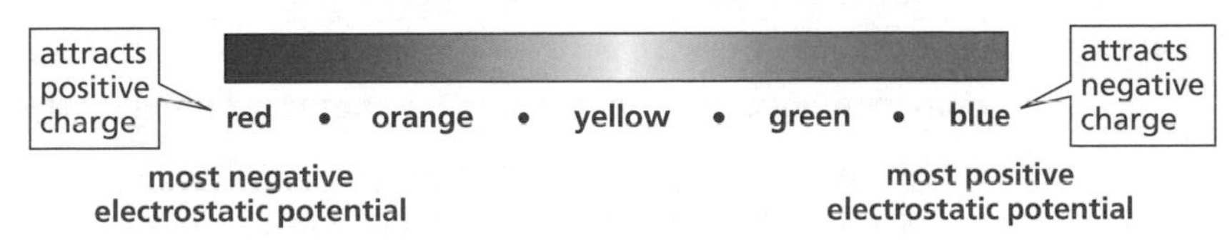

The colors on a potential map can also be used to estimate charge distribution. For example, the potential map for LiH indicates that the hydrogen atom is more electron-rich than the lithium atom. By comparing the three maps, we can tell that the hydrogen in LiH is more electron-rich than a hydrogen in H_2, and the hydrogen in HF is less electron-rich than a hydrogen in H_2.

A molecule's size and shape are determined by the number of electrons in the molecule and by the way these electrons move. Because a potential map roughly marks the "edge" of the molecule's electron cloud, the map tells us something about the relative size and shape of the molecule. Notice that a given kind of atom can have different sizes in different molecules. The negatively charged hydrogen in LiH is bigger than a neutral hydrogen in H_2, which, in turn, is bigger than the positively charged hydrogen in HF.

PROBLEM 11 ♦

After examining the potential maps for LiH, HF, and H_2, answer the following questions:

a. Which compounds are polar?
b. Why does LiH have the largest hydrogen?
c. Which compound has the hydrogen that would be most apt to attract a negatively charged molecule?

10.4 HOW THE STRUCTURE OF A COMPOUND IS REPRESENTED

First we will see how compounds are drawn using Lewis structures. Then we will look at the kinds of structures that are used more commonly for organic compounds.

Lewis Structures

The chemical symbols we have been using, in which the valence electrons are represented as dots, are called **Lewis structures**. Lewis structures are useful because they show us which atoms are bonded together and tell us whether any atoms possess *lone-pair electrons* or have a *formal charge*, two concepts we describe below. The Lewis structures for H_2O, H_3O^+, HO^-, and H_2O_2 are:

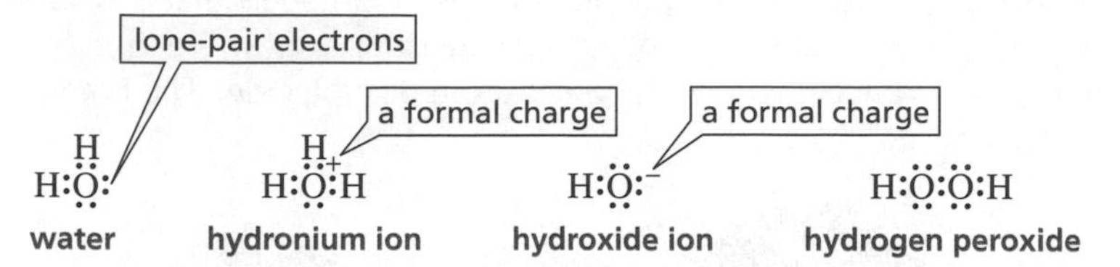

Notice that the atoms in Lewis structures are always lined up linearly or at right angles. Therefore, they do not tell us anything about the bond angles in the actual molecule.

When you draw a Lewis structure, make sure that hydrogen atoms are surrounded by no more than two electrons and that C, O, N, and halogen (F, Cl, Br, I) atoms are surrounded by no more than eight electrons, in accordance with the octet rule. Valence electrons not used in bonding are called **nonbonding electrons** or **lone-pair electrons**.

Once you have the atoms and the electrons in place, you must examine each atom to see whether a formal charge should be assigned to it. A **formal charge** is the *difference* between the number of valence electrons an atom has when it is not bonded to any other atoms and the number it "owns" when it is bonded. An atom "owns" all of its lone-pair electrons and half of its bonding (shared) electrons.

formal charge = number of valence electrons
− (number of lone-pair electrons + 1/2 number of bonding electrons)

For example, an oxygen atom has six valence electrons (Table 10.2). In water (H_2O), oxygen "owns" six electrons (four lone-pair electrons and half of the four bonding electrons). Because the number of electrons it "owns" is equal to the number of its valence electrons ($6 - 6 = 0$), the oxygen atom in water has no formal charge. The oxygen atom in the hydronium ion (H_3O^+) "owns" five electrons: two lone-pair electrons plus three (half of six) bonding electrons. Because the number of electrons it "owns" is one less than the number of its valence electrons ($6 - 5 = 1$), its formal charge is $+1$. The oxygen atom in the hydroxide ion (HO^-) "owns" seven electrons: six lone-pair electrons plus one (half of two) bonding electron. Because it "owns" one more electron than the number of its valence electrons ($6 - 7 = -1$), its formal charge is -1.

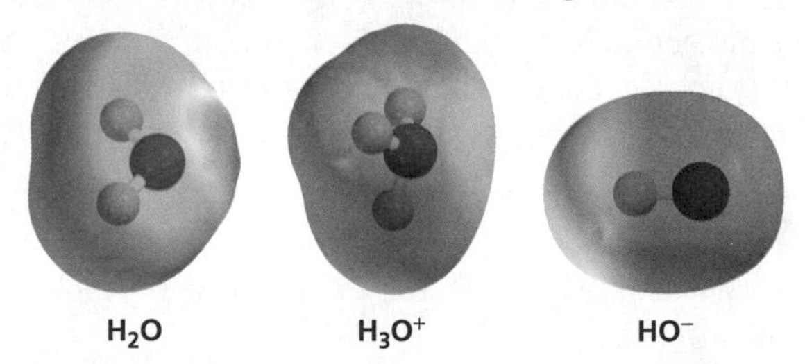

PROBLEM 12 ♦

A formal charge does not necessarily indicate that the atom with the formal change has greater or less electron density than atoms in the molecule without formal charges. We can see this by examining the potential maps for H_2O, H_3O^+, and HO^-.

a. Which atom bears the formal negative charge in the hydroxide ion?
b. Which atom has the greater electron density in the hydroxide ion?
c. Which atom bears the formal positive charge in the hydronium ion?
d. Which atom has the least electron density in the hydronium ion?

Nitrogen has five valence electrons (Table 10.2). Prove to yourself that the appropriate formal charges have been assigned to the nitrogen atoms in the following Lewis structures:

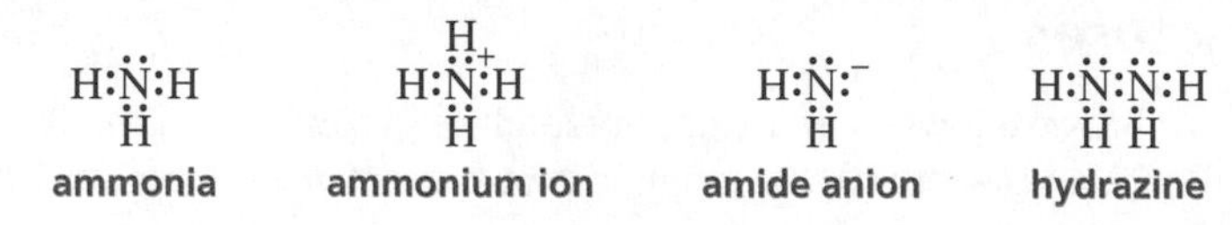

Carbon has four valence electrons. Take a moment to make sure you understand why the carbon atoms in the following Lewis structures have the indicated formal charges:

H H:C:H H	H H:C⁺ H	H H:C:⁻ H	H H:C· H	H H H:C:C:H H H
methane	**methyl cation a carbocation**	**methyl anion a carbanion**	**methyl radical**	**ethane**

A species containing a positively charged carbon atom is called a **carbocation**, and a species containing a negatively charged carbon atom is called a **carbanion**. (Recall that a *cation* is a positively charged ion and an *anion* is a negatively charged ion.) A species containing an atom with a single unpaired electron is called a **radical** (often called a **free radical**).

Hydrogen has one valence electron, and each halogen (F, Cl, Br, I) has seven valence electrons, so the following species have the indicated formal charges:

H^+	$H:^-$	H·	:Br:⁻	:Br·	:Br:Br:	:Cl:Cl:
hydrogen ion	**hydride ion**	**hydrogen radical**	**bromide ion**	**bromine radical**	**bromine**	**chlorine**

PROBLEM 13

Give each atom the appropriate formal charge:

a. CH_3—Ö—CH_3 (with H bonded to O)

b. H—C̈—H (with H bonded to C)

c. CH_3—N—CH_3 (with CH_3 above and CH_3 below N)

d. H—N—B—H (with H above and below N, and H above and below B)

chem place Tutorial: Formal charges

In studying the molecules in this section, notice that when the atoms do not bear a formal charge or an unpaired electron, hydrogen and the halogens always have *one* covalent bond, oxygen always has *two* covalent bonds, nitrogen always has *three* covalent bonds, and carbon has *four* covalent bonds. Atoms that have more bonds or fewer bonds than the number required for a neutral atom will have either a formal charge or an unpaired electron. These numbers are very important to remember when you are first drawing structures of organic compounds because they provide a quick way to recognize when you have made a mistake.

H—	:F— :Cl— :I— :Br—	:Ö— (with one bond down)	—N̈— (with one bond down)	—C— (with bonds up and down)
one bond	**one bond**	**two bonds**	**three bonds**	**four bonds**

When it is neutral:
C forms 4 bonds
N forms 3 bonds
O forms 2 bonds
H forms 1 bond
Halogen forms 1 bond

In the following Lewis structures notice that each atom has a filled outer shell. Also notice that since none of the molecules has a formal charge or an unpaired electron, H and Br each form one bond, O forms two bonds (these can be two single bonds or one double bond), N forms three bonds (these can be three single bonds, one double bond and one single bond, or one triple bond), and C forms a total of four bonds. (In drawing the Lewis structure for a compound that has two or more oxygen atoms, avoid oxygen–oxygen single bonds. These are weak bonds, and few compounds have them.)

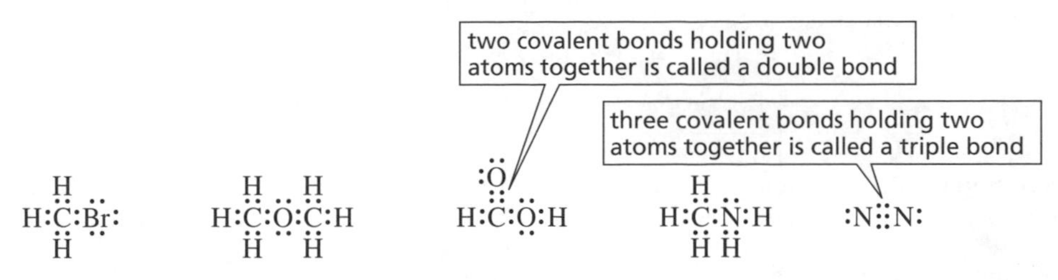

two covalent bonds holding two atoms together is called a double bond
three covalent bonds holding two atoms together is called a triple bond

We have seen that a pair of shared electrons can also be shown as a line between two atoms (Section 10.3). Compare the preceding structures with the following ones:

```
    H             H     H         :Ö           H
    |             |     |          ||          |    ..
H—C—Br:    H—C—Ö—C—H     H—C—Ö—H      H—C—N—H      :N≡N:
    |   ..        |  ..  |            ..        |  |
    H             H     H                      H  H
```

PROBLEM-SOLVING STRATEGY

Drawing Lewis Structures

Draw the Lewis structure for HNO_2.

1. Determine the total number of valence electrons (1 for H, 5 for N, and 6 for each O adds up to $1 + 5 + 12 = 18$).
2. Use the total number of valence electrons to form bonds and fill octets with lone-pair electrons.
3. If after all the electrons have been assigned, an atom (other than hydrogen) does not have a complete octet, use a lone pair to form a double bond to that atom.
4. Assign a formal charge to any atom whose number of valence electrons is not equal to the number of its lone-pair electrons plus one-half its bonding electrons. (None of the atoms in HNO_2 has a formal charge.)

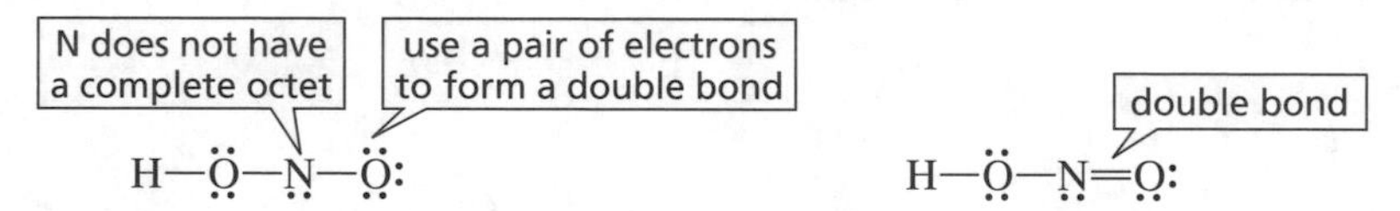

N does not have a complete octet
use a pair of electrons to form a double bond
H—Ö—N—Ö:
double bond
H—Ö—N=O:

18 electrons have been assigned

using one of oxygen's lone pairs to form a double bond gives N a complete octet

Now continue on to Problem 14.

PROBLEM 14 SOLVED

Draw the Lewis structure for each of the following:

a. NO_3^- **c.** $^-C_2H_5$ **e.** $CH_3\overset{+}{N}H_3$ **g.** HCO_3^-

b. NO_2^+ **d.** $^+C_2H_5$ **f.** NaOH **h.** H_2CO

Solution to 14a The only way we can arrange one N and three O's and avoid O—O single bonds is to place the three O's around the N. The total number of valence electrons is 23 (5 for N, and 6 for each of the three O's). Because the species has one negative charge, we must add 1 to the number of valence electrons, for a total of 24. We then use the 24 electrons to form bonds and fill octets with lone-pair electrons.

```
      :Ö:
       |
  :Ö—N—Ö:
       \
   incomplete octet
```

When all 24 electrons have been assigned, we see that N does not have a complete octet. We complete N's octet by using one of oxygen's lone pairs to form a double bond. (It does not make a difference which oxygen atom we choose.) When we check each atom to see whether it has a formal charge, we find that two of the O's are negatively charged and the N is positively charged, for an overall charge of −1.

```
        :Ö
         ||
  ⁻:Ö—N—Ö:⁻
         +
```

Solution to 14b The total number of valence electrons is 17 (5 for N and 6 for each of the two O's). Because the species has one positive charge, we must subtract 1 from the number of valence electrons, for a total of 16. The 16 electrons are used to form bonds and then fill octets with lone-pair electrons.

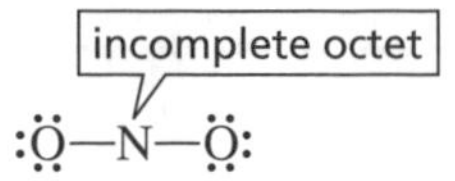

incomplete octet

:Ö—N—Ö:

Two double bonds are necessary to complete N's octet. The N has a formal charge of +1.

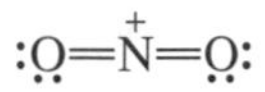

$:\underset{\cdot\cdot}{O}{=}\overset{+}{N}{=}\underset{\cdot\cdot}{O}:$

chem place Tutorial: Lewis structure

PROBLEM 15♦

a. Draw two Lewis structures for C_2H_6O.
b. Draw three Lewis structures for C_3H_8O.

(*Hint:* The two Lewis structures in part **a** are **constitutional isomers**, molecules that have the same atoms, but differ in the way the atoms are connected. The three Lewis structures in part **b** are also constitutional isomers.)

Kekulé Structures

In **Kekulé structures**, the bonding electrons are drawn as lines and the lone-pair electrons are usually left out entirely, unless they are needed to draw attention to some chemical property of the molecule. (Although lone-pair electrons are not shown, you should remember that neutral nitrogen, oxygen, and halogen atoms always have them: one pair in the case of nitrogen, two pairs in the case of oxygen, and three pairs in the case of a halogen.)

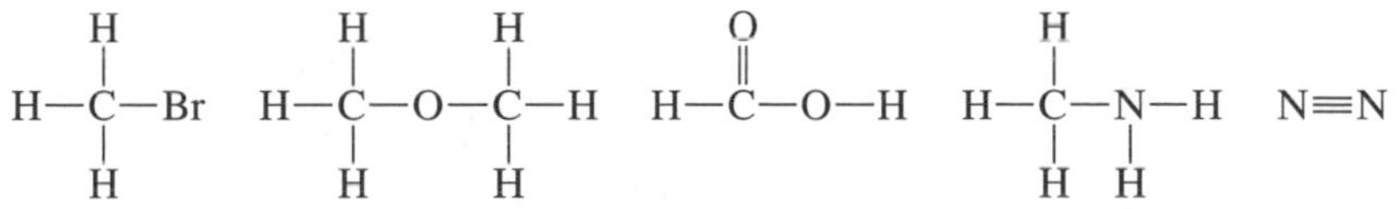

```
   H          H       H          O            H
   |          |       |          ‖            |
H—C—Br    H—C—O—C—H    H—C—O—H    H—C—N—H    N≡N
   |          |       |                       |  |
   H          H       H                       H  H
```

Condensed Structures

Frequently, structures are simplified by omitting some (or all) of the covalent bonds and listing atoms bonded to a particular carbon (or nitrogen or oxygen) next to it with subscripts as necessary. These structures are called **condensed structures**. Compare the following examples with the Kekulé structures shown above:

CH_3Br CH_3OCH_3 HCO_2H CH_3NH_2 N_2

You can find more examples of condensed structures and the conventions commonly used to create them in Table 10.5. Notice that since none of the molecules in Table 10.5 has a formal charge or an unpaired electron, each C has four bonds, each N has three bonds, each O has two bonds, and each H or halogen has one bond.

PROBLEM 16♦

Draw the lone-pair electrons that are not shown in the following structures:

a. $CH_3CH_2NH_2$ **c.** CH_3CH_2OH **e.** CH_3CH_2Cl
b. CH_3NHCH_3 **d.** CH_3OCH_3 **f.** $HONH_2$

Table 10.5 Kekulé and Condensed Structures

Kekulé structure	Condensed structures

Atoms bonded to a carbon are shown to the right of the carbon. Atoms other than H can be shown hanging from the carbon.

```
    H  H  H  H  H  H
    |  |  |  |  |  |
 H—C—C—C—C—C—C—H
    |  |  |  |  |  |
    H  Br H  H  Cl H
```

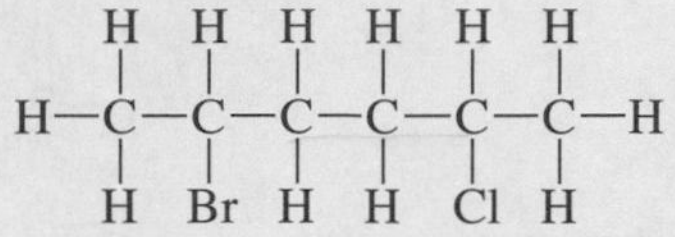

$CH_3CHBrCH_2CH_2CHClCH_3$ or

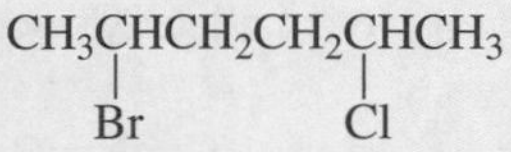

```
CH3CHCH2CH2CHCH3
   |        |
   Br       Cl
```

Repeating CH_2 groups can be shown in parentheses.

```
    H  H  H  H  H  H
    |  |  |  |  |  |
 H—C—C—C—C—C—C—H
    |  |  |  |  |  |
    H  H  H  H  H  H
```

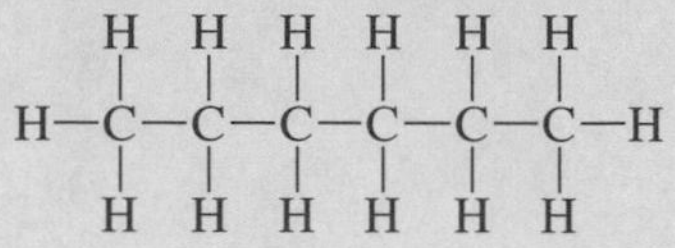

$CH_3CH_2CH_2CH_2CH_2CH_3$ or $CH_3(CH_2)_4CH_3$

Groups bonded to a carbon can be shown (in parentheses) to the right of the carbon, or hanging from the carbon.

```
    H  H  H    H  H  H
    |  |  |    |  |  |
 H—C—C—C—C—C—C—H
    |  |  |    |  |  |
    H  H  CH3  H  OH H
```

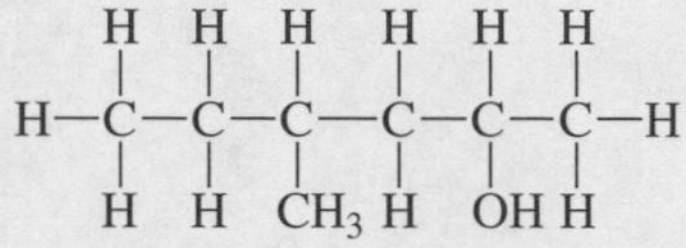

$CH_3CH_2CH(CH_3)CH_2CH(OH)CH_3$ or

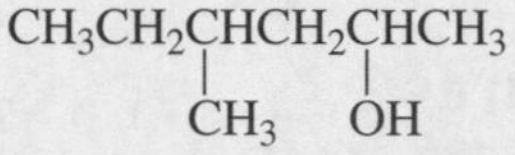

```
CH3CH2CHCH2CHCH3
      |    |
      CH3  OH
```

Groups bonded to the far-right carbon are not put in parentheses.

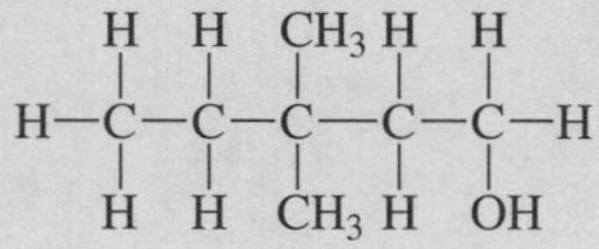

```
    H  H  CH3 H  H
    |  |  |   |  |
 H—C—C—C—C—C—H
    |  |  |   |  |
    H  H  CH3 H  OH
```

$CH_3CH_2C(CH_3)_2CH_2CH_2OH$ or

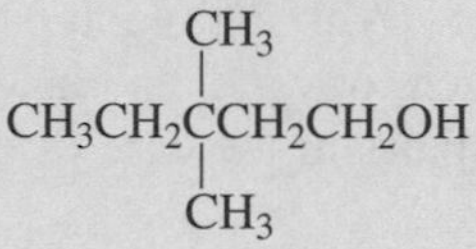

```
       CH3
       |
CH3CH2CCH2CH2OH
       |
       CH3
```

Two or more identical groups considered bonded to the "first" atom on the left can be shown (in parentheses) to the left of that atom, or hanging from the atom.

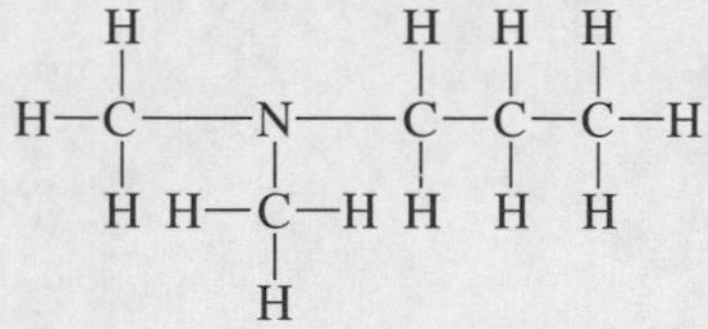

```
    H         H  H  H
    |         |  |  |
 H—C———N———C—C—C—H
    |    |    |  |  |
    H  H—C—H  H  H  H
         |
         H
```

$(CH_3)_2NCH_2CH_2CH_3$ or

```
CH3NCH2CH2CH3
   |
   CH3
```

```
    H    H    H  H  H
    |    |    |  |  |
 H—C———C———C—C—C—H
    |    |    |  |  |
    H  H—C—H  H  H  H
         |
         H
```

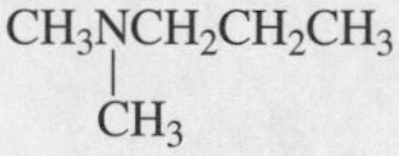

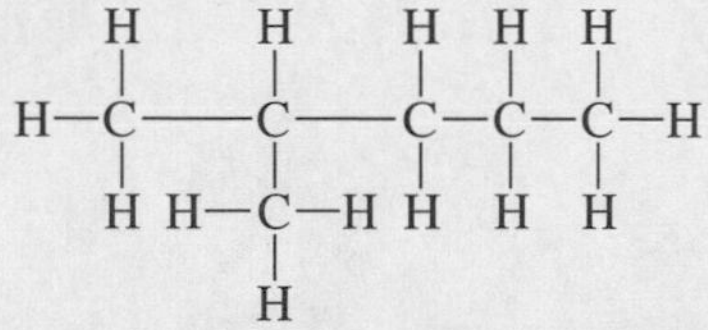

$(CH_3)_2CHCH_2CH_2CH_3$ or

```
CH3CHCH2CH2CH3
   |
   CH3
```

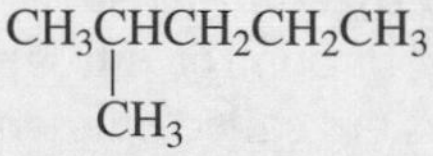

An oxygen doubly bonded to a carbon can be shown hanging off the carbon or to the right of the carbon.

```
      O
      ||
CH3CH2CCH3
```

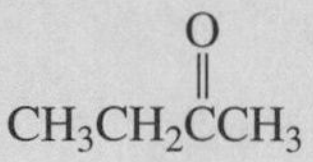

or $CH_3CH_2COCH_3$ or $CH_3CH_2C(=O)CH_3$

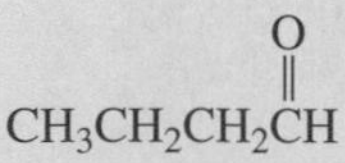

```
         O
         ||
CH3CH2CH2CH
```

or $CH_3CH_2CH_2CHO$ or $CH_3CH_2CH_2CH=O$

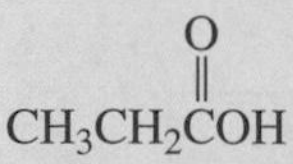

```
      O
      ||
CH3CH2COH
```

or $CH_3CH_2CO_2H$ or CH_3CH_2COOH

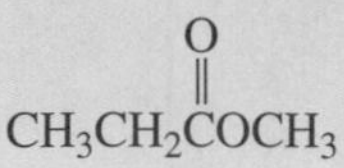

```
      O
      ||
CH3CH2COCH3
```

or $CH_3CH_2CO_2CH_3$ or $CH_3CH_2COOCH_3$

PROBLEM 17 ♦

Draw condensed structures for the compounds represented by the following models (black = C, gray = H, red = O, blue = N, green = Cl):

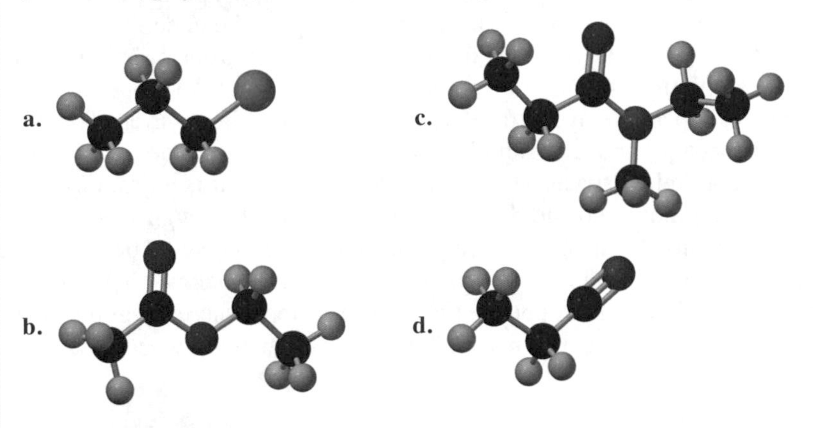

PROBLEM 18 ♦

Which of the atoms in the molecular models in Problem 17 have:

a. three lone pairs **b.** two lone pairs **c.** one lone pair **d.** no lone pairs

PROBLEM 19

Expand the following condensed structures to show the covalent bonds and lone-pair electrons:

a. $CH_3NH(CH_2)_2CH_3$
b. $(CH_3)_2CHCl$
c. $(CH_3)_3CBr$
d. $(CH_3)_3C(CH_2)_3CH(CH_3)_2$

10.5 ATOMIC ORBITALS

We have seen that electrons are distributed into different atomic orbitals (Table 10.2), three-dimensional regions around the nucleus where electrons are most likely to be found. The **Heisenberg uncertainty principle**, however, states that both the precise location and the momentum of an atomic particle cannot be simultaneously determined. This means that we can never say precisely where an electron is—we can only describe its probable location. Mathematical calculations indicate that an *s* atomic orbital is a sphere with the nucleus at its center, and experimental evidence supports this theory. Thus, when we say that an electron occupies a 1*s* orbital, we mean that there is a greater than 90% probability that the electron is in the space defined by the sphere.

An orbital tells us the volume of space around the nucleus where an electron is most likely to be found.

Because the second shell lies farther from the nucleus than the first shell (Section 10.2), the average distance from the nucleus is greater for an electron in a 2*s* orbital than it is for an electron in a 1*s* orbital. A 2*s* orbital, therefore, is represented by a larger sphere. Because of the greater size of a 2*s* orbital, the average electron density there is less than the average electron density in a 1*s* orbital.

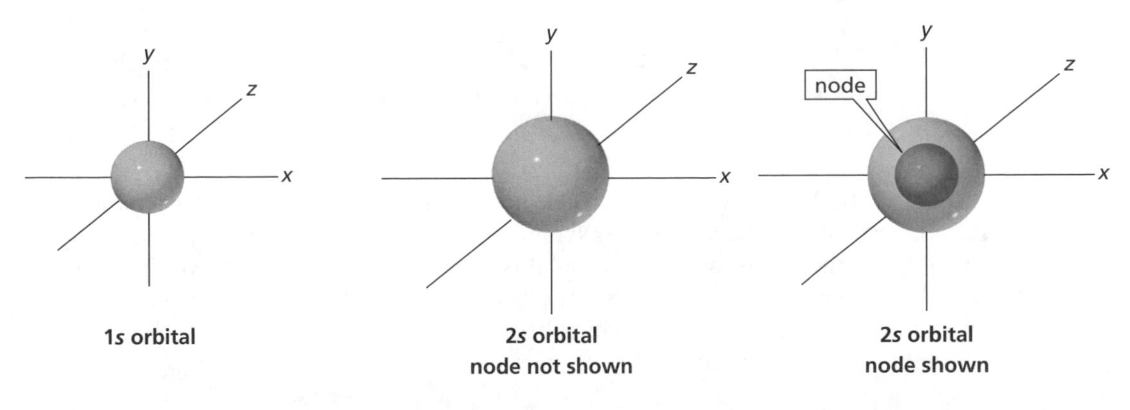

An electron in a 1*s* orbital can be anywhere within the 1*s* sphere, but a 2*s* orbital has a region where the probability of finding an electron falls to zero. This is called a **node**, or, more precisely a **radial node** since this absence of electron density lies at one set distance from the nucleus. So a 2*s* electron can be found anywhere within the 2*s* sphere—including the region of space defined by the 1*s* sphere—except at the node.

To understand why nodes occur, you need to remember that electrons have both particlelike and wavelike properties. A node is a consequence of the wavelike properties of an electron. There are two types of waves: traveling waves and standing waves. Traveling waves move through space; light is an example of a traveling wave. A standing wave, in contrast, is confined to a limited space. A vibrating string of a guitar is an example of a standing wave—the string moves up and down, but does not travel through space. If you were to write a wave equation for the guitar string, the wave function would be (+) in the region above where the guitar string is at rest and (−) in the region below where the guitar string is at rest—the regions are of opposite phase. The regions where the guitar string has no transverse displacement are called *nodes*. A node is at the region where a standing wave has an amplitude of zero.

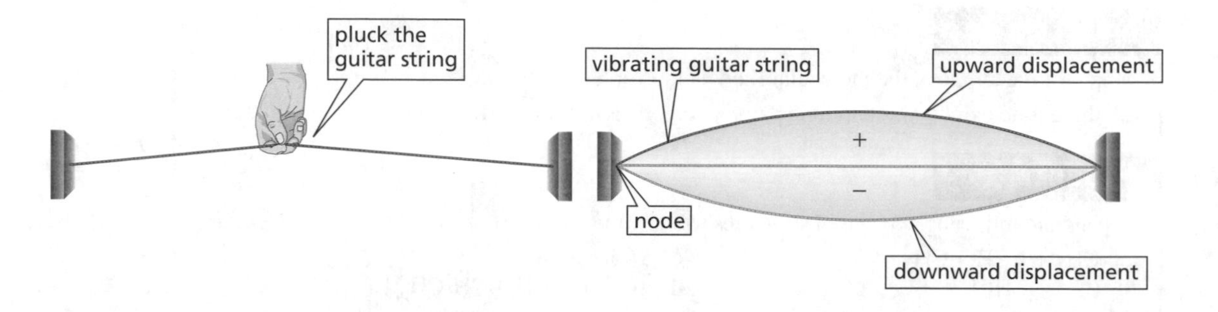

An electron behaves like a standing wave, but, unlike the wave created by a vibrating guitar string, it is three dimensional. This means that the node of a 2*s* orbital is actually a spherical surface within the 2*s* orbital. Because the electron wave has zero amplitude at the node, there is zero probability of finding an electron at the node.

Unlike *s* orbitals, which resemble spheres, *p* orbitals have two lobes. Generally, the lobes are depicted as teardrop shaped, but computer-generated representations reveal that they are shaped more like doorknobs (as shown on the right below). Like the vibrating guitar string, the lobes are of opposite phase, which can be designated by plus (+) and minus (−) or by two different colors. (In this context, + and − indicate the phase of the orbital; they do not indicate charge.) The node of the *p* orbital is a plane—called a **nodal plane**—that passes through the center of the nucleus, between its two lobes. There is zero probability of finding an electron in the nodal plane of the *p* orbital.

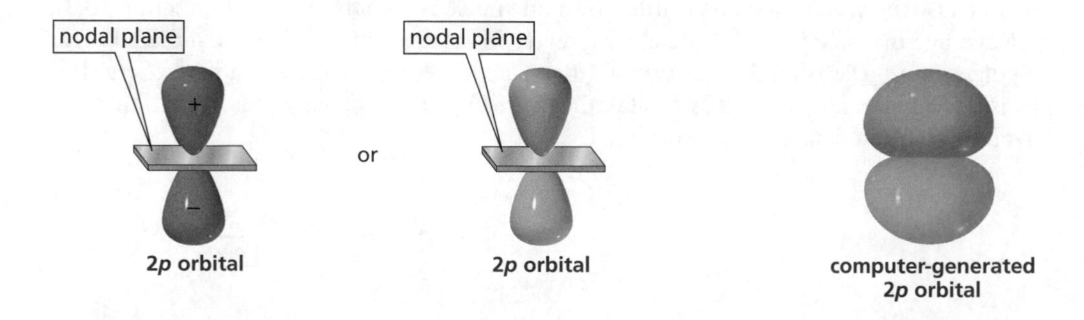

In Section 10.2, we saw that the second and higher numbered shells each contain three degenerate *p* orbitals. The p_x orbital is symmetrical about the *x*-axis, the p_y orbital is symmetrical about the *y*-axis, and the p_z orbital is symmetrical about the *z*-axis. This means that each *p* orbital is perpendicular to the other two *p* orbitals. The energy of a 2*p* orbital is slightly greater than that of a 2*s* orbital because the average location of an electron in a 2*p* orbital is farther away from the nucleus.

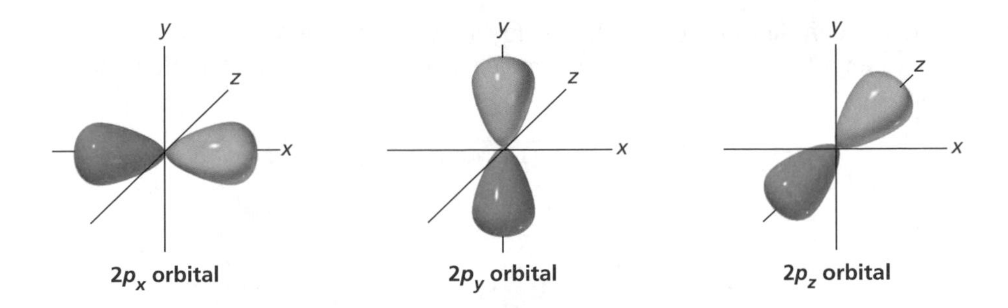

10.6 AN INTRODUCTION TO MOLECULAR ORBITAL THEORY

How do atoms form covalent bonds in order to form molecules? The Lewis model, which shows atoms attaining a complete octet by sharing electrons, tells only part of the story. A drawback of the model is that it treats electrons like particles and does not take into account their wavelike properties.

Molecular orbital (MO) theory combines the tendency of atoms to fill their octets by sharing electrons (the Lewis model) with their wavelike properties, assigning electrons to a volume of space called an orbital. According to MO theory, covalent bonds result when atomic orbitals combine to form *molecular orbitals*. A **molecular orbital** belongs to the whole molecule rather than to a single atom. Like an atomic orbital, which describes the volume of space around an atom's nucleus where an electron is likely to be found, a molecular orbital describes the volume of space around a molecule where an electron is likely to be found. Molecular orbitals, too, have specific sizes, shapes, and energies.

Let's look first at the bonding in a hydrogen molecule (H_2). Imagine a meeting of two separate H atoms. As one atom with its 1*s* atomic orbital approaches the other with its 1*s* atomic orbital, the orbitals begin to overlap. The atoms continue to move closer, and the amount of overlap increases until the orbitals combine to form a molecular orbital. The covalent bond that is formed when the two *s* orbitals overlap is called a **sigma** (σ) bond. A σ bond is cylindrically symmetrical—the electrons in the bond are symmetrically distributed about an imaginary line connecting the centers of the two atoms joined by the bond.

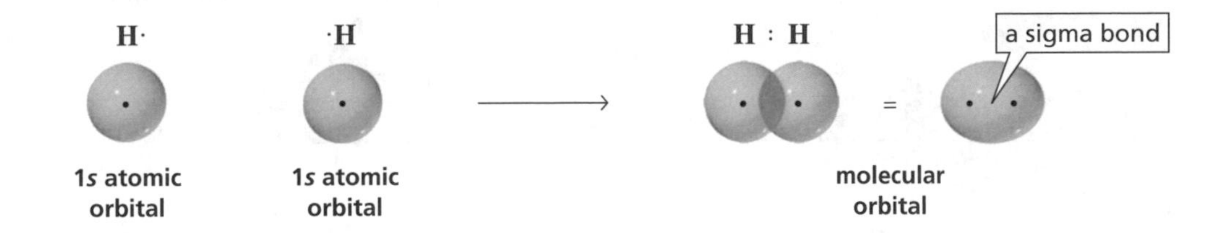

An atomic orbital surrounds an atom.

A molecular orbital surrounds a molecule.

As the two orbitals start to overlap, energy is released (stability is increased) because the electron in each atom is attracted both to its own nucleus and to the positively charged nucleus of the other atom (Figure 10.2). The attraction of the negatively charged electrons for the two positively charged nuclei is what holds the atoms together. The more the orbitals overlap, the more the energy decreases until the atoms are so close that their positively charged nuclei start to repel each other. This repulsion causes a large increase in energy. Figure 10.2 shows that minimum energy (maximum stability) is achieved when the nuclei are a certain distance apart. This distance is the **bond length** of the new covalent bond. The bond length of the H—H bond is 0.74 Å.

Minimum energy corresponds to maximum stability.

As Figure 10.2 shows, energy is released when a covalent bond forms. When the H—H bond forms, 105 kcal/mol (or 439 kJ/mol)* of energy is released. Breaking the bond requires precisely the same amount of energy. Thus, the **bond strength**, also called

*Joules are the Système International (SI) units for energy, although many chemists use calories (1kcal = 4.184 kJ). We will use both in this book.

the **bond dissociation energy**, is the energy required to break a bond, or the energy released when a bond is formed. Every covalent bond has a characteristic bond length and bond strength.

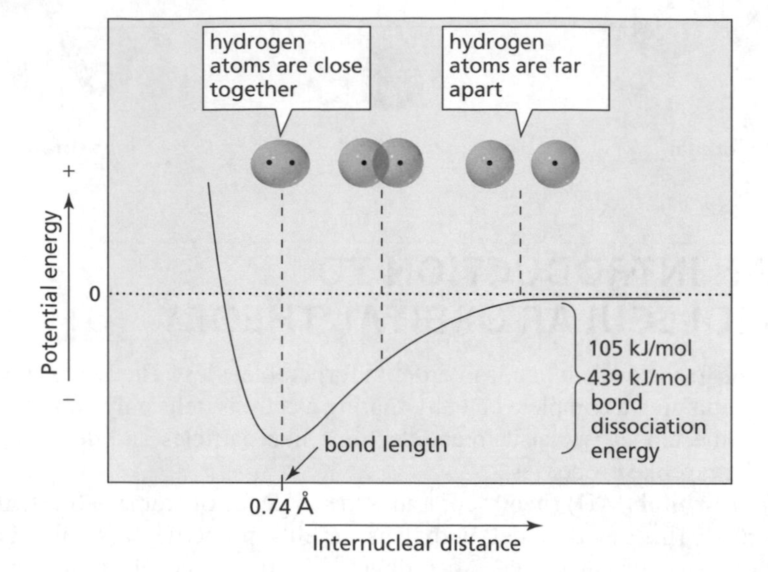

▶ **Figure 10.2**
The change in energy that occurs as two 1*s* atomic orbitals approach each other. The internuclear distance at minimum energy is the length of the H—H covalent bond.

Orbitals are conserved. In other words, the number of molecular orbitals formed must equal the number of atomic orbitals combined. In describing the formation of an H—H bond, we combined two atomic orbitals but discussed only one molecular orbital. Where is the other molecular orbital? We will see that it is there, but it does not contain any electrons.

Atomic orbitals can combine in two different ways: constructively and destructively. They can combine in a constructive, additive manner, just as two light waves or sound waves may reinforce each other (Figure 10.3). The constructive combination of two *s* orbitals is called a **σ (sigma) bonding molecular orbital**. Atomic orbitals can also combine in a destructive way, canceling each other. The cancellation is similar to the darkness that results when two light waves cancel each other or to the resulting silence when two sound waves cancel each other (Figure 10.3). The destructive combination of two *s* orbitals is called a σ^* **antibonding molecular orbital**. An antibonding orbital is indicated by an asterisk (*).

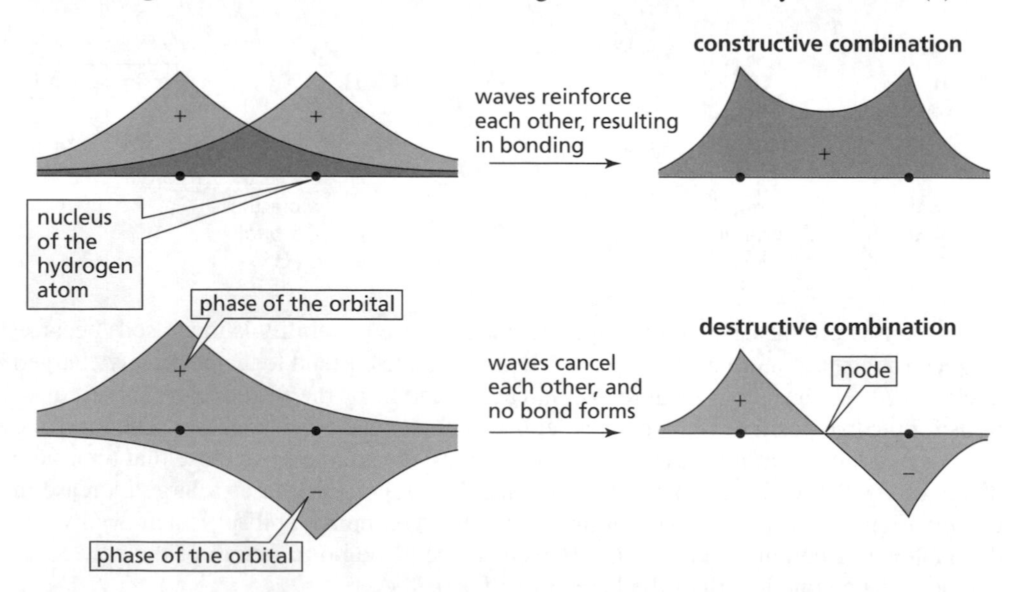

▶ **Figure 10.3**
The wave functions of two hydrogen atoms can interact to reinforce each other (*top*) or can interact to cancel each other (*bottom*). Note that waves that interact constructively are in-phase (have the same phase), whereas waves that interact destructively are out-of-phase (have different phases).

The σ bonding molecular orbital and σ^* antibonding molecular orbital are shown in the molecular orbital (MO) diagram in Figure 10.4. In an MO diagram, the energies of the orbitals are represented as horizontal lines; the bottom line is the lowest energy level, the top line the highest energy level. We see that any electrons in the bonding molecular orbital will most likely be found between the nuclei, attracting both nuclei simultaneously. This increased electron density between the nuclei is what binds the atoms together.

Because there is a node between the nuclei in the antibonding molecular orbital, any electrons in that orbital are more likely to be found anywhere except between the nuclei, so the nuclei are more exposed to one another and will be forced apart by electrostatic repulsion. Thus, electrons that occupy this orbital detract from, rather than aid, the formation of a bond between the atoms.

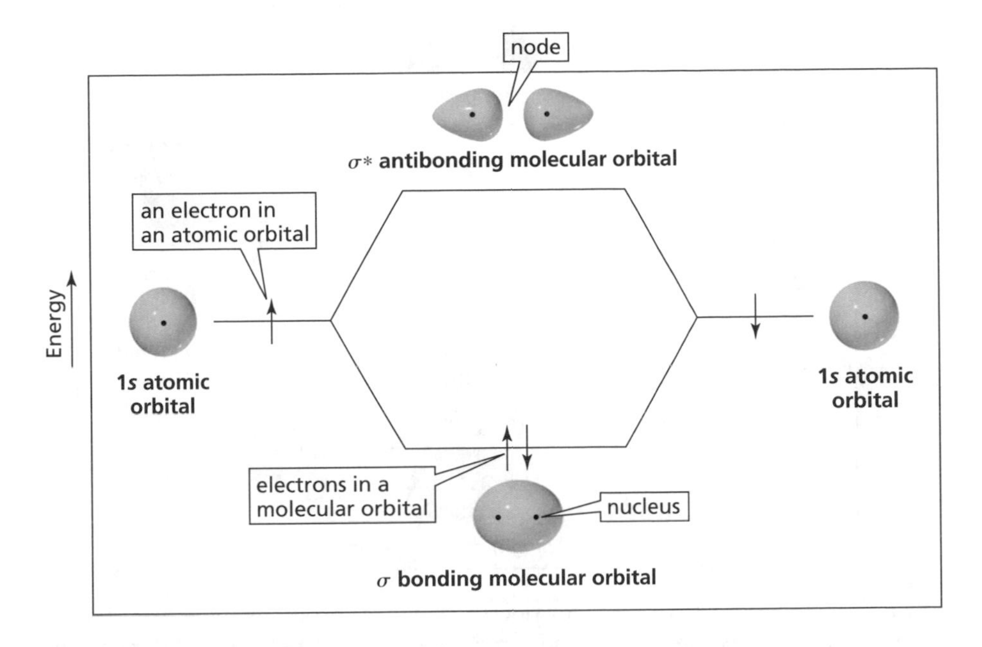

◀ **Figure 10.4**
Atomic orbitals of H· and molecular orbitals of H_2. Before covalent bond formation, each electron is in an atomic orbital. After covalent bond formation, both electrons are in the bonding molecular orbital. The antibonding molecular orbital is empty.

The MO diagram shows that the bonding molecular orbital is lower in energy, and therefore more stable, than the individual atomic orbitals. This is because the more nuclei an electron "feels," the more stable it is. The antibonding molecular orbital, with less electron density between the nuclei, is less stable—is of higher energy—than the atomic orbitals.

When two atomic orbitals overlap, two molecular orbitals are formed—one lower in energy and one higher in energy than the atomic orbitals.

Electrons are assigned to the molecular orbitals using the same rules used to assign electrons to atomic orbitals: electrons always occupy available orbitals with the lowest energy (the aufbau principle), and no more than two electrons can occupy a molecular orbital (the Pauli exclusion principle). Thus, the two electrons of the H—H bond occupy the lower energy bonding molecular orbital (Figure 10.4), where they are attracted to both positively charged nuclei. It is this electrostatic attraction that gives a covalent bond its strength. Therefore, the greater the overlap of the atomic orbitals, the stronger is the covalent bond. *The strongest covalent bonds are formed by electrons that occupy the molecular orbitals with the lowest energy.*

In-phase overlap forms a bonding MO; out-of-phase overlap forms an antibonding MO.

The MO diagram in Figure 10.4 allows us to predict that H_2^+ would not be as stable as H_2 because H_2^+ has only one electron in the bonding orbital. Using the same diagram, we can also predict that He_2 does not exist: because each He atom would bring two electrons, He_2 would have four electrons—two filling the lower energy bonding molecular orbital and the remaining two filling the higher energy antibonding molecular orbital. The two electrons in the antibonding molecular orbital would cancel the advantage to bonding gained by the two electrons in the bonding molecular orbital.

chem place Tutorial: H_2 bond formation

PROBLEM 20 ♦

Predict whether or not He_2^+ exists.

When *p* orbitals overlap, the side of one *p* orbital overlaps the side of the other *p* orbital. The bond that is formed is called a **pi (π) bond**. Side-to-side overlap of two in-phase *p* atomic orbitals (blue lobes overlap blue lobes and green lobes overlap green lobes) forms a π bonding molecular orbital, whereas side-to-side overlap of two out-of-phase *p* orbitals (blue lobes overlap green lobes) forms a π^* antibonding

Side-to-side overlap of two *p* atomic orbitals forms a π bond. All other covalent bonds in organic molecules are σ bonds.

molecular orbital (Figure 10.5). The p bonding molecular orbital has one node—a nodal plane that passes through both nuclei. The antibonding molecular orbital has two nodal planes.

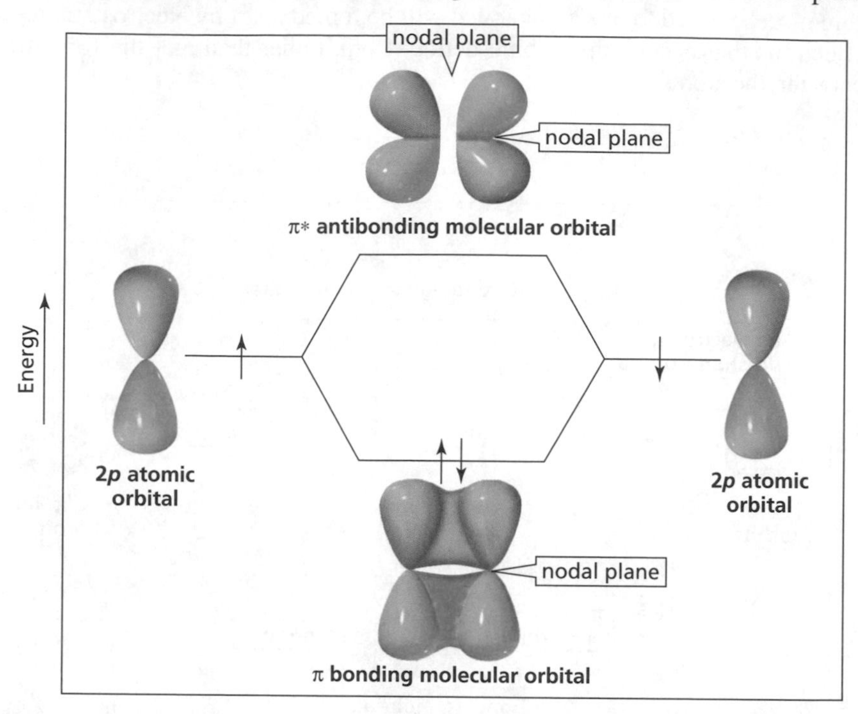

▶ **Figure 10.5**
Side-to-side overlap of two parallel *p* orbitals to form a π bonding molecular orbital and a π* antibonding molecular orbital.

Now let's look at the MO diagram for side-to-side overlap of a *p* orbital of carbon with a *p* orbital of oxygen—the orbitals are the same type, but they belong to different kinds of atoms. When the two *p* atomic orbitals combine to form molecular orbitals, the atomic orbital of the more electronegative atom contributes more to the bonding molecular orbital, and the atomic orbital of the less electronegative atom contributes more to the antibonding molecular orbital (Figure 10.6). This means that if we were to put electrons in the bonding MO, they would be more apt to be around the oxygen atom than around the carbon atom. Thus, both Lewis theory and molecular orbital theory tell us that the electrons shared by carbon and oxygen are not shared equally—the oxygen atom of a carbon–oxygen bond has a partial negative charge and the carbon atom has a partial positive charge.

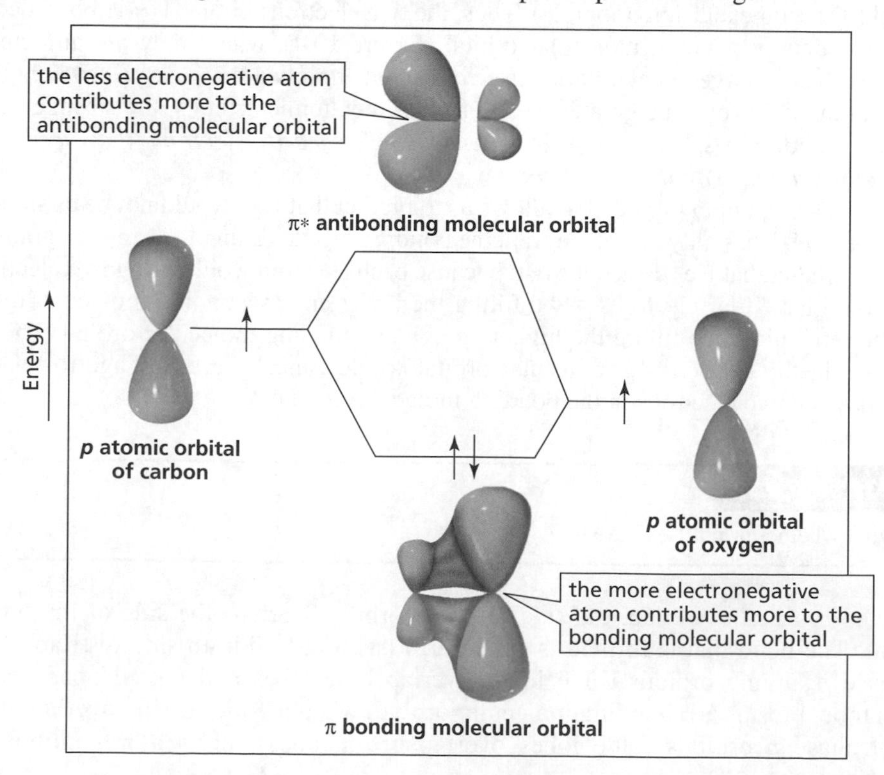

▶ **Figure 10.6**
Side-to-side overlap of a *p* orbital of carbon with a *p* orbital of oxygen to form a π bonding molecular orbital and a π* antibonding molecular orbital.

Organic chemists find that the information obtained from MO theory, where valence electrons occupy bonding and antibonding molecular orbitals, does not always yield the needed information about the bonds in a molecule. The **valence-shell electron-pair repulsion (VSEPR) model** combines the Lewis concept of shared electron pairs and lone-pair electrons with the concept of atomic orbitals and adds a third principle: *the minimization of electron repulsion.* In this model, atoms share electrons by overlapping their atomic orbitals, and because electron pairs repel each other, the bonding electrons and lone-pair electrons around an atom are positioned as far apart as possible. Thus, a Lewis structure gives us a first approximation of the structure of a simple molecule, and VSEPR gives us a first glance at the shape of the molecule.

You can find a more extensive discussion of molecular orbital theory in Special Topic VI in the *Study Guide and Solutions Manual.*

Because organic chemists generally think of chemical reactions in terms of the changes that occur in the bonds of the reacting molecules, the VSEPR model often provides the easiest way to visualize chemical change. However, the model is inadequate for some molecules because it does not allow for antibonding orbitals. We will use both the MO and the VSEPR models in this book. Our choice will depend on which model provides the best description of the molecule under discussion. We will use the VSEPR model in Sections 10.7–10.13.

PROBLEM 21 ♦

Indicate the kind of molecular orbital (σ, σ^*, π, or π^*) that results when atomic orbitals are combined as indicated:

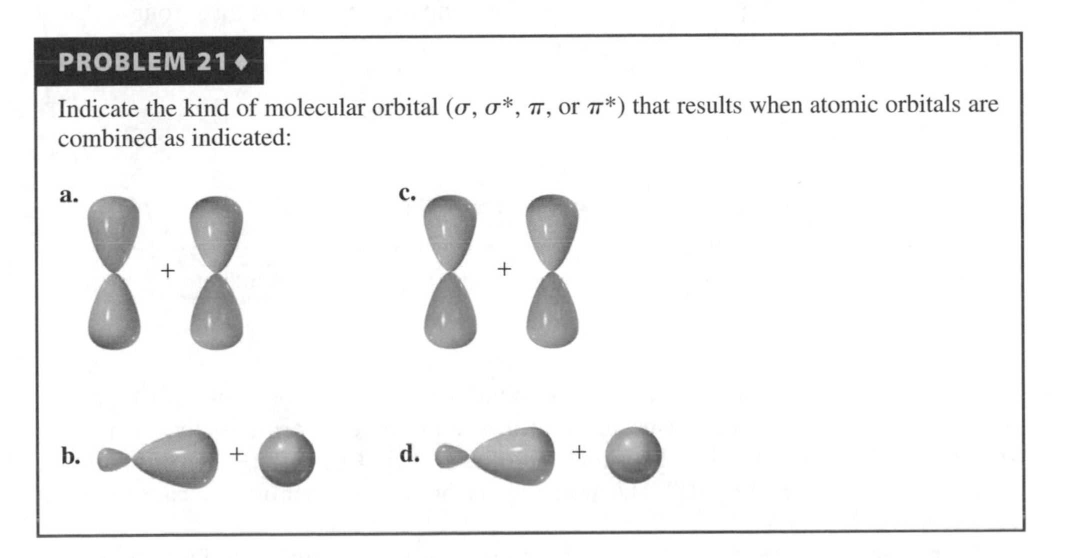

10.7 HOW SINGLE BONDS ARE FORMED IN ORGANIC COMPOUNDS

We will begin the discussion of bonding in organic compounds by looking at the bonding in methane, a compound with only one carbon atom. Then we will examine the bonding in ethane, a compound with two carbons attached by a carbon–carbon single bond.

The Bonds in Methane

Methane (CH_4) has four covalent C—H bonds. Because all four bonds have the same length (1.10 Å) and all the bond angles are the same (109.5°), we can conclude that the four C—H bonds in methane are identical. Four different ways to represent a methane molecule are shown here.

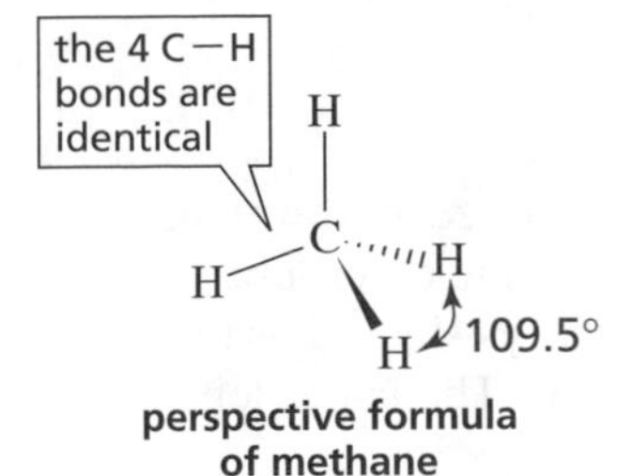

perspective formula of methane

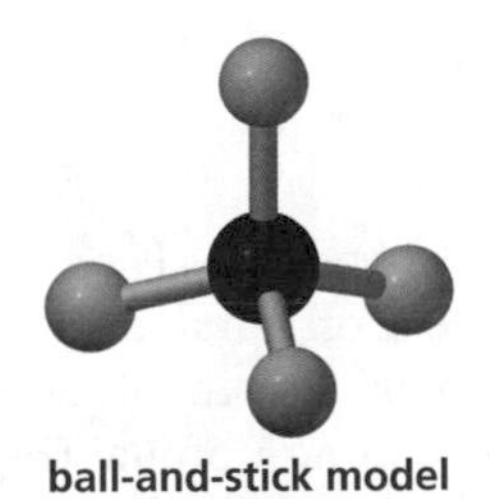
ball-and-stick model of methane

space-filling model of methane

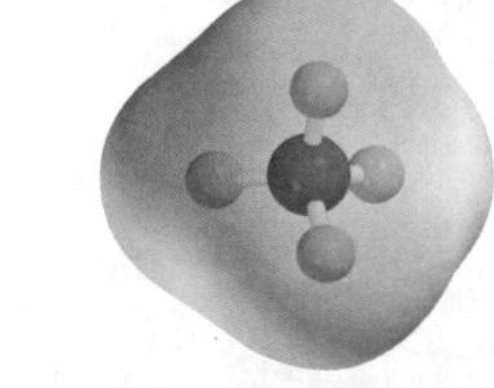
electrostatic potential map for methane

In a **perspective formula**, bonds in the plane of the paper are drawn as solid lines, bonds protruding out of the plane of the paper toward the viewer are drawn as solid wedges, and those projecting back from the plane of the paper away from the viewer are drawn as hatched wedges.

The potential map of methane shows that neither carbon nor hydrogen carries much of a charge: there are neither red areas, representing partially negatively charged atoms, nor blue areas, representing partially positively charged atoms. (Compare this map with the potential map for water on p. 427.) The absence of partially charged atoms can be explained by the similar electronegativities of carbon and hydrogen, which cause them to share their bonding electrons relatively equally. Methane is therefore a **nonpolar molecule**.

You may be surprised to learn that carbon forms four covalent bonds since you know that carbon has only two unpaired electrons in its ground-state electronic configuration (Table 10.2). But if carbon formed only two covalent bonds, it would not complete its octet. We therefore need to come up with an explanation that accounts for carbon's forming four covalent bonds.

If one of the electrons in carbon's 2*s* orbital were promoted into the empty 2*p* orbital, the new electronic configuration would have four unpaired electrons; thus, four covalent bonds could be formed.

But we have seen that the four C—H bonds in methane are identical. How can they be identical if carbon uses an *s* orbital and three *p* orbitals to form these four bonds? Wouldn't the bond formed with the *s* orbital be different from the three bonds formed with *p* orbitals? The four C—H bonds are identical because carbon uses *hybrid orbitals*.

Hybrid orbitals are mixed orbitals that result from combining atomic orbitals. The concept of combining orbitals, called **hybridization**, was first proposed by Linus Pauling in 1931. If the one *s* and three *p* orbitals of the second shell are all combined and then apportioned into four equal orbitals, each of the four resulting orbitals will be one part *s* and three parts *p*. This type of mixed orbital is called an sp^3 (pronounced "*s-p*-three," not "*s-p*-cubed") orbital. (The superscript 3 means that three *p* orbitals were mixed with one *s* orbital—the superscript 1 on the *s* is implied—form the hybrid orbitals.) Each sp^3 orbital has 25% *s* character and 75% *p* character. The four sp^3 orbitals are degenerate—they all have the same energy.

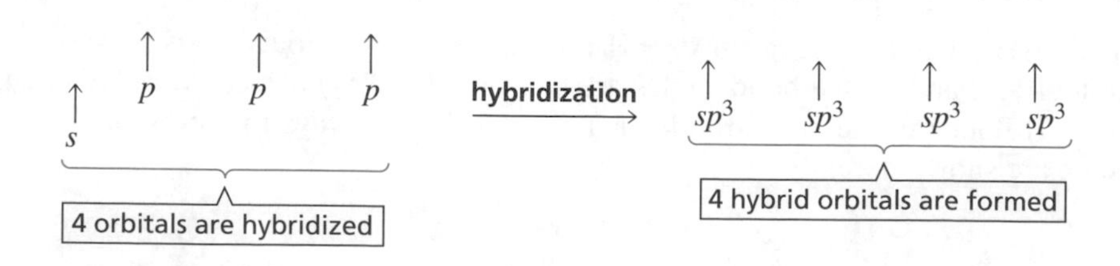

Like a *p* orbital, an sp^3 orbital has two lobes. The lobes differ in size, however, because the *s* orbital adds to one lobe of the *p* orbital and subtracts from the other lobe of the *p* orbital (Figure 10.7). The stability of an sp^3 orbital reflects its composition; it is more stable than a *p* orbital, but not as stable as an *s* orbital (Figure 10.8). The larger lobe of the sp^3 orbital is used in covalent bond formation.

BIOGRAPHY

Linus Carl Pauling (1901–1994) *was born in Portland, Oregon. A friend's home chemistry laboratory sparked Pauling's early interest in science. He received a Ph.D. from the California Institute of Technology and remained there for most of his academic career. He received the Nobel Prize in Chemistry in 1954 for his work on molecular structure. Like Einstein, Pauling was a pacifist, winning the 1962 Nobel Peace Prize for his work on behalf of nuclear disarmament.*

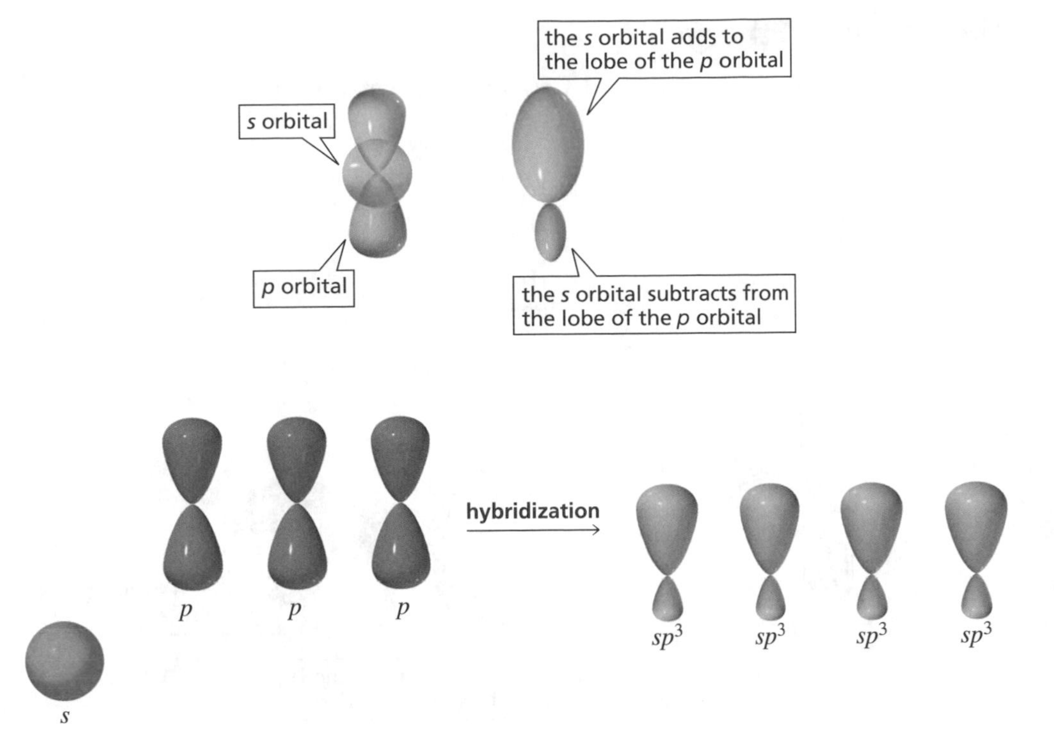

Figure 10.7
The *s* orbital adds to one lobe of the *p* orbital and subtracts from the other lobe of the *p* orbital.

Figure 10.8
An *s* orbital and three *p* orbitals hybridize to form four sp^3 orbitals. An sp^3 orbital is more stable than a *p* orbital, but not as stable as an *s* orbital.

The four sp^3 orbitals adopt a spatial arrangement that keeps them as far away from each other as possible. They do this because electrons repel each other, and moving as far from each other as possible minimizes the repulsion (Section 10.6). When four orbitals move as far from each other as possible, they point toward the corners of a regular tetrahedron—a pyramid with four faces, each an equilateral triangle (Figure 10.9a). Each of the four C—H bonds in methane is formed from overlap of an sp^3 orbital of carbon with the *s* orbital of a hydrogen (Figure 10.9b). This explains why the four C—H bonds are identical.

Electron pairs stay as far from each other as possible.

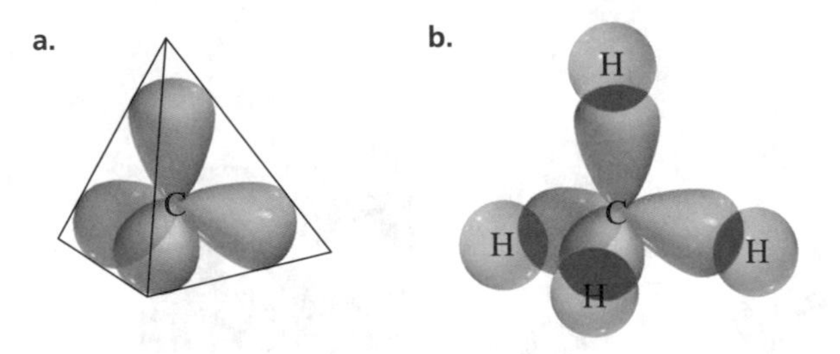

Figure 10.9
(a) The four sp^3 orbitals are directed toward the corners of a tetrahedron, causing each bond angle to be 109.5°.
(b) An orbital of methane, showing the overlap of each sp^3 orbital of carbon with the *s* orbital of a hydrogen. (For clarity, the smaller lobes of the sp^3 orbitals are not shown.)

The angle between any two lines that point from the center to the corners of a tetrahedron is 109.5°. The bond angles in methane therefore are 109.5°. This is called a **tetrahedral bond angle**. A carbon, such as the one in methane, that forms covalent bonds using four equivalent sp^3 orbitals is called a **tetrahedral carbon**.

Hybrid orbital theory may appear to have been contrived just to make things fit—and that is exactly the case. Nevertheless, it gives us a very good picture of the bonding in organic compounds.

NOTE TO THE STUDENT
It is important to understand what molecules look like in three dimensions. Therefore be sure to visit the textbook's website (http://www.chemplace.com) and look at the three-dimensional representations of molecules that can be found in the molecule gallery prepared for each chapter.

The Bonds in Ethane

The two carbon atoms in ethane (CH_3CH_3) are tetrahedral. Each carbon uses four sp^3 orbitals to form four covalent bonds (Figure 10.10):

H H
H—C—C—H
H H
ethane

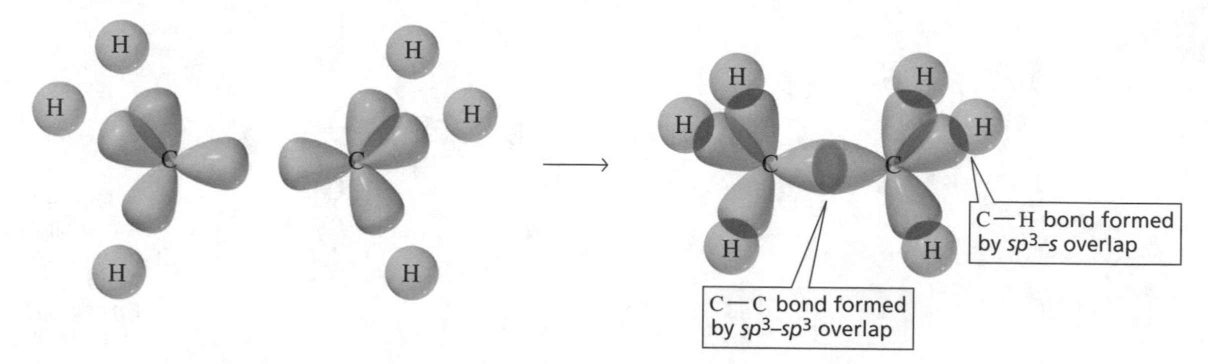

▲ Figure 10.10
An orbital picture of ethane. The C—C bond is formed by sp^3–sp^3 overlap, and each C—H bond is formed by sp^3–s overlap. (The smaller lobes of the sp^3 orbitals are not shown.)

One sp^3 orbital of one carbon overlaps an sp^3 orbital of the other carbon to form the C—C bond. Each of the remaining three sp^3 orbitals of each carbon overlaps the s orbital of a hydrogen to form a C—H bond. Thus, the C—C bond is formed by sp^3–sp^3 overlap, and each C—H bond is formed by sp^3–s overlap. Each of the bond angles in ethane is nearly the tetrahedral bond angle of 109.5°, and the length of the C—C bond is 1.54 Å. Ethane, like methane, is a nonpolar molecule.

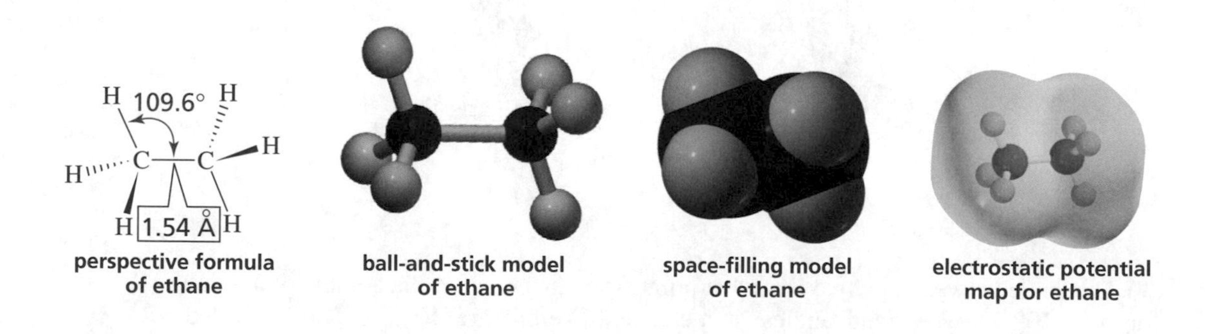

perspective formula of ethane **ball-and-stick model of ethane** **space-filling model of ethane** **electrostatic potential map for ethane**

All single bonds found in organic compounds are sigma bonds.

Sigma bonds are cylindrically symmetrical.

All the bonds in methane and ethane are sigma (σ) bonds because they are all formed by the end-on overlap of atomic orbitals. One bond connecting two atoms is called a **single bond**. *All single bonds found in organic compounds are sigma bonds.*

The MO diagram illustrating the overlap of an sp^3 orbital of one carbon with an sp^3 orbital of another carbon shows that the two sp^3 orbitals overlap end-on (Figure 10.11). End-on overlap forms a cylindrically symmetrical bond that is, therefore, a σ bond (Section 10.6). The electron density of the σ bonding MO is concentrated between the nuclei, which causes the back lobes (the nonoverlapping green lobes) to be quite small.

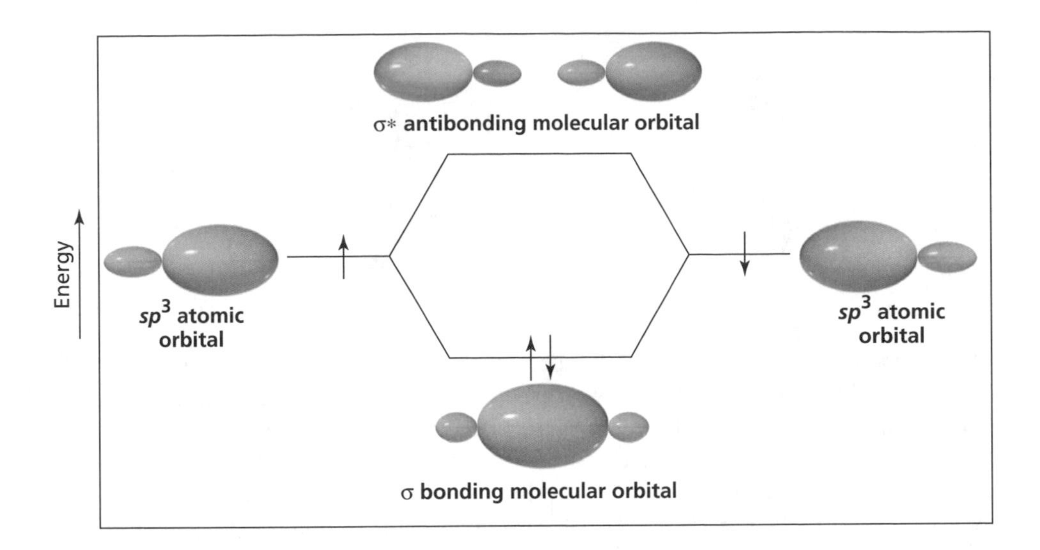

◀ **Figure 10.11**
End-on overlap of two sp^3 orbitals to form a σ bonding molecular orbital and a σ^* antibonding molecular orbital.

PROBLEM 22 ♦

What orbitals are used to form the 10 covalent bonds in propane ($CH_3CH_2CH_3$)?

10.8 HOW A DOUBLE BOND IS FORMED: THE BONDS IN ETHENE

Each of the carbon atoms in ethene (also called ethylene) forms four bonds, but each is bonded to only three atoms:

H₂C=CH₂ (structure)

ethene
ethylene

To bond to three atoms, each carbon hybridizes three atomic orbitals: an *s* orbital and two of the *p* orbitals. Because three orbitals are hybridized, three hybrid orbitals are obtained. These are called sp^2 orbitals. After hybridization, each carbon atom has three degenerate sp^2 orbitals and one unhybridized *p* orbital:

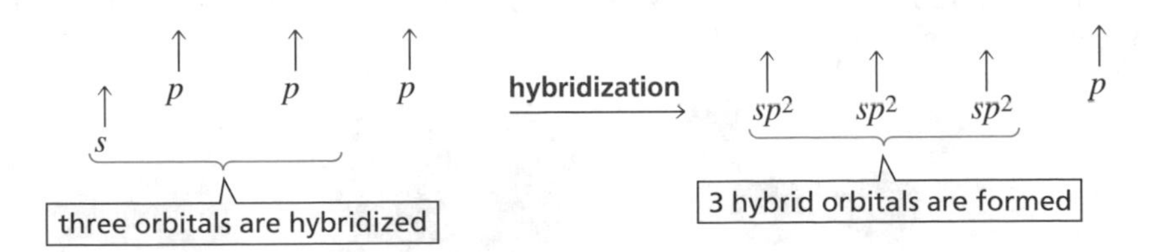

To minimize electron repulsion, the three sp^2 orbitals need to get as far from each other as possible. Therefore, the axes of the three orbitals lie in a plane, directed toward the corners of an equilateral triangle with the carbon nucleus at the center. This means that the bond angles are all close to 120°. Because an sp^2 hybridized carbon is bonded to three atoms that define a plane, it is called a **trigonal planar carbon**. The unhybridized *p* orbital is perpendicular to the plane defined by the axes of the sp^2 orbitals (Figure 10.12).

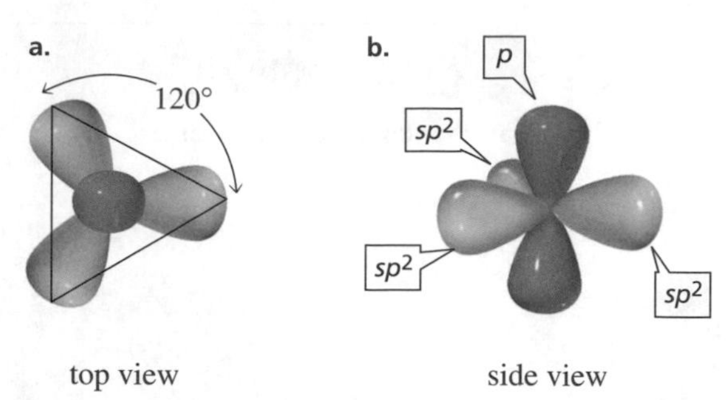

▶ **Figure 10.12**
(a) The three degenerate sp^2 orbitals lie in a plane.
(b) The unhybridized *p* orbital is perpendicular to the plane.
(The smaller lobes of the sp^2 orbitals are not shown.)

The carbons in ethene form two bonds with each other. Two bonds connecting two atoms is called a **double bond**. The two carbon–carbon bonds in the double bond are not identical. One of them results from the overlap of an sp^2 orbital of one carbon with an sp^2 orbital of the other carbon; this is a sigma (σ) bond because it is cylindrically symmetrical (Figure 10.13a). Each carbon uses its other two sp^2 orbitals to overlap the *s* orbital of a hydrogen to form the C—H bonds. The second carbon–carbon bond results from side-to-side overlap of the two unhybridized *p* orbitals. Side-to-side overlap of *p* orbitals forms a pi (π) bond (Figure 10.13b). Thus, one of the bonds in a double bond is a σ bond, and the other is a π bond (Figure 10.13c). All the C—H bonds are σ bonds.

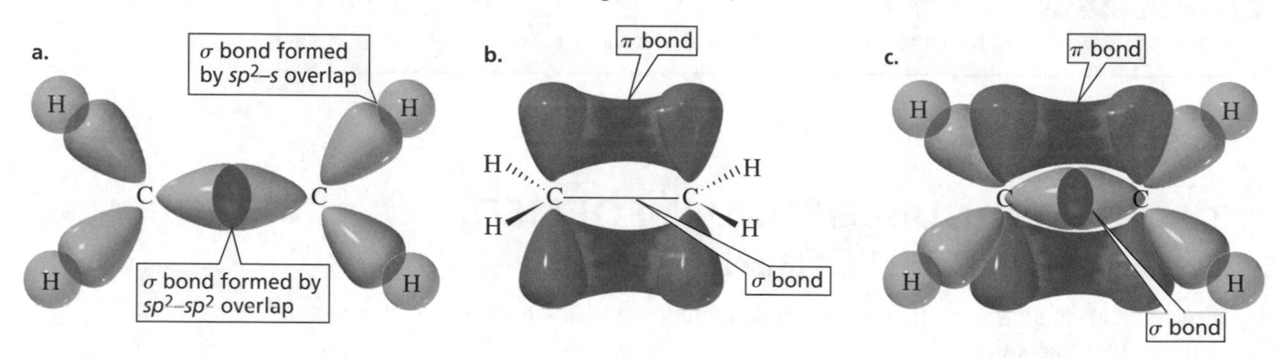

▲ **Figure 10.13**
(a) One C—C bond in ethene is a σ bond formed by sp^2–sp^2 overlap, and the C—H bonds are σ bonds formed by sp^2–s overlap. (b) The second C—C bond is a π bond formed by side-to-side overlap of a *p* orbital of one carbon with a *p* orbital of the other carbon. (c) There is an accumulation of electron density above and below the plane containing the two carbons and four hydrogens.

The two *p* orbitals that overlap to form the π bond must be parallel to each other for maximum overlap to occur. This forces the triangle formed by one carbon and two hydrogens to lie in the same plane as the triangle formed by the other carbon and two hydrogens. As a result, all six atoms of ethene lie in the same plane, and the electrons in the *p* orbitals occupy a volume of space above and below the plane (Figure 10.13c). The potential map for ethene shows that it is a nonpolar molecule with a slight accumulation of negative charge (the pale orange area) above the two carbons. (If you could turn the potential map over to show the hidden side, a similar accumulation of negative charge would be found there.)

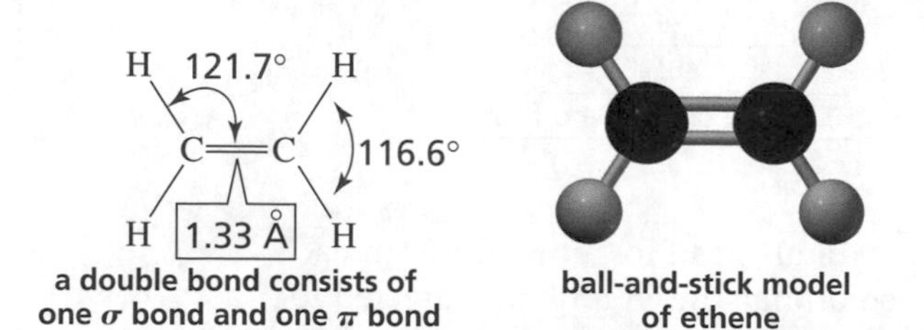

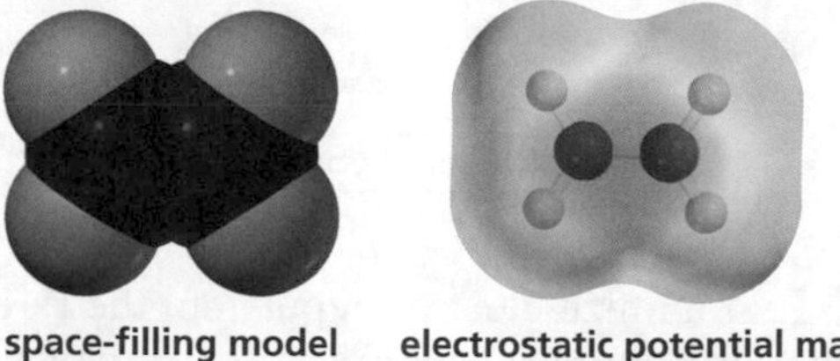

Four electrons hold the carbons together in a carbon–carbon double bond; only two electrons hold the carbons together in a carbon–carbon single bond. With more electrons holding the carbons together, a carbon–carbon double bond is stronger (174 kcal/mol or 728 kJ/mol) and shorter (1.33 Å) than a carbon–carbon single bond (90 kcal/mol or 377 kJ/mol, and 1.54 Å).

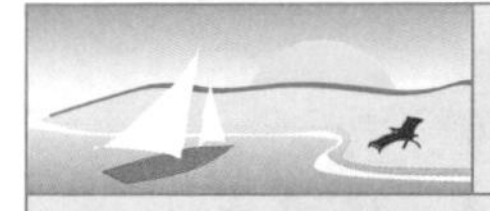

Diamond, Graphite, and Fullerenes: Substances Containing Only Carbon Atoms

The difference that hybridization can make is illustrated by diamond and graphite. Diamond is the hardest of all substances. Graphite, in contrast, is a slippery, soft solid most familiar to us as the "lead" in pencils. Both materials, in spite of their very different physical properties, contain only carbon atoms. The two substances differ solely in the nature of the bonds holding the carbon atoms together.

Diamond consists of a rigid three-dimensional network of carbon atoms, with each bonded to four others via sp^3 orbitals. The carbon atoms in graphite, on the other hand, are sp^2 hybridized, so each bonds to only three other carbons. This trigonal planar arrangement causes the atoms in graphite to lie in flat, layered sheets. Since there are no covalent bonds between the sheets, they can shear off from neighboring sheets.

Diamond and graphite have been known since ancient times—but a third substance found in nature that contains only carbon atoms was discovered just 25 years ago. Like graphite, fullerenes consist solely of sp^2 carbons, but instead of forming planar sheets, the carbons join to form spherical structures.

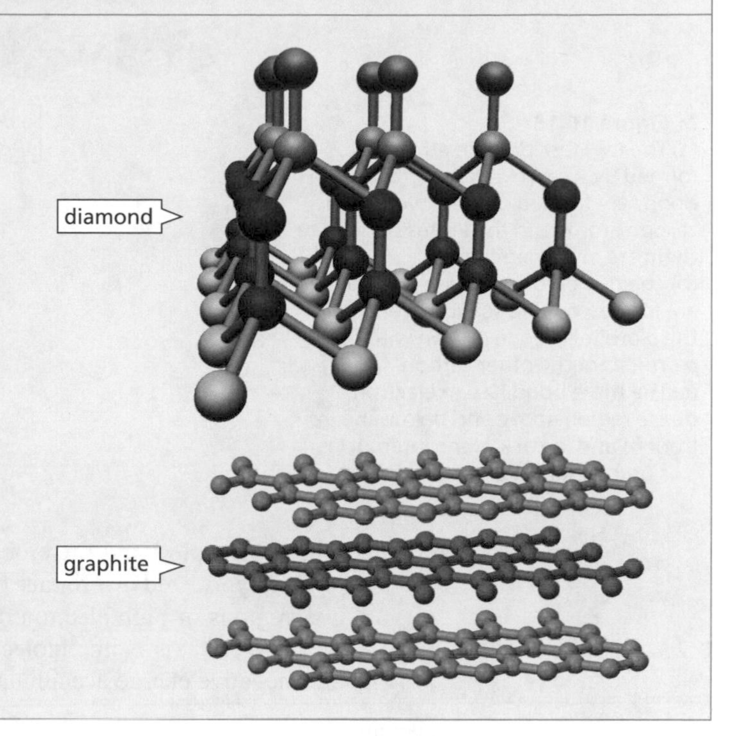

10.9 HOW A TRIPLE BOND IS FORMED: THE BONDS IN ETHYNE

The carbon atoms in ethyne (also called acetylene) are each bonded to only two atoms—a hydrogen and another carbon:

$$H{-}C{\equiv}C{-}H$$

ethyne
acetylene

Because each carbon forms covalent bonds with two atoms, only two of each carbon's orbitals are hybridized: an *s* and a *p*. Two degenerate *sp* orbitals result. Each carbon atom in ethyne, therefore, has two *sp* orbitals and two unhybridized *p* orbitals. To minimize electron repulsion, the two *sp* orbitals point in opposite directions (Figure 10.14).

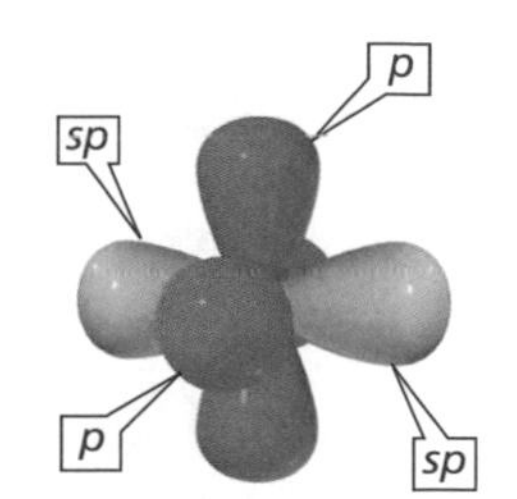

▲ **Figure 10.14**
The two *sp* orbitals are oriented 180° away from each other, perpendicular to the two unhybridized *p* orbitals. (The smaller lobes of the *sp* orbitals are not shown.)

The carbon atoms in ethyne are held together by three bonds. Three bonds connecting two atoms is called a **triple bond**. One of the *sp* orbitals of one carbon in ethyne overlaps an *sp* orbital of the other carbon to form a carbon–carbon σ bond. The other *sp* orbital of each carbon overlaps the *s* orbital of a hydrogen to form a C—H s bond (Figure 10.15a). Because the two *sp* orbitals point in opposite directions, the bond angles are 180°. The two unhybridized *p* orbitals are perpendicular to each other, and both are perpendicular to the *sp* orbitals. Each of the unhybridized *p* orbitals engages in side-to-side overlap with a parallel *p* orbital on the other carbon, with the result that two π bonds are formed (Figure 10.15b).

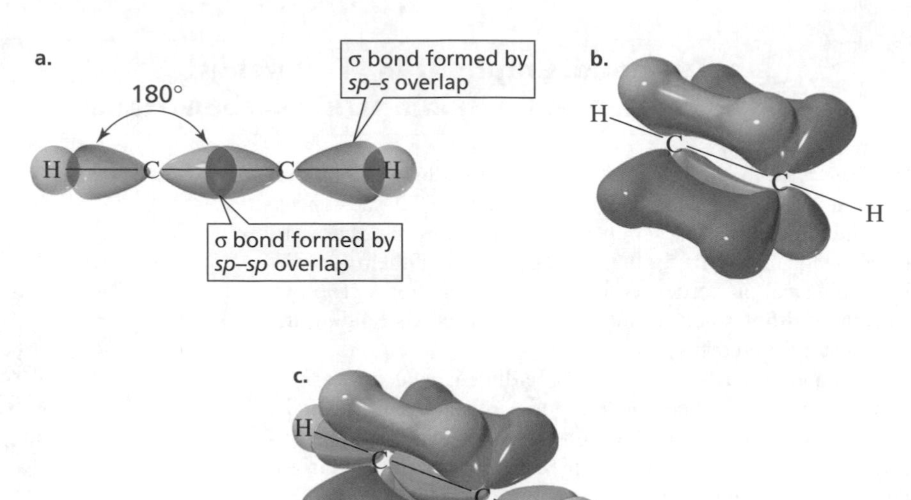

▶ **Figure 10.15**
(a) The C—C σ bond in ethyne is formed by *sp–sp* overlap, and the C—H bonds are formed by *sp–s* overlap. The carbon atoms and the atoms bonded to them are in a straight line.
(b) The two carbon–carbon π bonds are formed by side-to-side overlap of the *p* orbitals of one carbon with the *p* orbitals of the other carbon.
(c) The triple bond has an electron-dense region above and below and in front of and in back of the internuclear axis of the molecule.

A triple bond therefore consists of one σ bond and two π bonds. Because the two unhybridized *p* orbitals on each carbon are perpendicular to each other, they create regions of high electron density above and below *and* in front of and back of the internuclear axis of the molecule (Figure 10.15c). The potential map for ethyne shows that negative charge accumulates in a cylinder that wraps around the egg-shaped molecule.

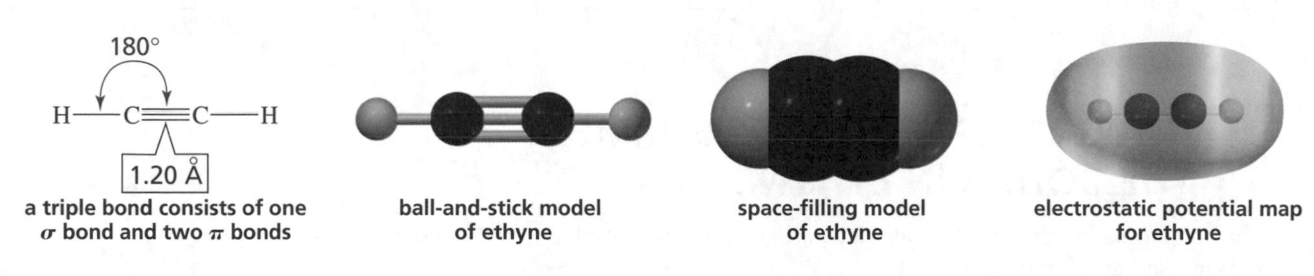

Because the two carbon atoms in a triple bond are held together by six electrons, a triple bond is stronger (231 kcal/mol or 967 kJ/mol) and shorter (1.20 Å) than a double bond (174 kcal/mol or 728 kJ/mol, and 1.33 Å).

PROBLEM 23 SOLVED

For each of the given species:

a. Draw its Lewis structure.
b. Describe the orbitals used by each carbon atom in bonding and indicate the approximate bond angles.

1. HCOH **2.** CCl_4 **3.** CH_3COH **4.** HCN

Solution to 23a1. Our first attempt at a Lewis structure (drawing the atoms in the order given by the condensed structure) shows that carbon is the only atom that does not form the needed number of bonds.

H—C—O—H

If we place a double bond between carbon and oxygen and move an H, all the atoms end up with the correct number of bonds. Lone-pair electrons are used to give each atom a filled outer shell. When we check to see if any atom needs to be assigned a formal charge, we find that none of them does.

:O:
‖
H—C—H

Solution to 23b1. Because the carbon atom forms a double bond, we know that carbon uses sp^2 orbitals (as it does in ethene) to bond to the two hydrogens and the oxygen. It uses its "left-over" p orbital to form the second bond to oxygen. Because carbon is sp^2 hybridized, the bond angles are approximately 120°.

120° 120° 120° (structure of $H_2C{=}O$)

10.10 THE BONDS IN THE METHYL CATION, THE METHYL RADICAL, AND THE METHYL ANION

Not all carbon atoms form four bonds. A carbon with a positive charge, a negative charge, or an unpaired electron forms only three bonds. Now we will see what orbitals carbon uses when it forms three bonds.

The Methyl Cation ($^+CH_3$)

The positively charged carbon in the methyl cation is bonded to three atoms, so it hybridizes three orbitals—an s orbital and two p orbitals. Therefore, it forms its three covalent bonds using sp^2 orbitals. Its unhybridized p orbital remains empty. The positively charged carbon and the three atoms bonded to it lie in a plane. The p orbital stands perpendicular to the plane.

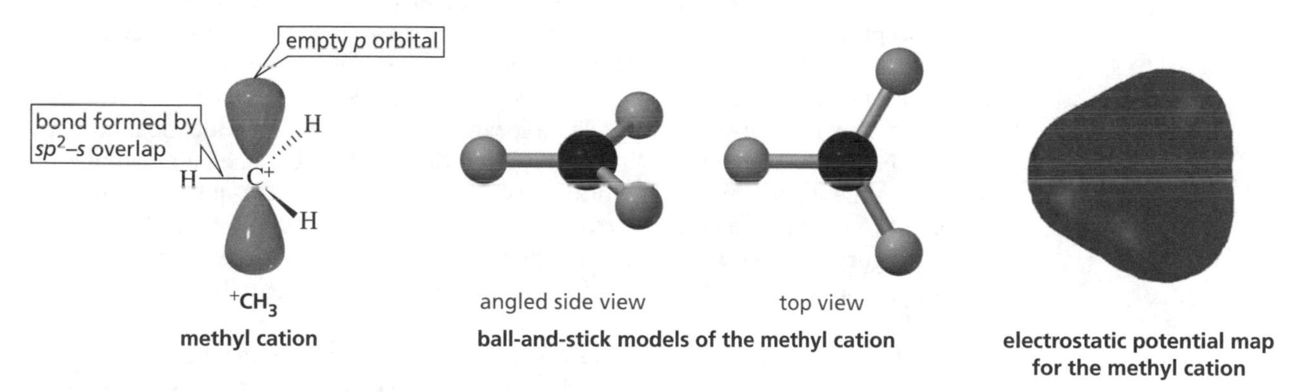

$^+CH_3$
methyl cation

ball-and-stick models of the methyl cation

electrostatic potential map for the methyl cation

The Methyl Radical ($\cdot CH_3$)

The carbon atom in the methyl radical is also sp^2 hybridized. The methyl radical differs by one unpaired electron from the methyl cation. That electron is in the p orbital, with half of the electron density in each lobe. Notice the similarity in the ball-and-stick models of the methyl cation and the methyl radical. The potential maps, however, are quite different because of the additional electron in the methyl radical.

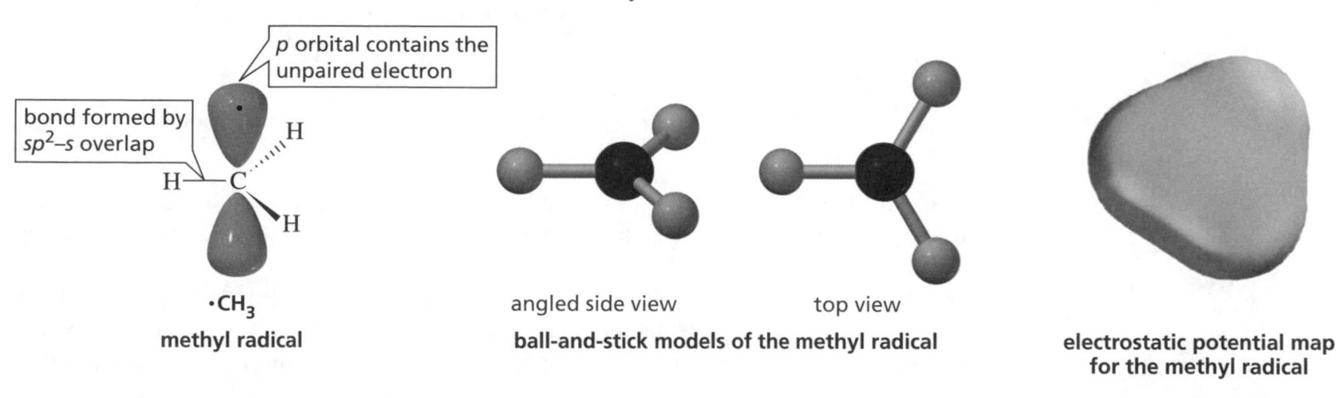

$\cdot CH_3$
methyl radical

ball-and-stick models of the methyl radical

electrostatic potential map for the methyl radical

The Methyl Anion ($\bar{:}CH_3$)

The negatively charged carbon in the methyl anion has three pairs of bonding electrons and one lone pair. The four pairs of electrons are farthest apart when the four orbitals containing the bonding and lone-pair electrons point toward the corners of a tetrahedron. In other words, a negatively charged carbon is sp^3 hybridized. In the methyl anion, three of carbon's sp^3 orbitals each overlap the s orbital of a hydrogen, and the fourth sp^3 orbital holds the lone pair.

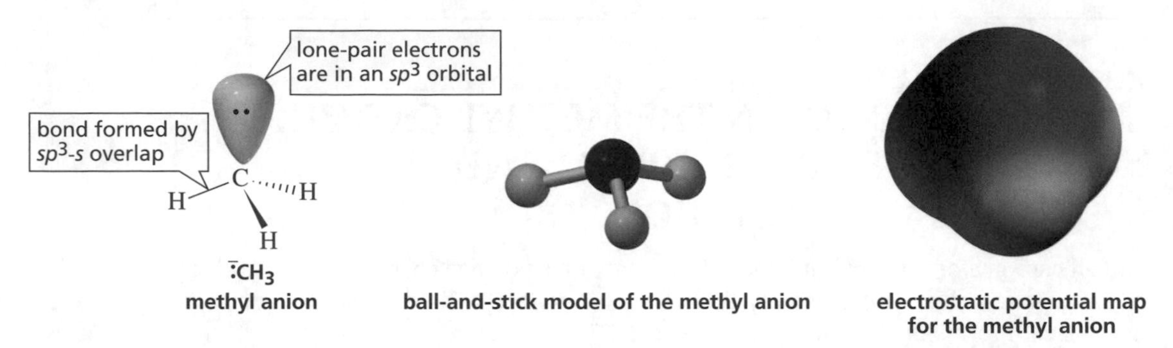

Take a moment to compare the potential maps for the methyl cation, the methyl radical, and the methyl anion.

10.11 THE BONDS IN WATER

The oxygen atom in water (H_2O) forms two covalent bonds. Because the electronic configuration of oxygen shows that it has two unpaired electrons (Table 10.2), oxygen does not need to promote an electron to form the number of covalent bonds (two) required to achieve an outer shell of eight electrons—that is, to complete its octet. But this simple picture presents a problem. Oxygen has two pairs of nonbonding electrons. These two lone pairs are energetically identical, which means that they must be in identical orbitals. However, the electronic configuration of oxygen indicates that one lone pair occupies an s orbital and the other occupies a p orbital, which would make them nonidentical. Furthermore, if oxygen uses p orbitals to form the two O—H bonds, as predicted by its electronic configuration, we would expect a bond angle of about 90° because the two p orbitals are at right angles to each other. However, the experimentally observed bond angle is 104.5°.

The bond angles in a molecule indicate which orbitals are used in bond formation.

The identity of the lone pairs and the observed bond angle can be explained if we assume that oxygen uses hybrid orbitals to form covalent bonds—just as carbon does. The s orbital and the three p orbitals must hybridize to produce four identical sp^3 orbitals.

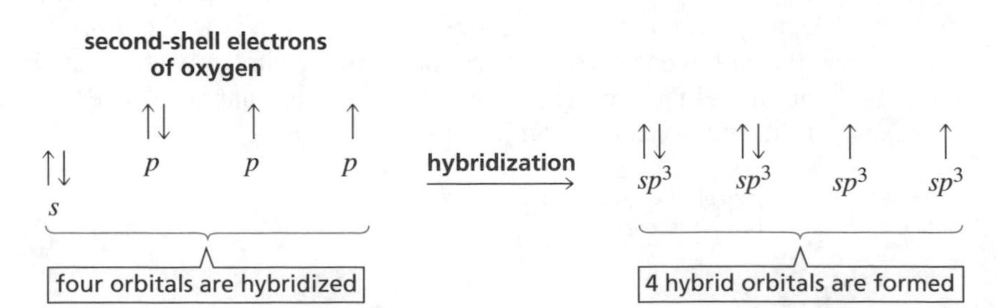

Each of the two O—H bonds is formed by the overlap of an sp^3 orbital of oxygen with the s orbital of a hydrogen. A lone pair occupies each of the two remaining sp^3 orbitals.

The bond angle in water (104.5°) is a little smaller than the bond angle in methane (109.5°) presumably because each of the lone pairs is held by only one nucleus, which makes a lone pair more diffuse than a bonding pair that is shared by two nuclei and is therefore relatively confined between them. Consequently, lone pairs exert more electron repulsion, causing the O—H bonds to squeeze closer together, thereby decreasing the bond angle.

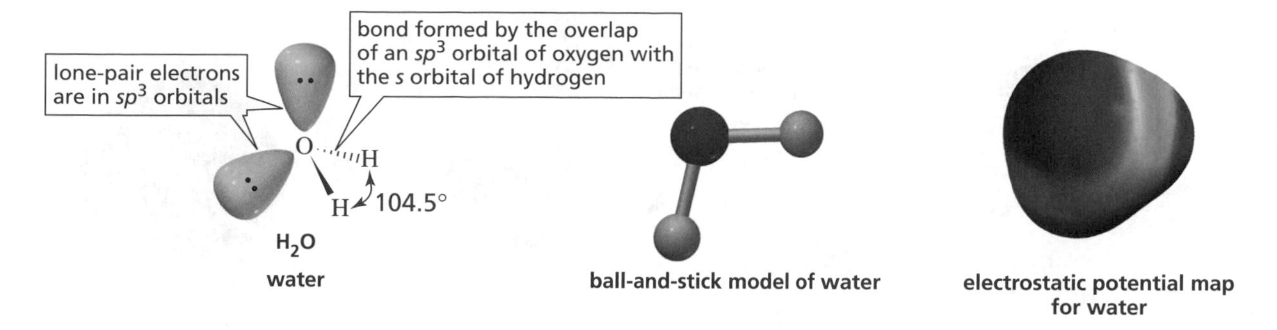

Compare the potential map for water with that for methane. Water is a polar molecule; methane is nonpolar.

PROBLEM 24♦

The bond angles in H_3O^+ are greater than _______ and less than _______.

Water—A Unique Compound

Water is the most abundant compound found in living organisms. Its unique properties have allowed life to originate and evolve. Its high heat of fusion (the heat required to convert a solid to a liquid) protects organisms from freezing at low temperatures because a lot of heat must be removed from water to freeze it. Its high heat capacity (the heat required to raise the temperature of a substance by a given amount) minimizes temperature changes in organisms, and its high heat of vaporization (the heat required to convert a liquid to a gas) allows animals to cool themselves with a minimal loss of body fluid. Because liquid water is denser than ice, ice formed on the surface of water floats and insulates the water below. That is why oceans and lakes don't freeze from the bottom up, and why plants and aquatic animals can survive when the ocean or lake they live in freezes.

10.12 THE BONDS IN AMMONIA AND IN THE AMMONIUM ION

The experimentally observed bond angles in NH_3 are 107.3°. The bond angles indicate that nitrogen also uses hybrid orbitals when it forms covalent bonds. Like carbon and oxygen, the one s and three p orbitals of the second shell of nitrogen hybridize to form four degenerate sp^3 orbitals:

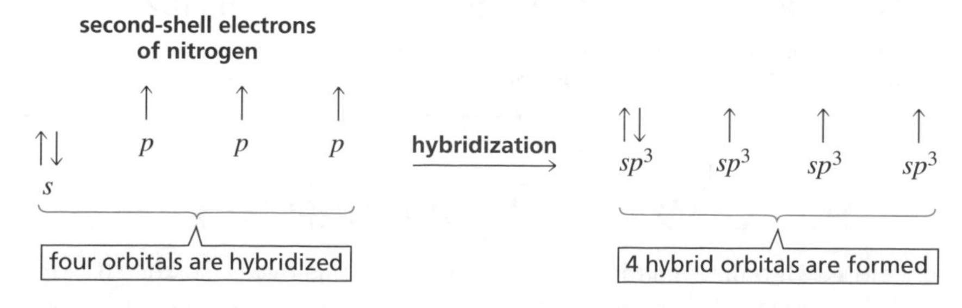

Each of the N—H bonds in NH_3 is formed from the overlap of an sp^3 orbital of nitrogen with the s orbital of a hydrogen. The single lone pair occupies an sp^3 orbital. The bond angle (107.3°) is smaller than the tetrahedral bond angle (109.5°) because of the relatively diffuse lone pair. Notice that the bond angles in NH_3 (107.3°) are larger than the bond angles in H_2O (104.5°) because nitrogen has only one lone pair, whereas oxygen has two lone pairs.

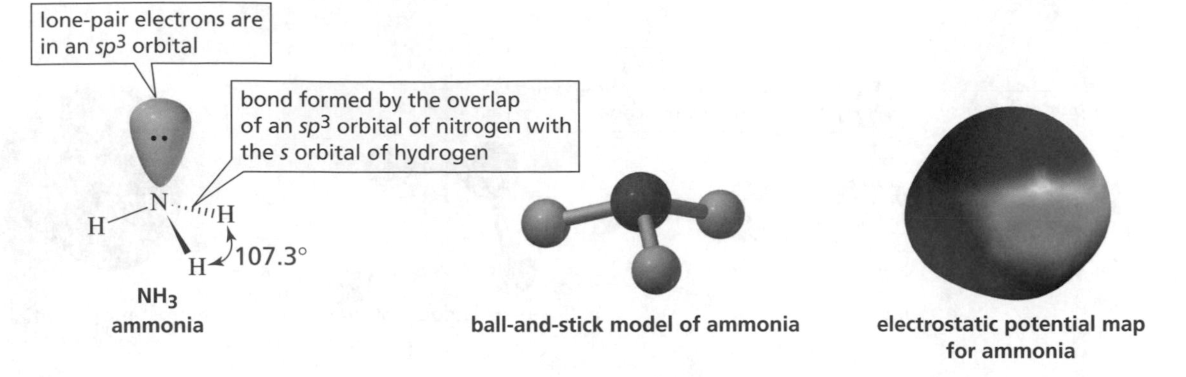

Because the ammonium ion ($^+NH_4$) has four identical N—H bonds and no lone pairs, all the bond angles are 109.5°, just like the bond angles in methane.

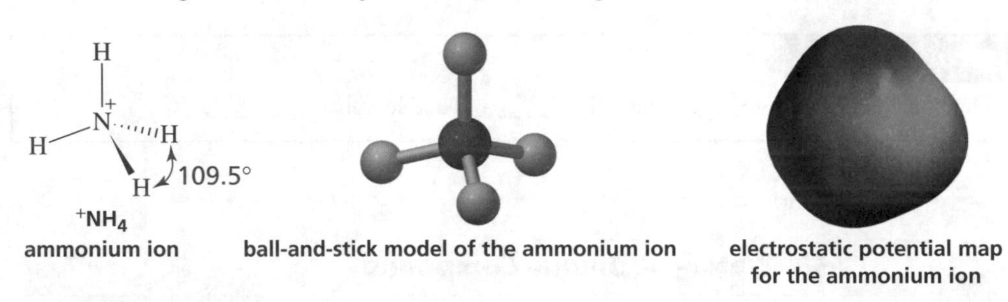

PROBLEM 25 ♦

Predict the approximate bond angles in the methyl carbanion.

PROBLEM 26 ♦

According to the potential map for the ammonium ion, which atom has the greatest electron density?

PROBLEM 27 ♦

Compare the potential maps for methane, ammonia, and water. Which is the most polar molecule? Which is the least polar?

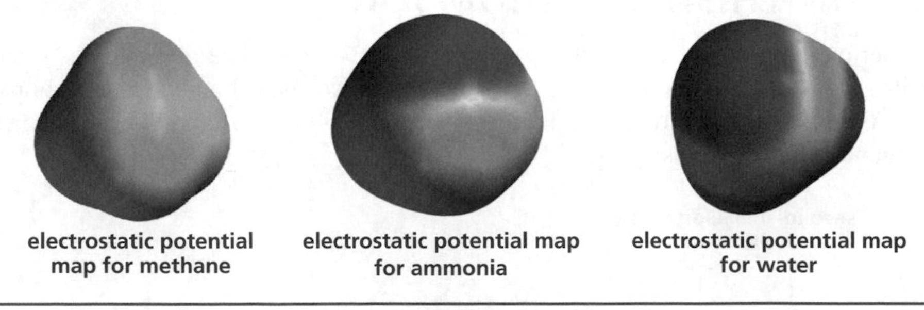

10.13 THE BOND IN A HYDROGEN HALIDE

Fluorine, chlorine, bromine, and iodine are known as the halogens, so HF, HCl, HBr, and HI are called hydrogen halides. Bond angles will not help us determine the orbitals that form a hydrogen halide bond, as they did with other molecules, because hydrogen halides have only one bond and therefore no bond angles. We do know, however, that a halogen's three lone pairs are energetically identical and that lone-pair electrons position themselves to minimize electron repulsion. Both of these observations suggest that the halogen's three lone pairs are in hybrid orbitals. Therefore, we will assume that the hydrogen–halogen bond is formed by the overlap of an sp^3 orbital of the halogen with the *s* orbital of hydrogen.

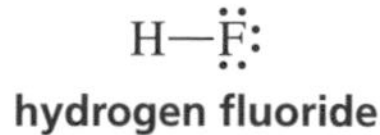

hydrogen fluoride

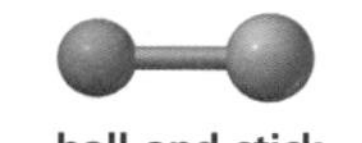

ball-and-stick model of hydrogen fluoride

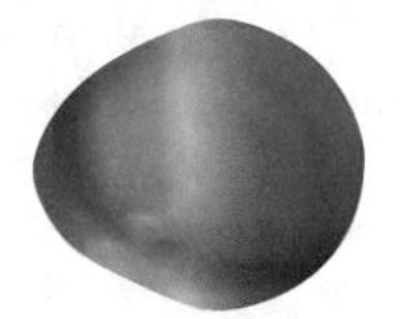

electrostatic potential map for hydrogen fluoride

In the case of fluorine, the sp^3 orbital used in bond formation belongs to the second shell of electrons. In chlorine, the sp^3 orbital belongs to the third shell. Because the average distance from the nucleus is greater for an electron in the third shell than it is for an electron in the second shell, the average electron density is less in a $3sp^3$ orbital than it is in a $2sp^3$ orbital. This means that the electron density in the region where the *s* orbital of hydrogen overlaps the sp^3 orbital of the halogen decreases as the size of the halogen increases (Figure 10.16). Therefore, the hydrogen–halogen bond becomes longer and weaker as the size (atomic weight) of the halogen increases (Table 10.6).

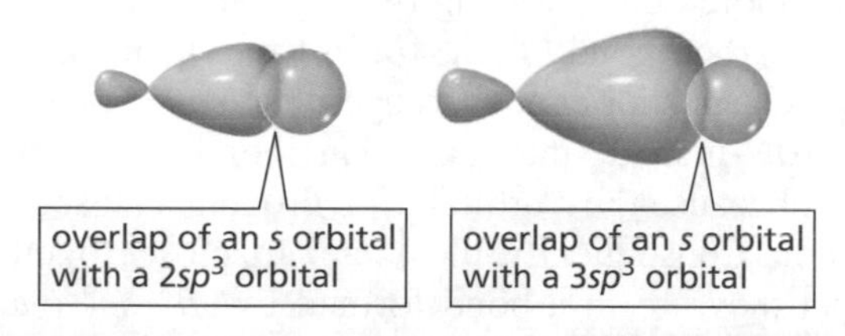

◀ **Figure 10.16**
There is greater electron density in the region of overlap of an *s* orbital with a $2sp^3$ orbital than in the region of overlap of an *s* orbital with a $3sp^3$ orbital.

Table 10.6 Hydrogen–Halogen Bond Lengths and Bond Strengths

Hydrogen halide	Bond length (Å)	Bond strength (kcal/mol)	Bond strength (kJ/mol)
H—F	0.917	136	571
H—Cl	1.2746	103	432
H—Br	1.4145	87	366
H—I	1.6090	71	298

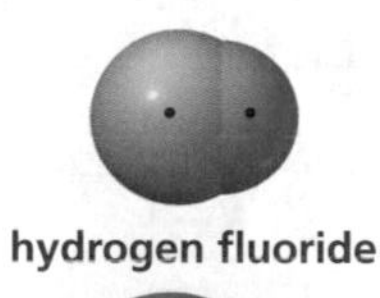

hydrogen fluoride

hydrogen chloride

hydrogen bromide

hydrogen iodide

PROBLEM 28 ♦

a. Predict the relative lengths and strengths of the bonds in Cl_2 and Br_2.
b. Predict the relative lengths and strengths of the carbon–halogen bonds in CH_3F, CH_3Cl, and CH_3Br.

PROBLEM 29 ♦

a. Which bond would be longer?
b. Which bond would be stronger?
1. C—Cl or C—I **2.** C—C or C—Cl **3.** H—Cl or H—F

10.14 SUMMARY: HYBRIDIZATION, BOND LENGTHS, BOND STRENGTHS, AND BOND ANGLES

We have seen that all *single bonds* are σ bonds. All *double bonds* are composed of one σ bond and one π bond. All *triple bonds* are composed of one σ bond and two π bonds. The easiest way to determine the hybridization of a carbon, oxygen, or nitrogen

The hybridization of a C, O, or N is $sp^{(3 \text{ minus the number of } \pi \text{ bonds})}$.

atom is to look at the number of π bonds it forms: if it forms no π bonds, it is sp^3 hybridized; if it forms one π bond, it is sp^2 hybridized; if it forms two π bonds, it is sp hybridized. The exceptions are carbocations and carbon radicals, which are sp^2 hybridized—not because they form a π bond, but because they have an empty or a half-filled p orbital (Section 10.10).

$CH_3—\ddot{N}H_2$: sp^3, sp^3

$(CH_3)_2C=\ddot{N}—\ddot{N}H_2$: sp^3, sp^2, sp^2, sp^3

$CH_3—C≡N:$: sp^3, sp, sp

$CH_3—\ddot{O}H$: sp^3, sp^3

$CH_3C(=\ddot{O})CH_3$: sp^3, sp^2, sp^3; O ← sp^2

$:\ddot{O}=C=\ddot{O}:$: sp^2, sp, sp^2

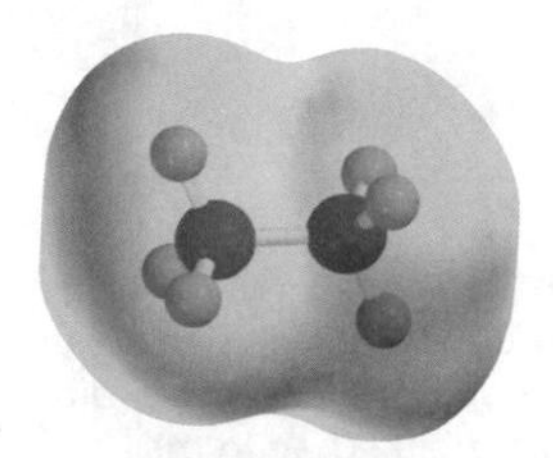

Ethane

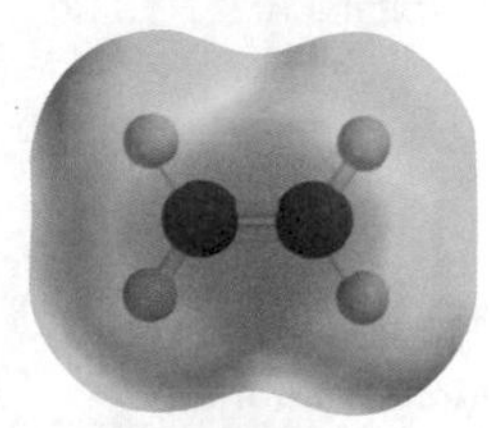

Ethene

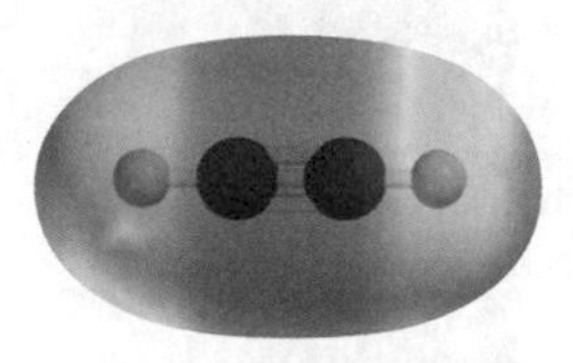

Ethyne

In comparing the lengths and strengths of carbon–carbon single, double, and triple bonds, we see that the more bonds holding two carbon atoms together, the shorter and stronger is the carbon–carbon bond (Table 10.7): triple bonds are shorter and stronger than double bonds, which are shorter and stronger than single bonds.

The data in Table 10.7 indicate that a C—H σ bond is shorter and stronger than a C—C σ bond. This is because the s orbital of hydrogen is closer to the nucleus than is the sp^3 orbital of carbon. Consequently, the nuclei are closer together in a bond formed by sp^3–s overlap than they are in a bond formed by sp^3–sp^3 overlap. In addition to being shorter, a C—H σ bond is stronger than a C—C σ bond because there is greater electron density in the region of overlap of an sp^3 orbital with an s orbital than in the region of overlap of an sp^3 orbital with an sp^3 orbital.

The length and strength of a C—H bond depend on the hybridization of the carbon atom to which the hydrogen is attached. The more s character in the orbital used by carbon to form the bond, the shorter and stronger is the bond—again, because an s orbital is closer to the nucleus than is a p orbital. So a C—H bond formed by an sp carbon (50% s) is shorter and stronger than a C—H bond formed by an sp^2 carbon (33.3% s), which in turn is shorter and stronger than a C—H bond formed by an sp^3 carbon (25% s).

A double bond (a σ bond plus a π bond) is stronger (174 kcal/mol) than a single bond (a σ bond), but it is not twice as strong, so we can conclude that the π bond of a

Table 10.7 Comparison of the Bond Angles and the Lengths and Strengths of the Carbon–Carbon and Carbon–Hydrogen Bonds in Ethane, Ethene, and Ethyne

Molecule	Hybridization of carbon	Bond angles	Length of C—C bond (Å)	Strength of C—C bond (kcal/mol)	Strength of C—C bond (kJ/mol)	Length of C—H bond (Å)	Strength of C—H bond (kcal/mol)	Strength of C—H bond (kJ/mol)
$H_3C—CH_3$ ethane	sp^3	109.5°	1.54	90	377	1.10	101	423
$H_2C=CH_2$ ethene	sp^2	120°	1.33	174	728	1.08	111	466
H—C≡C—H ethyne	sp	180°	1.20	231	967	1.06	131	548

double bond is weaker than the σ bond. Table 10.7 indicates that the strength of a C—C σ bond formed by sp^3–sp^3 overlap is 90 kJ/mol. However, a C—C σ bond formed by sp^2–sp^2 overlap is expected to be stronger because of the greater *s* character in the overlapping orbitals; it has been estimated to be ~112 kcal/mol. We can conclude then, that the strength of the π bond of ethene is about 62 kcal/mol, because $174 - 112 = 62$. We expected the π bond to be weaker than the σ bond because side-to-side overlap that forms a π bond is less effective than the end-on overlap that forms a σ bond (Section 10.6).

The shorter the bond, the stronger it is.

A π bond is weaker than a σ bond.

The bond angle, too, depends on the orbital used by carbon to form the bond. The greater the amount of *s* character in the orbital, the larger is the bond angle. For example, *sp* carbons have bond angles of 180°, sp^2 carbons have bond angles of 120°, and sp^3 carbons have bond angles of 109.5°.

You may wonder how an electron "knows" what orbital it should go into. In fact, electrons know nothing about orbitals. They simply occupy the space around atoms in the most stable arrangement possible. It is chemists who use the concept of orbitals to explain this arrangement.

The greater the electron density in the region of orbital overlap, the stronger the bond.

The more *s* character in an orbital, the shorter and stronger the bond it forms.

The more *s* character in the orbitals, the larger the bond angle they form.

PROBLEM 30 ♦

Which of the bonds in a carbon–oxygen double bond has more effective orbital–orbital overlap, the σ bond or the π bond?

PROBLEM 31 ♦

Would you expect a C—C σ bond formed by sp^2–sp^2 overlap to be stronger or weaker than a C—C σ bond formed by sp^3–sp^3 overlap?

PROBLEM 32

a. What is the hybridization of each of the carbon atoms in the following compound?

$$CH_3\underset{\displaystyle CH_3}{\underset{|}{C}}HCH{=}CHCH_2C{\equiv}CCH_3$$

b. What is the hybridization of each of the carbon and oxygen atoms in the following compounds?

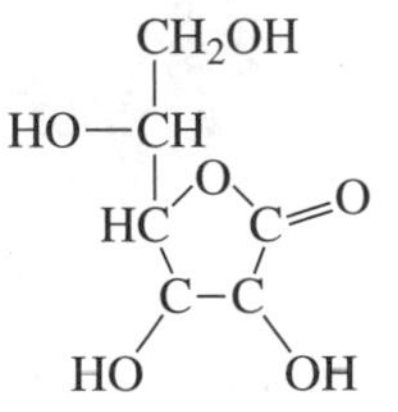

vitamin C

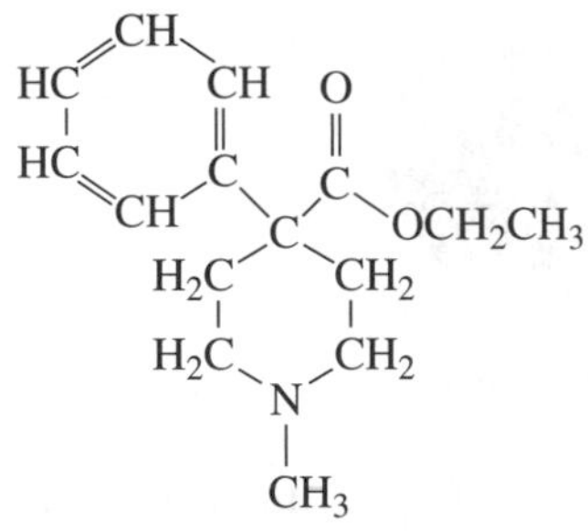

demerol

chem place Tutorial: Hybridization 1

Tutorial: Hybridization 2

PROBLEM-SOLVING STRATEGY

Predicting Bond Angles

Predict the approximate bond angle of the C—N—H bond in $(CH_3)_2NH$.

First we need to determine the hybridization of the central atom (the N). Because the nitrogen atom forms only single bonds, we know it is sp^3 hybridized. Next we look to see if there are lone pairs that will affect the bond angle. A neutral nitrogen has one lone pair. Based on these observations, we can predict that the C—N—H bond angle will be about 107.3°, the same as the H—N—H bond angle in NH_3, another compound with a neutral sp^3 nitrogen.

Now continue on to Problem 33.

PROBLEM 33 ♦

Predict the approximate bond angles:

a. the C—N—C bond angle in $(CH_3)_2\overset{+}{N}H_2$
b. the C—N—H bond angle in $CH_3CH_2NH_2$
c. the H—C—N bond angle in $(CH_3)_2NH$
d. the H—C—O bond angle in CH_3OCH_3

PROBLEM 34

Describe the orbitals used in bonding and the bond angles in the following compounds. (*Hint:* See Table 10.7.)

a. BeH_2
b. BH_3
c. CCl_4
d. CO_2
e. HCOOH
f. N_2

10.15 THE DIPOLE MOMENTS OF MOLECULES

In Section 10.3, we saw that in molecules with one covalent bond, the dipole moment of the molecule is identical to the dipole moment of the bond. When molecules have more than one covalent bond, the geometry of the molecule must be taken into account because both the *magnitude* and the *direction* of the individual bond dipole moments (the vector sum) determine the overall dipole moment of the molecule. Totally symmetrical molecules, therefore, have no dipole moment. For example, let's look at the dipole moment of carbon dioxide (CO_2). Because the carbon is bonded to two atoms, it uses *sp* orbitals to form the C—O σ bonds. The remaining two *p* orbitals on carbon form the two C—O π bonds. The *sp* orbitals form a bond angle of 180°, so the individual carbon–oxygen bond dipole moments cancel each other. Therefore, carbon dioxide has a dipole moment of 0 D. Another symmetrical molecule is carbon tetrachloride (CCl_4). The four atoms bonded to the sp^3 carbon atom are identical and project symmetrically out from the carbon atom. Thus, as with CO_2, the symmetry of the molecule causes the bond dipole moments to cancel. Methane also has no dipole moment.

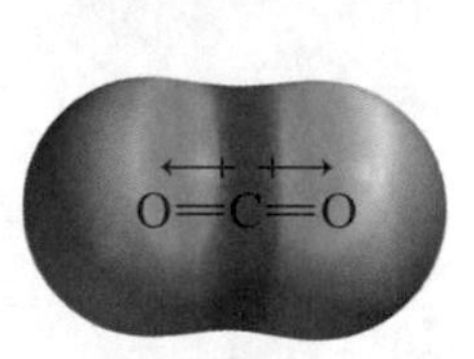

carbon dioxide
μ = 0 D

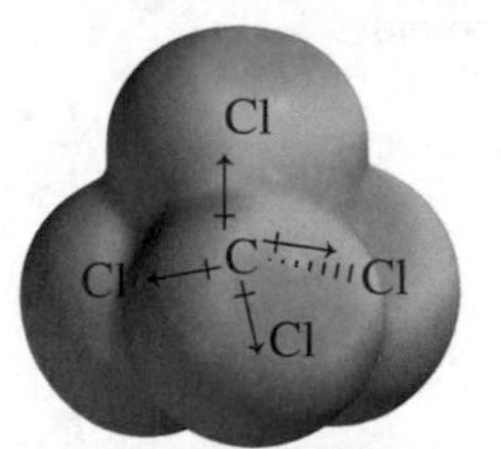

carbon tetrachloride
μ = 0 D

The dipole moment of chloromethane (CH_3Cl) is greater (1.87 D) than the dipole moment of the C—Cl bond (1.5 D) because the C—H dipoles are oriented so that they reinforce the dipole of the C—Cl bond: all the electrons are pulled in the same relative direction. The dipole moment of water (1.85 D) is greater than the dipole moment of a single O—H bond (1.5 D) because the dipoles of the two O—H bonds reinforce each other. The lone-pair electrons also contribute to the dipole moment. Similarly, the dipole moment of ammonia (1.47 D) is greater than the dipole moment of a single N—H bond (1.3 D).

Cl
C
H H H

chloromethane
μ = 1.87 D

O
H H

water
μ = 1.85 D

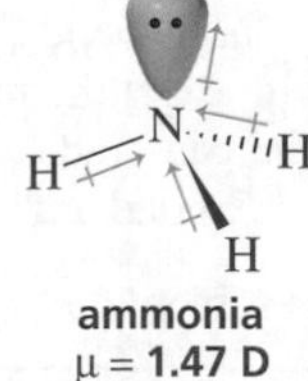

ammonia
μ = 1.47 D

PROBLEM 35 ♦

If the dipole moment of CH_3F is 1.847 D and the dipole moment of CD_3F is 1.858 D, which is more electronegative, hydrogen or deuterium?

PROBLEM 36

Account for the difference in the shape and color of the potential maps for ammonia and the ammonium ion in Section 10.12.

PROBLEM 37 ♦

Which of the following molecules would you expect to have a dipole moment of zero? To answer parts g and h, you may need to consult your answers to Problem 34a and b.

a. CH_3CH_3
b. $H_2C{=}O$
c. CH_2Cl_2
d. NH_3
e. $H_2C{=}CH_2$
f. $H_2C{=}CHBr$
g. $BeCl_2$
h. BF_3

10.16 AN INTRODUCTION TO ACIDS AND BASES

Early chemists called any compound that tasted sour an acid (from *acidus*, Latin for "sour"). Some familiar acids are citric acid (found in lemons and other citrus fruits), acetic acid (found in vinegar), and hydrochloric acid (found in stomach acid—the sour taste associated with vomiting). Compounds that neutralize acids, eliminating their acidic properties, were called bases, or alkaline compounds ("ash" in Arabic is *al kalai*). Glass cleaners and solutions designed to unclog drains are familiar alkaline solutions.

There are two definitions for the terms *acid* and *base,* the Brønsted–Lowry definitions and the Lewis definitions (Section 10.27). According to Brønsted and Lowry, an **acid** is a species that donates a proton, and a **base** is a species that accepts a proton. (Remember that positively charged hydrogen ions are called protons.) In the reaction shown below, hydrogen chloride (HCl) is an acid because it donates a proton to water, and water is a base because it accepts a proton from HCl. Water can accept a proton because it has two lone pairs, either of which can form a covalent bond with a proton. In the reverse reaction, H_3O^+ is an acid because it donates a proton to Cl^-, and Cl^- is a base because it accepts a proton from H_3O^+. The reaction of an acid with a base is called an **acid–base reaction** or a **proton-transfer reaction**. Both an acid and a base must be present in an acid–base reaction, because an acid cannot donate a proton unless a base is present to accept it.

$$\underset{\text{an acid}}{HCl:} + \underset{\text{a base}}{H_2\ddot{O}:} \rightleftharpoons \underset{\text{a base}}{:\ddot{Cl}:^-} + \underset{\text{an acid}}{H_3\ddot{O}^+}$$

Notice that according to the Brønsted–Lowry definitions, *any species that has a hydrogen can potentially act as an acid, and any compound possessing a lone pair can potentially act as a base.*

When a compound loses a proton, the resulting species is called its **conjugate base**. Thus, Cl^- is the conjugate base of HCl, and H_2O is the conjugate base of H_3O^+. When a compound accepts a proton, the resulting species is called its **conjugate acid**. Thus, HCl is the conjugate acid of Cl^-, and H_3O^+ is the conjugate acid of H_2O.

In a reaction between ammonia and water, ammonia (NH_3) is a base because it accepts a proton, and water is an acid because it donates a proton. Thus, HO^- is the conjugate

B I O G R A P H Y

Born in Denmark, **Johannes Nicolaus Brønsted (1879–1947)** *studied engineering before he switched to chemistry, eventually becoming a professor of chemistry at the University of Copenhagen. During World War II, he became known for his anti-Nazi position and consequently was elected to the Danish parliament in 1947. He died before he could take his seat.*

B I O G R A P H Y

Thomas M. Lowry (1874–1936) *was born in England, the son of an army chaplain. He earned a Ph.D. at Central Technical College, London (now Imperial College). He was head of chemistry at Westminster Training College and, later, at Guy's Hospital in London. In 1920, he became a professor of chemistry at Cambridge University.*

base of H_2O, and $^+NH_4$ is the conjugate acid of NH_3. In the reverse reaction, ammonium ion ($^+NH_4$) is an acid because it donates a proton, and hydroxide ion (HO^-) is a base because it accepts a proton.

conjugate base of $^+NH_4$		conjugate acid of HO^-		conjugate acid of NH_3		conjugate base of H_2O
$\ddot{N}H_3$	+	$H_2\ddot{O}:$	⇌	$^+NH_4$	+	$H\ddot{O}:^-$
a base		an acid		an acid		a base

Notice that water can behave as either an acid or a base. It can behave as an acid because it has a proton that it can donate, but it can also behave as a base because it has a lone pair that can accept a proton. In Section 10.19, we will see how we can predict that water acts as a base in the first reaction and acts as an acid in the second reaction.

A strong base has a high affinity for a proton.

Acidity is a measure of the tendency of a compound to give up a proton. **Basicity** is a measure of a compound's affinity for a proton. A strong acid is one that has a strong tendency to give up its proton. This means that its conjugate base must be weak because it has little affinity for the proton. A weak acid has little tendency to give up its proton, indicating that its conjugate base is strong because it has a high affinity for the proton. Thus, the following important relationship exists between an acid and its conjugate base: *the stronger the acid, the weaker is its conjugate base*. For example, since HBr is a stronger acid than HCl, we know that Br^- is a weaker base than Cl^-.

The stronger the acid, the weaker is its conjugate base.

PROBLEM 38 ♦

a. What is the conjugate acid of each of the following?
1. NH_3 **2.** Cl^- **3.** HO^- **4.** H_2O

b. What is the conjugate base of each of the following?
1. NH_3 **2.** HBr **3.** HNO_3 **4.** H_2O

10.17 pK_a AND pH

When a strong acid such as hydrogen chloride is dissolved in water, almost all the molecules dissociate (break into ions), which means that the *products* are favored at equilibrium—the equilibrium lies to the right. When a much weaker acid, such as acetic acid, is dissolved in water, very few molecules dissociate, so the *reactants* are favored at equilibrium—the equilibrium lies to the left. Two half-headed arrows are used to designate equilibrium reactions. A longer arrow is drawn toward the species favored at equilibrium.

$$H\ddot{\underset{..}{Cl}}: + H_2\ddot{O}: \rightleftharpoons H_3\ddot{O}^+ + :\ddot{\underset{..}{Cl}}:^-$$

hydrogen chloride

$$CH_3C(=\ddot{O}:)\ddot{O}H + H_2\ddot{O}: \rightleftharpoons H_3\ddot{O}^+ + CH_3C(=\ddot{O}:)\ddot{O}:^-$$

acetic acid

The degree to which an acid (HA) dissociates in aqueous solution is indicated by the **equilibrium constant** of the reaction, K_{eq}. Brackets are used to indicate the concentration in moles/liter, that is, the molarity (M).

$$HA + H_2O \rightleftharpoons H_3O^+ + A^-$$

$$K_{eq} = \frac{[H_3O^+][A^-]}{[H_2O][HA]}$$

The degree to which an acid (HA) dissociates is normally determined in a dilute solution, so the concentration of water remains nearly constant. The equilibrium expression, therefore, can be rewritten using a new constant called the **acid dissociation constant**, (K_a).

$$K_a = \frac{[H_3O^+][A^-]}{[HA]} = K_{eq}[H_2O]$$

The acid dissociation constant is the equilibrium constant multiplied by the molar concentration of water (55.5 M).

The larger the acid dissociation constant, the stronger is the acid—that is, the greater is its tendency to give up a proton. Hydrogen chloride, with an acid dissociation constant of 10^7, is a stronger acid than acetic acid, with an acid dissociation constant of 1.74×10^{-5}. For convenience, the strength of an acid is generally indicated by its $\mathbf{p}\boldsymbol{K}_\mathbf{a}$ value rather than its K_a value, where

$$pK_a = -\log K_a$$

The pK_a of hydrogen chloride is -7 and the pK_a of acetic acid, a much weaker acid, is 4.76. Notice that *the smaller the* pK_a*, the stronger the acid.*

The stronger the acid, the smaller is its $\mathbf{p}\boldsymbol{K}_\mathbf{a}$ value.

very strong acids	$pK_a < 1$
moderately strong acids	$pK_a = 1-3$
weak acids	$pK_a = 3-5$
very weak acids	$pK_a = 5-15$
extremely weak acids	$pK_a > 15$

Unless otherwise stated, the pK_a values given in this text indicate the strength of the acid *in water*. You see how the pK_a value of an acid is affected when the solvent is changed.

The concentration of positively charged hydrogen ions in a solution is indicated by **pH**. This concentration can be described as either $[H^+]$ or, because a hydrogen ion in water is solvated, as $[H_3O^+]$.

$$pH = -\log[H^+]$$

The lower the pH, the more acidic is the solution. Acidic solutions have pH values less than 7; basic solutions have pH values greater than 7. The pH values of some commonly encountered solutions are shown in the margin. The pH of a solution can be changed simply by adding acid or base to the solution. Do not confuse pH and pK_a: the pH scale is used to describe the acidity of a *solution*; the pK_a is characteristic of a particular *compound*, much like a melting point or a boiling point—it indicates the tendency of the compound to give up its proton. The importance of organic acids and bases will become clear when we discuss how and why organic compounds react.

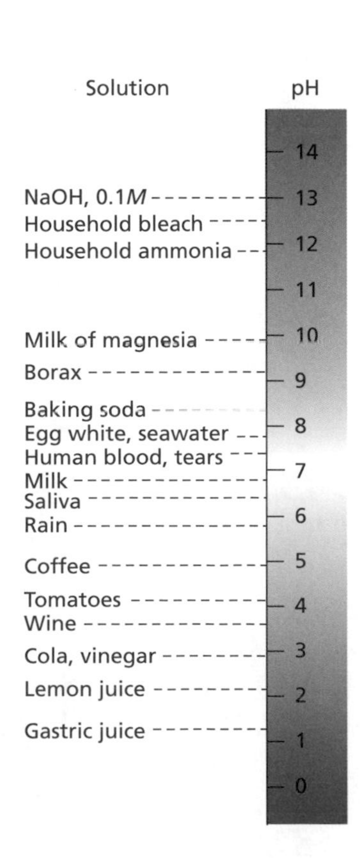

Acid Rain

Rain is mildly acidic (pH = 5.5) because when water reacts with the CO_2 in the air, a weak acid—carbonic acid (pK_a = 6.4)—is formed.

$$CO_2 + H_2O \rightleftharpoons \underset{\text{carbonic acid}}{H_2CO_3}$$

In some parts of the world, rain has been found to be much more acidic—with pH values as low as 4.3. Acid rain is formed where sulfur dioxide and nitrogen oxides are produced, because when water reacts with these gases, strong acids—sulfuric acid (pK_a = −5.0) and nitric acid (pK_a = −1.3)—are formed. Burning fossil fuels for the generation of electric power is the factor most responsible for forming these acid-producing gases.

Acid rain has many deleterious effects. It can destroy aquatic life in lakes and streams; it can make soil so acidic that crops cannot grow; and it can cause the deterioration of paint and building materials, including monuments and statues that are part of our cultural heritage. Marble—a form of calcium carbonate—decays because acid reacts with CO_3^{2-} to form carbonic acid, which decomposes to CO_2 and H_2O, the reverse of the reaction shown to the left.

$$CO_3^{2-} \overset{H^+}{\rightleftharpoons} HCO_3^- \overset{H^+}{\rightleftharpoons} H_2CO_3 \rightleftharpoons CO_2 + H_2O$$

photo taken in 1935

photo taken in 1994

Statue of George Washington in Washington Square Park, in Greenwich Village, New York.

PROBLEM 39 ♦

a. Which is a stronger acid, one with a pK_a of 5.2 or one with a pK_a of 5.8?
b. Which is a stronger acid, one with an acid dissociation constant of 3.4×10^{-3} or one with an acid dissociation constant of 2.1×10^{-4}?

PROBLEM 40 ♦

An acid has a K_a of 4.53×10^{-6} in water. What is its K_{eq}? ($[H_2O]$ = 55.5 M)

PROBLEM-SOLVING STRATEGY

Determining K_a from pK_a

Vitamin C has a pK_a value of 4.17. What is its K_a value?

You will need a calculator to answer this question. Remember that $pK_a = -\log K_a$.

1. Enter the pK_a value on your calculator.
2. Multiply it by −1.
3. Determine the inverse log by pressing the key labeled 10^x.

   You should find that vitamin C has a K_a value of 6.76×10^{-5}.

Now continue on to Problem 41.

PROBLEM 41 ♦

chem place Tutorial: Introduction to Acids

Butyric acid, the compound responsible for the unpleasant odor and taste of sour milk, has a pK_a value of 4.82. What is its K_a value? Is it a stronger or a weaker acid than vitamin C?

PROBLEM 42

Antacids are compounds that neutralize stomach acid. Write the equations that show how Milk of Magnesia, Alka-Seltzer, and Tums remove excess acid.

a. Milk of Magnesia: $Mg(OH)_2$
b. Alka-Seltzer: $KHCO_3$ and $NaHCO_3$
c. Tums: $CaCO_3$

PROBLEM 43 ♦

Are the following body fluids acidic or basic?

a. bile (pH = 8.4) **b.** urine (pH = 5.9) **c.** spinal fluid (pH = 7.4)

10.18 ORGANIC ACIDS AND BASES

The most common organic acids are carboxylic acids—compounds that have a COOH group. Acetic acid and formic acid are examples of carboxylic acids. Carboxylic acids have pK_a values ranging from about 3 to 5. (They are weak acids.) The pK_a values of a wide variety of organic compounds are given in Appendix C.

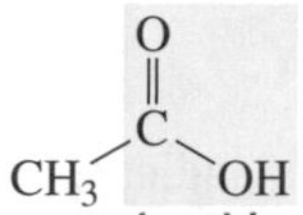

CH_3COOH	$HCOOH$
acetic acid	formic acid
$pK_a = 4.76$	$pK_a = 3.75$

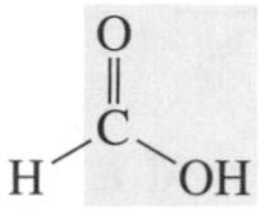

Alcohols—compounds that have an OH group—are much weaker acids than carboxylic acids, with pK_a values close to 16. Methyl alcohol and ethyl alcohol are examples of alcohols.

CH_3OH	CH_3CH_2OH
methyl alcohol	ethyl alcohol
$pK_a = 15.5$	$pK_a = 15.9$

A compound with an NH_2 group is an amine. Amines and ammonia have such high pK_a values that they rarely behave as acids—they are much more likely to act as bases. In fact, they are the most common organic bases.

CH_3NH_2	NH_3
methylamine	ammonia
$pK_a = 40$	$pK_a = 36$

We can assess the strength of a base by considering the strength of its conjugate acid, as indicated by its pK_a value—remembering that the stronger the acid, the weaker is its conjugate base. For example, from their pK_a values we see that protonated methylamine is a stronger acid than protonated ethylamine, which means that methylamine is a weaker base than ethylamine. (A protonated compound is a compound that has gained an additional proton.) Notice that the pK_a values of protonated amines are in the range of 10 to 11.

$CH_3\overset{+}{N}H_3$	$CH_3CH_2\overset{+}{N}H_3$
protonated methylamine	protonated ethylamine
$pK_a = 10.7$	$pK_a = 11.0$

Protonated alcohols and protonated carboxylic acids are very strong acids. For example, protonated methyl alcohol has a pK_a of -2.5, protonated ethyl alcohol has a pK_a of -2.4, and protonated acetic acid has a pK_a of -6.1.

$CH_3\overset{+}{O}H_2$	$CH_3CH_2\overset{+}{O}H_2$	$CH_3C(=\overset{+}{O}H)OH$
protonated methanol	protonated ethanol	protonated acetic acid
$pK_a = -2.5$	$pK_a = -2.4$	$pK_a = -6.1$

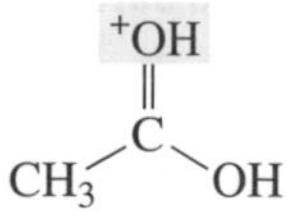

Notice that it is the sp^2 oxygen of the carboxylic acid that is protonated (acquires the proton).

We have seen that water can behave both as an acid and as a base. An alcohol behaves similarly: it can behave as an acid and donate a proton, or as a base and accept a proton.

a curved arrow indicates where the electrons start from and where they end up

new bond

a curved arrow indicates where the electrons start from and where they end up

$$CH_3\ddot{O}{-}H + H{-}\ddot{O}{:}^- \rightleftharpoons CH_3\ddot{O}{:}^- + H{-}\ddot{O}{-}H$$

an acid

$$CH_3\ddot{O}{-}H + H{-}\ddot{O}^+{-}H \;(\text{with } H) \rightleftharpoons CH_3\ddot{O}^+{-}H \;(\text{with } H) + H{-}\ddot{O}{-}H$$

a base

new bond

Chemists frequently use curved arrows to indicate the bonds that are broken and formed as reactants are converted into products. The arrows show where the electrons start from and where they end up. In an acid–base reaction, one arrow is drawn *from* a lone pair on the base (the tail of the arrow) *to* the proton of the acid (the point of the arrow). A second arrow is drawn *from* the electrons that the proton shared *to* the atom on which they are left behind. These are called "curved" arrows to distinguish them from the "straight" arrows used to link reactants with products in the equation for a chemical reaction. Notice that the curved arrows let you follow the electrons to see how bonds are being formed and broken.

A carboxylic acid also can behave as an acid and donate a proton, or as a base and accept a proton.

$$CH_3C(=\ddot{O}{:})\ddot{O}{-}H + H{-}\ddot{O}{:}^- \rightleftharpoons CH_3C(=\ddot{O}{:})\ddot{O}{:}^- + H{-}\ddot{O}{-}H$$

an acid

$$CH_3C(=\ddot{O}{:})\ddot{O}{-}H + H{-}\ddot{O}^+{-}H \;(\text{with } H) \rightleftharpoons CH_3C(={}^+\ddot{O}{-}H)O{-}H + H{-}\ddot{O}{-}H$$

a base

Similarly, an amine can behave as an acid and donate a proton, or as a base and accept a proton.

$$CH_3\ddot{N}H{-}H + H{-}\ddot{O}^- \rightleftharpoons CH_3\ddot{N}H^- + H{-}\ddot{O}{-}H$$

an acid

$$CH_3\ddot{N}H{-}H + H{-}\ddot{O}^+{-}H \;(\text{with } H) \rightleftharpoons CH_3\overset{+}{N}H_3 + H{-}\ddot{O}{-}H$$

a base

It is important to know the approximate pK_a values of the various classes of compounds we have discussed. An easy way to remember them is in units of five, as shown in Table 10.8. (R is used when the particular carboxylic acid, alcohol, or amine is not specified.) Protonated alcohols, protonated carboxylic acids, and protonated water have pK_a values less than 0, carboxylic acids have pK_a values of about 5, protonated amines have pK_a values of about 10, and alcohols and water have pK_a values of about 15.

Be sure to learn the approximate pK_a values given in Table 10.8.

Table 10.8 Approximate pK_a Values

$pK_a < 0$	$pK_a \sim 5$	$pK_a \sim 10$	$pK_a \sim 15$
$R\overset{+}{O}H_2$ a protonated alcohol	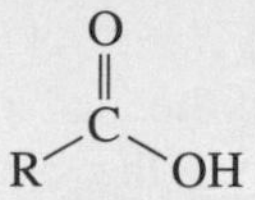 $RC(=O)OH$ a carboxylic acid	$R\overset{+}{N}H_3$ a protonated amine	ROH an alcohol
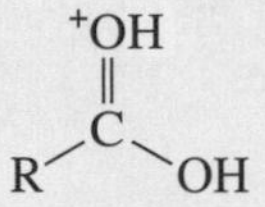 $RC(={}^{+}OH)OH$ a protonated carboxylic acid			H_2O water
H_3O^+ protonated water			

PROBLEM 44 ♦

Draw the conjugate acid of each of the following:

a. CH_3CH_2OH b. $CH_3CH_2O^-$ c. $CH_3CH_2NH_2$ d. 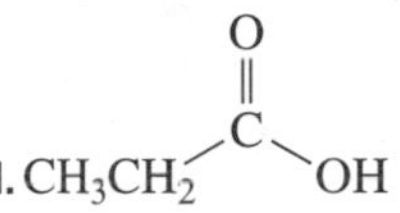 $CH_3CH_2C(=O)OH$

PROBLEM 45 ♦

a. Which is a stronger base, CH_3COO^- or $HCOO^-$? (The pK_a of CH_3COOH is 4.8; the pK_a of HCOOH is 3.8.)

b. Which is a stronger base, HO^- or $^-NH_2$? (The pK_a of H_2O is 15.7; the pK_a of NH_3 is 36.)

c. Which is a stronger base, H_2O or CH_3OH? (The pK_a of H_3O^+ is -1.7; the pK_a of $CH_3\overset{+}{O}H_2$ is -2.5.)

PROBLEM 46 ♦

Using the pK_a values in Section 10.18, rank the following species in order of decreasing base strength (that is, list the strongest base first):

CH_3NH_2 CH_3NH^- CH_3OH CH_3O^- $CH_3C(=O)O^-$

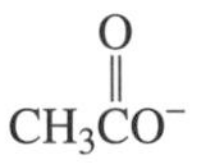

chem place Tutorial: Important pK_a values

10.19 HOW TO PREDICT THE OUTCOME OF AN ACID–BASE REACTION

Now let's see how we can predict that water will act as a base in the first reaction in Section 10.16 and as an acid in the second reaction. To determine which of two reactants will be the acid, we need to compare their pK_a values: in the first reaction, the pK_a of hydrogen chloride is -7 and the pK_a of water is 15.7. Because hydrogen chloride is the stronger acid, it will donate a proton to water. Water, therefore, is a base in this reaction. When we compare the pK_a values of the two reactants of the second reaction, we see that the pK_a of ammonia is 36 and the pK_a of water is 15.7. In this case, water is the stronger acid, so it donates a proton to ammonia. Water, therefore, is an acid in this reaction.

$$\underset{pK_a = -7}{\underset{\text{this is the acid}}{HCl}} + \underset{pK_a = 15.7}{H_2O} \qquad\qquad \underset{pK_a = 36}{NH_3} + \underset{pK_a = 15.7}{\underset{\text{this is the acid}}{H_2O}}$$

10.20 HOW TO DETERMINE THE POSITION OF EQUILIBRIUM

Strong reacts to form weak.

To determine the position of equilibrium for an acid–base reaction (that is, whether reactants or products are favored at equilibrium), we need to compare the pK_a value of the acid on the left of the arrow with the pK_a value of the acid on the right of the arrow. The equilibrium favors *reaction* of the stronger acid (the one with the lower pK_a) and *formation* of the weaker acid (the one with the higher pK_a). In other words, *strong reacts to form weak.* Thus, the equilibrium lies away from the stronger acid and toward the weaker acid. Notice that the stronger acid has the weaker conjugate base.

$$\underset{\substack{\textbf{stronger acid} \\ pK_a = 4.8}}{CH_3C(=O)OH} + \underset{\textbf{stronger base}}{NH_3} \rightleftharpoons \underset{\textbf{weaker base}}{CH_3C(=O)O^-} + \underset{\substack{\textbf{weaker acid} \\ pK_a = 9.4}}{\overset{+}{N}H_4}$$

$$\underset{\substack{\textbf{weaker acid} \\ pK_a = 15.9}}{CH_3CH_2OH} + \underset{\textbf{weaker base}}{CH_3NH_2} \rightleftharpoons \underset{\textbf{stronger base}}{CH_3CH_2O^-} + \underset{\substack{\textbf{stronger acid} \\ pK_a = 10.7}}{CH_3\overset{+}{N}H_3}$$

PROBLEM 47

a. Write an equation showing CH_3OH reacting as an acid with NH_3 and an equation showing it reacting as a base with HCl.
b. Write an equation showing NH_3 reacting as an acid with CH_3O^- and an equation showing it reacting as a base with HBr.

PROBLEM 48

a. For each of the acid–base reactions in Section 10.18, compare the pK_a values of the acids on either side of the equilibrium arrows to prove that the equilibrium lies in the direction indicated. (The pK_a values you need can be found in Section 10.18 or in Problem 45.)
b. Do the same for the equilibria in Section 10.16. (The pK_a of $^+NH_4$ is 9.4.)

PROBLEM 49

Ethyne has a pK_a value of 25, water has a pK_a value of 15.7, and ammonia (NH_3) has a pK_a value of 36. Draw the equation, showing equilibrium arrows that indicate whether reactants or products are favored, for the acid–base reaction of ethyne with:

a. HO^- **b.** $^-NH_2$
c. Which would be a better base to use if you wanted to remove a proton from ethyne, HO^- or $^-NH_2$?

The precise value of the equilibrium constant can be calculated by dividing the K_a of the reactant acid by the K_a of the product acid.

$$K_{eq} = \frac{K_a \text{ reactant acid}}{K_a \text{ product acid}}$$

Thus, the equilibrium constant for the reaction of acetic acid with ammonia is 4.0×10^4, and the equilibrium constant for the reaction of ethyl alcohol with methylamine is 6.3×10^{-6}. The calculations are:

for the reaction of acetic acid with ammonia:

$$K_{eq} = \frac{10^{-4.8}}{10^{-9.4}} = 10^{4.6} = 4.0 \times 10^4$$

for the reaction of ethyl alcohol with methylamine:

$$K_{eq} = \frac{10^{-15.9}}{10^{-10.7}} = 10^{-5.2} = 6.3 \times 10^{-6}$$

PROBLEM 50♦

Calculate the equilibrium constant for the acid–base reaction between the reactants in each of the following pairs:

a. $HCl + H_2O$
b. $CH_3COOH + H_2O$
c. $CH_3NH_2 + H_2O$
d. $CH_3\overset{+}{N}H_3 + H_2O$

chem place Tutorial: Acid-Base Reaction

10.21 HOW THE STRUCTURE OF AN ACID AFFECTS ITS pK_a VALUE

The strength of an acid is determined by the stability of the conjugate base formed when the acid gives up its proton: the more stable the base, the stronger is its conjugate acid. A stable base is a base that readily bears the electrons it formerly shared with a proton. In other words, stable bases are weak bases—they do not share their electrons well—allowing us to say, *the weaker the base, the stronger is its conjugate acid*, or *the more stable the base, the stronger is its conjugate acid.*

The weaker the base, the stronger is its conjugate acid.

Stable bases are weak bases.

The more stable the base, the stronger is its conjugate acid.

Electronegativity

Two factors that affect the stability of a base are its *electronegativity* and its size. The atoms in the second row of the periodic table are all similar in size, but they have very different electronegativities, which increase across the row from left to right. Of the atoms shown, carbon is the least electronegative and fluorine is the most electronegative.

relative electronegativities: C < N < O < F (most electronegative)

If we look at the acids formed by attaching hydrogens to these elements, we see that the most acidic compound is the one that has its hydrogen attached to the most electronegative atom. Thus, HF is the strongest acid and methane is the weakest acid.

relative acidities: $CH_4 < NH_3 < H_2O < HF$ (strongest acid)

If we look at the stabilities of the conjugate bases of these acids, we find that they too increase from left to right because the more electronegative the atom, the better it can bear its negative charge. Thus, we see that the strongest acid has the most stable (most electronegative) conjugate base.

relative stabilities: $^-CH_3 < {}^-NH_2 < HO^- < F^-$ (most stable)

We therefore can conclude that *when the atoms are similar in size, the strongest acid will have its hydrogen attached to the most electronegative atom.*

When atoms are similar in size, the strongest acid will have its hydrogen attached to the most electronegative atom.

The effect that the electronegativity of the atom bonded to a hydrogen has on the acidity of that hydrogen can be appreciated when the pK_a values of alcohols and amines are compared. Because oxygen is more electronegative than nitrogen, an alcohol is more acidic than an amine.

CH_3OH	CH_3NH_2
methyl alcohol	methylamine
pK_a = 15.5	pK_a = 40

Similarly, a protonated alcohol is more acidic than a protonated amine.

$CH_3\overset{+}{O}H_2$	$CH_3\overset{+}{N}H_3$
protonated methyl alcohol	**protonated methylamine**
pK_a = −2.5	**pK_a = 10.7**

Hybridization

An *sp* carbon is more electronegative than an sp^2 carbon, which is more electronegative than an sp^3 carbon.

The hybridization of an atom affects the acidity of a hydrogen bonded to the atom because its hybridization affects its electronegativity: an *sp* hybridized atom is more electronegative than the same atom that is sp^2 hybridized, which is more electronegative than the same atom that is sp^3 hybridized.

relative electronegativities of carbon atoms

most electronegative $sp > sp^2 > sp^3$ least electronegative

Because the electronegativity of carbon atoms follows the order $sp > sp^2 > sp^3$, ethyne is a stronger acid than ethene, and ethene is a stronger acid than ethane—the most acidic compound is the one with the hydrogen attached to the most electronegative atom.

most acidic			least acidic
	$HC{\equiv}CH$	$H_2C{=}CH_2$	CH_3CH_3
	ethyne	**ethene**	**ethane**
	pK_a = 25	**pK_a = 44**	**pK_a > 60**

Why does the hybridization of the atom affect its electronegativity? Electronegativity is a measure of the ability of an atom to pull the bonding electrons toward itself. Thus, the most electronegative atom will be the one with its bonding electrons closest to the nucleus. The average distance of a 2*s* electron from the nucleus is less than the average distance of a 2*p* electron from the nucleus. Therefore, an *sp* hybridized atom with 50% *s* character is the most electronegative, an sp^2 hybridized atom with 33.3% *s* character is next, and an sp^3 hybridized atom with 25% *s* character is the least electronegative.

Pulling the electrons closer to the nucleus stabilizes the carbanion. Once again we see that the stronger the acid, the more stable (weaker) is its conjugate base. Notice that the weakest base is the least electron-rich (less red).

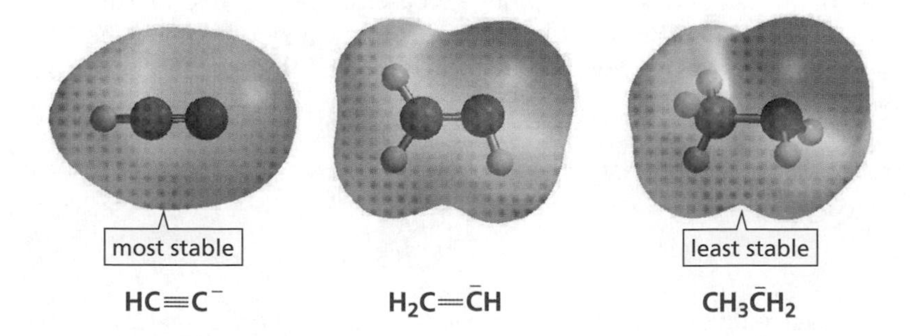

$HC{\equiv}C^-$ $\quad$ $H_2C{=}\bar{C}H$ $\quad$ $CH_3\bar{C}H_2$

Size

In comparing atoms that are very different in size, the *size* of the atom is more important than its *electronegativity* in determining how well it bears its negative charge. For example, as we proceed down a column in the periodic table, the atoms get larger and their electronegativity *decreases*. But the stability of the bases increases down the column, so the strength of the conjugate acids *increases*. Thus, HI is the strongest acid of the hydrogen halides, even though iodine is the least electronegative of the halogens.

Therefore, *when atoms are very different in size, the strongest acid will have its hydrogen attached to the largest atom.*

Size overrides electronegativity.

relative electronegativities: F > Cl > Br > I

most electronegative (F); largest (I)

relative stabilities: F^- < Cl^- < Br^- < I^-

most stable (I^-)

relative acidities: HF < HCl < HBr < HI

strongest acid (HI)

Why does the size of an atom have such a significant effect on the stability of the base that it more than overcomes any difference in electronegativity? The valence electrons of F^- are in a 2sp^3 orbital, the valence electrons of Cl^- are in a 3sp^3 orbital, those of Br^- are in a 4sp^3 orbital, and those of I^- are in a 5sp^3 orbital. The volume of space occupied by a 3sp^3 orbital is significantly greater than the volume of space occupied by a 2sp^3 orbital because a 3sp^3 orbital extends out farther from the nucleus. Because its negative charge is spread over a larger volume of space, Cl^- is more stable than F^-.

When atoms are very different in size, the strongest acid will have its hydrogen attached to the largest atom.

Thus, as the halide ion increases in size, its stability increases because its negative charge is spread over a larger volume of space (its electron density decreases). The *more stable the halide ion is as a base, the stronger is its conjugate acid.* Therefore, HI is the strongest acid of the hydrogen halides because I^- is the most stable halide ion, even though iodine is the least electronegative of the halogens (Table 10.9). The potential maps illustrate the large difference in size of the hydrogen halides:

Table 10.9 The pK_a Values of Some Simple Acids

CH_4 pK_a = 60	NH_3 pK_a = 36	H_2O pK_a = 15.7	HF pK_a = 3.2
		H_2S pK_a = 7.0	HCl pK_a = −7
			HBr pK_a = −9
			HI pK_a = −10

HF

HCl

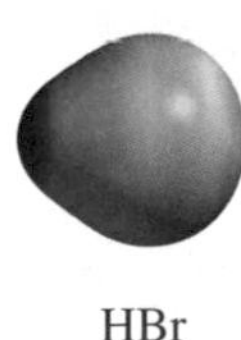
HBr

HI

In summary, as we move across a row of the periodic table, the atoms' orbitals have approximately the same volume, so it is electronegativity that determines the stability of the base and, therefore, the acidity of a proton bonded to that base. As we move down a column of the periodic table, the volume of the orbitals increases. The increase in volume causes the electron density of the orbital to decrease. The electron density of the orbitals is more important than electronegativity in determining the stability of a base and, therefore, the acidity of its conjugate acid.

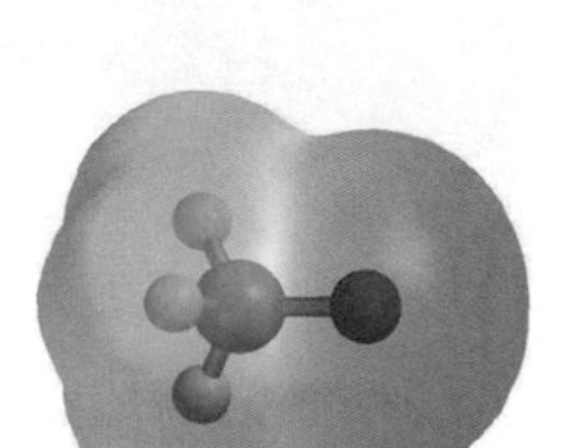

CH_3O^-

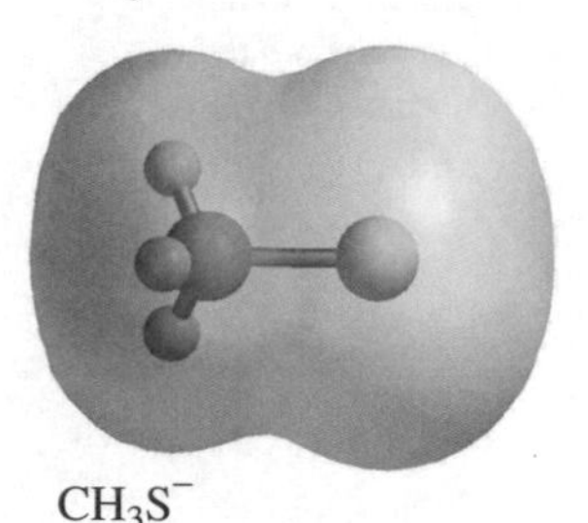

CH_3S^-

PROBLEM 51♦

a. Which is more electronegative, oxygen or sulfur?
b. Which is a stronger acid, H_2O or H_2S?
c. Which is a stronger acid, CH_3OH or CH_3SH?

PROBLEM 52♦

For each of the following pairs, indicate which is the stronger acid:
a. HCl or HBr

b. $CH_3CH_2CH_2\overset{+}{N}H_3$ or $CH_3CH_2CH_2\overset{+}{O}H_2$

c.

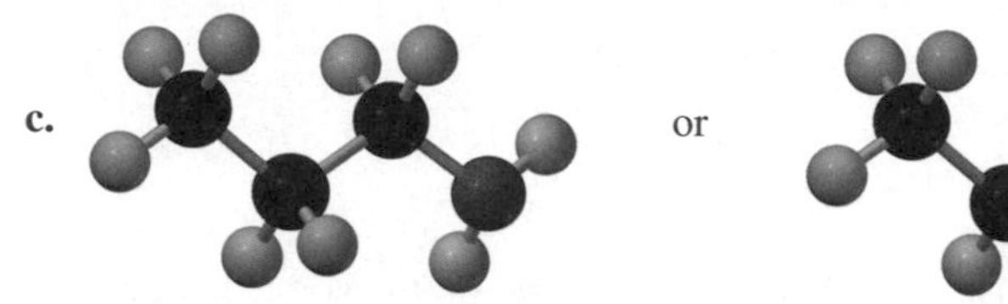

d.

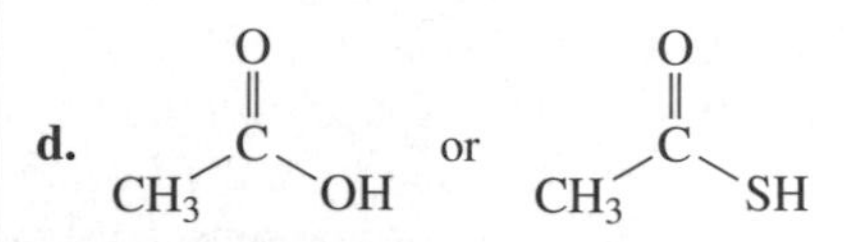

PROBLEM 53♦

a. Which of the halide ions (F^-, Cl^-, Br^-, I^-) is the strongest base?
b. Which is the weakest base?

PROBLEM 54♦

For each of the following pairs, indicate which is the stronger base:

a. H_2O or HO^- **b.** H_2O or NH_3 **c.** $CH_3\overset{O}{\overset{\|}{C}}O^-$ or CH_3O^- **d.** CH_3O^- or CH_3S^-

10.22 HOW SUBSTITUENTS AFFECT THE STRENGTH OF AN ACID

Although the acidic proton of each of the following four carboxylic acids is attached to the same atom (an oxygen atom), the four compounds have different acidities as reflected in their pK_a values:

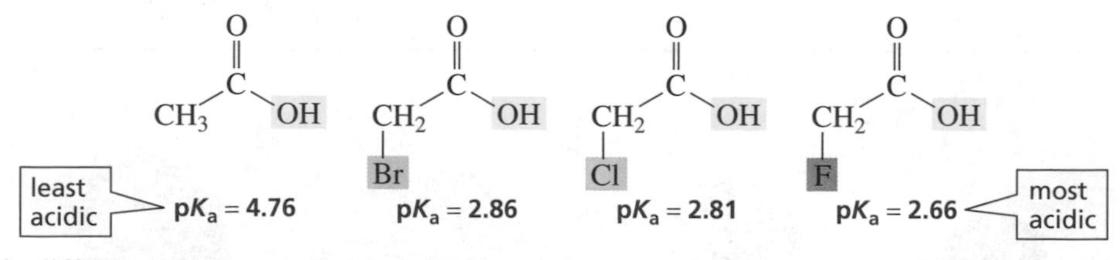

This difference indicates that in addition to the nature of the atom to which the hydrogen is bonded, there must be another factor that affects acidity.

From the pK_a values of the four carboxylic acids, we see that replacing one of the hydrogen atoms of the CH_3 group with a halogen atom affects the acidity of the compound. (The term for replacing an atom in a compound is *substitution*, and the new atom is called a *substituent*.) The acidity increases because a halogen is more electronegative than hydrogen. An electronegative halogen atom pulls the bonding electrons toward itself. Pulling electrons through sigma (σ) bonds is called **inductive electron withdrawal**. If we look at the conjugate base of a carboxylic acid, we see that inductive electron withdrawal stabilizes the base by *decreasing the electron density* about the oxygen atom. Stabilizing a base increases the acidity of its conjugate acid.

Inductive electron withdrawal increases the strength of an acid.

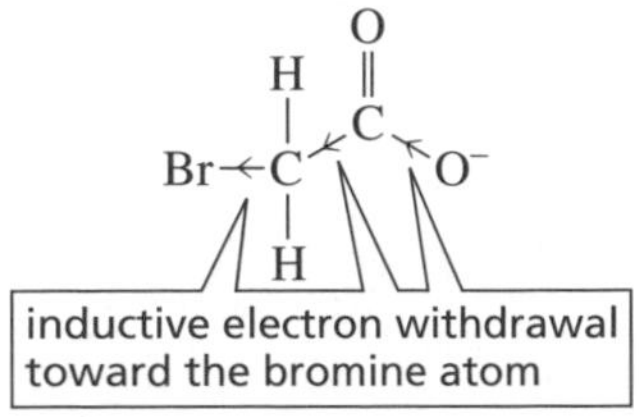

$$Br \leftarrow CH_2 \rightarrow C(=O)O^-$$

inductive electron withdrawal toward the bromine atom

As the pK_a values of the four carboxylic acids on page 444 show, inductive electron withdrawal increases the acidity of a compound. The greater the electron-withdrawing ability (electronegativity) of the halogen substituent, the more the acidity is increased because the more its conjugate base is stabilized. Thus, the fluoro-substituted compound is the strongest acid.

The effect of a substituent on the acidity of a compound decreases as the distance between the substituent and the acidic proton increases.

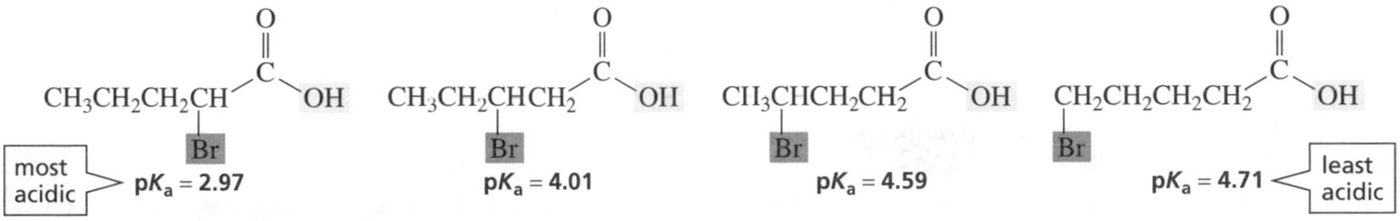

$CH_3CH_2CH_2CH(Br)COOH$	$CH_3CH_2CH(Br)CH_2COOH$	$CH_3CH(Br)CH_2CH_2COOH$	$CH_2(Br)CH_2CH_2CH_2COOH$
pK_a = 2.97 (most acidic)	pK_a = 4.01	pK_a = 4.59	pK_a = 4.71 (least acidic)

PROBLEM-SOLVING STRATEGY

Determining Relative Acid Strength from Structure

a. Which is a stronger acid?

$$CH_3CH(F)CH_2OH \quad \text{or} \quad CH_3CH(Br)CH_2OH$$

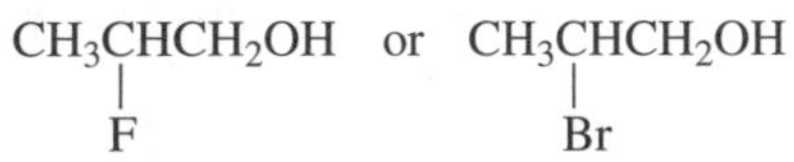

When you are asked to compare two items, pay attention to how they differ; ignore where they are the same. These two compounds differ only in the halogen atom attached to the middle carbon of the molecule. Because fluorine is more electronegative than bromine, there is greater electron withdrawal from the oxygen atom in the fluorinated compound. The fluorinated compound, therefore, will have the more stable conjugate base, so it will be the stronger acid.

b. Which is a stronger acid?

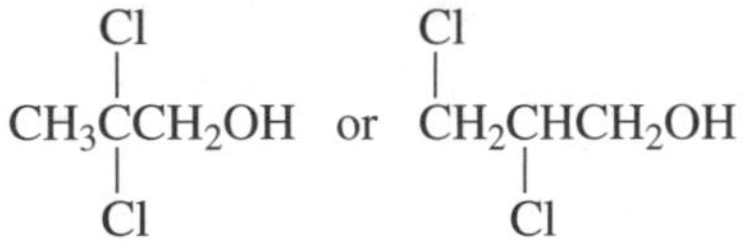

$$CH_3C(Cl)_2CH_2OH \quad \text{or} \quad CH_2(Cl)CH(Cl)CH_2OH$$

These two compounds differ in the location of one of the chlorine atoms. Because the second chlorine in the compound on the left is closer to the O—H bond than is the second chlorine in the compound on the right, the former is more effective at withdrawing electrons from the oxygen atom. Thus, the compound on the left will have the more stable conjugate base, so it will be the stronger acid.

Now continue on to Problem 55.

PROBLEM 55 ♦

For each of the following pairs, indicate which is the stronger acid:

a. $CH_3OCH_2CH_2OH$ or $CH_3CH_2CH_2CH_2OH$

b. $CH_3CH_2CH_2\overset{+}{N}H_3$ or $CH_3CH_2CH_2\overset{+}{O}H_2$

c. $CH_3OCH_2CH_2CH_2OH$ or $CH_3CH_2OCH_2CH_2OH$

d. 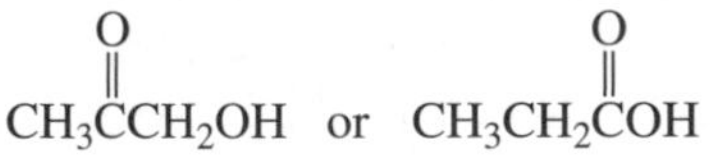 $CH_3C(=O)CH_2OH$ or $CH_3CH_2C(=O)OH$

PROBLEM 56 ♦

List the following compounds in order of decreasing acidity:

$CH_3CH(F)CH_2OH$ $CH_3CH_2CH_2OH$ $CH_2(Cl)CH_2CH_2OH$ $CH_3CH(Cl)CH_2OH$

PROBLEM 57 ♦

For each of the following pairs, indicate which is the stronger base:

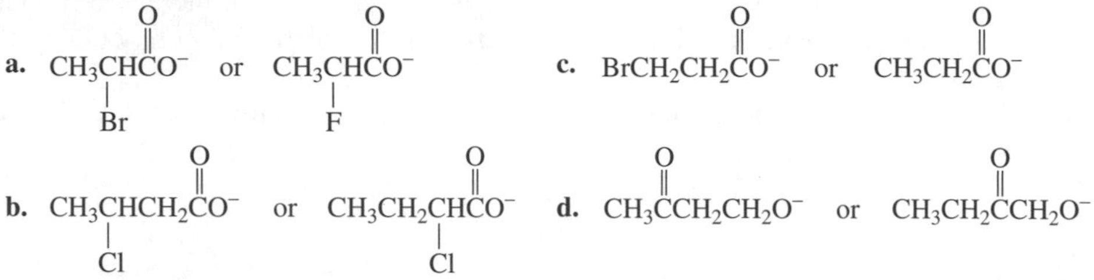

a. $CH_3CH(Br)C(=O)O^-$ or $CH_3CH(F)C(=O)O^-$

b. $CH_3CH(Cl)CH_2C(=O)O^-$ or $CH_3CH_2CH(Cl)C(=O)O^-$

c. $BrCH_2CH_2C(=O)O^-$ or $CH_3CH_2C(=O)O^-$

d. $CH_3C(=O)CH_2CH_2O^-$ or $CH_3CH_2C(=O)CH_2O^-$

PROBLEM 58 SOLVED

If HCl is a weaker acid than HBr, why is $ClCH_2COOH$ a stronger acid than $BrCH_2COOH$?

Solution To compare the acidities of HCl and HBr, we need to compare the stabilities of their conjugate bases, Cl^- and Br^-. Because we know that size is more important than electronegativity in determining stability, we know that Br^- is more stable than Cl^-. Therefore, HBr is a stronger acid than HCl. In comparing the acidities of the two carboxylic acids, we need to compare the stabilities of their conjugate bases, $RCOO^-$ and $R'COO^-$. (Notice that an O—H bond is broken in both compounds.) The only way the conjugate bases differ is in the electronegativity of the atom that is pulling electrons away from the negatively charged oxygen. Because Cl is more electronegative than Br, Cl exerts greater inductive electron withdrawal. Thus, it has a greater stabilizing effect on the base that is formed when the proton leaves, so the chloro-substituted compound is the stronger acid.

10.23 AN INTRODUCTION TO DELOCALIZED ELECTRONS

We have seen that a carboxylic acid has a pK_a value of about 5, whereas the pK_a value of an alcohol is about 15. Because a carboxylic acid is a much stronger acid than an alcohol, we know that a carboxylic acid has a considerably more stable conjugate base.

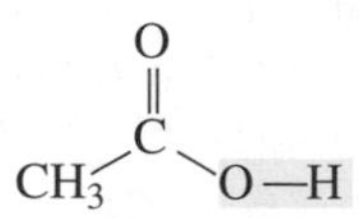

$CH_3C(=O)O{-}H$ $pK_a = 4.76$ $CH_3CH_2O{-}H$ $pK_a = 15.9$

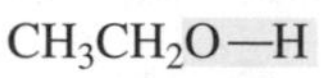

Two factors cause the conjugate base of a carboxylic acid to be more stable than the conjugate base of an alcohol. First, the conjugate base of a carboxylic acid has a doubly bonded oxygen in place of two hydrogens in the conjugate base of an alcohol. Inductive electron withdrawal by this electronegative oxygen decreases the electron density of the negatively charged oxygen. Second, oxygen's electron density is further decreased by *electron delocalization*.

When an alcohol loses a proton, the negative charge resides on its single oxygen atom: electrons that belong to only one atom are called *localized* electrons. In contrast, when a carboxylic acid loses a proton, the negative charge is shared by both oxygen atoms because the electrons are *delocalized*.

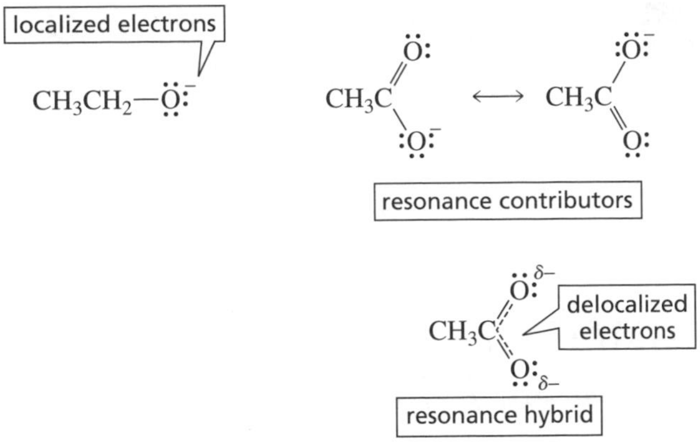

localized electrons

$CH_3CH_2{-}\ddot{\underset{..}{O}}{:}^-$

$CH_3C(=\ddot{O}{:}){-}{:}\ddot{O}{:}^- \longleftrightarrow CH_3C({-}{:}\ddot{O}{:}^-){=}\ddot{O}{:}$

resonance contributors

CH_3C (with $\ddot{O}{:}^{\delta-}$ and $\ddot{O}{:}^{\delta-}$ joined by dotted bonds) — delocalized electrons

resonance hybrid

The two structures shown for the conjugate base of the carboxylic acid are called **resonance contributors**. Neither resonance contributor alone represents the actual structure of the conjugate base. Instead, the actual structure—called a **resonance hybrid**—is a composite of the two resonance contributors. The double-headed arrow between the two resonance contributors is used to indicate that the actual structure is a hybrid. Notice that the two resonance contributors differ only in the location of their π electrons and lone-pair electrons—all the atoms stay in the same place. In the resonance hybrid, an electron pair is spread over *two oxygens and a carbon*. The negative charge is shared equally by the two oxygens, and both carbon–oxygen bonds are the same length—they are not as long as a single bond, but they are longer than a double bond. A resonance hybrid can be drawn by using dotted lines to show the delocalized electrons.

Delocalized electrons are shared by more than two atoms.

The following potential maps show that the negative charge is on one oxygen in the conjugate base of the alcohol (red region) and is shared by both oxygens in the conjugate base of the carboxylic acid (orange-red region):

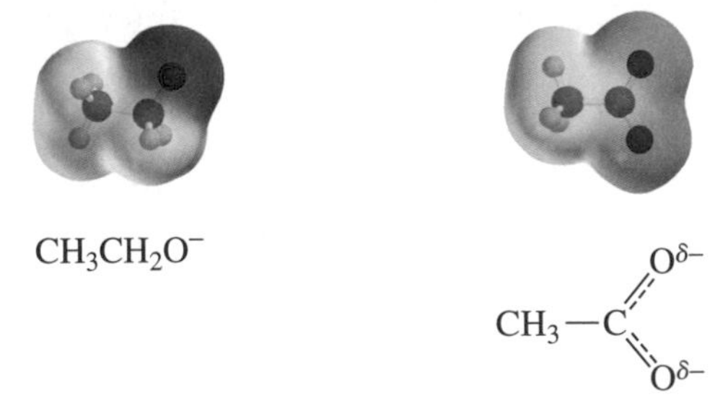

$CH_3CH_2O^-$

$CH_3{-}C(\text{---}O^{\delta-})(\text{---}O^{\delta-})$

Thus, the combination of inductive electron withdrawal and the ability of two atoms to share the negative charge makes the conjugate base of the carboxylic acid more stable than the conjugate base of the alcohol.

PROBLEM 59 ♦

Which compound would you expect to be a stronger acid? Why?

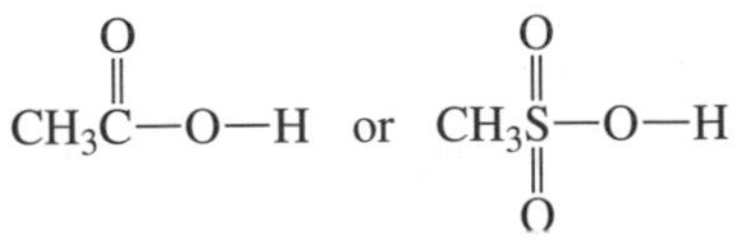

$CH_3C(=O){-}O{-}H$ or $CH_3S(=O)_2{-}O{-}H$

PROBLEM 60 ♦

Draw resonance contributors for the following compounds:

a. 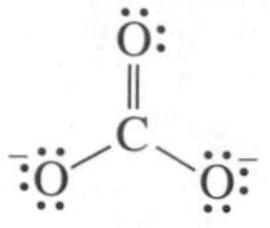 CO_3^{2-} (O═C with two O^-)   **b.** 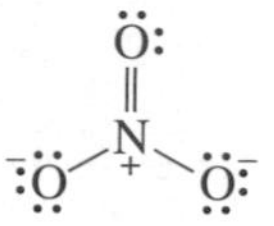 NO_3^- (O═N^+ with two O^-)

10.24 A SUMMARY OF THE FACTORS THAT DETERMINE ACID STRENGTH

We have seen that the strength of an acid depends on five factors: the *size* of the atom to which the hydrogen is attached, the *electronegativity* of the atom to which the hydrogen is attached, the *hybridization* of the atom to which the hydrogen is attached, *inductive effects*, and *electron delocalization*. All five factors affect acidity by stabilizing the conjugate base.

1. **Size:** As the atom attached to the hydrogen increases in size (going down a column of the periodic table), the strength of the acid increases.
2. **Electronegativity:** As the atom attached to the hydrogen increases in electronegativity (going across a row of the periodic table), the strength of the acid increases.

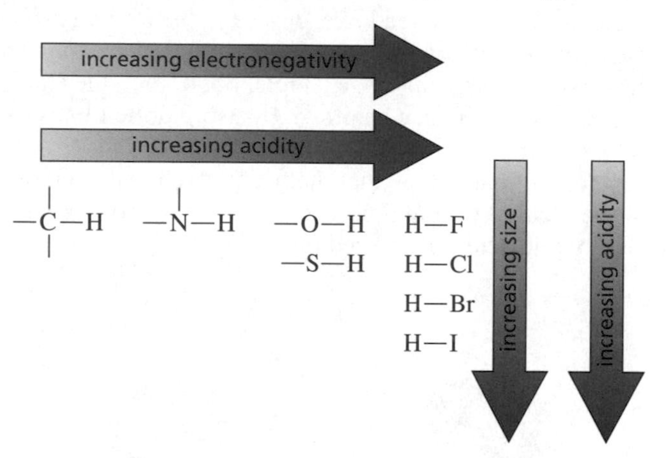

3. **Hybridization:** The relative electronegativities of an atom are: $sp > sp^2 > sp^3$. Because hybridization affects the electronegativity of an atom, a hydrogen attached to an *sp* carbon is the most acidic and a hydrogen attached to an sp^3 carbon is the least acidic.

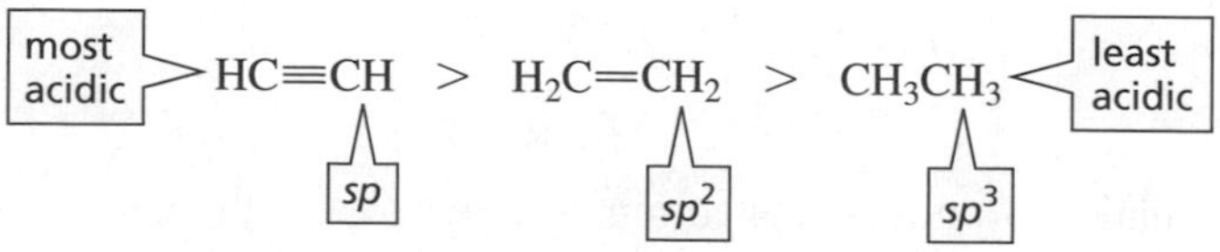

most acidic $HC{\equiv}CH > H_2C{=}CH_2 > CH_3CH_3$ least acidic

(*sp*, sp^2, sp^3)

4. **Inductive effect:** An electron-withdrawing group increases acid strength: the more electronegative the electron-withdrawing group and the closer it is to the acidic hydrogen, the stronger is the acid.

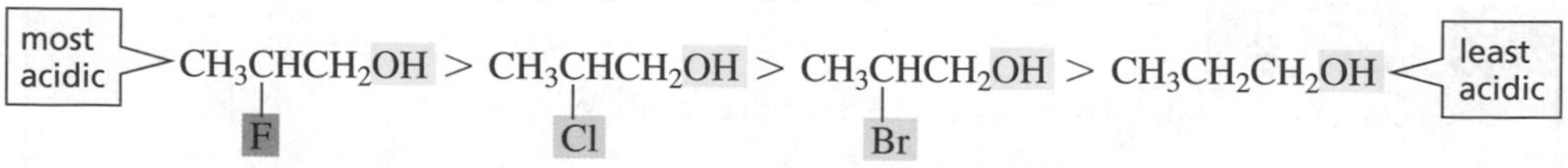

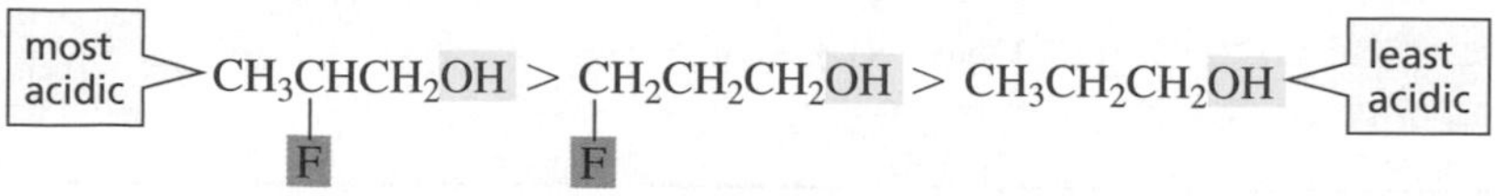

most acidic $CH_3CH(F)CH_2OH > CH_3CH(Cl)CH_2OH > CH_3CH(Br)CH_2OH > CH_3CH_2CH_2OH$ least acidic

most acidic $CH_3CH(F)CH_2OH > CH_2(F)CH_2CH_2OH > CH_3CH_2CH_2OH$ least acidic

5. **Electron delocalization:** An acid whose conjugate base has delocalized electrons is more acidic than a similar acid whose conjugate base has only localized electrons.

more acidic $RC(=O)OH$ RCH_2OH less acidic

more stable $RC(O^{\delta-})O^{\delta-}$ RCH_2O^- less stable

PROBLEM 61 ♦

Using the table of pK_a values given in Appendix II, answer the following:

a. Which is the most acidic organic compound in the table?
b. Which is the least acidic organic compound in the table?
c. Which is the most acidic carboxylic acid in the table?
d. Which is more electronegative, an sp^3 oxygen or an sp^2 oxygen? (*Hint:* Pick a compound in Appendix II with a hydrogen attached to an sp^2 oxygen and one with a hydrogen attached to an sp^3 oxygen, and compare their pK_avalues.)
e. What compounds illustrate that the relative electronegativities of a hybridized nitrogen atom are $sp > sp^2 > sp^3$?
f. Which is more acidic, HNO_3 or HNO_2? Why?

10.25 HOW pH AFFECTS THE STRUCTURE OF AN ORGANIC COMPOUND

Whether a given acid will lose a proton in an aqueous solution depends both on the pK_a of the acid and the pH of the solution. The relationship between the two is given by the **Henderson–Hasselbalch equation**. This is an extremely useful equation because it tells us whether a compound will exist in its acidic form (with its proton retained) or in its basic form (with its proton removed) at a particular pH.

the Henderson–Hasselbalch equation

$$pK_a = pH + \log\frac{[HA]}{[A^-]}$$

The Henderson–Hasselbalch equation tells us that when the pH of a solution equals the pK_a of the compound that undergoes dissociation, the concentration of the compound in its acidic form [HA] will equal the concentration of the compound in its basic form $[A^-]$ (because log 1 = 0). If the pH of the solution is less than the pK_a of the compound, the compound will exist primarily in its acidic form. If the pH of the solution is greater than the pK_a of the compound, the compound will exist primarily in its basic form. In other words, *compounds exist primarily in their acidic forms in solutions that are more acidic than their* pK_a *values and primarily in their basic forms in solutions that are more basic than their* pK_a *values.*

A compound will exist primarily in its acidic form if the pH of the solution is less than the compound's pK_a.

A compound will exist primarily in its basic form if the pH of the solution is greater than the compound's pK_a.

If we know the pH of the solution and the pK_a of the compound, the Henderson–Hasselbalch equation allows us to calculate precisely how much of the compound will be in its acidic form, and how much will be in its basic form. For example, when a compound with a pK_a of 5.2 is in a solution of pH 5.2, half the compound will be in the acidic form and the other half will be in the basic form (Figure 10.17). If the pH is one unit less than the pK_a of the compound (pH = 4.2), there will be 10 times more compound present in the acidic form than in the basic form (because log 10 = 1). If the pH is two units less than the pK_a of the compound (pH = 3.2), there will be 100 times more compound present in the acidic form than in the basic form (because log 100 = 2). If the pH is 6.2, there will be 10 times more compound in the basic form than in the acidic form, and at pH = 7.2 there will be 100 times more compound present in the basic form than in the acidic form.

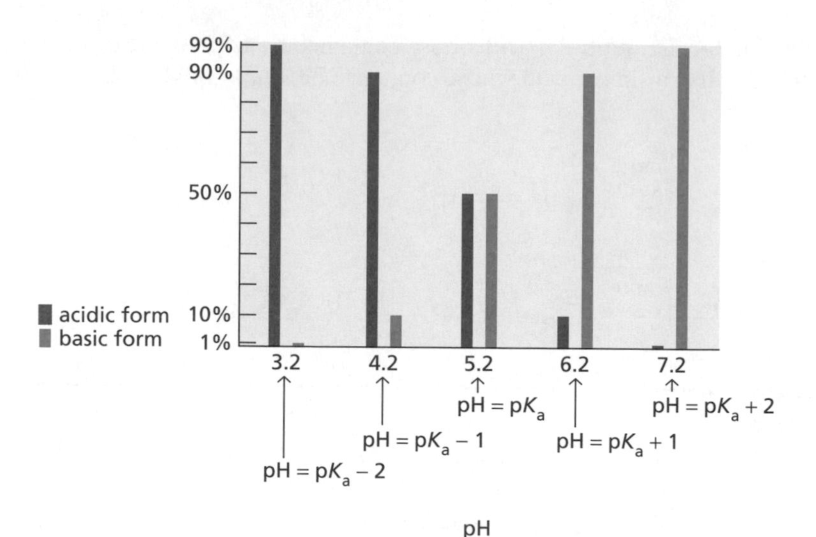

▶ **Figure 10.17**
The relative amounts of a compound with a pK_a of 5.2 in the acidic and basic forms at different pH values.

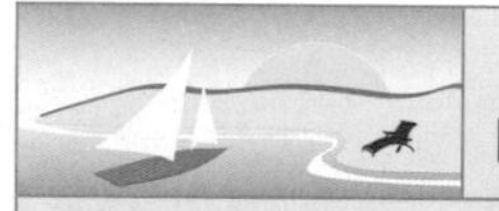

Derivation of the Henderson–Hasselbalch Equation

The Henderson–Hasselbalch equation can be derived from the expression that defines the acid dissociation constant:

$$K_a = \frac{[H_3O^+][A^-]}{[HA]}$$

Taking the logarithms of both sides of the equation remembering that when things are multiplied their logs are added, we obtain

$$\log K_a = \log [H_3O^+] + \log \frac{[A^-]}{[HA]}$$

Multiplying both sides of the equation by −1 give us

$$-\log K_a = -\log[H_3O^+] - \log \frac{[A^-]}{[HA]}$$

Substituting and remembering that when a fraction is inverted, the sign of its log changes, we get

$$pK_a = pH + \log \frac{[HA]}{[A^-]}$$

PROBLEM-SOLVING STRATEGY

Determining the Structure at a Particular pH

Write the form in which the following compounds will predominate in a solution of pH 5.5:

a. CH_3CH_2OH (pK_a = 15.9)
b. $CH_3CH_2\overset{+}{O}H_2$ (pK_a = −2.5)
c. $CH_3\overset{+}{N}H_3$ (pK_a = 11.0)

To answer this kind of question, we need to compare the pH of the solution with the pK_a value of the compound's dissociable proton.

a. The pH of the solution is more acidic (5.5) than the pK_a value of the OH group (15.9). Therefore, the compound will exist primarily as CH_3CH_2OH (with its proton).
b. The pH of the solution is more basic (5.5) than the pK_a value of the $^+OH_2$ group (−2.5). Therefore, the compound will exist primarily as CH_3CH_2OH (without its proton).
c. The pH of the solution is more acidic (5.5) than the pK_a value of the $^+NH_3$ group (11.0). Therefore, the compound will exist primarily as $CH_3\overset{+}{N}H_3$ (with its proton).

Now continue on to Problem 62.

PROBLEM 62 ♦

For each of the following compounds, shown in their acidic forms, write the form that will predominate in a solution of pH = 5.5:

a. CH_3COOH (pK_a = 4.76)
b. $CH_3CH_2\overset{+}{N}H_3$ (pK_a = 11.0)
c. H_3O^+ (pK_a = −1.7)
d. HBr (pK_a = −9)
e. $^+NH_4$ (pK_a = 9.4)
f. $HC{\equiv}N$ (pK_a = 9.1)
g. HNO_2 (pK_a = 3.4)
h. HNO_3 (pK_a = −1.3)

PROBLEM 63 ♦ SOLVED

a. Indicate whether a carboxylic acid (RCOOH) with a pK_a value of 4.5 will have more charged molecules or more neutral molecules in a solution with the following pH:

1. pH = 1 **3.** pH = 5 **5.** pH = 10
2. pH = 3 **4.** pH = 7 **6.** pH = 13

b. Answer the same question for a protonated amine ($R\overset{+}{N}H_3$) with a pK_a value of 9.
c. Answer the same question for an alcohol (ROH) with a pK_a value of 15.

Solution to 63a First determine whether the compound is charged or neutral in its acidic form and charged or neutral in its basic form: a carboxylic acid is neutral in its acidic form (RCOOH) and charged in its basic form ($RCOO^-$). Then compare the pH and pK_a values remembering that if the pH of the solution is less than the pK_a value of the compound, more molecules will be in the acidic form, but if the pH is greater than the pK_a value of the compound, more molecules will be in the basic form. Therefore, at pH = 1 and 3, there will be more neutral molecules, and at pH = 5, 7, 10, and 13, there will be more charged molecules.

You are what you're in: a compound will be mostly in the acidic form in an acidic solution (pH < pK_a) and mostly in the basic form in a basic solution (pH > pK_a).

PROBLEM 64 ♦

A naturally occurring amino acid such as alanine has both a carboxylic acid group and an amine group. The pK_a values of the two groups are shown.

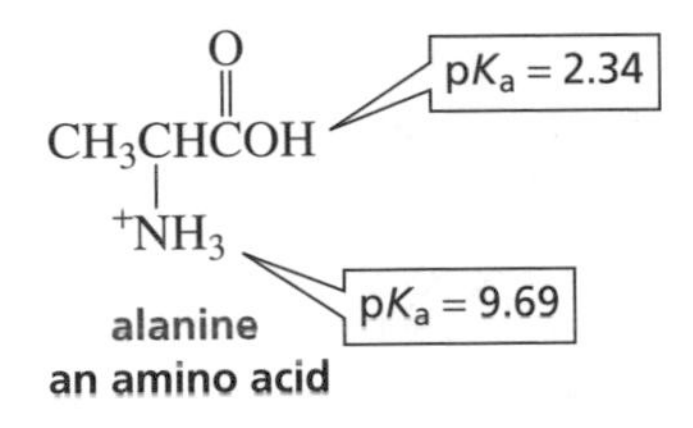

a. Draw the structure of alanine in a solution at physiological pH (pH 7.3).
b. Is there a pH at which alanine will be neutral (neither group will have a charge)?
c. At what pH will alanine have no net charge (the amount of negative charge will be the same as the amount of positive charge)?

The Henderson–Hasselbalch equation can be very useful in the laboratory for separating the compounds in a mixture. Water and diethyl ether are liquids of very limited mutual solubility and, therefore, will form two layers when combined; the ether layer will lie above the more dense water layer. Charged compounds are more soluble in water, whereas neutral compounds are more soluble in diethyl ether. Two compounds, such as a carboxylic acid (RCOOH) with a pK_a of 5.0 and a protonated amine (RNH_3^+) with a pK_a of 10.0, dissolved in a mixture of water and diethyl ether, can be separated by adjusting the pH of the water layer. For example, if the pH of the water layer is 2, the carboxylic acid and the protonated amine will both be in their acidic forms because the pH of the water is less than the pK_a values of both compounds. The acidic form of a carboxylic acid is neutral, whereas the acidic form of an amine is charged. Therefore, the carboxylic acid will be more soluble in the ether layer, and the protonated amine will be more soluble in the water layer.

acidic form		basic form
RCOOH	$\rightleftharpoons$	$RCOO^-$ + H^+
$R\overset{+}{N}H_3$	$\rightleftharpoons$	RNH_2 + H^+

For the most effective separation, the pH of the water layer should be at least two units away from the pK_a values of the compounds being separated. Then the relative amounts of the compounds in their acidic and basic forms will be at least 100:1 (Figure 10.17).

PROBLEM 65 ♦ SOLVED

a. At what pH will the concentration of a compound with a pK_a of 8.4 be 100 times greater in its basic form than in its acidic form?
b. At what pH will the concentration of a compound with a pK_a of 3.7 be 10 times greater in its acidic form than in its basic form?
c. At what pH will the concentration of a compound with a pK_a of 8.4 be 100 times greater in its acidic form than in its basic form?
d. At what pH will 50% of a compound with a pK_a of 7.3 be in its basic form?
e. At what pH will the concentration of a compound with a pK_a of 4.6 be 10 times greater in its basic form than in its acidic form?

Solution to 65a If the concentration in the basic form is 100 times greater than the concentration in the acidic form, the Henderson–Hasselbalch equation becomes

$$\begin{aligned} pK_a &= \text{pH} + \log 1/100 \\ 8.4 &= \text{pH} + \log .01 \\ 8.4 &= \text{pH} - 2.0 \\ \text{pH} &= 10.4 \end{aligned}$$

There is a faster way to get the answer: if 100 times more compound is present in the basic form than in the acidic form, the pH will be two units more basic than the pK_a. Thus, pH = 8.4 + 2.0 = 10.4.

Solution to 65b If 10 times more compound is present in the acidic form than in the basic form, the pH will be one unit more acidic than the pK_a. Thus, pH = 3.7 − 1.0 = 2.7.

PROBLEM 66 ♦

For each of the following compounds, indicate the pH at which
a. 50% of the compound will be in a form that possesses a charge.
b. more than 99% of the compound will be in a form that possesses a charge.
1. CH_3CH_2COOH (pK_a = 4.9)
2. $CH_3\overset{+}{N}H_3$ (pK_a = 10.7)

PROBLEM 67 ♦

As long as the pH is greater than ________, more than 50% of a protonated amine with a pK_a of 10.4 will be in its neutral, nonprotonated form.

10.26 BUFFER SOLUTIONS

A solution of a weak acid (HA) and its conjugate base (A^-) is called a **buffer solution**. A buffer solution will maintain nearly constant pH when small amounts of acid or base are added to it, because the weak acid can donate a proton to any HO^- added to the solution, and its conjugate base can accept any H^+ that is added to the solution.

can donate an H^+ to HO^-

$$HA + HO^- \longrightarrow A^- + H_2O$$

$$A^- + H_3O^+ \longrightarrow HA + H_2O$$

can accept an H^+ from H_3O^+

NOTE TO THE STUDENT

Buffer solutions are discussed in detail in Special Topic I in the *Study Guide and Solutions Manual*. By working the problems you will find there, you will see the usefulness of the Henderson–Hasselbalch equation for dealing with buffer solutions.

PROBLEM 68 ♦

Write the equation that shows how a buffer made by dissolving CH_3COOH and $CH_3COO^-Na^+$ in water prevents the pH of a solution from changing appreciably when:

a. a small amount of H^+ is added to the solution.
b. a small amount of HO^- is added to the solution.

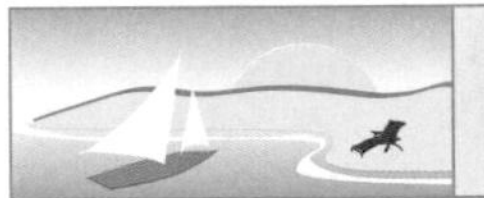

Blood: A Buffered Solution

Blood is the fluid that transports oxygen to all the cells of the human body. The normal pH of human blood is 7.3 to 7.4. Death will result if this pH decreases to a value less than ~6.8 or increases to a value greater than ~8.0 for even a few seconds.

Oxygen is carried to cells by a protein in the blood called hemoglobin (HbH^+). When hemoglobin binds O_2, hemoglobin loses a proton, which would make the blood more acidic if it did not contain a buffer to maintain its pH.

$$HbH^+ + O_2 \rightleftharpoons HbO_2 + H^+$$

A carbonic acid/bicarbonate (H_2CO_3 / HCO_3^-) buffer controls the pH of blood. An important feature of this buffer is that carbonic acid decomposes to CO_2 and H_2O:

$$CO_2 + H_2O \rightleftharpoons \underset{\text{carbonic acid}}{H_2CO_3} \rightleftharpoons \underset{\text{bicarbonate}}{HCO_3^-} + H^+$$

During exercise our metabolism speeds up, producing large amounts of CO_2. The increased concentration of CO_2 shifts the equilibrium between carbonic acid and bicarbonate to the right, which increases the concentration of H^+. Significant amounts of lactic acid are also produced during exercise, and this further increases the concentration of H^+. Receptors in the brain respond to the increased concentration of H^+ by triggering a reflex that increases the rate of breathing. Hemoglobin then releases more oxygen to the cells and more CO_2 is eliminated by exhalation. Both processes decrease the concentration of H^+ in the blood by shifting both equilibria to the left.

Thus, any disorder that decreases the rate and depth of ventilation, such as emphysema, will decrease the pH of the blood—a condition called acidosis. In contrast, any excessive increase in the rate and depth of ventilation, as with hyperventilation due to anxiety, will increase the pH of blood—a condition called alkalosis.

10.27 LEWIS ACIDS AND BASES

In 1923, G. N. Lewis (page 400) offered new definitions for the terms *acid* and *base*. He defined an acid as *a species that accepts a share in an electron pair* and a base as *a species that donates a share in an electron pair*. All proton-donating acids fit the Lewis definition because all proton-donating acids lose a proton and the proton accepts a share in an electron pair.

the curved arrow indicates where the electrons start from and where they end up

$$\underset{\text{acid}}{H^+} + \underset{\text{base}}{:NH_3} \rightleftharpoons H{-}\overset{+}{N}H_3$$

acid: accepts a share in an electron pair
base: donates a share in an electron pair
new bond

Lewis acids, however, are not limited to compounds that donate protons. Compounds such as aluminum chloride ($AlCl_3$), boron trifluoride (BF_3), and borane (BH_3) are acids according to the Lewis definition because they have unfilled valence orbitals and thus can accept a share in an electron pair. These compounds react with a compound that has a lone pair, just as a proton reacts with ammonia. Thus, the Lewis definition of an acid includes all proton-donating compounds and some additional compounds that do not have protons. Throughout this text, the term *acid* is used to mean a Brønsted-Lowery proton-donating acid, and the term **Lewis acid** is used to refer to non-proton-donating acids such as $AlCl_3$ or BF_3.

Lewis base: Have pair, will share.

Lewis acid: Need two from you.

All bases are **Lewis bases** because they all have a pair of electrons that they can share, either with a proton or with an atom such as aluminum or boron.

the curved arrow indicates where the electrons start from and where they end up

$$AlCl_3 + CH_3\ddot{O}CH_3 \rightleftharpoons Cl_3\overset{-}{Al}-\overset{+}{O}(CH_3)-CH_3$$

new bond

aluminum trichloride a Lewis acid; dimethyl ether a Lewis base

$$BH_3 + :NH_3 \rightleftharpoons H_3\overset{-}{B}-\overset{+}{N}H_3$$

borane a Lewis acid; ammonia a Lewis base

PROBLEM 69

Give the products of the following reactions using arrows to show where the pair of electrons starts and where it ends up.

a. $ZnCl_2 + CH_3\ddot{O}H \rightleftharpoons$

b. $FeBr_3 + :\ddot{Br}:^- \rightleftharpoons$

c. $AlCl_3 + :\ddot{Cl}:^- \rightleftharpoons$

PROBLEM 70

Show how each of the following compounds reacts with HO^-:

a. CH_3OH **b.** $^+NH_4$ **c.** $CH_3\overset{+}{N}H_3$ **d.** BF_3 **e.** $^+CH_3$ **f.** $FeBr_3$ **g.** $AlCl_3$ **h.** CH_3COOH

SUMMARY

Organic compounds are compounds that contain carbon. The **atomic number** of an atom is the number of protons in its nucleus. The **mass number** of an atom is the sum of its protons and neutrons. **Isotopes** have the same atomic number, but different mass numbers.

An **atomic orbital** indicates where there is a high probability of finding an electron. The closer the atomic orbital is to the nucleus, the lower is its energy. **Degenerate orbitals** have the same energy. Electrons are assigned to orbitals following the **aufbau principle**, the **Pauli exclusion principle**, and **Hund's rule**.

The **octet rule** states that an atom will give up, accept, or share electrons in order to fill its outer shell or attain an outer shell with eight electrons. **Electropositive** elements readily lose electrons; **electronegative** elements readily acquire electrons. The **electronic configuration** of an atom describes the orbitals occupied by the atom's electrons. Electrons in inner shells are called **core electrons**; electrons in the outermost shell are called **valence electrons**. **Lone-pair electrons** are valence electrons that are not used in bonding. Attractive forces between opposite charges are called **electrostatic attractions**. An **ionic bond** is formed by a transfer of electrons; a **covalent bond** is formed by sharing electrons. A **polar covalent bond** is a covalent bond between atoms with different **electronegativites**. Therefore, a polar covalent bond has a **dipole**, measured by a **dipole moment**. The **dipole moment** of a molecule depends on the magnitudes and directions of the bond dipole moments.

Lewis structures indicate which atoms are bonded together and show **lone pairs** and **formal charges**. A **carbocation** has a positively charged carbon, a **carbanion** has a negatively charged carbon, and a **radical** has an unpaired electron.

According to **molecular orbital (MO) theory**, covalent bonds result when atomic orbitals combine to form **molecular orbitals**. Atomic orbitals combine to give a **bonding MO** and a higher energy **antibonding MO**. Cylindrically symmetrical bonds are called **sigma** (σ) bonds; **pi** (π) bonds form when p orbitals overlap side to side. Bond strength is measured by the **bond dissociation energy**. A σ bond is stronger than a π bond. All **single bonds** in organic compounds are σ bonds, a **double bond** consists of one σ bond and one π bond, and a **triple bond** consists of one σ bond and two π bonds.

Triple bonds are shorter and stronger than double bonds, which are shorter and stronger than single bonds.

To form four bonds, carbon promotes an electron from a 2*s* to a 2*p* orbital. C, N, and O form bonds using **hybrid orbitals**. The **hybridization** of C, N, or O depends on the number of π bonds the atom forms: no π bonds means that the atom is sp^3 **hybridized**, one π bond indicates that it is sp^2 **hybridized**, and two π bonds signifies that it is *sp* **hybridized**. Exceptions are carbocations and carbon radicals, which are sp^2 hybridized. The more *s* character in the orbital used to form a bond, the shorter and stronger the bond and the larger the bond angle. Bonding and lone-pair electrons around an atom are positioned as far apart as possible.

An **acid** is a species that donates a proton, and a **base** is a species that accepts a proton. A **Lewis acid** is a species that accepts a share in an electron pair; a **Lewis base** is a species that donates a share in an electron pair.

Acidity is a measure of the tendency of a compound to give up a proton. **Basicity** is a measure of a compound's affinity for a proton. The stronger the acid, the weaker is its conjugate base. The strength of an acid is given by the **acid dissociation constant** (K_a). Approximate pK_a values are as follows: protonated alcohols, protonated carboxylic acids, protonated water < 0; carboxylic acids ~ 5; protonated amines ~ 10; alcohols and water ~ 15. The **pH** of a solution indicates the concentration of positively charged hydrogen ions in the solution. In **acid–base reactions**, the equilibrium favors reaction of the strong acid and formation of the weak acid. Curved arrows indicate the bonds that are broken and formed as reactants are converted into products.

The strength of an acid is determined by the stability of its conjugate base: the more stable the base, the stronger is its conjugate acid. When atoms are similar in size, the more acidic compound will have its hydrogen attached to the more electronegative atom. When atoms are very different in size, the more acidic compound will have its hydrogen attached to the larger atom. Hybridization affects acidity because an *sp* hybridized atom is more electronegative than an sp^2 hybridized atom, which is more electronegative than an sp^3 hybridized atom. **Inductive electron withdrawal** increases acidity: the more electronegative the electron-withdrawing group and the closer it is to the acidic hydrogen, the stronger is the acid.

Delocalized electrons, which are electrons shared by more than two atoms, stabilize a compound. A **resonance hybrid** is a composite of the **resonance contributors**, structures that differ only in the location of their lone-pair and π electrons.

The **Henderson–Hasselbalch equation** gives the relationship between pK_a and pH: a compound exists primarily in its acidic form in solutions more acidic than its pK_a value and primarily in its basic form in solutions more basic than its pK_a value. A **buffer solution** contains both a weak acid and its conjugate base.

KEY TERMS

acid (p. 433)
acid–base reaction (p. 433)
acid dissociation constant (K_a) (p. 435)
acidity (p. 434)
antibonding molecular orbital (p. 414)
atomic number (p. 396)
atomic orbital (p. 397)
atomic weight (p. 396)
aufbau principle (p. 397)
base (p. 433)
basicity (p. 434)
bond (p. 401)
bond dissociation energy (p. 414)
bond length (p. 413)
bond strength (p. 413)
bonding molecular orbital (p. 414)
buffer solution (p. 452)
carbanion (p. 407)
carbocation (p. 407)
condensed structure (p. 409)
conjugate acid (p. 433)
conjugate base (p. 433)
constitutional isomer (p. 409)
core electrons (p. 399)
covalent bond (p. 401)
debye (D) (p. 404)
degenerate orbitals (p. 397)
delocalized electrons (p. 446)
dipole (p. 403)
dipole moment (μ) (p. 403)
double bond (p. 422)
electronegative (p. 400)
electronegativity (p. 402)
electropositive (p. 400)
electrostatic attraction (p. 401)
electrostatic potential map (p. 405)
equilibrium constant (p. 435)
excited-state electronic configuration (p. 397)
formal charge (p. 406)
free radical (p. 407)
ground-state electronic configuration (p. 397)
Heisenberg uncertainty principle (p. 411)
Henderson–Hasselbalch equation (p. 449)
Hund's rule (p. 398)
hybrid orbital (p. 418)
hybridization (p. 418)
hydride ion (p. 401)
hydrogen ion (p. 401)
inductive electron withdrawal (p. 444)
ionic bond (p. 401)
ionic compound (p. 401)
isotopes (p. 396)
Kekulé structure (p. 409)
Lewis acid (p. 453)
Lewis base (p. 454)
Lewis structure (p. 405)
lone-pair electrons (p. 406)
mass number (p. 396)
molecular orbital (p. 413)
molecular orbital (MO) theory (p. 413)
molecular weight (p. 396)
nodal plane (p. 412)
node (p. 412)
nonbonding electrons (p. 406)
nonpolar covalent bond (p. 402)
nonpolar molecule (p. 418)
octet rule (p. 400)
orbital (p. 397)
organic compound (p. 394)
Pauli exclusion principle (p. 397)
perspective formula (p. 418)
pH (p. 435)
pi (π) bond (p. 415)
pK_a (p. 435)
polar covalent bond (p. 402)
proton (p. 401)
proton-transfer reaction (p. 433)
quantum mechanics (p. 396)
radial node (p. 412)
radical (p. 407)
resonance contributors (p. 447)
resonance hybrid (p. 447)
sigma (σ) bond (p. 413)
sigma bonding molecular orbital (p. 414)
single bond (p. 420)
tetrahedral bond angle (p. 419)
tetrahedral carbon (p. 419)
trigonal planar carbon (p. 421)
triple bond (p. 423)
valence electrons (p. 399)
valence-shell electron-pair repulsion (VSEPR) model (p. 417)
wave equation (p. 397)
wave function (p. 397)

PROBLEMS

71. Draw a Lewis structure for each of the following species:

a. H_2CO_3 **b.** CO_3^{2-} **c.** CH_2O **d.** N_2H_4 **e.** CH_3NH_2 **f.** $CH_3N_2^+$ **g.** CO_2 **h.** NH_2O^-

72. What is the hybridization of the central atom of each of the following species? Are the bonds around it linear, trigonal planar, or tetrahedral?

a. NH_3 **b.** BH_3 **c.** $^-CH_3$ **d.** $\cdot CH_3$ **e.** $^+NH_4$ **f.** $^+CH_3$ **g.** HCN **h.** $C(CH_3)_4$ **i.** H_3O^+ **j.** $H_2C{=}O$

73. Draw the condensed structure of a compound that contains only carbon and hydrogen atoms and that has

a. three sp^3 hybridized carbons.
b. one sp^3 hybridized carbon and two sp^2 hybridized carbons.
c. two sp^3 hybridized carbons and two sp hybridized carbons.

74. a. List the following alcohols in order of decreasing acidity (that is, list the most acidic alcohol first):

CCl_3CH_2OH	CH_2ClCH_2OH	$CHCl_2CH_2OH$
$K_a = 5.75 \times 10^{-13}$	$K_a = 1.29 \times 10^{-13}$	$K_a = 4.90 \times 10^{-13}$

b. Explain the relative acidities.

75. Predict the approximate bond angles:

a. the C—N—H bond angle in $(CH_3)_2NH$
b. the C—N—C bond angle in $(CH_3)_2NH$
c. the C—N—C bond angle in $(CH_3)_2\overset{+}{N}H_2$
d. the C—O—C bond angle in CH_3OCH_3
e. the C—O—H bond angle in CH_3OH
f. the H—C—H bond angle in $H_2C{=}O$
g. the F—B—F bond angle in $^-BF_4$
h. the C—C—N bond angle in $CH_3C{\equiv}N$
i. the C—C—N bond angle in $CH_3CH_2NH_2$

76. Draw the ground-state electronic configuration for:

a. Ca **b.** Ca^{2+} **c.** Ar **d.** Mg^{2+}

77. List the bonds in order of decreasing polarity (that is, list the most polar bond first).

a. C—O, C—F, C—N **b.** C—Cl, C—I, C—Br **c.** H—O, H—N, H—C **d.** C—H, C—C, C—N

78. Which is the stronger base?

a. HS^- or HO^- **b.** CH_3O^- or $CH_3\overset{-}{N}H$ **c.** CH_3OH or CH_3O^- **d.** Cl^- or Br^-

79. Write the Kekulé structure for each of the following compounds:

a. CH_3CHO **b.** CH_3OCH_3 **c.** CH_3COOH **d.** $(CH_3)_3COH$ **e.** $CH_3CH(OH)CH_2CN$ **f.** $(CH_3)_2CHCH(CH_3)CH_2C(CH_3)_3$

80. Draw curved arrows to show the electron flow in the following reactions:

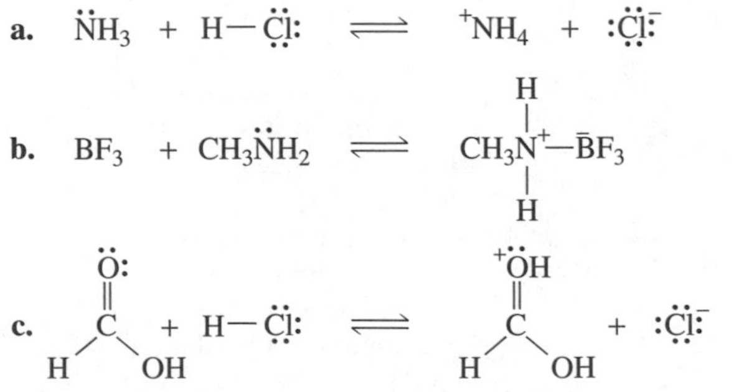

a. $\ddot{N}H_3 + H{-}\ddot{\underset{..}{Cl}}{:} \rightleftharpoons {}^+NH_4 + {:}\ddot{\underset{..}{Cl}}{:}^-$

b. $BF_3 + CH_3\ddot{N}H_2 \rightleftharpoons CH_3\overset{+}{N}H_2{-}\overset{-}{B}F_3$ (N bearing two H)

c. $H{-}C({=}\ddot{O}{:}){-}OH + H{-}\ddot{\underset{..}{Cl}}{:} \rightleftharpoons H{-}C({=}\overset{+}{\ddot{O}}H){-}OH + {:}\ddot{\underset{..}{Cl}}{:}^-$

81. Show the direction of the dipole moment in each of the following bonds (use the electronegativities given in Table 10.3):

a. $H_3C{-}Br$ **b.** $H_3C{-}Li$ **c.** $HO{-}NH_2$ **d.** I—Br **e.** $H_3C{-}OH$ **f.** $(CH_3)_2N{-}H$

82. What is the hybridization of the indicated atom in each of the following molecules?

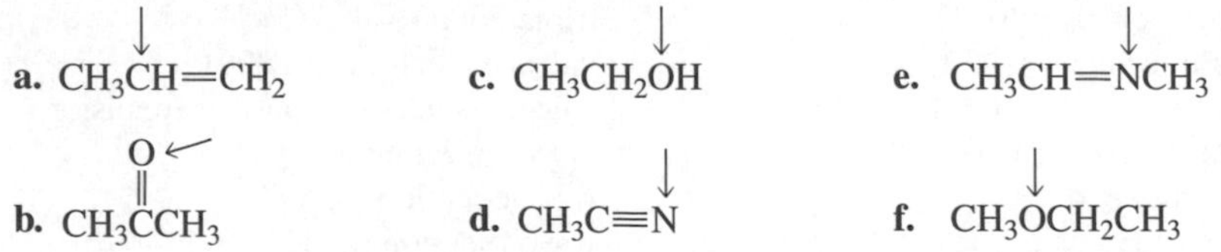

a. $CH_3\underset{\downarrow}{C}H{=}CH_2$ (arrow on CH carbon)
b. $CH_3\overset{O}{\overset{\|}{C}}CH_3$ (arrow on O)
c. $CH_3CH_2\underset{\downarrow}{O}H$ (arrow on O)
d. $CH_3C{\equiv}N$ (arrow on N)
e. $CH_3CH{=}NCH_3$ (arrow on N)
f. $CH_3OCH_2CH_3$ (arrow on O)

83. Draw the missing lone-pair electrons and assign the missing formal charges.

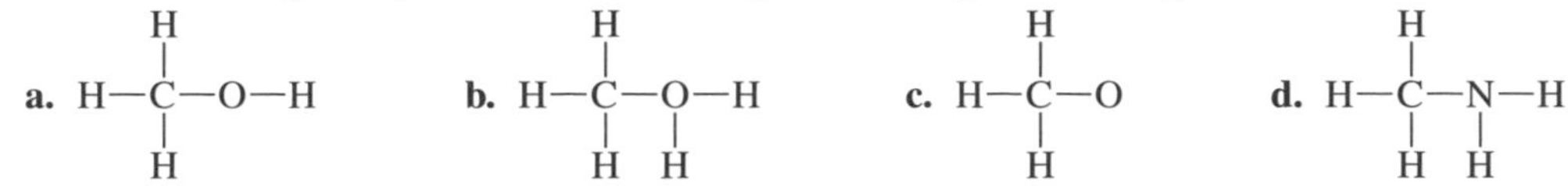

84. a. List the following carboxylic acids in order of decreasing acidity:

$CH_3CH_2CH_2COOH$ $K_a = 1.52 \times 10^{-5}$

$CH_3CH_2CHCOOH$ (Cl on C-2) $K_a = 1.39 \times 10^{-3}$

$ClCH_2CH_2CH_2COOH$ $K_a = 2.96 \times 10^{-5}$

CH_3CHCH_2COOH (Cl on C-3) $K_a = 8.9 \times 10^{-5}$

b. How does the presence of an electronegative substituent such as Cl affect the acidity of a carboxylic acid?

c. How does the location of the substituent affect the acidity of the carboxylic acid?

85. Draw the products of the following reactions:

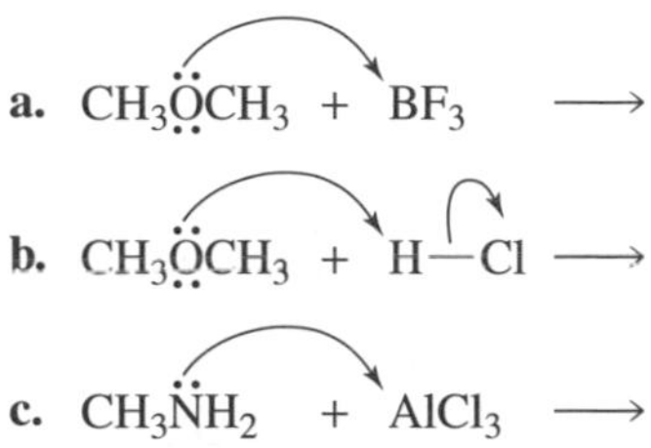

a. $CH_3\ddot{O}CH_3 + BF_3 \longrightarrow$

b. $CH_3\ddot{O}CH_3 + H{-}Cl \longrightarrow$

c. $CH_3\ddot{N}H_2 + AlCl_3 \longrightarrow$

86. a. Which of the indicated bonds in each molecule is shorter?

b. Indicate the hybridization of the C, O, and N atoms in each of the molecules.

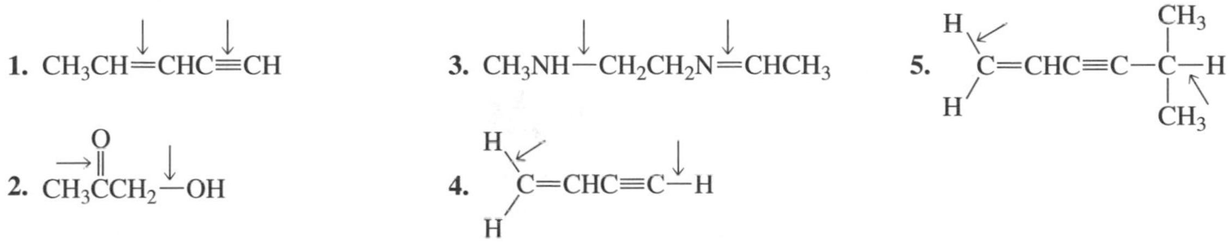

1. $CH_3CH{=}CHC{\equiv}CH$

2. $CH_3\overset{O}{\overset{\|}{C}}CH_2{-}OH$

3. $CH_3NH{-}CH_2CH_2N{=}CHCH_3$

4. $H_2C{=}CHC{\equiv}C{-}H$

5. $H_2C{=}CHC{\equiv}C{-}CH(CH_3)_2$

87. List the following compounds in order of decreasing acidity.

CH_3CH_2OH $CH_3CH_2NH_2$ CH_3CH_2SH $CH_3CH_2CH_3$

88. For each of the following compounds, draw the form in which it will predominate at pH = 3, pH = 6, pH = 10, and pH = 14:

a. CH_3COOH $pK_a = 4.8$

b. $CH_3CH_2\overset{+}{N}H_3$ $pK_a = 11.0$

c. CF_3CH_2OH $pK_a = 12.4$

89. Do the sp^2 carbons and the indicated sp^3 carbons lie in the same plane?

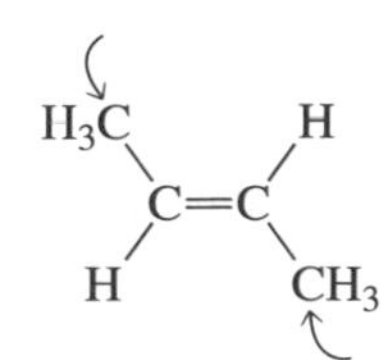

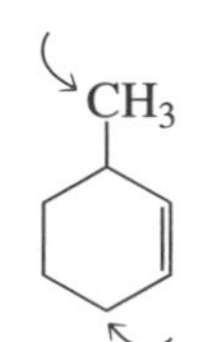

90. Give the products of the following acid–base reactions, and indicate whether reactants or products are favored at equilibrium (use the pK_a values that are given in Section 10.18):

a. $CH_3\overset{O}{\overset{\|}{C}}OH + CH_3O^- \rightleftharpoons$

b. $CH_3\overset{O}{\overset{\|}{C}}OH + CH_3NH_2 \rightleftharpoons$

c. $CH_3CH_2OH + {}^-NH_2 \rightleftharpoons$

d. $CH_3CH_2OH + HCl \rightleftharpoons$

91. a. List the following alcohols in order of decreasing acidity:
b. Explain the relative acidities.

$$CH_2{=}CHCH_2OH \qquad CH_3CH_2CH_2OH \qquad HC{\equiv}CCH_2OH$$

92. Which of the following species have a bond angle of 109.5°?

$$H_2O \quad H_3O^+ \quad {}^+CH_3 \quad BF_3 \quad NH_3 \quad {}^+NH_4 \quad {}^-CH_3$$

93. For each of the following molecules, indicate the hybridization of each carbon atom and give the approximate values of all the bond angles:

a. $CH_3C{\equiv}CH$ **b.** $CH_3CH{=}CH_2$ **c.** $CH_3CH_2CH_3$ **d.** $CH_2{=}CH{-}CH{=}CH_2$

94. a. Estimate the pK_a value of each of the following acids without using a calculator (that is, between 3 and 4, between 9 and 10, etc.):
1. nitrous acid (HNO_2), $K_a = 4.0 \times 10^{-4}$
2. nitric acid (HNO_3), $K_a = 22$
3. bicarbonate (HCO_3^-), $K_a = 6.3 \times 10^{-11}$
4. hydrogen cyanide (HCN), $K_a = 7.9 \times 10^{-10}$
5. formic acid (HCOOH), $K_a = 2.0 \times 10^{-4}$

b. Determine the pK_a values, using a calculator.
c. Which is the strongest acid?

95. Histamine is the compound that causes the symptoms associated with the common cold and with allergic responses. Which of the two nitrogen atoms in the ring is the most basic? Explain its greater basicity.

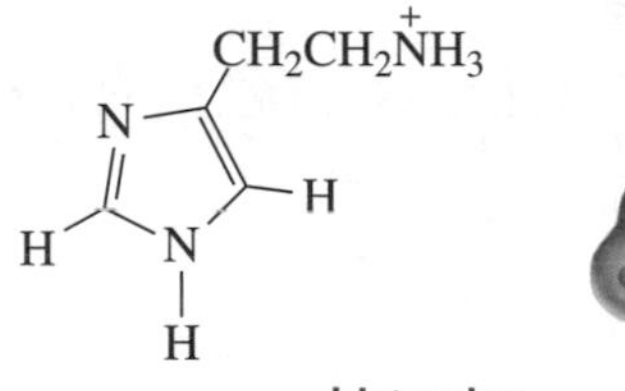

histamine

96. a. List the following carboxylic acids in order of decreasing acidity:

$CH_3CH_2CH(Br)COOH$	$CH_3CH_2CH_2COOH$	$CH_3CH_2CH(OH)COOH$	$CH_3CH_2CH(Cl)COOH$
$K_a = 1.02 \times 10^{-3}$	$K_a = 1.51 \times 10^{-5}$	$K_a = 6.03 \times 10^{-5}$	$K_a = 1.45 \times 10^{-3}$

b. Which is a more electronegative substituent, Cl or OH?

97. Draw a Lewis structure for each of the following species:

a. $CH_3N_2^+$ **b.** CH_2N_2 **c.** N_3^- **d.** N_2O (arranged NNO)

98. a. For each of the following pairs of reactions, indicate which one has the more favorable equilibrium constant (that is, which one most favors products):
1. $CH_3CH_2OH + NH_3 \rightleftharpoons CH_3CH_2O^- + \overset{+}{N}H_4$
   or
   $CH_3OH + NH_3 \rightleftharpoons CH_3O^- + \overset{+}{N}H_4$
2. $CH_3CH_2OH + NH_3 \rightleftharpoons CH_3CH_2O^- + \overset{+}{N}H_4$
   or
   $CH_3CH_2OH + CH_3NH_2 \rightleftharpoons CH_3CH_2O^- + CH_3\overset{+}{N}H_3$

b. Which of the four reactions has the most favorable equilibrium constant?

99. Citrus fruits are rich in citric acid, a compound with three COOH groups. Explain why:
a. The first pK_a (for the COOH group in the center of the molecule) is lower than the pK_a of acetic acid.

b. The third pK_a is greater than the pK_a of acetic acid.

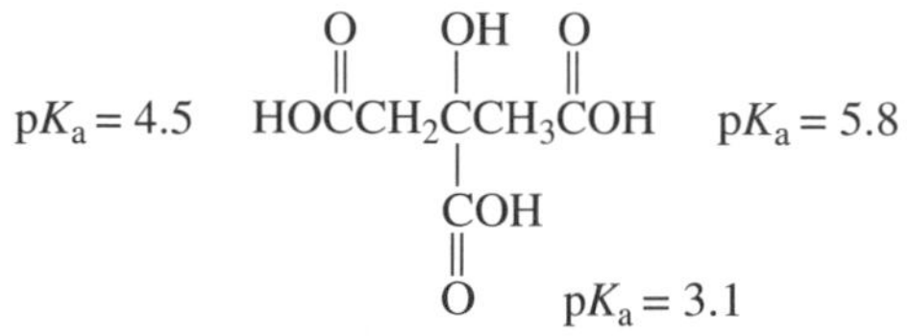

$$
\begin{array}{ccc}
 & \text{O} \quad \text{OH} \quad \text{O} & \\
 & \| \qquad | \qquad \| & \\
pK_a = 4.5 & \text{HOCCH}_2\text{CCH}_3\text{COH} & pK_a = 5.8 \\
 & | & \\
 & \text{COH} & \\
 & \| & \\
 & \text{O} \qquad pK_a = 3.1 &
\end{array}
$$

100. The following compound has two isomers:

$$\text{ClCH}{=}\text{CHCl}$$

One isomer has a dipole moment of 0 D, and the other has a dipole moment of 2.95 D. Propose structures for the two isomers that are consistent with these data.

101. Explain why the following compound is not stable:

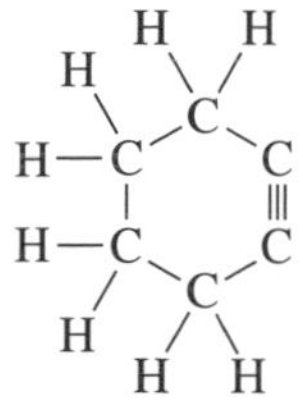

$$
\begin{array}{c}
\text{H} \quad \text{H} \\
\text{H} \quad \diagdown \; \diagup \\
\diagdown \; \text{C} \\
\text{H}-\text{C} \qquad \text{C} \\
| \qquad\quad ||| \\
\text{H}-\text{C} \qquad \text{C} \\
\diagup \; \text{C} \\
\text{H} \quad \diagup \; \diagdown \\
\text{H} \quad \text{H}
\end{array}
$$

102. Given that pH + pOH = 14 and that the concentration of water in a solution of water is 55.5 M, show that the pK_a of water is 15.7. (*Hint:* pOH = $-\log [HO^-]$.)

103. Water and diethyl ether are immiscible liquids. Charged compounds dissolve in water, and uncharged compounds dissolve in ether. Given that $C_6H_{11}COOH$ has a pK_a of 4.8 and $C_6H_{11}\overset{+}{N}H_3$ has a pK_a of 10.7.

a. What pH would you make the water layer in order to cause both compounds to dissolve in it?

b. What pH would you make the water layer in order to cause the acid to dissolve in the water layer and the amine to dissolve in the ether layer?

c. What pH would you make the water layer in order to cause the acid to dissolve in the ether layer and the amine to dissolve in the water layer?

104. How could you separate a mixture of the following compounds? The reagents available to you are water, ether, 1.0 M HCl, and 1.0 M NaOH. (*Hint:* See Problem 103.)

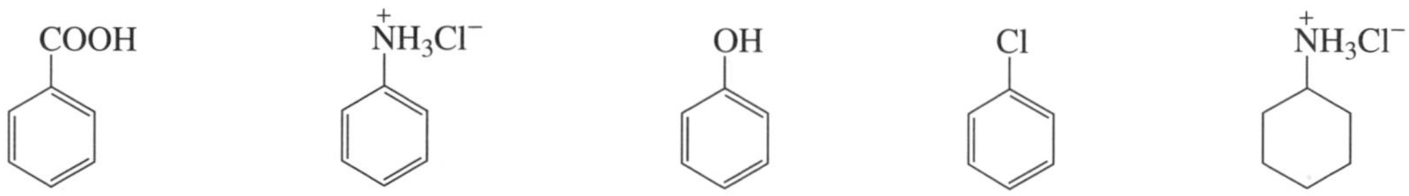

COOH (benzene ring)	$\overset{+}{N}H_3Cl^-$ (benzene ring)	OH (benzene ring)	Cl (benzene ring)	$\overset{+}{N}H_3Cl^-$ (cyclohexane ring)
$pK_a = 4.17$	$pK_a = 4.60$	$pK_a = 9.95$		$pK_a = 10.66$

105. Show that $K_{eq} = \dfrac{K_a \text{ reactant acid}}{K_a \text{ product acid}} = \dfrac{[\text{products}]}{[\text{reactants}]}$

For help in answering Problems 106–108, see Special Topic I in the *Study Guide and Solutions Manual*.

106. Carbonic acid has a pK_a of 6.1 at physiological temperature. Is the carbonic acid/bicarbonate buffer system that maintains the pH of the blood at 7.3 better at neutralizing excess acid or excess base?

107. a. If an acid with a pK_a of 5.3 is in an aqueous solution of pH 5.7, what percentage of the acid is present in the acidic form?

b. At what pH will 80% of the acid exist in the acidic form?

108. Calculate the pH values of the following solutions:

a. a 1.0 M solution of acetic acid (pK_a = 4.76)

b. a 0.1 M solution of protonated methylamine (pK_a = 10.7)

c. a solution containing 0.3 M HCOOH and 0.1 M $HCOO^-$ (pK_a of HCOOH = 3.76)

CHAPTER

11

An Introduction to Organic Compounds

Nomenclature, Physical Properties, and Representation of Structure

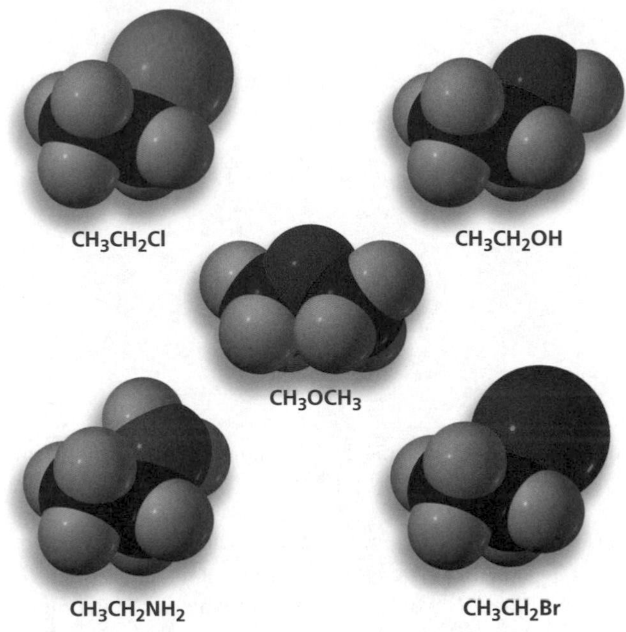

IN THIS BOOK, THE PRESENTATION OF ORGANIC CHEMISTRY IS ORGANIZED ACCORDING TO HOW organic compounds react. When a compound undergoes a reaction, a new compound is synthesized. In other words, while you are learning how organic compounds react, you are simultaneously learning how to synthesize organic compounds.

$$Y \longrightarrow Z$$

Y is reacting   Z is being synthesized

The main classes of compounds that are synthesized by the reactions we will look at are alkanes, alkyl halides, ethers, alcohols, and amines. As we learn about the reactions and synthesis of organic compounds, we will need to be able to refer to them by name. Therefore, we will begin the study of organic chemistry by learning how to name these five classes of compounds.

First we will see how *alkanes* are named because their names form the basis for the names of all the other organic compounds. **Alkanes** are composed of only carbon atoms and hydrogen atoms and contain only *single bonds*. Compounds that contain only carbon and hydrogen are called **hydrocarbons**. Thus, an alkane is a hydrocarbon that has only single bonds.

Alkanes in which the carbons form a continuous chain with no branches are called **straight-chain alkanes**. The names of several straight-chain alkanes are listed in Table 11.1. It is important that you learn the names of at least the first 10.

The family of alkanes shown in the table is an example of a homologous series. A **homologous series** (*homos* is Greek for "the same as") is a family of compounds in which each member differs from the one before it in the series by one **methylene (CH_2) group**. The members of a homologous series are called **homologs**. Propane ($CH_3CH_2CH_3$) and butane ($CH_3CH_2CH_2CH_3$) are homologs.

If you look at the relative numbers of carbon and hydrogen atoms in the alkanes listed in Table 11.1, you will see that the general molecular formula for an alkane is C_nH_{2n+2}, where n is any integer. So, if an alkane has one carbon, it must have four hydrogens; if it has two carbons, it must have six hydrogens.

Table 11.1 Nomenclature and Physical Properties of Straight-Chain Alkanes

Number of carbons	Molecular formula	Name	Condensed structure	Boiling point (°C)	Melting point (°C)	Density[a] (g/mL)
1	CH_4	methane	CH_4	−167.7	−182.5	
2	C_2H_6	ethane	CH_3CH_3	−88.6	−183.3	
3	C_3H_8	propane	$CH_3CH_2CH_3$	−42.1	−187.7	
4	C_4H_{10}	butane	$CH_3CH_2CH_2CH_3$	−0.5	−138.3	
5	C_5H_{12}	pentane	$CH_3(CH_2)_3CH_3$	36.1	−129.8	0.5572
6	C_6H_{14}	hexane	$CH_3(CH_2)_4CH_3$	68.7	−95.3	0.6603
7	C_7H_{16}	heptane	$CH_3(CH_2)_5CH_3$	98.4	−90.6	0.6837
8	C_8H_{18}	octane	$CH_3(CH_2)_6CH_3$	125.7	−56.8	0.7026
9	C_9H_{20}	nonane	$CH_3(CH_2)_7CH_3$	150.8	−53.5	0.7177
10	$C_{10}H_{22}$	decane	$CH_3(CH_2)_8CH_3$	174.0	−29.7	0.7299
11	$C_{11}H_{24}$	undecane	$CH_3(CH_2)_9CH_3$	195.8	−25.6	0.7402
12	$C_{12}H_{26}$	dodecane	$CH_3(CH_2)_{10}CH_3$	216.3	−9.6	0.7487
13	$C_{13}H_{28}$	tridecane	$CH_3(CH_2)_{11}CH_3$	235.4	−5.5	0.7546
⋮	⋮	⋮	⋮	⋮	⋮	⋮
20	$C_{20}H_{42}$	eicosane	$CH_3(CH_2)_{18}CH_3$	343.0	36.8	0.7886
21	$C_{21}H_{44}$	heneicosane	$CH_3(CH_2)_{19}CH_3$	356.5	40.5	0.7917
⋮	⋮	⋮	⋮	⋮	⋮	⋮
30	$C_{30}H_{62}$	triacontane	$CH_3(CH_2)_{28}CH_3$	449.7	65.8	0.8097

[a]Density is temperature dependent. The densities given are those determined at 20 °C ($d^{20°}$).

We have seen that carbon forms four covalent bonds and hydrogen forms only one covalent bond (Section 10.4). This means that there is only one possible structure for an alkane with molecular formula CH_4 (methane) and only one structure for an alkane with molecular formula C_2H_6 (ethane). We examined the structures of these compounds in Section 10.7. There is also only one possible structure for an alkane with molecular formula C_3H_8 (propane).

name	Kekulé structure	condensed structure	ball-and-stick model
methane	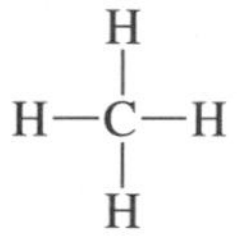 H—C—H with H above and below C	CH_4	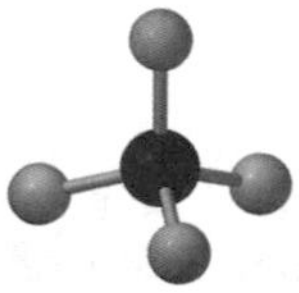
ethane	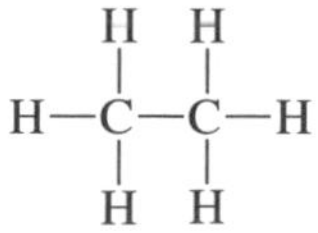 H—C—C—H with H above and below each C	CH_3CH_3	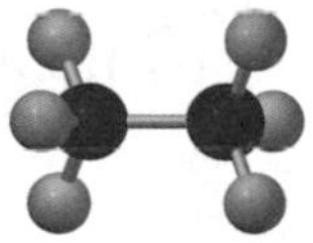
propane	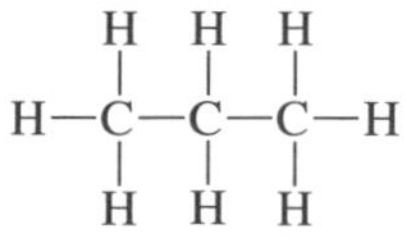 H—C—C—C—H with H above and below each C	$CH_3CH_2CH_3$	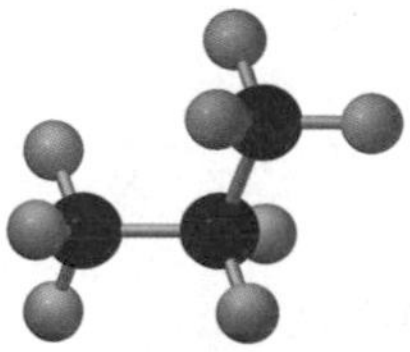
butane	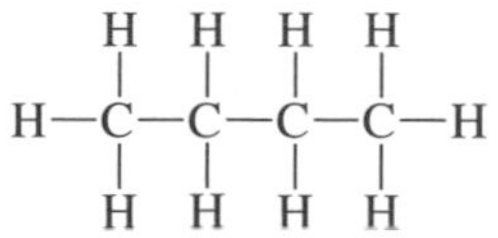 H—C—C—C—C—H with H above and below each C	$CH_3CH_2CH_2CH_3$	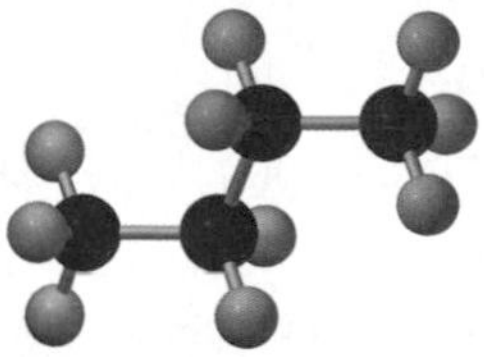

However, there are two possible structures for an alkane with molecular formula C_4H_{10}. In addition to butane—a straight-chain alkane—there is a branched butane called isobutane. Both of these structures fulfill the requirement that each carbon forms four bonds and each hydrogen forms one bond.

$CH_3CH_2CH_2CH_3$ **butane**

CH_3CHCH_3 with CH_3 on C-2 **isobutane**

$CH_3CH—$ with CH_3 **an "iso" structural unit**

Compounds such as butane and isobutane that have the same molecular formula but differ in the order in which the atoms are connected are called **constitutional isomers**—their molecules have different constitutions. In fact, isobutane got its name because it is an "iso"mer of butane. The structural unit consisting of a carbon bonded to a hydrogen and two CH_3 groups—that occurs in isobutane—has come to be called "iso." Thus, the name isobutane tells you that the compound is a four-carbon alkane with an iso structural unit.

There are three alkanes with molecular formula C_5H_{12}. You have already learned how to name two of them. Pentane is the straight-chain alkane. Isopentane, as its name indicates, has an iso structural unit and five carbons. We cannot name the other branched-chain alkane without defining a name for a new structural unit. (For now, ignore the names written in blue.)

$CH_3CH_2CH_2CH_2CH_3$ **pentane**

$CH_3CHCH_2CH_3$ with CH_3 on C-2 **isopentane**

CH_3CCH_3 with two CH_3 on C-2 **2,2-dimethylpropane**

There are five constitutional isomers with molecular formula C_6H_{14}. Again, we are able to name only two of them, unless we define new structural units.

common name: / **systematic name:**

$CH_3CH_2CH_2CH_2CH_2CH_3$ **hexane** / **hexane**

$CH_3CHCH_2CH_2CH_3$ with CH_3 on C-2 **isohexane** / **2-methylpentane**

$CH_3CCH_2CH_3$ with two CH_3 on C-2 **2,2-dimethylbutane**

$CH_3CH_2CHCH_2CH_3$ with CH_3 on C-3 **3-methylpentane**

$CH_3CH—CHCH_3$ with CH_3 on C-2 and C-3 **2,3-dimethylbutane**

There are nine alkanes with molecular formula C_7H_{16}. We can name only two of them (heptane and isoheptane).

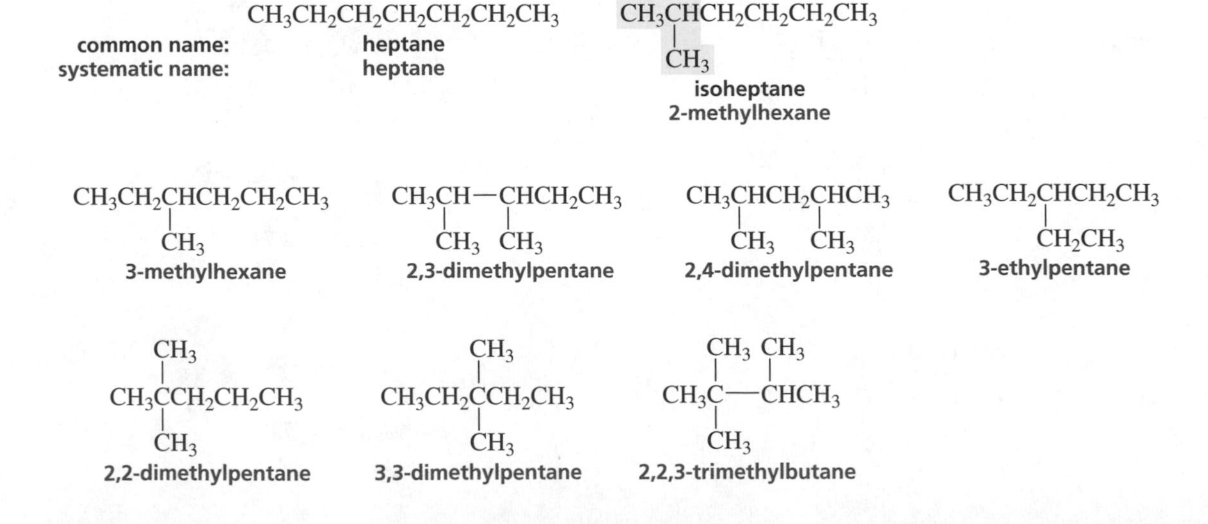

The number of constitutional isomers increases rapidly as the number of carbons in an alkane increases. For example, there are 75 alkanes with molecular formula $C_{10}H_{22}$ and 4347 alkanes with molecular formula $C_{15}H_{32}$. To avoid having to memorize the names of thousands of structural units, chemists have devised rules for creating systematic names that describe the compound's structure. That way, only the rules have to be learned. Because the name describes the structure, these rules make it possible to deduce the structure of a compound from its name.

This method of nomenclature is called **systematic nomenclature**. It is also called **IUPAC nomenclature** because it was designed by a commission of the International Union of Pure and Applied Chemistry (abbreviated IUPAC and pronounced "eye-you-pack") at a meeting in Geneva, Switzerland, in 1892. The IUPAC rules have been continually revised by the commission since then. A name such as isobutane—a nonsystematic name—is called a **common name**. When both names are shown in this book, common names will be shown in red and systematic (IUPAC) names in blue. Before we can understand how a systematic name for an alkane is constructed, we must learn how to name alkyl substituents.

11.1 HOW ALKYL SUBSTITUENTS ARE NAMED

Removing a hydrogen from an alkane results in an **alkyl substituent** (or an alkyl group). Alkyl substituents are named by replacing the "ane" ending of the alkane with "yl." The letter "R" is used to indicate any alkyl group.

CH_3— a methyl group; CH_3CH_2— an ethyl group; $CH_3CH_2CH_2$— a propyl group; $CH_3CH_2CH_2CH_2$— a butyl group

$CH_3CH_2CH_2CH_2CH_2$— a pentyl group; R— any alkyl group

If a hydrogen in an alkane is replaced by an OH, the compound becomes an **alcohol**; if it is replaced by an NH_2, the compound becomes an **amine**; if it is replaced by a halogen, the compound becomes an **alkyl halide**, and if it is replaced by an OR, the compound becomes an **ether**.

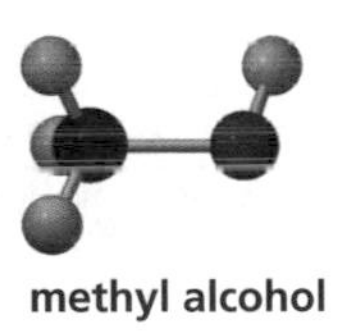
methyl alcohol

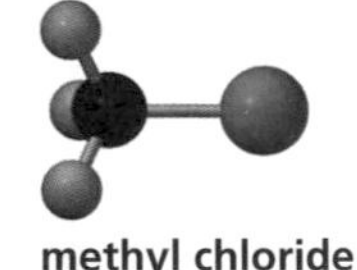
methyl chloride

methylamine

R—OH an alcohol; R—NH_2 an amine; R—X an alkyl halide (X = F, Cl, Br, or I); R—O—R an ether

The alkyl group name followed by the name of the class of the compound (alcohol, amine, etc.) yields the common name of the compound. The two alkyl groups in ethers are listed in alphabetical order. The following examples show how alkyl group names are used to build common names:

CH_3OH	$CH_3CH_2NH_2$	$CH_3CH_2CH_2Br$	$CH_3CH_2CH_2CH_2Cl$
methyl alcohol	ethylamine	propyl bromide	butyl chloride
CH_3I	CH_3CH_2OH	$CH_3CH_2CH_2NH_2$	$CH_3CH_2OCH_3$
methyl iodide	ethyl alcohol	propylamine	ethyl methyl ether

Notice that for most compounds there is a space between the name of the alkyl group and the name of the class of compound. For amines, however, the entire name is written as one word.

PROBLEM 1 ♦

Name each of the following:

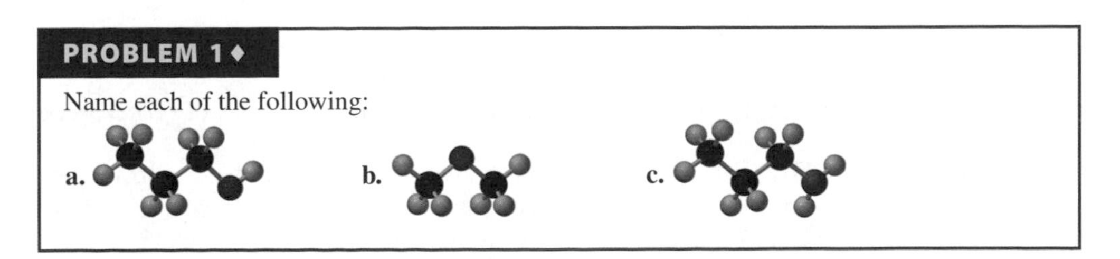

Two alkyl groups—the propyl group and the isopropyl group—have three carbons. A propyl group is obtained when a hydrogen is removed from a *primary carbon* of propane. A **primary carbon** is a carbon bonded to only one other carbon. An isopropyl group is obtained when a hydrogen is removed from the *secondary carbon* of propane. A **secondary carbon** is a carbon bonded to two other carbons. Notice that an isopropyl group, as its name indicates, has its three carbon atoms arranged as an iso structural unit.

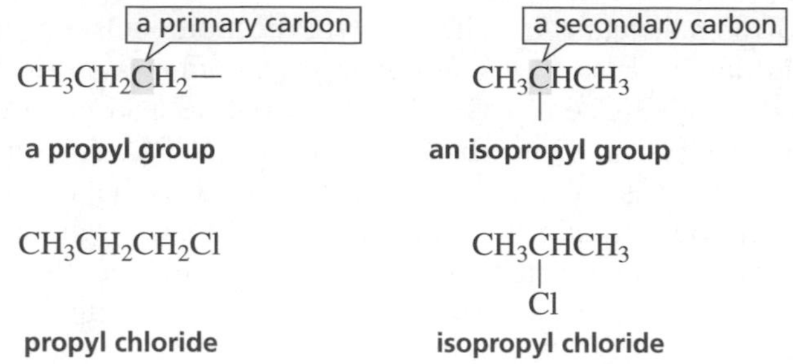

a primary carbon

$CH_3CH_2CH_2—$

a propyl group

a secondary carbon

CH_3CHCH_3
 |

an isopropyl group

$CH_3CH_2CH_2Cl$

propyl chloride

CH_3CHCH_3
 |
 Cl

isopropyl chloride

Molecular structures can be drawn in different ways. Isopropyl chloride, for example, is drawn below in two different ways. Both representations depict the same compound, although, at first glance, the two-dimensional representations appear to be different: the methyl groups are placed at opposite ends in one structure and at right angles in the other. The structures are identical, however, because carbon is tetrahedral. The four groups bonded to the central carbon—a hydrogen, a chlorine, and two methyl groups—point to the corners of a tetrahedron. If you rotate the three-dimensional model on the right 90° in a clockwise direction, you should be able to see that the two models are the same.

two different ways to draw isopropyl chloride

CH_3CHCH_3
 |
 Cl

CH_3CHCl
 |
 CH_3

Build models of the two representations of isopropyl chloride to see that they represent the same compound.

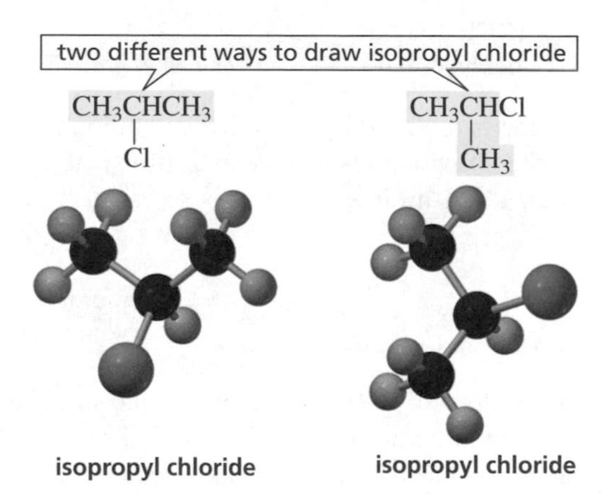

isopropyl chloride **isopropyl chloride**

There are four alkyl groups that have four carbons. Two of them, the butyl and isobutyl groups, have a hydrogen removed from a primary carbon. A *sec*-butyl group has a hydrogen removed from a secondary carbon (*sec*-, often abbreviated *s*-, stands for secondary), and a *tert*-butyl group has a hydrogen removed from a tertiary carbon (*tert*-, sometimes abbreviated *t*-, stands for tertiary). A **tertiary carbon** is a carbon that is bonded to three other carbons. Notice that the isobutyl group is the only group with an iso structural unit.

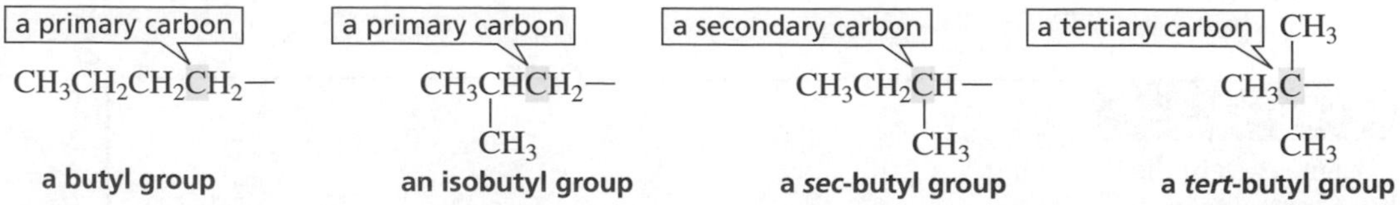

a primary carbon

$CH_3CH_2CH_2CH_2—$

a butyl group

a primary carbon

$CH_3CHCH_2—$
 |
 CH_3

an isobutyl group

a secondary carbon

$CH_3CH_2CH—$
 |
 CH_3

a *sec*-butyl group

a tertiary carbon

 CH_3
 |
$CH_3C—$
 |
 CH_3

a *tert*-butyl group

A primary carbon is bonded to one carbon, a secondary carbon is bonded to two carbons, and a tertiary carbon is bonded to three carbons.

The names of straight-chain alkyl groups often have the prefix "*n*" (for "normal") to emphasize that the carbons are in an unbranched chain. If a name does not have a prefix such as "*n*" or "iso," we assume that the carbons are in an unbranched chain.

$CH_3CH_2CH_2CH_2Br$	$CH_3CH_2CH_2CH_2CH_2F$
butyl bromide	**pentyl fluoride**
or	or
***n*-butyl bromide**	***n*-pentyl fluoride**

Like the carbons, the hydrogens in a molecule are also referred to as primary, secondary, and tertiary. **Primary hydrogens** are attached to primary carbons, **secondary hydrogens** to secondary carbons, and **tertiary hydrogens** to tertiary carbons.

Primary hydrogens are attached to a primary carbon, secondary hydrogens to a secondary carbon, and tertiary hydrogens to a tertiary carbon.

primary hydrogens: $CH_3CH_2CH_2CH_2OH$

secondary hydrogens: CH_3CH_2CHOH (with CH_3 on the third carbon)

tertiary hydrogen: CH_3CHCH_2OH (with CH_3 on the second carbon)

A chemical name must specify one compound only. The prefix "*sec*," therefore, can only be used with *sec*-butyl compounds. The name "*sec*-pentyl" cannot be used because pentane has two different secondary carbons, which means that removing a hydrogen from a secondary carbon of pentane produces one of two different alkyl groups, depending on which hydrogen is removed. As a result, *sec*-pentyl chloride would specify two different alkyl chorides, and, therefore, it is not a correct name.

A name must specify one compound only.

Both alkyl halides have five carbon atoms with a chlorine attached to a secondary carbon, but two compounds cannot be named *sec*-pentyl chloride.

$CH_3CHCH_2CH_2CH_3$ (Cl on the second carbon) $CH_3CH_2CHCH_2CH_3$ (Cl on the third carbon)

The prefix "*tert*" can be used for both *tert*-butyl and *tert*-pentyl compounds because each of these substituent names describes only one alkyl group. The name "*tert*-hexyl" cannot be used because it describes two different alkyl groups.

$CH_3C(CH_3)_2{-}Br$ — ***tert*-butyl bromide**

$CH_3C(CH_3)(CH_2CH_3){-}Br$ — ***tert*-pentyl bromide**

$CH_3CH_2C(CH_2CH_3)(CH_3){-}Br$ $CH_3CH_2CH_2C(CH_3)(CH_3){-}Br$

Both alkyl bromides have six carbon atoms with a bromine attached to a tertiary carbon, but two compounds cannot be named *tert*-hexyl bromide.

If you examine the following structures, you will see that whenever the prefix "iso" is used, the iso structural unit will be at one end of the molecule and any group replacing a hydrogen will be at the other end:

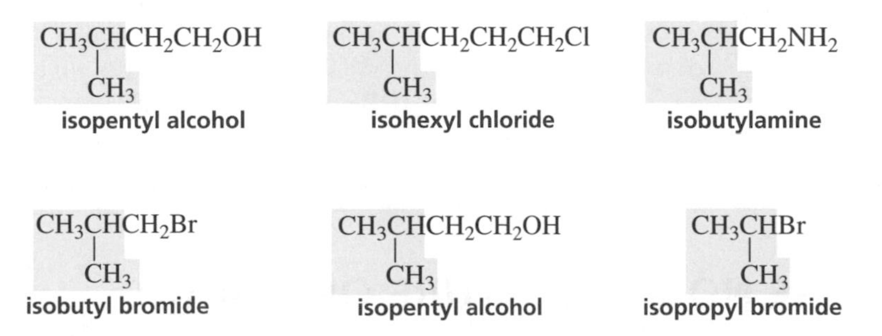

Notice that an iso group has a methyl group on the next-to-the-last carbon in the chain. Notice also that all isoalkyl compounds have the substituent (OH, Cl, NH_2, etc.) on a primary carbon, except for isopropyl, which has the substituent on a secondary carbon. Thus, the isopropyl group could have been called a *sec*-propyl group. Either name would have been appropriate because the group has an iso structural unit and a hydrogen has been removed from a secondary carbon. Chemists decided to call it isopropyl, however, which means that "*sec*" is used only for *sec*-butyl.

Alkyl group names are used so frequently that you need to learn them. Some of the most common alkyl group names are compiled in Table 11.2.

Table 11.2 Names of Some Common Alkyl Groups

methyl	CH_3	isobutyl	CH_3CHCH_2	pentyl	$CH_3CH_2CH_2CH_2CH_2$
ethyl	CH_3CH_2		CH_3	isopentyl	$CH_3CHCH_2CH_2$
propyl	$CH_3CH_2CH_2$	*sec*-butyl	CH_3CH_2CH		CH_3
isopropyl	CH_3CH		CH_3	hexyl	$CH_3CH_2CH_2CH_2CH_2CH_2$
	CH_3		CH_3	isohexyl	$CH_3CHCH_2CH_2CH_2$
butyl	$CH_3CH_2CH_2CH_2$	*tert*-butyl	CH_3C		CH_3
			CH_3		

PROBLEM 2 ♦

Draw the structure and give the systematic name of a compound with molecular formula C_5H_{12} that has

a. one tertiary carbon.

b. no secondary carbons.

PROBLEM 3 ♦

Draw the structures and name the four constitutional isomers with molecular formula C_4H_9Br.

PROBLEM 4 ♦

Which of the following statements can be used to prove that carbon is tetrahedral?

a. Methyl bromide does not have constitutional isomers.
b. Tetrachloromethane does not have a dipole moment.
c. Dibromomethane does not have constitutional isomers.

PROBLEM 5 ♦

Write a structure for each of the following:

a. isopropyl alcohol
b. isopentyl fluoride
c. *sec*-butyl iodide
d. *tert*-pentyl alcohol
e. *tert*-butylamine
f. *n*-octyl bromide

chem place Tutorial: Degree of alkyl substitution

PROBLEM 6 ♦

Name the following:

a. $CH_3OCH_2CH_3$

b. $CH_3OCH_2CH_2CH_3$

c. $CH_3CH_2CHNH_2$ (with CH_3 on the CH)

d. $CH_3CH_2CH_2CH_2OH$

e. CH_3CHCH_2Br (with CH_3 on the CH)

f. CH_3CH_2CHCl (with CH_3 on the CH)

11.2 THE NOMENCLATURE OF ALKANES

The systematic name of an alkane is obtained using the following rules:

1. Determine the number of carbons in the longest continuous carbon chain. This chain is called the **parent hydrocarbon**. The name that indicates the number of carbons in the parent hydrocarbon becomes the alkane's "last name." For example, a parent hydrocarbon with eight carbons would be called *octane*. The longest continuous chain is not always a straight chain; sometimes you have to "turn a corner" to obtain the longest continuous chain.

First, determine the number of carbons in the longest continuous chain.

$\overset{8}{CH_3}\overset{7}{CH_2}\overset{6}{CH_2}\overset{5}{CH_2}\overset{4}{CH}\overset{3}{CH_2}\overset{2}{CH_2}\overset{1}{CH_3}$ with CH_3 on C4

4-methyloctane

$\overset{8}{CH_3}\overset{7}{CH_2}\overset{6}{CH_2}\overset{5}{CH_2}\overset{4}{CH}CH_2CH_3$ with $\underset{3}{CH_2}\underset{2}{CH_2}\underset{1}{CH_3}$ on C4

4-ethyloctane

three different alkanes with an eight-carbon parent hydrocarbon

$CH_3CH_2CH_2\overset{4}{CH}\overset{3}{CH_2}\overset{2}{CH_2}\overset{1}{CH_3}$ with $\underset{5}{CH_2}\underset{6}{CH_2}\underset{7}{CH_2}\underset{8}{CH_3}$ on C4

4-propyloctane

2. The name of any alkyl substituent that hangs off the parent hydrocarbon is placed in front of the name of the parent hydrocarbon, together with a number to designate the carbon to which the alkyl substituent is attached. The carbons in the parent chain are numbered in the direction that gives the substituent as low a number as possible. The substituent's name and the name of the parent hydrocarbon are joined into one word, preceded by a hyphen that connects the number and the substituent's name.

$\overset{1}{CH_3}\overset{2}{CH}\overset{3}{CH_2}\overset{4}{CH_2}\overset{5}{CH_3}$ with CH_3 on C2

2-methylpentane

$\overset{6}{CH_3}\overset{5}{CH_2}\overset{4}{CH_2}\overset{3}{CH}\overset{2}{CH_2}\overset{1}{CH_3}$ with CH_2CH_3 on C3

3-ethylhexane

$\overset{1}{CH_3}\overset{2}{CH_2}\overset{3}{CH_2}\overset{4}{CH}\overset{5}{CH_2}\overset{6}{CH_2}\overset{7}{CH_2}\overset{8}{CH_3}$ with $CHCH_3$ (bearing CH_3) on C4

4-isopropyloctane

Number the chain in the direction that gives the substituent the lower number.

Notice that only systematic names have numbers; common names never contain numbers.

$CH_3CHCH_2CH_2CH_3$ with CH_3 on C2

common name: isohexane
systematic name: 2-methylpentane

Numbers are used only for systematic names, never for common names.

3. If more than one substituent is attached to the parent hydrocarbon, the chain is numbered in the direction that will produce a name containing the lowest of the possible numbers. The substituents are listed in alphabetical (not numerical) order, with each substituent preceded by the appropriate number. In the following example, the correct name (5-ethyl-3-methyloctane) contains a 3 as its lowest number, whereas the incorrect name (4-ethyl-6-methyloctane) contains a 4 as its lowest number:

$CH_3CH_2CHCH_2CHCH_2CH_2CH_3$ with CH_3 and CH_2CH_3 substituents

5-ethyl-3-methyloctane
not
4-ethyl-6-methyloctane
because 3 < 4

Substituents are listed in alphabetical order.

If two or more substituents are the same, the prefixes "di," "tri," and "tetra" are used to indicate how many identical substituents the compound has. The numbers indicating the locations of the identical substituents are listed together, separated by commas. Notice that there must be as many numbers in a name as there are substituents. The prefixes "di," "tri," "tetra," "*sec*," and "*tert*" are ignored in alphabetizing substituent groups, but the prefixes "iso" and "cyclo" ("cyclo" is introduced in Section 11.3) are not ignored.

$CH_3CH_2CHCH_2CHCH_3$ with two CH_3 substituents

2,4-dimethylhexane

$CH_3CH_2CCH_2CH_2CHCH_3$ with CH_2CH_3 and CH_3 on the quaternary carbon and CH_3 on the CH

5-ethyl-2,5-dimethylheptane

A number and a word are separated by a hyphen; numbers are separated by a comma.

di, tri, tetra, *sec*, and *tert* are ignored in alphabetizing.

iso and cyclo are not ignored in alphabetizing.

CH_2CH_3 CH_3
$CH_3CH_2CCH_2CH_2CHCHCH_2CH_2CH_3$
CH_2CH_3 CH_2CH_3
3,3,6-triethyl-7-methyldecane

CH_3
$CH_3CH_2CH_2CHCH_2CH_2CHCH_3$
CH_3CHCH_3
5-isopropyl-2-methyloctane

4. When numbering in either direction leads to the same lowest number for one of the substituents, the chain is numbered in the direction that gives the lowest possible number to one of the remaining substituents.

CH_3
$CH_3CCH_2CHCH_3$
CH_3 CH_3
2,2,4-trimethylpentane
not
2,4,4-trimethylpentane
because 2 < 4

CH_3 CH_2CH_3
$CH_3CH_2CHCHCH_2CHCH_2CH_3$
CH_3
6-ethyl-3,4-dimethyloctane
not
3-ethyl-5,6-dimethyloctane
because 4 < 5

5. If the same substituent numbers are obtained in both directions, the first group listed receives the lower number.

Only if the same set of numbers is obtained in both directions does the first group listed get the lower number.

Cl
$CH_3CHCHCH_3$
Br
2-bromo-3-chlorobutane
not
3-bromo-2-chlorobutane

CH_2CH_3
$CH_3CH_2CHCH_2CHCH_2CH_3$
CH_3
3-ethyl-5-methylheptane
not
5-ethyl-3-methylheptane

6. If a compound has two or more chains of the same length, the parent hydrocarbon is the chain with the greatest number of substituents.

In the case of two hydrocarbon chains with the same number of carbons, choose the one with the most substituents.

3 4 5 6
$CH_3CH_2CHCH_2CH_2CH_3$
$^2CHCH_3$
$^1CH_3$
3-ethyl-2-methylhexane (two substituents)

1 2 3 4 5 6
$CH_3CH_2CHCH_2CH_2CH_3$
$CHCH_3$
CH_3
not
3-isopropylhexane (one substituent)

7. Names such as "isopropyl," "*sec*-butyl," and "*tert*-butyl" are acceptable substituent names in the IUPAC system of nomenclature, but systematic substituent names are preferred. Systematic substituent names are obtained by numbering the alkyl substituent starting at the carbon attached to the parent hydrocarbon. This means that the carbon attached to the parent hydrocarbon is always the number-1 carbon of the substituent. In a compound such as 4-(1-methylethyl)octane, the substituent name is in parentheses; the number inside the parentheses indicates a position on the substituent, whereas the number outside the parentheses indicates a position on the parent hydrocarbon. (Note that if a prefix such as "di" is part of a branch name, it *is* included in the alphabetization.)

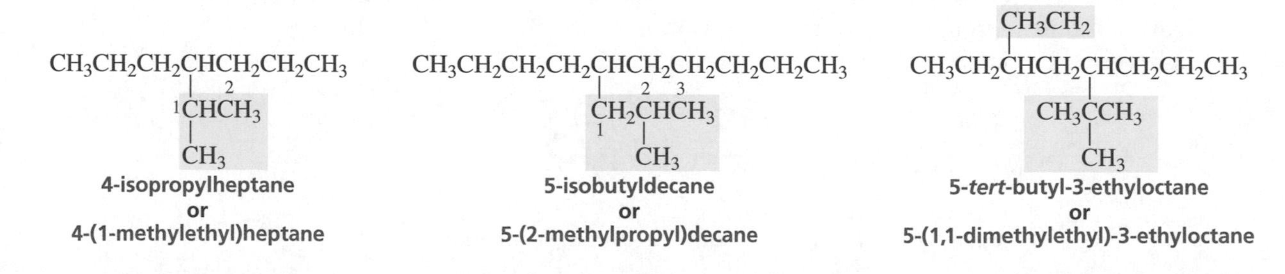

Some substituents have only a systematic name.

$$\begin{array}{c} CH_2CH_2CH_3 \\ | \\ CH_3CH_2CH_2CH_2CHCH_2CHCH_2CH_2CH_3 \\ | \\ CH_3CHCHCH_3 \\ | \\ CH_3 \end{array}$$

6-(1,2-dimethylpropyl)-4-propyldecane

$$\begin{array}{c} CH_3 \quad\quad CH_3 \\ | \quad\quad | \\ CH_3CHCHCH_2CHCH_2CHCH_2CH_3 \\ | \quad\quad | \\ CH_3 \quad\quad CH_2CH_2CH_2CH_2CH_3 \end{array}$$

2,3-dimethyl-5-(2-methylbutyl)decane

These rules will allow you to name thousands of alkanes, and eventually you will learn the additional rules necessary to name many other kinds of compounds. The rules are important for looking up a compound in the scientific literature, because it usually will be listed by its systematic name. Nevertheless, you must still learn common names because they are so entrenched in chemists' vocabularies that they are widely used in scientific conversation and are often found in the literature.

Look at the systematic names (the ones written in blue) for the isomeric hexanes and isomeric heptanes shown on page 462 to make sure you understand how they are constructed.

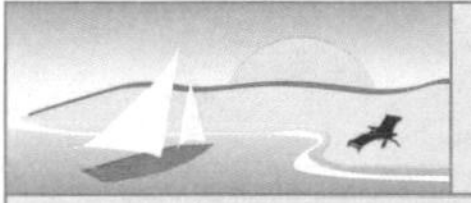

Octane Number

Gasoline engines like those used in most cars operate by creating a series of carefully-timed, controlled explosions. In the engine cylinders, fuel is mixed with air, compressed, and then ignited by a spark. When the fuel used is too easily ignited, however, the heat of compression can initiate combustion before the spark plug fires. A pinging or knocking may then be heard in the running engine.

As the quality of the fuel improves, the engine is less likely to knock. The quality of a fuel is indicated by its octane number. Straight-chain hydrocarbons have low octane numbers and make poor fuels. Heptane, for example, with an arbitrarily assigned octane number of 0, causes engines to knock badly. Branched-chain alkanes have more hydrogens bonded to primary carbons. These are the bonds that require the most energy to break and, therefore, make combustion more difficult to initiate, thereby reducing knocking. 2,2,4-Trimethylpentane, for example, does not cause knocking and has arbitrarily been assigned an octane number of 100.

The octane number of a gasoline is determined by comparing its knocking with the knocking of mixtures of heptane and 2,2,4-trimethylpentane. The octane number given to the gasoline corresponds to the percent of 2,2,4-trimethylpentane in the matching mixture. Thus, a gasoline with an octane rating of 91 has the same "knocking" property as a mixture of 91% 2,2,4-trimethylpentane and 9% heptane. The term *octane number* originated from the fact that 2,2,4-trimethylpentane contains eight carbons. Because slightly different methods are used to determine the octane number, gasoline in Canada and the United States will have an octane number that is 4 to 5 points less than the same gasoline in Europe and Australia.

$$CH_3CH_2CH_2CH_2CH_2CH_2CH_3$$

heptane
octane number = 0

$$\begin{array}{c} CH_3 \;\; CH_3 \\ | \quad\;\; | \\ CH_3CCH_2CHCH_3 \\ | \\ CH_3 \end{array}$$

2,2,4-trimethylpentane
octane number = 100

PROBLEM 7♦

Draw the structure for each of the following:

a. 2,3-dimethylhexane
b. 4-isopropyl-2,4,5-trimethylheptane
c. 4,4-diethyldecane
d. 2,2-dimethyl-4-propyloctane
e. 4-isobutyl-2,5-dimethyloctane
f. 4-(1,1-dimethylethyl)octane

PROBLEM 8 SOLVED

a. Draw the 18 isomeric octanes.
b. Give each isomer its systematic name.
c. How many isomers have common names?
d. Which isomers contain an isopropyl group?
e. Which isomers contain a *sec*-butyl group?
f. Which isomers contain a *tert*-butyl group?

Solution to 8a Start with the isomer with an eight-carbon continuous chain. Then draw isomers with a seven-carbon continuous chain plus one methyl group. Next, draw isomers with a six-carbon continuous chain plus two methyl groups or one ethyl group. Then draw isomers with a five-carbon continuous chain plus three methyl groups or one methyl group and one ethyl group. Finally, draw a four-carbon continuous chain with four methyl groups. (You will be able to tell whether you have drawn duplicate structures by your answers to Problem 8b, because if two structures have the same systematic name, they represent the same compound.)

PROBLEM 9♦

Give the systematic name for each of the following:

a. $CH_3CH_2CHCH_2CCH_3$ (with CH_3 on the third carbon; two CH_3 groups on the fifth carbon)

b. $CH_3CH_2C(CH_3)_3$

c. $CH_3CH_2CH_2CHCH_2CH_2CH_3$ (with $CH_3CHCH_2CH_3$ attached to the fourth carbon)

d. $CH_3CHCH_2CH_2CCH_3$ (with CH_3 on the second carbon; two CH_3 groups on the fifth carbon)

e. $CH_3CH_2C(CH_2CH_3)_2CH(CH_3)CH(CH_2CH_2CH_3)_2$

f. $CH_3C{-}CHCH_2CH_3$ (with CH_3 and $CH_2CH_2CH_3$ on the second carbon; $CH_2CH_2CH_3$ on the third carbon)

g. $CH_3CH_2C(CH_2CH_3)_2CH_2CH_2CH_3$

h. $CH_3CH_2CH_2CH_2CHCH_2CH_2CH_3$ (with $CH(CH_3)_2$ on the fifth carbon)

i. $CH_3CHCH_2CH_2CHCH_3$ (with CH_2CH_3 on the second carbon; CH_3 on the fifth carbon)

chem place Tutorial: Basic nomenclature of alkanes

PROBLEM 10♦

Draw the structure and give the systematic name of a compound with molecular formula C_5H_{12} that has

a. only primary and secondary hydrogens.
b. only primary hydrogens.
c. one tertiary hydrogen.
d. two secondary hydrogens.

11.3 THE NOMENCLATURE OF CYCLOALKANES • SKELETAL STRUCTURES

Cycloalkanes are alkanes with their carbon atoms arranged in a ring. Because of the ring, a cycloalkane has two fewer hydrogens than an acyclic (noncyclic) alkane with the same number of carbons. This means that the general molecular formula for a cycloalkane is C_nH_{2n}. Cycloalkanes are named by adding the prefix "cyclo" to the alkane name that signifies the number of carbons in the ring.

cyclopropane	cyclobutane	cyclopentane	cyclohexane
CH_2, $H_2C{-}CH_2$	$H_2C{-}CH_2$, $H_2C{-}CH_2$	CH_2, H_2C CH_2, $H_2C{-}CH_2$	CH_2, H_2C CH_2, H_2C CH_2, CH_2

Cycloalkanes are almost always written as **skeletal structures**. Skeletal structures show the carbon–carbon bonds as lines, but do not show the carbons or the hydrogens bonded to carbons. Atoms other than carbon are shown, and hydrogens bonded to atoms other than carbon are shown. Each vertex in a skeletal structure represents a carbon, and each carbon is understood to be bonded to the appropriate number of hydrogens to give the carbon four bonds.

cyclopropane cyclobutane cyclopentane cyclohexane

Acyclic molecules can also be represented by skeletal structures. In skeletal structures of acyclic molecules, the carbon chains are represented by zigzag lines. Again, each vertex represents a carbon, and carbons are assumed to be present where a line begins or ends.

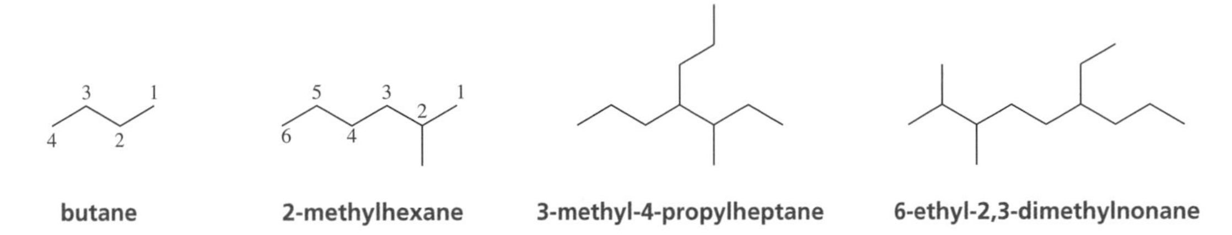

butane 2-methylhexane 3-methyl-4-propylheptane 6-ethyl-2,3-dimethylnonane

The rules for naming cycloalkanes resemble the rules for naming acyclic alkanes:

1. In a cycloalkane with an attached alkyl substituent, the ring is the parent hydrocarbon unless the substituent has more carbons than the ring. In that case, the substituent is the parent hydrocarbon and the ring is named as a substituent. There is no need to number the position of a single substituent on a ring.

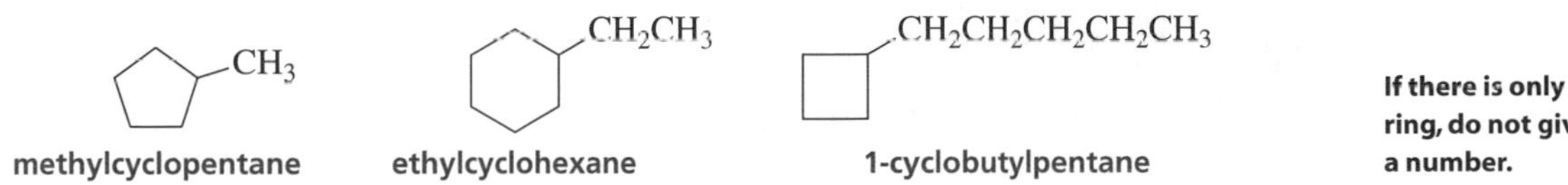

methylcyclopentane ethylcyclohexane 1-cyclobutylpentane

If there is only one substituent on a ring, do not give that substituent a number.

2. If the ring has two different substituents, they are listed in *alphabetical order* and the number-1 position is given to the substituent listed first.

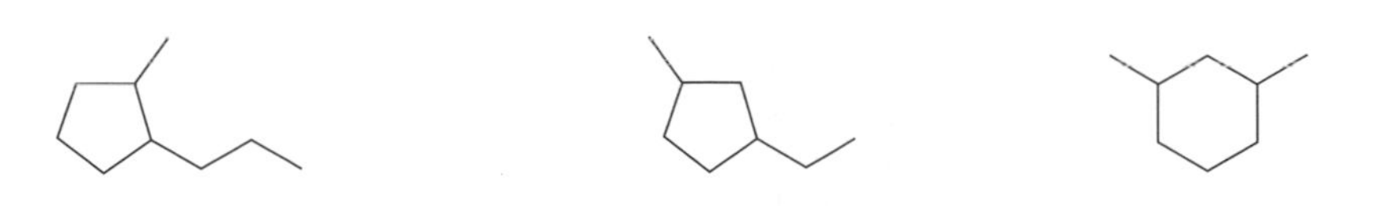

1-methyl-2-propylcyclopentane 1-ethyl-3-methylcyclopentane 1,3-dimethylcyclohexane

3. If there are more than two substituents on the ring, they are listed in alphabetical order, and the substituent given the number-1 position is the one that results in a second substituent getting as low a number as possible. If two substituents have the same low numbers, the ring is numbered—either clockwise or counterclockwise—in the direction that gives the third substituent the lowest possible number. For example, the correct name of the compound below on the left is 4-ethyl-2-methyl-1-propylcyclohexane, not 5-ethyl-1-methyl-2-propylcyclohexane:

4-ethyl-2-methyl-1-propylcyclohexane
not
1-ethyl-3-methyl-4-propylcyclohexane
because 2 < 3
not
5-ethyl-1-methyl-2-propylcyclohexane
because 4 < 5

1,1,2-trimethylcyclopentane
not
1,2,2-trimethylcyclopentane
because 1 < 2
not
1,1,5-trimethylcyclopentane
because 2 < 5

PROBLEM-SOLVING STRATEGY

Interpreting a Skeletal Structure

Write the number of hydrogens attached to each of the indicated carbons in the following compound:

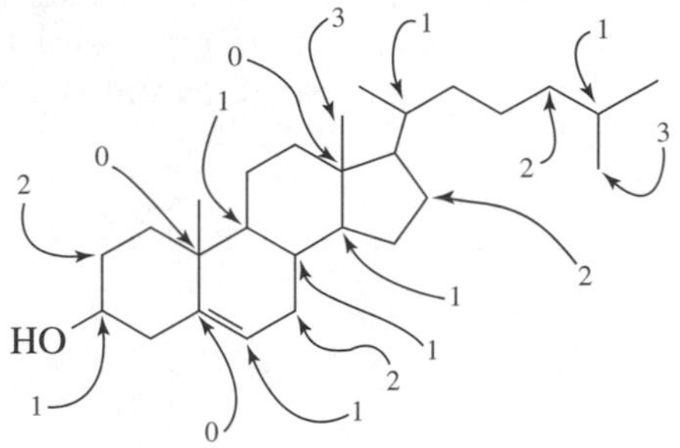

cholesterol

All the carbons in the compound are neutral, so each needs to be bonded to four atoms. Thus if the carbon has only one bond showing, it must be attached to three hydrogens that are not shown; if the carbon has two bonds showing, it must be attached to two hydrogens that are not shown, and so on.

Now continue on to Problem 11.

PROBLEM 11

Write the number of hydrogens attached to each of the indicated carbons in the following compound:

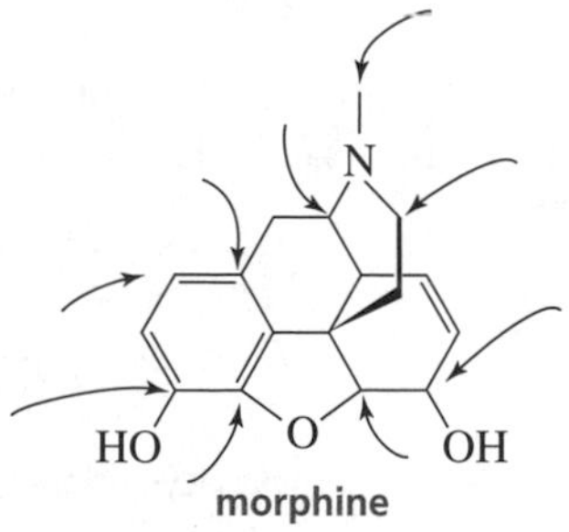

morphine

PROBLEM 12♦

Convert the following condensed structures into skeletal structures (remember that condensed structures show atoms but few, if any, bonds, whereas skeletal structures show bonds but few, if any, atoms):

a. $CH_3CH_2CH_2CH_2CH_2CH_2OH$

b. $CH_3CH_2CH_2CH_2CH_2CH_3$

c. $CH_3CH_2\overset{\overset{CH_3}{|}}{C}HCH_2\overset{\overset{CH_3}{|}}{C}HCH_2CH_3$

d. $CH_3CH_2CH_2CH_2OCH_3$

e. $CH_3CH_2NHCH_2CH_2CH_3$

f. $CH_3\overset{\overset{CH_3}{|}}{C}HCH_2CH_2\underset{\underset{Br}{|}}{C}HCH_3$

PROBLEM 13

Convert the structures in Problem 9 into skeletal structures.

PROBLEM 14

Draw the condensed and skeletal structures for:

a. 3,4-diethyl-2-methylheptane

b. 2,2,5-trimethylhexane

PROBLEM 15 ♦

Give the systematic name for each of the following:

a.

b.

c.

d.

e.

f.

g.

h.

chem place Tutorial: Alkyl group nomenclature

Tutorial: Advanced alkane nomenclature

11.4 THE NOMENCLATURE OF ALKYL HALIDES

The number of alkyl groups attached to the carbon to which the halogen is bonded determines whether an alkyl halide is primary, secondary, or tertiary.

An **alkyl halide** is a compound in which a hydrogen of an alkane has been replaced by a halogen. Alkyl halides are classified as primary, secondary, or tertiary, depending on the carbon to which the halogen is attached. **Primary alkyl halides** have a halogen bonded to a primary carbon, **secondary alkyl halides** have a halogen bonded to a secondary carbon, and **tertiary alkyl halides** have a halogen bonded to a tertiary carbon (Section 11.1). The lone-pair electrons on the halogens are generally not shown unless they are needed to draw your attention to some chemical property of the atom.

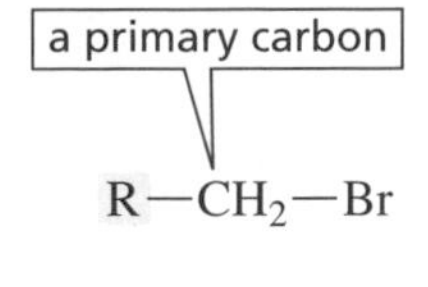

a primary alkyl halide

a secondary carbon

$R—CH—R$ (with Br on CH)

a secondary alkyl halide

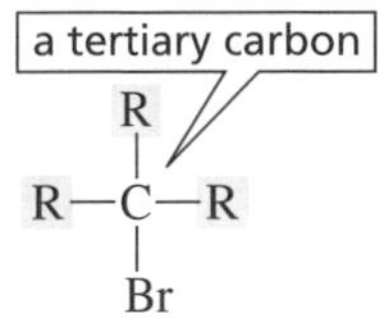

a tertiary alkyl halide

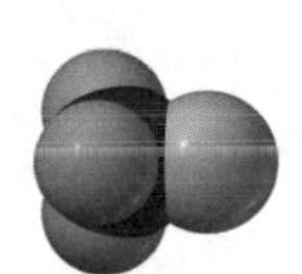

CH_3F
methyl fluoride

CH_3Cl
methyl chloride

CH_3Br
methyl bromide

CH_3I
methyl iodide

The common names of alkyl halides consist of the name of the alkyl group, followed by the name of the halogen—with the "ine" ending of the halogen name replaced by "ide" (that is, fluoride, chloride, bromide, iodide).

	CH_3Cl	CH_3CH_2F	CH_3CHI (with CH_3 on CH)	CH_3CH_2CHBr (with CH_3 on CH)
common name:	methyl chloride	ethyl fluoride	isopropyl iodide	*sec*-butyl bromide
systematic name:	chloromethane	fluoroethane	2-iodopropane	2-bromobutane

In the IUPAC system, alkyl halides are named as substituted alkanes. The prefixes for the halogens end with "o" (that is, "fluoro," "chloro," "bromo," "iodo"). Therefore, alkyl halides are often called haloalkanes. Notice that although a name must specify only one compound, a compound can have more than one name.

A compound can have more than one name, but a name must specify only one compound.

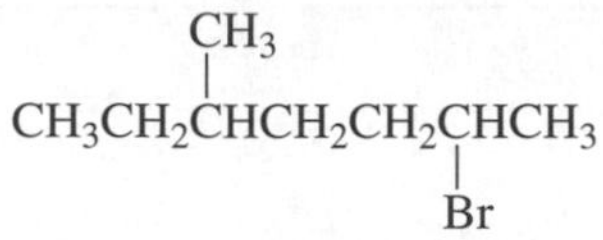

$$\underset{\text{Br}}{\overset{\text{CH}_3}{\text{CH}_3\text{CH}_2\text{CHCH}_2\text{CH}_2\text{CHCH}_3}}$$

2-bromo-5-methylheptane

Cl

1-chloro-6,6-dimethylheptane

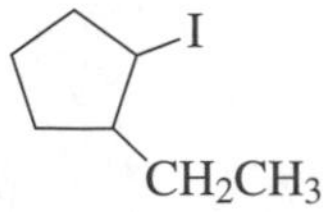

I

CH_2CH_3

1-ethyl-2-iodocyclopentane

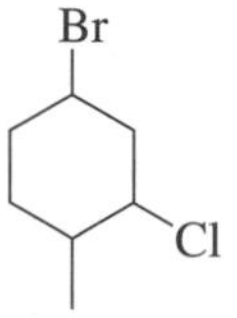

Br

Cl

4-bromo-2-chloro-1-methylcyclohexane

PROBLEM 16♦

Give two names for each of the following, and tell whether each alkyl halide is primary, secondary, or tertiary:

a. 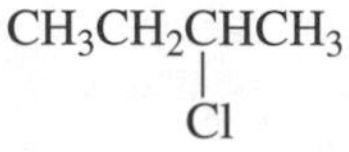 $CH_3CH_2CHCH_3$ (Cl on C-2)

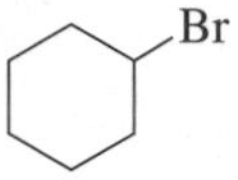

b. (cyclohexane with Br)

c. $CH_3CHCH_2CH_2CH_2Cl$ (CH_3 on C-2)

d. 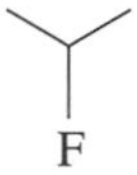 (skeletal structure with F)

PROBLEM 17

Draw the structures and provide systematic names for parts **a**, **b**, and **c** by substituting a chlorine for a hydrogen of methylcyclohexane:

a. a primary alkyl halide

b. a tertiary alkyl halide

c. three secondary alkyl halides

11.5 THE NOMENCLATURE OF ETHERS

Chemists sometimes neglect the prefix "di" when they name symmetrical ethers. Try not to make this oversight a habit.

An **ether** is a compound in which an oxygen is bonded to two alkyl substituents. If the alkyl substituents are identical, the ether is a **symmetrical ether**. If the substituents are different, the ether is an **unsymmetrical ether**.

R—O—R
a symmetrical ether

R—O—R′
an unsymmetrical ether

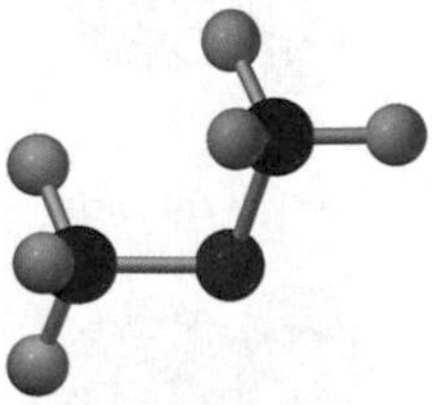

dimethyl ether

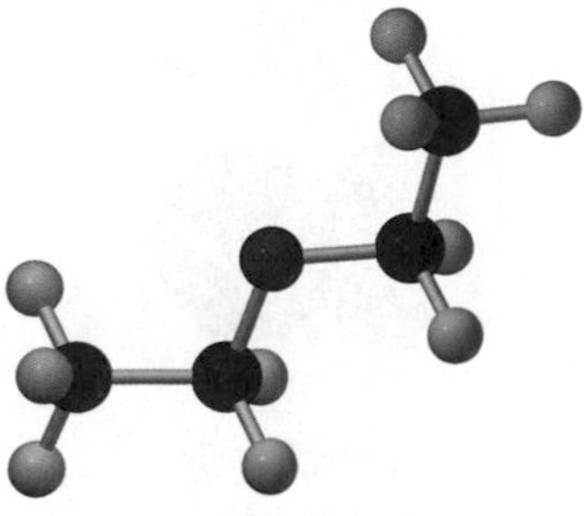

diethyl ether

The common name of an ether consists of the names of the two alkyl substituents (in alphabetical order), followed by the word "ether." The smallest ethers are almost always named by their common names.

$CH_3OCH_2CH_3$
ethyl methyl ether

$CH_3CH_2OCH_2CH_3$
diethyl ether
often called ethyl ether

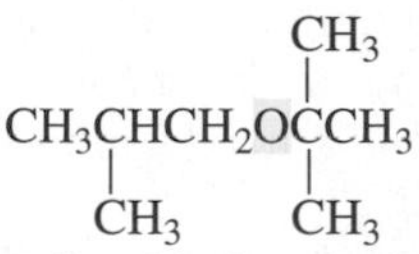

$CH_3CHCH_2OCCH_3$ (with CH_3 on C-2 and two CH_3 on the quaternary carbon)
***tert*-butyl isobutyl ether**

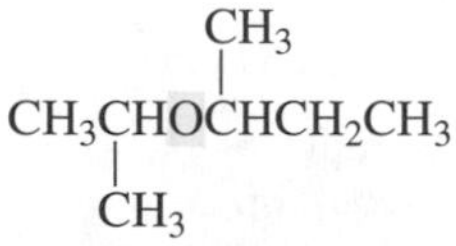

$CH_3CHOCHCH_2CH_3$ (with CH_3 on each CH)
***sec*-butyl isopropyl ether**

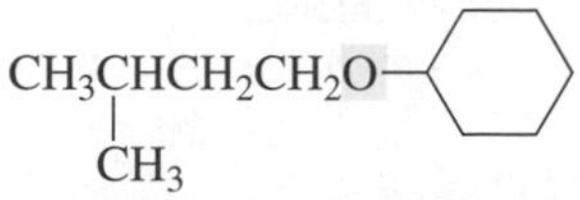

$CH_3CHCH_2CH_2O$—cyclohexyl (with CH_3 on C-2)
cyclohexyl isopentyl ether

The IUPAC system names an ether as an alkane with an RO substituent. The substituents are named by replacing the "yl" ending in the name of the alkyl substituent with "oxy."

CH_3O- **methoxy**; CH_3CH_2O- **ethoxy**; $CH_3CH(CH_3)O-$ **isopropoxy**; $CH_3CH_2CH(CH_3)O-$ ***sec*-butoxy**; $CH_3C(CH_3)_2O-$ ***tert*-butoxy**

$CH_3CH(OCH_3)CH_2CH_3$ **2-methoxybutane**

$CH_3CH_2CH(CH_3)CH_2CH_2OCH_2CH_3$ **1-ethoxy-3-methylpentane**

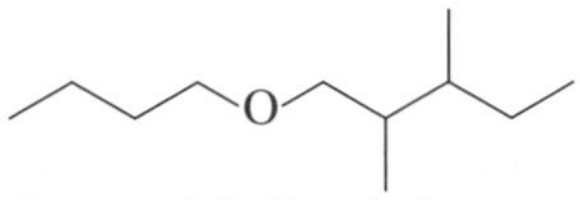

(skeletal structure) **1-butoxy-2,3-dimethylpentane**

$CH_3CH(CH_3)OCH_2CH_2CH_2CH_2OCH(CH_3)CH_3$ **1,4-diisopropoxybutane**

chem place Tutorial: Nomenclature of ethers

Tutorial: Ether nomenclature

PROBLEM 18♦

a. Give the systematic (IUPAC) name for each of the following ethers:

1. $CH_3OCH_2CH_3$
2. $CH_3CH_2OCH_2CH_3$
3. $CH_3CH_2CH_2CH_2CH(OCH_3)CH_2CH_2CH_3$
4. $CH_3CH(CH_3)OCH_2CH_2CH(CH_3)CH_3$
5. 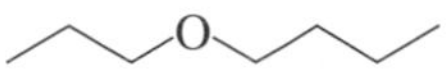 (skeletal structure)
6. 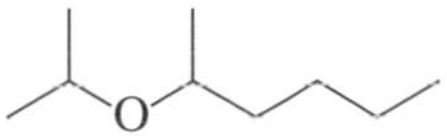 (skeletal structure)

b. Do all of these ethers have common names?

c. What are their common names?

11.6 THE NOMENCLATURE OF ALCOHOLS

The number of alkyl groups attached to the carbon to which the OH group is attached determines whether an alcohol is primary, secondary, or tertiary.

An **alcohol** is a compound in which a hydrogen of an alkane has been replaced by an OH group. Alcohols are classified as **primary alcohols**, **secondary alcohols**, or **tertiary alcohols**, depending on whether the OH group is bonded to a primary, secondary, or tertiary carbon—just like the way alkyl halides are classified.

$R-CH_2-OH$ **a primary alcohol**; $R-CH(R)-OH$ **a secondary alcohol**; $R-C(R)(R)-OH$ **a tertiary alcohol**

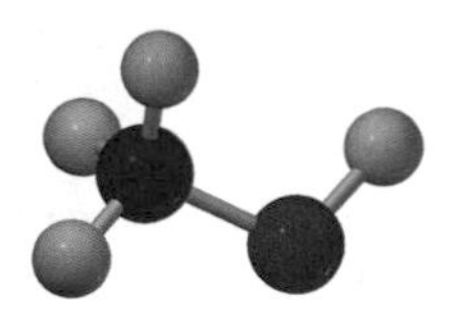
methyl alcohol

The common name of an alcohol consists of the name of the alkyl group to which the OH group is attached, followed by the word "alcohol."

CH_3CH_2OH **ethyl alcohol**; $CH_3CH_2CH_2OH$ **propyl alcohol**; $CH_3CH(CH_3)OH$ **isopropyl alcohol**; $CH_3CH(CH_3)CH_2OH$ **isobutyl alcohol**

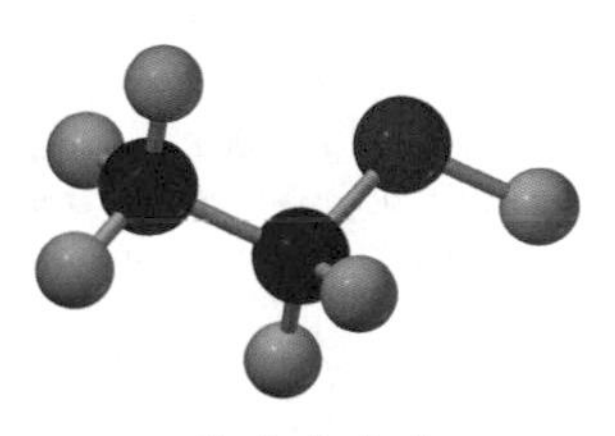
ethyl alcohol

The **functional group** is the center of reactivity in an organic molecule. In an alcohol, the OH is the functional group. The IUPAC system uses *suffixes* to denote certain functional groups. The systematic name of an alcohol, for example, is obtained by replacing the "e" at the end of the name of the parent hydrocarbon with the suffix "ol."

CH_3OH **methanol**; CH_3CH_2OH **ethanol**

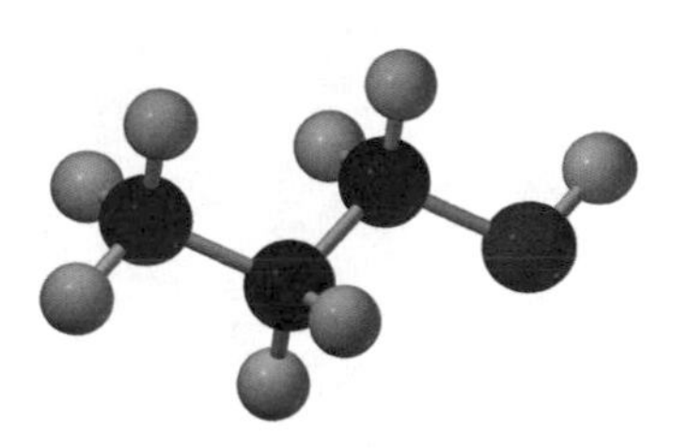
propyl alcohol

When necessary, the position of the functional group is indicated by a number immediately preceding the name of the alcohol or immediately preceding the suffix. The most recently approved IUPAC names are those with the number immediately preceding the suffix. However, names with the number preceding the name of the alcohol have been in use for a long time, so those are the ones most likely to appear in the literature, on reagent bottles, and on standardized tests. They will also be the ones that appear most often in this book.

$CH_3CH_2CHCH_2CH_3$ (OH on C-3)
3-pentanol
or
pentan-3-ol

3-methyl-1-hexanol
or
3-methylhexan-1-ol

The following rules are used to name a compound that has a functional group suffix:

1. The parent hydrocarbon is the longest continuous chain *containing the functional group.*
2. The parent hydrocarbon is numbered in the direction that gives the *functional group suffix the lowest possible number.*

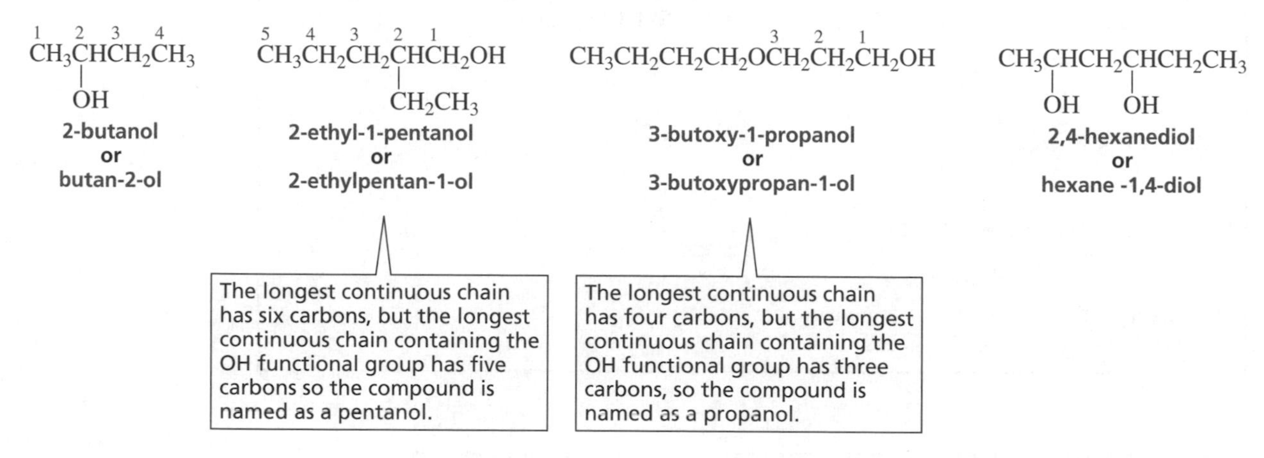
2-butanol
or
butan-2-ol
2-ethyl-1-pentanol
or
2-ethylpentan-1-ol
3-butoxy-1-propanol
or
3-butoxypropan-1-ol
2,4-hexanediol
or
hexane -1,4-diol
The longest continuous chain has six carbons, but the longest continuous chain containing the OH functional group has five carbons so the compound is named as a pentanol.
The longest continuous chain has four carbons, but the longest continuous chain containing the OH functional group has three carbons, so the compound is named as a propanol.

3. If there are two OH groups, the suffix "diol" is added to the name of the parent hydrocarbon.

$CH_3CHCH_2CHCH_2CH_3$ (OH on C-2 and C-4)
2,4-hexanediol
or
hexane-1,4-diol

When there is only a substituent, the substituent gets the lowest possible number.

When there is only a functional group suffix, the functional group suffix gets the lowest possible number.

When there is both a functional group suffix and a substituent, the functional group suffix gets the lowest possible number.

4. If there is a functional group suffix and a substituent, the functional group suffix gets the lowest possible number.

$HOCH_2CH_2CH_2Br$ — **3-bromo-1-propanol**

$ClCH_2CH_2CHCH_3$ (OH on C-2) — **4-chloro-2-butanol**

$CH_3CCH_2CHCH_3$ (two CH_3 on C-4, OH on C-2) — **4,4-dimethyl-2-pentanol**

5. If counting in either direction gives the same number for the functional group suffix, the chain is numbered in the direction that gives a substituent the lowest possible number. Notice that a number is not needed to designate the position of a functional group suffix in a cyclic compound, because it is assumed to be at the 1-position.

$CH_3CHCHCH_2CH_3$ (Cl, OH) — **2-chloro-3-pentanol** **not** **4-chloro-3-pentanol**

$CH_3CH_2CH_2CHCH_2CHCH_3$ (OH, CH_3) — **2-methyl-4-heptanol** **not** **6-methyl-4-heptanol**

3-methylcyclohexanol **not** **5-methylcyclohexanol**

6. If there is more than one substituent, the substituents are listed in alphabetical order.

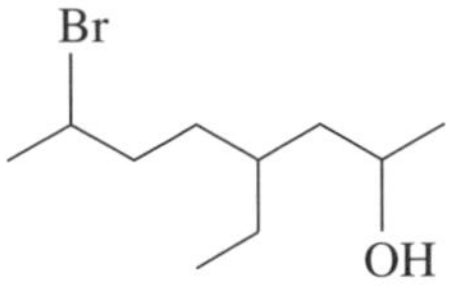

7-bromo-4-ethyl-2-octanol 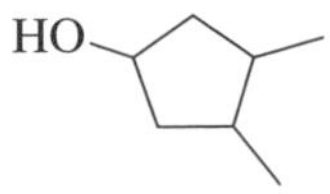 **3,4-dimethylcyclopentanol** 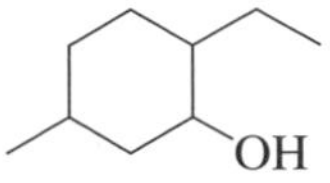 **2-ethyl-5-methylcyclohexanol**

Remember that the name of a substituent is stated *before* the name of the parent hydrocarbon, and the functional group suffix is stated *after* the name of the parent hydrocarbon.

[substituent] [parent hydrocarbon] [functional group suffix]

PROBLEM 19

Draw the structures of a homologous series of alcohols that have from one to six carbons, and then give each of them a common name and a systematic name.

PROBLEM 20 ♦

Give each of the following a systematic name, and indicate whether each is a primary, secondary, or tertiary alcohol:

a. $CH_3CH_2CH_2CH_2CH_2OH$

b. $CH_3C(CH_3)(OH)CH_2CH_2CH_2Cl$

c. $CH_3CH(CH_3)CH_2CH(OH)CH_2CH_3$

d. $CH_3CH(CH_3)CH_2CH(OH)CH_2CH(OH)CH_2CH_3$

PROBLEM 21 ♦

Write the structures of all the tertiary alcohols with molecular formula $C_6H_{14}O$, and give each a systematic name.

PROBLEM 22 ♦

Give each of the following a systematic name, and indicate whether each is a primary, secondary, or tertiary alcohol:

a. Cl, OH

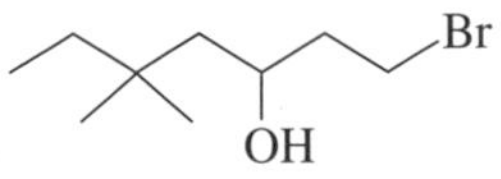

b. OH

c. Br, OH

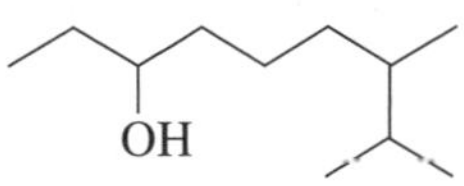

d. HO

chem place Tutorial: Nomenclature of alcohols

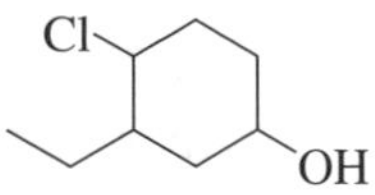

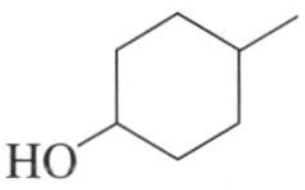

11.7 THE NOMENCLATURE OF AMINES

An **amine** is a compound in which one or more hydrogens of ammonia have been replaced by alkyl groups. There are **primary amines, secondary amines**, and **tertiary amines**. The classification depends on how many alkyl groups are bonded to the nitrogen. Primary amines have one alkyl group bonded to the nitrogen, secondary amines have two, and tertiary amines have three.

The number of alkyl groups attached to the nitrogen determines whether an amine is primary, secondary, or tertiary.

NH_3	$R{-}NH_2$	$R{-}NH{-}R$	$R{-}N(R){-}R$
ammonia	**a primary amine**	**a secondary amine**	**a tertiary amine**

Notice that the number of alkyl groups *attached to the nitrogen* determines whether an amine is primary, secondary, or tertiary. For an alkyl halide or an alcohol, on the other hand, the number of alkyl groups *attached to the carbon* to which the halogen or the OH is bonded determines the classification (Sections 11.4 and 11.6).

nitrogen is attached to one alkyl group

carbon is attached to three alkyl groups

$R_3C{-}NH_2$
a primary amine

$R_3C{-}Cl$
a tertiary alkyl chloride

$R_3C{-}OH$
a tertiary alcohol

The common name of an amine consists of the names of the alkyl groups bonded to the nitrogen, in alphabetical order, followed by "amine." The entire name is written as one word (unlike the common names of alcohols, ethers, and alkyl halides, in which "alcohol," "ether," and "halide" are separate words).

CH_3NH_2
methylamine

$CH_3NHCH_2CH_2CH_3$
methylpropylamine

$CH_3CH_2NHCH_2CH_3$
diethylamine

$CH_3N(CH_3)CH_3$
trimethylamine

$CH_3N(CH_3)CH_2CH_2CH_2CH_3$
butyldimethylamine

$CH_3CH_2N(CH_3)CH_2CH_2CH_3$
ethylmethylpropylamine

The IUPAC system uses the suffix "amine" to denote the amine functional group. The "e" at the end of the name of the parent hydrocarbon is replaced by "amine"—similar to the way in which alcohols are named. Also similar to the way alcohols are named, a number identifies the carbon to which the nitrogen is attached, and the number can appear before the name of the parent hydrocarbon or before "amine." The name of any alkyl group bonded to nitrogen is preceded by an "*N*" (in italics) to indicate that the group is bonded to a nitrogen rather than to a carbon.

$\overset{4}{C}H_3\overset{3}{C}H_2\overset{2}{C}H_2\overset{1}{C}H_2NH_2$
1-butanamine
or
butan-1-amine

$\overset{1}{C}H_3\overset{2}{C}H_2\overset{3}{C}H(NHCH_2CH_3)\overset{4}{C}H_2\overset{5}{C}H_2\overset{6}{C}H_3$
***N*-ethyl-3-hexanamine**
or
***N*-ethylhexan-3-amine**

$\overset{3}{C}H_3\overset{2}{C}H_2\overset{1}{C}H_2N(CH_3)CH_2CH_3$
***N*-ethyl-*N*-methyl-1-propanamine**
or
***N*-ethyl-*N*-methylpropan-1-amine**

The substituents—regardless of whether they are attached to the nitrogen or to the parent hydrocarbon—are listed in alphabetical order, and then an "*N*" or a number is assigned to each one. The chain is numbered in the direction that gives the functional group suffix the lowest number.

$\overset{4}{C}H_3\overset{3}{C}H(Cl)\overset{2}{C}H_2\overset{1}{C}H_2NHCH_3$
3-chloro-*N*-methyl-1-butanamine

$\overset{1}{C}H_3\overset{2}{C}H_2\overset{3}{C}H(NHCH_2CH_3)\overset{4}{C}H_2\overset{5}{C}H(CH_3)\overset{6}{C}H_3$
***N*-ethyl-5-methyl-3-hexanamine**

Br, N (skeletal structure, carbons numbered 5 4 3 2 1)
4-bromo-*N*,*N*-dimethyl-2-pentanamine

CH_2CH_3, $NHCH_2CH_2CH_3$ (on cyclohexane ring)
2-ethyl-*N*-propylcyclohexanamine

Nitrogen compounds with four alkyl groups bonded to the nitrogen—thereby giving the nitrogen a positive formal charge—are called **quaternary ammonium salts**. Their names consist of the names of the alkyl groups in alphabetical order, followed by "ammonium" (all in one word), and then the name of the accompanying anion as a separate word.

$$\underset{\text{tetramethylammonium hydroxide}}{CH_3-\overset{\overset{CH_3}{|}}{\underset{\underset{CH_3}{|}}{N^+}}-CH_3\ \ HO^-} \qquad \underset{\text{ethyldimethylpropylammonium chloride}}{CH_3CH_2CH_2-\overset{\overset{CH_3}{|}}{\underset{\underset{CH_2CH_3}{|}}{N^+}}-CH_3\ \ Cl^-}$$

Bad-Smelling Compounds

Amines are associated with some of nature's unpleasant odors. Amines with relatively small alkyl groups, for example, have a fishy smell. Thus, fermented shark, a traditional dish in Iceland, smells exactly like triethylamine. The amines putrescine and cadaverine are poisonous compounds formed when amino acids are degraded. Because the body excretes them in the quickest ways possible, their odors may be detected in the urine and breath. They are also responsible for the odor of decaying flesh.

H_2N–(CH₂)₄–NH_2
1,4-butanediamine
putrescine

H_2N–(CH₂)₅–NH_2
1,5-pentanediamine
cadaverine

Table 11.3 summarizes the ways in which alkyl halides, ethers, alcohols, and amines are named.

Table 11.3 Summary of Nomenclature

	Systematic name	Common name
Alkyl halide	substituted alkane CH_3Br bromomethane CH_3CH_2Cl chloroethane	alkyl group to which halogen is attached, plus *halide* CH_3Br methyl bromide CH_3CH_2Cl ethyl chloride
Ether	substituted alkane CH_3OCH_3 methoxymethane $CH_3CH_2OCH_3$ methoxyethane	alkyl groups attached to oxygen, plus *ether* CH_3OCH_3 dimethyl ether $CH_3CH_2OCH_3$ ethyl methyl ether
Alcohol	functional group suffix is *ol* CH_3OH methanol CH_3CH_2OH ethanol	alkyl group to which OH is attached, plus *alcohol* CH_3OH methyl alcohol CH_3CH_2OH ethyl alcohol
Amine	functional group suffix is *amine* $CH_3CH_2NH_2$ ethanamine $CH_3CH_2CH_2NHCH_3$ *N*-methyl-1-propanamine	alkyl groups attached to N, plus *amine* $CH_3CH_2NH_2$ ethylamine $CH_3CH_2CH_2NHCH_3$ methylpropylamine

PROBLEM 23♦

Tell whether the following are primary, secondary, or tertiary:

a. $CH_3-\overset{\overset{CH_3}{|}}{\underset{\underset{CH_3}{|}}{C}}-Br$ **b.** $CH_3-\overset{\overset{CH_3}{|}}{\underset{\underset{CH_3}{|}}{C}}-OH$ **c.** $CH_3-\overset{\overset{CH_3}{|}}{\underset{\underset{CH_3}{|}}{C}}-NH_2$

PROBLEM 24♦

Give a common name (if it has one) and a systematic name for each of the following amines and tell whether each is a primary, secondary, or tertiary amine:

a. $CH_3CH_2CH_2CH_2CH_2CH_2NH_2$

b. $CH_3CH(CH_3)CH_2NHCH(CH_3)CH_2CH_3$

c. $(CH_3CH_2)_2NCH_3$

d. $CH_3CH_2CH_2NHCH_2CH_2CH_2CH_3$

e. $CH_3CH_2CH_2N(CH_2CH_3)CH_2CH_3$

f. 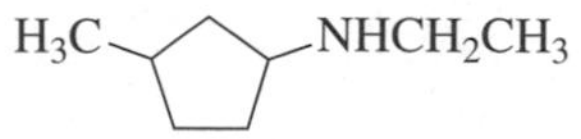 H_3C–(cyclopentane)–$NHCH_2CH_3$

PROBLEM 25♦

Draw the structure for each of the following:

a. 2-methyl-*N*-propyl-1-propanamine
b. *N*-ethylethanamine
c. 5-methyl-1-hexanamine
d. methyldipropylamine
e. *N,N*-dimethyl-3-pentanamine
f. cyclohexylethylmethylamine

chem place Tutorial: Summary of systematic nomenclature

PROBLEM 26♦

For each of the following, give the systematic name and the common name (if it has one), and indicate whether it is a primary, secondary, or tertiary amine:

a. 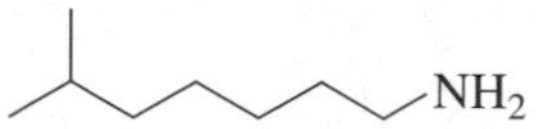 NH_2

b. 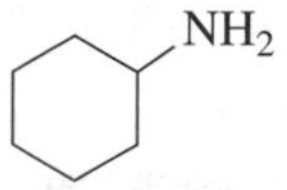 NH_2

c.  H N

d. 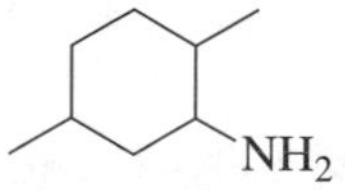 NH_2

11.8 THE STRUCTURES OF ALKYL HALIDES, ALCOHOLS, ETHERS, AND AMINES

The classes of compounds we have been looking at in this chapter have structural resemblances to the simpler compounds. Let's begin by looking at alkyl halides and their resemblance to alkanes. Both classes of compounds have the same geometry; the only difference is that a C—X bond of an alkyl halide (where X denotes a halogen) has replaced a C—H bond of the alkane. The C—X bond of an alkyl halide is formed from the overlap of an sp^3 orbital of the halogen with an sp^3 orbital of carbon. Fluorine uses a $2sp^3$ orbital to overlap with a $2sp^3$ orbital of carbon, chlorine uses a $3sp^3$ orbital, bromine a $4sp^3$ orbital, and iodine a $5sp^3$ orbital. As you can see in Table 11.4, because the electron density of the orbital decreases with increasing volume, the C—X bond becomes longer and weaker as the size of the halogen increases. Notice that this is the same trend shown by the H—X bond of hydrogen halides in Table 10.6.

Now consider the geometry of the oxygen in an alcohol, which is the same as the geometry of the oxygen in water. In fact, an alcohol molecule can be thought of structurally as a water molecule with an alkyl group in place of one of the hydrogens. The oxygen atom in an alcohol is sp^3 hybridized, as it is in water. One of the sp^3 orbitals of oxygen overlaps an sp^3 orbital of a carbon, one sp^3 orbital overlaps the *s* orbital of a hydrogen, and the other two sp^3 orbitals each contain a lone pair.

Table 11.4 Carbon–Halogen bond lengths and bond strengths

	Orbital interactions	Bond lengths	Bond strength (kcal/mol)	Bond strength (kJ/mol)
$H_3C{-}F$		1.39 Å	108	451
$H_3C{-}Cl$		1.78 Å	84	350
$H_3C{-}Br$		1.93 Å	70	294
$H_3C{-}I$		2.14 Å	57	239

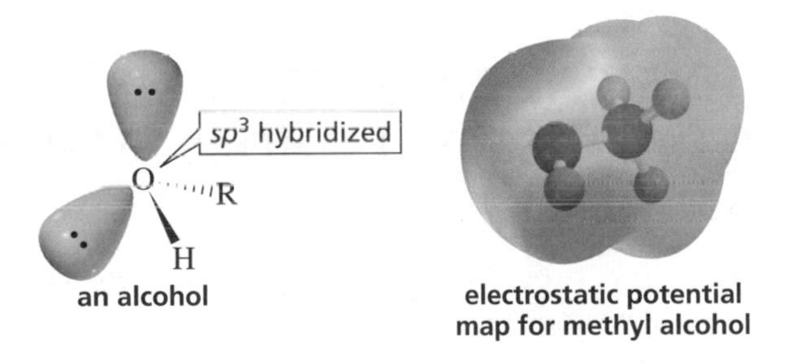

an alcohol

electrostatic potential map for methyl alcohol

The oxygen in an ether also has the same geometry as the oxygen in water. An ether molecule can be thought of structurally as a water molecule with alkyl groups in place of both hydrogens.

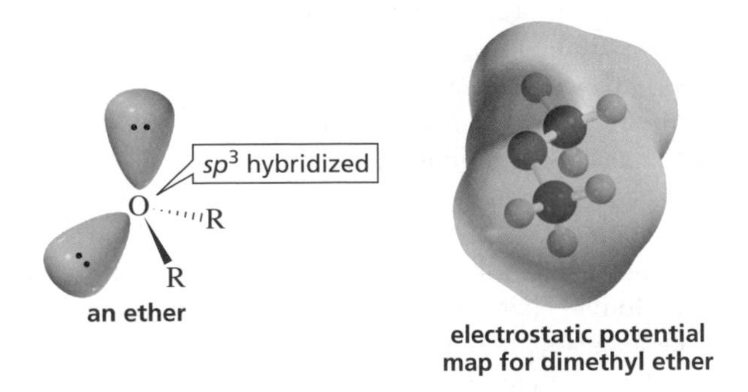

an ether

electrostatic potential map for dimethyl ether

The nitrogen in an amine has the same geometry as the nitrogen in ammonia. It is sp^3 hybridized as in ammonia, with one, two, or three of the hydrogens replaced by alkyl groups. Remember that the number of hydrogens replaced by alkyl groups determines whether the amine is primary, secondary, or tertiary (Section 11.7).

sp^3 hybridized

H_3C—N—H, H — **methylamine** **a primary amine**

H_3C—N—CH_3, H — **dimethylamine** **a secondary amine**

H_3C—N—CH_3, CH_3 — **trimethylamine** **a tertiary amine**

electrostatic potential maps for

methylamine **dimethylamine** **trimethylamine**

PROBLEM 27 ♦

Predict the approximate size of the following bond angles.

a. the C—O—C bond angle in an ether
b. the C—N—C bond angle in a secondary amine
c. the C—O—H bond angle in an alcohol
d. the C—N—C bond angle in a quaternary ammonium salt

11.9 THE PHYSICAL PROPERTIES OF ALKANES, ALKYL HALIDES, ALCOHOLS, ETHERS, AND AMINES

B I O G R A P H Y

Johannes Diderik van der Waals (1837–1923) *was a Dutch physicist. He was born in Leiden, the son of a carpenter, and was largely self-taught when he entered the University of Leiden, where he earned a Ph.D. Van der Waals was a professor of physics at the University of Amsterdam from 1877 to 1907. He won the 1910 Nobel Prize in Physics for his research on the gaseous and liquid states of matter.*

Now we will look at the physical properties of the classes of compounds whose names and structures we have just examined.

Boiling Points

The **boiling point (bp)** of a compound is the temperature at which the liquid form becomes a gas (vaporizes). In order for a compound to vaporize, the forces that hold the individual molecules close to each other in the liquid must be overcome. This means that the boiling point of a compound depends on the strength of the attractive forces between the individual molecules. If the molecules are held together by strong forces, a lot of energy will be needed to pull the molecules away from each other and the compound will have a high boiling point. In contrast, if the molecules are held together by weak forces, only a small amount of energy will be needed to pull the molecules away from each other and the compound will have a low boiling point.

The attractive forces between alkane molecules are relatively weak. Alkanes contain only carbon and hydrogen atoms, and the electronegativities of carbon and hydrogen are similar. As a result, the bonds in alkanes are nonpolar—there are no significant partial charges on any of the atoms. Therefore, alkanes are neutral (nonpolar) molecules. The nonpolar nature of alkanes gives them their oily feel.

However, it is only the average charge distribution over the alkane molecule that is neutral. The electrons are moving continuously, and at any instant the electron density on one side of the molecule can be slightly greater than that on the other side, causing the molecule to have a temporary dipole. Recall that a molecule with a dipole has a negative end and a positive end.

A temporary dipole in one molecule can induce a temporary dipole in a nearby molecule. As a result, the (temporarily) negative side of one molecule ends up adjacent to the (temporarily) positive side of another, as shown in Figure 11.1. Because the dipoles in the molecules are induced, the interactions between the molecules are called **induced-dipole–induced-dipole interactions**. The molecules of an alkane are held together by these induced-dipole–induced-dipole interactions, which are known as **van der Waals forces**. Van der Waals forces are the weakest of all the intermolecular attractions.

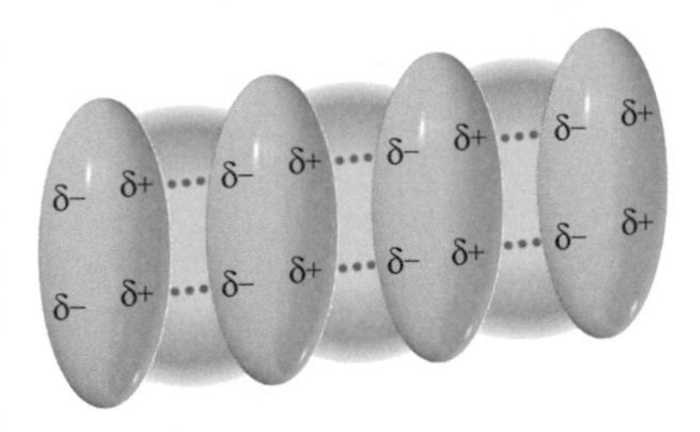

▲ **Figure 11.1**
Van der Waals forces are induced-dipole–induced-dipole interactions.

The magnitude of the van der Waals forces that hold alkane molecules together depends on the area of contact between the molecules. The greater the area of contact, the stronger the van der Waals forces and the greater the amount of energy needed to overcome them. If you look at the boiling points of the alkanes listed in Table 11.1, you will see that they increase as their size increases. This relationship holds because each additional methylene (CH_2) group increases the area of contact between the molecules. The four smallest alkanes have boiling points below room temperature (which is about 25 °C), so they exist as gases at room temperature.

Because the strength of the van der Waals forces depends on the area of contact between the molecules, branching in a compound lowers the compound's boiling point by reducing the area of contact. If you think of pentane, an unbranched alkane, as a cigar and think of branched 2,2-dimethylpropane as a tennis ball, you can see that branching decreases the area of contact between molecules: two cigars make contact over a greater area than do two tennis balls. Thus, if two alkanes have the same molecular weight, the more highly branched alkane will have a lower boiling point.

$CH_3CH_2CH_2CH_2CH_3$
pentane
bp = 36.1 °C

$CH_3CH(CH_3)CH_2CH_3$
2-methylbutane
bp = 27.9 °C

$CH_3C(CH_3)_2CH_3$
2,2-dimethylpropane
bp = 9.5 °C

PROBLEM 28 ♦

What is the smallest alkane that is a liquid at room temperature, which is generally taken to be 20 °C to 25 °C?

The boiling points of a series of ethers, alkyl halides, alcohols, or amines also increase with increasing molecular weight because of the increase in van der Waals forces. The boiling points of these compounds, however, are also affected by the polar C—Z bond (where Z denotes N, O, F, Cl, or Br). Recall that the C—Z bond is polar because nitrogen, oxygen, and the halogens are more electronegative than the carbon to which they are attached.

$$R-\overset{\delta+}{C}-\overset{\delta-}{Z} \qquad Z = N, O, F, Cl, \text{ or } Br$$

Molecules with polar bonds are attracted to one another because they can align themselves in such a way that the positive end of one dipole is adjacent to the negative end of another dipole. These electrostatic attractive forces, called **dipole–dipole interactions**, are stronger than van der Waals forces, but not as strong as ionic or covalent bonds.

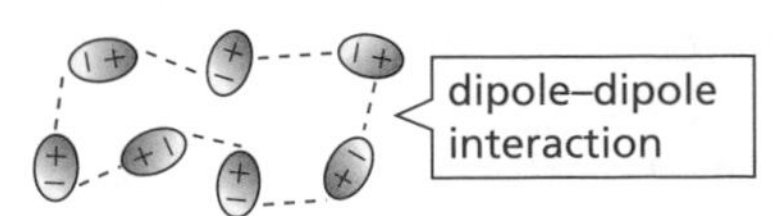

As you can see in Table 11.5, ethers generally have higher boiling points than alkanes of comparable molecular weight. This is because both van der Waals forces and dipole–dipole interactions must be overcome for an ether to boil.

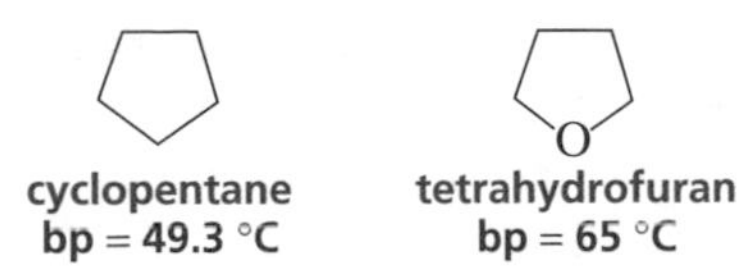

The boiling point of a compound depends on the strength of the attraction between the individual molecules.

Table 11.5 Comparative Boiling Points (°C)

Alkanes	Ethers	Alcohols	Amines
$CH_3CH_2CH_3$	CH_3OCH_3	CH_3CH_2OH	$CH_3CH_2NH_2$
−42.1	−23.7	78	16.6
$CH_3CH_2CH_2CH_3$	$CH_3OCH_2CH_3$	$CH_3CH_2CH_2OH$	$CH_3CH_2CH_2NH_2$
−0.5	10.8	97.4	47.8

Alcohols have much higher boiling points than ethers with similar molecular weights (as Table 11.5 also shows) because, in addition to van der Waals forces and the dipole–dipole interactions of the polar C—O bond, alcohols can form **hydrogen bonds**. A hydrogen bond is a special kind of dipole–dipole interaction that occurs between a hydrogen that is bonded to an oxygen, nitrogen, or fluorine and the lone-pair electrons of an oxygen, nitrogen, or fluorine in another molecule.

The length of the covalent bond between oxygen and hydrogen is 0.96 Å. The hydrogen bond between an oxygen of one molecule and a hydrogen of another molecule is almost twice as long (1.69−1.79 Å), which means that a hydrogen bond is not as strong as an O—H covalent bond. A hydrogen bond is, however, stronger than other dipole–dipole interactions. The strongest hydrogen bonds are linear, meaning the two electronegative atoms and the hydrogen between them lie on a straight line.

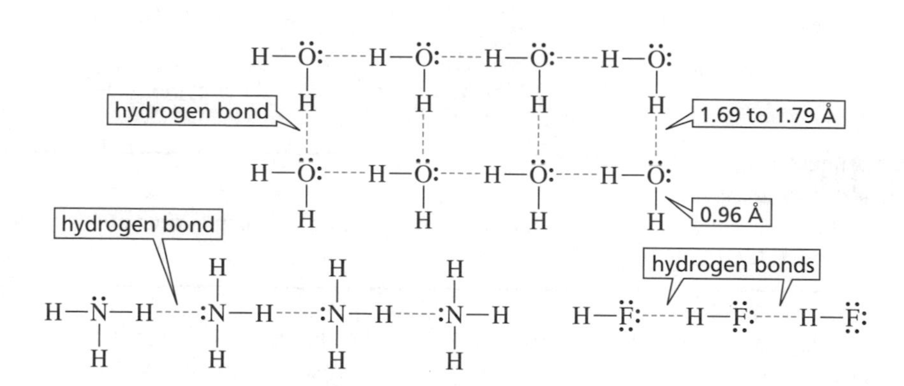

Hydrogen bonds are stronger than other dipole–dipole interactions, which are stronger than van der Waals forces.

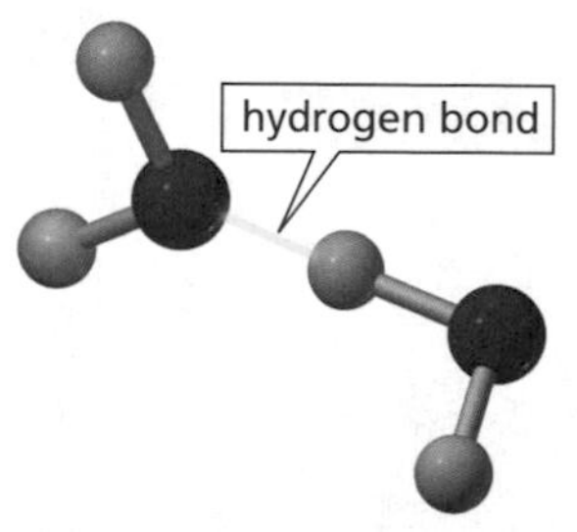

hydrogen bonding in water

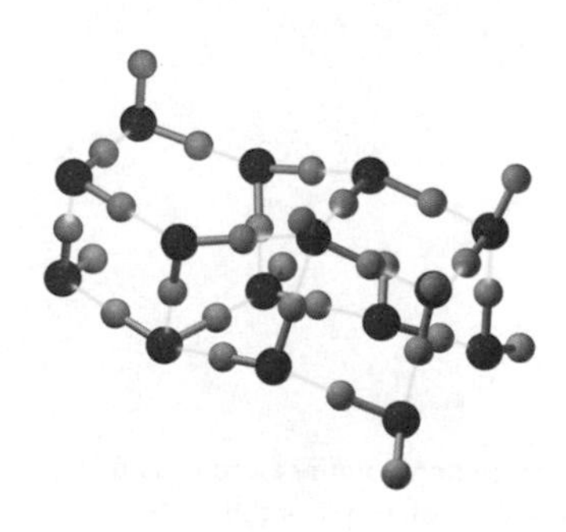

Although each individual hydrogen bond is weak, requiring about 5 kcal/mol (or 21 kJ/mol) to break, there are many such bonds holding alcohol molecules together. The extra energy required to break these hydrogen bonds is the reason alcohols have much higher boiling points than ethers with similar molecular weights.

The boiling point of water illustrates the dramatic effect that hydrogen bonding has on boiling points. Water has a molecular weight of 18 and a boiling point of 100 °C. The alkane nearest in size is methane, with a molecular weight of 16. Methane boils at −167.7 °C.

Primary and secondary amines also form hydrogen bonds, so these amines have higher boiling points than ethers with similar molecular weights. Nitrogen is not as electronegative as oxygen, however, which means that the hydrogen bonds between amine molecules are weaker than the hydrogen bonds between alcohol molecules. An amine, therefore, has a lower boiling point than an alcohol with a similar molecular weight (Table 11.5).

Because primary amines have two N—H bonds, hydrogen bonding is more significant in primary amines than in secondary amines. Tertiary amines cannot form hydrogen bonds between their own molecules because they do not have a hydrogen attached to the nitrogen. Consequently, when we compare amines with the same molecular weight and similar structures, we find that a primary amine has a higher boiling point than a secondary amine and a secondary amine has a higher boiling point than a tertiary amine.

NH_2 a primary amine bp = 97 °C

$\overset{H}{N}$ a secondary amine bp = 84 °C

N a tertiary amine bp = 65 °C

Hydrogen bonds play an important role in biology. We will see that proteins are shaped by hydrogen bonding and DNA relies on hydrogen bonding to copy all its hereditary information.

PROBLEM-SOLVING STRATEGY

Predicting Hydrogen Bonding

a. Which of the following compounds will form hydrogen bonds between its molecules?

1. $CH_3CH_2CH_2OH$ **2.** $CH_3CH_2CH_2F$ **3.** $CH_3OCH_2CH_3$

b. Which of these compounds will form hydrogen bonds with a solvent such as ethanol?

To solve this type of question, start by defining the kind of compound that will do what is being asked.

a. A hydrogen bond forms when a hydrogen attached to an O, N, or F of one molecule interacts with a lone pair on an O, N, or F of another molecule. Therefore, a compound that will form hydrogen bonds with itself must have a hydrogen bonded to an O, N, or F. Only compound 1 will be able to form hydrogen bonds with itself.

b. Ethanol has an H bonded to an O, so it will be able to form hydrogen bonds with a compound that has a lone pair on an O, N, or F. All three compounds will be able to form hydrogen bonds with ethanol.

Now continue on to Problem 29.

PROBLEM 29♦

a. Which of the following will form hydrogen bonds between its molecules?

1. $CH_3CH_2CH_2COOH$

2. $CH_3CH_2N(CH_3)_2$

3. $CH_3CH_2CH_2CH_2Br$

4. $CH_3CH_2CH_2NHCH_3$

5. $CH_3CH_2OCH_2CH_2OH$

6. $CH_3CH_2CH_2CH_2F$

b. Which of the preceding compounds will form hydrogen bonds with a solvent such as ethanol?

Both van der Waals forces and dipole–dipole interactions must be overcome for an alkyl halide to boil. Moreover, as the halogen atom increases in size, these interactions become stronger. A larger electron cloud means that the van der Waals contact area is greater and the electron cloud's polarizability is also greater. **Polarizability** indicates how readily an electron cloud can be distorted. The larger the atom, the more loosely it holds the electrons in its outermost shell, and the more they can be distorted to create a strong induced dipole. Therefore, an alkyl fluoride has a lower boiling point than an alkyl chloride with the same alkyl group. Similarly, alkyl chlorides have lower boiling points than alkyl bromides, which have lower boiling points than alkyl iodides (Table 11.6).

A more extensive tables of physical properties can be found in Appendix B.

Table 11.6 Comparative Boiling Points of Alkanes and Alkyl Halides (°C)

—Y	H	F	Cl	Br	I
$CH_3—Y$	−161.7	−78.4	−24.2	3.6	42.4
$CH_3CH_2—Y$	−88.6	−37.7	12.3	38.4	72.3
$CH_3CH_2CH_2—Y$	−42.1	−2.5	46.6	71.0	102.5
$CH_3CH_2CH_2CH_2—Y$	−0.5	32.5	78.4	101.6	130.5
$CH_3CH_2CH_2CH_2CH_2—Y$	36.1	62.8	107.8	129.6	157.0

Drugs Bind to Their Receptors

Many drugs exert their physiological effects by binding to specific binding sites called *receptors*. A drug binds to a receptor using the same kinds of bonding interactions—van der Waals interactions, dipole–dipole interactions, hydrogen bonding—that molecules use to bind to each other. The most important factor in the interaction between a drug and its receptor is a snug fit. Therefore, drugs with similar shapes often have similar physiological effects. For example, each of the compounds shown here has a nonpolar, planar six-membered ring and substituents with similar polarities, and they all have anti-inflammatory activity. Salicylic acid has been used for the relief of fever and arthritic pain since 500 B.C. In 1897, acetylsalicylic acid (aspirin) was found to be a more potent anti-inflammatory agent and less irritating to the stomach; it became commercially available in 1899.

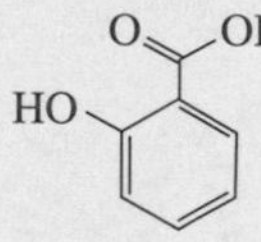

salicylic acid

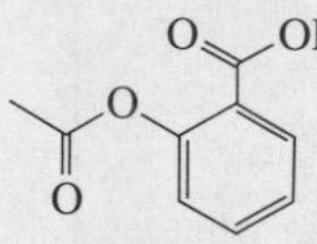

acetylsalicylic acid

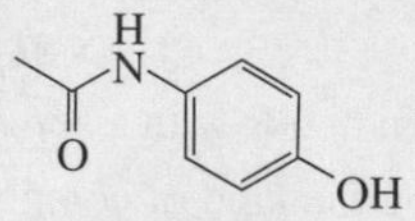

acetaminophen
Tylenol®

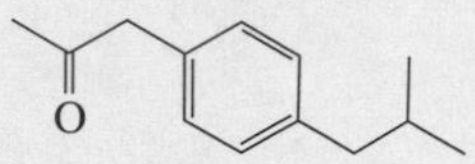

ibufenac

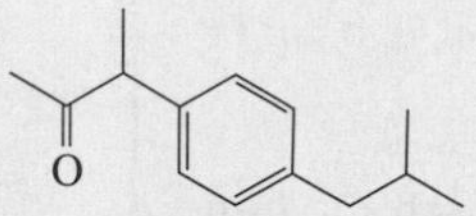

ibuprofen
Advil®

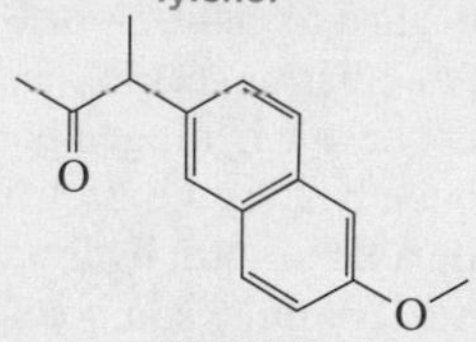

naproxen
Aleve®

Changing the relative positions of the substituents on the ring produced acetaminophen (Tylenol), which was introduced in 1955. It became a widely used drug because it causes no gastric irritation. However, its effective dose is not far from its toxic dose. Subsequently, ibufenac emerged; adding a methyl group to ibufenac produced ibuprofen (Advil), a much safer drug. Naproxen (Aleve), which has twice the potency of ibuprofen, was introduced in 1976.

PROBLEM 30

Explain why

a. H_2O has a higher boiling point than CH_3OH (65 °C).
b. H_2O has a higher boiling point than NH_3 (−33 °C).
c. H_2O has a higher boiling point than HF (20 °C).

PROBLEM 31 ♦

List the following compounds in order of decreasing boiling point:

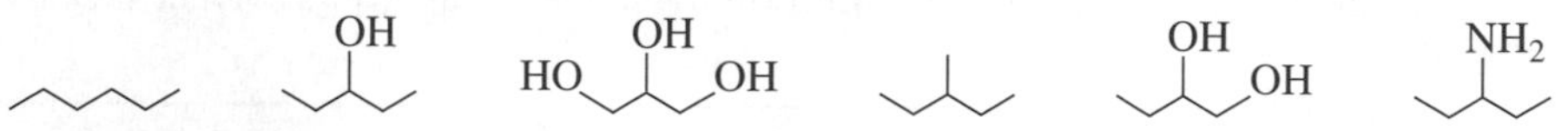

PROBLEM 32

List the compounds in each set in order of decreasing boiling point:

a.

b.

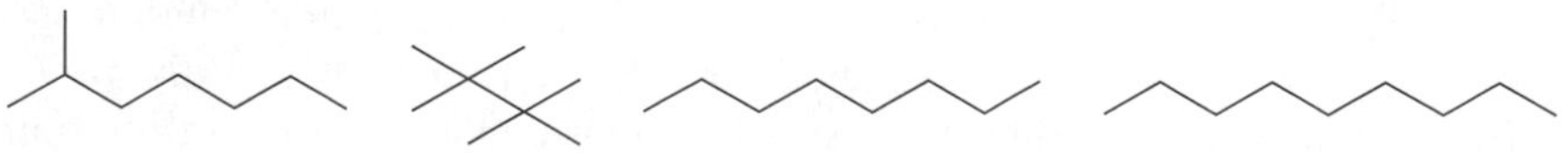

c.

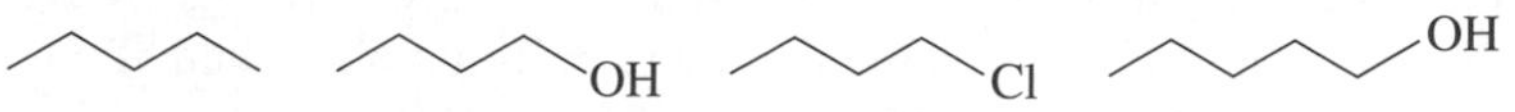

Melting Points

The **melting point (mp)** of a compound is the temperature at which its solid form is converted into a liquid. If you examine the melting points of the alkanes listed in Table 11.1, you will see that they increase (with a few exceptions) as the molecular weight increases. The increase in melting point is less regular than the increase in boiling point because, in addition to the intermolecular attractions we considered above, the melting point is influenced by the type of **packing** (that is, the arrangement, including the closeness and compactness, of the molecules) in the crystal lattice. The tighter the fit, the more energy is required to break the lattice and melt the compound.

Figure 11.2 shows that the melting points of alkanes with an even number of carbons fall on a smooth curve (the red line). The melting points of alkanes with an odd number of carbons also fall on a smooth curve (the green line). The two curves do not overlap, however, because alkanes with an odd number of carbons pack less tightly than alkanes with an even number of carbons.

Alkanes with an odd number of carbons pack less tightly because the molecules, each a zigzag chain with its ends tilted the same way, can lie next to each other with a methyl group on the end of one facing and repelling the methyl group on the end of the other, thus increasing the average distance between the chains. Consequently, they have weaker intermolecular attractions and correspondingly lower melting points.

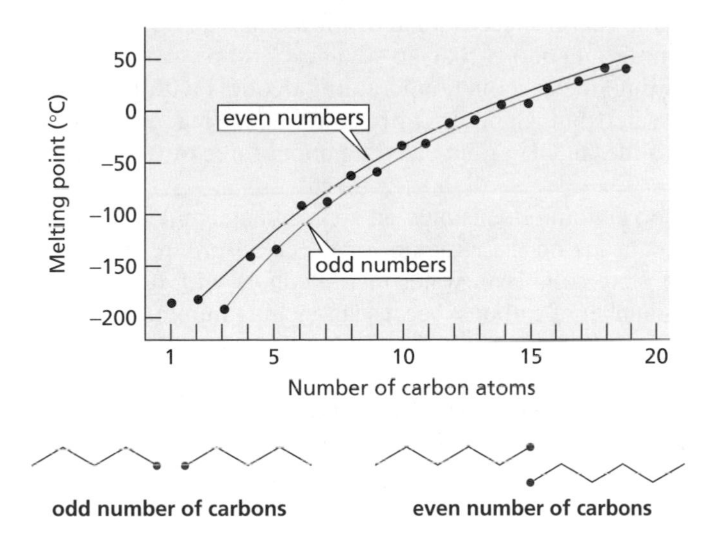

◀ Figure 11.2
Melting points of straight-chain alkanes. Alkanes with an even number of carbons fall on a melting-point curve that is higher than the melting-point curve for alkanes with an odd number of carbons.

Solubility

"Like dissolves like."

The general rule that governs **solubility** is "like dissolves like." In other words, *polar compounds dissolve in polar solvents, and nonpolar compounds dissolve in nonpolar solvents*. The reason "polar dissolves polar" is that a polar solvent, such as water, has partial charges that can interact with the partial charges on a polar compound. The negative poles of the solvent molecules surround the positive pole of the polar compound, and the positive poles of the solvent molecules surround the negative pole of the polar compound. Clustering of the solvent molecules around the polar molecules separates them from each other, which is what makes them dissolve. The interaction between solvent molecules and solute molecules (molecules dissolved in a solvent) is called **solvation**.

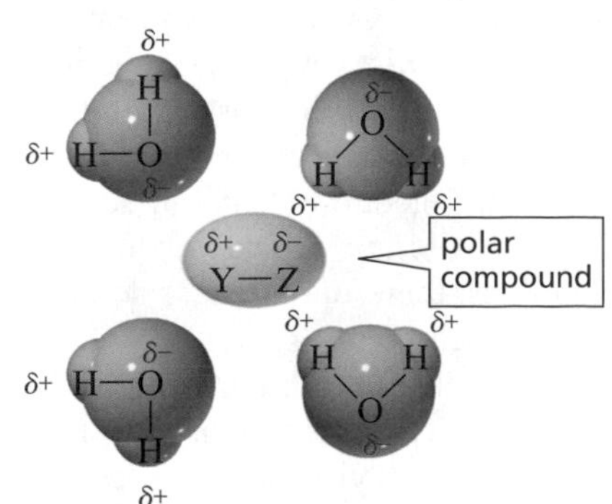

solvation of a polar compound by water

Because nonpolar compounds have no net charge, polar solvents are not attracted to them. In order for a nonpolar molecule to dissolve in a polar solvent such as water, the nonpolar molecule would have to push the water molecules apart, disrupting their hydrogen bonding. Hydrogen bonding is strong enough to exclude the nonpolar compound. In contrast, nonpolar solutes dissolve in nonpolar solvents because the van der Waals interactions between solvent molecules and solute molecules are about the same as between solvent–solvent molecules and solute–solute molecules.

Alkanes are nonpolar, which causes them to be soluble in nonpolar solvents and insoluble in polar solvents such as water. The densities of alkanes (Table 11.1) increase with increasing molecular weight, but even a 30-carbon alkane (density at 20 °C, or $d^{20°} = 0.8097$ g/mL) is less dense than water ($d^{20°} = 1.00$ g/mL). This means that a mixture of an alkane and water will separate into two distinct layers, with the less dense alkane floating on top. The Alaskan oil spill of 1989, the Persian Gulf spill of 1991, and the spill off the northwest coast of Spain in 2002 are large-scale examples of this phenomenon. (Crude oil is primarily a mixture of alkanes.)

Oil from a 70,000-ton oil spill in 1996 off the coast of Wales.

An alcohol has both a nonpolar alkyl group and a polar OH group. So is an alcohol molecule nonpolar or polar? Is it soluble in a nonpolar solvent, or is it soluble in water? The answer depends on the size of the alkyl group. As the alkyl group increases in size, becoming a more significant fraction of the alcohol molecule, the compound becomes less and less soluble in water. In other words, the molecule becomes more and more like an alkane. Groups with four carbons tend to straddle the dividing line at room temperature: alcohols with fewer than four carbons are soluble in water, but alcohols with more than four carbons are insoluble in water. In other words, an OH group can drag about three or four carbons into solution in water.

The four-carbon dividing line is only an approximate guide because the solubility of an alcohol also depends on the structure of the alkyl group. Alcohols with branched alkyl groups are more soluble in water than alcohols with nonbranched alkyl groups having the same number of carbons, because branching minimizes the contact surface of the nonpolar portion of the molecule. So *tert*-butyl alcohol is more soluble than *n*-butyl alcohol in water.

Similarly, the oxygen atom of an ether can drag only about three carbons into solution in water (Table 11.7). Diethyl ether—an ether with four carbons—is not soluble in water.

Table 11.7 Solubilities of Ethers in Water

2 C's	CH_3OCH_3	soluble
3 C's	$CH_3OCH_2CH_3$	soluble
4 C's	$CH_3CH_2OCH_2CH_3$	slightly soluble (10 g/100 g H_2O)
5 C's	$CH_3CH_2OCH_2CH_2CH_3$	minimally soluble (1.0 g/100 g H_2O)
6 C's	$CH_3CH_2CH_2OCH_2CH_2CH_3$	insoluble (0.25 g/100 g H_2O)

Low-molecular-weight amines are soluble in water because amines can form hydrogen bonds with water. Comparing amines with the same number of carbons, we find that primary amines are more soluble than secondary amines because primary amines have two hydrogens that can engage in hydrogen bonding. Tertiary amines, like primary and secondary amines, have lone-pair electrons that can accept hydrogen bonds, but unlike primary and secondary amines, tertiary amines do not have hydrogens to donate for hydrogen bonds. Tertiary amines, therefore, are less soluble in water than are secondary amines with the same number of carbons.

Alkyl halides have some polar character, but only alkyl fluorides have an atom that can form a hydrogen bond with water. This means that alkyl fluorides are the most water soluble of the alkyl halides. The other alkyl halides are less soluble in water than ethers or alcohols with the same number of carbons (Table 11.8).

Table 11.8 Solubilities of Alkyl Halides in Water

CH_3F	CH_3Cl	CH_3Br	CH_3I
very soluble	soluble	slightly soluble	slightly soluble
CH_3CH_2F	CH_3CH_2Cl	CH_3CH_2Br	CH_3CH_2I
soluble	slightly soluble	slightly soluble	slightly soluble
$CH_3CH_2CH_2F$	$CH_3CH_2CH_2Cl$	$CH_3CH_2CH_2Br$	$CH_3CH_2CH_2I$
slightly soluble	slightly soluble	slightly soluble	slightly soluble
$CH_3CH_2CH_2CH_2F$	$CH_3CH_2CH_2CH_2Cl$	$CH_3CH_2CH_2CH_2Br$	$CH_3CH_2CH_2CH_2I$
insoluble	insoluble	insoluble	insoluble

PROBLEM 33♦

Rank the following groups of compounds in order of decreasing solubility in water:

a. OH, O OH OH, OH O

b. $CH_3CH_2CH_2OH$ $CH_3CH_2CH_2CH_2Cl$ $CH_3CH_2CH_2CH_2OH$ $HOCH_2CH_2CH_2OH$

PROBLEM 34♦

In which solvent would cyclohexane have the lowest solubility, 1-pentanol, diethyl ether, ethanol, or hexane?

11.10 ROTATION OCCURS ABOUT CARBON–CARBON SINGLE BONDS

We have seen that a carbon–carbon single bond (a σ bond) is formed when an sp^3 orbital of one carbon overlaps an sp^3 orbital of another carbon. Figure 11.3 shows that rotation about a carbon–carbon single bond can occur without any change in the amount of orbital overlap. The different spatial arrangements of the atoms that result from rotation about a single bond are called **conformations**. Molecules with different conformations are called **conformational isomers** or **conformers**.

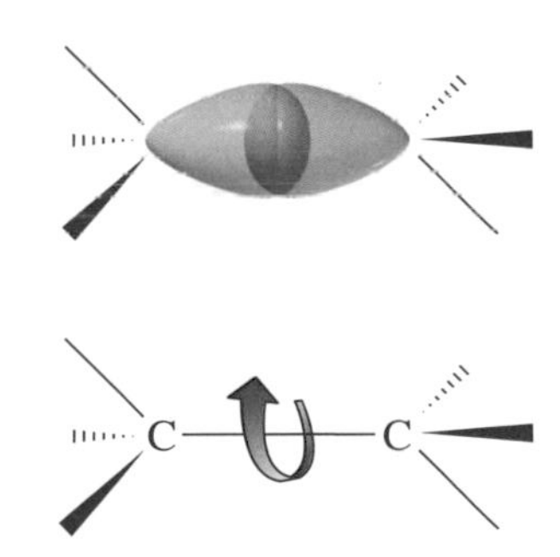

▲ Figure 11.3
A carbon–carbon bond is formed by the overlap of cylindrically symmetrical sp^3 orbitals. Therefore, rotation about the bond can occur without changing the amount of orbital overlap.

The conformers produced by rotation about the carbon–carbon bond of ethane represent a continuum between the two extremes shown below: a *staggered conformer* and an *eclipsed conformer*. An infinite number of conformers between these two extremes are also possible.

Our drawings of molecules are two-dimensional attempts to communicate three-dimensional structures. Chemists commonly use *Newman projections* to represent the three-dimensional spatial arrangements resulting from rotation about a σ bond. A **Newman projection** assumes that the viewer is looking along the longitudinal axis of a particular C—C bond. The carbon in front is represented by a point (where three lines are seen to intersect), and the carbon at the back is represented by a circle. The three lines emanating from each of the carbons represent its other three bonds.

$H_3C{-}CH_3$
ethane

Newman projections

60°

staggered conformer from rotation about the C—C bond in ethane

eclipsed conformer from rotation about the C—C bond in ethane

BIOGRAPHY

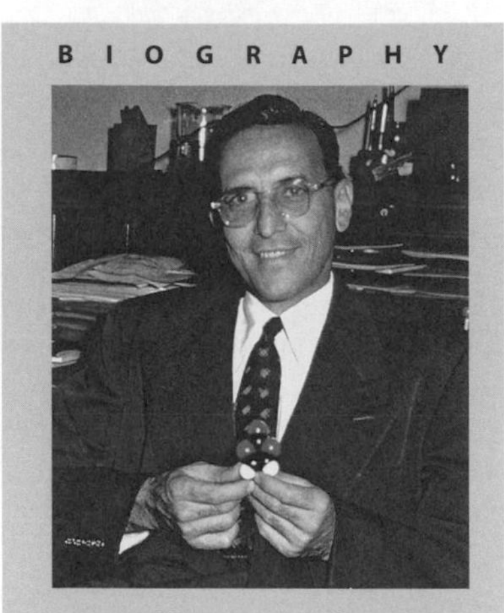

Melvin S. Newman (1908–1993) *was born in New York. He received a Ph.D. from Yale University in 1932 and was a professor of chemistry at Ohio State University from 1936 to 1973. He first suggested his technique for drawing organic molecules in 1952.*

A **staggered conformer** is more stable, and therefore lower in energy, than an **eclipsed conformer**. Because of this energy difference, rotation about a carbon–carbon single bond is not completely free since an energy barrier must be overcome when rotation about the C—C bond occurs (Figure 11.4). However, the energy barrier in ethane is small enough (2.9 kcal/mol or 12 kJ/mol) to allow continuous rotation. A molecule's conformation changes from staggered to eclipsed millions of times per second at room temperature. Because of this continuous interconversion, the conformers cannot be separated from each other. Nevertheless, at any one time approximately 99% of the ethane molecules will be in a staggered conformation because of its greater stability, and only 1% will be in the less stable eclipsed conformation. The investigation of the various conformations of a compound and their relative stabilities is called **conformational analysis**.

Figure 11.4 shows the potential energies of all the conformers of ethane obtained in one complete 360° rotation about the C—C bond. Notice that staggered conformers are at energy minima, whereas eclipsed conformers are at energy maxima.

Why is a staggered conformer more stable than an eclipsed conformer? The major contribution to the energy difference between them is a stabilizing interaction between the C—H σ bonding orbital on one carbon and the C—H σ^* antibonding orbital on the other carbon: the electrons in the filled bonding orbital move partially into the unoccupied antibonding orbital. This interaction is greatest in a staggered conformation because only in this conformation are the two orbitals parallel. Such a delocalization of electrons by the overlap of an σ orbital with an empty orbital is called **hyperconjugation**.

A staggered conformer is more stable than an eclipsed conformer.

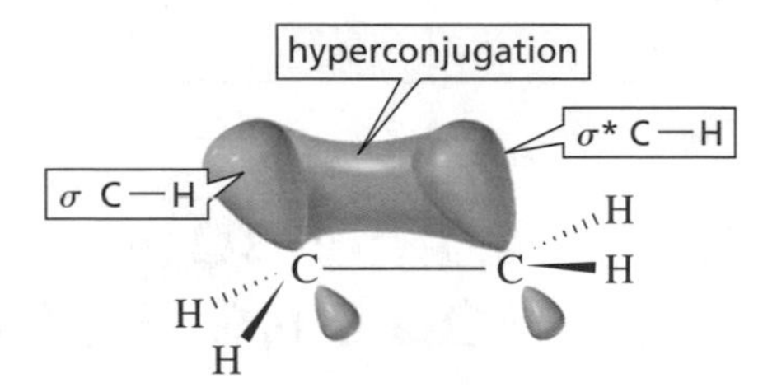

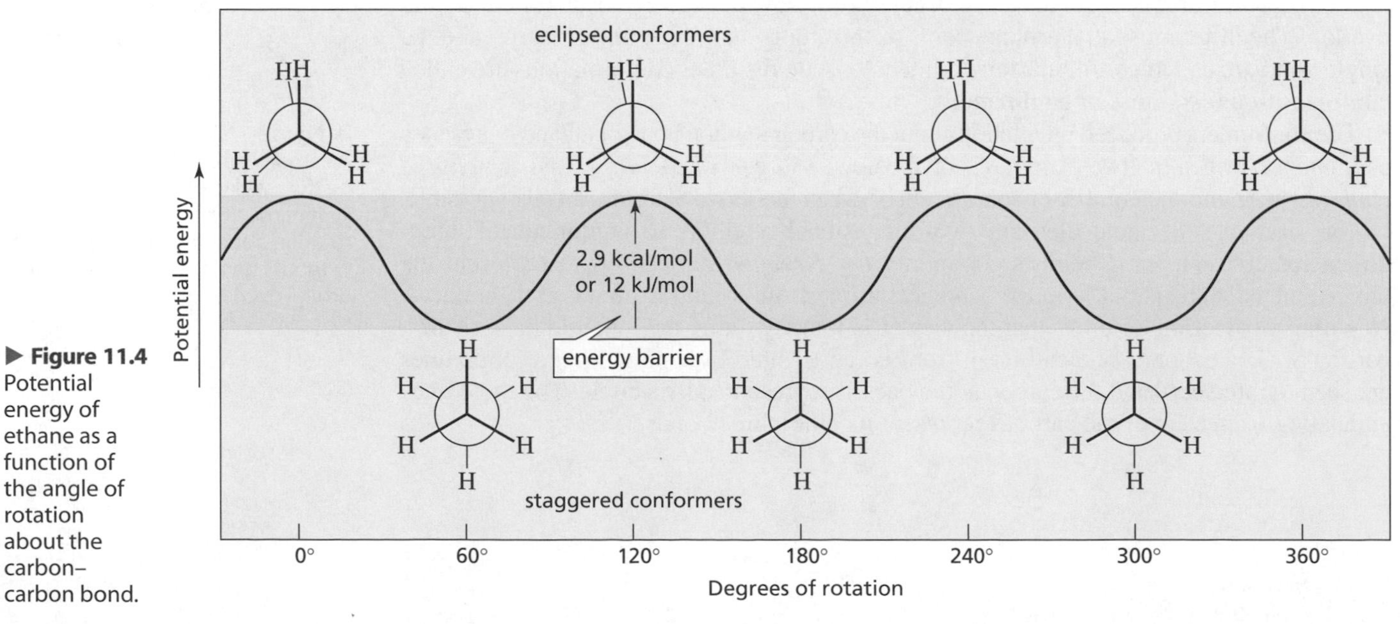

▶ **Figure 11.4**
Potential energy of ethane as a function of the angle of rotation about the carbon–carbon bond.

Butane has three carbon–carbon single bonds, and rotation can occur about each of them. The Newman projections below show the staggered and eclipsed conformers that result from rotation about the C-1—C-2 bond:

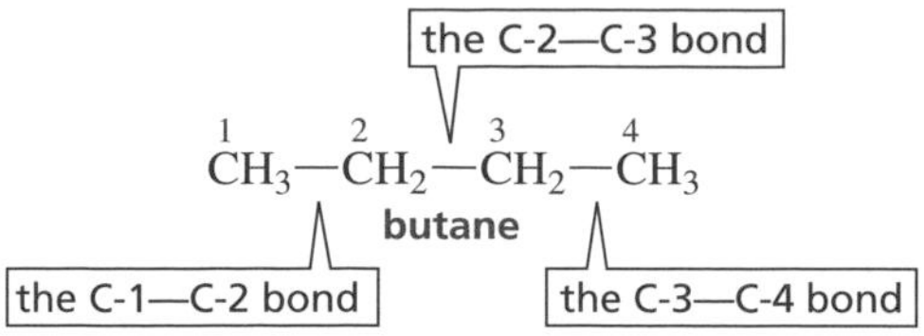

the C-2—C-3 bond

$\overset{1}{C}H_3-\overset{2}{C}H_2-\overset{3}{C}H_2-\overset{4}{C}H_3$

butane

the C-1—C-2 bond

the C-3—C-4 bond

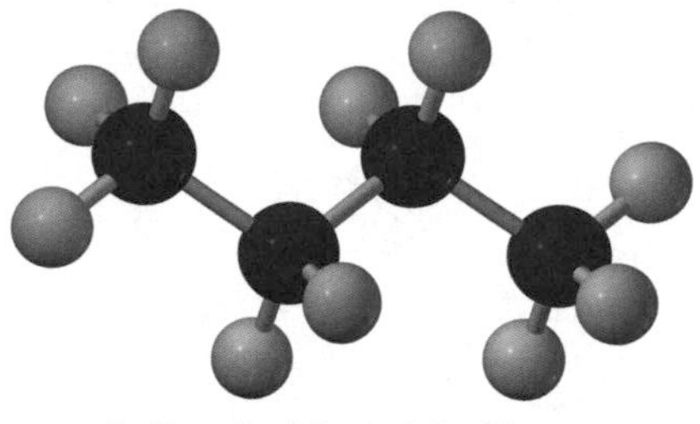

ball-and-stick model of butane

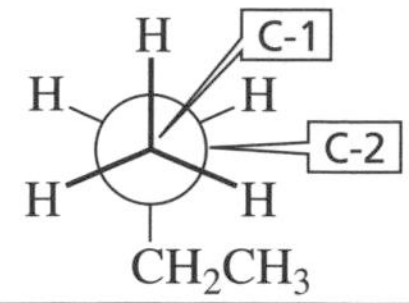

C-1 C-2 CH_2CH_3

staggered conformer that results from rotation about the C-1—C-2 bond in butane

C-3 C-4 CH_2CH_3

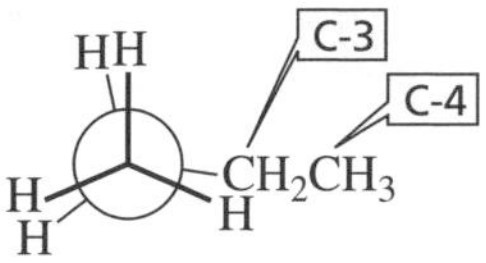

eclipsed conformer that results from rotation about the C-1—C-2 bond in butane

Notice that the carbon with the lower number is placed in the foreground in a Newman projection.

Although the staggered conformers resulting from rotation about the C-1—C-2 bond in butane all have the same energy, the staggered conformers resulting from rotation about the C-2—C-3 bond do not. The staggered and eclipsed conformers from rotation about the C-2—C-3 bond in butane are:

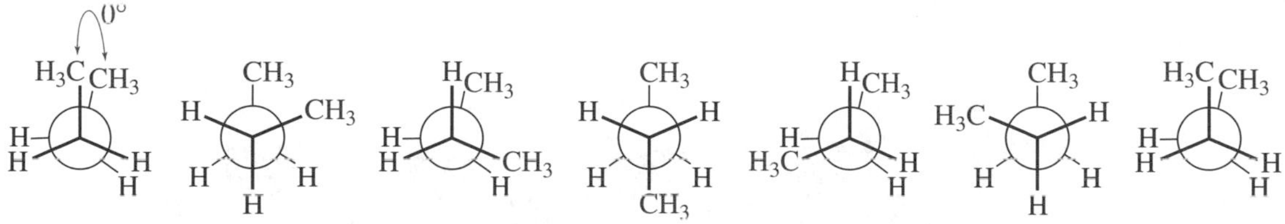

$0°$

A B C D E F A

Of the staggered conformers, D, in which the two methyl groups are as far apart as possible, is more stable than the other two staggered conformers (B and F). The most stable staggered conformer (in this case, D) is called the **anti conformer**, and the other two staggered conformers (in this case, B and F) are called **gauche** ("goesh") **conformers**. (*Anti* is Greek for "opposite of"; *gauche* is French for "left.") In the anti conformer, the largest substituents are opposite each other; in a gauche conformer, they are adjacent. The two gauche conformers have the same energy, which is higher than the energy of the anti conformer.

The anti and gauche conformers do not have the same energy because of steric strain. **Steric strain** is the strain experienced by a molecule (that is, the additional energy it possesses) when atoms or groups are close enough to one another for their electron clouds to repel each other. There is more steric strain in a gauche conformer than in the anti conformer because the two substituents (in this case, the two methyl groups of butane) are closer together in a gauche conformer. This type of steric strain is called a **gauche interaction**. In general, steric strain in molecules increases as the size of the interacting atoms or groups increases.

The eclipsed conformers resulting from rotation about the C-2—C-3 bond in butane also have different energies. The eclipsed conformer in which the two methyl groups are closest to each other (A) is less stable than the eclipsed conformer in which they are farther apart (C and E).

The energies of the conformers obtained from rotation about the C-2—C-3 bond of butane are shown in Figure 11.5. The letters in Figure 11.5 correspond to the letters that identify the above structures. The degree of rotation of each conformer is identified by the dihedral angle—the angle formed in a Newman projection by a bond on the nearer carbon and a bond on the far carbon. For example, the conformer in which one methyl

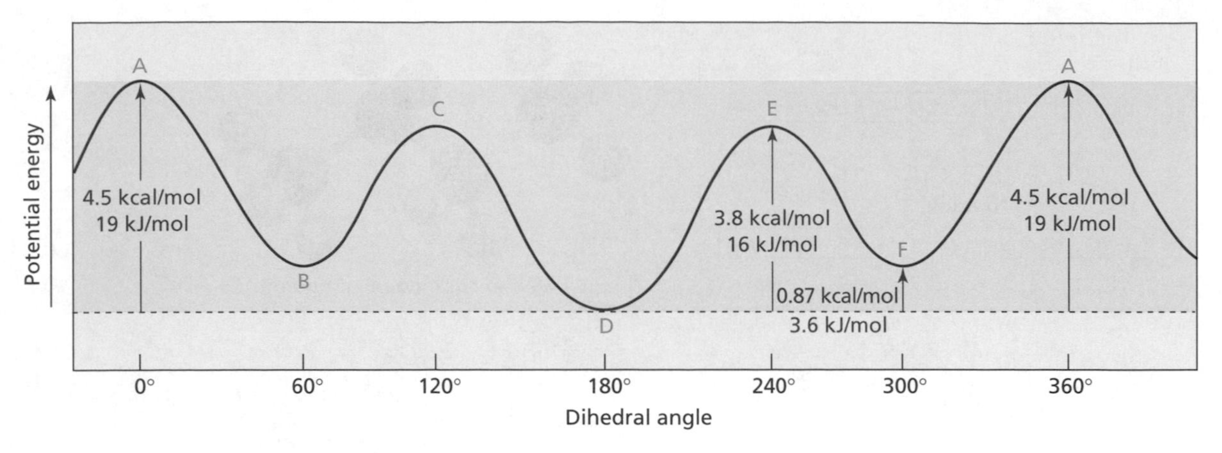

▶ **Figure 11.5** Potential energy of butane as a function of the degree of rotation about the C-2—C-3 bond. Green letters refer to the conformers (A–F) shown on page 491.

group stands directly in front of the other—the least stable conformer—has a dihedral angle of 0°.

Because there is continuous rotation about all the C—C single bonds in a molecule, organic molecules with C—C single bonds are not static balls and sticks—they have many interconvertible conformers. The relative number of molecules in a particular conformation at any one time depends on its stability: the more stable it is, the greater the fraction of molecules that will be in that conformation. Most molecules, therefore, are in staggered conformations at any given instant, and more molecules are in the anti conformation than in a gauche conformation. The preference for the staggered conformation gives carbon chains a tendency to adopt zigzag arrangements, as seen in the ball-and-stick model of decane.

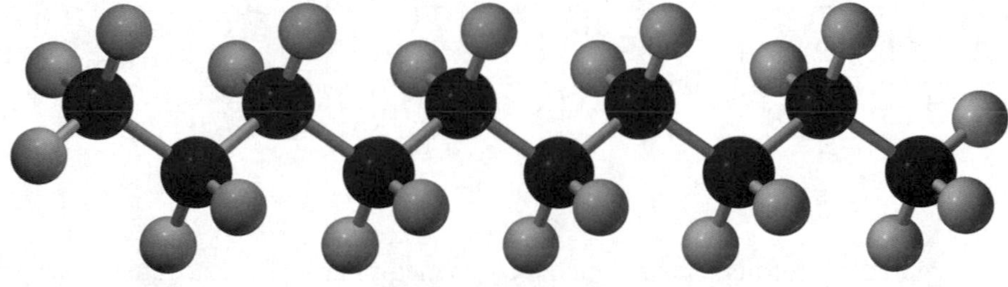

ball-and-stick model of decane

PROBLEM 35

a. Draw all the staggered and eclipsed conformers that result from rotation about the C-2—C-3 bond of pentane.
b. Draw a potential-energy diagram for rotation about the C-2—C-3 bond of pentane through 360°, starting with the least stable conformer.

PROBLEM 36♦

Using Newman projections, draw the most stable conformer for each of the following:
a. 3-methylpentane, viewed along the C-2—C-3 bond
b. 3-methylhexane, viewed along the C-3—C-4 bond
c. 3,3-dimethylhexane, viewed along the C-3—C-4 bond

11.11 SOME CYCLOALKANES HAVE ANGLE STRAIN

Early chemists observed that cyclic compounds found in nature generally have five- or six-membered rings. Compounds with three- and four-membered rings are much less common. This observation suggests that compounds with five- and six-membered rings are more stable than compounds with three- or four-membered rings.

In 1885, the German chemist Adolf von Baeyer proposed that the instability of three- and four-membered rings is due to angle strain. We know that, ideally, an sp^3 carbon has bond angles of 109.5°. Baeyer suggested that the stability of a cycloalkane could be predicted by assessing the difference between this ideal bond angle and the bond angle in the planar cycloalkane. The bond angles in an equilateral triangle, for example, are 60°, representing a 49.5° deviation from the tetrahedral 109.5°. According to Baeyer, this deviation causes **angle strain**, and thus instability, in cyclopropane.

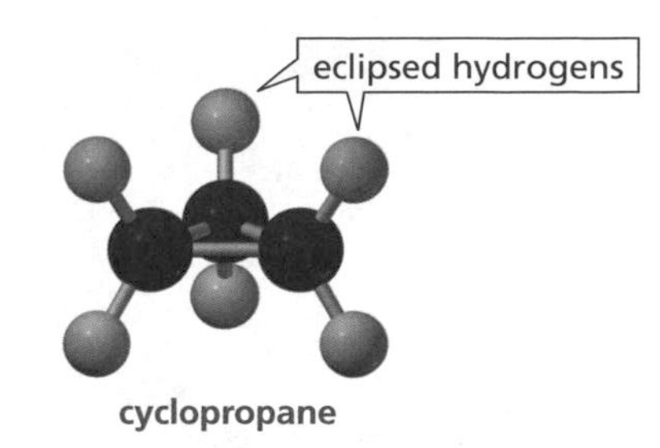

The angle strain in a three-membered ring can be understood by looking at the overlap of the orbitals that form the σ bonds in cyclopropane (Figure 11.6). Normal σ bonds are formed by the overlap of two sp^3 orbitals that point directly at each other. In cyclopropane, the overlapping orbitals cannot point directly at each other, so the amount of overlap between them is less than in a normal C—C bond. The smaller degree of overlap causes the C—C bonds in cyclopropane to be weaker than normal C—C bonds. This weakness is what we have described as angle strain.

a.

b.

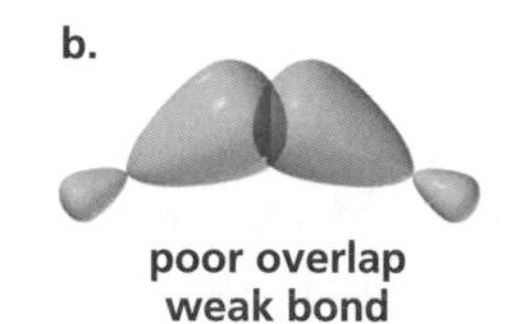

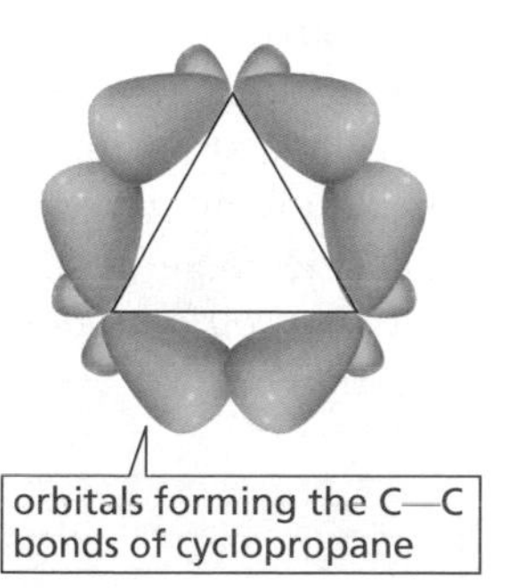

◀ **Figure 11.6**
(a) Overlap of sp^3 orbitals in a normal σ bond.
(b) Overlap sp^3 of orbitals in cyclopropane.

Because the C—C bonding orbitals in cyclopropane cannot point directly at each other, the bonds they form have shapes that resemble bananas and, consequently, are sometimes called **banana bonds**. In addition to the angle strain of the C—C bonds, all the adjacent C—H bonds in cyclopropane are eclipsed rather than staggered, making it even more unstable.

The bond angles in a hypothetical planar cyclobutane molecule would have to be compressed from 109.5° to 90°, the bond angle associated with a planar four-membered ring. Planar cyclobutane would therefore have less angle strain than cyclopropane because the bond angles in cyclobutane are only 19.5° away from the ideal bond angle. It would, however, have eight pairs of eclipsed hydrogens, compared with six pairs in cyclopropane. Because of the eclipsed hydrogens, a cyclobutane molecule is not planar.

Highly Strained Hydrocarbons

Organic chemists have been able to synthesize some highly strained cyclic hydrocarbons, such as bicyclo[1.1.0]butane, cubane, and prismane. Bicyclo[1.1.0]butane was synthesized by David Lemal, Fredric Menger, and George Clark at the University of Wisconsin. Cubane was synthesized by Philip Eaton and Thomas Cole Jr. at the University of Chicago. Prismane was synthesized by Thomas Katz and Nancy Acton at Columbia University.

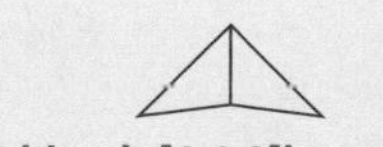

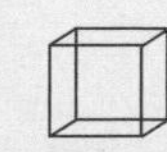

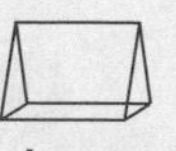

Philip Eaton, the first to synthesize cubane, also synthesized octanitrocubane, which is cubane with an NO_2 group bonded to each of the eight corners. It turned out to be less powerful an explosive than expected.

PROBLEM 37◆

The bond angles in a regular polygon with n sides are equal to

$$180° - \frac{360°}{n}$$

a. What are the bond angles in a regular octagon?
b. What are the bond angles in a regular nonagon?

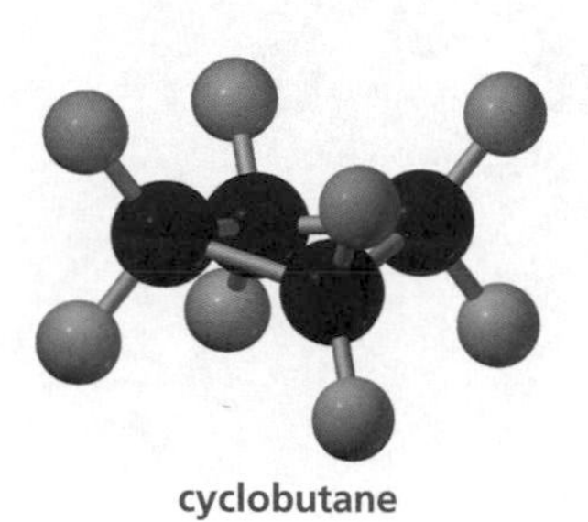
cyclobutane

Baeyer predicted that cyclopentane would be the most stable of the cycloalkanes because its bond angles (108°) are closest to the ideal tetrahedral bond angle. He predicted that cyclohexane, with bond angles of 120°, would be less stable and that as the number of sides in the cycloalkanes increases beyond six, their stability would decrease.

Contrary to what Baeyer predicted, however, cyclohexane is more stable than cyclopentane. Furthermore, cyclic compounds do not thereafter become less and less stable as the number of sides increases. The mistake Baeyer made was to assume that all cyclic molecules are planar. Because three points define a plane, the carbons of cyclopropane must lie in a plane. The other cycloalkanes, however, are not planar but twist and bend in order to attain a structure that maximizes their stability by minimizing ring strain and the number of eclipsed hydrogens. Therefore, instead of being planar as in the hypothetical example described on page 101, the cyclobutane molecule is bent, with one of its methylene groups extending at an angle of about 25° from the plane defined by the other three carbons.

If the cyclopentane ring were planar, as Baeyer had predicted, it would have essentially no angle strain, but it would have 10 pairs of eclipsed hydrogens. So cyclopentane puckers, allowing some of the hydrogens to become nearly staggered but, in the process, the molecule acquires some angle strain. The puckered form of cyclopentane is called the *envelope conformation*, because the shape of the ring resembles a squarish envelope with the flap up.

Von Baeyer and Barbituric Acid

Johann Friedrich Wilhelm Adolf von Baeyer (1835–1917), a German chemist, was a professor of chemistry at the University of Strasbourg and later at the University of Munich. In 1864, he discovered barbituric acid—the first of a group of sedatives known as barbiturates—and named it after a woman named Barbara. Who Barbara was is not certain. Some say she was his girlfriend, but because Baeyer discovered barbituric acid in the same year that Prussia defeated Denmark, some believe he named it after Saint Barbara, the patron saint of artillerymen. Baeyer is also known as the first to synthesize indigo, the dye used in the manufacture of blue jeans. He received the Nobel Prize in Chemistry in 1905 for his work in synthetic organic chemistry.

PROBLEM 38 ♦

The effectiveness of a barbiturate as a sedative is related to its ability to penetrate the nonpolar membrane of a cell. Which of the following barbiturates would you expect to be the more effective sedative?

hexethal

barbital

cyclopentane

11.12 CONFORMERS OF CYCLOHEXANE

The cyclic compounds most commonly found in nature contain six-membered rings because carbon rings of that size can exist in a conformation—called a *chair conformer*—that is almost completely free of strain. All the bond angles in a **chair conformer** are 111°, which is very close to the ideal tetrahedral bond angle of 109.5°, and all the adjacent bonds are staggered (Figure 11.7).

chair conformer of cyclohexane

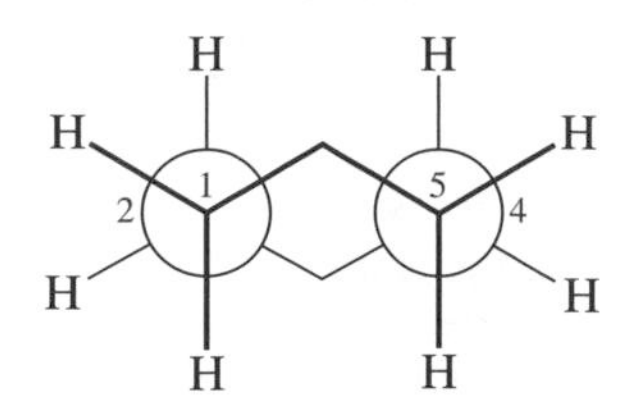

Newman projection of the chair conformer

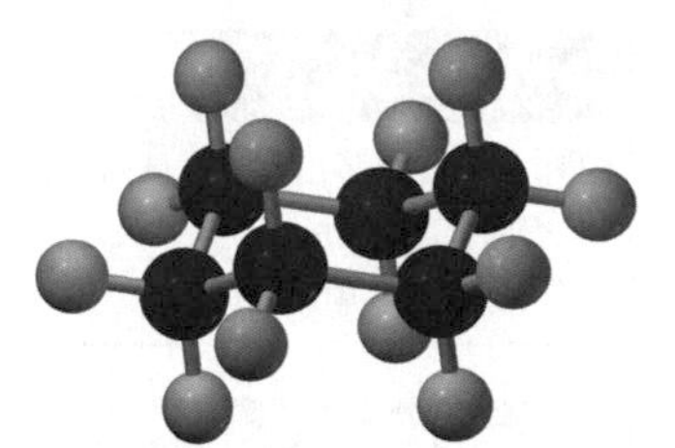
ball-and-stick model of the chair conformer

◀ **Figure 11.7**
The chair conformer of cyclohexane, a Newman projection of the chair conformer showing that all the bonds are staggered, and a ball-and-stick model.

The chair conformer is such an important conformer that you should learn how to draw it:

1. Draw two parallel lines of the same length, slanted upward and beginning at the same height.

2. Connect the tops of the lines with a V whose left side is slightly longer than its right side. Connect the bottoms of the lines with an inverted V. (The bottom-left and top-right lines should be parallel; and the top-left and bottom-right lines should be parallel.) This completes the framework of the six-membered ring.

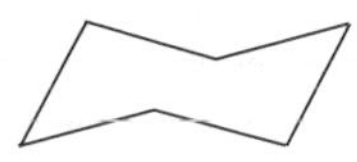

3. Each carbon has an axial bond and an equatorial bond. The **axial bonds** (red lines) are vertical and alternate above and below the ring. The axial bond on one of the uppermost carbons is up, the next is down, the next is up, and so on.

axial bonds

4. The **equatorial bonds** (red lines with blue balls) point outward from the ring. Because the bond angles are greater than 90°, the equatorial bonds are on a slant. If the axial bond points up, the equatorial bond on the same carbon is on a downward slant. If the axial bond points down, the equatorial bond on the same carbon is on an upward slant.

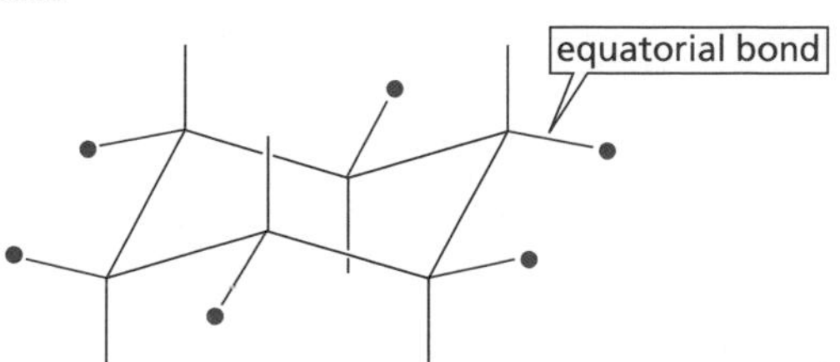

Notice that each equatorial bond is parallel to two ring bonds (two carbons over).

Remember that in this depiction cyclohexane is viewed edge-on. The lower bonds of the ring are in front and the upper bonds of the ring are in back.

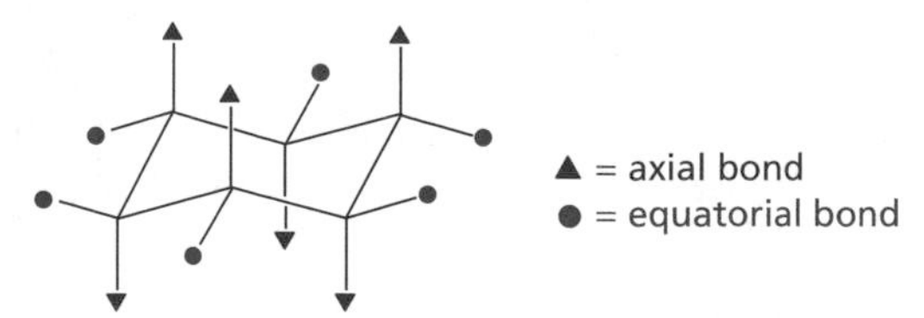

PROBLEM 39

Draw 1,2,3,4,5,6-hexachlorocyclohexane with

a. all the chloro groups in axial positions.
b. all the chloro groups in equatorial positions.

PROBLEM-SOLVING STRATEGY

Calculating the Strain Energy of a Cycloalkane

If we assume that cyclohexane is completely free of strain, we can use the **heat of formation**—the heat given off when a compound is formed from its elements under standard conditions—to calculate the total strain energy of the other cycloalkanes. Taking the heat of formation of cyclohexane (Table 11.9) and dividing by 6 for its six CH_2 groups gives us a value of -4.92 kcal/mol for a "strainless" CH_2 group ($-29.5/6 = -4.92$). With this value, we can calculate the heat of formation of any other "strainless" cycloalkane: we simply multiply the number of CH_2 groups in its ring by -4.92 kcal/mol. The total strain in the compound is the difference between its "strainless" heat of formation and its actual heat of formation (Table 11.9). For example, cyclopentane has a "strainless" heat of formation of $(5)(-4.92) = -24.6$ kcal/mol and an actual heat of formation of -18.4 kcal/mol. Therefore, cyclopentane has a total strain energy of 6.2 kcal/mol, because $[-18.4 - (-24.6) = 6.2]$. Dividing the total strain energy by the number of CH_2 groups in the cyclic compound gives the strain energy per CH_2 group.

Now continue on to Problem 40.

PROBLEM 40♦

Calculate the total strain energy of cycloheptane.

Table 11.9 Heats Formation and Strain Energies of Cyloalkanes

	Heat of formation (kcal/mol)	"Strainless" heat of formation (kcal/mol)	Total Strain energy (kcal/mol)	Strain energy per CH_2 group (kcal/mol)
cyclopropane	+12.7	-14.6	27.3	9.1
cyclobutane	+6.8	-19.7	26.5	6.6
cyclopentane	-18.4	-24.6	6.2	1.2
cyclohexane	-29.5	-29.5	0	0
cycloheptane	-28.2	-34.4	6.2	0.9
cyclooctane	-29.7	-39.4	9.7	1.2
cyclononane	-31.7	-44.3	12.6	1.4
cyclodecane	-36.9	-49.2	12.3	1.2
cycloundecane	-42.9	-54.1	11.2	1.0

Bonds that are equatorial in one chair conformer are axial in the other chair conformer.

Cyclohexane rapidly interconverts between two stable chair conformers because of the ease of rotation about its C—C bonds. This interconversion is called **ring flip** (Figure 11.8). When the two chair conformers interconvert, bonds that are equatorial in one chair conformer become axial in the other chair conformer and vice versa.

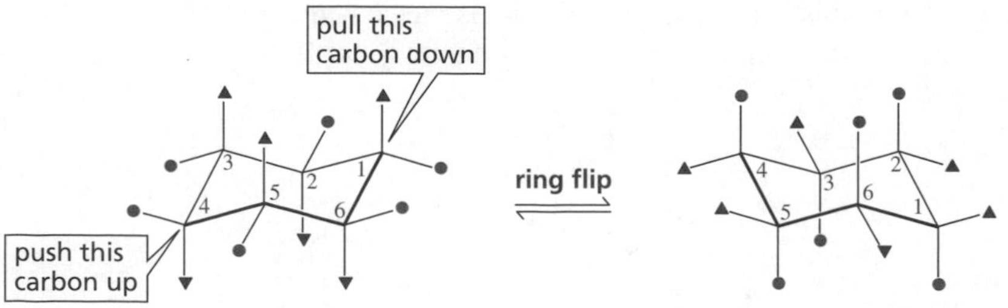

pull this carbon down
push this carbon up
ring flip

▶ Figure 11.8
The bonds that are axial in one chair conformer are equatorial in the other chair conformer. The bonds that are equatorial in one chair conformer are axial in the other chair conformer.

Cyclohexane can also exist as a **boat conformer**, shown in Figure 11.9. Like the chair conformer, the boat conformer is free of angle strain. However, the boat conformer is not as stable because some of the bonds are eclipsed. The boat conformer is further destabilized by the close proximity of the **flagpole hydrogens**—the hydrogens at the "bow" and "stern" of the boat—which causes steric strain.

flagpole hydrogens

boat conformer of cyclohexane

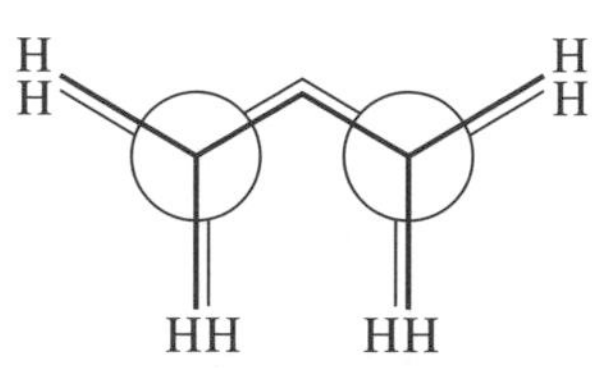

Newman projection of the boat conformer

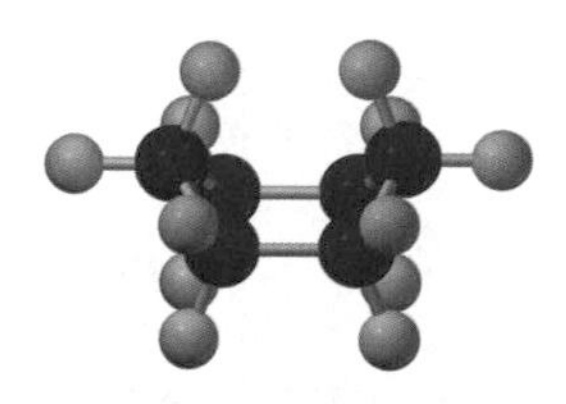

ball-and-stick model of the boat conformer

◀ **Figure 11.9**
The boat conformer of cyclohexane, a Newman projection of the boat conformer showing that some of the bonds are eclipsed, and a ball-and-stick model.

The conformers that cyclohexane assumes when interconverting from one chair conformer to the other are shown in Figure 11.10. To convert from the boat conformer to a chair conformer, one of the two topmost carbons of the boat conformer must be pulled down so that it becomes the bottommost carbon of the chair conformer. When the carbon is pulled down just a little, the **twist-boat** (or **skew-boat**) **conformer** is obtained. The twist-boat conformer is more stable than the boat conformer because the flagpole hydrogens have moved away from each other, thus relieving some steric strain. When the carbon is pulled down to the point where it is in the same plane as the sides of the boat, the very unstable **half-chair conformer** is obtained. Pulling the carbon down farther produces the *chair conformer*. The graph in Figure 11.10 shows the energy of a cyclohexane molecule as it interconverts from one chair conformer to the other; the energy barrier for interconversion is 12.1 kcal/mol (50.6 kJ/mol). From this value, it can be calculated that cyclohexane undergoes 10^5 ring flips per second at room temperature. In other words, the two chair conformers are in rapid equilibrium.

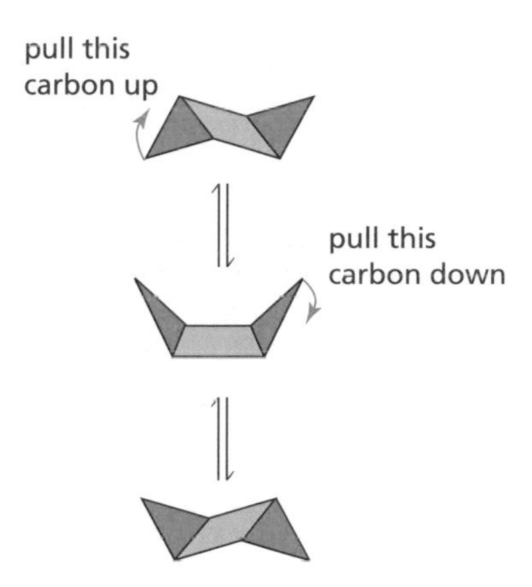

Build a model of cyclohexane. Convert it from one chair conformer to the other by pulling the topmost carbon down and pushing the bottommost carbon up.

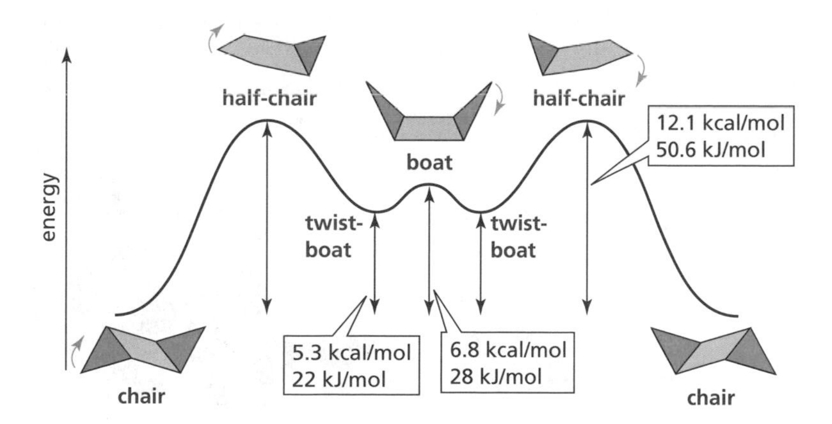

◀ **Figure 11.10**
The conformers of cyclohexane—and their relative energies—as one chair conformer interconverts to the other chair conformer.

The chair conformers are the most stable of cyclohexane's conformers, so at any instant more molecules of cyclohexane are in a chair conformation than in any other conformation. For every 10,000 molecules of cyclohexane in a chair conformation, there is no more than one molecule in the next most stable conformation, the twist-boat.

Go to the website to see three-dimensional representations of the conformers of cyclohexane.

11.13 CONFORMERS OF MONOSUBSTITUTED CYCLOHEXANES

Unlike cyclohexane, which has two equivalent chair conformers, the two chair conformers of a monosubstituted cyclohexane, such as methylcyclohexane, are not equivalent. The methyl substituent is in an equatorial position in one conformer and in an axial position in the other (Figure 11.11), because as we have just seen, substituents that are equatorial in one chair conformer are axial in the other (Figure 11.8).

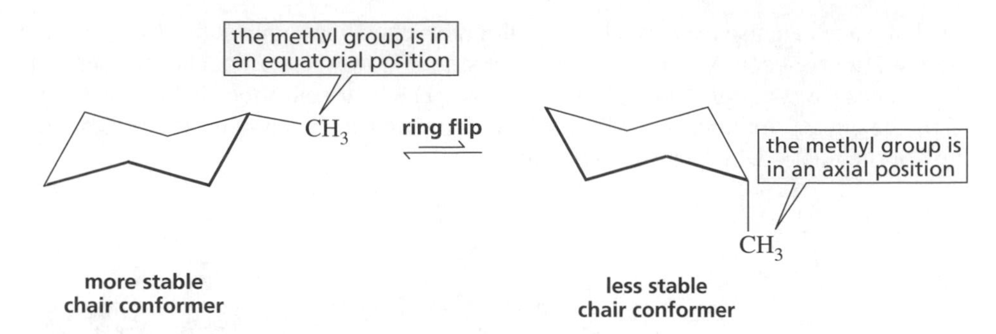

▶ **Figure 11.11**
A substituent is in an equatorial position in one chair conformer and in an axial position in the other. The conformer with the substituent in the equatorial position is more stable.

The chair conformer with the methyl substituent in an equatorial position is the more stable of the two conformers because a substituent has more room and, therefore, fewer steric interactions when it is in an equatorial position. This can be best understood from a drawing like that in Figure 11.12a, which shows that when the methyl group is in an equatorial position, it extends into space, away from the rest of the molecule.

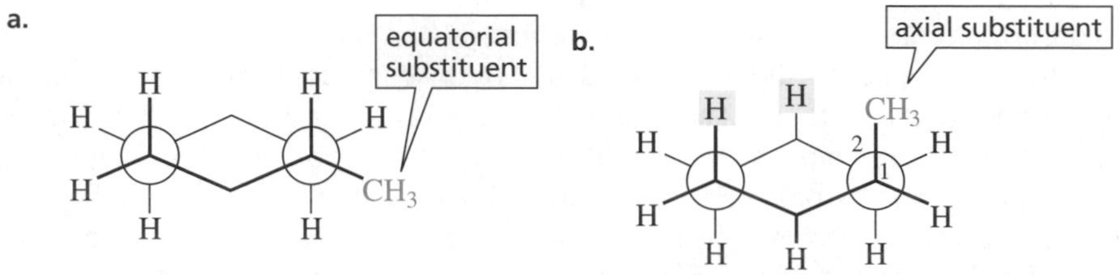

▶ **Figure 11.12**
a. An equatorial substituent
b. An axial substituent

In contrast, because the three axial bonds on the same side of the ring are parallel to each other, any axial substituent will be relatively close to the axial substituents on the other two carbons (Figure 11.12b).

Because the interacting hydrogens or substituents are in 1,3-positions relative to each other, these unfavorable steric interactions are called **1,3-diaxial interactions**. If you take a few minutes to build models, you will see that a substituent has more room if it is in an equatorial position than if it is in an axial position.

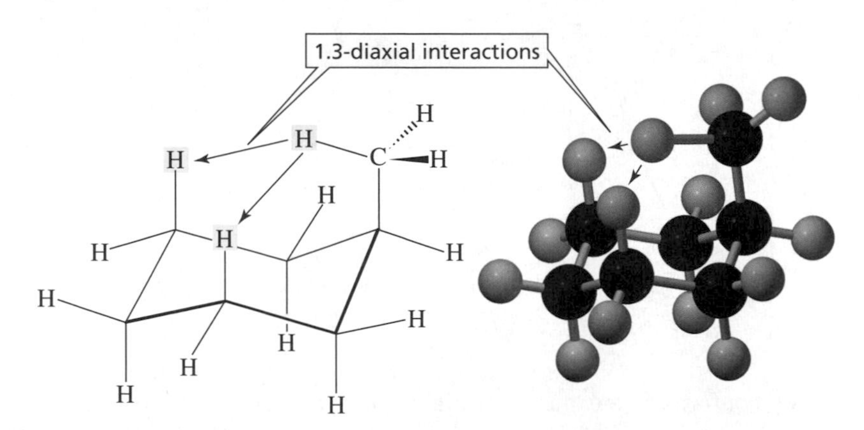

A gauche conformer of butane and the axially substituted conformer of methylcyclohexane are compared in Figure 11.13. Notice that the gauche interaction in butane is the same as a 1,3-diaxial interaction in methylcyclohexane. Butane has one gauche interaction and methylcyclohexane has two 1,3-diaxial interactions.

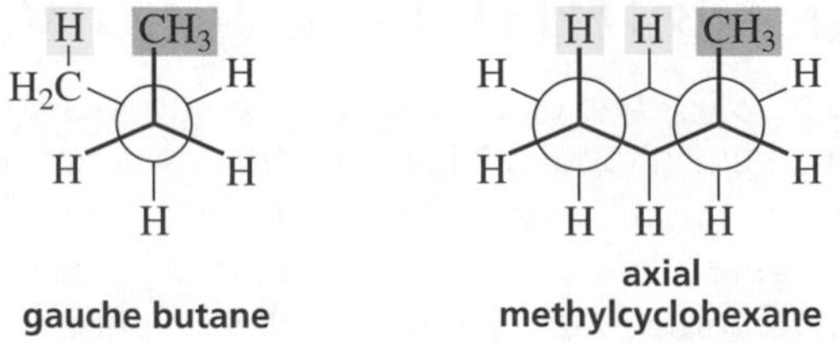

▶ **Figure 11.13**
The steric strain of gauche butane is the same as the steric strain between an axial methyl group of methylcyclohexane and one of its axial hydrogens. Butane has one gauche interaction between a methyl group and a hydrogen; methylcyclohexane has two.

gauche butane **axial methylcyclohexane**

In Section 11.10, we saw that the gauche interaction between the methyl groups of butane caused a gauche conformer to be 0.87 kcal/mol (3.6 kJ/mol) less stable than the anti conformer. Because there are two such gauche interactions in the chair conformer of methylcyclohexane when the methyl group is in an axial position, this conformer is 1.74 kcal/mol (7.2 kJ/mol) less stable than the chair conformer with the methyl group in the equatorial position.

Because of the difference in stability of the two chair conformers, a sample of methylcyclohexane or any other substituted cycloalkane will at any point in time contain more chair conformers with the substituent in the equatorial position than with the substituent in the axial position. The relative amounts of the two chair conformers depend on the substituent (Table 11.10).

Table 11.10 Equilibrium Constants for Several Monosubstituted Cyclohexanes at 25 °C

Substituent	Axial $\underset{}{\overset{K_{eq}}{\rightleftharpoons}}$ Equatorial	Substituent	Axial $\underset{}{\overset{K_{eq}}{\rightleftharpoons}}$ Equatorial
H	1	CN	1.4
CH_3	18	F	1.5
CH_3CH_2	21	Cl	2.4
$CH_3CH(CH_3)$	35	Br	2.2
$CH_3C(CH_3)_2$	4800	I	2.2
		HO	5.4

The substituent with the greater bulk in the vicinity of the 1,3-diaxial hydrogens will have a greater preference for the equatorial position because it will have stronger 1,3-diaxial interactions. For example, the experimental equilibrium constant (K_{eq}) for the conformers of methylcyclohexane (Table 11.10) indicates that 95% of methylcyclohexane molecules have the methyl group in the equatorial position at 25 °C:

$$K_{eq} = \frac{[\text{equatorial conformer}]}{[\text{axial conformer}]} = \frac{18}{1}$$

$$\%\text{ of equatorial conformer} = \frac{[\text{equatorial conformer}]}{[\text{equatorial conformer}] + [\text{axial conformer}]} \times 100$$

$$\%\text{ of equatorial conformer} = \frac{18}{18 + 1} \times 100 = 95\%$$

In *tert*-butylcyclohexane, where the 1,3-diaxial interactions are even more destabilizing because a *tert*-butyl group is larger than a methyl group, more than 99.9% of the molecules have the *tert*-butyl group in the equatorial position.

The larger the substituent on a cyclohexane ring, the more the equatorial-substituted conformer will be favored.

PROBLEM 41 ♦

The chair conformer of fluorocyclohexane is 0.25 kcal/mol more stable when the fluoro substituent is in the equatorial position than when it is in the axial position. How much more stable is 1-fluoropropane when it is in the anti conformation than when it is in a gauche conformation?

PROBLEM 42 ♦

From the data in Table 11.10, calculate the percentage of molecules of cyclohexanol that have the OH group in the equatorial position at 25 °C.

11.14 CONFORMERS OF DISUBSTITUTED CYCLOHEXANES

The cis isomer of a disubstituted cyclic compound has its substituents on the same side of the ring.

The trans isomer of a disubstituted cyclic compound has its substituents on opposite sides of the ring.

If a cyclohexane ring has two substituents, we must take both substituents into account when predicting which of the two chair conformers is more stable. Let's use 1,4-dimethylcyclohexane as an example. First of all, note that there are two different dimethylcyclohexanes. One has both methyl substituents on the *same side* of the cyclohexane ring (both point downward); it is called the cis isomer (*cis* is Latin for "on this side"). The other has the two methyl substituents on *opposite sides* of the ring (one points upward and one points downward); it is called the **trans isomer** (*trans* is Latin for "across").

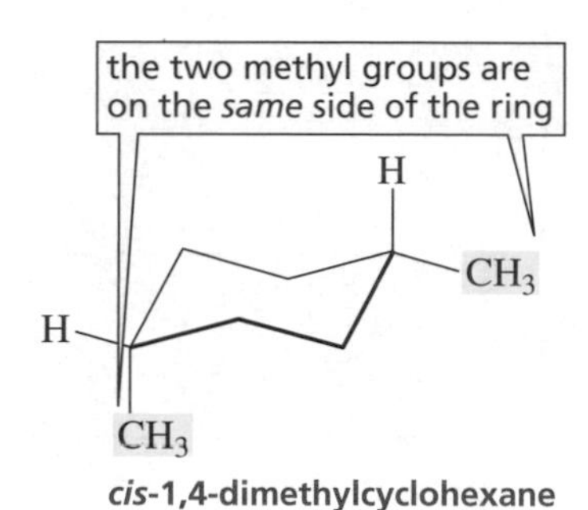

cis-1,4-dimethylcyclohexane

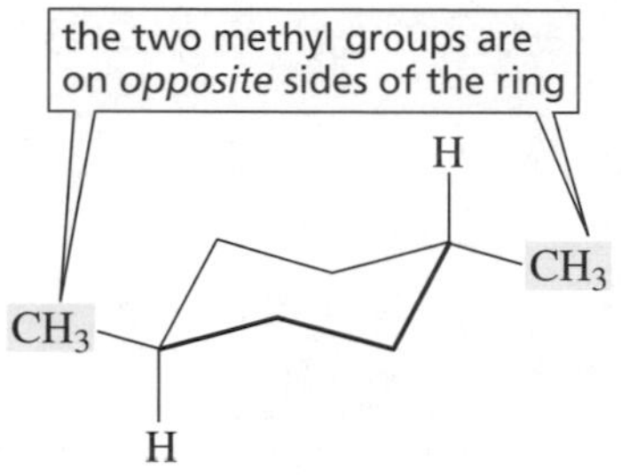

the two methyl groups are on *opposite* sides of the ring
H
CH_3
CH_3
H
trans-1,4-dimethylcyclohexane

cis-1,4-Dimethylcyclohexane and *trans*-1,4-dimethylcyclohexane are examples of **cis–trans isomers** or **geometric isomers**; cis–trans isomers are compounds containing the same atoms, and the atoms are linked in the same order, but the atoms exhibit two different spatial arrangements. The cis and trans isomers are different compounds with different melting and boiling points. They can, therefore, be separated from one another.

PROBLEM-SOLVING STRATEGY

Differentiating Cis–Trans Isomers

Is the conformer of 1,2-dimethylcyclohexane with one methyl group in an equatorial position and the other in an axial position the cis isomer or the trans isomer?

H
CH_3
H
CH_3

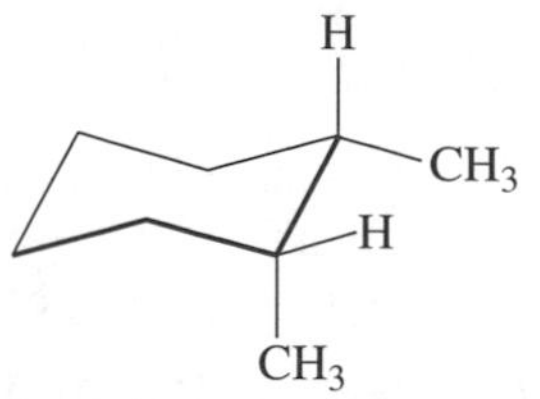

Is this the cis isomer or the trans isomer?

To solve this kind of problem we need to determine whether the two substituents are on the same side of the ring (cis) or on opposite sides of the ring (trans). If the bonds bearing the substituents are both pointing upward or both pointing downward, the compound is the cis isomer; if one bond is pointing upward and the other downward, the compound is the trans isomer. Because the conformer in question has both methyl groups attached to downward-pointing bonds, it is the cis isomer.

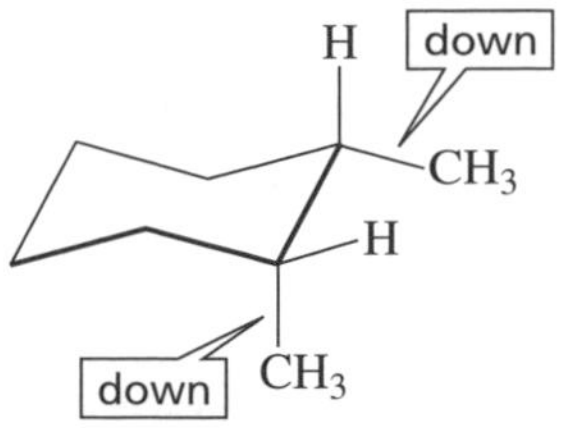

the cis isomer 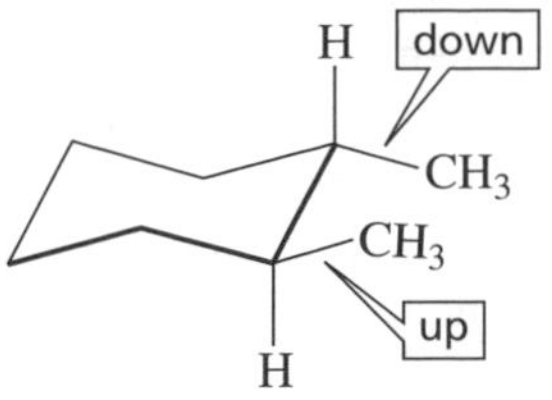 **the trans isomer**

The isomer that is the most misleading when drawn in two dimensions is a *trans*-1,2-disubstituted isomer. At first glance, the methyl groups of *trans*-1,2-dimethylcyclohexane (on the right, above) appear to be oriented in the same direction, so you might think the compound is the cis isomer. Closer inspection shows, however, that one bond points upward and the other downward, so we know that it is the trans isomer. Alternatively, if you look at the two axial hydrogens, they are clearly trans (one points straight up and the other straight down), so the methyl groups must also be trans.

Now continue on to Problem 43.

PROBLEM 43 ♦

Determine whether each of the following is a cis isomer or a trans isomer:

a.

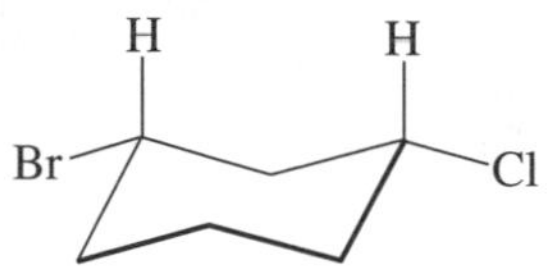

d.

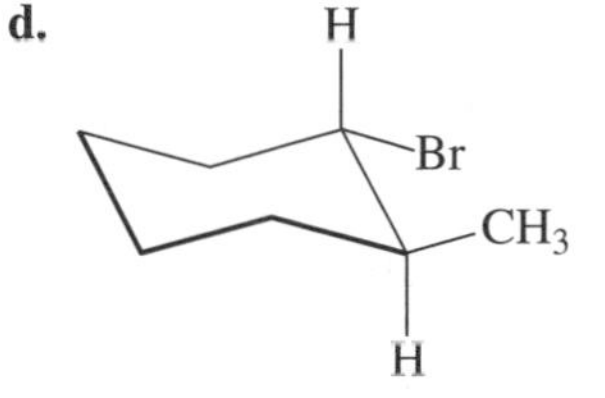

b.

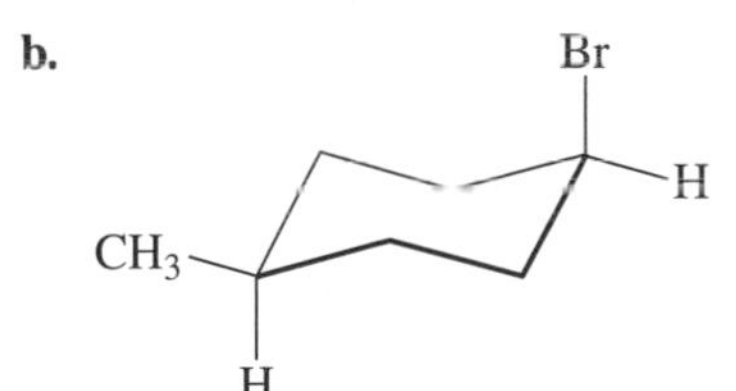

e.

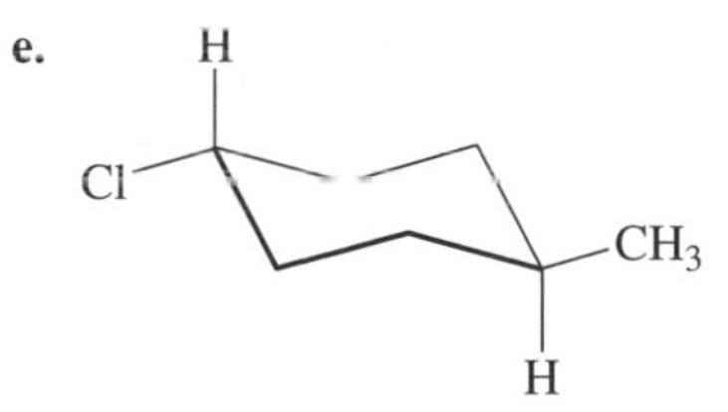

c.

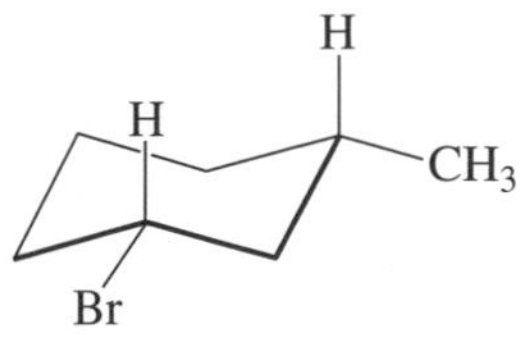

f.

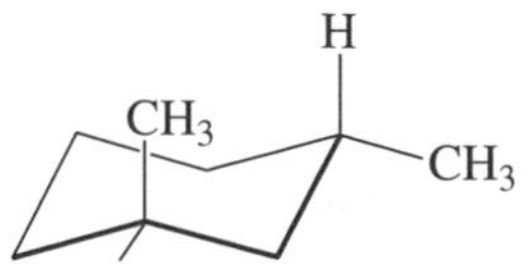

Every compound with a cyclohexane ring has two chair conformers; thus, both the cis and the trans isomers of disubstituted cyclohexanes have two chair conformers. Let's compare the structures of the two chair conformers of *cis*-1,4-dimethylcyclohexane to see if we can predict any difference in their stabilities.

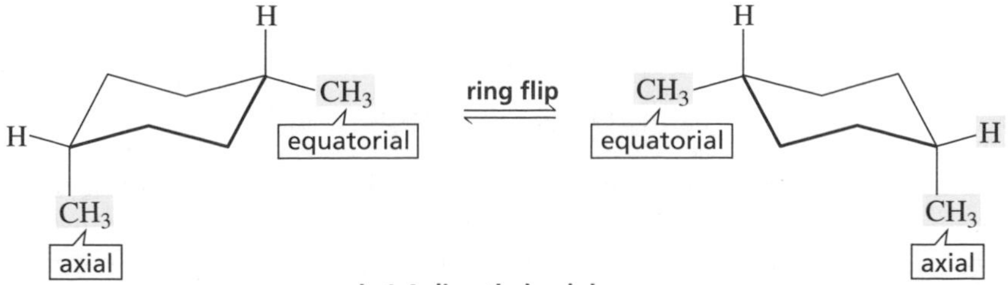

ring flip

***cis*-1,4-dimethylcyclohexane**

The conformer shown on the left has one methyl group in an equatorial position and one methyl group in an axial position. The conformer shown on the right also has one methyl group in an equatorial position and one methyl group in an axial position. Therefore, both chair conformers are equally stable.

In contrast, the two chair conformers of *trans*-1,4-dimethylcyclohexane have different stabilities because one has both methyl substituents in equatorial positions and the other has both methyl groups in axial positions. The conformer with both substituents in equatorial positions is more stable.

axial CH_3 — H — CH_3 equatorial — CH_3 equatorial — H — ring flip — H — H — CH_3 axial

more stable — less stable

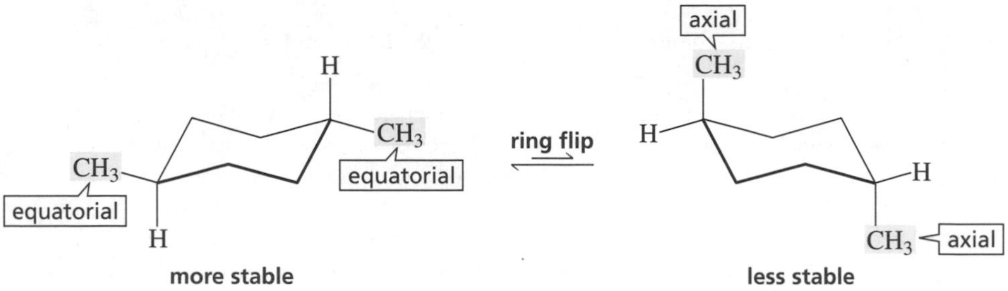

***trans*-1,4-dimethylcyclohexane**

The chair conformer with both substituents in axial positions has four 1,3-diaxial interactions, causing it to be about 4 × 0.87 kcal/mol = 3.5 kcal/mol (or 14.6 kJ/mol) less stable than the chair conformer with both methyl groups in equatorial positions. We can, therefore, predict that *trans*-1,4-dimethylcyclohexane will exist almost entirely in the chair conformer with both substituents in equatorial positions.

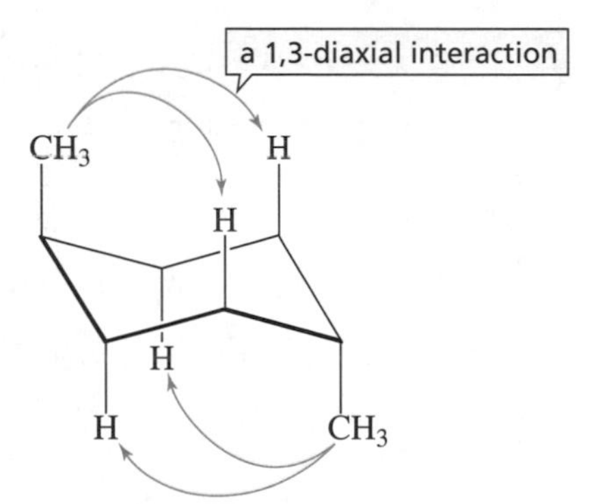

this chair conformer has four 1,3-diaxial interactions

Now let's look at the geometric isomers of 1-*tert*-butyl-3-methylcyclohexane. Both substituents of the cis isomer are in equatorial positions in one conformer and in axial positions in the other conformer. The conformer with both substituents in equatorial positions is more stable.

H — H — CH_3 — C — CH_3 — CH_3 — CH_3 — ring flip — H — H — CH_3 — CH_3 — C — CH_3 — CH_3

more stable — less stable

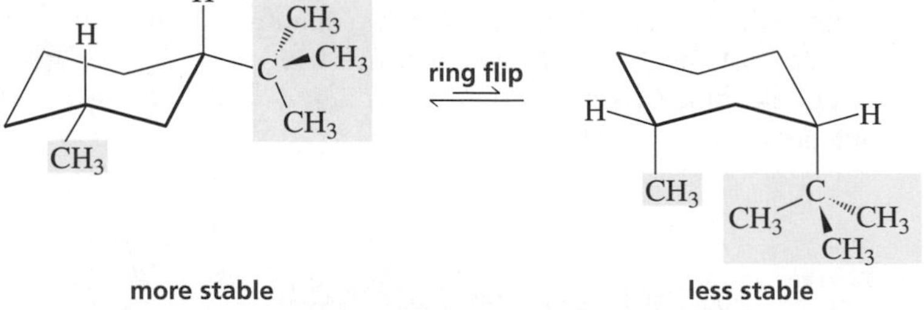

***cis*-1-*tert*-butyl-3-methylcyclohexane**

Both conformers of the trans isomer have one substituent in an equatorial position and the other in an axial position. Because the *tert*-butyl group is larger than the methyl group, the 1,3-diaxial interactions will be stronger when the *tert*-butyl group is in the axial position. Therefore, the conformer with the *tert*-butyl group in the equatorial position is more stable.

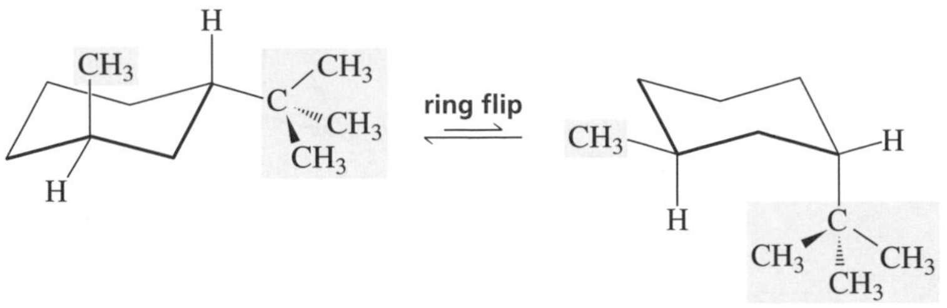

***trans*-1-*tert*-butyl-3-methylcyclohexane**

PROBLEM 44♦

Which will have a higher percentage of the diequatorial-substituted conformer compared with the diaxial-substituted conformer: *trans*-1,4-dimethylcyclohexane or *cis*-1-*tert*-butyl-3-methylcyclohexane?

PROBLEM 45 SOLVED

a. Draw the more stable chair conformer of *cis*-1-ethyl-2-methylcyclohexane.
b. Draw the more stable conformer of *trans*-1-ethyl-2-methylcyclohexane.
c. Which is more stable, *cis*-1-ethyl-2-methylcyclohexane or *trans*-1-ethyl-2-methylcyclohexane?

Solution to 45a If the two substituents of a 1,2-disubstituted cyclohexane are to be on the same side of the ring, one must be in an equatorial position and the other must be in an axial position. The more stable chair conformer is the one in which the larger of the two substituents (the ethyl group) is in the equatorial position.

PROBLEM 46♦

For each of the following disubstituted cyclohexanes, indicate whether the substituents in the two chair conformers would be both equatorial in one chair conformer and both axial in the other *or* one equatorial and one axial in each of the chair conformers:

a. *cis*-1,2-
b. *trans*-1,2-
c. *cis*-1,3-
d. *trans*-1,3-
e. *cis*-1,4-
f. *trans*-1,4-

PROBLEM 47♦

a. Calculate the energy difference between the two chair conformers of *trans*-1,4-dimethylcyclohexane.
b. What is the energy difference between the two chair conformers of *cis*-1,4-dimethylcyclohexane?

11.15 FUSED CYCLOHEXANE RINGS

When two cyclohexane rings are fused together, the second ring can be considered to be a pair of substituents bonded to the first ring. As with any disubstituted cyclohexane, the two substituents can be either cis or trans. The trans isomer (in which one substituent bond points upward and the other downward) has both substituents in the equatorial position. The cis isomer has one substituent in the equatorial position and one in the axial position. **Trans-fused** rings, therefore, are more stable than **cis-fused** rings.

equatorial H equatorial H — **trans-fused rings more stable**

equatorial H H axial — **cis-fused rings less stable**

BIOGRAPHY

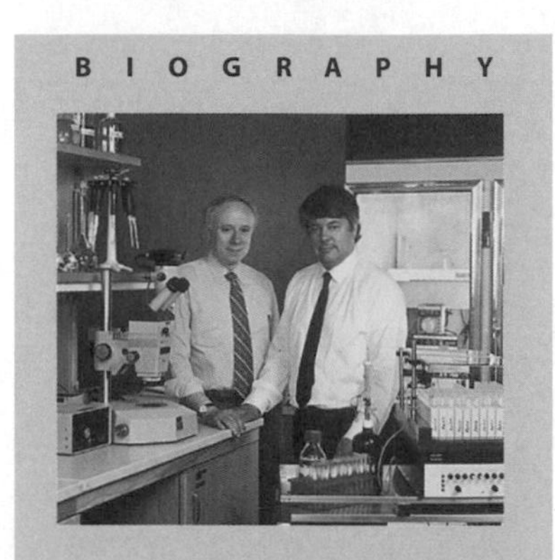

Michael S. Brown *and* **Joseph Leonard Goldstein** *shared the 1985 Nobel Prize in Physiology or Medicine for their work on the regulation of cholesterol metabolism and the treatment of disease caused by elevated cholesterol levels in the blood. Brown was born in New York in 1941, Goldstein in South Carolina in 1940. They are both professors of medicine at the University of Texas Southwestern Medical Center.*

Hormones are chemical messengers—organic compounds synthesized in glands and delivered by the bloodstream to target tissues in order to stimulate or inhibit some process. Many hormones are **steroids**. The four rings in steroids are designated A, B, C, and D. The B, C, and D rings are all trans fused, and in most naturally occurring steroids, the A and B rings are also trans fused.

A B C D — **the steroid ring system**

A B C D — all the rings are trans fused

The most abundant member of the steroid family in animals is **cholesterol**, the precursor of all other steroids. Cholesterol is an important component of cell membranes. Its ring structure makes it more rigid than other membrane components.

H_3C H_3C H H H HO — **cholesterol**

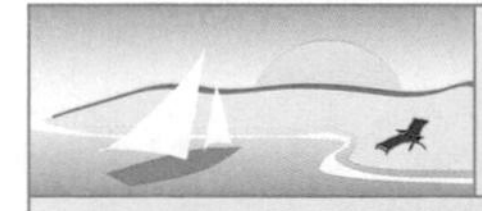

Cholesterol and Heart Disease

Cholesterol is probably the best-known steroid because of the widely publicized correlation between cholesterol levels in the blood and heart disease. This compound is synthesized in the liver and is present in almost all body tissues. Cholesterol is also found in many foods, but we do not require it in our diet because the body can synthesize all we need. A diet high in cholesterol can lead to high levels of cholesterol in the bloodstream, and the excess can accumulate on the walls of arteries, restricting the flow of blood. This disease of the circulatory system is known as *atherosclerosis* and is a primary cause of heart disease. Cholesterol travels through the bloodstream packaged in particles that are classified according to their density. Low-density lipoprotein (LDL) particles transport cholesterol from the liver to other tissues. Receptors on the surfaces of cells bind LDL particles, allowing them to be brought into the cell so that it can use the cholesterol. High-density lipoprotein (HDL) is a cholesterol scavenger, removing cholesterol from the surfaces of membranes and delivering it back to the liver, where it is converted into bile acids. LDL is the so-called "bad" cholesterol, whereas HDL is the "good" cholesterol. The more cholesterol we eat, the less the body synthesizes. But this does not mean that dietary cholesterol has no effect on the total amount of cholesterol in the bloodstream, because dietary cholesterol also inhibits the synthesis of the LDL receptors. So the more cholesterol we eat, the less the body synthesizes, but also the less the body can get rid of by bringing it into target cells.

Clinical Treatment of High Cholesterol

Statins are the newest class of cholesterol-reducing drugs. Statins reduce serum cholesterol levels by inhibiting the enzyme that catalyzes the formation of a compound needed for the synthesis of cholesterol. As a consequence of diminished cholesterol synthesis in the liver, the liver forms more LDL receptors—the receptors that help clear LDL (the so-called "bad" cholesterol) from the bloodstream. Studies show that for every 10% that cholesterol is reduced, deaths from coronary heart disease are reduced by 15% and total death risk is reduced by 11%.

Lovastatin and simvastatin are natural statins used clinically under the trade names Mevacor and Zocor. Atorvastatin (Lipitor), a synthetic statin, is now the most popular statin. It has greater potency and lasts longer in the body than natural statins because the products of its breakdown are as active as the parent drug in reducing cholesterol levels. Therefore, smaller doses of the drug may be administered. In addition, Lipitor is less polar than lovastatin and simvastatin, so it persists longer in liver cells, where it is needed. Lipitor has been the most widely prescribed drug in the United States for the past two years.

lovastatin
Mevacor®

simvastatin
Zocor®

atorvastatin
Lipitor®

SUMMARY

Alkanes are **hydrocarbons** that contain only single bonds. Their general molecular formula is C_nH_{2n+2}. **Constitutional isomers** have the same molecular formula, but their atoms are linked differently. Alkanes are named by determining the number of carbons in their **parent hydrocarbon**—the longest continuous chain. Substituents are listed in alphabetical order, with a number to designate their position on the chain. When there is only a substituent, the substituent gets the lower of the possible numbers; when there is only a functional group suffix, the functional group suffix gets the lower of the possible numbers; when there is both a functional group suffix and a substituent, the functional group suffix gets the lower of the possible numbers. A **functional group** is a center of reactivity in a molecule.

Alkyl halides and **ethers** are named as substituted alkanes. **Alcohols** and **amines** are named using a functional group suffix. **Systematic names** can contain numbers; **common names** never do. A compound can have more than one name, but a name must specify only one compound. Whether alkyl halides or alcohols are **primary**, **secondary**, or **tertiary** depends on whether the X (halogen) or OH group is bonded to a primary, secondary, or tertiary carbon. A **primary carbon** is bonded to one carbon, a **secondary carbon** is bonded to two carbons, and a **tertiary carbon** is bonded to three carbons. Whether amines are **primary**, **secondary**, or **tertiary** depends on the number of alkyl groups bonded to the nitrogen. Compounds with four alkyl groups bonded to nitrogen are called **quaternary ammonium salts**.

The oxygen of an alcohol or an ether has the same geometry as the oxygen in water; the nitrogen of an amine has the same geometry as the nitrogen in ammonia. The greater the attractive forces between molecules—**van der Waals forces, dipole–dipole interactions, hydrogen bonds**—the higher is the **boiling point** of the compound. A **hydrogen bond** is an interaction between a hydrogen bonded to an O, N, or F and a lone pair of an O, N, or F in another molecule. In a series of homologs, the boiling point increases with increasing molecular weight. Branching lowers the boiling point. **Polarizability** indicates the ease with which an electron cloud can be distorted: larger atoms are more polarizable.

Polar compounds dissolve in polar solvents, and nonpolar compounds dissolve in nonpolar solvents. The interaction between a solvent and a molecule or an ion dissolved in that solvent is called **solvation**. The oxygen of an alcohol or an ether can usually drag three or four carbons into solution in water.

Rotation about a C—C bond results in two extreme **conformations**, staggered and eclipsed, that rapidly interconvert. A **staggered conformer** is more stable than an **eclipsed conformer** because of **hyperconjugation**. There can be two different staggered conformers: the **anti conformer** is more stable than a **gauche conformer** because of **steric strain**—repulsion between the electron clouds of atoms or groups. The steric strain in a gauche conformer is called a **gauche interaction**.

Five- and six-membered rings are more stable than three- and four-membered rings because of the **angle strain** that results when bond angles deviate from the ideal bond angle of 109.5°. In a process called **ring flip**, cyclohexane rapidly interconverts between two stable chair conformers. **Bonds** that are **axial** in one chair conformer are **equatorial** in the other and vice versa. The chair conformer with a substituent in the equatorial position is more stable, because there is more room, and hence less steric strain, in an equatorial position. A substituent in an axial position experiences unfavorable **1,3-diaxial interactions**. In the case of disubstituted cyclohexanes, the more stable conformer will have its larger substituent in the equatorial position. Cis and trans isomers are called **geometric isomers** or **cis–trans isomers**. A **cis isomer** has its two substituents on the same side of the ring; a **trans isomer** has its substituents on opposite sides of the ring. Cis and trans isomers are different compounds. **Conformers** are different conformations of the same compound.

KEY TERMS

alcohol (p. 475)
alkane (p. 460)
alkyl halide (p. 473)
alkyl substituent (p. 463)
amine (p. 477)
angle strain (p. 493)
anti conformer (p. 491)
axial bond (p. 495)
banana bond (p. 493)
boat conformer (p. 497)
boiling point (bp) (p. 482)
chair conformer (p. 494)
cis fused (p. 503)
cis isomer (p. 500)
cis–trans isomers (p. 500)
common name (p. 463)
conformation (p. 489)
conformational analysis (p. 490)
conformational isomers (p. 489)
conformer (p. 489)
constitutional isomers (p. 462)
cycloalkane (p. 470)
1,3-diaxial interaction (p. 498)
dipole–dipole interaction (p. 483)
eclipsed conformer (p. 490)
equatorial bond (p. 495)
ether (p. 474)
flagpole hydrogen (p. 497)
functional group (p. 475)
gauche conformer (p. 491)
gauche interaction (p. 491)
geometric isomers (p. 500)
half-chair conformer (p. 497)
heat of formation (p. 496)
homolog (p. 460)
homologous series (p. 460)
hormones (p. 504)
hydrocarbon (p. 460)
hydrogen bond (p. 484)
hyperconjugation (p. 490)
induced-dipole–induced-dipole interaction (p. 483)
IUPAC nomenclature (p. 463)
melting point (mp) (p. 487)
methylene (CH_2) group (p. 460)
Newman projection (p. 489)
packing (p. 487)
parent hydrocarbon (p. 466)
polarizability (p. 485)
primary alcohol (p. 475)
primary alkyl halide (p. 473)
primary amine (p. 477)
primary carbon (p. 464)
primary hydrogen (p. 465)
quaternary ammonium salt (p. 479)
ring flip (p. 496)
secondary alcohol (p. 475)
secondary alkyl halide (p. 473)
secondary amine (p. 477)
secondary carbon (p. 464)
secondary hydrogen (p. 465)
skeletal structure (p. 470)
skew-boat conformer (p. 497)
solubility (p. 487)
solvation (p. 487)
staggered conformer (p. 490)
steric strain (p. 491)
steroids (p. 504)
straight-chain alkane (p. 460)
symmetrical ether (p. 474)
systematic nomenclature (p. 463)
tertiary alcohol (p. 475)
tertiary alkyl halide (p. 473)
tertiary amine (p. 477)
tertiary carbon (p. 464)
tertiary hydrogen (p. 465)
trans fused (p. 503)
trans isomer (p. 500)
twist-boat conformer (p. 497)
unsymmetrical ether (p. 474
van der Waals forces (p. 483)

PROBLEMS

48. Draw a condensed and a skeletal structure for each of the following:

a. *sec*-butyl *tert*-butyl ether
b. isoheptyl alcohol
c. *sec*-butylamine
d. isopentyl bromide
e. 4,5-diisopropylnonane
f. triethylamine
g. 4-*tert*-butylheptane
h. 5,5-dibromo-2-methyloctane
i. 3-ethoxy-2-methylhexane
j. 5-(1,2-dimethylpropyl)nonane
k. 3,4-dimethyloctane
l. 4-(1-methylethyl)nonane

49. List the following compounds in order of decreasing boiling point. (Label the highest boiling compound #1.)

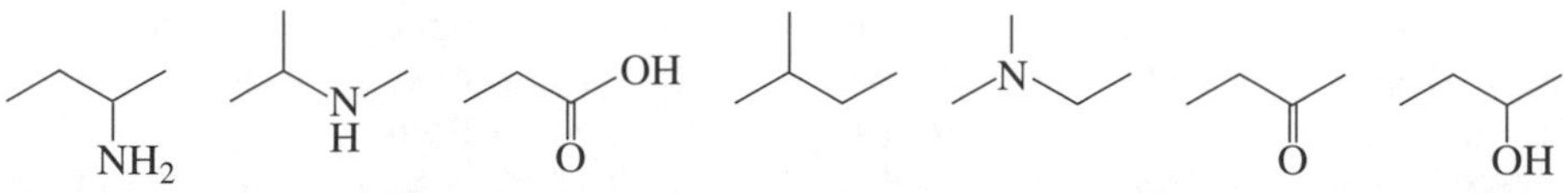

NH_2 N H   OH O   N   O   OH

50. a. Give the systematic name for each of the following:

1. $(CH_3)_3CCH_2CH_2CH_2CH(CH_3)_2$

2. 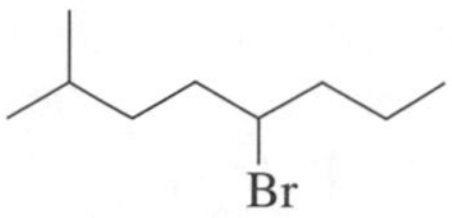 Br

3. $CH_3CHCH_2CHCH_2CH_3$ (with CH_3 and OH substituents)

4. $(CH_3CH_2)_4C$

5. $BrCH_2CH_2CH_2CH_2CH_2NHCH_2CH_3$

6.

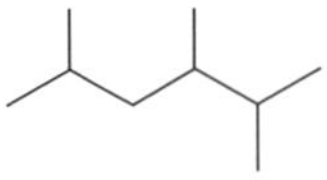

7. $CH_3CH_2CHOCH_2CH_3$ (with $CH_2CH_2CH_2CH_3$ on the CH)

8. $CH_3OCH_2CH_2CH_2OCH_3$

9. 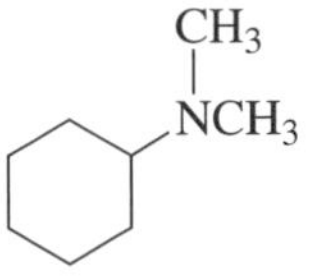 (cyclohexane with NCH_3 bearing CH_3)

10. 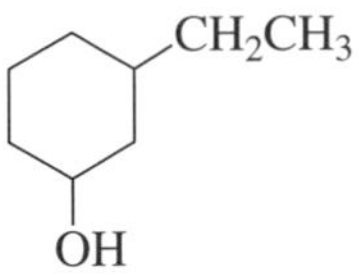 (cyclohexane with CH_2CH_3 and OH)

11. 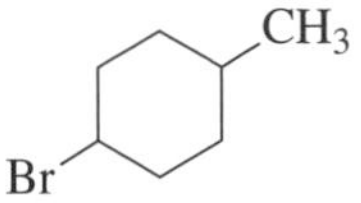 (cyclohexane with CH_3 and Br)

b. Draw skeletal structures for these compounds.

51. Which of the following structures represents a cis isomer?

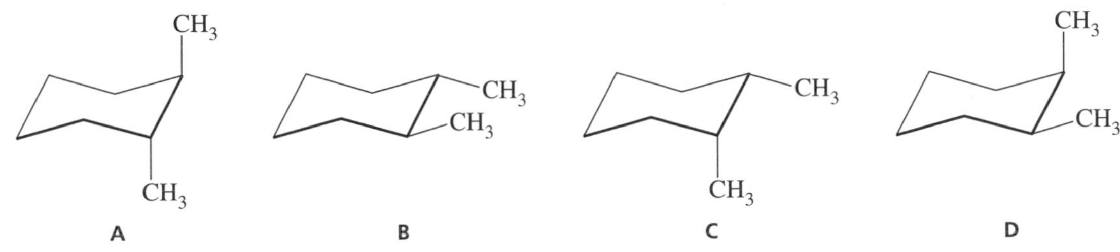

52. a. How many primary carbons does each of the following compounds have?

1. 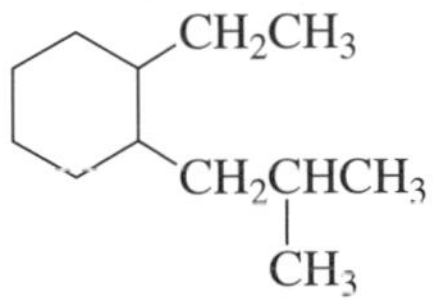 (cyclohexane with CH_2CH_3 and CH_2CHCH_3 bearing CH_3)

2.

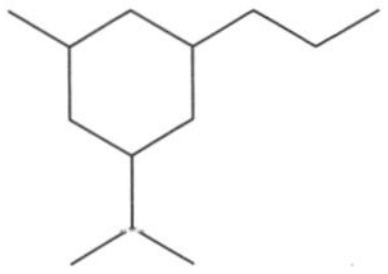

b. How many secondary carbons does each one have?

c. How many tertiary carbons does each one have?

53. Which of the following conformers of isobutyl chloride is the most stable?

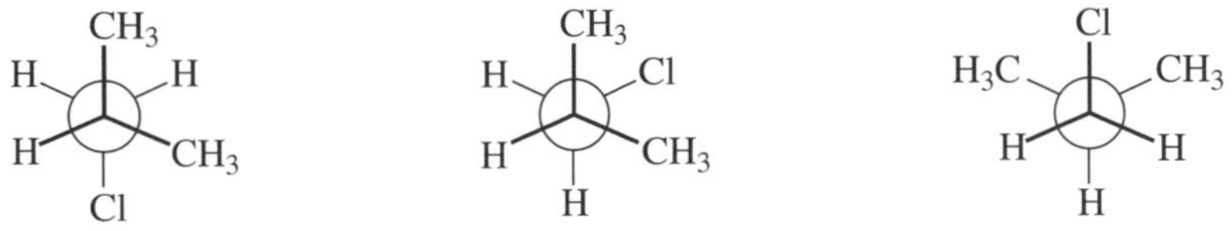

(Newman projections: front groups CH_3, H, H / back groups H, CH_3, Cl; front CH_3, H, H / back Cl, CH_3, H; front Cl, H, H / back H_3C, CH_3, H)

54. Draw the structural formula for an alkane that has

a. six carbons, all secondary

b. eight carbons and only primary hydrogens

c. seven carbons with two isopropyl groups

55. Give two names for each of the following:

a. $CH_3CH_2CHCH_3$ (with NH_2 on CH)

b. $CH_3CH_2CHCH_3$ (with Cl on CH)

c. $CH_3CH_2CHNHCH_2CH_3$ (with CH_3 on CH)

d. $CH_3CH_2CH_2OCH_2CH_3$

e. $CH_3CHCH_2CH_2CH_3$ (with CH_3 on CH)

f. CH_3CHNH_2 (with CH_3 on CH)

g. CH_3CBr (with CH_3 and CH_2CH_3 on C)

h. $CH_3CHCH_2CH_2CH_2OH$ (with CH_3 on CH)

i. 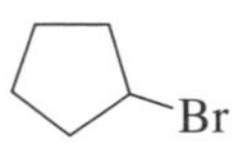 (cyclopentane with Br)

j. 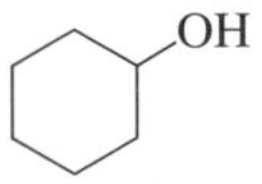 (cyclohexane with OH)

56. Which compound has
- **a.** the higher boiling point: 1-bromopentane or 1-bromohexane?
- **b.** the higher boiling point: pentyl chloride or isopentyl chloride?
- **c.** the greater solubility in water: 1-butanol or 1-pentanol?
- **d.** the higher boiling point: 1-hexanol or 1-methoxypentane?
- **e.** the higher melting point: hexane or isohexane?
- **f.** the higher boiling point: 1-chloropentane or 1-pentanol?
- **g.** the higher boiling point: 1-bromopentane or 1-chloropentane?
- **h.** the higher boiling point: diethyl ether or butyl alcohol?
- **i.** the greater density: heptane or octane?
- **j.** the higher boiling point: isopentyl alcohol or isopentylamine?
- **k.** the higher boiling point: hexylamine or dipropylamine?

57.
- **a.** Draw Newman projections of the two conformers of *cis*-1,3-dimethylcyclohexane.
- **b.** Which of the conformers would predominate at equilibrium?
- **c.** Draw Newman projections of the two conformers of the trans isomer.
- **d.** Which of the conformers would predominate at equilibrium?

58. Ansaid and Motrin belong to the group of drugs known as nonsteroidal anti-inflammatory drugs (NSAIDs). Both are only slightly soluble in water, but one is a little more soluble than the other. Which of the drugs has the greater solubility in water?

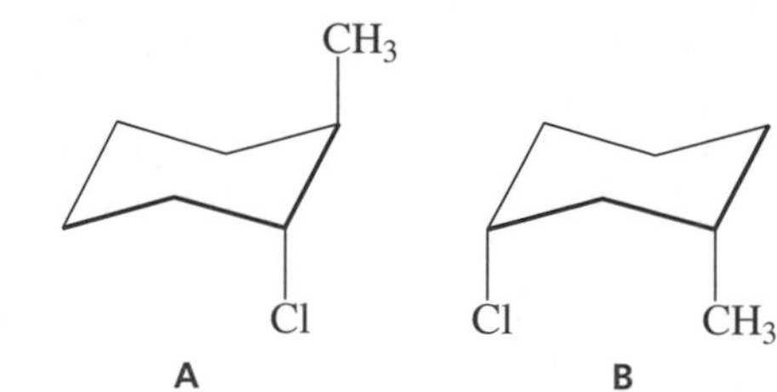

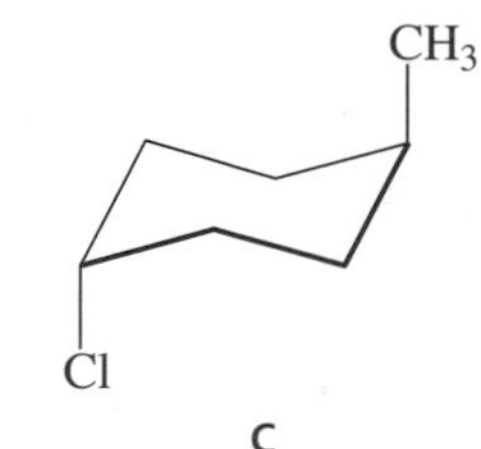

59. Draw a picture of the hydrogen bonding in methanol.

60. A student was given the structural formulas of several compounds and was asked to give them systematic names. How many did the student name correctly? Correct those that are misnamed.
- **a.** 4-bromo-3-pentanol
- **b.** 2,2-dimethyl-4-ethylheptane
- **c.** 5-methylcyclohexanol
- **d.** 1,1-dimethyl-2-cyclohexanol
- **e.** 5-(2,2-dimethylethyl)nonane
- **f.** isopentyl bromide
- **g.** 3,3-dichlorooctane
- **h.** 5-ethyl-2-methylhexane
- **i.** 1-bromo-4-pentanol
- **j.** 3-isopropyloctane
- **k.** 2-methyl-2-isopropylheptane
- **l.** 2-methyl-*N*,*N*-dimethyl-4-hexanamine

61. Which of the following conformers has the highest energy?

A B C

62. Give systematic names for all the alkanes with molecular formula C_7H_{16} that do not have any secondary hydrogens.

63. Draw skeletal structures for the following:
- **a.** 5-ethyl-2-methyloctane
- **b.** 1,3-dimethylcyclohexane
- **c.** 2,3,3,4-tetramethylheptane
- **d.** propylcyclopentane
- **e.** 2-methyl-4-(1-methylethyl)octane
- **f.** 2,6-dimethyl-4-(2-methylpropyl)decane

64. For rotation about the C-3—C-4 bond of 2-methylhexane:
- **a.** Draw the Newman projection of the most stable conformer.
- **b.** Draw the Newman projection of the least stable conformer.
- **c.** About which other carbon–carbon bonds may rotation occur?
- **d.** How many of the carbon–carbon bonds in the compound have staggered conformers that are all equally stable?

65. Draw all the isomers that have molecular formula $C_5H_{11}Br$. (*Hint:* There are eight such isomers.)
- **a.** Give the systematic name for each of the isomers.
- **b.** Give a common name for each isomer that has a common name.

c. How many isomers do not have common names?
d. How many of the isomers are primary alkyl halides?
e. How many of the isomers are secondary alkyl halides?
f. How many of the isomers are tertiary alkyl halides?

66. Give the systematic name for each of the following:

a.

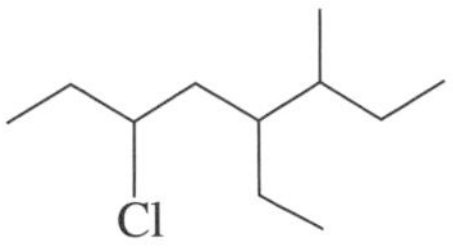

b.  OH

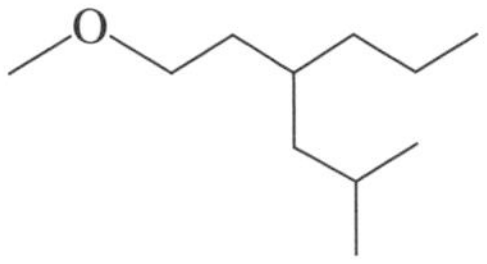

c.

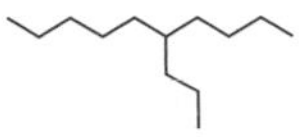

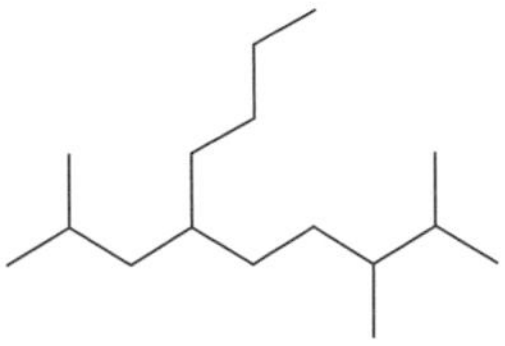

d. 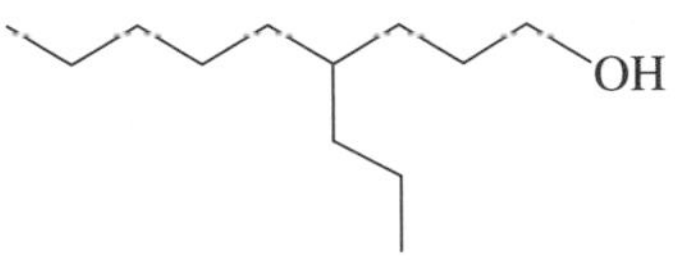 OH

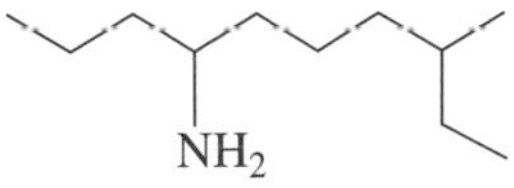

e.

f. Cl

g. O

h.

i. NH_2

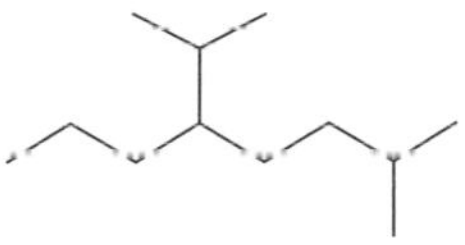

j.

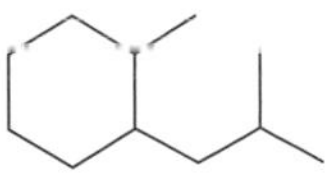

67. Draw the two chair conformers for each of the following, and indicate which conformer is more stable:

a. *cis*-1-ethyl-3-methylcyclohexane
b. *trans*-1-ethyl-2-isopropylcyclohexane
c. *trans*-1-ethyl-2-methylcyclohexane
d. *cis*-1,2-diethylcyclohexane
e. *cis*-1-ethyl-3-isopropylcyclohexane
f. *cis*-1-ethyl-4-isopropylcyclohexane

68. Why are lower molecular weight alcohols more soluble in water than higher molecular weight alcohols?

69. a. Draw a potential energy diagram for rotation about the C—C bond of 1,2-dichloroethane through 360°, starting with the least stable conformer. The anti conformer is 1.2 kcal/mol more stable than a gauche conformer. A gauche conformer has two energy barriers, 5.2 kcal/mol and 9.3 kcal/mole.

b. Draw the conformer that would be present in greatest concentration.
c. How much more stable is the most stable staggered conformer than the most stable eclipsed conformer?
d. How much more stable is the most stable staggered conformer than the least stable eclipsed conformer?

70. How many ethers have molecular formula $C_5H_{12}O$? Draw their structures and give each a systematic name. What are their common names?

71. Draw the most stable conformer of the following molecule:

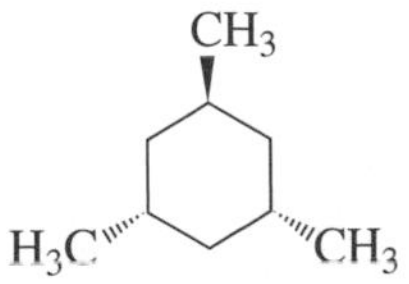

CH_3

H_3C CH_3

72. Give the systematic name for each of the following:

a. 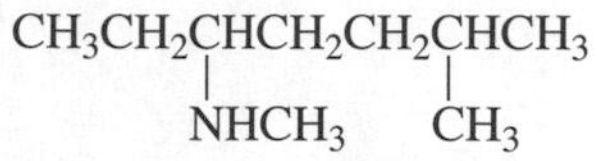 $CH_3CH_2CHCH_2CH_2CHCH_3$ (with $NHCH_3$ and CH_3 substituents)

b. 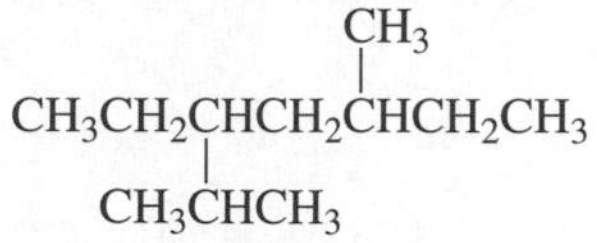 $CH_3CH_2CHCH_2CHCH_2CH_3$ (with CH_3CHCH_3 and CH_3 substituents)

c. 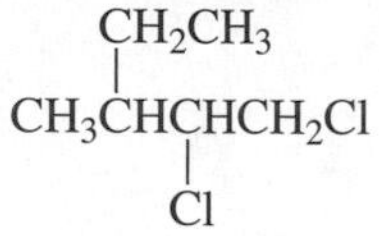 CH_2CH_3 attached to $CH_3CHCHCH_2Cl$ with Cl

d. 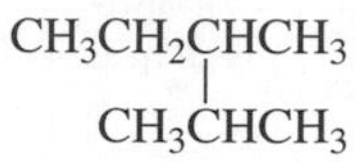 $CH_3CH_2CHCH_3$ with CH_3CHCH_3

e.

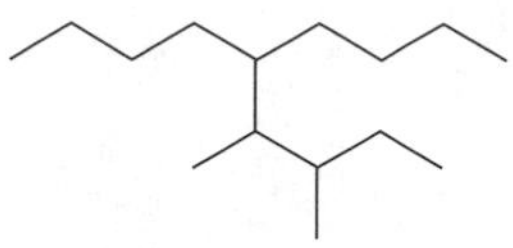

f.

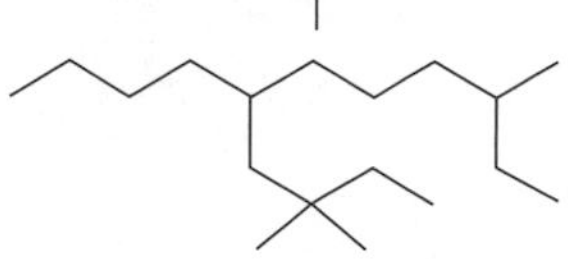

73. Calculate the energy difference between the two chair conformers of *trans*-1,2-dimethylcyclohexane.

74. The most stable form of glucose (blood sugar) is a six-membered ring in a chair conformation with its five substituents all in equatorial positions. Draw the most stable conformer of glucose by putting the OH groups on the appropriate bonds in the structure on the right.

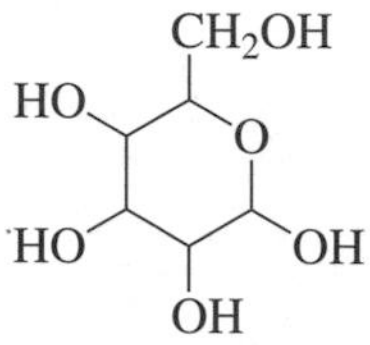

CH_2OH HO O HO OH OH

glucose

CH_2OH O

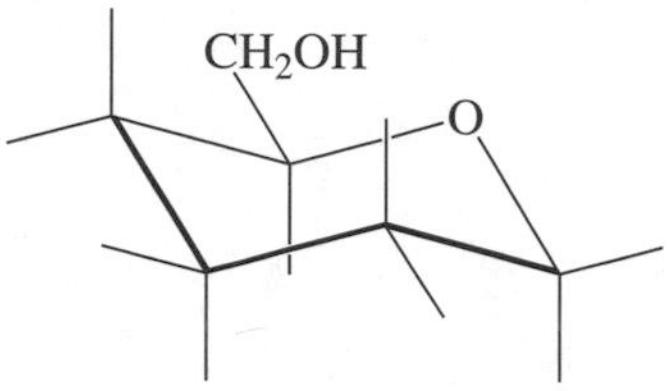

75. Give the systematic name for each of the following:

a. 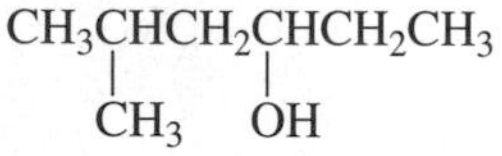 $CH_3CHCH_2CHCH_2CH_3$ (with CH_3 and OH)

b. 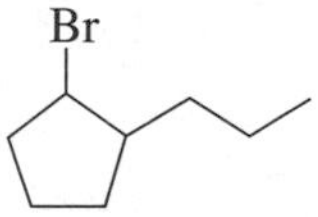 Br

c. 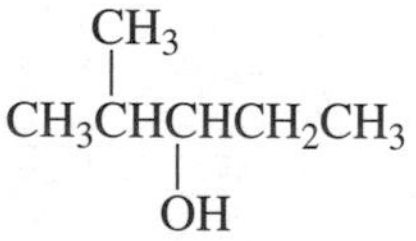 $CH_3CHCHCH_2CH_3$ (with CH_3 and OH)

d. 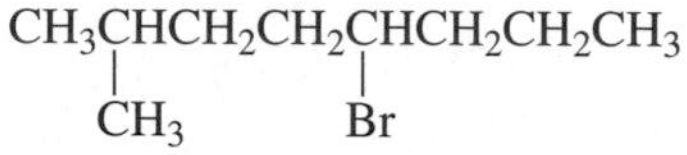 $CH_3CHCH_2CH_2CHCH_2CH_2CH_3$ (with CH_3 and Br)

e. 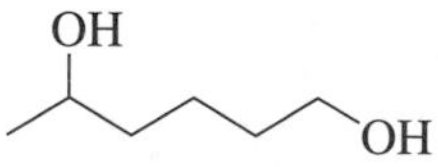 OH OH

f. 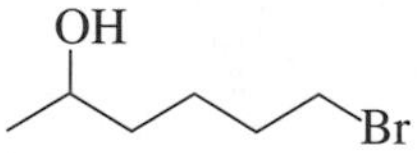 OH Br

g. 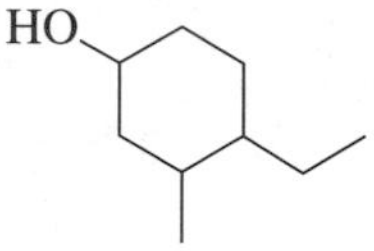 HO

h. 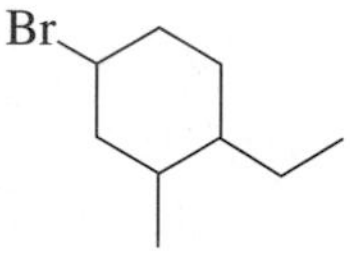 Br

76. Explain the following facts:

a. 1-Hexanol has a higher boiling point than 3-hexanol.

b. Diethyl ether has very limited solubility in water, but tetrahydrofuran is completely soluble.

O

tetrahydrofuran

77. One of the chair conformers of *cis*-1,3-dimethylcyclohexane has been found to be 5.4 kcal/mol (or 23 kJ/mol) less stable than the other. How much steric strain does a 1,3-diaxial interaction between two methyl groups introduce into the conformer?

78. Bromine is a larger atom than chlorine, but the equilibrium constants in Table 11.10 indicate that a chloro substituent has a greater preference for the equatorial position than a bromo substituent does. Suggest an explanation for this fact.

79. Name the following:

a. OH Br

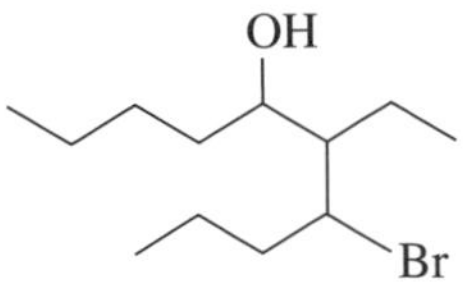

b. Cl

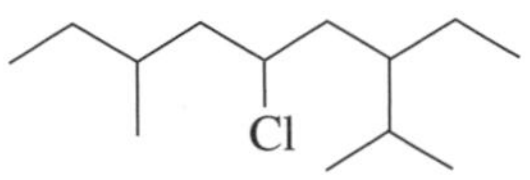

c. OH

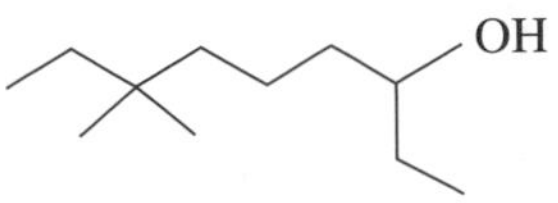

80. Using the data obtained in Problem 77, calculate the amount of steric strain in each of the chair conformers of 1,1,3-trimethylcyclohexane. Which conformer would predominate at equilibrium?

81. Using the data obtained in Problem 73, calculate the percentage of molecules of *trans*-1,2-dimethylcyclohexane that will have both methyl groups in equatorial positions.

CHAPTER

12

Alkenes

Structure, Nomenclature, and an Introduction to Reactivity • Thermodynamics and Kinetics

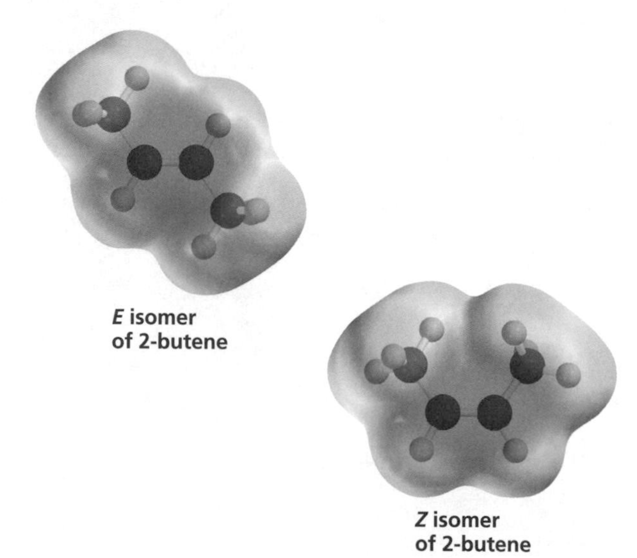

Tomatoes are shipped green so they will arrive unspoiled. Ripening can be started by exposure to ethene.

WE SAW THAT ALKANES ARE HYDROCARBONS THAT CONTAIN ONLY CARBON–CARBON *SINGLE* bonds. Hydrocarbons that contain a carbon–carbon *double* bond are called **alkenes**. Early chemists noted that an oily substance was formed when ethene ($H_2C{=}CH_2$), the smallest alkene, reacted with chlorine. On the basis of this observation, alkenes were originally called *olefins* ("oil forming").

Alkenes play many important roles in biology. Ethene, for example, is a plant hormone—a compound that controls growth and other changes in the plant's tissues. Among other things, ethene affects seed germination, flower maturation, and fruit ripening. Many of the flavors and fragrances produced by plants also belong to the alkene family.

OH

citronellol
in rose and
geranium oils

limonene
in lemon and
orange oils

β-phellandrene
oil of eucalyptus

We will begin our study of alkenes by looking at their structures and how they are named. Then we will examine a reaction of an alkene, paying close attention to the steps by which it occurs and the energy changes that accompany them. You will see that some of the discussion in the chapter revolves around concepts with which you are already familiar, while some of the information is new and will broaden the foundation of knowledge that you will be building on in subsequent chapters.

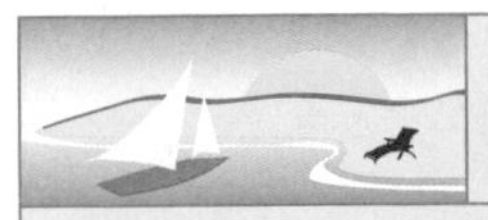

Pheromones

Insects communicate by releasing pheromones—chemical substances that other insects of the same species detect with their antennae. Many of the sex, alarm, and trail pheromones are alkenes. Interfering with an insect's ability to send or receive chemical signals is an environmentally safe way to control insect populations. For example, traps containing synthetic sex attractants have been used to capture such crop-destroying insects as the gypsy moth and the boll weevil.

muscalure
sex attractant of the housefly

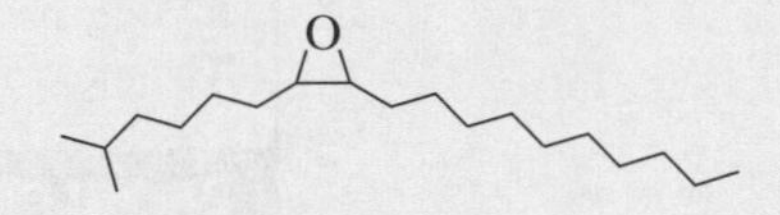

sex attractant of the gypsy moth

12.1 MOLECULAR FORMULAS AND THE DEGREE OF UNSATURATION

We have seen that the general molecular formula for a noncyclic alkane is C_nH_{2n+2}. We have also seen that the general molecular formula for a cyclic alkane is C_nH_{2n} because the cyclic structure reduces the number of hydrogens by two. Noncyclic compounds are also called **acyclic** compounds (the prefix "*a*" is Greek for "non" or "not").

The general molecular formula for an *acyclic alkene* is also C_nH_{2n} because, as a result of the double bond, an alkene has two fewer hydrogens than an alkane with the same number of carbons. Thus, the general molecular formula for a *cyclic alkene* must be C_nH_{2n-2}.

$CH_3CH_2CH_2CH_2CH_3$	$CH_3CH_2CH_2CH{=}CH_2$	(cyclopentane)	(cyclopentene)
an alkane	an alkene	a cyclic alkane	a cyclic alkene
C_5H_{12}	C_5H_{10}	C_5H_{10}	C_5H_8
C_nH_{2n+2}	C_nH_{2n}	C_nH_{2n}	C_nH_{2n-2}

We can therefore make the following statement: *the general molecular formula for a hydrocarbon is* C_nH_{2n+2} *minus two hydrogens for every* π *bond or ring in the molecule.* The total number of π bonds and rings in an alkene is called the alkene's **degree of unsaturation**. Thus, C_8H_{14}, which is missing four hydrogens from C_nH_{2n+2}, has two degrees of unsaturation. In other words, the sum of its π bonds and rings is two.

several compounds with molecular formula C_8H_{14}

A: $CH_3CH{=}CH(CH_2)_3CH{=}CH_2$

B: (1-ethylcyclohexene, CH_2CH_3)

C: (bicyclic structure)

D: $CH_3(CH_2)_5C{\equiv}CH$

The general molecular formula for a hydrocarbon is C_nH_{2n+2} minus two hydrogens for every π bond or ring present in the molecule.

Because alkanes contain the maximum number of C—H bonds possible—that is, they are saturated with hydrogen—they are called **saturated hydrocarbons**. In contrast, alkenes are called **unsaturated hydrocarbons** because they have fewer than the maximum number of hydrogens.

$CH_3CH_2CH_2CH_3$
a saturated hydrocarbon

$CH_3CH{=}CHCH_3$
an unsaturated hydrocarbon

PROBLEM 1♦ SOLVED

Determine the molecular formula for each of the following:

a. a 5-carbon hydrocarbon with one π bond and one ring.
b. a 4-carbon hydrocarbon with two π bonds and no rings.
c. a 10-carbon hydrocarbon with one π bond and two rings.

Solution to 1a For a 5-carbon hydrocarbon with no π bonds and no rings, $C_nH_{2n+2} = C_5H_{12}$. A 5-carbon hydrocarbon with one π bond and one ring has four fewer hydrogens, because two hydrogens are subtracted for every π bond or ring in the molecule. The molecular formula is therefore C_5H_8.

PROBLEM 2♦ SOLVED

Determine the degree of unsaturation for hydrocarbons with the following molecular formulas:

a. $C_{10}H_{16}$ **b.** $C_{20}H_{34}$ **c.** C_8H_{16} **d.** $C_{12}H_{20}$ **e.** $C_{40}H_{56}$

Solution to 2a For a 10-carbon hydrocarbon with no π bonds and no rings, $C_nH_{2n+2} = C_{10}H_{22}$. A 10-carbon compound with molecular formula $C_{10}H_{16}$ has six fewer hydrogens. The degree of unsaturation is therefore 6/2 = 3.

PROBLEM 3

Determine the degree of unsaturation, and then draw possible structures, for compounds with the following molecular formulas:

a. C_3H_6 **b.** C_3H_4 **c.** C_4H_6

12.2 THE NOMENCLATURE OF ALKENES

We have seen that the IUPAC system uses a suffix to denote certain functional groups. The double bond is the functional group of an alkene, and its presence is denoted by the suffix "ene." Therefore, the systematic (IUPAC) name of an alkene is obtained by replacing the "ane" ending of the corresponding alkane with "ene." For example, a two-carbon alkene is called ethene, and a three-carbon alkene is called propene. Ethene also is frequently called by its common name: ethylene.

	$H_2C{=}CH_2$	$CH_3CH{=}CH_2$		
systematic name:	**ethene**	**propene**	**cyclopentene**	**cyclohexene**
common name:	**ethylene**	**propylene**		

Most alkene names need a number to indicate the position of the double bond. (The four names above do not because there is no ambiguity.) The IUPAC rules apply to alkenes as well:

Number the longest continuous chain containing the functional group in the direction that gives the functional group suffix the lowest possible number.

1. The longest continuous chain containing the functional group (in this case, the carbon–carbon double bond) is numbered in a direction that gives the functional group suffix the lowest possible number. For example, 1-butene signifies that the double bond is between the first and second carbons of butene; 2-hexene signifies that the double bond is between the second and third carbons of hexene.

$\overset{4}{C}H_3\overset{3}{C}H_2\overset{2}{C}H{=}\overset{1}{C}H_2$ **1-butene**

$\overset{1}{C}H_3\overset{2}{C}H{=}\overset{3}{C}H\overset{4}{C}H_3$ **2-butene**

$\overset{1}{C}H_3\overset{2}{C}H{=}\overset{3}{C}H\overset{4}{C}H_2\overset{5}{C}H_2\overset{6}{C}H_3$ **2-hexene**

$\overset{6}{C}H_3\overset{5}{C}H_2\overset{4}{C}H_2\overset{3}{C}H_2\overset{2}{C}(={}^{1}CH_2)CH_2CH_2CH_3$ **2-propyl-1-hexene**

the longest continuous chain has eight carbons but the longest continuous chain containing the functional group has six carbons, so the parent name of the compound is hexene

Notice that 1-butene does not have a common name. You might be tempted to call it "butylene," which is analogous to "propylene" for propene, but butylene is not an appropriate name. A name must be unambiguous, and "butylene" could signify either 1-butene or 2-butene.

2. For a compound with two double bonds, the suffix is "diene."

$\overset{1}{C}H_3\overset{2}{C}H{=}\overset{3}{C}H{-}\overset{4}{C}H{=}\overset{5}{C}H\overset{6}{C}H_2\overset{7}{C}H_3$ **2,4-heptadiene**

$\overset{5}{C}H_3\overset{4}{C}H{=}\overset{3}{C}H{-}\overset{2}{C}H{=}\overset{1}{C}H_2$ **1,3-pentadiene**

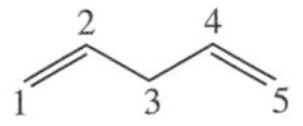

1,4-pentadiene

3. The name of a substituent is stated before the name of the longest continuous chain that contains the functional group, together with a number to designate the carbon to which the substituent is attached. Notice that *if a compound's name contains both a functional group suffix and a substituent, the functional group suffix gets the lowest possible number.*

When there are both a functional group suffix and a substituent, the functional group suffix gets the lowest possible number.

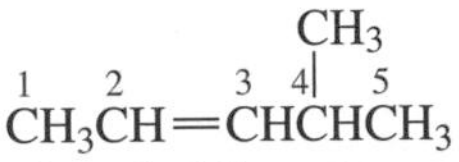

$CH_3CH{=}CHCH(CH_3)CH_3$ **4-methyl-2-pentene**

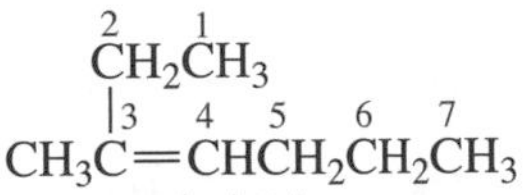

$CH_3C(CH_2CH_3){=}CHCH_2CH_2CH_3$ **3-methyl-3-heptene**

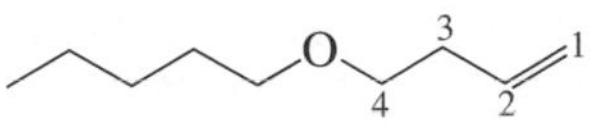

4-pentoxy-1-butene

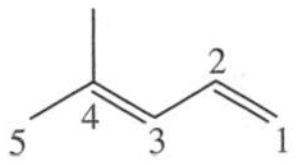

4-methyl-1,3-pentadiene

4. If a chain has more than one substituent, the substituents are stated in alphabetical order, using the same rules for alphabetizing discussed earlier. Then the appropriate number is assigned to each substituent.

Substituents are stated in alphabetical order.

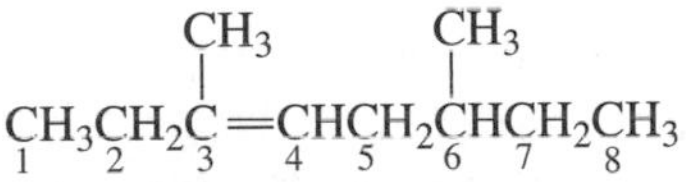

$CH_3CH_2C(CH_3){=}CHCH_2CH(CH_3)CH_2CH_3$ **3,6-dimethyl-3-octene**

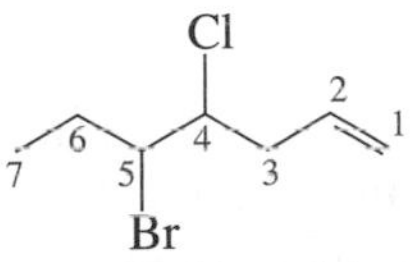

5-bromo-4-chloro-1-heptene

5. If counting in either direction results in the same number for the alkene functional group suffix, the correct name is the one containing the lowest substituent number. For example, 2,5-dimethyl-4-octene is a 4-octene whether the longest continuous chain is numbered from left to right or from right to left. If you number from left to right, the substituents are at positions 4 and 7, but if you number from right to left, they are at positions 2 and 5. Of those four substituent numbers, 2 is the lowest, so the compound is named 2,5-dimethyl-4-octene, *not* 4,7-dimethyl-4-octene.

A substituent receives the lowest possible number only if there is no functional group suffix or if the same number for the functional group suffix is obtained in both directions.

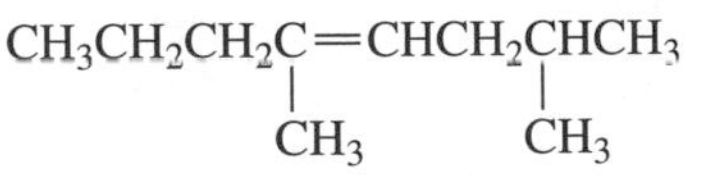

$CH_3CH_2CH_2C(CH_3){=}CHCH_2CH(CH_3)CH_3$
2,5-dimethyl-4-octene
not
4,7-dimethyl-4-octene
because 2 < 4

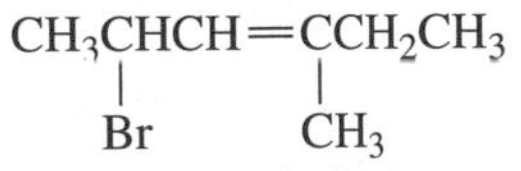

$CH_3CH(Br)CH{=}C(CH_3)CH_2CH_3$
2-bromo-4-methyl-3-hexene
not
5-bromo-3-methyl-3-hexene
because 2 < 3

6. A number is not needed to denote the position of the double bond in a cyclic alkene because the ring is always numbered so that the double bond is between carbons 1 and 2. To assign numbers to any substituents, count around the ring in the direction (clockwise or counterclockwise) that puts the lowest number into the name.

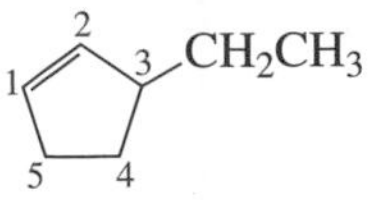

3-ethylcyclopentene 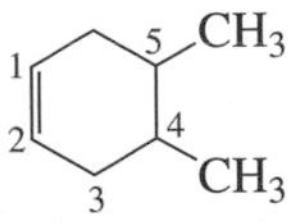 **4,5-dimethylcyclohexene** 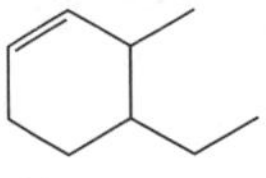 **4-ethyl-3-methylcyclohexene**

For example, 1,6-dichlorocyclohexene is *not* called 2,3-dichlorocyclohexene because 1,6-dichlorocyclohexene has the lowest substituent number (1), even though it does not have the lowest sum of substituent numbers (1 + 6 = 7 versus 2 + 3 = 5).

Cl
Cl

1,6-dichlorocyclohexene
not
2,3-dichlorocyclohexene
because 1 < 2

5-ethyl-1-methylcyclohexene
not
4-ethyl-2-methylcyclohexene
because 1 < 2

7. If counting in either direction leads to the same number for the alkene functional group suffix and the same lowest number or numbers for one or more of the substituents, then ignore those substituents and choose the direction that gives the lowest number to one of the remaining substituents.

$CH_3CH(CH_3)CH_2CH{=}C(CH_2CH_3)CH_2CH(Br)CH_3$

2-bromo-4-ethyl-7-methyl-4-octene
not
7-bromo-5-ethyl-2-methyl-4-octene
because 4 < 5

Cl
Br

6-bromo-3-chloro-4-methylcyclohexene
not
3-bromo-6-chloro-5-methylcyclohexene
because 4 < 5

The sp^2 carbons of an alkene are called **vinylic carbons**. An sp^3 carbon that is adjacent to a vinylic carbon is called an **allylic carbon**.

vinylic carbons

$RCH_2{-}CH{=}CH{-}CH_2R$

allylic carbons

Two groups containing a carbon–carbon double bond are used in common names—the **vinyl group** and the **allyl group**. The vinyl group is the smallest possible group containing a vinylic carbon; the allyl group is the smallest possible group containing an allylic carbon. When "vinyl" or "allyl" is used in a name, the substituent must be attached to the vinylic or allylic carbon, respectively. A hydrogen bonded to a vinylic carbon is called a **vinylic hydrogen**; a hydrogen bonded to an allylic carbon is called an **allylic hydrogen**.

	$CH_2{=}CH{-}$	$CH_2{=}CHCH_2{-}$
	the vinyl group	**the allyl group**
	$CH_2{=}CHCl$	$CH_2{=}CHCH_2Br$
systematic name:	**chloroethene**	**3-bromopropene**
common name:	**vinyl chloride**	**allyl bromide**

Notice how the groups shown below can be used as substituent names in systematic nomenclature.

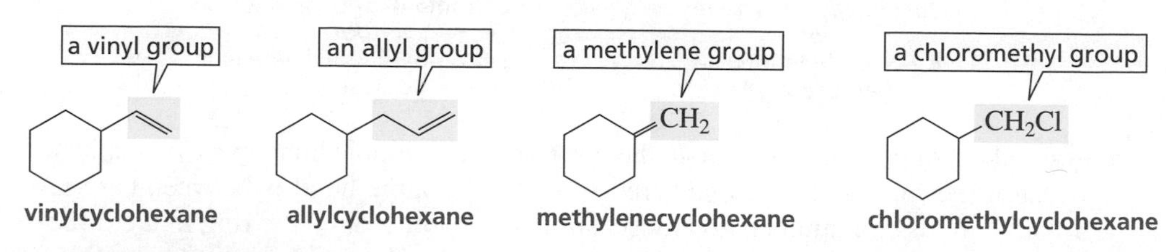

vinylcyclohexane **allylcyclohexane** **methylenecyclohexane** **chloromethylcyclohexane**

PROBLEM 4♦

Draw the structure for each of the following:

a. 3,3-dimethylcyclopentene
b. 6-bromo-2,3-dimethyl-2-hexene
c. ethyl vinyl ether
d. allyl alcohol

PROBLEM 5♦

Give the systematic name for each of the following:

a. $CH_3CHCH{=}CHCH_3$ with CH_3 on C-2

b. $CH_3CH_2C{=}CCHCH_3$ with CH_3 on C-3, CH_3 on C-4, Cl on C-5

c. Br-substituted cyclopentene

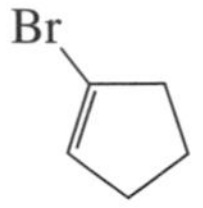

d. $BrCH_2CH_2CH{=}CCH_3$ with CH_2CH_3 on C-4

e. 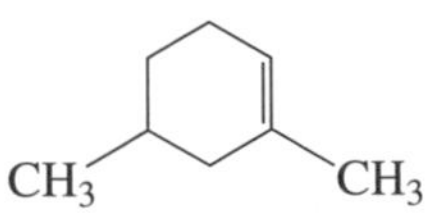 cyclohexene with two CH_3 groups

f. $CH_3CH{=}CHOCH_2CH_2CH_2CH_3$

g.

chem place Tutorial: Alkene nomenclature

Tutorial: Common names of alkyl groups

12.3 THE STRUCTURE OF ALKENES

The structure of the smallest alkene (ethene) was described in Section 10.8. Other alkenes have similar structures. Each double-bonded carbon of an alkene has three sp^2 orbitals that lie in a plane with angles of 120°. Each of these sp^2 orbitals overlaps an orbital of another atom to form a σ bond. Thus, one of the carbon–carbon bonds in a double bond is a σ bond, formed by the overlap of an sp^2 orbital of one carbon with an sp^2 orbital of the other carbon. The second carbon–carbon bond in the double bond (the π bond) is formed from side-to-side overlap of the remaining p orbital of one of the sp^2 carbons with the remaining p orbital of the other sp^2 carbon. Because three points determine a plane, each sp^2 carbon and the two atoms singly bonded to it lie in a plane. In order to achieve maximum orbital–orbital overlap, the two p orbitals must be parallel to each other. Therefore, all six atoms of the double-bond system are in the same plane.

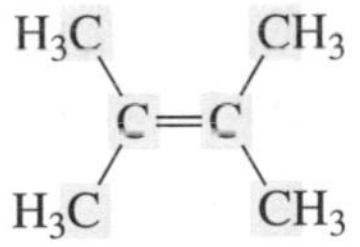

$(H_3C)_2C{=}C(CH_3)_2$

the six carbon atoms are in the same plane

It is important to remember that the π bond consists of the cloud of electrons distributed above and below the plane defined by the two sp^2 carbons and the four atoms bonded to them.

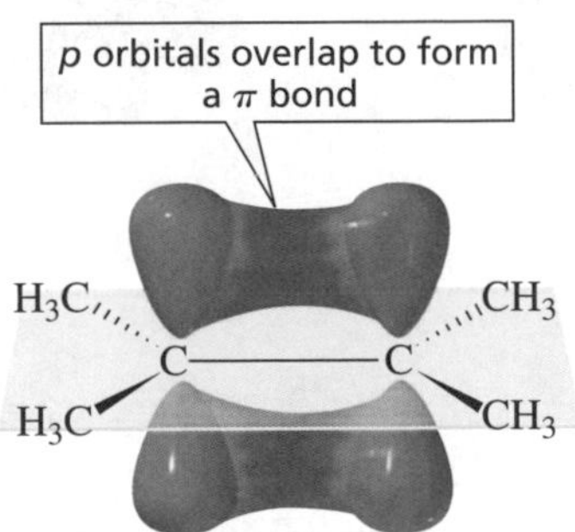

PROBLEM 6♦ **SOLVED**

For each of the following compounds, tell how many carbons are in its planar double-bond system:

a. 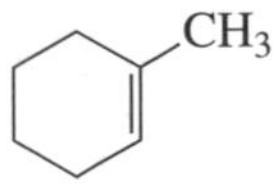 (1-methylcyclohexene, CH_3) b. 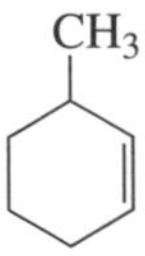 (CH_3-substituted cyclohexene) c. 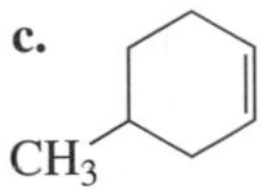 (CH_3-substituted cyclohexene) d. 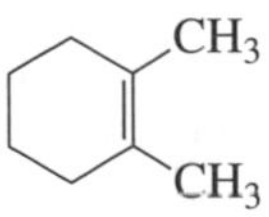 (CH_3, CH_3 on cyclohexene)

Solution to 6a Five carbons are in its planar double-bond system: the two sp^2 carbons (blue dots) and the three carbons bonded to the sp^2 carbons (red dots).

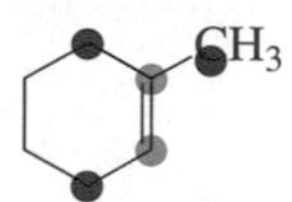
CH3

12.4 ALKENES CAN HAVE CIS AND TRANS ISOMERS

We have just seen that the two *p* orbitals forming the π bond must be parallel to achieve maximum overlap. Therefore, rotation about a double bond does not readily occur. If rotation were to occur, the two *p* orbitals would cease to overlap, and the π bond would break (Figure 12.1). The energy barrier to rotation about a double bond is about 62 kcal/mol or 259 kJ/mol. Compare this to the energy barrier 2.9 kcal/mol or 12 kJ/mol to rotation about a carbon–carbon single bond.

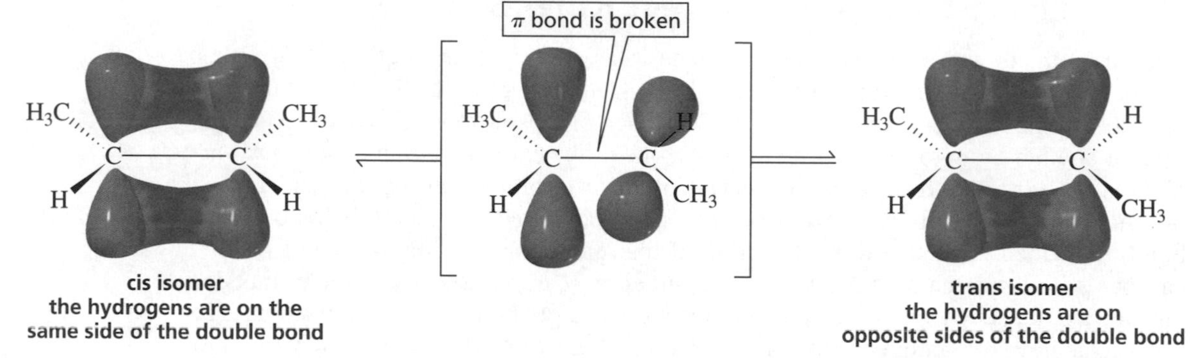
π bond is broken
H3C
CH3
H
C
C
cis isomer
the hydrogens are on the
same side of the double bond
trans isomer
the hydrogens are on
opposite sides of the double bond

▶ **Figure 12.1**
Rotation about the carbon–carbon double bond would break the π bond.

Because of the high energy barrier to rotation about a carbon–carbon double bond, an alkene such as 2-butene can exist in two distinct forms: the hydrogens bonded to the sp^2 carbons can be on the same side of the double bond or on opposite sides of the double bond.

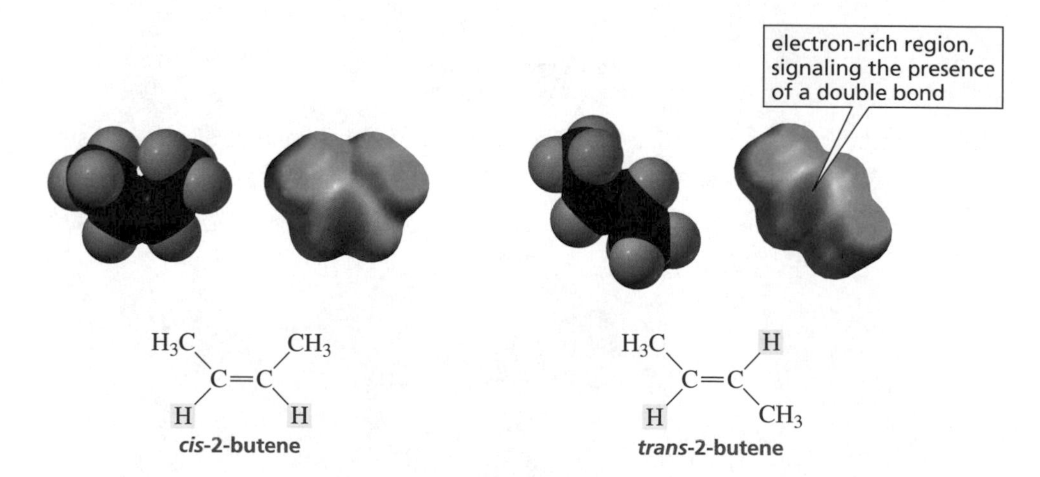
electron-rich region,
signaling the presence
of a double bond
H3C
CH3
C=C
H
H
cis-2-butene
trans-2-butene

The compound with the hydrogens on the same side of the double bond is called the **cis isomer**, and the compound with the hydrogens on opposite sides of the double bond is called the **trans isomer**. A pair of isomers such as *cis*-2-butene and *trans*-2-butene are called **cis–trans isomers** or **geometric isomers**. This should remind you of the cis–trans isomers of disubstituted cyclohexanes—the cis isomer had its substituents on the same side of the ring, and the trans isomer had its substituents on opposite sides of the ring. Notice that the cis and trans isomers have the same molecular formula and the same bonds but have different configurations—they differ in the way the atoms are oriented in space.

Do not confuse the terms *conformation* and *configuration.*

- Conformations are different spatial arrangements of the same compound (for example, anti and gauche conformers). They cannot be separated. Some conformations are more stable than others.

Different Conformations

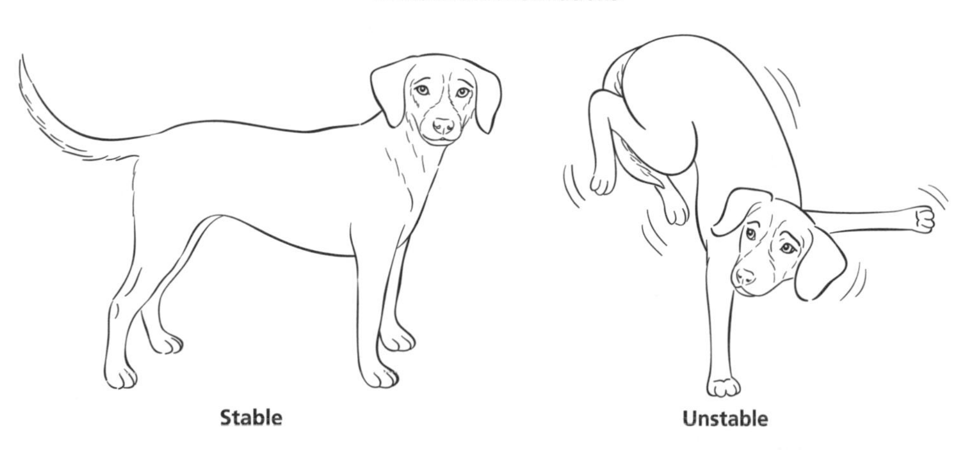

- Compounds with different configurations are different compounds. They can be separated from each other. Bonds have to be broken to interconvert compounds with different configurations.

Different Configurations

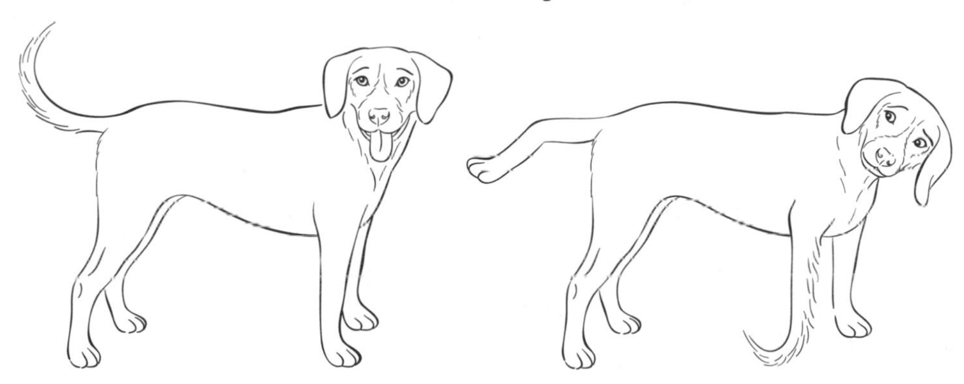

If one of the sp^2 carbons of the double bond is attached to two identical substituents, there is only one possible structure for the alkene. In other words, cis and trans isomers are not possible for an alkene that has identical substituents attached to one of the sp^2 carbons.

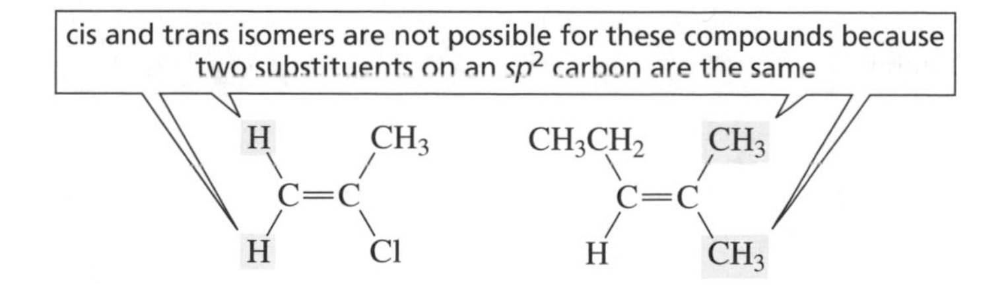

PROBLEM 7♦

a. Which of the following compounds can exist as cis–trans isomers?
b. For those compounds, draw and label the cis and trans isomers.

1. $CH_3CH{=}CHCH_2CH_2CH_3$
2. $CH_3CH_2C{=}CHCH_3$ (with CH_2CH_3 on the C)
3. $CH_3CH{=}CHCH_3$
4. $CH_3CH_2CH{=}CH_2$

PROBLEM 8

Draw skeletal structures for all the compounds in Problem 7, including any cis–trans isomers.

PROBLEM 9♦

Draw three alkenes with molecular formula C_5H_{10} that do not have cis–trans isomers.

Because of the energy barrier to rotation about a double bond, cis and trans isomers of alkenes cannot interconvert (except under conditions extreme enough to overcome the energy barrier and break the π bond). This means that they can be separated from each other. In other words, the two isomers are different compounds with different physical properties, such as different boiling points and different dipole moments. Notice that *trans*-2-butene and *trans*-1,2-dichloroethene, unlike their respective cis isomers, have dipole moments (μ) of zero because the bond dipole moments cancel.

cis-2-butene
bp = 3.7 °C
μ = 0.33 D

trans-2-butene
bp = 0.9 °C
μ = 0 D

cis-1,2-dichloroethene
bp = 60.3 °C
μ = 2.95 D

trans-1,2-dichloroethene
bp = 47.5 °C
μ = 0 D

Because cis and trans isomers can be interconverted (in the absence of any added reagents) only when the molecule absorbs sufficient heat or light energy to cause the π bond to break, cis–trans interconversion is not a practical laboratory process.

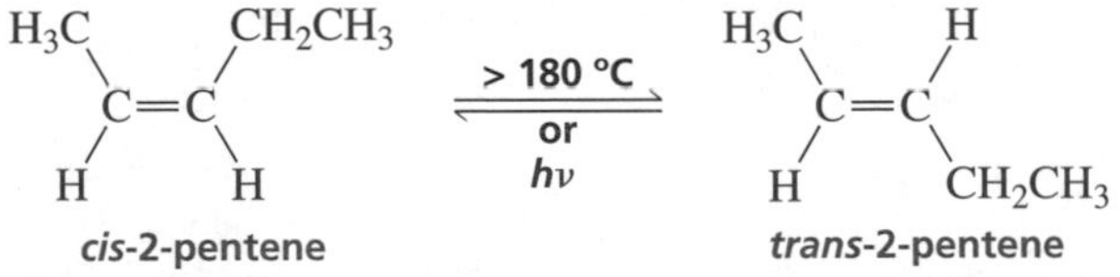

cis-2-pentene ⇌ (> 180 °C or $h\nu$) *trans*-2-pentene

Cis–Trans Interconversion in Vision

The ability to see depends in part on a cis–trans interconversion that takes place in our eyes. A protein called opsin binds to *cis*-retinal (formed from vitamin A) in photoreceptor cells (called rod cells) in the retina of the eye to form rhodopsin. When rhodopsin absorbs light, a double bond interconverts between the cis and trans configurations, triggering a nerve impulse that plays an important role in vision. *trans*-Retinal is then released from opsin, isomerizing back to *cis*-retinal, and another cycle begins. To trigger the nerve impulse, a group of about 500 rod cells must register five to seven rhodopsin isomerizations within a few tenths of a second.

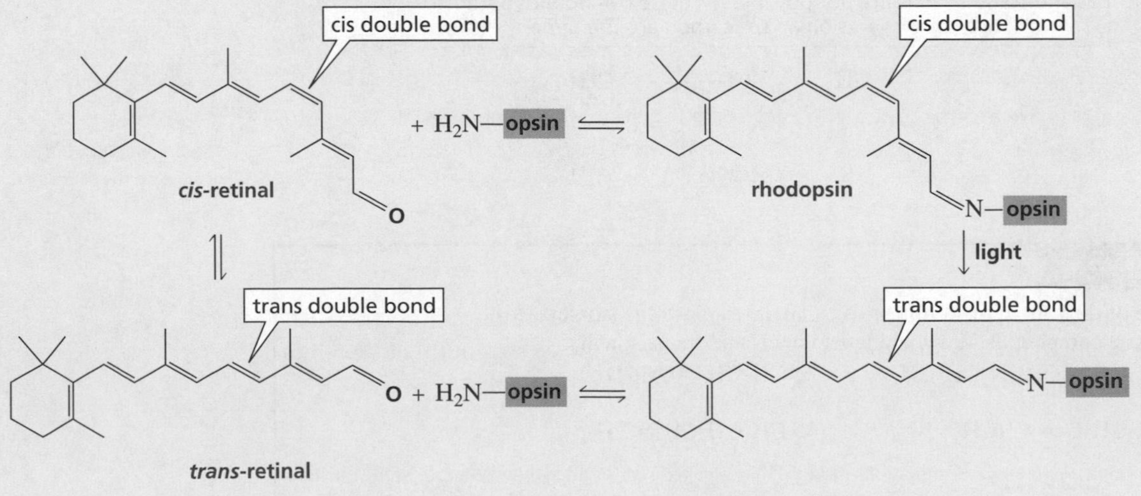

cis double bond

cis-retinal + H_2N—opsin ⇌ rhodopsin

light

trans double bond

trans-retinal + H_2N—opsin ⇌

PROBLEM 10♦

Which of the following compounds have a dipole moment of zero?

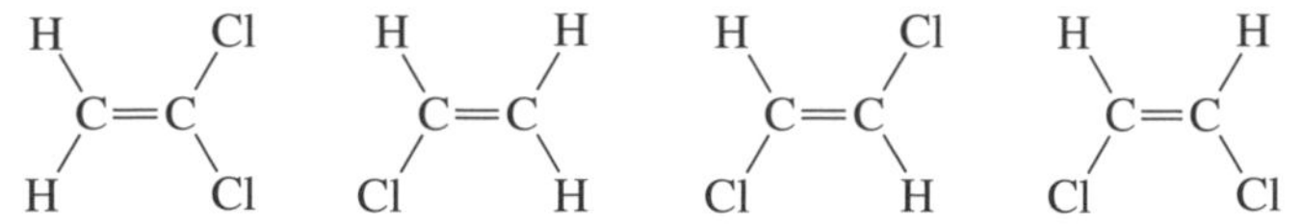

A: H, H on one carbon; Cl, Cl on the other carbon (C=C)
B: H, Cl on one carbon; H, H on the other carbon (C=C)
C: H, Cl on one carbon; Cl, H on the other carbon (C=C)
D: H, Cl on one carbon; H, Cl on the other carbon (C=C)

12.5 NAMING ALKENES USING THE *E,Z* SYSTEM

As long as each of the sp^2 carbons of an alkene is bonded to only one substituent, we can use the terms *cis* and *trans* to designate the structure of the alkene: *if the hydrogens are on the same side of the double bond, it is the cis isomer; if they are on opposite sides of the double bond, it is the trans isomer.* But how do we designate the isomers of a compound such as 1-bromo-2-chloropropene?

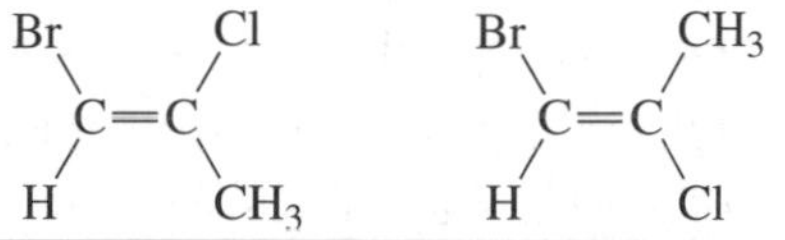

Br, H on one carbon; Cl, CH_3 on the other (C=C) — Br, H on one carbon; CH_3, Cl on the other (C=C)

Which isomer is cis and which is trans?

The *E,Z* system of nomenclature was devised for alkenes with two substituents on one or both of the sp^2 carbons.*

To name an isomer by the *E,Z* system, we first determine the relative priorities of the two groups bonded to one of the sp^2 carbons and then the relative priorities of the two groups bonded to the other sp^2 carbon. (The rules for assigning relative priorities are explained below.)

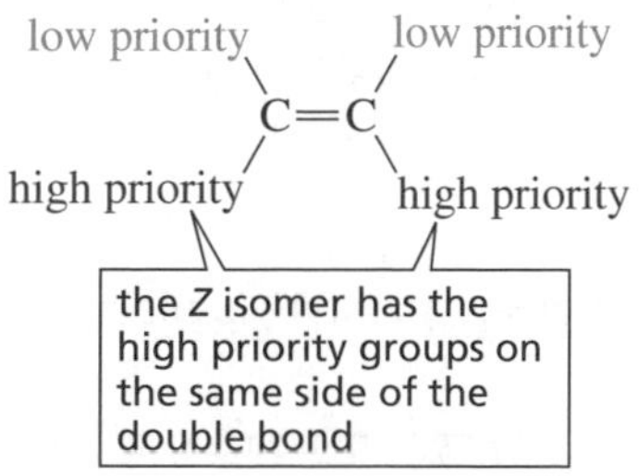

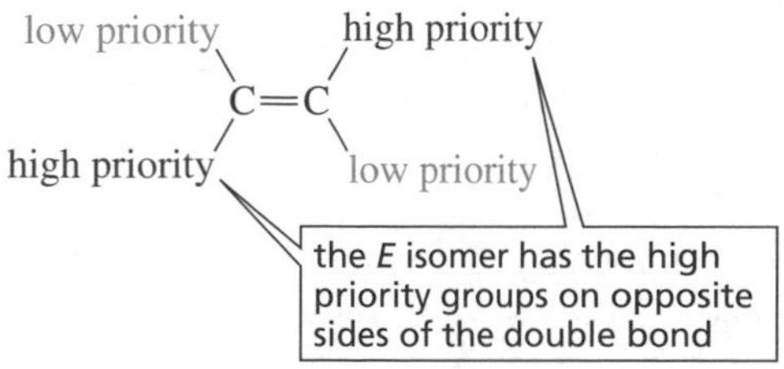

low priority, high priority on one carbon; low priority, high priority on the other (C=C)

the *Z* isomer has the high priority groups on the same side of the double bond

low priority, high priority on one carbon; high priority, low priority on the other (C=C)

the *E* isomer has the high priority groups on opposite sides of the double bond

If the two high-priority groups (one from each carbon) are on the same side of the double bond, it is the *Z* isomer (*Z* is for *zusammen*, German for "together"). If the high-priority groups are on opposite sides of the double bond, it is the *E* isomer (*E* is for *entgegen*, German for "opposite").

The *Z* isomer has the high-priority groups on the same side.

The relative priorities of the two groups bonded to an sp^2 carbon are determined using the following rules:

1. The relative priorities of the two groups depend on the atomic numbers of the atoms bonded directly to the sp^2 carbon. The greater the atomic number, the higher the priority.

*The IUPAC prefers the *E* and *Z* designations because they can be used for all alkene isomers. Many chemists, however, continue to use the "cis" and "trans" designations for simple molecules.

The greater the atomic number of the atom bonded to the sp^2 carbon, the higher the priority of the substituent.

For example, in the following pair of isomers, one of the sp^2 carbons is bonded to a Br and to an H:

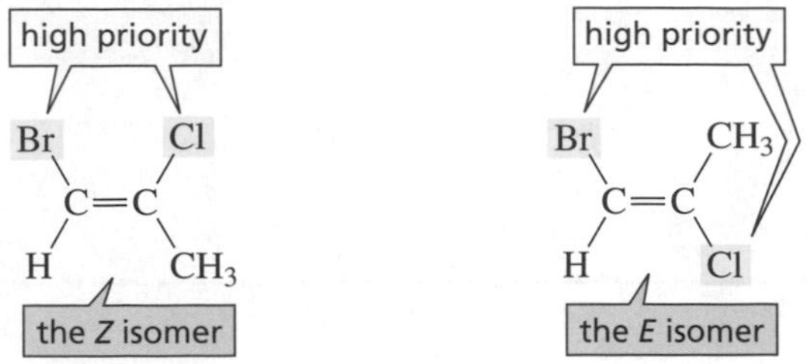

high priority | high priority

Br, Cl / C=C / H, CH_3 — the *Z* isomer

Br, CH_3 / C=C / H, Cl — the *E* isomer

Bromine has a greater atomic number than hydrogen, so **Br** has a higher priority than **H**. The other sp^2 carbon is bonded to a Cl and to a C. Chlorine has the greater atomic number, so **Cl** has a higher priority than **C**. (Notice that you use the atomic number of C, not the mass of the CH_3 group, because the priorities are based on the atomic numbers of atoms, *not* on the masses of groups.) The isomer on the left has the high-priority groups (Br and Cl) on the same side of the double bond, so it is the **Z isomer**. (Zee groups are on Zee Zame Zide.) The isomer on the right has the high-priority groups on opposite sides of the double bond, so it is the ***E* isomer**.

2. If the two groups bonded to an sp^2 carbon start with the same atom (there is a tie), you then move outward from the point of attachment and consider the atomic numbers of the atoms that are attached to the "tied" atoms.

If the atoms attached to the sp^2 carbon are the same, the atoms attached to the tied atoms are compared; the one with the greater atomic number belongs to the group with the higher priority.

For example, in the following pair of isomers, both atoms bonded to the sp^2 carbon on the left are C's (in a CH_2Cl group and a CH_2CH_2Cl group), so there is a tie.

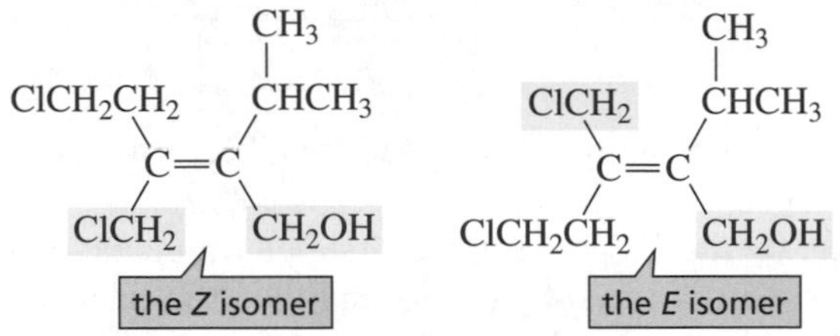

$ClCH_2CH_2$, $CHCH_3$ (with CH_3) / C=C / $ClCH_2$, CH_2OH — the *Z* isomer

$ClCH_2$, $CHCH_3$ (with CH_3) / C=C / $ClCH_2CH_2$, CH_2OH — the *E* isomer

The C of the CH_2Cl group is bonded to **Cl, H, H,** and the C of the CH_2CH_2Cl group is bonded to **C, H, H**. Cl has a greater atomic number than C, so the CH_2Cl group has the higher priority. Both atoms bonded to the other sp^2 carbon are C's (in a CH_2OH group and a $CH(CH_3)_2$ group), so there is a tie on that side as well. The C of the CH_2OH group is bonded to **O**, **H**, and **H**, and the C of the $CH(CH_3)_2$ group is bonded to **C**, **C**, and **H**. Of these six atoms, O has the greatest atomic number, so **CH_2OH** has a higher priority than **$CH(CH_3)_2$**. (Note that you do not add the atomic numbers; you consider the single atom with the greatest atomic number.) The *E* and *Z* isomers are as shown above.

3. If an atom is doubly bonded to another atom, the priority system treats it as if it were singly bonded to two of those atoms. If an atom is triply bonded to another atom, the priority system treats it as if it were singly bonded to three of those atoms.

If an atom is doubly bonded to another atom, treat it as if it were singly bonded to two of those atoms.

If an atom is triply bonded to another atom, treat it as if it were singly bonded to three of those atoms.

For example, one of the sp^2 carbons in the following pair of isomers is bonded to a CH_2CH_2OH group and to a $CH_2C{\equiv}CH$ group:

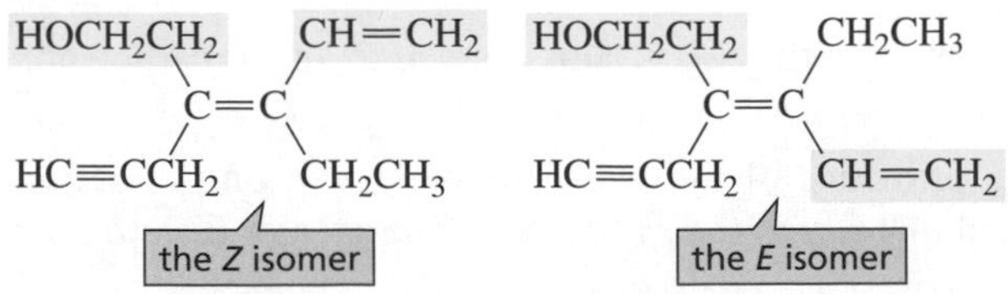

$HOCH_2CH_2$, $CH{=}CH_2$ / C=C / $HC{\equiv}CCH_2$, CH_2CH_3 — the *Z* isomer

$HOCH_2CH_2$, CH_2CH_3 / C=C / $HC{\equiv}CCH_2$, $CH{=}CH_2$ — the *E* isomer

Because the carbons immediately bonded to the sp^2 carbon on the left are both bonded to **C**, **H**, and **H**, we ignore them and turn our attention to the groups attached to them. One of these groups is CH_2OH, and the other is $C{\equiv}CH$. One C is bonded to **H**, **H**, and **O**; the triple-bonded C is considered to be bonded to **C**, **C**, and **C**. Of the six atoms, O has the greatest atomic number, so $\mathbf{CH_2OH}$ has a higher priority than $\mathbf{C{\equiv}CH}$. Both atoms that are bonded to the other sp^2 carbon are C's, so they are tied. The first carbon of the CH_2CH_3 group is bonded to **C**, **H**, and **H**. The first carbon of the $CH{=}CH_2$ group is bonded to an H and doubly bonded to a C, so it is considered to be bonded to **H**, **C**, and **C**. One **C** cancels in each of the two groups, leaving **H** and **H** in the CH_2CH_3 group and **H** and **C** in the $CH{=}CH_2$ group. C has a greater atomic number than H, so $\mathbf{CH{=}CH_2}$ has a higher priority than $\mathbf{CH_2CH_3}$.

Cancel atoms that are identical in the two groups; use the remaining atoms to determine the group with the higher priority.

4. If two isotopes (atoms with the same atomic number, but different mass numbers) are being compared, the mass number is used to determine the relative priorities. In the following pair of isomers, for example, one of the sp^2 carbons is bonded to a deuterium (D) and a hydrogen (H):

If atoms have the same atomic number, but different mass numbers, the one with the greater mass number has the higher priority.

(H)(D)C=C($CH(CH_3)CH_3$)($CH{=}CH_2$) — the *Z* isomer

(H)(D)C=C($CH{=}CH_2$)($CH(CH_3)CH_3$) — the *E* isomer

Deuterium and hydrogen have the same atomic number, but D has a greater mass number, so **D** has a higher priority than **H**. The C's that are bonded to the other sp^2 carbon are *both* bonded to **C**, **C**, and **H**, so we must go to the next set of atoms to break the tie. The second carbon of the $CH(CH_3)_2$ group is bonded to **H**, **H**, and **H**, whereas the second carbon of the $CH{=}CH_2$ group is bonded to **H**, **H**, and **C**. (Notice that to get the third atom, you can go back along the double bond.) Therefore, $\mathbf{CH{=}CH_2}$ has a higher priority than $\mathbf{CH(CH_3)_2}$.

PROBLEM 11 ♦

Assign relative priorities to each set of substituents:

a. $-Br$, $-I$, $-OH$, $-CH_3$
b. $-CH_2CH_2OH$, $-OH$, $-CH_2Cl$, $-CH{=}CH_2$

PROBLEM 12

Draw and label the *E* and *Z* isomers for each of the following:

a. $CH_3CH_2CH{=}CHCH_3$

b. $CH_3CH_2C(Cl){=}CHCH_2CH_3$

c. $CH_3CH_2C(CH_2CH_2CH_2CH_3){=}C(CH(CH_3)CH_3)CH_2Cl$

d. $HOCH_2CH_2C(CH{=}O){=}C(C(CH_3)_3)C{\equiv}CH$

chem place Tutorial: *E* and *Z* nomenclature

PROBLEM 13

Draw skeletal structures for each pair of isomers in Problem 12.

PROBLEM 14 ♦

Name each of the following:

a. **b.** **c.** Cl

PROBLEM-SOLVING STRATEGY

Drawing *E,Z* Structures

Draw the structure of (*E*)-1-bromo-2-methyl-2-butene.

First draw the compound without specifying the isomer so you can see what substituents are bonded to the sp^2 carbons. Then determine the relative priorities of the two groups bonded to each of the sp^2 carbons.

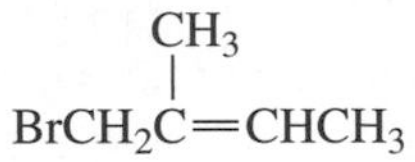

$$BrCH_2\overset{\displaystyle CH_3}{\overset{|}{C}}{=}CHCH_3$$

The sp^2 carbon on the right is attached to a CH_3 and an H: CH_3 has the higher priority. The other sp^2 carbon is attached to a CH_3 and a CH_2Br: CH_2Br has the higher priority. To draw the *E* isomer, put the two high-priority substituents on opposite sides of the double bond.

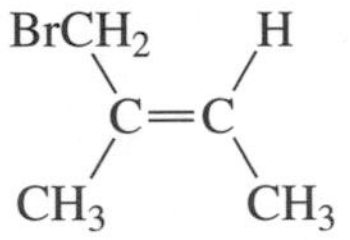

BrCH₂ and H on top; C=C; CH₃ and CH₃ on bottom:

$$\begin{matrix} BrCH_2 & & H \\ & C{=}C & \\ CH_3 & & CH_3 \end{matrix}$$

Now continue on to Problem 15.

PROBLEM 15

Draw the structure of (*Z*)-3-isopropyl-2-heptene.

PROBLEM-SOLVING STRATEGY

Drawing Isomers for Compounds with Two Double Bonds

How many isomers does the following compound have?

$$ClCH_2CH{=}CHCH{=}CHCH_2CH_3$$

It has four isomers because each of its double bonds can have either the *E* or the *Z* configuration. Thus, there are *E-E*, *Z-Z*, *E-Z*, and *Z-E* isomers.

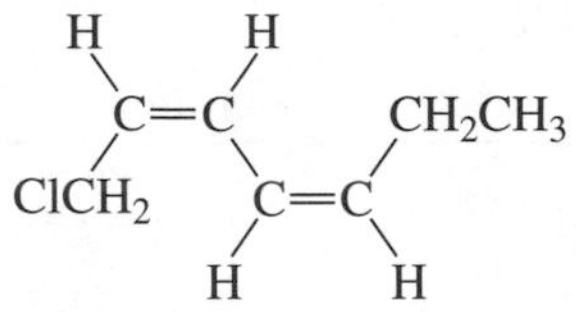

$$\begin{matrix} H & & H & & \\ & C{=}C & & & CH_2CH_3 \\ ClCH_2 & & & C{=}C & \\ & & H & & H \end{matrix}$$

(2*Z*,4*Z*)-1-chloro-2,4-heptadiene

$$\begin{matrix} H & & H & & \\ & C{=}C & & & H \\ ClCH_2 & & & C{=}C & \\ & & H & & CH_2CH_3 \end{matrix}$$

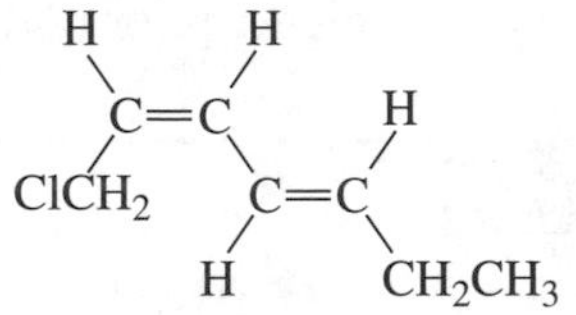

(2*Z*,4*E*)-1-chloro-2,4-heptadiene

$$\begin{matrix} ClCH_2 & & H & & \\ & C{=}C & & & CH_2CH_3 \\ H & & & C{=}C & \\ & & H & & H \end{matrix}$$

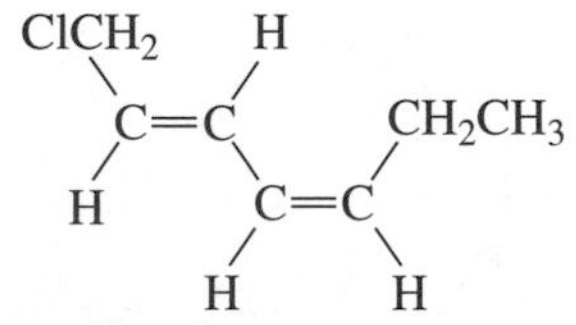

(2*E*,4*Z*)-1-chloro-2,4-heptadiene

$$\begin{matrix} ClCH_2 & & H & & \\ & C{=}C & & & H \\ H & & & C{=}C & \\ & & H & & CH_2CH_3 \end{matrix}$$

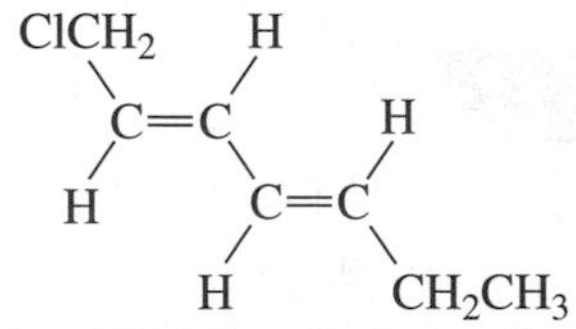

(2*E*,4*E*)-1-chloro-2,4-heptadiene

Now continue on to Problem 16.

PROBLEM 16

Draw the isomers for the following compounds, and name each one:

a. 2-methyl-2,4-hexadiene **b.** 2,4-heptadiene **c.** 1,3-pentadiene

12.6 HOW ALKENES REACT • CURVED ARROWS SHOW THE FLOW OF ELECTRONS

There are many millions of organic compounds. If you had to memorize how each of them reacts, studying organic chemistry would not be a very pleasant experience. Fortunately, organic compounds can be divided into families, and all the members of a family react in similar ways. What makes learning organic chemistry even easier is that only a few rules govern the reactivity of each family.

The family that an organic compound belongs to is determined by its functional group. The **functional group** is the center of reactivity of a molecule. You are already familiar with the functional group of an alkene: the carbon–carbon double bond. All compounds with a carbon–carbon double bond react in similar ways, whether the compound is a small molecule like ethene or a large molecule like cholesterol.

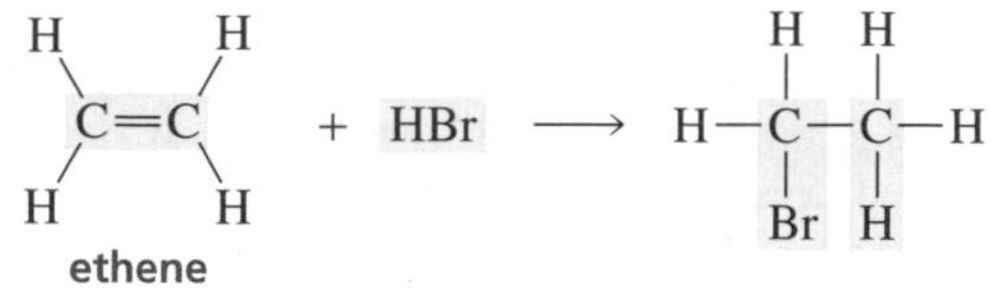

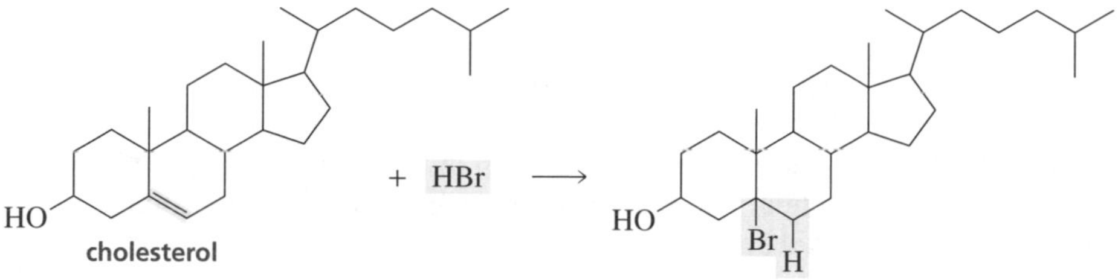

$$H_2C{=}CH_2 + HBr \longrightarrow H{-}\underset{Br}{\overset{H}{C}}{-}\underset{H}{\overset{H}{C}}{-}H$$

ethene

$$\text{cholesterol} + HBr \longrightarrow \text{(HO, Br, H product)}$$

cholesterol

First, we need to understand *why* a functional group reacts the way it does. It is not sufficient to know that a compound with a carbon–carbon double bond reacts with HBr to form a product in which the H and Br atoms have taken the place of the π bond; we also need to understand *why* the compound reacts with HBr. In each chapter that discusses the reactivity of a particular functional group, we will see how the nature of the functional group allows us to predict the kind of reactions it will undergo. Then, when you are confronted with a reaction you have never seen before, knowledge of how the structure of the molecule affects its reactivity will help you predict the products of the reaction.

In essence, organic chemistry is all about the interaction between electron-rich atoms or molecules and electron-deficient atoms or molecules. These are the forces that make chemical reactions happen. From this observation follows a very important rule for predicting the reactivity of organic compounds: *electron-rich atoms or molecules are attracted to electron-deficient atoms or molecules.* Each time you study a new functional group, remember that the reactions it undergoes can be explained by this very simple rule.

Electron-rich atoms or molecules are attracted to electron-deficient atoms or molecules.

Therefore, to understand how a functional group reacts, you must first learn to recognize electron-deficient and electron-rich atoms and molecules. An electron-deficient atom or molecule is called an **electrophile**. Literally, "electrophile" means "electron loving" (*phile* is the Greek suffix for "loving"). An electrophile looks for a pair of electrons. An electrophile has either a positive charge or an incomplete octet that can accept electrons.

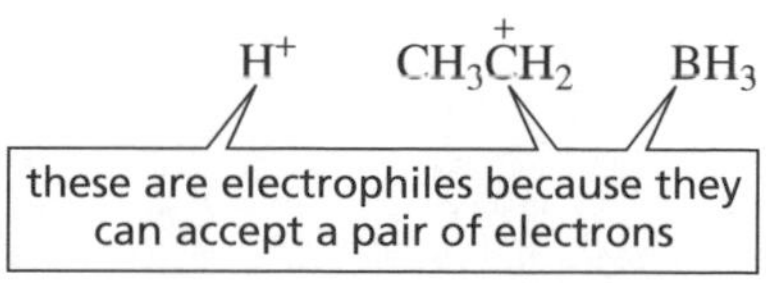

$$H^+ \qquad CH_3\overset{+}{C}H_2 \qquad BH_3$$

these are electrophiles because they can accept a pair of electrons

An electron-rich atom or molecule is called a **nucleophile**. A nucleophile has a pair of electrons it can share. Because a nucleophile has electrons to share and an electrophile is seeking electrons, it should not be surprising that they attract each other. Thus, the preceding rule can be restated as *a nucleophile reacts with an electrophile.*

A nucleophile reacts with an electrophile.

$$H\ddot{\underset{..}{O}}{:}^- \qquad {:}\ddot{\underset{..}{Cl}}{:}^- \qquad CH_3\ddot{N}H_2 \qquad H_2\ddot{O}{:}$$

these are nucleophiles because they have a pair of electrons to share

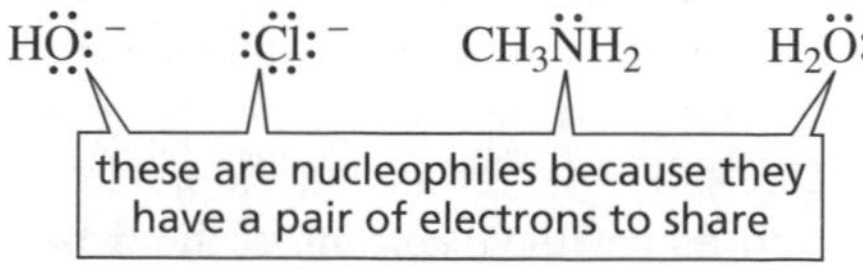

PROBLEM 17

Identify the nucleophile and the electrophile in the following acid–base reactions.

a. $AlCl_3 + NH_3 \rightleftharpoons Cl_3\overset{-}{Al}-\overset{+}{N}H_3$

b. $H-Br + HO^- \rightleftharpoons Br^- + H_2O$

Let's now see how the rule "a nucleophile reacts with an electrophile" allows us to predict the characteristic reaction of an alkene. We have seen that the π bond of an alkene consists of a cloud of electrons above and below the σ bond. As a result of this cloud of electrons, an alkene is an electron-rich molecule—it is a nucleophile. (Notice the relatively electron-rich pale orange area in the electrostatic potential maps for *cis*- and *trans*-2-butene in Section 12.4.) We have also seen that a π bond is weaker than a σ bond. The π bond, therefore, is the bond that is most easily broken when an alkene undergoes a reaction. For these reasons, we can predict that an alkene will react with an electrophile, and, in the process, the π bond will break. So if a reagent such as hydrogen bromide is added to an alkene, the alkene (a nucleophile) will react with the partially positively charged hydrogen (an electrophile) of hydrogen bromide; the product of the reaction will be a carbocation. In the second step of the reaction, the positively charged carbocation (an electrophile) will react with the negatively charged bromide ion (a nucleophile) to form an alkyl halide.

$$CH_3CH{=}CHCH_3 + \overset{\delta+}{H}-\overset{\delta-}{Br} \longrightarrow CH_3\overset{+}{C}H-\underset{\underset{H}{|}}{C}HCH_3 + Br^- \longrightarrow CH_3\underset{\underset{Br}{|}}{C}H-\underset{\underset{H}{|}}{C}HCH_3$$

nucleophile (CH3CH=CHCH3); electrophile (H–Br); electrophile (carbocation); nucleophile (Br⁻)

a carbocation

2-bromobutane
an alkyl halide

The step-by-step description of the process by which reactants (for example, alkene + HBr) are changed into products (an alkyl halide) is called the **mechanism of the reaction**. To help us understand a mechanism, curved arrows are drawn to show how the electrons move as new covalent bonds are formed and existing covalent bonds are broken. Each arrow represents the simultaneous movement of two electrons (an electron pair) from an electron-rich center (at the tail of the arrow) toward an electron-deficient center (at the point of the arrow). In this way, the arrows show which bonds are formed and which are broken.

Curved arrows show the flow of electrons; they are drawn from an electron-rich center to an electron-deficient center.

An arrowhead with two barbs signifies the movement of two electrons.

$$CH_3CH{=}CHCH_3 + \overset{\delta+}{H}-\overset{\delta-}{\ddot{Br}:} \longrightarrow CH_3\overset{+}{C}H-\underset{\underset{H}{|}}{C}HCH_3 + :\ddot{Br}:^-$$

a curved arrow indicates where the electrons start from and where they end up

σ bond breaks

π bond has broken

new σ bond has formed

For the reaction of 2-butene with HBr, an arrow is drawn to show that the two electrons of the π bond of the alkene are attracted to the partially positively charged hydrogen of HBr. The hydrogen is not immediately free to accept this pair of electrons because it is already bonded to a bromine, and hydrogen can be bonded to only one atom at a time. However, as the π electrons of the alkene move toward the hydrogen, the H—Br bond breaks, with bromine keeping the bonding electrons. Notice that the π electrons are pulled away from one carbon, but remain attached to the other. Thus, the two electrons that originally formed the π bond now form a new σ bond between carbon and the hydrogen from HBr. The product is positively charged, because the sp^2 carbon that did not form the new bond with hydrogen has lost a share in an electron pair (the electrons of the π bond).

In the second step of the reaction, a lone pair on the negatively charged bromide ion forms a bond with the positively charged carbon of the carbocation. Notice that in both steps of the reaction *a nucleophile reacts with an electrophile.*

$$CH_3\overset{+}{C}H{-}CHCH_3(H) + :\ddot{Br}:^- \longrightarrow CH_3CH(Br){-}CHCH_3(H)$$

new σ bond

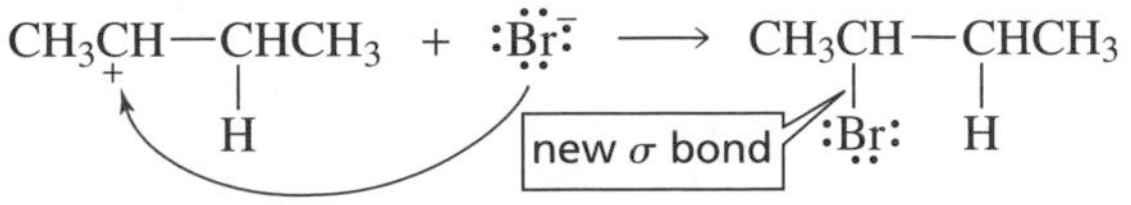

A curved arrow indicates where the electrons start from and where they end up.

Solely from the knowledge that a nucleophile reacts with an electrophile and a π bond is the weakest bond in an alkene, we have been able to predict that the product of the reaction of 2-butene and HBr is 2-bromobutane. The overall reaction involves the addition of 1 mole of HBr to 1 mole of the alkene. The reaction, therefore, is called an **addition reaction**. Because the first step of the reaction is the addition of an electrophile (H^+) to the alkene, the reaction is more precisely called an **electrophilic addition reaction**. *Electrophilic addition reactions are the characteristic reactions of alkenes.*

At this point, you may think it would be easier just to memorize the fact that 2-bromobutane is the product of the reaction, without trying to understand the mechanism that explains why 2-bromobutane is the product. Keep in mind, however, that you will soon be encountering a great many reactions, and you will not be able to memorize them all. *It will be a lot easier to learn a dozen mechanisms that are based on similar rules than to try to memorize thousands of reactions.* And if you understand the mechanism of each reaction, the unifying principles of organic chemistry will soon be clear to you, making mastery of the material much easier and a lot more fun.

PROBLEM 18♦

Which of the following are electrophiles, and which are nucleophiles?

H^- $\quad CH_3O^-$ $\quad CH_3C{\equiv}CH$ $\quad CH_3\overset{+}{C}HCH_3$ $\quad NH_3$

PROBLEM 19

Draw the consequence of following the incorrect arrows in item 1 of the box on page 528, "A Few Words about Curved Arrows." What is wrong with the structures that you obtain?

PROBLEM 20

Use curved arrows to show the movement of electrons in each of the following reaction steps. (*Hint*: Look at the starting material and look at the products, then draw the arrows.)

a. 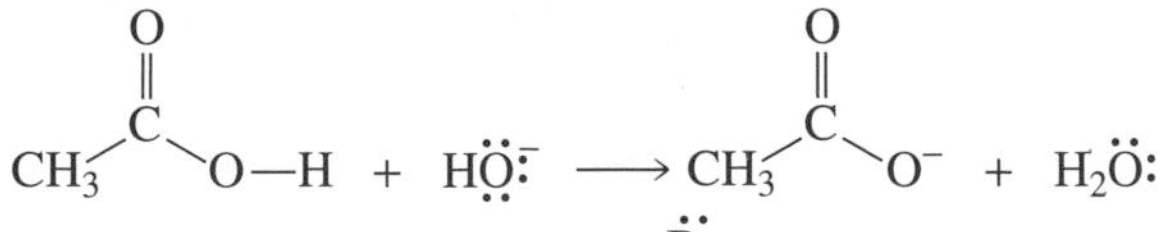 $CH_3C(=O){-}O{-}H + H\ddot{O}:^- \longrightarrow CH_3C(=O){-}O^- + H_2\ddot{O}:$

b. 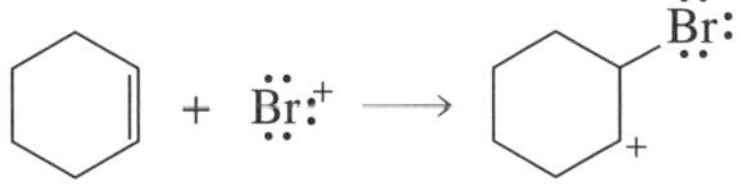 cyclohexene $+ :\ddot{Br}:^+ \longrightarrow$ bromocyclohexyl cation ($:\ddot{Br}:$, $+$)

c. 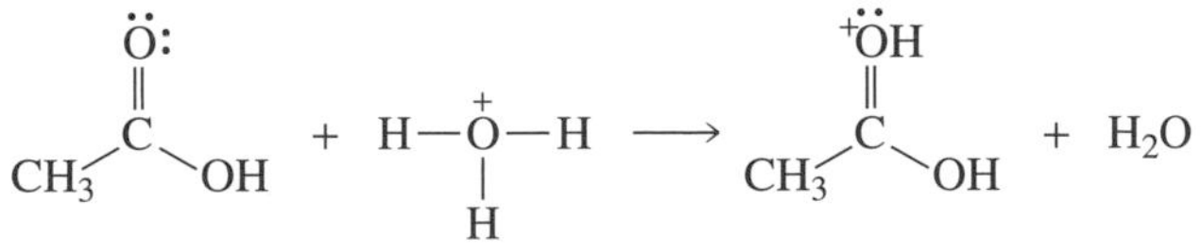 $CH_3C(=\ddot{O}:){-}OH + H{-}\overset{+}{\ddot{O}}{-}H(H) \longrightarrow CH_3C(=\overset{+}{\ddot{O}}H){-}OH + H_2O$

d. 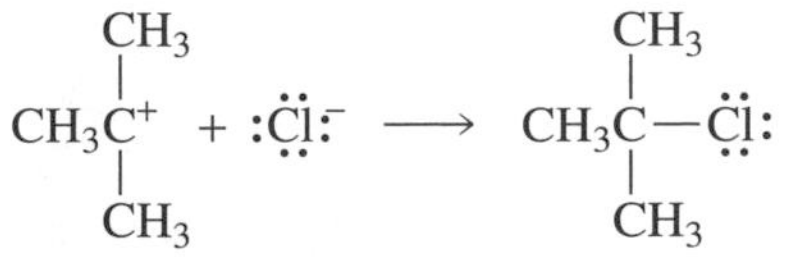 $CH_3\overset{+}{C}(CH_3)_2 + :\ddot{Cl}:^- \longrightarrow CH_3C(CH_3)_2{-}\ddot{Cl}:$

PROBLEM 21

For each of the reactions in Problem 20, indicate which reactant is the nucleophile and which is the electrophile.

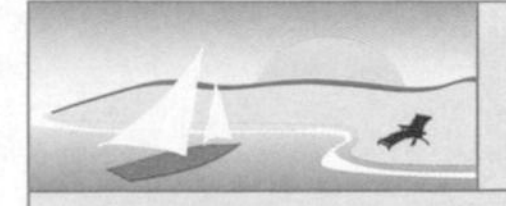

A Few Words about Curved Arrows

1. Draw the arrows so that they point in the direction of the electron flow and never against the flow. This means that *an arrow will point away from a negative charge and toward a positive charge.* An arrow is used to show both the bond that forms and the bond that breaks.

correct: $CH_3-C(CH_3)(O^-)-Br \longrightarrow CH_3-C(=O)-CH_3 + Br^-$

incorrect: $CH_3-C(CH_3)(O^-)-Br \longrightarrow CH_3-C(=O)-CH_3 + Br^-$

correct: $CH_3-\overset{+}{O}(H)-H \longrightarrow CH_3-O-H + H^+$

incorrect: $CH_3-\overset{+}{O}(H)-H \longrightarrow CH_3-O-H + H^+$

2. Curved arrows are meant to indicate the movement of electrons. *Never use a curved arrow to indicate the movement of an atom.* For example, do not use an arrow as a lasso to remove a proton, as shown in the equation on the right:

correct: $CH_3C(=\overset{+}{O}H)CH_3 \longrightarrow CH_3C(=O)CH_3 + H^+$

incorrect: $CH_3C(=\overset{+}{O}H)CH_3 \longrightarrow CH_3C(=O)CH_3 + H^+$

3. *The head of a curved arrow always points at an atom or at a bond.* Never draw the head of the arrow pointing out into space.

correct: $CH_3C(=O)OCH_3 + HO^- \longrightarrow CH_3C(O^-)(OH)OCH_3$

incorrect: $CH_3C(=O)CH_3 + HO^- \longrightarrow CH_3C(O^-)(OH)OCH_3$

4. *A curved arrow starts at an electron source; it does not start at an atom.* In the following example, the arrow starts at the electron-rich π bond, not at a carbon atom:

correct: $CH_3CH{=}CHCH_3 + H-Br \longrightarrow CH_3\overset{+}{C}H-CH(H)CH_3 + Br^-$

incorrect: $CH_3CH{=}CHCH_3 + H-Br \longrightarrow CH_3\overset{+}{C}H-CH(H)CH_3 + Br^-$

NOTE TO THE STUDENT

It is critically important that you learn how to draw curved arrows. Be sure to do the exercise in Special Topic II in the *Study Guide and Solutions Manual.* It should take no more than 15 minutes, yet it can make an enormous difference to your success in this course.

SUMMARY

An **alkene** is a hydrocarbon that contains a double bond. The double bond is the **functional group**, or center of reactivity of the alkene. The **functional group suffix** of an alkene is "ene." The general molecular formula for a hydrocarbon is C_nH_{2n+2}, minus two hydrogens for every π bond or ring in the molecule. The number of π bonds and rings is called the **degree of unsaturation**. Because alkenes contain fewer than the maximum number of hydrogens, they are called **unsaturated hydrocarbons**.

Rotation about the double bond is restricted, so an alkene can exist as **cis–trans isomers**. The **cis isomer** has its hydrogens on the same side of the double bond; the **trans isomer** has its hydrogens on opposite sides of the double bond. The ***Z* isomer** has the high-priority groups on the same side of the double bond; the ***E* isomer** has the high-priority groups on opposite sides of the double bond. The relative priorities depend on the atomic numbers of the atoms bonded directly to the sp^2 carbon.

All compounds with a particular **functional group** react similarly. Due to the cloud of electrons above and below its π bond, an alkene is an electron-rich species, or a **nucleophile**. Nucleophiles are attracted to electron-deficient species, called **electrophiles**. Alkenes undergo **electrophilic addition reactions**.

The description of the step-by-step process by which reactants are changed into products is called the **mechanism of the reaction**. **Curved arrows** show which bonds are formed and which are broken and the direction of the electron flow that accompanies these changes.

KEY TERMS

acyclic (p. 513)
addition reaction (p. 527)
alkene (p. 512)
allyl group (p. 516)
allylic carbon (p. 516)
allylic hydrogen (p. 516)
cis isomer (p. 518)
cis–trans isomers (p. 518)
degree of unsaturation (p. 513)
E isomer (p. 522)
electrophile (p. 525)
electrophilic addition reaction (p. 527)
functional group (p. 525)
geometric isomers (p. 518)
mechanism of the reaction (p. 526)
nucleophile (p. 525)
saturated hydrocarbon (p. 513)
trans isomer (p. 518)
unsaturated hydrocarbon (p. 513)
vinyl group (p. 516)
vinylic carbon (p. 516)
vinylic hydrogen (p. 516)
Z isomer (p. 522)

PROBLEMS

22. Give the systematic name for each of the following:

a. 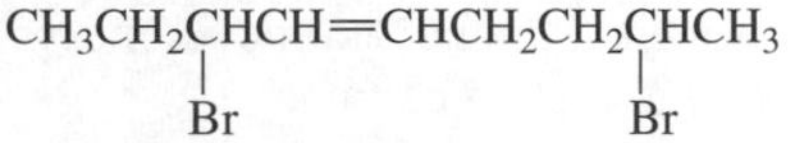 $CH_3CH_2CHCH{=}CHCH_2CH_2CHCH_3$ (with Br on C3 and Br on C8)

b. 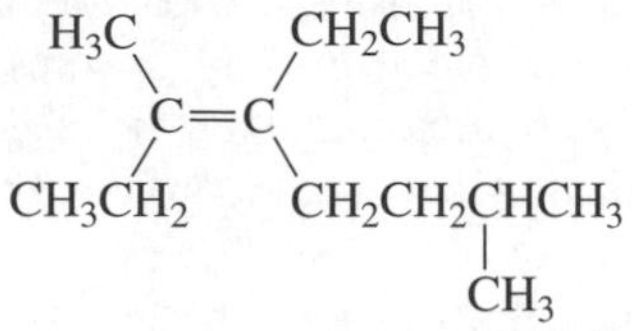 $(H_3C)(CH_3CH_2)C{=}C(CH_2CH_3)(CH_2CH_2CHCH_3)$, with CH_3 on the CH

c. (cyclopentene ring with CH_3 and CH_3)

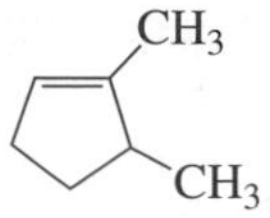

d. 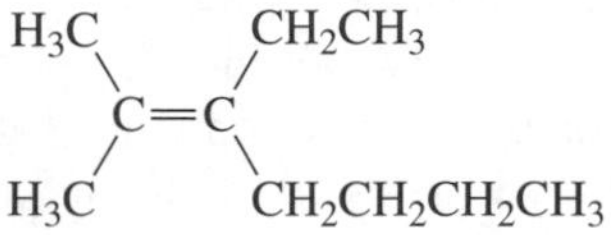 $(H_3C)(H_3C)C{=}C(CH_2CH_3)(CH_2CH_2CH_2CH_3)$

e. 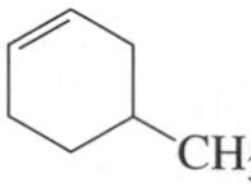 (cyclohexene ring with CH_3)

f. 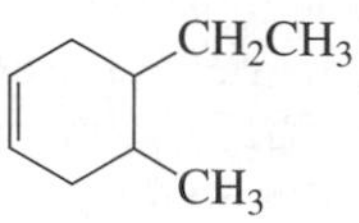 (cyclohexene ring with CH_2CH_3 and CH_3)

23. Give the structure of a hydrocarbon that has six carbon atoms and
- **a.** three vinylic hydrogens and two allylic hydrogens.
- **b.** three vinylic hydrogens and one allylic hydrogen.
- **c.** three vinylic hydrogens and no allylic hydrogens.

24. Draw the condensed structure for each of the following:
- **a.** (*Z*)-1,3,5-tribromo-2-pentene
- **b.** (*Z*)-3-methyl-2-heptene
- **c.** (*E*)-1,2-dibromo-3-isopropyl-2-hexene
- **d.** vinyl bromide
- **e.** 1,2-dimethylcyclopentene
- **f.** diallylamine

25. Draw the skeletal structures for the compounds in Problem 24.

26. **a.** Draw the condensed structures and give the systematic names for all alkenes with molecular formula C_6H_{12}, ignoring cis–trans isomers. (*Hint:* There are 13.)
b. Which of the compounds have *E* and *Z* isomers?

27. Name the following:

a. 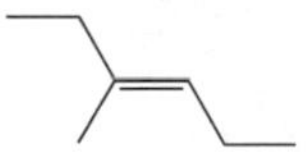 **b.** 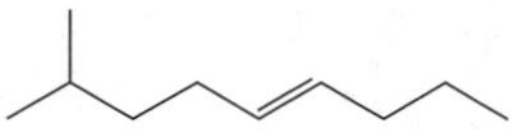 **c.** 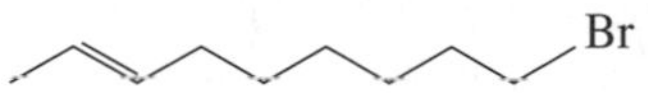 Br **d.** 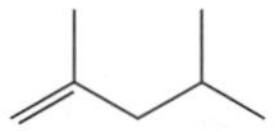 **e.** 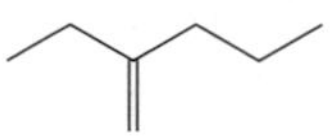 **f.**

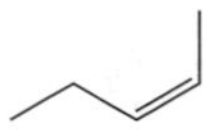

28. Draw curved arrows to show the flow of electrons responsible for the conversion of the reactants into the products:

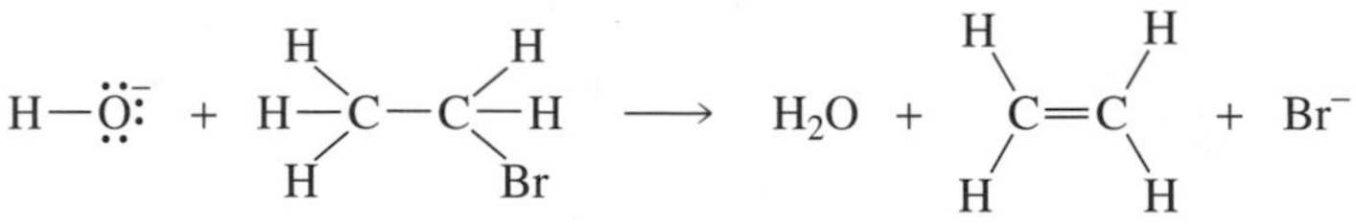

$$H{-}\ddot{\underset{..}{O}}{:}^{-} + H{-}\underset{H}{\overset{H}{C}}{-}\underset{Br}{\overset{H}{C}}{-}H \longrightarrow H_2O + \underset{H}{\overset{H}{}}C{=}C\underset{H}{\overset{H}{}} + Br^-$$

29. Tamoxifen slows the growth of some breast tumors by binding to estrogen receptors. Is tamoxifen an *E* or a *Z* isomer?

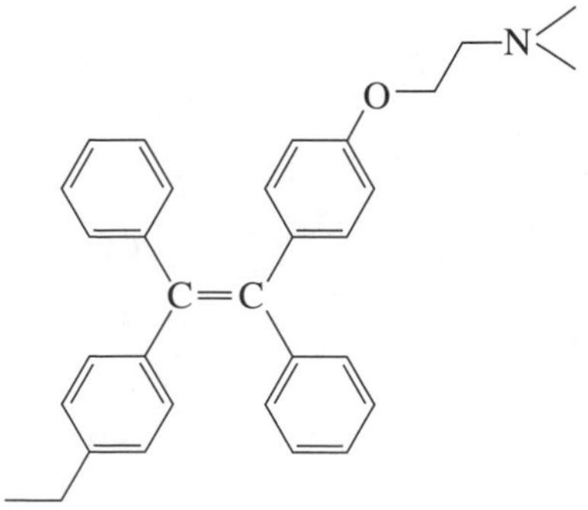

O N C=C

tamoxifen

30. Draw the skeletal structure of 6-*sec*-butyl-7-isopropyl-3,3-dimethyldecane.

31. In a reaction in which reactant A is in equilibrium with product B at 25 °C, what are the relative amounts of A and B present at equilibrium if $\Delta G°$ at 25 °C is
- **a.** 2.72 kcal/mol?
- **b.** 0.65 kcal/mol?
- **c.** −2.72 kcal/mol?
- **d.** −0.65 kcal/mol?

32. Several studies have shown that β-carotene, a precursor of vitamin A, may play a role in preventing cancer. β-Carotene has a molecular formula of $C_{40}H_{56}$ and contains two rings and no triple bonds. How many double bonds does it have?

33. For each pair of bonds, which has the greater strength? Briefly explain why.

a. CH_3—Cl or CH_3—Br (arrows point to the C—Cl and C—Br bonds)

b. I—Br or Br—Br (arrows point to the I—Br and Br—Br bonds)

34. Tell whether each of the following compounds has the *E* or the *Z* configuration:

a. H_3C and CH_3CH_2 on one carbon, CH_2CH_3 and CH_2CH_2Cl on the other: $(H_3C)(CH_3CH_2)C{=}C(CH_2CH_3)(CH_2CH_2Cl)$

b. $CH_3CH_2CH_2$ and $HC{\equiv}CCH_2$ on one carbon, $CH(CH_3)_2$ and $CH_2CH{=}CH_2$ on the other: $(CH_3CH_2CH_2)(HC{\equiv}CCH_2)C{=}C(CH(CH_3)_2)(CH_2CH{=}CH_2)$

c. H_3C and Br on one carbon, CH_2Br and $CH_2CH_2CH_2CH_3$ on the other: $(H_3C)(Br)C{=}C(CH_2Br)(CH_2CH_2CH_2CH_3)$

d. $CH_3C(=O)$ and $HOCH_2$ on one carbon, CH_2Br and CH_2CH_2Cl on the other: $(CH_3C(=O))(HOCH_2)C{=}C(CH_2Br)(CH_2CH_2Cl)$

35. Squalene, a hydrocarbon with molecular formula $C_{30}H_{50}$, is obtained from shark liver. (*Squalus* is Latin for "shark.") If squalene is an acyclic compound, how many π bonds does it have?

36. Assign relative priorities to each set of substituents:

a. $-CH_2CH_2CH_3$, $-CH(CH_3)_2$, $-CH{=}CH_2$, $-CH_3$

b. $-CH_2NH_2$, $-NH_2$, $-OH$, $-CH_2OH$

c. $-C({=}O)CH_3$, $-CH{=}CH_2$, $-Cl$, $-C{\equiv}N$

37. Draw the geometric isomers for the following compounds, and name each one:

a. 2-methyl-2,4-hexadiene **b.** 1,5-heptadiene **c.** 1,4-pentadiene

38. By following the curved red arrows, draw the product(s) of each of the reactions.

a. CH_3CH_2—$\ddot{B}r$: + :NH_3

b. $CH_3C({=}\ddot{O}{:})CH_3$ + $H\ddot{O}{:}^-$

c. $CH_3C(CH_3){=}C(CH_3)CH_3$ + H—$\ddot{C}l$:

39. How many of the following names are correct? Correct the incorrect names.

a. 3-pentene
b. 2-octene
c. 2-vinylpentane
d. 1-ethyl-1-pentene
e. 5-ethylcyclohexene
f. 5-chloro-3-hexene
g. 2-ethyl-2-butene
h. (*E*)-2-methyl-1-hexene
i. 2-methylcyclopentene

40. Draw structures for the following compounds:

a. (2*E*,4*E*)-1-chloro-3-methyl-2,4-hexadiene
b. (3*Z*,5*E*)-4-methyl-3,5-nonadiene
c. (3*Z*,5*Z*)-4,5-dimethyl-3,5-nonadiene
d. (3*E*,5*E*)-2,5-dibromo-3,5-octadiene

41. Given the reaction coordinate diagram for the reaction of A to form G, answer the following questions:

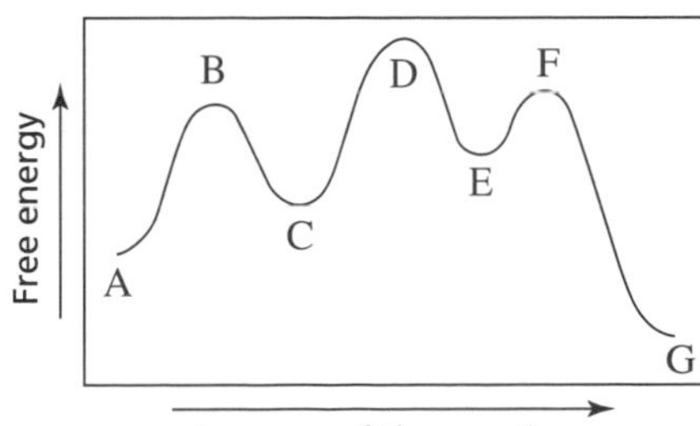

a. How many intermediates are formed in the reaction?
b. Which letters represent transition states?
c. What is the fastest step in the reaction?
d. Which is more stable, A or G?
e. Does A or E form faster from C?
f. What is the reactant of the rate-determining step?
g. Is the first step of the reaction exergonic or endergonic?
h. Is the overall reaction exergonic or endergonic?

i. Which is the more stable intermediate?
j. Which step in the forward direction has the smallest rate constant?
k. Which step in the reverse direction has the smallest rate constant?

42. a. What is the equilibrium constant of a reaction that is carried out at 25 °C (298 K) with $\Delta H° = 20$ kcal/mol and $\Delta S° = 25$ cal mol^{-1}K^{-1}?
b. What is the equilibrium constant of the same reaction carried out at 125 °C?

43. Using curved arrows, show the mechanism for the following reaction.

$$R_2C{=}\ddot{O}: \;+\; H{-}\overset{+}{\ddot{O}}{-}H\,(H) \;\rightleftharpoons\; R_2C{=}\overset{+}{\ddot{O}}H \;+\; H_2\ddot{O}: \;\rightleftharpoons\; R_2C(:\ddot{O}H)({-}\overset{+}{:O}H_2)\;+\;H_2\ddot{O}: \;\rightleftharpoons\; R_2C(:\ddot{O}H)(:\ddot{O}H) \;+\; H_3\overset{+}{O}:$$

44. a. For a reaction that is carried out at 25 °C, how much must $\Delta G°$ change in order to increase the equilibrium constant by a factor of 10?
b. How much must $\Delta H°$ change if $\Delta S° = 0$ kcal mol^{-1}K^{-1}?
c. How much must $\Delta S°$ change if $\Delta H° = 0$ kcal mol^{-1}?

45. Given that the twist-boat conformer of cyclohexane is 5.3 kcal/mole higher in free energy than the chair conformer, calculate the percentage of twist-boat conformers present in a sample of cyclohexane at 25 °C. Does your answer agree with the statement made in Section 11.12 about the relative number of molecules in these two conformations?

Calculating Kinetic Parameters

After obtaining rate constants at several temperatures, you can calculate E_a, $\Delta H^‡$, $\Delta G^‡$, and $\Delta S^‡$ for a reaction as follows:

- The Arrhenius equation allows E_a to be obtained from the slope of a plot of ln k versus $1/T$, because

$$\ln k_2 - \ln k_1 = -E_a/R\left(\frac{1}{T_2} - \frac{1}{T_1}\right)$$

- You can determine $\Delta H^‡$ at a given temperature from E_a because $\Delta H^‡ = E_a - RT$.
- You can determine $\Delta G^‡$, in kJ/mol, from the following equation, which relates $\Delta G^‡$ to the rate constant at a given temperature:

$$-\Delta G^‡ = RT \ln \frac{kh}{Tk_B}$$

In this equation, h is Planck's constant (6.62608×10^{-34} Js) and k_B is the Boltzmann constant (1.38066×10^{-23} JK^{-1})

- You can determine the entropy of activation from the other two kinetic parameters via the formula $\Delta S^‡ = (\Delta H^‡ - \Delta G^‡)/T$.

Use this information to answer Problem 46.

46. From the following rate constants, determined at five temperatures, calculate the experimental energy of activation and $\Delta G^‡$, $\Delta H^‡$, and $\Delta S^‡$ for the reaction at 30 °C:

Temperature	Observed rate constant
31.0 °C	2.11×10^{-5} s^{-1}
40.0 °C	4.44×10^{-5} s^{-1}
51.5 °C	1.16×10^{-4} s^{-1}
59.8 °C	2.10×10^{-4} s^{-1}
69.2 °C	4.34×10^{-4} s^{-1}

CHAPTER

13

Stereochemistry

The Arrangement of Atoms in Space: The Stereochemistry of Addition Reactions

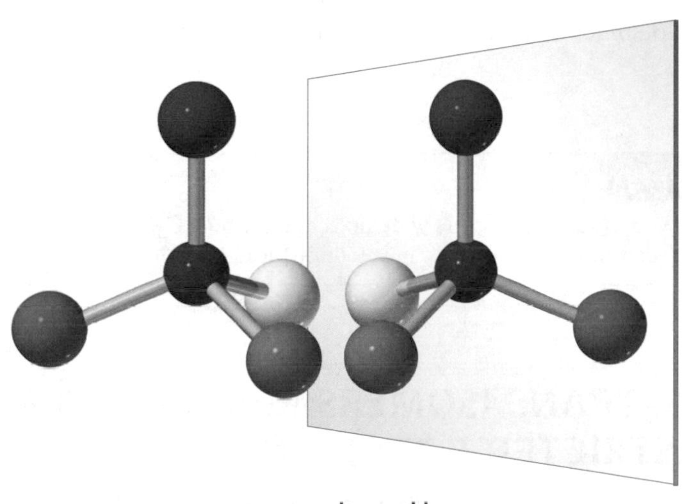

nonsuperimposable mirror images

COMPOUNDS WITH THE SAME MOLECULAR FORMULA BUT DIFFERENT STRUCTURES ARE called **isomers**. Isomers fall into two main classes: *constitutional isomers* and *stereoisomers*. **Constitutional isomers** differ in the way their atoms are connected. For example, ethanol and dimethyl ether are constitutional isomers; they have the same molecular formula (C_2H_6O), but the oxygen in ethanol is bonded to a carbon and to a hydrogen, whereas the oxygen in dimethyl ether is bonded to two carbons.

constitutional isomers

CH_3CH_2OH and CH_3OCH_3
ethanol, dimethyl ether

$CH_3CH_2CH_2CH_2Cl$ and $CH_3CH_2CH(Cl)CH_3$
1-chlorobutane, 2-chlorobutane

$CH_3CH_2CH_2CH_2CH_3$ and $CH_3CH(CH_3)CH_2CH_3$
pentane, isopentane

$CH_3C(=O)CH_3$ and $CH_3CH_2CH(=O)$
acetone, propionaldehyde

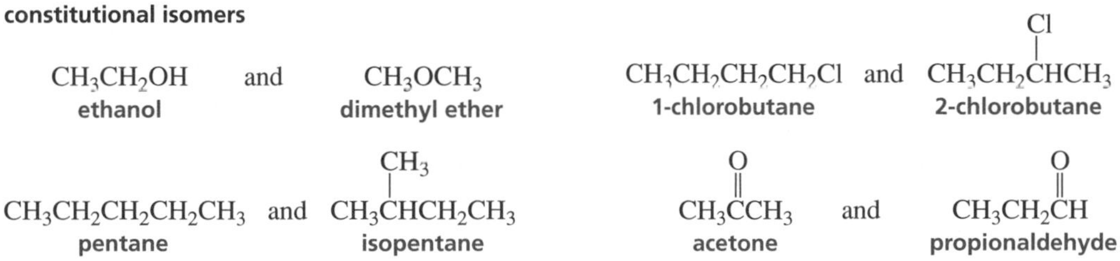

Unlike constitutional isomers, the atoms in stereoisomers are connected in the same way. **Stereoisomers** (also called **configurational isomers**) differ in the way their atoms are arranged in space. Like constitutional isomers, stereoisomers can be separated because they are different compounds; they can interconvert only if bonds are broken. There are two kinds of stereoisomers: *cis–trans isomers* and isomers that contain *asymmetric centers*.

chem place Tutorial: Isomerism

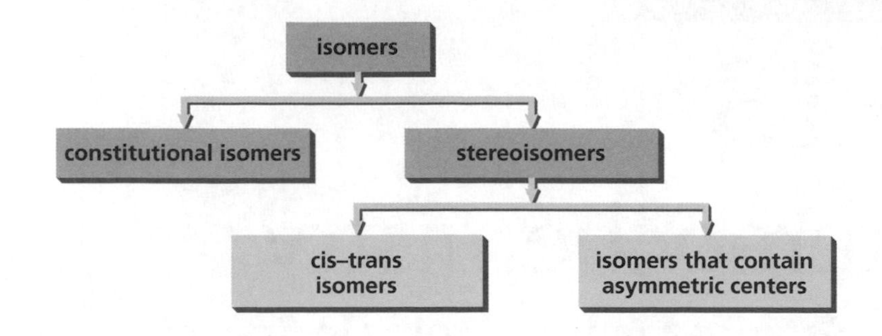

After reviewing cis–trans isomers, we will look at isomers that contain asymmetric centers, the only stereoisomers that you have not seen previously. Then we will go back and look at the reactions—and for those reactions with products that can have stereoisomers, see what specific stereoisomers are formed.

PROBLEM 1 ♦

a. Draw three constitutional isomers with molecular formula C_3H_8O.
b. How many constitutional isomers can you draw for $C_4H_{10}O$?

13.1 CIS–TRANS ISOMERS RESULT FROM RESTRICTED ROTATION

Cis–trans isomers (also called **geometric isomers**) result from restricted rotation. Restricted rotation can be caused either by a *double bond* or by a *cyclic structure*. We have seen that the restricted rotation about its carbon–carbon double bond causes an alkene such as 2-pentene to have cis and trans isomers. The **cis isomer** has the hydrogens on the *same side* of the double bond and the **trans isomer** has the hydrogens on *opposite sides* of the double bond. (Remember that *Z* and *E* are used instead of cis and trans for more complex molecules.)

As a result of restricted rotation about the bonds in a ring, cyclic compounds that have two substituents bonded to different carbons also have cis and trans isomers. The cis isomer has its substituents on the same side of the ring, whereas the trans isomer has its substituents on opposite sides of the ring.

cis-2-pentene

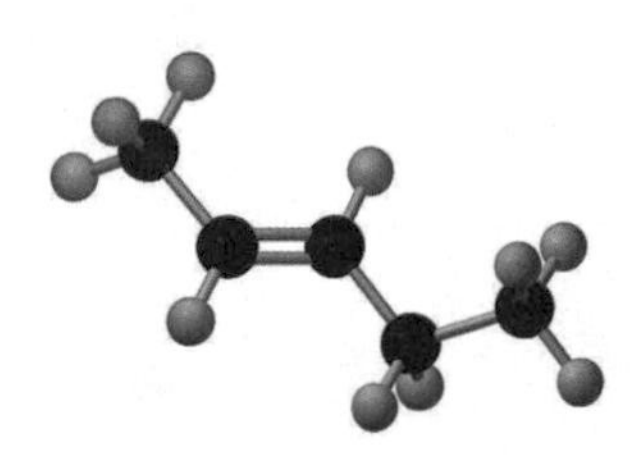

trans-2-pentene

cis-1-bromo-3-chlorocyclobutane

trans-1-bromo-3-chlorocyclobutane

cis-1,4-dimethylcyclohexane

trans-1,4-dimethylcyclohexane

PROBLEM 2

Draw the cis and trans isomers for the following:

a. 3-hexene
b. 2-methyl-3-heptene
c. 1-bromo-4-chlorocyclohexane
d. 1-ethyl-3-methylcyclobutane

13.2 A CHIRAL OBJECT HAS A NONSUPERIMPOSABLE MIRROR IMAGE

Why can't you put your right shoe on your left foot? Why can't you put your right glove on your left hand? It is because hands, feet, gloves, and shoes have right-handed and left-handed forms. An object with a right-handed and a left-handed form is said to be **chiral** (ky-ral), a word derived from the Greek word *cheir*, which means "hand."

A chiral object has a *nonsuperimposable mirror image*. In other words, its mirror image *is not the same* as an image of the object itself. A hand is chiral because when you look at your right hand in a mirror, you see not a right hand but a left hand (Figure 13.1). In contrast, a chair is not chiral; the reflection of the chair in the mirror looks the same as the chair itself. Objects that are not chiral are said to be **achiral**. An achiral object has a *superimposable mirror image*. Some other achiral objects are a table, a bowl, and a balloon (assuming they are simple and unadorned).

chiral objects

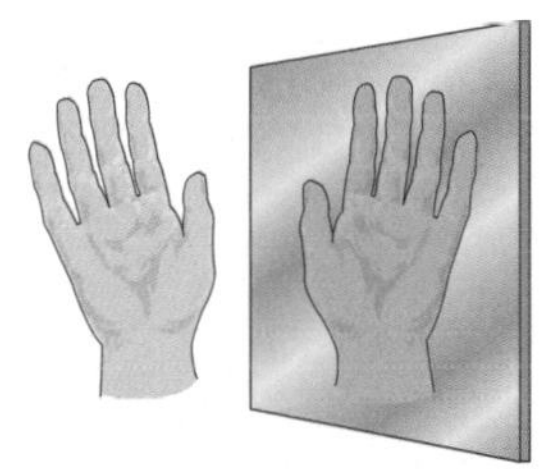
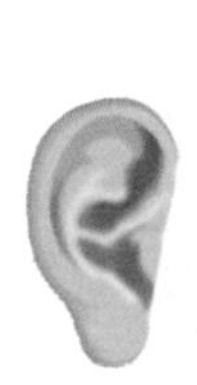
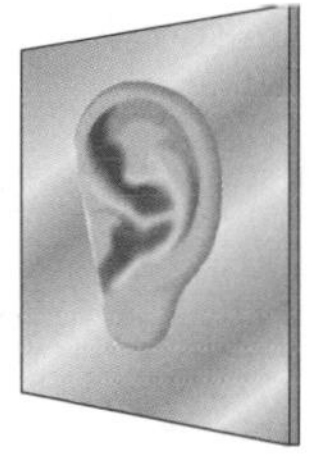
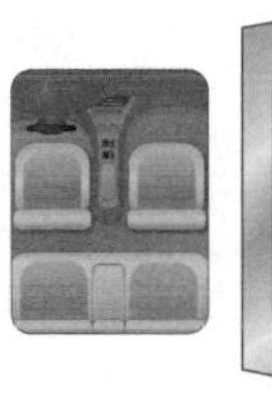
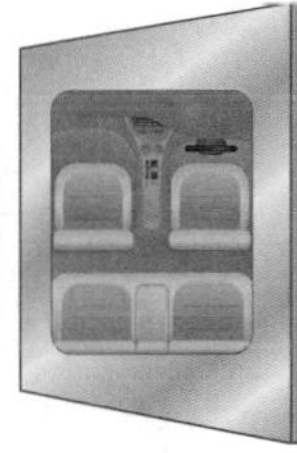

achiral objects

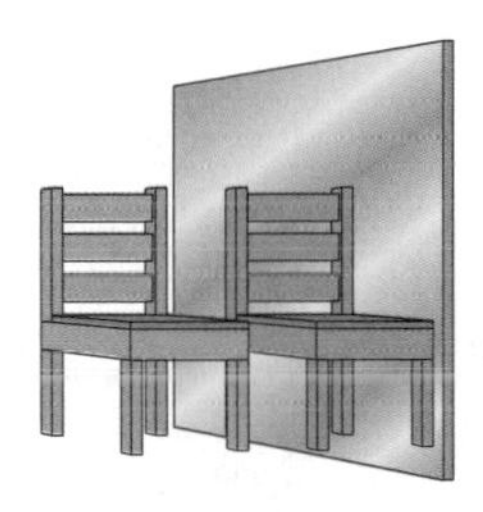

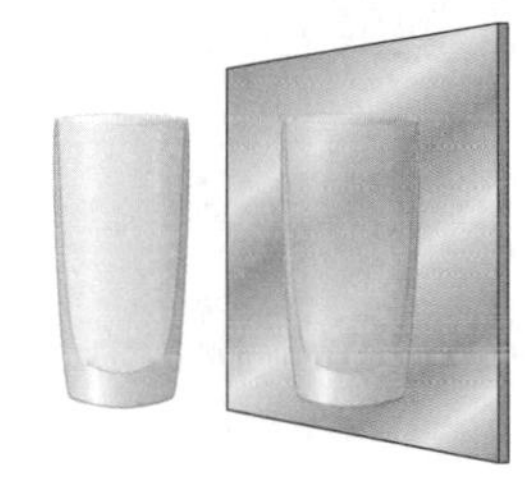

◀ **Figure 13.1**
Using a mirror to test for chirality. A chiral object is not the same as its mirror image—they are nonsuperimposable. An achiral object is the same as its mirror image—they are superimposable.

PROBLEM 3♦

Which of the following objects are chiral?

a. a mug with DAD written to one side of the handle
b. a mug with MOM written to one side of the handle
c. a mug with DAD written opposite the handle
d. a mug with MOM written opposite the handle
e. a wheelbarrow
f. a remote control device
g. a nail
h. a screw

PROBLEM 4♦

a. Name five capital letters that are chiral.
b. Name five capital letters that are achiral.

13.3 AN ASYMMETRIC CENTER IS A CAUSE OF CHIRALITY IN A MOLECULE

A molecule with an asymmetric center is chiral.

Objects are not the only things that can be chiral. Molecules can be chiral too. The usual *cause of chirality in a molecule is an asymmetric center*. (Other features that cause chirality are relatively uncommon and beyond the scope of this book, but you can see one example in Problem 82 at the end of this chapter.)

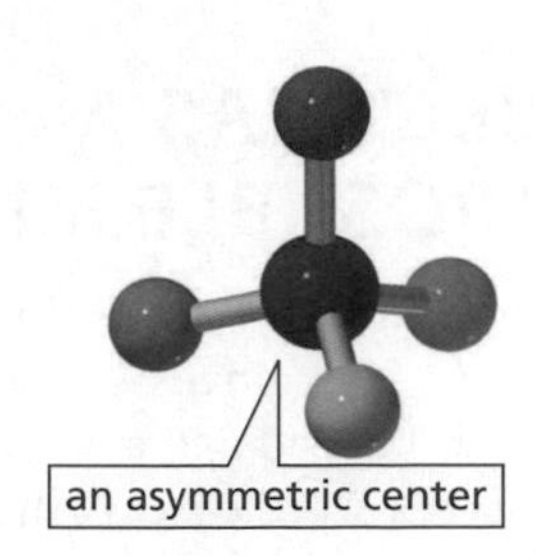

An **asymmetric center** (or chiral center) is an atom bonded to four different groups. Each of the compounds shown below has an asymmetric center indicated by a star. For example, the starred carbon in 4-octanol is an asymmetric center because it is bonded to four different groups (H, OH, $CH_2CH_2CH_3$, and $CH_2CH_2CH_2CH_3$). Notice that the atoms immediately bonded to the asymmetric center are not necessarily different from one another; the propyl and butyl groups are different even though the point at which they differ is several atoms away from the asymmetric center. The starred carbon in 2,4-dimethylhexane is an asymmetric center because it too is bonded to four different groups—(methyl, ethyl, isobutyl, and hydrogen).

$$CH_3CH_2CH_2\underset{\underset{OH}{|}}{\overset{*}{C}}HCH_2CH_2CH_2CH_3 \qquad CH_3\underset{\underset{Br}{|}}{\overset{*}{C}}HCH_2CH_3 \qquad CH_3\overset{\overset{CH_3}{|}}{C}HCH_2\underset{\underset{CH_3}{|}}{\overset{*}{C}}HCH_2CH_3$$

4-octanol **2-bromobutane** **2,4-dimethylhexane**

PROBLEM 5♦

Which of the following compounds have an asymmetric center?

a. $CH_3CH_2\underset{\underset{Cl}{|}}{C}HCH_3$

b. $CH_3CH_2\underset{\underset{CH_3}{|}}{C}HCH_3$

c. $CH_3CH_2\overset{\overset{CH_3}{|}}{\underset{\underset{Br}{|}}{C}}CH_2CH_2CH_3$

d. CH_3CH_2OH

e. $CH_3CH_2\underset{\underset{Br}{|}}{C}HCH_2CH_3$

f. $CH_2{=}CH\underset{\underset{NH_2}{|}}{C}HCH_3$

chem place Tutorial: Identification of asymmetric centers I

Tutorial: Identification of asymmetric centers II

Tutorial: Identification of asymmetric centers III

PROBLEM 6 SOLVED

Tetracycline is called a broad-spectrum antibiotic because it is active against a wide variety of bacteria. How many asymmetric centers does tetracycline have?

Solution Only sp^3 carbons can be asymmetric centers, because an asymmetric center must have four different groups attached to it. Therefore, we start by locating all the sp^3 carbons in tetracycline. (They are numbered in red.) Tetracycline has nine sp^3 carbons. Four of them (1, 2, 5, and 8) are not asymmetric centers because they are not bonded to four different groups. Tetracycline, therefore, has five asymmetric centers.

tetracycline

13.4 ISOMERS WITH ONE ASYMMETRIC CENTER

A compound with one asymmetric center, such as 2-bromobutane, can exist as two stereoisomers. The two stereoisomers are analogous to a left and a right hand. If we imagine a mirror between the two stereoisomers, we can see they are mirror images of each other. Moreover, they are nonsuperimposable mirror images and thus different molecules.

$CH_3\overset{*}{C}HCH_2CH_3$ (with Br on the starred C)

2-bromobutane

Br, CH_3CH_2, H, CH_3 on C | mirror | Br, H, CH_2CH_3, CH_3 on C

the two stereoisomers of 2-bromobutane

enantiomers

> **NOTE TO THE STUDENT**
>
> Prove to yourself that the two stereoisomers of 2-bromobutane are not identical by building ball-and-stick models to represent them and trying to superimpose one on the other; use four different-colored balls to represent the four different groups bonded to the asymmetric center. Special Topic IV in the *Study Guide and Solutions Manual* tells you what other models you should build as you go through this chapter.

Molecules that are nonsuperimposable mirror images of each other are called **enantiomers** (from the Greek *enantion*, which means "opposite"). Thus, the two stereoisomers of 2-bromobutane are enantiomers. A molecule that has a *nonsuperimposable* mirror image, like an object that has a *nonsuperimposable* mirror image, is *chiral*. Therefore, each member of a pair of enantiomers is chiral. Notice that chirality is a property of an entire object or an entire molecule.

A molecule that has a *superimposable* mirror image, like an object that has a *superimposable* mirror image, is *achiral*. To see that the achiral molecule on the right below is superimposable on its mirror image, mentally rotate it clockwise.

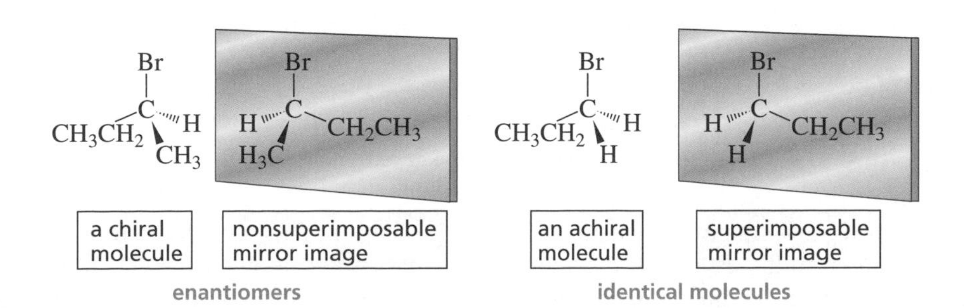

A chiral molecule has a nonsuperimposable mirror image.

An achiral molecule has a superimposable mirror image.

PROBLEM 7♦

Which of the compounds in Problem 5 can exist as enantiomers?

13.5 ASYMMETRIC CENTERS AND STEREOCENTERS

An asymmetric center is also called a **stereocenter** (or a **stereogenic center**), but they do not mean quite the same thing. A stereocenter is an atom at which the interchange of two groups produces a stereoisomer. Thus stereocenters include both (1) *asymmetric centers*, where the interchange of two groups produces an enantiomer, and (2) the sp^2 carbons of an alkene or the sp^3 carbons of a cyclic compound, where the interchange of two groups converts a cis isomer to a trans isomer (or a *Z* isomer to an *E* isomer) or vice versa. This means that although *all asymmetric centers are stereocenters*, not all stereocenters are asymmetric centers.

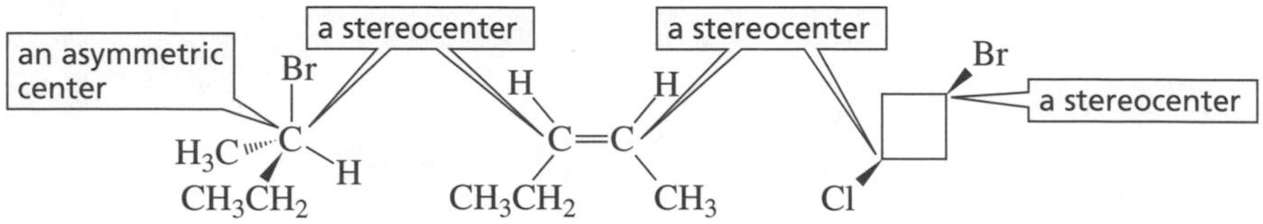

an asymmetric center
a stereocenter
a stereocenter
a stereocenter
Br
H_3C C H
CH_3CH_2
H H
C=C
CH_3CH_2 CH_3
Br
Cl

13.6 HOW TO DRAW ENANTIOMERS

Chemists draw enantiomers using either *perspective formulas* or *Fischer projections*. A **perspective formula** shows two of the bonds to the asymmetric center in the plane of the paper, one bond as a solid wedge protruding forward out of the paper, and the fourth bond as a hatched wedge extending behind the paper. The solid wedge and the hatched wedge must be adjacent to one another. When you draw the first enantiomer, the four groups bonded to the asymmetric center can be placed around it in any order. Then draw the second enantiomer by drawing the mirror image of the first.

A solid wedge represents a bond that extends out of the plane of the paper toward the viewer.

A hatched wedge represents a bond that points back from the plane of the paper away from the viewer.

When you draw a perspective formula, make sure that the two bonds in the plane of the paper are adjacent to one another; neither the solid wedge nor the hatched wedge should be drawn between them.

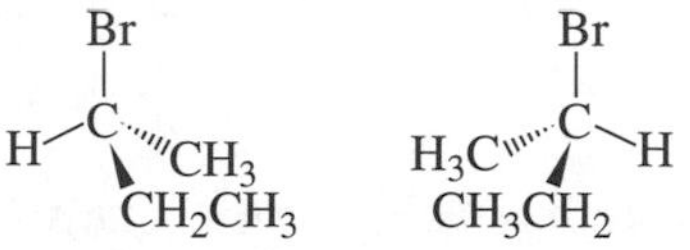

Br Br
H C CH_3 H_3C C H
CH_2CH_3 CH_3CH_2

perspective formulas of the enantiomers of 2-bromobutane

A **Fischer projection** is a shortcut for showing the three-dimensional arrangement of groups bonded to an asymmetric center. Devised in the late 1800s by Emil Fischer, when printing techniques could not handle wedges but only vertical and horizontal lines, it represents an asymmetric center as the point of intersection of two perpendicular lines. Horizontal lines represent the bonds that project out of the plane of the paper toward the viewer, and vertical lines represent the bonds that extend back from the plane of the paper away from the viewer. The carbon chain is usually drawn vertically, with C-1 at the top.

In a Fischer projection, horizontal lines project out of the plane of the paper toward the viewer, and vertical lines extend back from the plane of the paper away from the viewer.

asymmetric center
CH_3 CH_3
Br—H H—Br
CH_2CH_3 CH_2CH_3

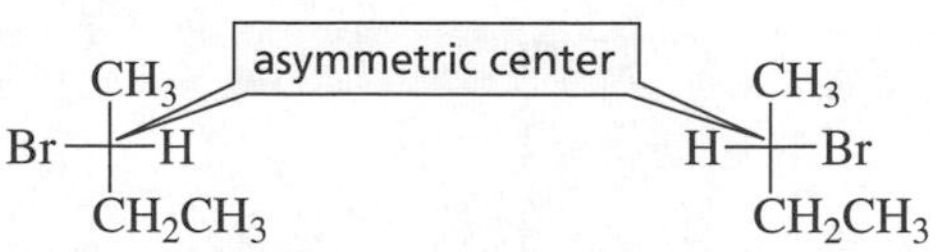

Fischer projections of the enantiomers of 2-bromobutane

When you draw enantiomers using a Fischer projection, you can put the four atoms or groups bonded to the asymmetric center around that center in any order. Then draw the second enantiomer by interchanging two of the atoms or groups. It does not matter which two you interchange. (Make models to convince yourself that this is true.) It is best to interchange the groups on the two horizontal bonds, because then the enantiomers look like mirror images on your paper.

Whether you are drawing perspective formulas or Fischer projections, interchanging two atoms or groups will produce the other enantiomer. Interchanging two atoms or groups a second time brings you back to the original molecule.

PROBLEM 8

Draw enantiomers for each of the following using:

a. perspective formulas.
b. Fischer projections.

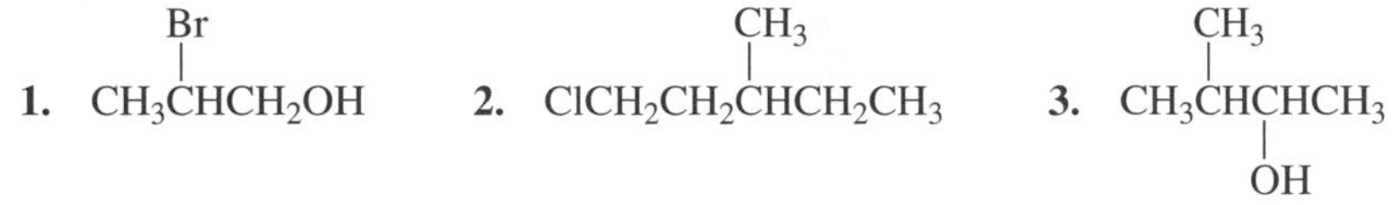

1. $CH_3CH(Br)CH_2OH$
2. $ClCH_2CH_2CH(CH_3)CH_2CH_3$
3. $CH_3CH(CH_3)CH(OH)CH_3$

PROBLEM 9 **SOLVED**

Do the following structures represent identical molecules or a pair of enantiomers?

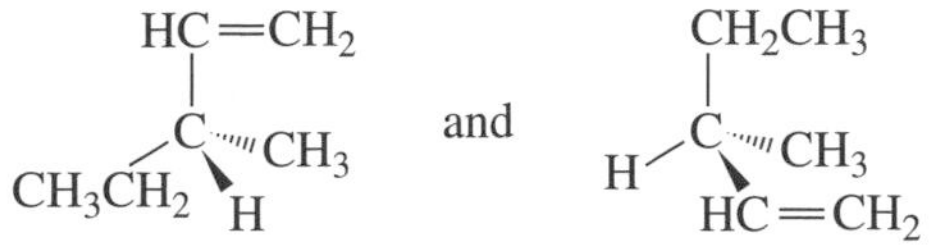

$HC{=}CH_2$ / C / CH_3CH_2 / CH_3 / H and CH_2CH_3 / C / H / CH_3 / $HC{=}CH_2$

Solution Interchanging two atoms or groups attached to an asymmetric center of a perspective formula produces an enantiomer. Interchanging two atoms or groups a second time brings you back to the original molecule. Because groups have to be interchanged twice to get from one structure to the other, the two structures represent identical molecules.

$HC{=}CH_2$ / C / CH_3CH_2 / CH_3 / H —interchange vinyl and H→ H / C / CH_3CH_2 / CH_3 / $HC{=}CH_2$ —interchange ethyl and H→ CH_2CH_3 / C / H / CH_3 / $HC{=}CH_2$

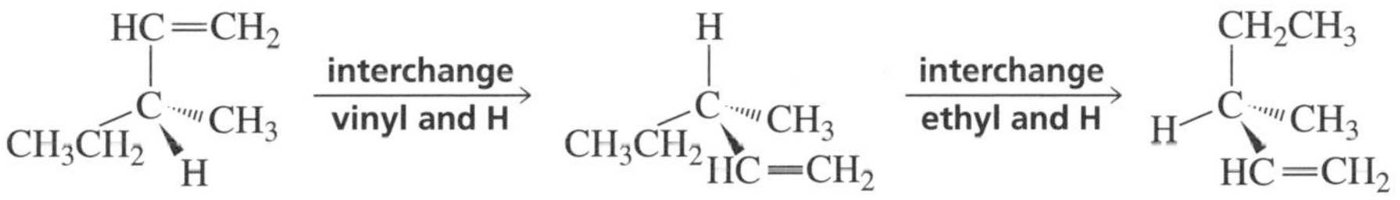

In Section 13.7 you will learn another way to determine if two structures represent identical molecules or enantiomers.

13.7 NAMING ENANTIOMERS BY THE *R,S* SYSTEM

How do we name the different stereoisomers of a compound like 2-bromobutane so that we know which one we are talking about? We need a system of nomenclature that indicates the arrangement of the atoms or groups about the asymmetric center. Chemists use the letters *R* and *S* for this purpose. For any pair of enantiomers with one asymmetric center, one member will have the ***R* configuration** and the other will have the ***S* configuration**. The *R,S* system was devised by R. S. Cahn, C. Ingold, and V. Prelog.

We will first look at how we can determine the configuration of a compound if we have a three-dimensional model.

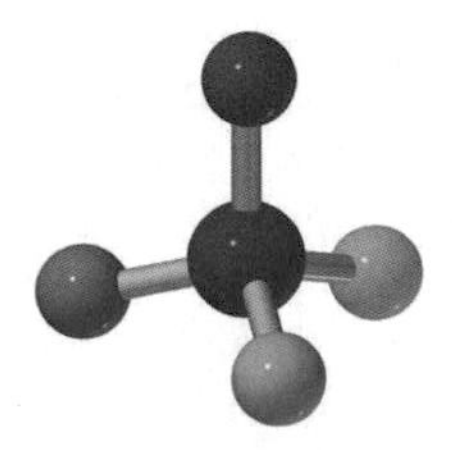

1. **Rank the groups (or atoms) bonded to the asymmetric center in order of priority.** The atomic numbers of the atoms directly attached to the asymmetric center determine the relative priorities. The higher the atomic number, the higher the priority. This should remind you of the way that relative priorities are determined for *E* and *Z* isomers, because the system of priorities was originally devised for the *R,S* system of nomenclature and was later adopted for the *E,Z* system.

B I O G R A P H Y

Born in London, England, **Robert Sidney Cahn (1899–1981)** *received an M.A. from Cambridge University and a doctorate in natural philosophy in France. He edited the* Journal of the Chemical Society *(London) from 1949 to 1963.*

B I O G R A P H Y

Sir Christopher Ingold (1893–1970), *born in Ilford, England, was a professor of chemistry at Leeds University (1924–1930) and at University College, London (1930–1970). In 1958 he was knighted by Queen Elizabeth II.*

B I O G R A P H Y

Vladimir Prelog (1906–1998) *was born in Sarajevo, Bosnia. In 1929 he received a Dr. Ing. degree from the Institute of Technology in Prague, Czechoslovakia. He taught at the University of Zagreb from 1935 until 1941, when he fled to Switzerland just ahead of the invading German army. He was a professor at the Swiss Federal Institute of Technology (ETH). For work that contributed to an understanding of how living organisms carry out chemical reactions, he shared the 1975 Nobel Prize in Chemistry with John Cornforth.*

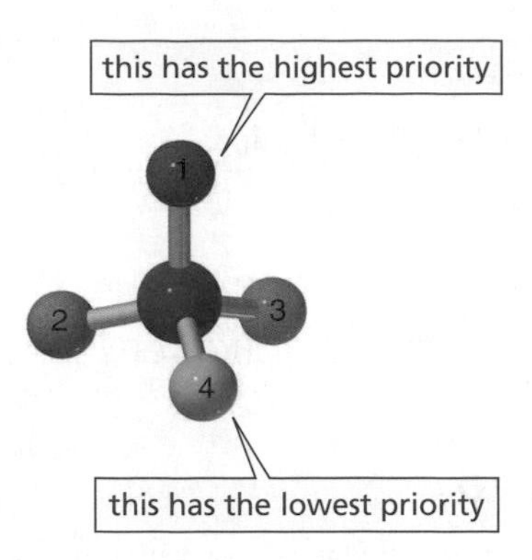

2. **Orient the molecule so that the group (or atom) with the lowest priority (4) is directed away from you. Then draw an imaginary arrow from the group (or atom) with the highest priority (1) to the group (or atom) with the next highest priority (2).** If the arrow points clockwise, the asymmetric center has the *R* configuration (*R* is for *rectus*, which is Latin for "right"). If the arrow points counterclockwise, the asymmetric center has the *S* configuration (*S* is for *sinister*, which is Latin for "left").

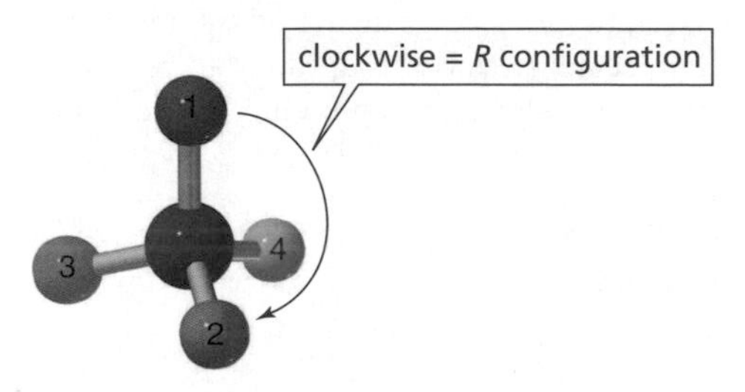

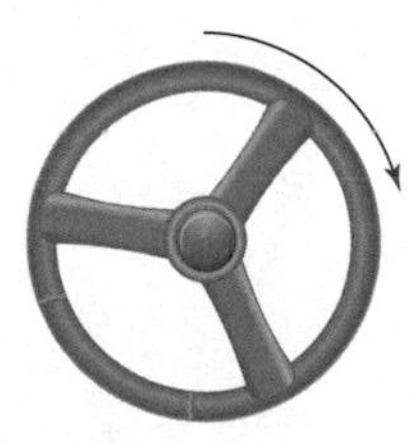
right turn

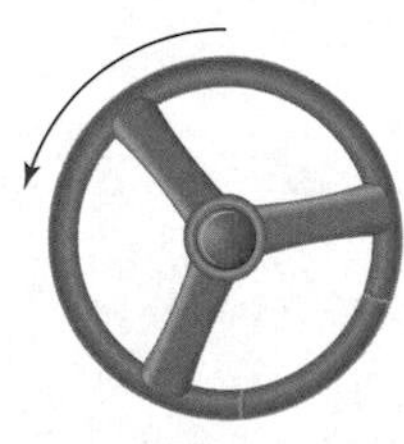
left turn

The molecule is oriented so that the group with the lowest priority points away from the viewer. If an arrow drawn from the highest priority group to the next-highest priority group points clockwise, the molecule has the *R* configuration.

If you forget which direction corresponds to which configuration, imagine driving a car and turning the steering wheel clockwise to make a right turn or counterclockwise to make a left turn.

PROBLEM 10♦

Which of the following molecular models are identical?

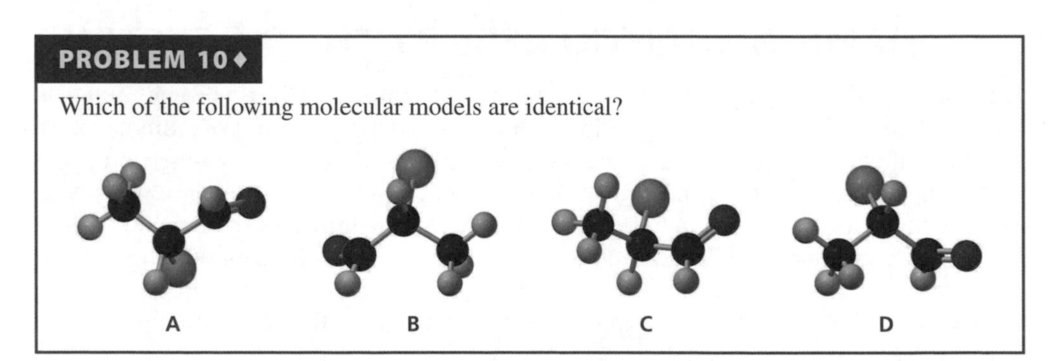

If you are able to visualize spatial relationships easily, the above two rules are all you need to determine whether the asymmetric center of a molecule written on a two-dimensional piece of paper has the *R* or the *S* configuration. Mentally rotate the molecule so that the group (or atom) with the lowest priority (4) is directed away from you, then draw an imaginary arrow from the group (or atom) with the highest priority to the group (or atom) with the next highest priority.

If you have trouble visualizing spatial relationships and you do not have access to a model, the following sets of instructions will allow you to determine the configuration about an asymmetric center without having to rotate the molecule mentally.

First, let's look at how you can determine the configuration of a compound drawn as a perspective formula. We will use the enantiomers of 2-bromobutane as an example.

Br — C(H)(CH_3)(CH_3CH_2)   Br — C(H)(CH_3)(CH_2CH_3)

the enantiomers of 2-bromobutane

1. Rank the groups (or atoms) that are bonded to the asymmetric center in order of priority. In our example, bromine has the highest priority (1), the ethyl group has the second highest priority (2), the methyl group is next (3), and hydrogen has the lowest priority (4). (Revisit Section 12.5 if you don't understand how these priorities are assigned.)

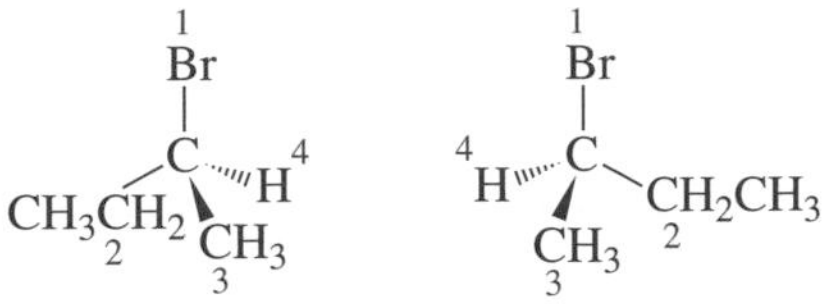

2. If the group (or atom) with the lowest priority (4) is bonded by a hatched wedge, draw an arrow from the group (or atom) with the highest priority (1) directly to the group (or atom) with the second highest priority (2). If the arrow points clockwise, the compound has the *R* configuration, and if it points counterclockwise, the compound has the *S* configuration.

the group with the lowest priority is bonded by a hatched wedge

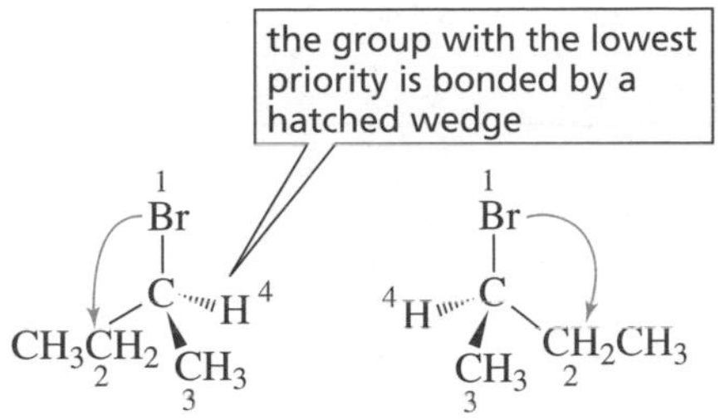

(*S*)-2-bromobutane **(*R*)-2-bromobutane**

Clockwise specifies *R* if the lowest priority substituent is on a hatched wedge.

Counterclockwise specifies *S* if the lowest priority substituent is on a hatched wedge.

3. If the group with the lowest priority (4) is not bonded by a hatched wedge, interchange group 4 with the group bonded by a hatched wedge. Then proceed as in step 2: Draw an arrow from the group (or atom) with the highest priority (1) to the group (or atom) with the second-highest priority (2). Because you have interchanged two groups, you are now determining the configuration of the *enantiomer* of the original molecule. So if the arrow points clockwise, the enantiomer (with the interchanged groups) has the *R* configuration, which means the original molecule has the *S* configuration. On the other hand, if the arrow points counterclockwise, the enantiomer (with the interchanged groups) has the *S* configuration, which means the original molecule has the *R* configuration.

what is its configuration?

switch CH_3 and H

this molecule has the *R* configuration; therefore, the molecule had the *S* configuration before the groups were switched

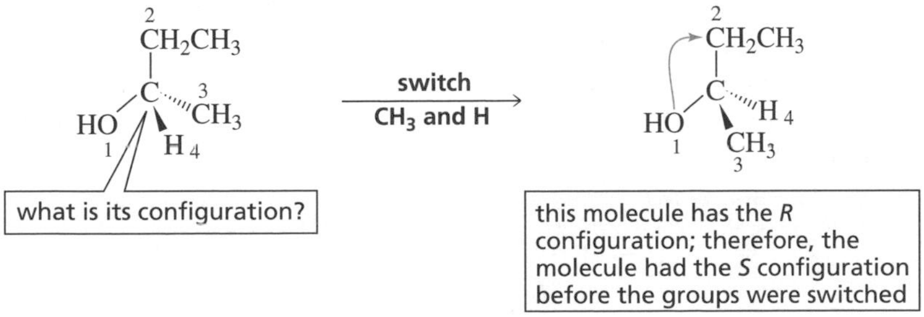

4. If there is a group between group (1) and group (2), make sure the arrow is drawn from (1) to (2) to (3) and **not** from (1) to (3) to (2).

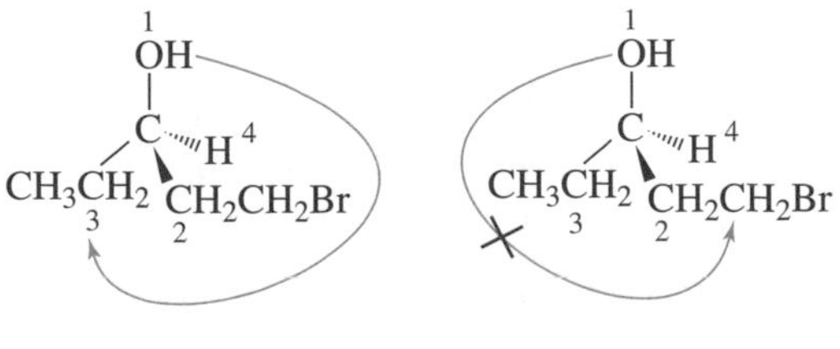

PROBLEM 11 ♦

Assign relative priorities to the groups or atoms within each of the following sets:

a. $-CH_2OH$ $-CH_3$ $-H$ $-CH_2CH_2OH$
b. $-CH{=}O$ $-OH$ $-CH_3$ $-CH_2OH$
c. $-CH(CH_3)_2$ $-CH_2CH_2Br$ $-Cl$ $-CH_2CH_2CH_2Br$
d. $-CH{=}CH_2$ $-CH_2CH_3$ (phenyl) $-CH_3$

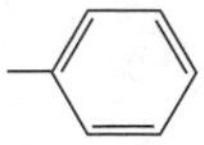

PROBLEM 12 ♦

Indicate whether each of the following structures has the *R* or the *S* configuration:

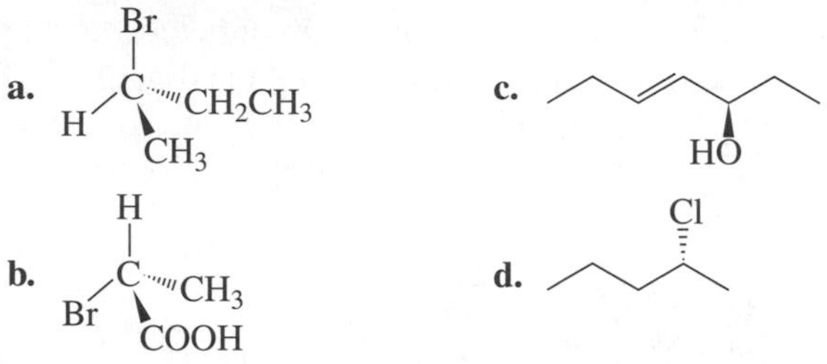

a. Br, H, CH_2CH_3, CH_3 on C
b. H, Br, CH_3, COOH on C
c. HO
d. Cl

Now let's see how to determine the configuration of a compound drawn as a Fischer projection.

1. Rank the groups (or atoms) that are bonded to the asymmetric center in order of priority.
2. Draw an arrow from the group (or atom) with the highest priority (1) to the group (or atom) with the next highest priority (2). If the arrow points clockwise, the enantiomer has the *R* configuration; if it points counterclockwise, the enantiomer has the *S* configuration, *provided that the group with the lowest priority (4) is on a vertical bond.*

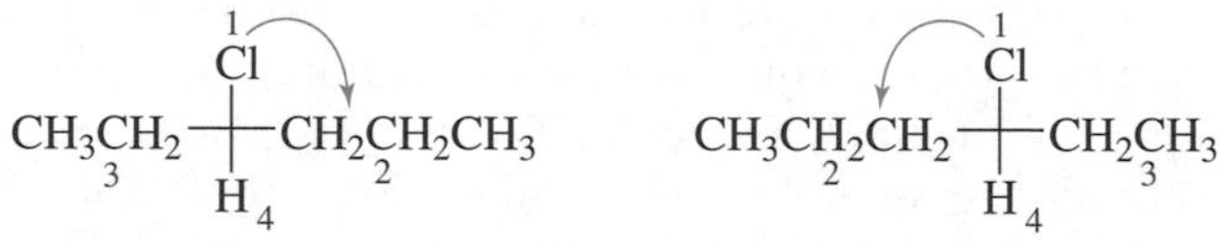

Cl 1; CH_3CH_2 3; $CH_2CH_2CH_3$ 2; H 4

(*R*)-3-chlorohexane

Cl 1; $CH_3CH_2CH_2$ 2; CH_2CH_3 3; H 4

(*S*)-3-chlorohexane

3. If the group (or atom) with the lowest priority is on a *horizontal bond,* the answer you get from the direction of the arrow will be the opposite of the correct answer. For example, if the arrow points clockwise, suggesting that the asymmetric center has the *R* configuration, it actually has the *S* configuration; if the arrow points counterclockwise, suggesting that the asymmetric center has the *S* configuration, it actually has the *R* configuration. In the following example, the group with the lowest priority is on a horizontal bond, so clockwise signifies the *S* configuration, not the *R* configuration.

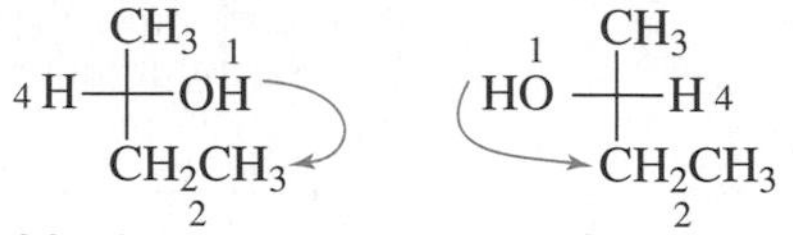

Clockwise specifies *R* if the lowest priority substituent is on a vertical bond.

Clockwise specifies *S* if the lowest priority substituent is on a horizontal bond.

CH_3 3; 4 H; OH 1; CH_2CH_3 2

(*S*)-2-butanol

CH_3 3; 1 HO; H 4; CH_2CH_3 2

(*R*)-2-butanol

4. If there is a group between group (1) and group (2), make sure the arrow is drawn from (1) to (2) to (3), as in the following structures, and not from (1) to (3) to (2).

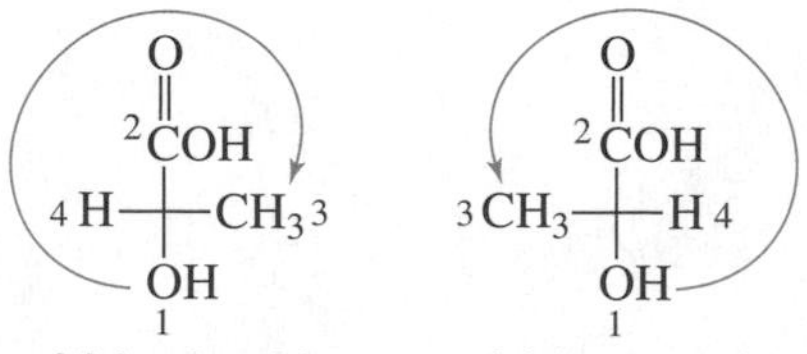

O; 2 COH; 4 H; CH_3 3; OH 1

(*S*)-lactic acid

O; 2 COH; 3 CH_3; H 4; OH 1

(*R*)-lactic acid

NOTE TO THE STUDENT

When comparing two Fischer projections to see if they are the same or different, never rotate one 90° or flip it "front-to-back," because that is a quick way to get a wrong answer. A Fischer projection can be rotated 180° in the plane of the paper, but that is the only way you can move it without risking an incorrect answer.

PROBLEM 13 ♦

Indicate the configuration of the following:

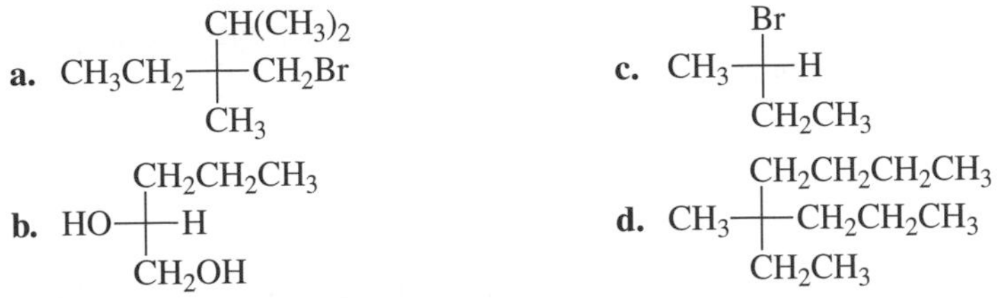

a. Fischer projection: top $CH(CH_3)_2$; left CH_3CH_2; right CH_2Br; bottom CH_3

b. Fischer projection: top $CH_2CH_2CH_3$; left HO; right H; bottom CH_2OH

c. Fischer projection: top Br; left CH_3; right H; bottom CH_2CH_3

d. Fischer projection: top $CH_2CH_2CH_2CH_3$; left CH_3; right $CH_2CH_2CH_3$; bottom CH_2CH_3

PROBLEM-SOLVING STRATEGY

Recognizing Pairs of Enantiomers

Do the structures represent identical molecules or a pair of enantiomers?

CH_3 (up), C, H (hashed), HO, $CH_2CH_2CH_3$ (wedge) and OH (up), C, CH_3 (hashed), $CH_3CH_2CH_2$, H (wedge)

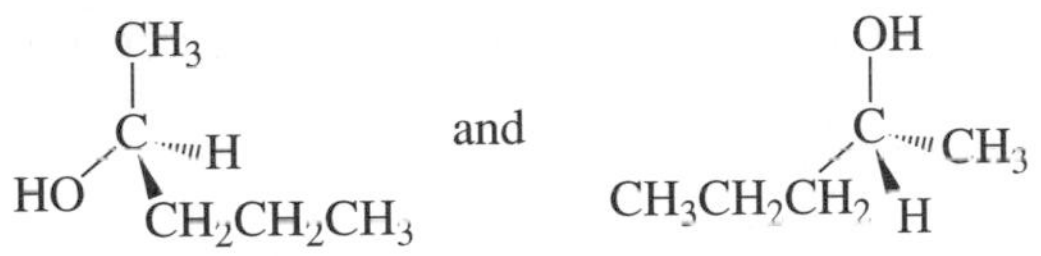

The easiest way to find out whether two molecules are enantiomers or identical molecules is to determine their configurations. If one has the *R* configuration and the other has the *S* configuration, they are enantiomers. If they both have the *R* configuration or both have the *S* configuration, they are identical molecules. Because the structure on the left has the *S* configuration and the structure on the right has the *R* configuration, we know that they represent a pair of enantiomers.

Now continue on to Problem 14.

PROBLEM 14 ♦ SOLVED

Do the following structures represent identical molecules or a pair of enantiomers?

a. HC=O (up), C, OH (hashed), $HOCH_2CH_2$, CH_2CH_3 (wedge) and HC=O (up), C, CH_2CH_2OH (hashed), CH_3CH_2, OH (wedge)

b. CH_2Br (up), C, Cl (hashed), H_3C, CH_2CH_3 (wedge) and Cl (up), C, CH_3 (hashed), CH_3CH_2, CH_2Br (wedge)

c. CH_2Br (up), C, OH (hashed), H, CH_3 (wedge) and H (up), C, CH_3 (hashed), HO, CH_2Br (wedge)

d. Fischer projection: top Cl; left CH_3; right CH_2CH_3; bottom H and Fischer projection: top CH_3; left H; right Cl; bottom CH_2CH_3

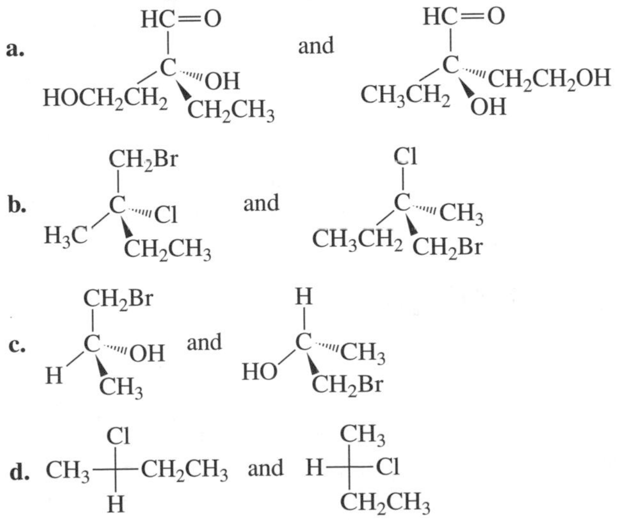

Solution to 14a The first structure shown in part **a** has the *R* configuration, and the second structure also has the *R* configuration. Because they both have the same configuration, the structures represent identical molecules.

PROBLEM-SOLVING STRATEGY

Drawing an Enantiomer with a Desired Configuration

(*S*)-Alanine is a naturally occurring amino acid. Draw its structure using a perspective formula.

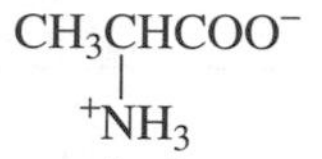

$$CH_3\underset{\underset{^{+}NH_3}{|}}{C}HCOO^-$$

alanine

First draw the bonds about the asymmetric center. Remember that the two bonds in the plane of the paper must be adjacent to one another.

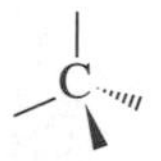

Put the group with the lowest priority on the hatched wedge. Put the group with the highest priority on any remaining bond.

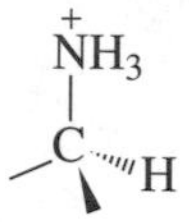

Because you have been asked to draw the *S* enantiomer, draw an arrow counterclockwise from the group with the highest priority to the next available bond and put the group with the next highest priority on that bond.

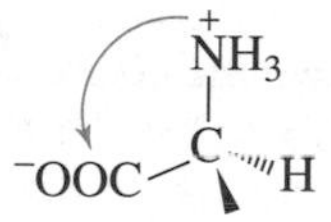

Put the remaining substituent on the last available bond.

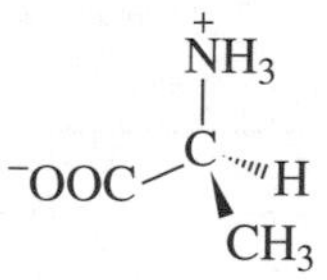

Now continue on to Problem 15.

PROBLEM 15

Draw perspective formulas for the following:

a. (*S*)-2-chlorobutane **b.** (*R*)-1,2-dibromobutane

13.8 CHIRAL COMPOUNDS ARE OPTICALLY ACTIVE

BIOGRAPHY

Born in Scotland, **William Nicol (1768–1851)** *was a professor at the University of Edinburgh. He developed the first prism that produced plane-polarized light. He also developed methods to produce thin slices of materials for use in microscopic studies.*

Enantiomers share many of the same properties; they have the same boiling points, the same melting points, and the same solubilities. In fact, all the physical properties of enantiomers are the same except those that stem from how groups bonded to the asymmetric center are arranged in space. One property that enantiomers do not share is the way they interact with plane-polarized light.

Normal light, such as that coming from a light bulb or the sun, consists of rays that oscillate in all directions. In contrast, all the rays in a beam of **plane-polarized light** oscillate in a single plane. Plane-polarized light is produced by passing normal light through a polarizer, such as a polarized lens or a Nicol prism. Only light oscillating in a certain plane can pass through.

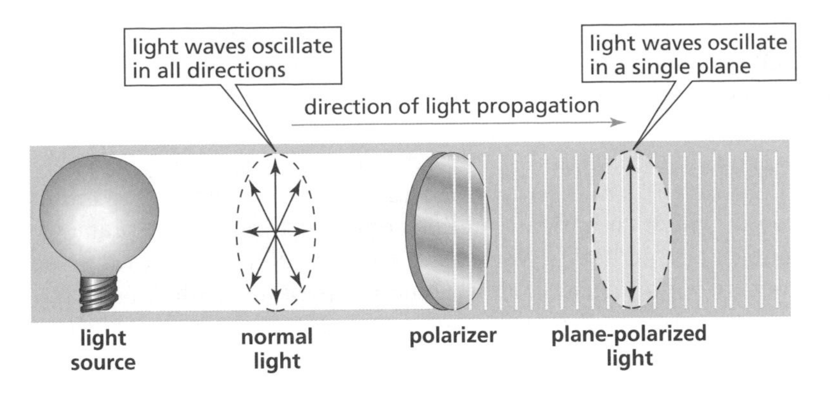

You can experience the effect of a polarized lens by wearing a pair of polarized sunglasses. Polarized sunglasses allow only light oscillating in a single plane to pass through, which is why they block reflections (glare) more effectively than nonpolarized sunglasses do.

In 1815, the physicist Jean-Baptiste Biot discovered that certain naturally occurring organic substances, such as camphor and oil of turpentine, are able to rotate the **plane of polarization** of plane-polarized light. He noted that some compounds rotated it clockwise and others counterclockwise, while some did not rotate it at all. He proposed that the ability to rotate the plane of polarization of plane-polarized light was attributable to some asymmetry in the molecules. Van't Hoff and Le Bel later determined that the asymmetry was associated with compounds having one or more asymmetric centers.

When plane-polarized light passes through a solution of achiral molecules, the light emerges from the solution with its plane of polarization unchanged. *An achiral compound does not rotate the plane of polarization of plane-polarized light.*

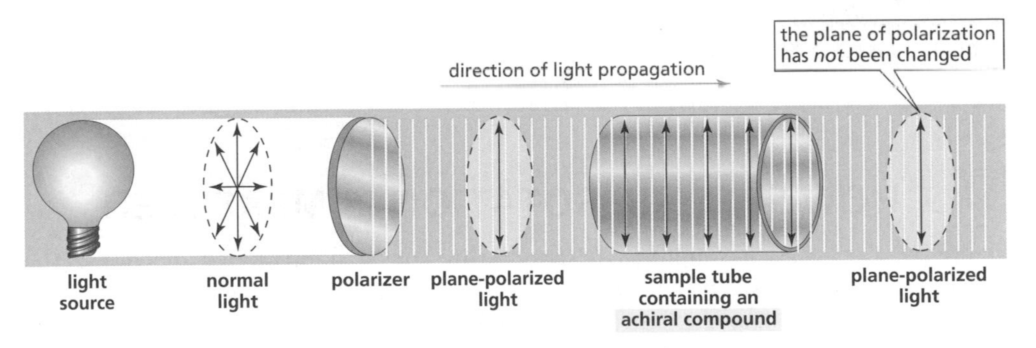

However, when polarized light passes through a solution of a chiral compound, the light emerges with its plane of polarization changed. Thus, *a chiral compound rotates the plane of polarization of plane-polarized light.* A chiral compound can rotate it clockwise or counterclockwise. If one enantiomer rotates it clockwise, its mirror image will rotate it exactly the same amount counterclockwise.

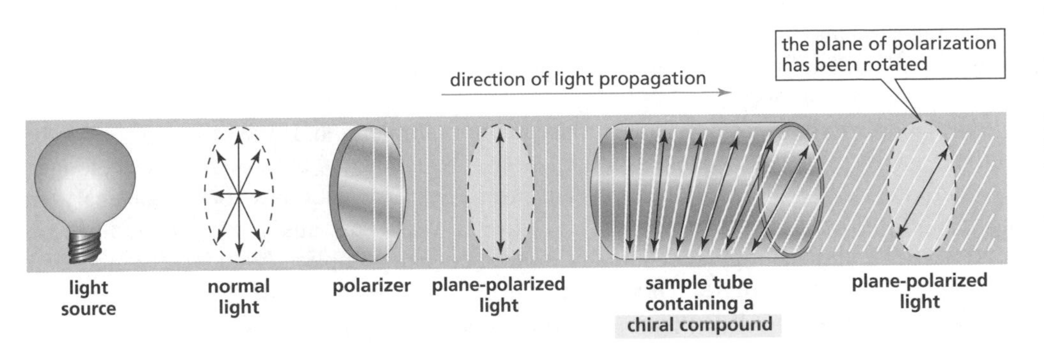

BIOGRAPHY

Born in France, **Jean-Baptiste Biot (1774–1862)** *was imprisoned for taking part in a street riot during the French Revolution. He became a professor of mathematics at the University of Beauvais and later a professor of physics at the Collège de France. He was awarded the Legion of Honor by Louis XVIII.*

BIOGRAPHY

Jacobus Hendricus van't Hoff (1852–1911), *a Dutch chemist, was a professor of chemistry at the University of Amsterdam and later at the University of Berlin. He received the first Nobel Prize in Chemistry (1901) for his work on solutions.*

BIOGRAPHY

Joseph Achille Le Bel (1847–1930), *a French chemist, inherited his family's fortune, which enabled him to establish his own laboratory. He and van't Hoff independently arrived at the reason for the optical activity of certain molecules. Although van't Hoff's explanation was more precise, both chemists are given credit for the work.*

When light is filtered through two polarized lenses at a 90° angle to one another, none of the light passes through.

A compound that rotates the plane of polarization of plane-polarized light is said to be **optically active**. In other words, chiral compounds are optically active, and achiral compounds are **optically inactive**.

If an optically active compound rotates the plane of polarization clockwise, the compound is said to be **dextrorotatory**, indicated in the compound's name by the prefix (+). If it rotates it counterclockwise, it is said to be **levorotatory**, indicated by (−). *Dextro* and *levo* are Latin prefixes for "to the right" and "to the left," respectively. Sometimes lowercase *d* and *l* are used instead of (+) and (−).

Do not confuse (+) and (−) with *R* and *S*. The (+) and (−) symbols indicate the direction in which an optically active compound rotates the plane of polarization of plane-polarized light, whereas *R* and *S* indicate the arrangement of the groups about an asymmetric center. Some compounds with the *R* configuration are (+) and some are (−). Likewise, some molecules with the *S* configuration are (+) and some are (−).

We can tell by looking at the structure of a compound whether it has the *R* or the *S* configuration, but the only way we can tell whether a compound is dextrorotatory (+) or levorotatory (−) is to put the compound in a polarimeter, an instrument that measures the direction and the amount the plane of polarization of plane-polarized light is rotated. For example, (*S*)-lactic acid and (*S*)-sodium lactate both have an *S* configuration, but (*S*)-lactic acid has been found to be dextrorotatory whereas (*S*)-sodium lactate is levorotatory. When we know the direction an optically active compound rotates the plane of polarization, we can incorporate (+) or (−) into its name.

CH_3, HO, H, COOH

(*S*)-(+)-lactic acid

CH_3, HO, H, $COO^- Na^+$

(*S*)-(−)-sodium lactate

PROBLEM 16♦

a. Is (*R*)-lactic acid dextrorotatory or levorotatory?
b. Is (*R*)-sodium lactate dextrorotatory or levorotatory?

13.9 HOW SPECIFIC ROTATION IS MEASURED

Figure 13.2 provides a simplified description of how a **polarimeter** functions. The amount of rotation caused by an optically active compound will vary with the wavelength of the light being used, so the light source in a polarimeter must produce monochromatic (single-wavelength) light. Most polarimeters use light from a sodium arc (called the sodium D-line; wavelength = 589 nm). In a polarimeter, monochromatic light passes through a polarizer and emerges as plane-polarized light. The polarized light then passes through a sample tube. If the tube is empty, or filled with an optically inactive solvent, the light emerges from it with its plane of polarization unchanged. The light then passes through an analyzer, which is a second polarizer mounted on an eyepiece with a dial marked in degrees. Before the start of an experiment, the user looks through the eyepiece and rotates the analyzer until he or she sees total darkness. At this point the analyzer is at a right angle to the first polarizer, so no light passes through. This analyzer setting corresponds to zero rotation.

The sample to be measured is then placed in the sample tube. If the sample is optically active, it will rotate the plane of polarization. The analyzer, therefore, will no longer block all the light, so some light reaches the user's eye. The user now rotates the analyzer again until no light passes through. The degree to which the analyzer is rotated can be read from the dial and represents the difference between an optically inactive sample and the optically active sample. This value, which is measured in degrees, is called the **observed rotation** (α). It is dependent on the number of optically active molecules that

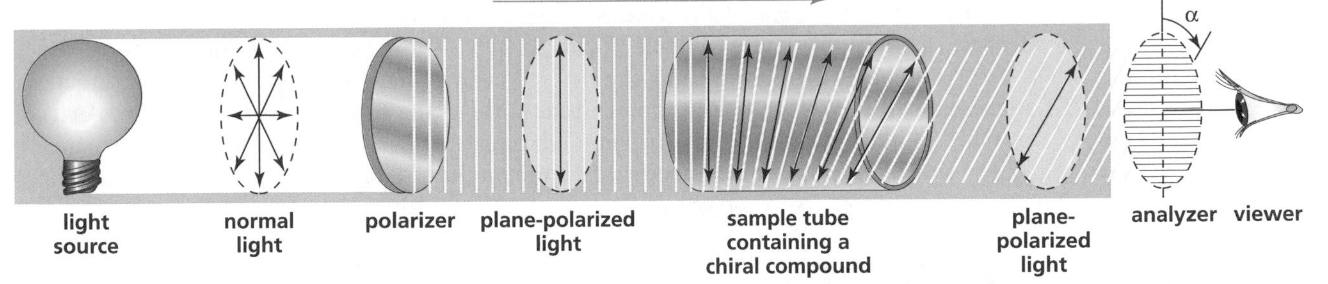

▲ **Figure 13.2**
A schematic drawing of a polarimeter.

the light encounters in the sample, which depends in turn on the concentration of the sample and the length of the sample tube. The observed rotation also depends on the temperature and the wavelength of the light source.

Each optically active compound has a characteristic specific rotation. A compound's **specific rotation** is the rotation caused by a solution of 1.0 g of the compound per milliliter of solution in a sample tube 1.0 decimeter long at a specified temperature and wavelength.* The specific rotation can be calculated from the observed rotation using the following formula:

$$[\alpha]_{\lambda}^{T} = \frac{\alpha}{l \times c}$$

where $[\alpha]$ is the specific rotation; T is temperature in °C; λ is the wavelength of the incident light (when the sodium D-line is used, λ is indicated as D); α is the observed rotation; l is the length of the sample tube in decimeters; and c is the concentration of the sample in grams per milliliter of solution.

If one enantiomer has a specific rotation of +5.75, the specific rotation of the other enantiomer must be −5.75, because the mirror-image molecule rotates the plane of polarization the same amount but in the opposite direction.

CH_2OH / CH_3—C—H / CH_2CH_3	CH_2OH / H—C—CH_3 / CH_3CH_2
(*R*)-2-methyl-1-butanol	**(*S*)-2-methyl-1-butanol**
$[\alpha]_{D}^{20\,°C} = +5.75$	$[\alpha]_{D}^{20\,°C} = -5.75$

The specific rotations of some common compounds are shown in Table 13.1.

Table 13.1 Specific Rotation of Some Naturally Occurring Compounds

Compound	Specific rotation
Cholesterol	− 31.5
Cocaine	− 16
Codeine	− 136
Morphine	− 132
Penicillin V	+ 233
Progesterone	+ 172
Sucrose (table sugar)	+ 66.5
Testosterone	+ 109

*Unlike observed rotation, which is measured in degrees, specific rotation has units of 10^{-1} deg cm^2 g^{-1}. In this book, values of specific rotation will be given without units.

A mixture of equal amounts of two enantiomers—such as (*R*)-(−)-lactic acid and (*S*)-(+)-lactic acid—is called a **racemic mixture** or a **racemate**. Racemic mixtures do not rotate the plane of polarization of plane-polarized light. They are optically inactive because for every molecule in a racemic mixture that rotates the plane of polarization in one direction, there is a mirror-image molecule that rotates the plane in the opposite direction. As a result, the light emerges from a racemic mixture with its plane of polarization unchanged. The symbol (±) is used to specify a racemic mixture. Thus, (±)-2-bromobutane indicates a mixture of 50% (+)-2-bromobutane and 50% (−)-2-bromobutane.

PROBLEM 17 ◆

The observed rotation of 2.0 g of a compound in 50 mL of solution in a polarimeter tube 20-cm long is +13.4°. What is the specific rotation of the compound?

PROBLEM 18 ◆

(*S*)-(+)-Monosodium glutamate (MSG) is a flavor enhancer used in many foods. Some people have an allergic reaction to MSG (headache, chest pain, and an overall feeling of weakness). "Fast food" often contains substantial amounts of MSG, which is widely used in Chinese food as well. (*S*)-(+)-MSG has a specific rotation of +24.

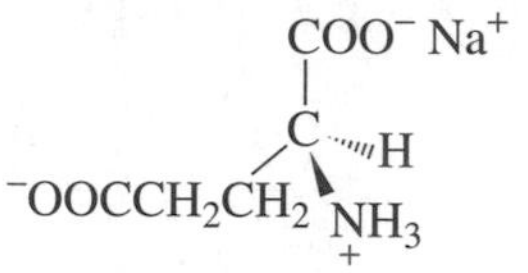

$COO^- Na^+$

$^-OOCCH_2CH_2$ — C — H, $\overset{+}{N}H_3$

(*S*)-(+)-monosodium glutamate

a. What is the specific rotation of (*R*)-(−)-monosodium glutamate?
b. What is the specific rotation of a racemic mixture of MSG?

13.10 ENANTIOMERIC EXCESS

Whether a particular sample consists of a single enantiomer or a mixture of enantiomers can be determined by its **observed specific rotation**, which is the specific rotation measured for a particular sample. For example, if a sample of (*S*)-(+)-2-bromobutane is **enantiomerically pure**—meaning only one enantiomer is present, it will have an *observed specific rotation* of +23.1 because the *specific rotation* of (*S*)-(+)-2-bromobutane is +23.1. If, however, the sample of 2-bromobutane is a racemic mixture, it will have an observed specific rotation of 0. If the observed specific rotation is positive but less than +23.1, we will know that the sample is a mixture of enantiomers and that the mixture contains more of the enantiomer with the *S* configuration than the enantiomer with the *R* configuration. The **enantiomeric excess (ee)** tells us how much of an excess of one enantiomer is in the mixture. It can be calculated from the observed specific rotation:

$$\textbf{enantiomeric excess} = \frac{\textbf{observed specific rotation}}{\textbf{specific rotation of the pure enantiomer}} \times 100\%$$

For example, if the sample of 2-bromobutane has an observed specific rotation of +9.2, the enantiomeric excess is 40%. In other words, the excess of one of the enantiomers comprises 40% of the mixture.

$$\textbf{enantiomeric excess} = \frac{+9.2}{+23.1} \times 100\% = 40\%$$

If the mixture has a 40% enantiomeric excess, 40% of the mixture is excess *S* enantiomer and 60% is a racemic mixture. Half of the racemic mixture plus the amount of excess *S* enantiomer equals the amount of the *S* enantiomer present in the mixture. Therefore, 70% of the mixture is the *S* enantiomer [(1/2 × 60) + 40] and 30% is the *R* enantiomer.

PROBLEM 19♦

(+)-Mandelic acid has a specific rotation of +158. What would be the observed specific rotation of each of the following mixtures?

a. 25% (−)-mandelic acid and 75% (+)-mandelic acid
b. 50% (−)-mandelic acid and 50% (+)-mandelic acid
c. 75% (−)-mandelic acid and 25% (+)-mandelic acid

PROBLEM 20♦

Naproxen, a nonsteroidal anti-inflammatory drug that is the active ingredient in Aleve (page 94), has a specific rotation of +66. One commercial preparation results in a mixture that has a 97% enantiomeric excess.

a. Does naproxen have the *R* or the *S* configuration?
b. What percent of each enantiomer is obtained from the commercial preparation?

PROBLEM 21 SOLVED

A solution prepared by mixing 10 mL of a 0.10 M solution of the *R* enantiomer of a compound and 30 mL of a 0.10 M solution of the *S* enantiomer was found to have an observed specific rotation of +4.8. What is the specific rotation of each of the enantiomers? (*Hint*: mL × M = millimole, abbreviated mmol)

Solution One (10 mL × 0.10 M) mmol of the *R* enantiomer is mixed with 3 (30 mL × 0.10 M) mmol of the *S* enantiomer; 1 mmol of the *R* enantiomer plus 1 mmol of the *S* enantiomer will form 2 mmol of a racemic mixture, so there will be 2 mmol of *S* enantiomer left over. Because 2 mmol out of 4 mmol is excess *S* enantiomer (2/4 = 0.50), the solution has a 50% enantiomeric excess.

$$\text{enantiomer excess} = \frac{\text{observed specific rotation}}{\text{specific rotation of the pure enantiomer}} \times 100\%$$

$$50\% = \frac{+4.8}{x} \times 100\%$$

$$\frac{50}{100} = \frac{+4.8}{x}$$

$$\frac{1}{2} = \frac{+4.8}{x}$$

$$x = 2\,(+4.8)$$

$$x = +9.6$$

The *S* enantiomer has a specific rotation of +9.6; the *R* enantiomer has a specific rotation of −9.6.

13.11 ISOMERS WITH MORE THAN ONE ASYMMETRIC CENTER

Many organic compounds have more than one asymmetric center. The more asymmetric centers a compound has, the more stereoisomers it can have. If we know the number of asymmetric centers, we can calculate the *maximum* number of stereoisomers for that compound: *a compound can have a maximum of* 2^n *stereoisomers, where* n *equals the number of asymmetric centers* (provided it does not also have stereocenters that would cause it to have cis–trans isomers; see Problem 22). For example, 3-chloro-2-butanol has two asymmetric centers. Therefore, it can have a maximum of four ($2^2 = 4$)

stereoisomers. The four stereoisomers are shown below both as perspective formulas and as Fischer projections.

$$\mathrm{CH_3\overset{*}{C}H(Cl)\overset{*}{C}H(OH)CH_3}$$

3-chloro-2-butanol

erythro enantiomers (1, 2) — threo enantiomers (3, 4)

perspective formulas of the stereoisomers of 3-chloro-2-butanol (staggered)

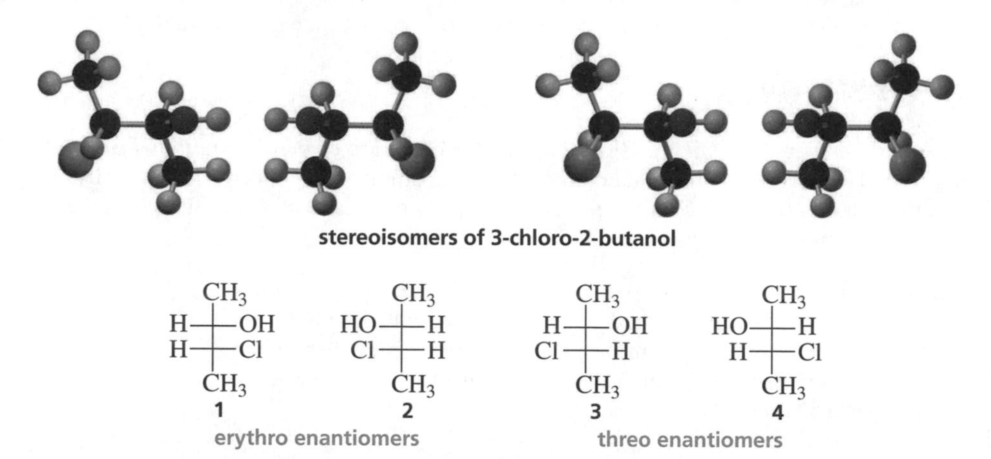

stereoisomers of 3-chloro-2-butanol

erythro enantiomers — threo enantiomers

Fischer projections of the stereoisomers of 3-chloro-2-butanol

The four stereoisomers of 3-chloro-2-butanol consist of two pairs of enantiomers. Stereoisomers **1** and **2** are nonsuperimposable mirror images. They, therefore, are enantiomers. Stereoisomers **3** and **4** are also enantiomers. Stereoisomers **1** and **3** are not identical, and they are not mirror images. Such stereoisomers are called **diastereomers**. *Diastereomers are stereoisomers that are not enantiomers.* Stereoisomers **1** and **4**, **2** and **3**, and **2** and **4** are also pairs of diastereomers. Notice that in a pair of diastereomers, the configuration of one of the asymmetric centers is the same but the configuration of the other asymmetric center is different. (Note that cis–trans isomers are also considered to be diastereomers, because they are stereoisomers that are not enantiomers.)

Diastereomers are stereoisomers that are not enantiomers.

Enantiomers have *identical physical properties* (except for the way they interact with polarized light) and *identical chemical properties*, so they react at the same rate with a given achiral reagent.

Diastereomers have *different physical properties*, meaning different melting points, boiling points, solubilities, specific rotations, and so on, and *different chemical properties*, so they react with a given achiral reagent at different rates.

When Fischer projections are drawn for stereoisomers with two adjacent asymmetric centers (such as those for 3-chloro-2-butanol), the enantiomers with similar groups on the same side of the carbon chain are called the **erythro enantiomers**. Those with similar groups on opposite sides are called the **threo enantiomers**. Therefore, **1** and **2** are the erythro enantiomers of 3-chloro-2-butanol (the hydrogens are on the same side), whereas **3** and **4** are the threo enantiomers. In each of the Fischer projections shown here, the horizontal bonds project out of the paper toward the viewer and the vertical bonds extend behind the paper away from the viewer. Groups can rotate freely about the carbon–carbon single bonds, but Fischer projections show the stereoisomers in their eclipsed conformations.

Because a Fischer projection does not show the three-dimensional structure of the molecule, and because it represents the molecule in a relatively unstable eclipsed conformation, most chemists prefer to use perspective formulas. Perspective formulas show the molecule's three-dimensional structure in a stable, staggered conformation, so they provide a more accurate representation of structure. When perspective formulas are drawn to show the stereoisomers in their less stable eclipsed conformations (those shown below), we can easily see that the erythro enantiomers have similar groups on the same side. We will use both perspective formulas and Fischer projections to depict the arrangement of groups bonded to an asymmetric center.

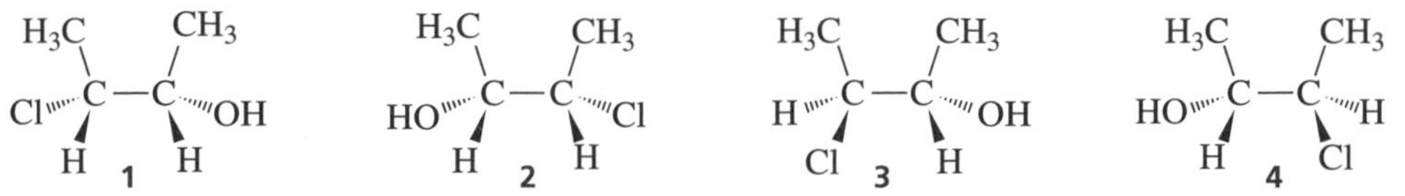

H₃C CH₃ / Cl C—C OH / H 1 H   H₃C CH₃ / HO C—C Cl / H 2 H   H₃C CH₃ / H C—C OH / Cl 3 H   H₃C CH₃ / HO C—C H / H 4 Cl

erythro enantiomers   threo enantiomers

perspective formulas of the stereoisomers of 3-chloro-2-butanol (eclipsed)

PROBLEM 22

The following compound has only one asymmetric center. Why then does it have four stereoisomers?

$$CH_3CH_2\overset{*}{C}HCH_2CH{=}CHCH_3$$
(Br on the starred carbon)

PROBLEM 23 ♦

Is the following statement correct?
A compound can have a maximum of 2^n stereoisomers, where n equals the number of stereocenters?

PROBLEM 24 ♦

a. Stereoisomers with two asymmetric centers are called ______ if the configuration of both asymmetric centers in one stereoisomer is the opposite of the configuration of the asymmetric centers in the other stereoisomer.
b. Stereoisomers with two asymmetric centers are called ______ if the configuration of both asymmetric centers in one stereoisomer is the same as the configuration of the asymmetric centers in the other stereoisomer.
c. Stereoisomers with two asymmetric centers are called ______ if one of the asymmetric centers has the same configuration in both stereoisomers and the other asymmetric center has the opposite configuration in the two stereoisomers.

PROBLEM 25 ♦

The stereoisomer of cholesterol found in nature is

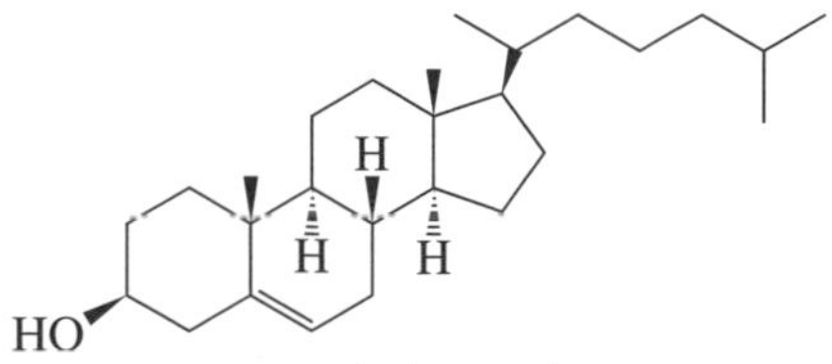

HO H H H

cholesterol

a. How many asymmetric centers does cholesterol have?
b. What is the maximum number of stereoisomers that cholesterol can have?

PROBLEM 26

Draw the stereoisomers of the following amino acids. Indicate pairs of enantiomers and pairs of diastereomers.

$CH_3CHCH_2{-}CHCOO^-$ (with CH_3 and $^+NH_3$ substituents)
leucine

$CH_3CH_2CH{-}CHCOO^-$ (with CH_3 and $^+NH_3$ substituents)
isoleucine

chem place Tutorial: Nonsuperimposable mirror image

1-Bromo-2-methylcyclopentane also has two asymmetric centers and four stereoisomers. Because the compound is cyclic, the substituents can be either cis or trans. The cis isomer exists as a pair of enantiomers, and the trans isomer exists as a pair of enantiomers.

Br CH$_3$ CH$_3$ Br Br CH$_3$ CH$_3$ Br

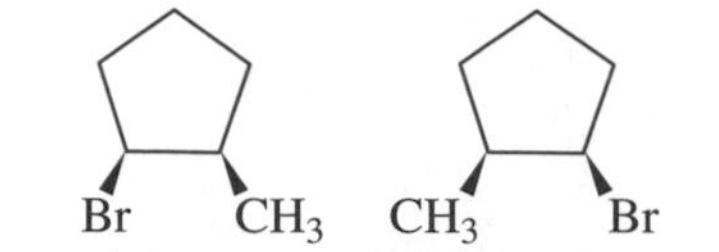

***cis*-1-bromo-2-methylcyclopentane** 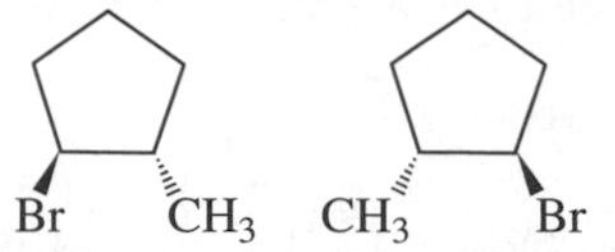 ***trans*-1-bromo-2-methylcyclopentane**

1-Bromo-3-methylcyclobutane does not have any asymmetric centers. The C-1 carbon has a bromine and a hydrogen attached to it, but its other two groups [$-CH_2CH(CH_3)CH_2-$] are identical; C-3 has a methyl group and a hydrogen attached to it, but its other two groups [$-CH_2CH(Br)CH_2-$] are identical. Because the compound does not have a carbon with four different groups attached to it, it has only two stereoisomers, the cis isomer and the trans isomer. The cis and trans isomers do not have enantiomers; they are achiral molecules.

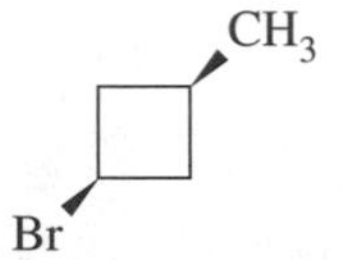

CH$_3$ CH$_3$

Br Br

***cis*-1-bromo-3-methylcyclobutane** 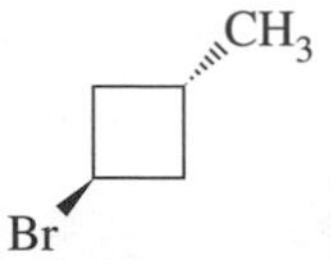 ***trans*-1-bromo-3-methylcyclobutane**

1-Bromo-3-methylcyclohexane has two asymmetric centers. The carbon that is bonded to a hydrogen and a bromine is also bonded to two different carbon-containing groups ($-CH_2CH(CH_3)CH_2CH_2CH_2-$ and $-CH_2CH_2CH_2CH(CH_3)CH_2-$), so it is an asymmetric center. The carbon that is bonded to a hydrogen and a methyl group is also bonded to two different carbon-containing groups, so it too is an asymmetric center.

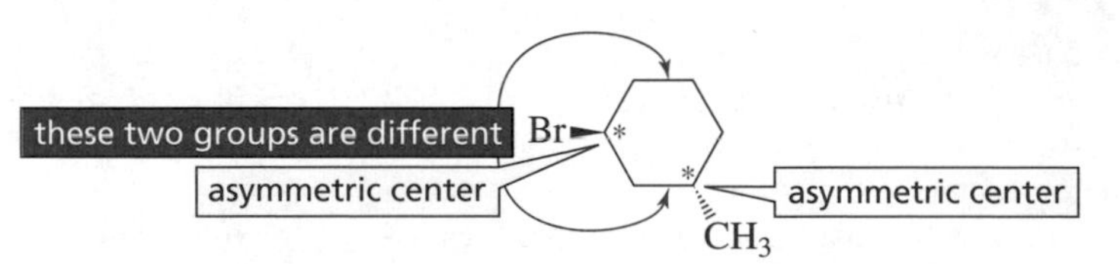

Because the compound has two asymmetric centers, it has four stereoisomers. Enantiomers can be drawn for the cis isomer, and enantiomers can be drawn for the trans isomer. Each of the stereoisomers is a chiral molecule.

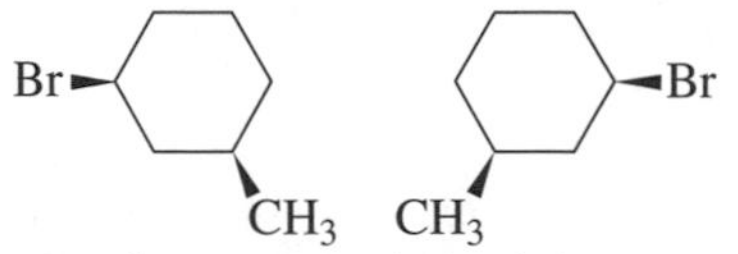

Br Br Br Br

CH$_3$ CH$_3$ CH$_3$ CH$_3$

***cis*-1-bromo-3-methylcyclohexane** 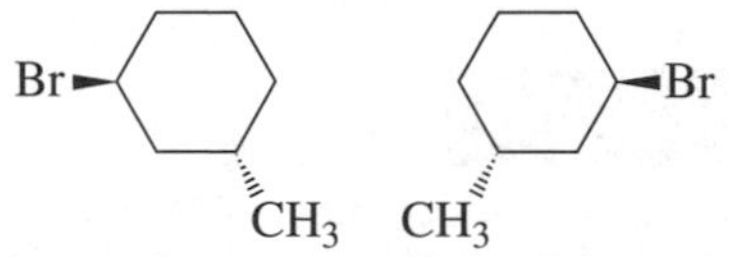 ***trans*-1-bromo-3-methylcyclohexane**

1-Bromo-4-methylcyclohexane has no asymmetric centers. Therefore, the compound has only one cis isomer and one trans isomer. Each of the stereoisomers is an achiral molecule.

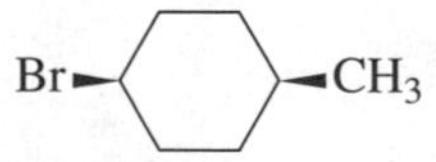

Br CH$_3$ Br CH$_3$

***cis*-1-bromo-4-methylcyclohexane** 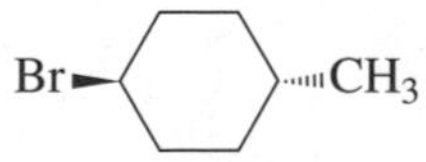 ***trans*-1-bromo-4-methylcyclohexane**

PROBLEM 27

Draw all possible stereoisomers for each of the following:

a. 2-chloro-3-hexanol
b. 2-bromo-4-chlorohexane
c. 2,3-dichloropentane
d. 1,3-dibromopentane

PROBLEM 28

Draw the stereoisomers of 2-methylcyclohexanol.

PROBLEM 29 ♦

Of all the possible cyclooctanes that have one chloro substituent and one methyl substituent, which ones do not have any asymmetric centers?

PROBLEM-SOLVING STRATEGY

Drawing Enantiomers and Diastereomers

Draw an enantiomer and a diastereomer for the following:

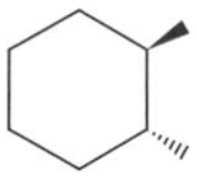

You can draw an enantiomer in one of two ways. You can change the configuration of all the asymmetric centers by changing all wedges to dashes and all dashes to wedges as in **A**. Or you can draw a mirror image of the compound as in **B**. Notice that since **A** and **B** are each an enantiomer of the given compound, **A** and **B** are identical molecules.

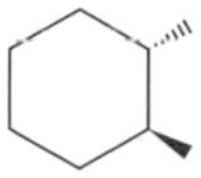

or

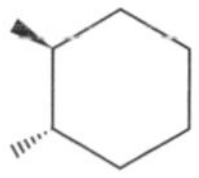

A B

You can draw a diastereomer by changing the configuration of only one of the asymmetric centers as in **C**.

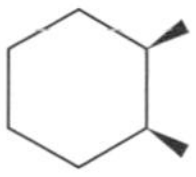

C

Now continue on to Problem 30.

PROBLEM 30

Draw a diastereomer for each of the following:

a. CH_3 / H—OH / H—OH / CH_3

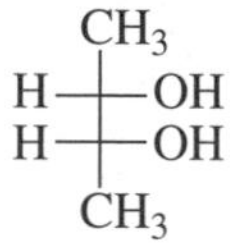

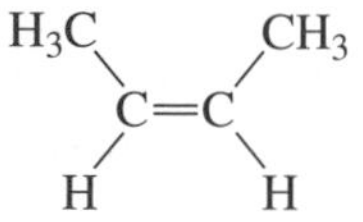

b. Cl Cl / H C—C H / CH_3CH_2 CH_3

c. H_3C CH_3 / C=C / H H

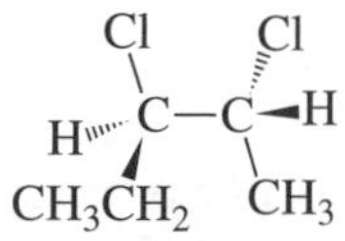

d. H H / HO CH_3

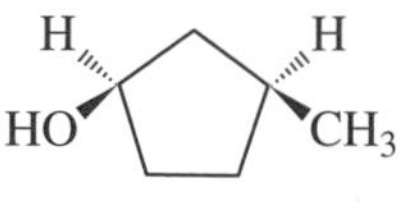

PROBLEM 31 ♦

Indicate whether each of the structures in the second row is an enantiomer of, a diastereomer of, or identical to the structure in the top row.

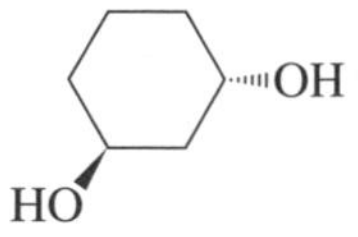

OH / HO

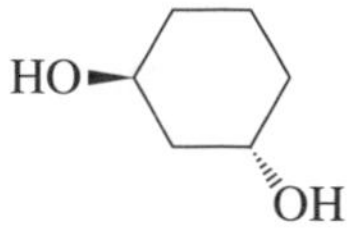

HO OH HO OH HO OH OH OH

A 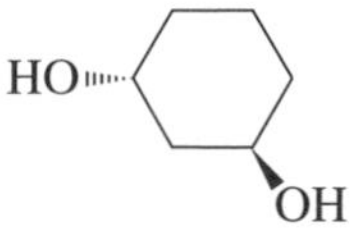 B 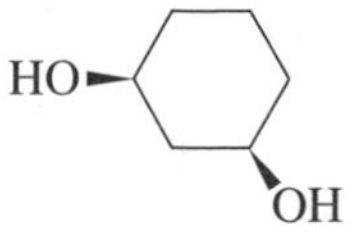 C 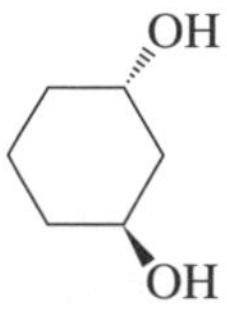 D

13.12 MESO COMPOUNDS HAVE ASYMMETRIC CENTERS BUT ARE OPTICALLY INACTIVE

In the examples we have just seen, the compounds with two asymmetric centers had four stereoisomers. However, some compounds with two asymmetric centers have only three stereoisomers. This is why we emphasized in Section 13.11 that the *maximum* number of stereoisomers a compound with n asymmetric centers can have is 2^n (unless it has stereocenters that are not asymmetric centers), instead of stating that a compound with n asymmetric centers has 2^n stereoisomers.

An example of a compound with two asymmetric centers that has only three stereoisomers is 2,3-dibromobutane.

$CH_3CHCHCH_3$ (Br on C-2 and C-3)

2,3-dibromobutane

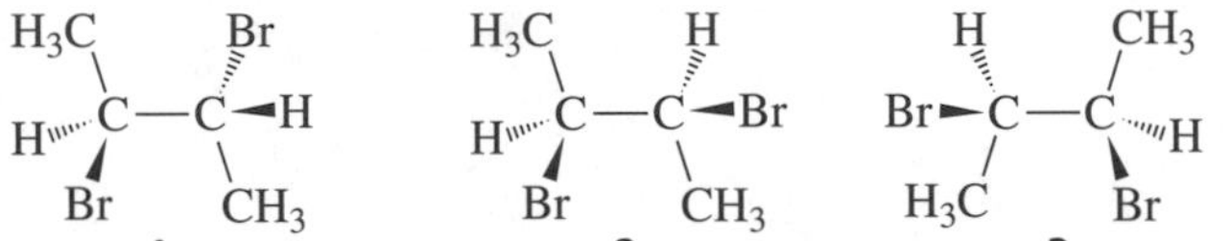

perspective formulas of the stereoisomers of 2,3-dibromobutane (staggered)

The "missing" isomer is the mirror image of **1** because **1** and its mirror image are the same molecule. This can be seen more clearly when the perspective formulas are drawn in eclipsed conformations or when Fischer projections are used.

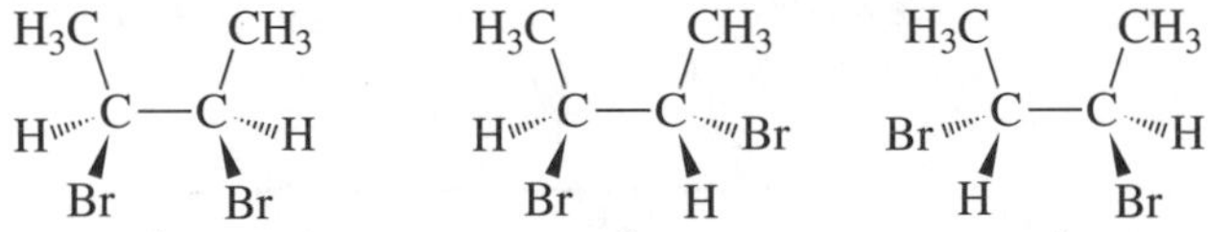

perspective formulas of the stereoisomers of 2,3-dibromobutane (eclipsed)

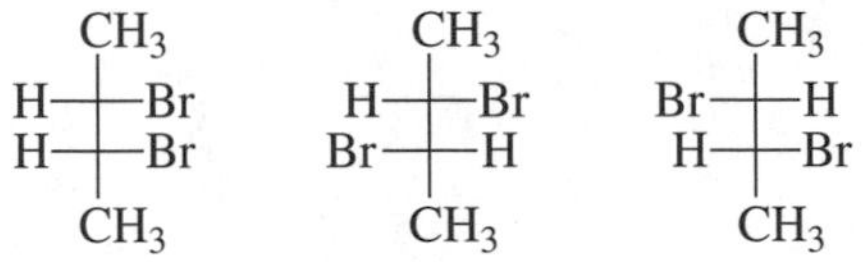

Fischer projections of the stereoisomers of 2,3-dibromobutane

It is easy to see from the following perspective formulas that **1** and its mirror image are identical. To convince yourself that the Fischer projection of **1** and its mirror image are identical, rotate the mirror image 180°. (*Remember, you can move Fischer projections only by rotating them* 180° *in the plane of the paper.*)

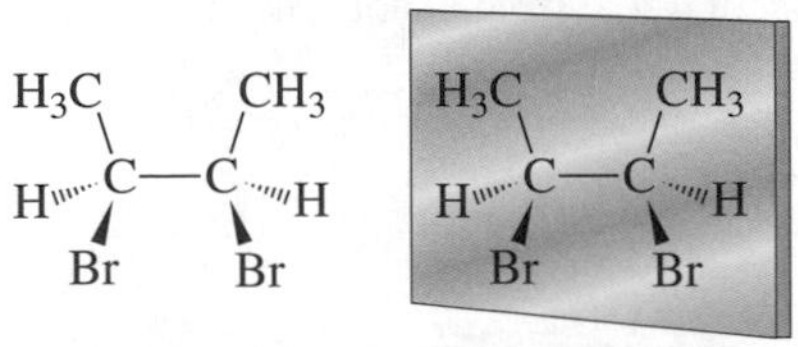

superimposable mirror image

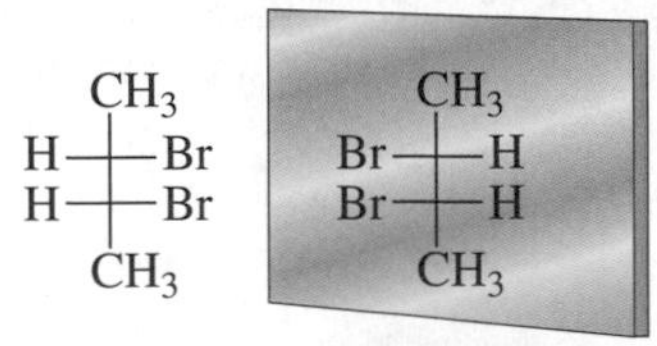

superimposable mirror image

A meso compound is achiral.

Stereoisomer **1** is called a meso compound. Even though a **meso** (mee-zo) **compound** has asymmetric centers, it is achiral. A meso compound does not rotate polarized light because it is superimposable on its mirror image. *Mesos* is the Greek word for "middle."

A meso compound can be recognized by the fact that it has two or more asymmetric centers and a plane of symmetry. A **plane of symmetry** cuts the molecule in half so that one half is the mirror image of the other. A molecule with a plane of symmetry does not have an enantiomer. Compare stereoisomer **1**, which has a plane of symmetry and thus no enantiomer, with stereoisomer **2**, which does not have a plane of symmetry and therefore *does* have an enantiomer. *If a compound has a plane of symmetry, it will not be optically active and will not have an enantiomer, even though it has asymmetric centers.*

A meso compound has two or more asymmetric centers and a plane of symmetry.

A chiral compound cannot have a plane of symmetry.

plane of symmetry

stereoisomer 1

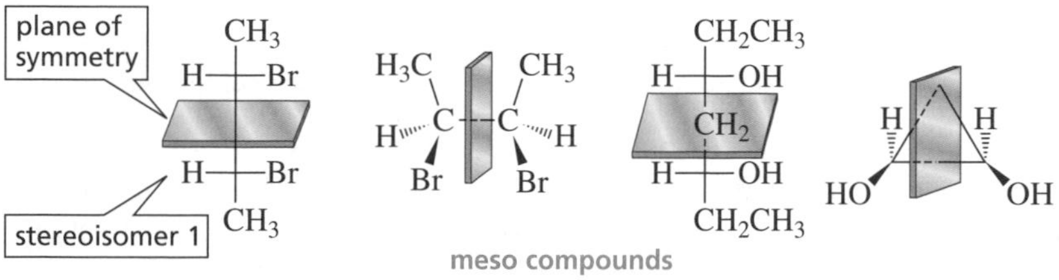

meso compounds

It is easy to recognize when a compound with two asymmetric centers has a stereoisomer that is a meso compound—the four atoms or groups bonded to one asymmetric center are identical to the four atoms or groups bonded to the other asymmetric center. *A compound with the same four atoms or groups bonded to two different asymmetric centers will have three stereoisomers: one will be a meso compound, and the other two will be enantiomers.*

If a compound has a plane of symmetry, it will not be optically active even though it has asymmetric centers.

If a compound with two asymmetric centers has the same four groups bonded to each of the asymmetric centers, one of its stereoisomers will be a meso compound.

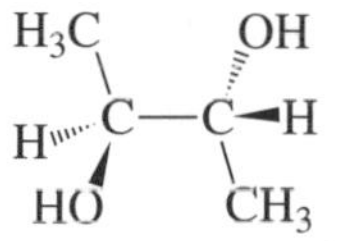

a meso compound

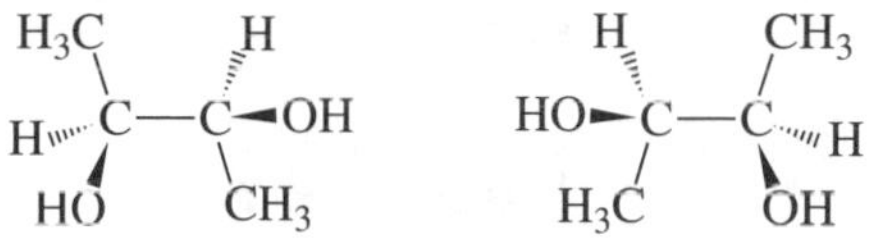

enantiomers

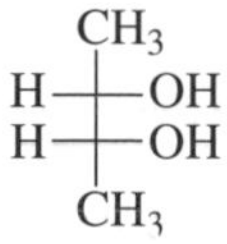

a meso compound

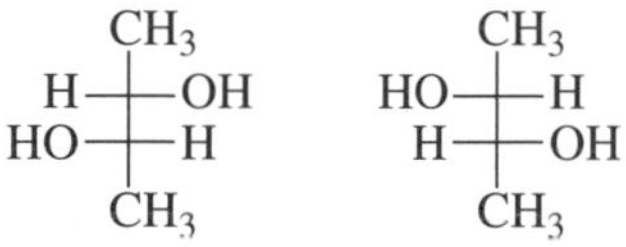

enantiomers

In the case of cyclic compounds, the cis isomer will be a meso compound and the trans isomer will be a pair of enantiomers.

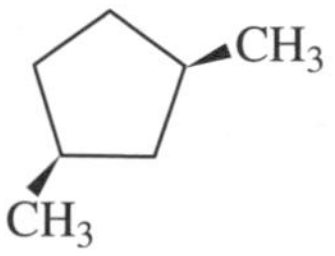

***cis*-1,3-dimethylcyclopentane**
a meso compound

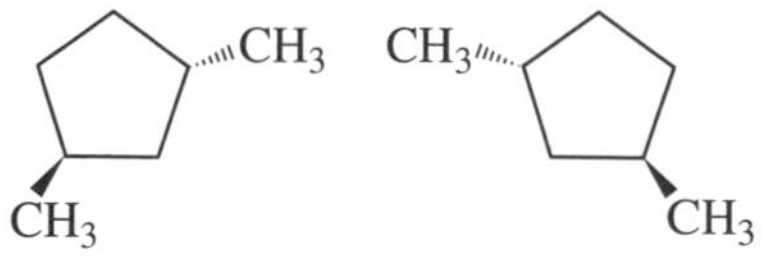

***trans*-1,3-dimethylcyclopentane**
a pair of enantiomers

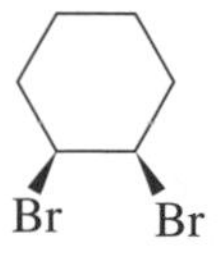

***cis*-1,2-dibromocyclohexane**
a meso compound

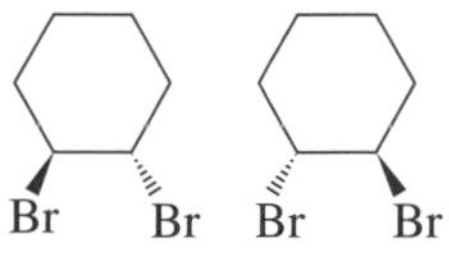

***trans*-1,2-dibromocyclohexane**
a pair of enantiomers

In the perspective formula shown above, *cis*-1,2-dibromocyclohexane appears to have a plane of symmetry. Remember, however, that cyclohexane is not a planar hexagon but exists preferentially in the chair conformation, and the chair conformation of *cis*-1,2-dibromocyclohexane does not have a plane of symmetry. Only the much less stable boat conformation of *cis*-1,2-dibromocyclohexane has a plane of symmetry. This issue raises the question of whether *cis*-1,2-dibromocyclohexane is a meso compound. The answer is yes. If a molecule has an achiral conformer (that is, a conformer with a plane of symmetry), the molecule is achiral, even if the achiral confomer is not the most stable conformer. An achiral molecule with two asymmetric centers is a meso compound.

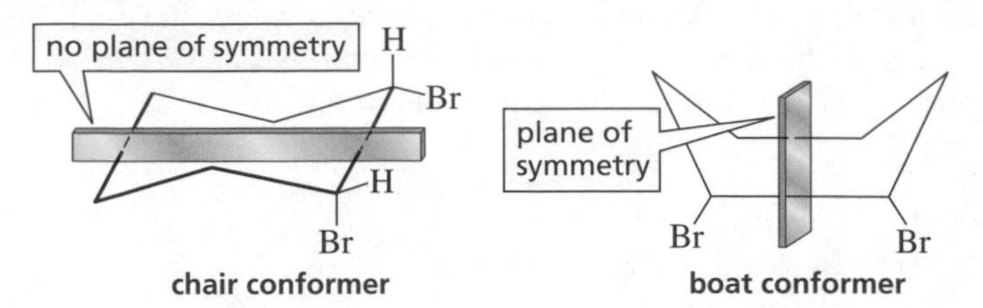

This rule holds for acyclic compounds as well. We have just seen that 2,3-dibromobutane is an achiral meso compound because it has a plane of symmetry. To find its plane of symmetry, however, we had to look at a relatively unstable eclipsed conformation. The more stable staggered conformation does not have a plane of symmetry. 2,3-Dibromobutane is still a meso compound, however, because it has a conformation that has a plane of symmetry.

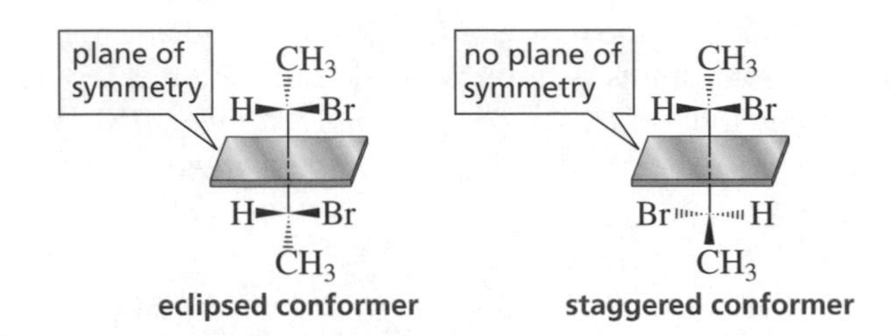

PROBLEM-SOLVING STRATEGY

Recognizing whether a Compound has a Stereoisomer that is a Meso Compound

Which of the following compounds has a stereoisomer that is a meso compound?

A 2,3-dimethylbutane
B 3,4-dimethylhexane
C 2-bromo-3-methylpentane
D 1,3-dimethylcyclohexane
E 1,4-dimethylcyclohexane
F 1,2-dimethylcyclohexane
G 3,4-diethylhexane
H 1-bromo-2-methylcyclohexane

Check each compound to see if it has the necessary requirements for having a stereoisomer that is a meso compound. That is, does it have two asymmetric centers, and if so, do they each have the same four substituents attached to them?

Compounds **A**, **E**, and **G** do *not* have a stereoisomer that is a meso compound because they do not have any asymmetric centers.

$CH_3CH(CH_3)CH(CH_3)CH_3$ **A** 1,4-dimethylcyclohexane (CH_3, CH_3) **E** $CH_3CH_2CH(CH_2CH_3)CH(CH_2CH_3)CH_2CH_3$ **G**

chem place Tutorial: Optical activity

Tutorial: Identification of stereoisomers with multiple asymmetric centers

Tutorial: Plane of symmetry

Compounds **C** and **H** each have two asymmetric centers. They do *not* have a stereoisomer that is a meso compound, however, because each of the asymmetric centers is *not* bonded to the same four substituents.

$CH_3CH(Br)CH(CH_3)CH_2CH_3$ **C** 1-bromo-2-methylcyclohexane (CH_3, Br) **H**

Compounds **B**, **D**, and **F** have two asymmetric centers, and each asymmetric center is bonded to the same four substituents. Therefore, these compounds have a stereoisomer that is a meso compound.

$CH_3CH_2CH(CH_3)CH(CH_3)CH_2CH_3$ **B** 1,3-dimethylcyclohexane (CH_3, CH_3) **D** 1,2-dimethylcyclohexane (CH_3, CH_3) **F**

In the case of the acyclic compound, the isomer that is the meso compound is the one that has a plane of symmetry when the compound is drawn in its eclipsed conformation (**B**). For the cyclic compounds, the cis isomer is the meso compound (**D** and **F**).

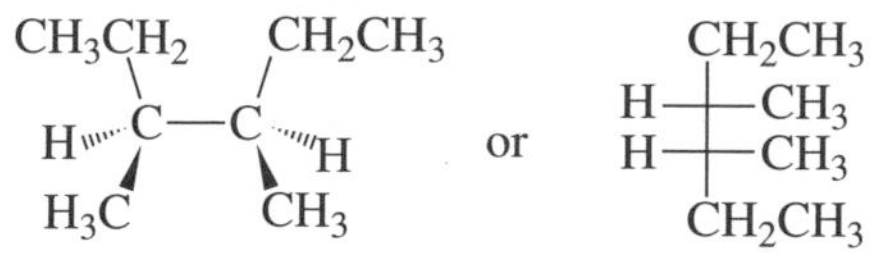

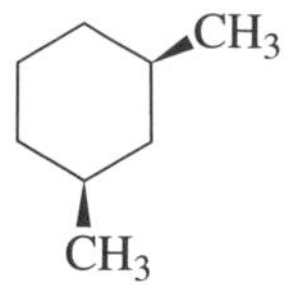

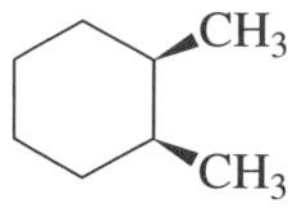

Now continue on to Problem 32.

PROBLEM 32♦

Which of the following compounds has a stereoisomer that is a meso compound?

A 2,4-dibromohexane
B 2,4-dibromopentane
C 2,4-dimethylpentane
D 1,3-dichlorocyclohexane
E 1,4-dichlorocyclohexane
F 1,2-dichlorocyclobutane

PROBLEM 33 SOLVED

Which of the following compounds are chiral?

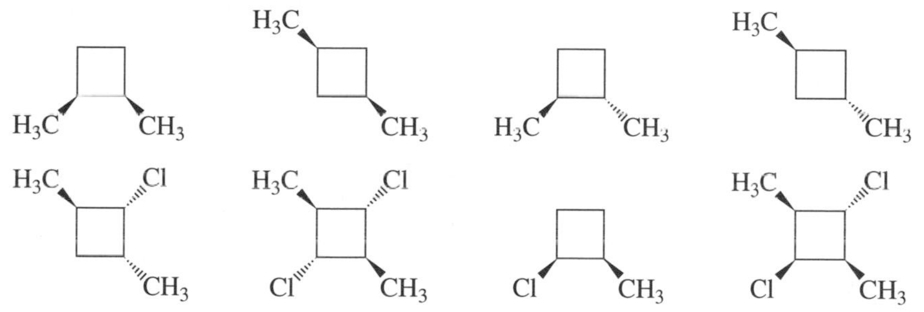

Solution In the top row of compounds, only the third compound is chiral. The first compound has a plane of symmetry, and a chiral molecule does not have a plane of symmetry; the second and fourth compounds do not have any asymmetric centers and each has a plane of symmetry. In the bottom row, the first and third compounds are chiral. The second and fourth compounds each have a plane of symmetry. Thus, only the following compounds are chiral.

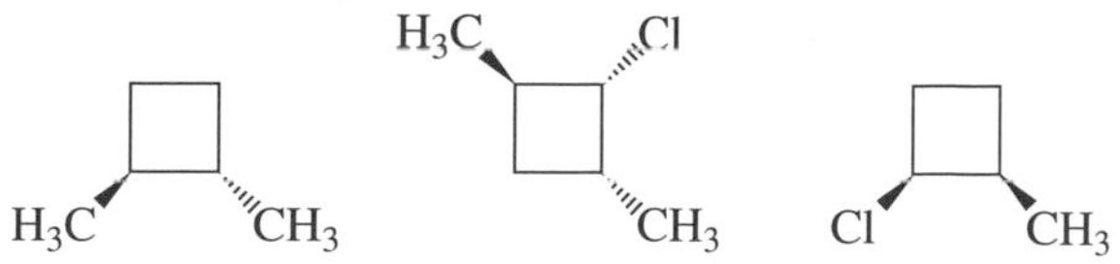

PROBLEM 34

Draw all the stereoisomers for each of the following compounds:

a. 1-bromo-2-methylbutane
b. 1-chloro-3-methylpentane
c. 2-methyl-1-propanol
d. 2-bromo-1-butanol
e. 3-chloro-3-methylpentane
f. 3-bromo-2-butanol
g. 3,4-dichlorohexane
h. 2,4-dichloropentane
i. 2,4-dichloroheptane
j. 1,2-dichlorocyclobutane
k. 1,3-dichlorocyclohexane
l. 1,4-dichlorocyclohexane
m. 1-bromo-2-chlorocyclobutane
n. 1-bromo-3-chlorocyclobutane

13.13 HOW TO NAME ISOMERS WITH MORE THAN ONE ASYMMETRIC CENTER

If a compound has more than one asymmetric center, the steps used to determine whether an asymmetric center has the *R* or the *S* configuration must be applied to each of the asymmetric centers individually. As an example, let's name one of the stereoisomers of 3-bromo-2-butanol.

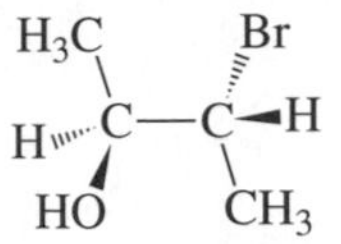

a stereoisomer of 3-bromo-2-butanol

First, we will determine the configuration at C-2. The OH group has the highest priority, the C-3 carbon (the C attached to Br, C, H) has the next-highest priority, CH_3 is next, and H has the lowest priority. Because the group with the lowest priority is bonded by a hatched wedge, we can immediately draw an arrow from the group with the highest priority to the group with the next highest priority. That arrow points counterclockwise, so the configuration at C-2 is *S*.

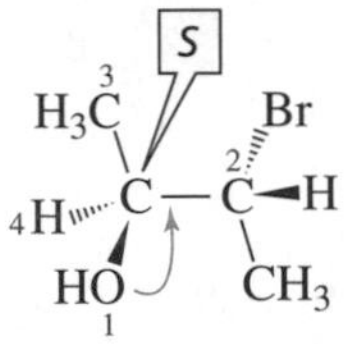

Now we need to determine the configuration at C-3. Because the group with the lowest priority (H) is not bonded by a hatched wedge, we must put it there by temporarily switching two groups.

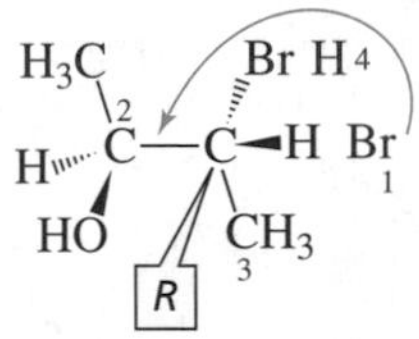

The arrow going from **1** (Br, the highest priority group) to **2** (the C attached to O, C, H) to **3** (the methyl group) points counterclockwise, suggesting C-3 has the *S* configuration. However, because we switched two groups before we drew the arrow, C-3 has the opposite configuration—it has the *R* configuration. Thus, the isomer is named (2*S*,3*R*)-3-bromo-2-butanol.

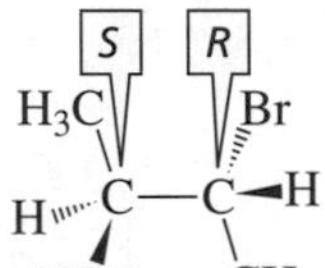

(2*S*,3*R*)-3-bromo-2-butanol

When Fischer projections are used, the procedure is similar. Just apply the steps to each asymmetric center that you learned for a Fischer projection with one asymmetric center. At C-2, the arrow from the group with the highest priority to the group with the next highest priority points clockwise, which would suggest an *R* configuration. However, the group with the lowest priority is on a horizontal bond, leading us to conclude that C-2 has the *S* configuration (Section 13.7).

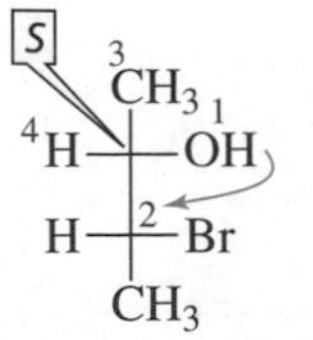

Repeating these steps for C-3 identifies that asymmetric center as having the *R* configuration. Thus, the isomer is named (2*S*,3*R*)-3-bromo-2-butanol.

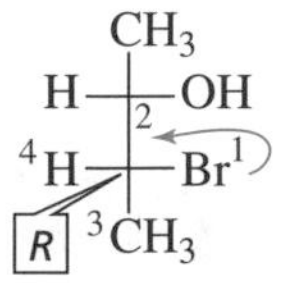

(2*S*,3*R*)-3-bromo-2-butanol

The four stereoisomers of 3-bromo-2-butanol are named as shown here. Take a few minutes to verify the names.

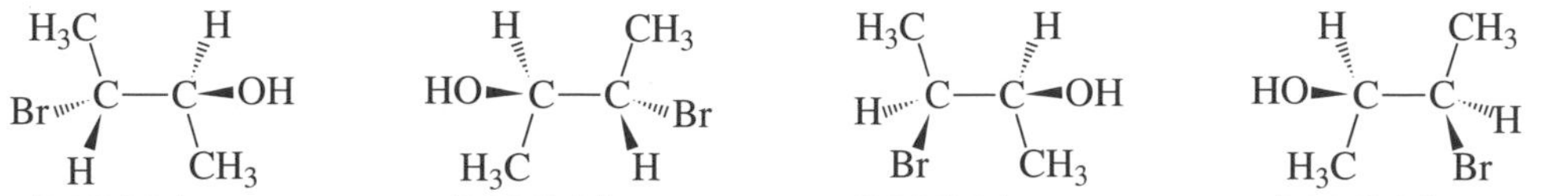

(2*S*,3*R*)-3-bromo-2-butanol **(2*R*,3*S*)-3-bromo-2-butanol** **(2*S*,3*S*)-3-bromo-2-butanol** **(2*R*,3*R*)-3-bromo-2-butanol**

perspective formulas of the stereoisomers of 3-bromo-2-butanol

(2*S*,3*R*)-3-bromo-2-butanol **(2*R*,3*S*)-3-bromo-2-butanol** **(2*S*,3*S*)-3-bromo-2-butanol** **(2*R*,3*R*)-3-bromo-2-butanol**

Fischer projections of the stereoisomers of 3-bromo-2-butanol

Notice that enantiomers have the opposite configuration at both asymmetric centers, whereas diastereomers have the same configuration at one asymmetric center and the opposite configuration at the other.

PROBLEM 35

Draw and name the four stereoisomers of 1,3-dichloro-2-pentanol using:

a. perspective formulas **b.** Fischer projections

Tartaric acid has three stereoisomers because each of its two asymmetric centers has the same set of four substituents. The meso compound and the pair of enantiomers are named as shown.

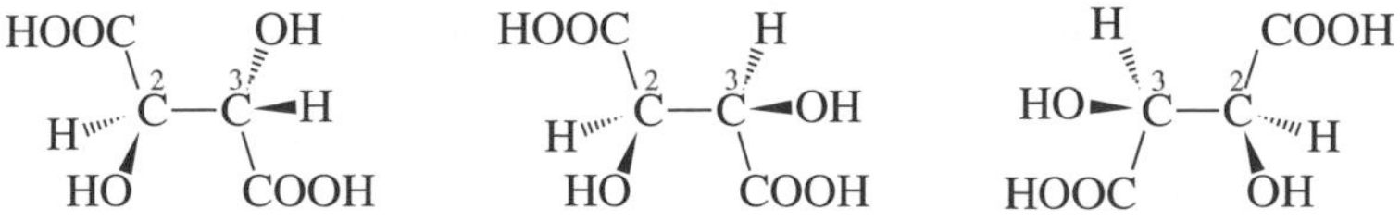

(2*R*,3*S*)-tartaric acid a meso compound **(2*R*,3*R*)-tartaric acid** **(2*S*,3*S*)-tartaric acid** a pair of enantiomers

perspective formulas of the stereoisomers of tartaric acid

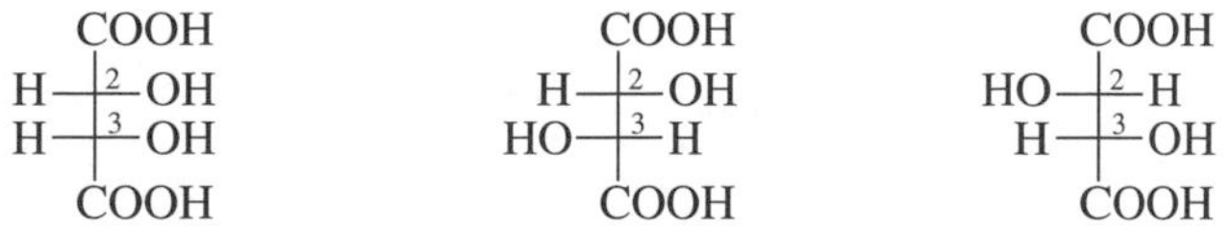

(2*R*,3*S*)-tartaric acid a meso compound **(2*R*,3*R*)-tartaric acid** **(2*S*,3*S*)-tartaric acid** a pair of enantiomers

Fischer projections of the stereoisomers of tartaric acid

The physical properties of the three stereoisomers of tartaric acid are listed in Table 13.2. The meso compound and either of the enantiomers are diastereomers. Notice that the physical properties of the enantiomers are the same, whereas the physical properties of the diastereomers are different.

Table 13.2 Physical Properties of the Stereoisomers of Tartaric Acid

	Melting point, °C	Specific rotation	Solubility, g/100 g H_2O at 15 °C
(2*R*,3*R*)-(+)-Tartaric acid	171	+11.98	139
(2*S*,3*S*)-(−)-Tartaric acid	171	−11.98	139
(2*R*,3*S*)-Tartaric acid (meso)	146	0	125
(±)-Tartaric acid	206	0	139

PROBLEM 36 ♦

Chloramphenicol is a broad-spectrum antibiotic that is particularly useful against typhoid fever. What is the configuration of each of its asymmetric centers?

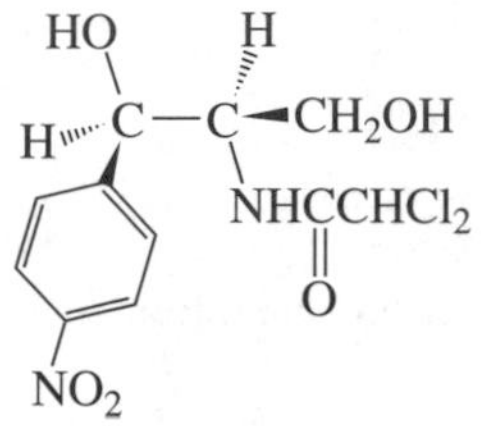

HO H

H C—C—CH_2OH

$NHCCHCl_2$

O

NO_2

chloramphenicol

PROBLEM-SOLVING STRATEGY

Drawing a Perspective Formula for a Compound with Two Asymmetric Centers

Draw a perspective formula for (2*S*,3*R*)-3-chloro-2-pentanol.

First write a condensed structure for the compound, ignoring the configuration at the asymmetric centers.

Cl

$CH_3CHCHCH_2CH_3$

OH

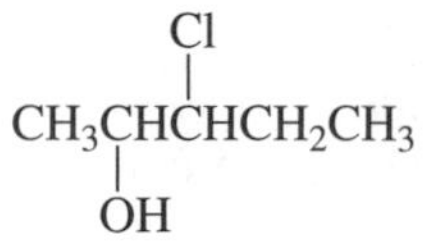

3-chloro-2-pentanol

Now draw the bonds about the asymmetric centers. Remember that the solid and hatched wedges must be adjacent.

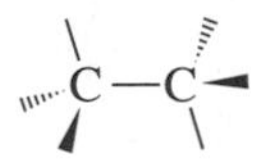

C—C

At each asymmetric center, put the group with the lowest priority on the hatched wedge.

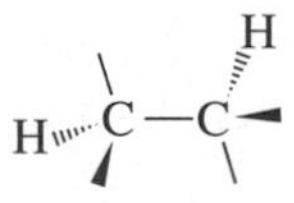

H

H C—C

At each asymmetric center, put the group with the highest priority on a bond so that an arrow will point clockwise, if you want the *R* configuration, or counterclockwise, if you want the *S* configuration, to the group with the next highest priority.

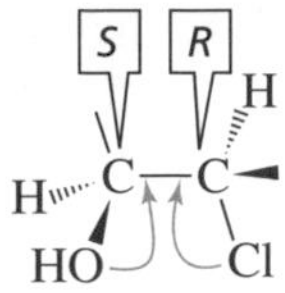

Put the remaining substituents on the last available bonds.

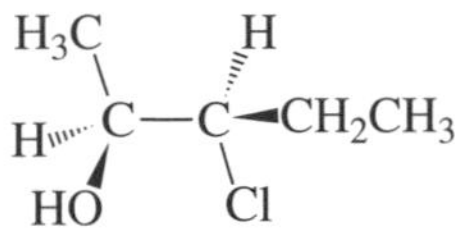

(2*S*,3*R*)-3-chloro-2-pentanol

Now continue on to Problem 37.

PROBLEM 37

Draw a perspective formula for each of the following:

a. (*S*)-3-chloro-1-pentanol
b. (2*R*,3*R*)-2,3-dibromopentane
c. (2*S*,3*R*)-3-methyl-2-pentanol
d. (*R*)-1,2-dibromobutane

PROBLEM 38♦

Threonine, an amino acid, has four stereoisomers. The isomer found in nature is (2*S*,3*R*)-threonine. Which of the following structures represents the naturally occurring amino acid?

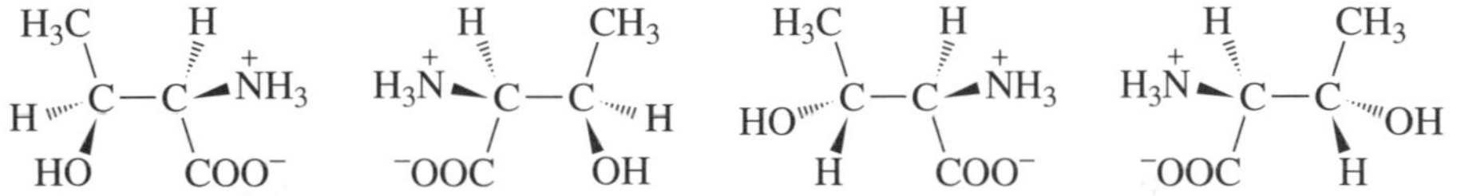

stereosiomers of threonine

PROBLEM 39♦

Name the following:

a.

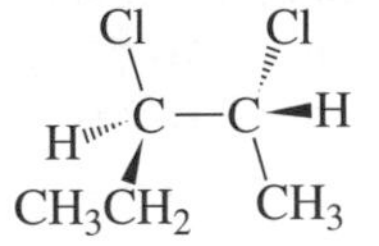

b.

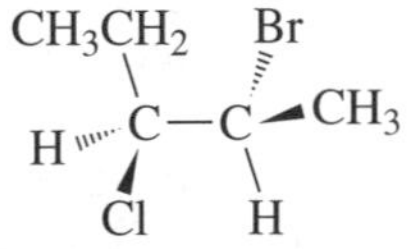

c.

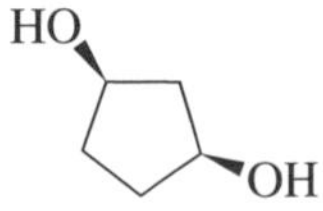

d.

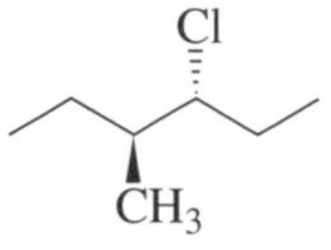

PROBLEM 40

Name the isomers you drew in Problem 28.

13.14 REACTIONS OF COMPOUNDS THAT CONTAIN AN ASYMMETRIC CENTER

When a compound containing an asymmetric center undergoes a reaction, the effect on the configuration of the asymmetric center depends on the reaction. If the reaction does not break any of the four bonds to the asymmetric center, then the relative positions of the groups bonded to the asymmetric center will not change. For example, when (*S*)-1-chloro-3-methylpentane reacts with hydroxide ion, OH substitutes for Cl. Because the reaction does not break any of the bonds to the asymmetric center, the reactant and product have the same **relative configuration**, meaning the groups maintain their relative positions, so that the CH_3CH_2 group is on the left, the CH_3 group is attached to a solid wedge, and the H is attached to a hatched wedge.

If a reaction does not break a bond to the asymmetric center, the reactant and the product will have the same relative configurations.

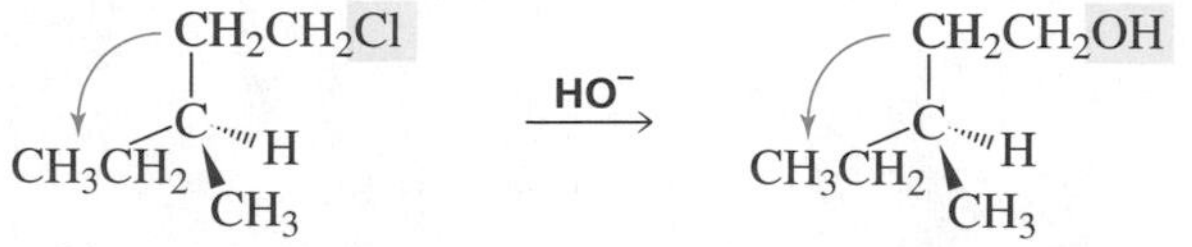

(*S*)-1-chloro-3-methylpentane $\xrightarrow{HO^-}$ (*S*)-3-methyl-1-pentanol

A Word of Warning. Even if the four groups bonded to the asymmetric center maintain their relative positions, an *S* reactant does not always form an *S* product as occurred in the preceding reaction, and an *R* reactant does not always form an *R* product. For example, in the reaction shown below, the groups maintain their relative positions during the reaction; thus the reactant and the product have the same *relative configurations*. Nevertheless, the reactant has the *S* configuration, but the product has the *R* configuration. Although the groups have maintained their relative positions, their relative priorities—as defined by the Cahn–Ingold–Prelog rules—have changed (the vinyl group has the highest priority in the reactant, whereas the propyl group has the highest priority in the product). The change in relative priorities—not any change in the relative positions of the groups—is what caused the *S* reactant to become an *R* product.

Two compounds with the same relative configuration do not necessarily have the same absolute configuration.

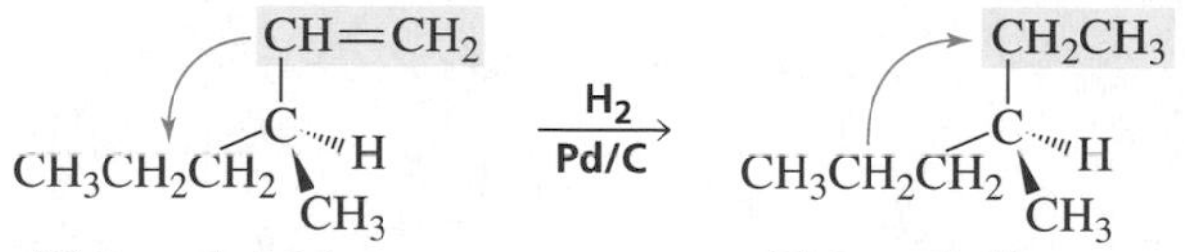

(*S*)-3-methyl-1-hexene $\xrightarrow[Pd/C]{H_2}$ (*R*)-3-methylhexane

The reactant and product in the preceding example have the same relative configuration, but because the reactant has the *S* configuration and the product has the *R* configuration, they have different absolute configurations. The **absolute configuration** is the compound's *actual* configuration. In other words, the configuration is known in an absolute sense rather than in a relative one. To know the *absolute configuration* of a compound is to know whether it has the *R* or the *S* configuration. To know that two compounds have the same *relative configuration* is to know that the groups attached to the asymmetric center in both compounds have the same relative positions.

We have just seen that if the reaction does not break any of the bonds to the asymmetric center, the reactant and product will have the same relative configuration. However, if the reaction *does break* a bond to the asymmetric center, the product can have the same relative configuration as the reactant, or it can have the opposite relative configuration. Which of the products is actually formed depends on the mechanism of the reaction. Therefore, we cannot predict what the configuration of the product will be unless we know the mechanism of the reaction.

If a reaction does break a bond to the asymmetric center, you cannot predict the configuration of the product unless you know the mechanism of the reaction.

has the same relative configuration as the reactant

has a relative configuration opposite to that of the reactant

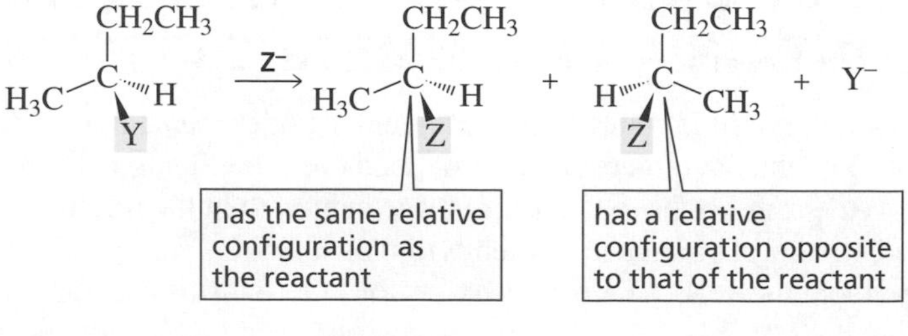

PROBLEM 41 SOLVED

(*S*)-(−)-2-Methyl-1-butanol can be converted to (+)-2-methylbutanoic acid without breaking any of the bonds to the asymmetric center. What is the configuration of (−)-2-methylbutanoic acid?

CH_2OH / CH_3CH_2–C–H / CH_3 **(*S*)-(−)-2-methyl-1-butanol**

$COOH$ / CH_3CH_2–C–H / CH_3 **(+)-2-methylbutanoic acid**

Solution We know that (+)-2-methylbutanoic acid has the relative configuration shown because it was formed from (*S*)-(−)-2-methyl-1-butanol without breaking any bonds to the asymmetric center. By looking at (+)-2-methylbutanoic acid, we know that it has the *S* configuration. We can conclude then that (−)-2-methylbutanoic acid has the *R* configuration.

PROBLEM 42 ♦

The stereoisomer of 1-iodo-2-methylbutane with the *R* configuration rotates the plane of polarization of plane-polarized light clockwise. The reaction shown below results in an alcohol that rotates the plane of polarization counterclockwise. What is the configuration of (+)-2-methyl-1-butanol?

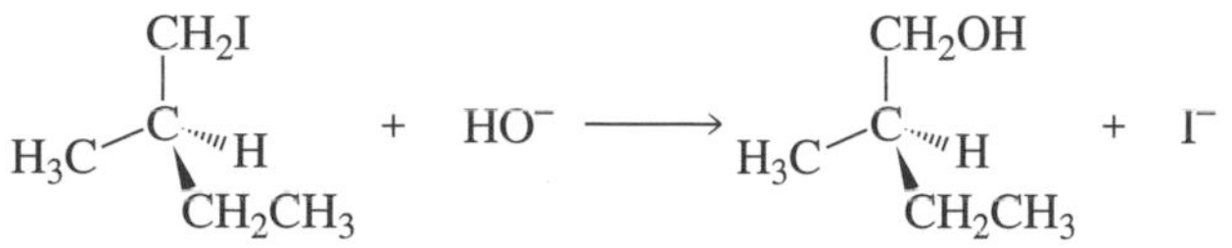

$$H_3C\text{–}C(CH_2I)(H)(CH_2CH_3) + HO^- \longrightarrow H_3C\text{–}C(CH_2OH)(H)(CH_2CH_3) + I^-$$

SUMMARY

Stereochemistry is the field of chemistry that deals with the structures of molecules in three dimensions. Compounds with the same molecular formula but different structures are called **isomers**; they fall into two classes: constitutional isomers and stereoisomers. **Constitutional isomers** differ in the way their atoms are connected. **Stereoisomers** differ in the way their atoms are arranged in space. There are two kinds of stereoisomers: **cis–trans isomers** and isomers that contain **asymmetric centers**.

A **chiral** molecule has a nonsuperimposable mirror image. An **achiral** molecule has a superimposable mirror image. The feature that is most often the cause of chirality is an asymmetric center. An **asymmetric center** is an atom (most often a carbon) bonded to four different atoms or groups.

Nonsuperimposable mirror-image molecules are called **enantiomers. Diastereomers** are stereoisomers that are not enantiomers. Enantiomers have identical physical and chemical properties; diastereomers have different physical and chemical properties. An achiral reagent reacts identically with both enantiomers; a chiral reagent reacts differently with each enantiomer. A **racemic mixture** is a mixture of equal amounts of two enantiomers.

The letters ***R*** and ***S*** indicate the **configuration** about an asymmetric center. If one member of a pair of stereoisomers has the *R* and the other has the *S* configuration, they are enantiomers; if they both have the *R* or both have the *S* configuration, they are identical molecules.

Chiral compounds are **optically active**, meaning that they rotate the plane of polarization of plane-polarized light; achiral compounds are **optically inactive**. If one enantiomer rotates the plane of polarization clockwise (+), its mirror image will rotate it the same amount counterclockwise (−). Each optically active compound has a characteristic **specific rotation**. A **racemic mixture**, indicated by ±, is optically inactive. A **meso compound** has two or more asymmetric centers and a plane of symmetry; it is optically inactive. A compound with the same four groups bonded to two different asymmetric centers will have three stereoisomers, a meso compound and a pair of enantiomers.

If a reaction does not break any bonds to the asymmetric center, the reactant and product will have the same **relative configuration**—their substituents will have the same relative positions. The **absolute configuration** is the actual configuration. If a reaction does break a bond to the asymmetric center, the configuration of the product will depend on the mechanism of the reaction.

KEY TERMS

absolute configuration (p. 562)
achiral (p. 535)
asymmetric center (p. 536)
chiral (p. 535)
cis isomer (p. 534)
cis–trans isomers (p. 534)
configurational isomers (p. 533)
constitutional isomers (p. 533)
dextrorotatory (p. 546)
diastereomer (p. 550)
enantiomers (p. 537)
enantiomerically pure (p. 548)
enantiomeric excess (ee) (p. 548)
erythro enantiomers (p. 550)
Fischer projection (p. 538)
geometric isomers (p. 534)
isomers (p. 533)
levorotatory (p. 546)
meso compound (p. 554)
observed rotation (p. 546)
observed specific rotation (p. 548)
optically active (p. 546)
optically inactive (p. 546)
perspective formula (p. 538)
plane of polarization (p. 545)
plane of symmetry (p. 554)
plane-polarized light (p. 544)
polarimeter (p. 546)
racemate (p. 548)
racemic mixture (p. 548)
R configuration (p. 539)
relative configuration (p. 562)
S configuration (p. 539)
specific rotation (p. 547)
stereocenter (p. 538)
stereochemistry (p. 563)
stereogenic center (p.538)
stereoisomers (p. 533)
threo enantiomers (p. 550)
trans isomer (p. 534)

PROBLEMS

43. Disregarding stereoisomers, give the structures of all compounds with molecular formula C_5H_{10}. Which ones can exist as stereoisomers?

44. Draw all possible stereoisomers for each of the following. Indicate if no stereoisomers are possible.

a. 1-bromo-2-chlorocyclohexane
b. 2-bromo-4-methylpentane
c. 1,2-dichlorocyclohexane
d. 2-bromo-4-chloropentane
e. 3-heptene
f. 1-bromo-4-chlorocyclohexane
g. 1,2-dimethylcyclopropane
h. 4-bromo-2-pentene
i. 3,3-dimethylpentane
j. 3-chloro-1-butene
k. 1-bromo-2-chlorocyclobutane
l. 1-bromo-3-chlorocyclobutane

45. Which of the following has an asymmetric center?

$CHBr_2Cl$ BHFCl CH_3CHCl_2 CHFBrCl BeHCl

46. Name each of the following compounds using *R,S* and *E,Z* designations where necessary:

a. $HC{=}CH_2$; C; CH_3CH_2; CH_3; H

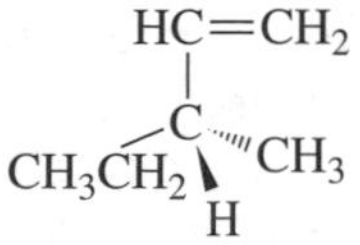

b. F, I; C=C; Cl, Br

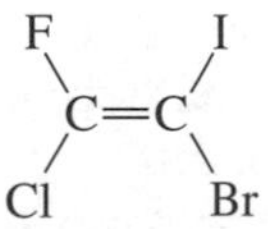

c. CH_3; HO—H; H—Cl; CH_2CH_3

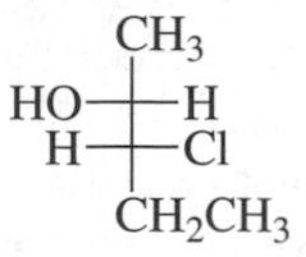

d. F, H; C=C; Cl, Br

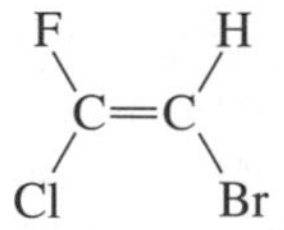

e. Br

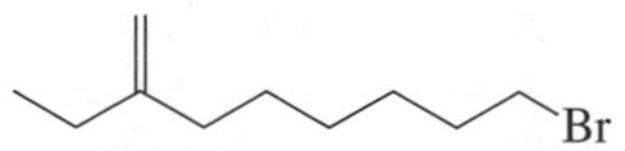

f. $BrCH_2CH_2$, $CH_2CH_2CHCH_3$ (CH_3); C=C; Br, CH_3

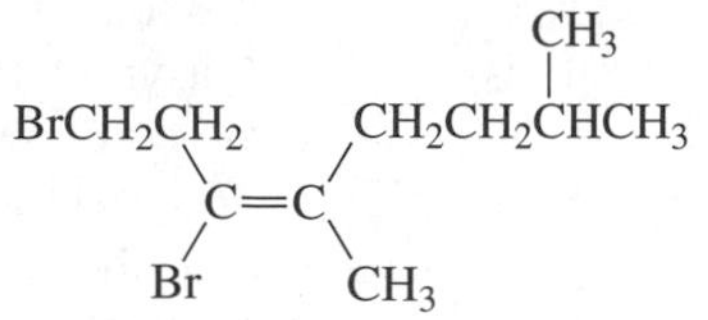

g. CH_2OH; HO—CH_3; $CH_2CH_2CH_2OH$

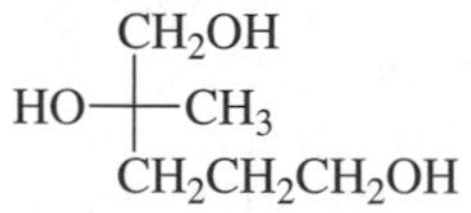

h. CH_3CH_2, Br; H—C—C—CH_3; HO, CH_2Br

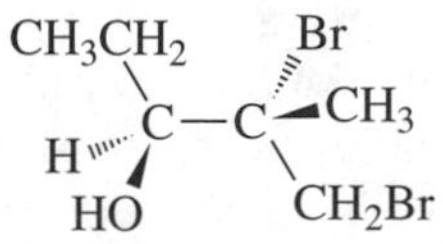

i. CH_3CH (CH_3), $CH_2CH_2CH_2CH_3$; C=C; H_3C, CH_2CH_2Cl

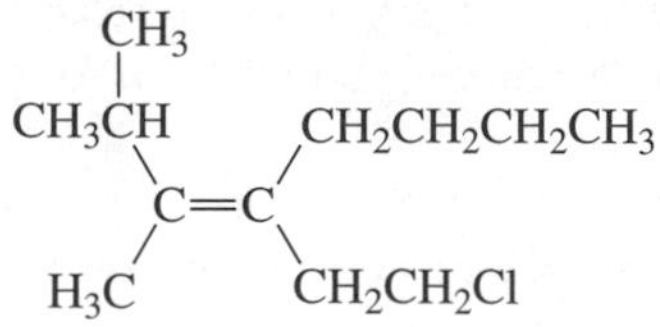

47. Mevacor is used clinically to lower serum cholesterol levels. How many asymmetric centers does Mevacor have?

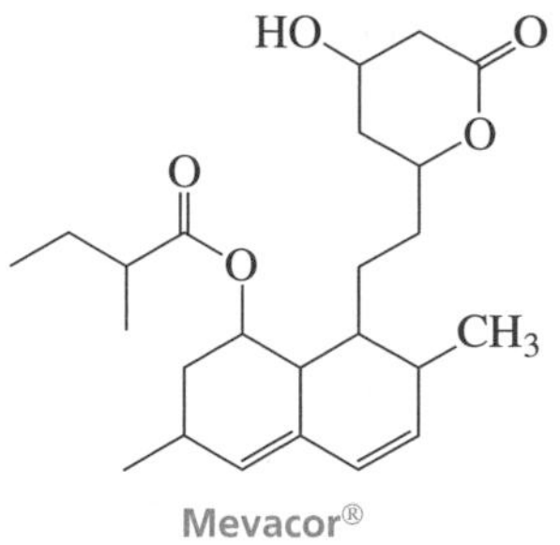

Mevacor®

48. Indicate whether each of the following pairs of compounds are identical or are enantiomers, diastereomers, or constitutional isomers:

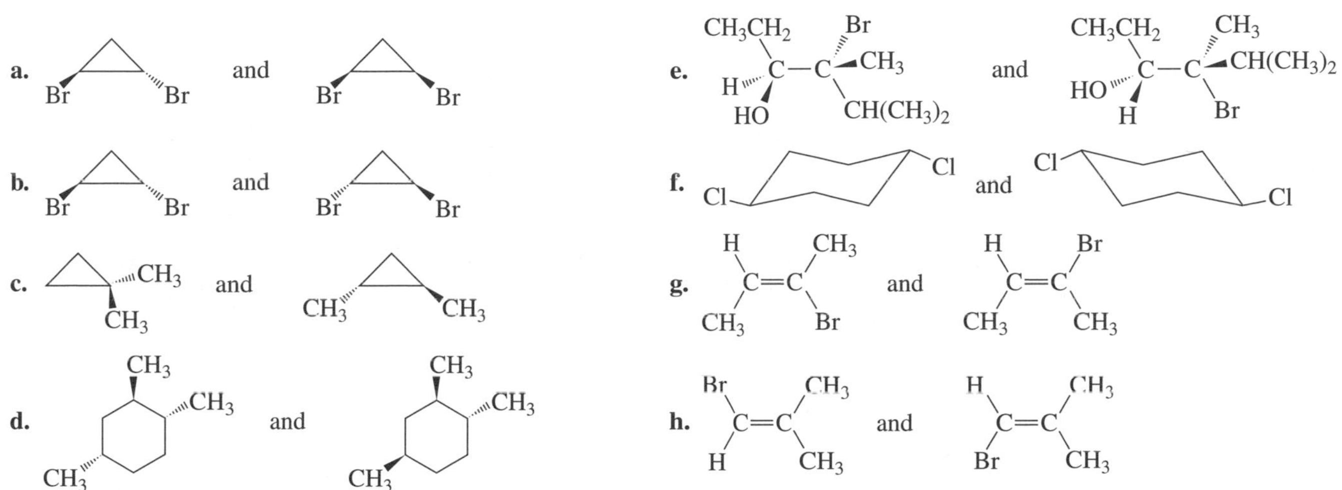

49. a. Give the product or products that would be obtained from the reaction of *cis*-2-butene and *trans*-2-butene with each of the following reagents. If a product can exist as stereoisomers, show which stereoisomers are obtained.

1. HCl
2. BH_3/THF followed by HO^-, H_2O_2, H_2O
3. a peroxyacid
4. Br_2 in CH_2Cl_2
5. $Br_2 + H_2O$
6. $H_2 + Pd/C$
7. $H_2O + H_2SO_4$
8. $CH_3OH + H_2SO_4$

b. With which reagents do the two alkenes react to give different products?

50. Which of the following are optically active?

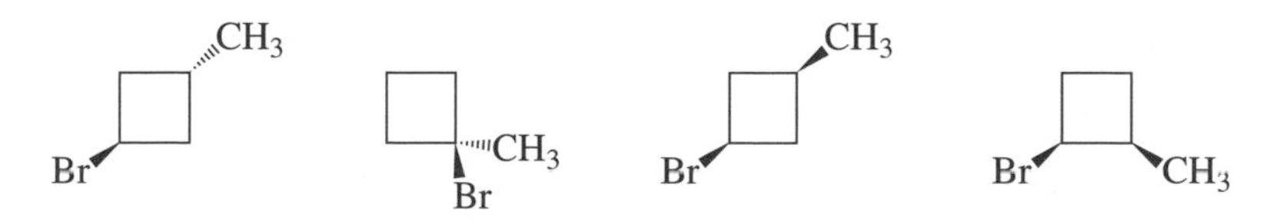

51. For many centuries, the Chinese have used extracts from a group of herbs known as ephedra to treat asthma. A compound named ephedrine that has been isolated from these herbs was found to be a potent dilator of air passages in the lungs.

a. How many stereoisomers are possible for ephedrine?

b. The stereoisomer shown below is the one that is pharmacologically active. What is the configuration of each of the asymmetric centers?

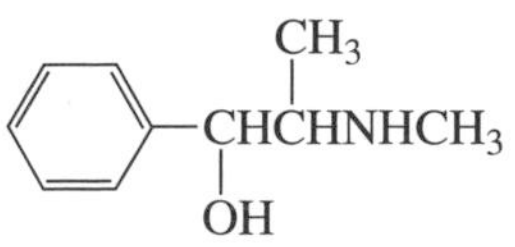

CH3 CHCHNHCH3 OH

ephedrine

H HO C—C NHCH3 H CH3

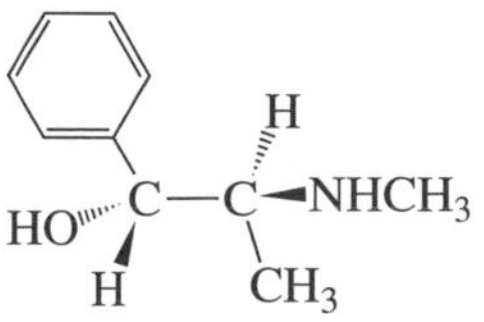

52. Which of the following compounds have an achiral stereoisomer?

a. 2,3-dichlorobutane
b. 2,3-dichloropentane
c. 2,3-dichloro-2,3-dimethylbutane
d. 1,3-dichlorocyclopentane
e. 1,3-dibromocyclobutane
f. 2,4-dibromopentane
g. 2,3-dibromopentane
h. 1,4-dimethylcyclohexane
i. 1,2-dimethylcyclopentane
j. 1,2-dimethylcyclobutane

53. Indicate whether each of the following pairs of compounds are identical or are enantiomers, diastereomers, or constitutional isomers:

a. 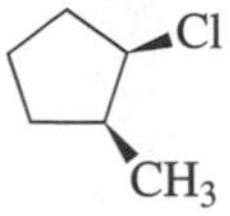 Cl, CH_3 and Cl, CH_3

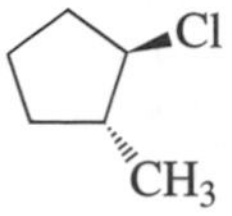

b. 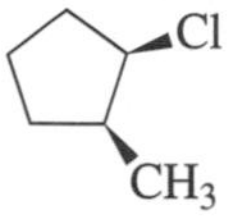 Cl, CH_3 and Cl, CH_3

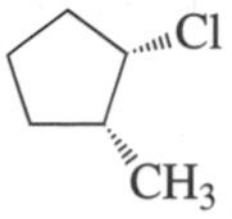

c. 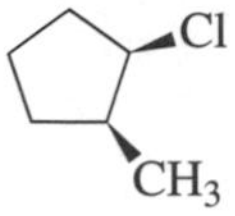 Cl, CH_3 and CH_3, Cl

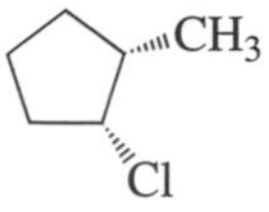

d. 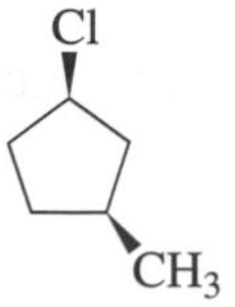 Cl, CH_3 and Cl, CH_3

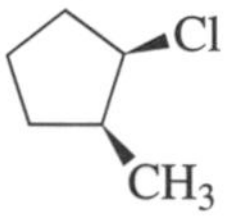

54. Give the products, including their configurations, obtained from the reaction of 1-ethylcyclohexene with the following reagents:

a. HBr
b. H_2, Pd/C
c. BH_3/THF followed by HO^-, H_2O_2, H_2O
d. Br_2/CH_2Cl_2

55. Citrate synthase, one of the enzymes in the series of enzyme-catalyzed reactions known as the citric acid cycle, catalyzes the synthesis of citric acid from oxaloacetic acid and acetyl-CoA. If the synthesis is carried out with acetyl-CoA that contains radioactive carbon (^{14}C) in the indicated position (Section 10.1), the isomer shown here is obtained.

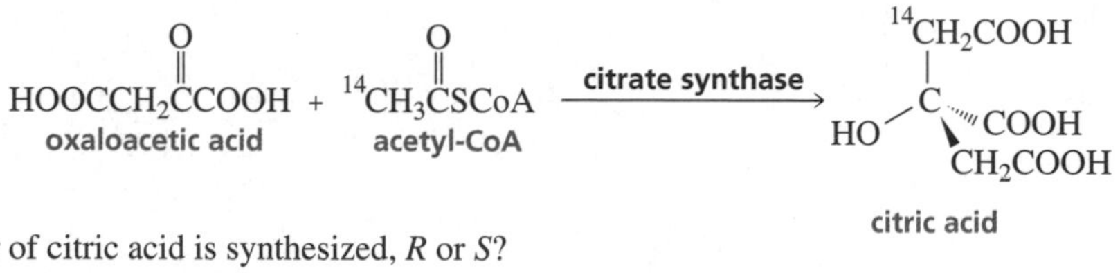

$$\underset{\text{oxaloacetic acid}}{HOOCCH_2\overset{O}{\overset{\|}{C}}COOH} + \underset{\text{acetyl-CoA}}{{}^{14}CH_3\overset{O}{\overset{\|}{C}}SCoA} \xrightarrow{\text{citrate synthase}} \underset{\text{citric acid}}{HO{-}C({}^{14}CH_2COOH)(COOH)(CH_2COOH)}$$

a. Which stereoisomer of citric acid is synthesized, *R* or *S*?
b. Why is the other stereoisomer not obtained?
c. If the acetyl-CoA used in the synthesis does not contain ^{14}C (Section 10.1), will the product of the reaction be chiral or achiral?

56. Give the products of the following reactions. If the products can exist as stereoisomers, show which stereoisomers are obtained.

a. *cis*-2-pentene + HCl
b. *trans*-2-pentene + HCl
c. 1-ethylcyclohexene + H_2O + H_2SO_4
d. 2,3-dimethyl-3-hexene + H_2, Pd/C
e. 1,2-dimethylcyclohexene + HCl
f. 1,2-dideuteriocyclohexene + H_2, Pd/C
g. 3,3-dimethyl-1-pentene + Br_2/CH_2Cl_2
h. (*E*)-3,4-dimethyl-3-heptene + H_2, Pd/C
i. (*Z*)-3,4-dimethyl-3-heptene + H_2, Pd/C
j. 1-chloro-2-ethylcyclohexene + H_2, Pd/C

57. Indicate whether each of the following pairs of compounds are identical or are enantiomers, diastereomers, or constitutional isomers:

a. 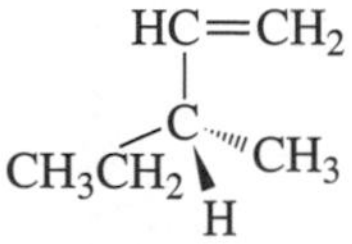 $HC{=}CH_2$, CH_3CH_2, CH_3, H and CH_2CH_3, H, CH_3, $HC{=}CH_2$

b. 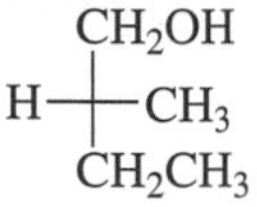 CH_2OH; H—CH_3; CH_2CH_3 and CH_2CH_3; CH_3—H; CH_2OH

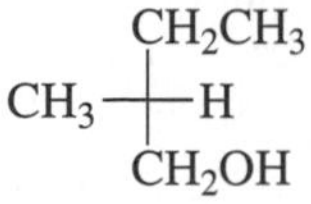

c. 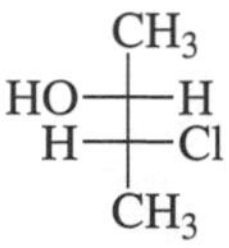 CH_3; HO—H; H—Cl; CH_3 and CH_3; H—OH; Cl—H; CH_3

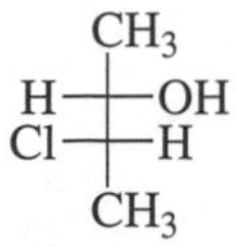

d. 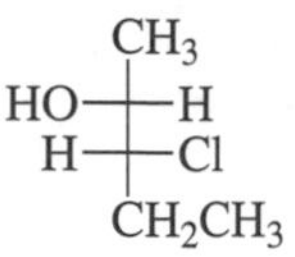 CH_3; HO—H; H—Cl; CH_2CH_3 and CH_2CH_3; HO—H; H—Cl; CH_3

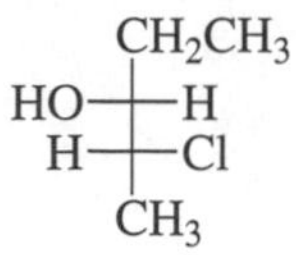

e. 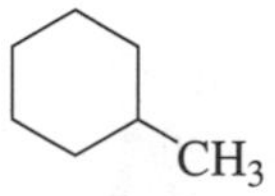 CH_3 and CH_2CH_3

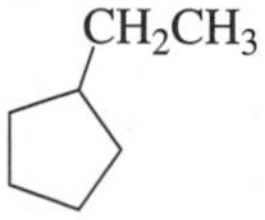

f. 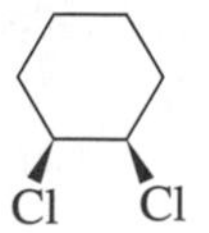 Cl Cl and  Cl Cl

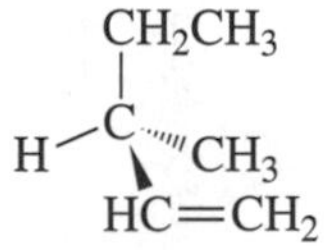

g. 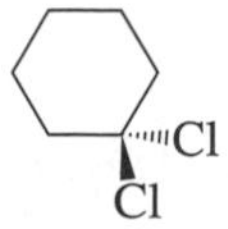 Cl, Cl and 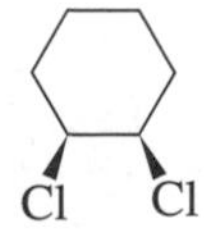 Cl Cl

h. 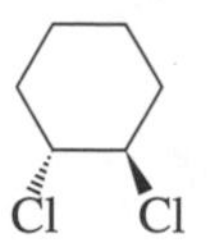 Cl Cl and Cl Cl

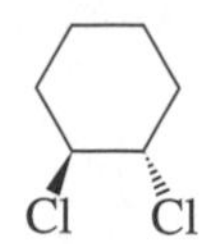

58. The specific rotation of (*R*)-(+)-glyceraldehyde is +8.7. If the observed specific rotation of a mixture of (*R*)-glyceraldehyde and (*S*)-glyceraldehyde is +1.4, what percent of glyceraldehyde is present as the *R* enantiomer?

59. Indicate whether each of the following structures is (*R*)-2-chlorobutane or (*S*)-2-chlorobutane. (Use models, if necessary.)

a. 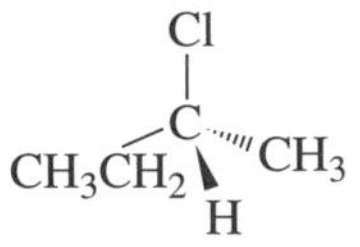

b. 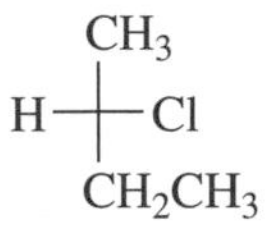

c. 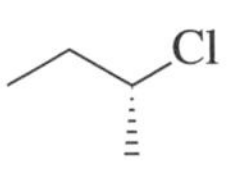

d. 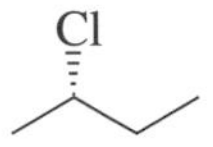

e. 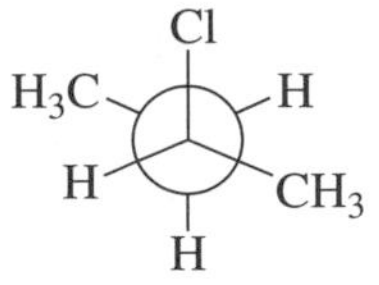

f. 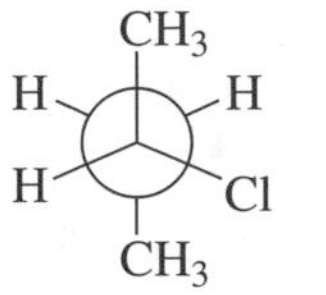

60. A solution of an unknown compound (3.0 g of the compound in 20 mL of solution), when placed in a polarimeter tube 2.0 dm long, was found to rotate the plane of polarized light 1.8° in a counterclockwise direction. What is the specific rotation of the compound?

61. Butaclamol is a potent antipsychotic that has been used clinically in the treatment of schizophrenia. How many asymmetric centers does it have?

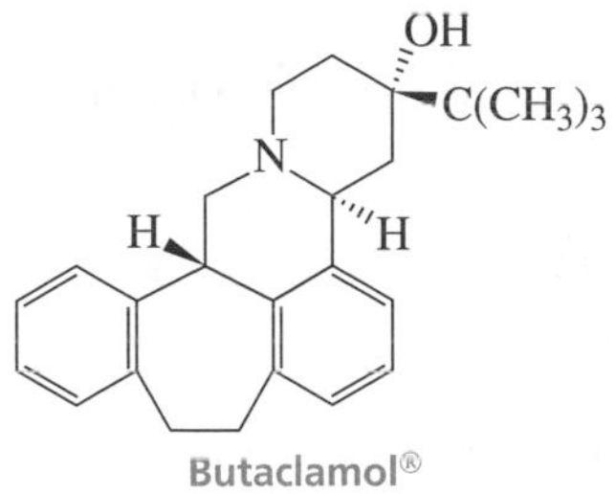

Butaclamol®

62. Explain how *R* and *S* are related to (+) and (−).

63. Give the products of the following reactions. If the products can exist as stereoisomers, show which stereoisomers are obtained.

a. *cis*-2-pentene + Br_2/CH_2Cl_2
b. *trans*-2-pentene + Br_2/CH_2Cl_2
c. 1-butene + HCl
d. methylcyclohexene + HBr
e. *trans*-3-hexene + Br_2/CH_2Cl_2
f. *cis*-3-hexene + Br_2/CH_2Cl_2
g. 3,3-dimethyl-1-pentene + HBr
h. *cis*-2-butene + HBr
i. (*Z*)-2,3-dichloro-2-butene + H_2, Pd/C
j. (*E*)-2,3-dichloro-2-butene + H_2, Pd/C
k. (*Z*)-3,4-dimethyl-3-hexene + H_2, Pd/C
l. (*E*)-3,4-dimethyl-3-hexene + H_2, Pd/C

64. a. Draw all possible stereoisomers for the following.

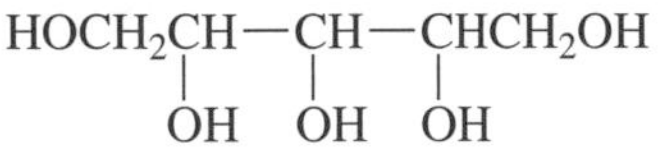

b. Which isomers are optically inactive (will not rotate the plane of polarization of plane-polarized light)?

65. Indicate the configuration of the asymmetric centers in the following molecules:

a. 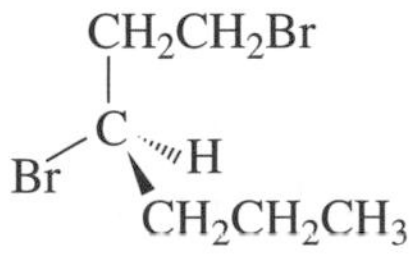

b. 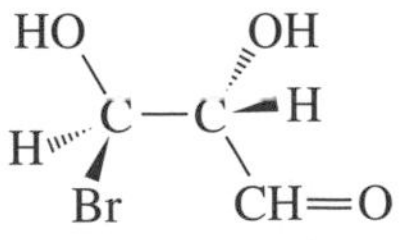

c. 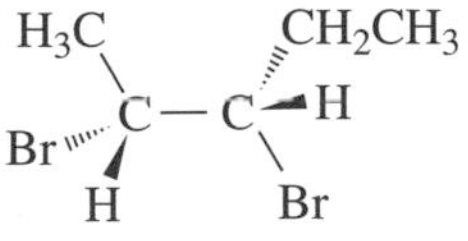

66. a. Draw all the isomers with molecular formula C_6H_{12} that contain a cyclobutane ring. (*Hint*: There are seven.)
b. Name the compounds without specifying the configuration of any asymmetric centers.
c. Identify:

1. constitutional isomers
2. stereoisomers
3. cis–trans isomers
4. chiral compounds
5. achiral compounds
6. meso compounds
7. enantiomers
8. diastereomers

67. A compound has a specific rotation of −39.0. A solution of the compound (0.187 g/mL) has an observed rotation of −6.52° when placed in a polarimeter tube 10 cm long. What is the percent of each enantiomer in the solution?

68. Indicate whether each of the following pairs of compounds are identical or are enantiomers, diastereomers, or constitutional isomers:

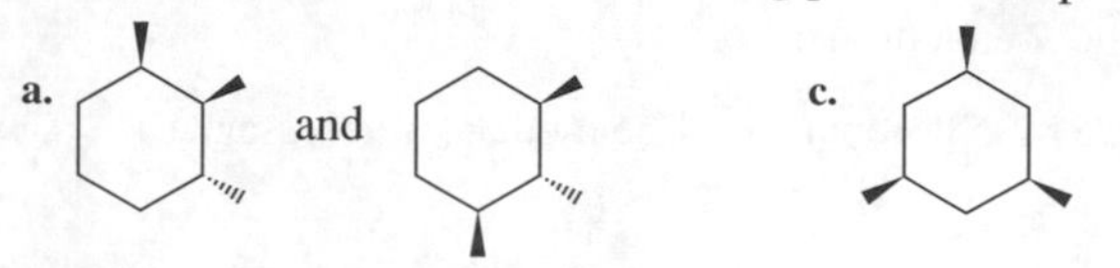

a. and c. 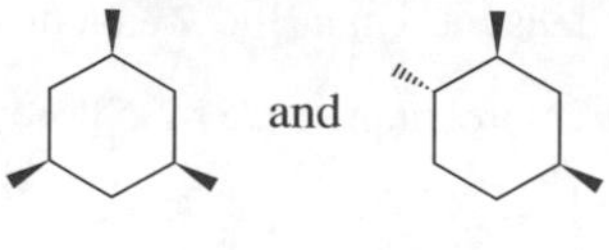 and

b. 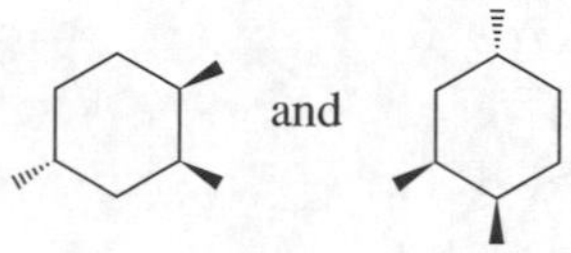 and d. 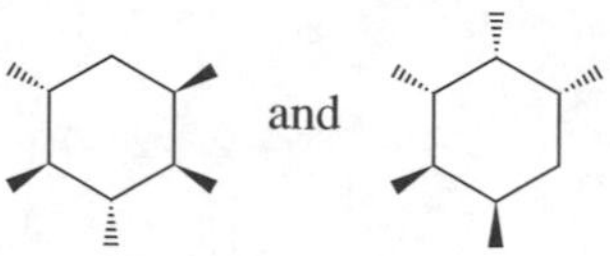 and

69. Draw structures for each of the following molecules:

a. (*S*)-1-bromo-1-chlorobutane
b. (2*R*,3*R*)-2,3-dichloropentane
c. an achiral isomer of 1,2-dimethylcyclohexane
d. a chiral isomer of 1,2-dibromocyclobutane
e. two achiral isomers of 3,4,5-trimethylheptane

70. Explain why the enantiomers of 1,2-dimethylaziridine can be separated, even though one of the "groups" attached to nitrogen is a lone pair.

enantiomers of 1,2-dimethylaziridine

71. Of the possible products shown for the following reaction, are there any that would not be formed?

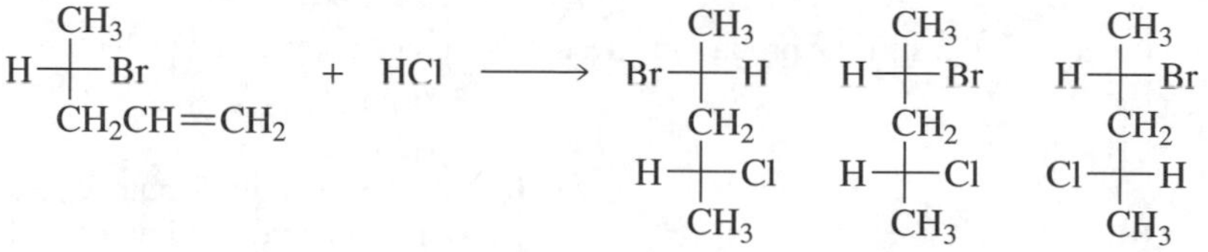

CH_3 / H—Br / $CH_2CH{=}CH_2$ + HCl ⟶ [CH_3 / Br—H / CH_2 / H—Cl / CH_3] [CH_3 / H—Br / CH_2 / H—Cl / CH_3] [CH_3 / H—Br / CH_2 / Cl—H / CH_3]

72. A sample of (*S*)-(+)-lactic acid was found to have an optical purity of 72%. How much *R* isomer is present in the sample?

73. Indicate whether each of the structures in the second row is an enantiomer of, a diastereomer of, or is identical to the structure in the top row.

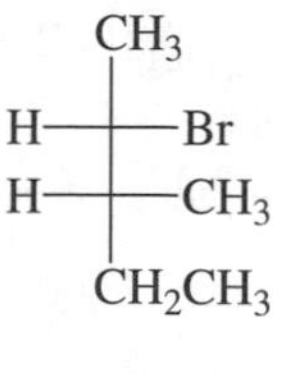

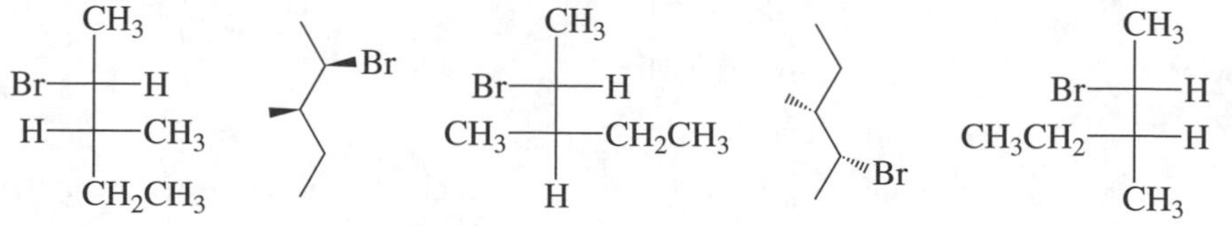

CH_3 / H—Br / H—CH_3 / CH_2CH_3

A: CH_3 / Br—H / H—CH_3 / CH_2CH_3

B: Br

C: CH_3 / Br—H / CH_3—CH_2CH_3 / H

D: Br

E: CH_3 / Br—H / CH_3CH_2—H / CH_3

74. Give the products of the following reactions including their configurations:

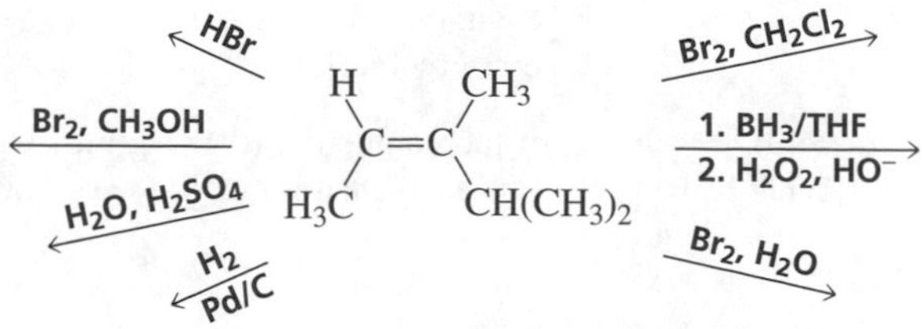

H, CH_3 / C=C / H_3C, $CH(CH_3)_2$

Reagents: HBr; Br_2, CH_3OH; H_2O, H_2SO_4; H_2 Pd/C; Br_2, CH_2Cl_2; 1. BH_3/THF 2. H_2O_2, HO^-; Br_2, H_2O

75. a. Using the wedge-and-dash notation, draw the nine stereoisomers of 1,2,3,4,5,6-hexachlorocyclohexane.
b. From the nine stereoisomers, identify one pair of enantiomers.
c. Draw the most stable conformation of the most stable stereoisomer.

76. Tamiflu is used for the prevention and treatment of flu. What is the configuration of each of its asymmetric centers?

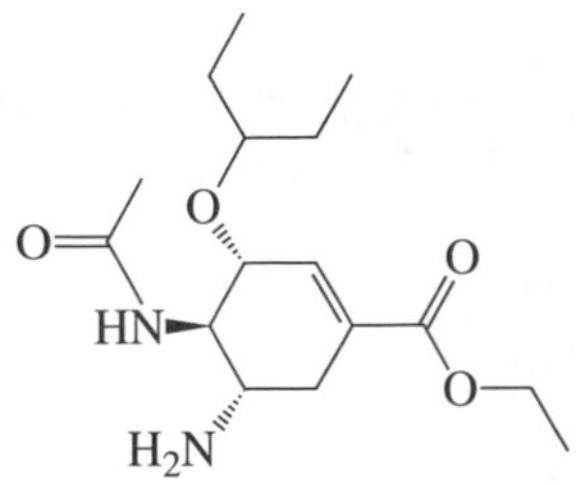

O HN O O O H_2N

Tamiflu®

77. A student decided that the configuration of the asymmetric centers in a sugar such as D-glucose could be determined rapidly by simply assigning the *R* configuration to an asymmetric center with an OH group on the right and the *S* configuration to an asymmetric center with an OH group on the left. Is he correct?

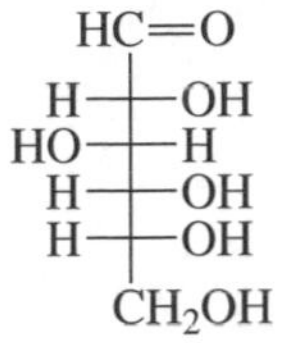

HC=O
H—OH
HO—H
H—OH
H—OH
CH_2OH

D-glucose

78. When fumarate reacts with D_2O in the presence of the enzyme fumarase, only one isomer of the product is formed, as shown below. Is the enzyme catalyzing a syn or an anti addition of D_2O?

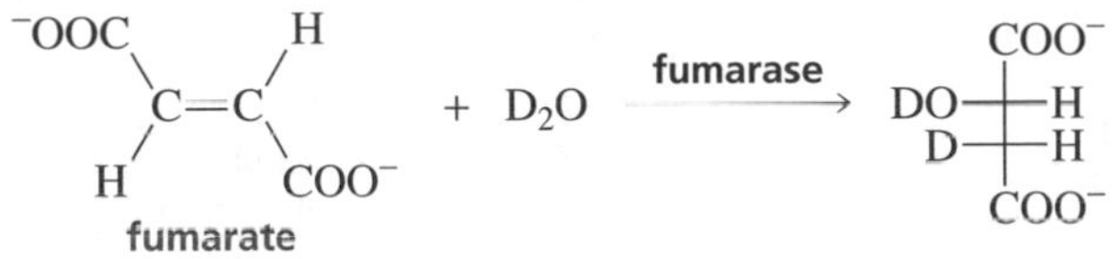

^{-}OOC, H, C=C, H, COO^{-} + D_2O —fumarase→ COO^{-}, DO—H, D—H, COO^{-}

fumarate

79. When (*S*)-(+)-1-chloro-2-methylbutane reacts with chlorine, one of the products is ( )-1,4-dichloro-2-methylbutane. Does this product have the *R* or the *S* configuration?

80. Indicate the configuration of the asymmetric centers in the following molecules:

a. 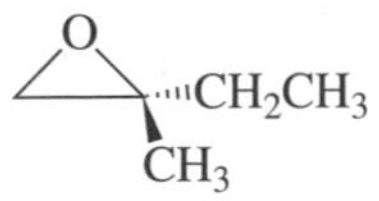 O, CH_2CH_3, CH_3 **b.** 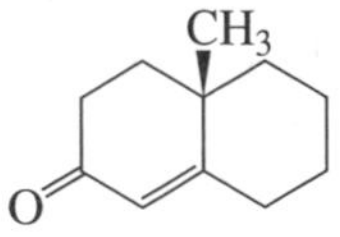 CH_3, O **c.** 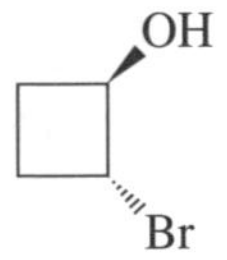 OH, Br

81. a. Draw the two chair conformers for each of the stereoisomers of *trans*-1-*tert*-butyl-3-methylcyclohexane.
b. For each pair, indicate which conformer is more stable.

82. a. Do the following compounds have any asymmetric centers?
1. $CH_2{=}C{=}CH_2$
2. $CH_3CH{=}C{=}CHCH_3$

b. Are the compounds chiral? (*Hint*: Make models.)

83. Is the following compound optically active?

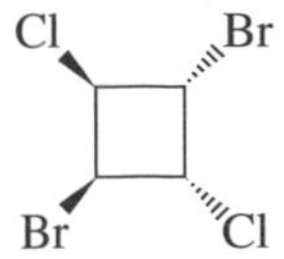

Cl, Br, Br, Cl

CHAPTER

14

Substitution Reactions of Alkyl Halides

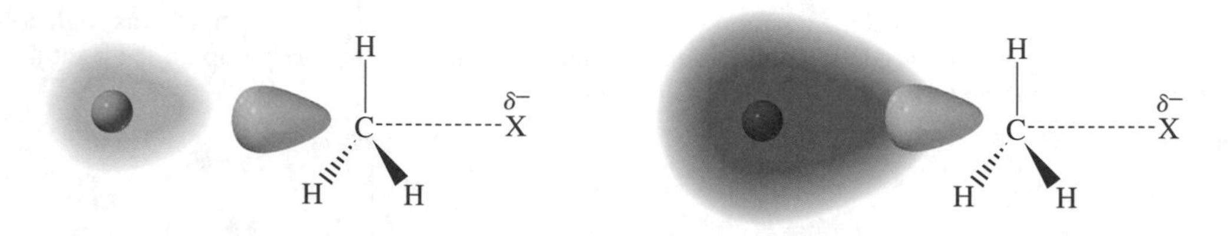

AN ELECTRONEGATIVE ATOM OR AN ELECTRON-WITHDRAWING GROUP ATTACHED TO AN sp^3 carbon creates a polar bond. A compound with such a bond can undergo substitution reactions and/or elimination reactions.

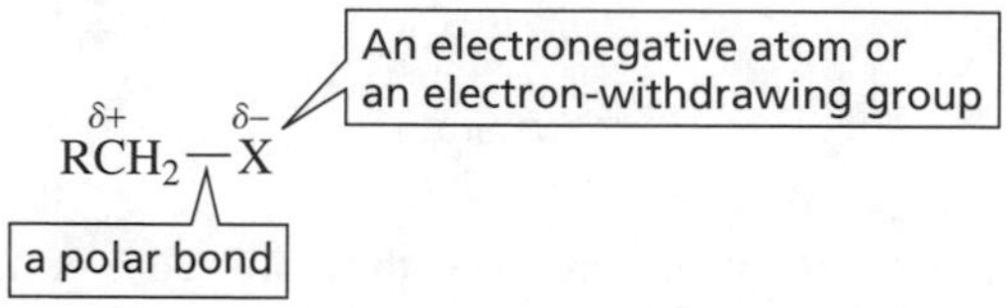

$$\overset{\delta+}{RCH_2}-\overset{\delta-}{X}$$

a polar bond

An electronegative atom or an electron-withdrawing group

In a **substitution reaction**, the electronegative atom or electron-withdrawing group is replaced by another atom or group. In an **elimination reaction**, the electronegative atom or electron-withdrawing group is eliminated, along with a hydrogen from an adjacent carbon. The atom or group that is *substituted* or *eliminated* in these reactions is called a **leaving group**.

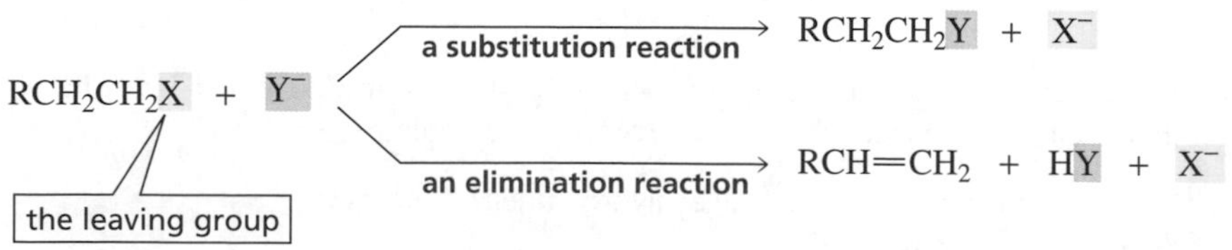

$$RCH_2CH_2X + Y^- \xrightarrow{\text{a substitution reaction}} RCH_2CH_2Y + X^-$$

$$RCH_2CH_2X + Y^- \xrightarrow{\text{an elimination reaction}} RCH{=}CH_2 + HY + X^-$$

the leaving group (X)

This chapter focuses on the substitution reactions of alkyl halides—compounds in which the leaving group is a halide ion (F^-, Cl^-, Br^-, or I^-). The nomenclature of alkyl halides was discussed in Section 11.4.

alkyl halides

R—F	R—Cl	R—Br	R—I
an alkyl fluoride	**an alkyl chloride**	**an alkyl bromide**	**an alkyl iodide**

Alkyl halides are a good family of compounds with which to start the study of substitution and elimination reactions because they have relatively good leaving groups; that is, the halide ions are easily displaced. After studying the reactions of alkyl halides, you will be prepared to look at the substitution and elimination reactions of compounds with poor leaving groups—those that are more difficult to displace.

Substitution reactions are important in organic chemistry because they make it possible to convert readily available alkyl halides into a wide variety of other compounds. Substitution reactions are also important in the cells of plants and animals. We will see, however, that because alkyl halides are insoluble in water, and cells exist in predominantly aqueous environments, biological systems use compounds in which the group that is replaced is more polar than a halogen and, therefore, more soluble in water.

Survival Compounds

For a long time chemists thought that only a few organic compounds containing halogen atoms (organohalides) occurred in nature. Now, however, over 5000 naturally occurring organohalides are known. Several marine organisms, including sponges, corals, and algae, synthesize organohalides that they use to deter predators. For example, red algae synthesize a toxic, foul-tasting organohalide that keeps predators from eating them. One predator that is not deterred, however, is a mollusk called a sea hare. After consuming red algae, a sea hare converts the algae's organohalide into a structurally similar compound it uses for its own defense. Unlike other mollusks, a sea hare does not have a shell. Its method of defense is to surround itself with a slimy substance that contains the organohalide, thereby protecting itself from carnivorous fish.

Humans synthesize organohalides to defend against infection. The human immune system has an enzyme that kills invading bacteria by halogenating them.

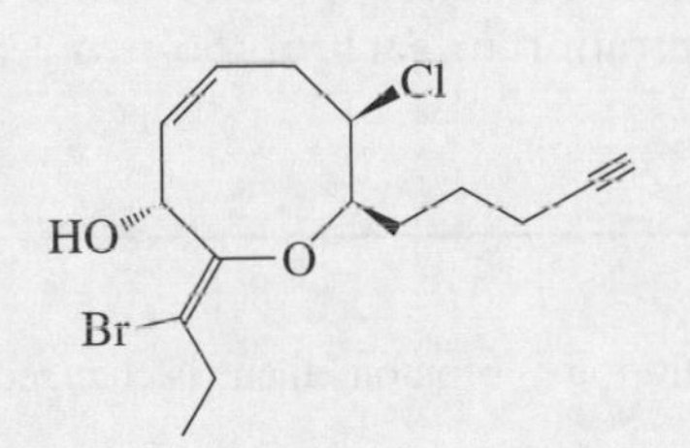

synthesized by red algae

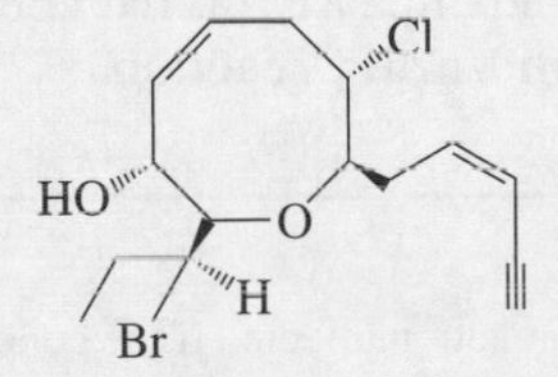

synthesized by the sea hare

a sea hare

14.1 THE MECHANISM FOR AN S_N2 REACTION

You will see that there are two different mechanisms by which a substitution reaction can take place. As you would expect, each of these mechanisms involves the *reaction of a nucleophile with an electrophile*. In both mechanisms, the atom or group that replaces the leaving group is a nucleophile. The substitution reactions therefore are more precisely called **nucleophilic substitution reactions**.

Perhaps you have been wondering how the mechanism for a reaction is determined. Remember that a mechanism describes the step-by-step process by which reactants are converted into products. It is a theory that fits the accumulated experimental evidence pertaining to the reaction. We can learn a great deal about a reaction's mechanism by studying its **kinetics**—the factors that affect the rate of the reaction.

The rate of the reaction of bromomethane with hydroxide ion—a nucleophilic substitution reaction—depends on the concentrations of both reagents. If the concentration of bromomethane in the reaction mixture is doubled, the rate of the reaction doubles. Likewise,

BIOGRAPHY

Edward Davies Hughes (1906–1963), *born in northern Wales, earned a Ph.D. from the University of Wales and a D.Sc. from the University of London, where he worked with Sir Christopher Ingold. He was a professor of chemistry at University College, London.*

if the concentration of the nucleophile (hydroxide ion) is doubled, the rate of the reaction doubles. If the concentrations of both reactants are doubled, the rate of the reaction quadruples.

$$CH_3Br + HO^- \longrightarrow CH_3OH + Br^-$$

bromomethane methanol

Because we know the relationship between the rate of the reaction and the concentration of the reactants, we can write a rate law for the reaction (Section 3.8):

$$\textbf{rate} \propto \textbf{[alkyl halide][nucleophile]}$$

The proportionality sign ($\propto$) can be replaced by an equals sign and a proportionality constant (k).

The proportionality constant is called a **rate constant**. The magnitude of the rate constant for a particular reaction indicates how difficult it is for the reactants to overcome the energy barrier of the reaction—how hard it is to reach the transition state. The larger the rate constant, the lower is the energy barrier and, therefore, the easier it is for the reactants to reach the transition state.

$$\text{rate} = k\,\text{[alkyl halide][nucleophile]}$$

the rate constant

The **rate law** tells us which molecules are involved in the transition state of the rate-determining step of the reaction. From the rate law for the reaction of bromomethane with hydroxide ion, for example, we know that *both* bromomethane and hydroxide ion are involved in the rate-determining transition state. Because the rate of this reaction depends linearly on the concentration of each of the two reactants, the reaction is a **second-order reaction**.

PROBLEM 1 ♦

How is the rate of the reaction affected if the concentration of bromomethane is changed from 1.00 M to 0.50 M?

BIOGRAPHY

Sir Christopher Ingold (1893–1970), *in addition to determining the mechanism for the* S_N2 *reaction, was a member of the group that developed the system of nomenclature for enantiomers. He also participated in developing resonance theory.*

The reaction of bromomethane with hydroxide ion is an example of an **S_N2 reaction**, where "S" stands for substitution, "N" for nucleophilic, and "2" for bimolecular. **Bimolecular** means that two molecules are involved in the transition state of the rate-determining step. In 1937, Edward Hughes and Christopher Ingold proposed a mechanism for an S_N2 reaction. They based their mechanism on the following three pieces of *experimental evidence*:

1. The rate of the substitution reaction depends on the concentration of the alkyl halide *and* on the concentration of the nucleophile, indicating that both reactants are involved in the transition state of the rate-determining step.
2. As the hydrogens of bromomethane are successively replaced with methyl groups, the rate of the substitution reaction with a given nucleophile becomes progressively slower (Table 14.1).
3. The substitution reaction of an alkyl halide in which the halogen is bonded to an asymmetric center leads to the formation of only one stereoisomer, and the configuration of the asymmetric center in the product is inverted relative to its configuration in the reacting alkyl halide.

Hughes and Ingold proposed that an S_N2 reaction is a *concerted* reaction (that is, it takes place in a single step), so no intermediates are formed. The nucleophile attacks the electrophilic carbon that bears the leaving group, and displaces the leaving group.

Table 14.1 Relative Rates of S_N2 Reactions for Several Alkyl Halides

$$R{-}Br + Cl^- \xrightarrow{S_N2} R{-}Cl + Br^-$$

Alkyl halide	Class of alkyl halide	Relative rate
$CH_3{-}Br$	methyl	1200
$CH_3CH_2{-}Br$	primary	40
$CH_3CH_2CH_2{-}Br$	primary	16
$CH_3CH(CH_3){-}Br$	secondary	1
$CH_3C(CH_3)_2{-}Br$	tertiary	too slow to measure

MECHANISM FOR THE S_N2 REACTION OF AN ALKYL HALIDE

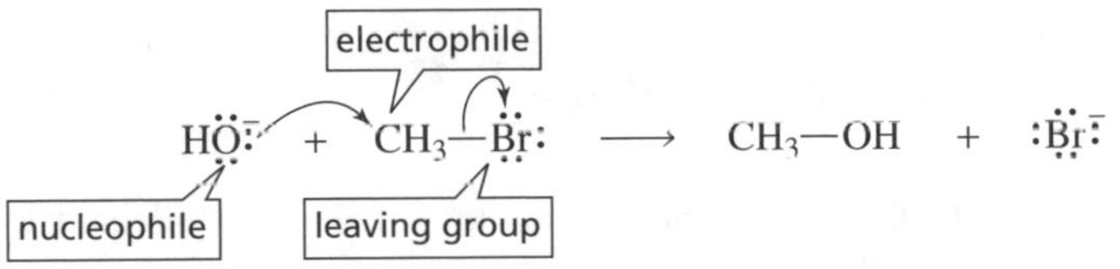

$$HO^- + CH_3{-}Br \longrightarrow CH_3{-}OH + Br^-$$

electrophile

nucleophile

leaving group

An S_N2 reaction is a one-step reaction.

A productive collision is one that leads to the formation of the product. A productive collision in an S_N2 reaction requires the nucleophile to hit the carbon on the side opposite the side bonded to the leaving group. Therefore, the carbon is said to undergo **back-side attack**. Why must the nucleophile attack from the back side? The simplest explanation is that the leaving group blocks the approach of the nucleophile to the front side of the molecule.

Molecular orbital theory also explains back-side attack. To form a bond, the LUMO (lowest unoccupied molecular orbital) of one species must interact with the HOMO (highest occupied molecular orbital) of the other. When the nucleophile approaches the alkyl halide, the filled nonbonding molecular orbital (the HOMO) of the nucleophile must interact with the empty σ^* antibonding molecular orbital (the LUMO) associated with the C—Br bond. Figure 14.1a shows that in a back-side attack, a bonding interaction occurs between the nucleophile and the larger lobe of σ^*. Compare this with what happens when the nucleophile approaches the front side of the carbon (Figure 14.1b): Both a bonding and an antibonding interaction occur, and the two cancel each other, so no bond forms. Consequently, a nucleophile always approaches an sp^3 carbon from its back side. (We saw back-side attack previously in the reaction of a bromide ion with a cyclic bromonium ion.)

A nucleophile attacks the back side of the carbon that is bonded to the leaving group.

How does Hughes and Ingold's mechanism account for the three pieces of experimental evidence? The mechanism shows that the alkyl halide and the nucleophile come together in the transition state of the one-step reaction. Therefore, increasing the concentration of either of them makes their collision more probable. Thus, the reaction will follow second-order kinetics, exactly as observed.

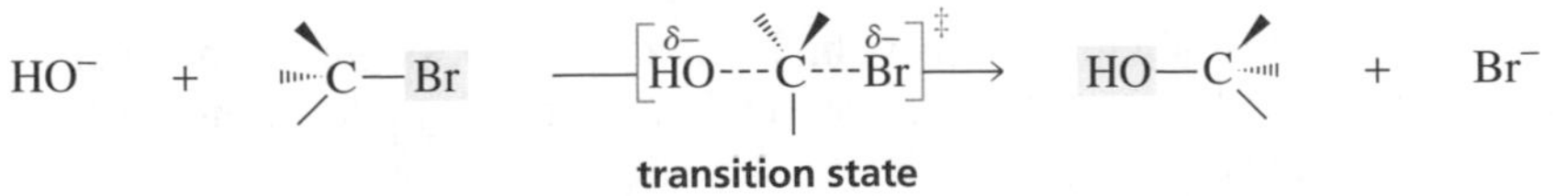

$$HO^- + C{-}Br \longrightarrow \left[\overset{\delta-}{HO}\text{---}C\text{---}\overset{\delta-}{Br}\right]^{\ddagger} \longrightarrow HO{-}C + Br^-$$

transition state

▶ Figure 14.1
(a) Back-side attack results in a bonding interaction between the HOMO (the filled nonbonding orbital) of the nucleophile and the LUMO (the empty σ^* antibonding orbital) of C—Br.
(b) Front-side attack results in both a bonding and an antibonding interaction that cancel each other out.

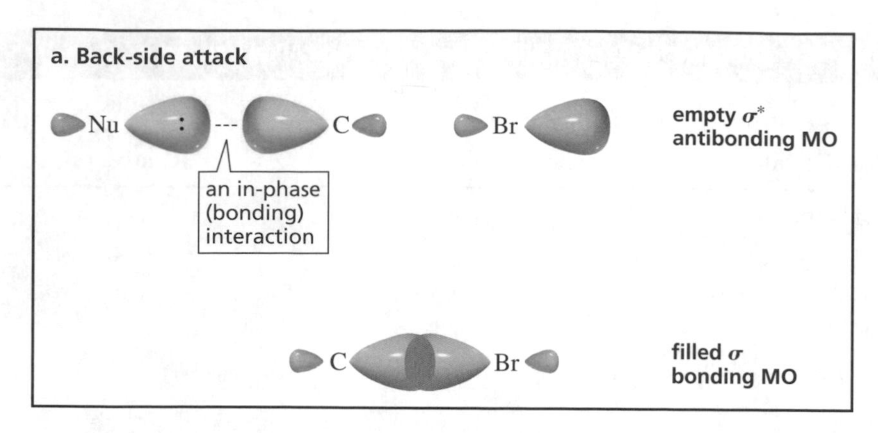

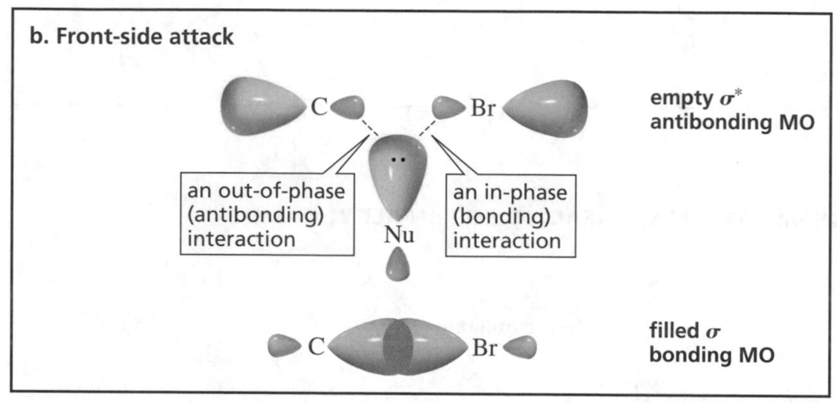

B I O G R A P H Y

Viktor Meyer (1848–1897) *was born in Germany. To prevent him from becoming an actor, his parents persuaded him to enter the University of Heidelberg, where he earned a Ph.D. in 1867 at the age of 18. Meyer was a professor of chemistry at the Universities of Stuttgart and Heidelberg. He coined the term* stereochemistry *for the study of molecular shapes and was the first to describe the effect of steric hindrance on a reaction.*

Bulky substituents attached to the carbon that undergoes back-side attack will decrease the nucleophile's access to the carbon's back side and will therefore decrease the rate of the reaction (Figure 14.2). This explains why substituting methyl groups for the hydrogens in bromomethane progressively slows the rate of the substitution reaction (Table 14.1).

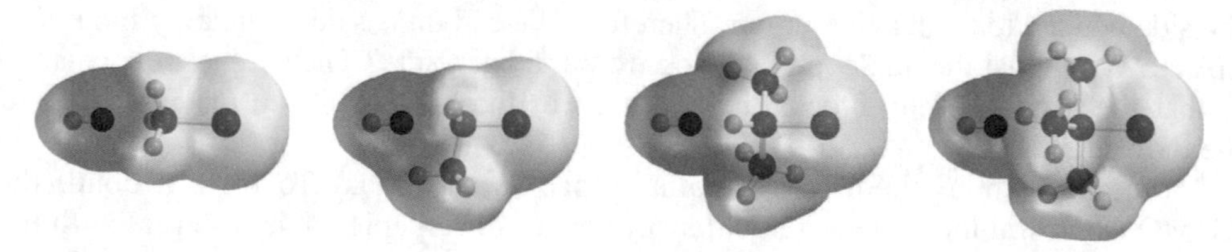

▲ Figure 14.2
The approach of HO^- to a methyl halide, a primary alkyl halide, a secondary alkyl halide, and a tertiary alkyl halide. Increasing the bulk of the substituents bonded to the carbon that is undergoing nucleophilic attack decreases access to the back side of the carbon, thereby decreasing the rate of the S_N2 reaction.

Steric effects are effects caused by the fact that groups occupy a certain volume of space (Section 11.10). A steric effect that decreases reactivity is called **steric hindrance**. Steric hindrance occurs when groups are in the way at a reaction site. Steric hindrance causes alkyl halides to have the following relative reactivities in an S_N2 reaction because, *generally*, primary alkyl halides are less sterically hindered than secondary alkyl halides, which, in turn, are less sterically hindered than tertiary alkyl halides:

The relative lack of steric hindrance causes methyl halides and primary alkyl halides to be the most reactive alkyl halides in S_N2 reactions.

relative reactivities of alkyl halides in an S_N2 reaction

most reactive > methyl halide > 1° alkyl halide > 2° alkyl halide > 3° alkyl halide < too unreactive to undergo an S_N2 reaction

Tertiary alkyl halides cannot undergo S_N2 reactions.

The three alkyl groups of a tertiary alkyl halide make it impossible for the nucleophile to come within bonding distance of the tertiary carbon, so tertiary alkyl halides are unable to undergo S_N2 reactions.

The reaction coordinate diagrams for the S_N2 reaction of *unhindered* bromomethane (Figure 14.3a) and for the S_N2 reaction of a *sterically hindered* secondary alkyl bromide (Figure 14.3b) show that steric hindrance raises the energy of the transition state, slowing the reaction.

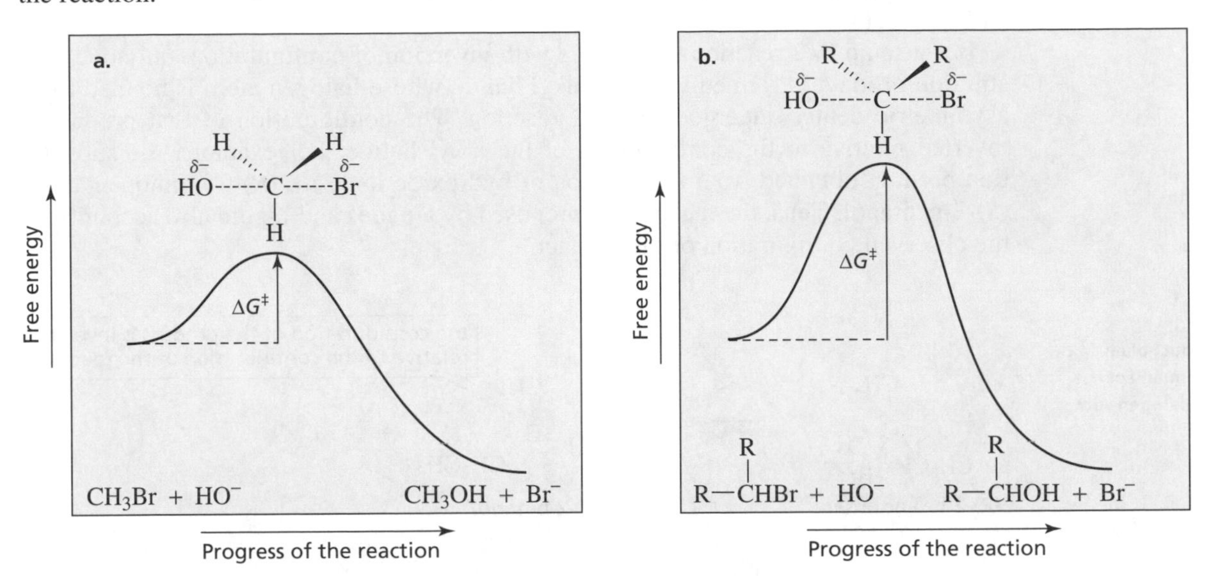

▲ **Figure 14.3**
Reaction coordinate diagrams for (a) the S_N2 reaction of bromomethane with hydroxide ion; (b) an S_N2 reaction of a sterically hindered secondary alkyl bromide with hydroxide ion.

PROBLEM 2 ♦

Does increasing the energy barrier for an S_N2 reaction increase or decrease the magnitude of the rate constant for the reaction?

The rate of an S_N2 reaction depends not only on the *number* of alkyl groups attached to the carbon that is undergoing nucleophilic attack, but also on their size. For example, while bromoethane and 1-bromopropane are both primary alkyl halides, bromoethane is more than twice as reactive in an S_N2 reaction (Table 14.1) because the bulkier alkyl group on the carbon undergoing nucleophilic attack in 1-bromopropane provides more steric hindrance to back-side attack. Also, although 1-bromo-2,2-dimethylpropane is a primary alkyl halide, it undergoes S_N2 reactions very slowly because its single alkyl group is unusually bulky.

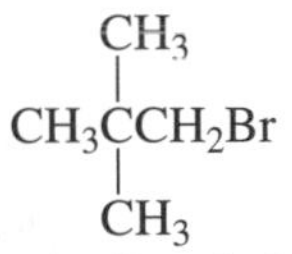

CH_3
CH_3CCH_2Br
CH_3
1-bromo-2,2-dimethylpropane

Now we will look at the third piece of experimental evidence used by Hughes and Ingold to arrive at their proposed mechanism. Figure 14.4 shows that as the nucleophile approaches the back side of the carbon of bromomethane, the C—H bonds begin to move away from the nucleophile and its attacking electrons. By the time the transition state is reached, the C—H bonds are all in the same plane and the carbon is pentacoordinate (fully bonded to three atoms and partially bonded to two) rather than tetrahedral. As the nucleophile gets closer to the carbon and the bromine moves farther away from it, the C—H bonds continue to move in the same direction. Eventually, the bond between carbon and the nucleophile is fully formed, and the bond between carbon and bromine is completely broken, so the carbon is once again tetrahedral.

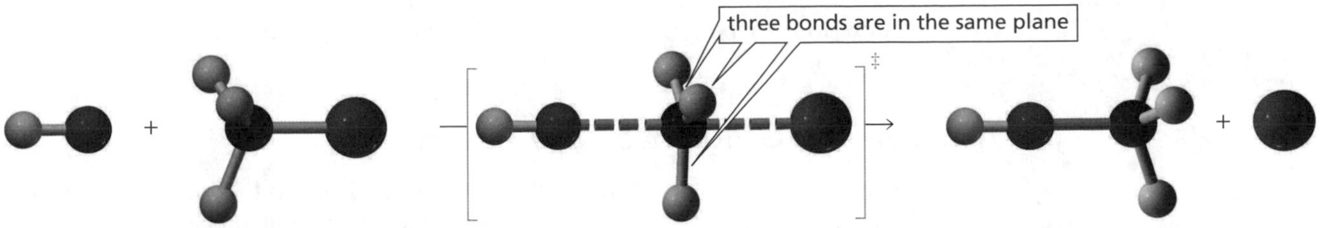

three bonds are in the same plane

▲ **Figure 14.4**
An S_N2 reaction between hydroxide ion and bromomethane.

chem place Tutorial: S_N2

Tutorial: S_N2: a concerted reaction

Tutorial: Steric hindrance in the S_N2 reaction

The carbon at which substitution occurs has inverted its configuration during the course of the reaction, just like an umbrella tends to invert in a windstorm. This **inversion of configuration** is called a *Walden inversion*, after Paul Walden, who first discovered that the configuration of a compound becomes inverted during the course of an S_N2 reaction.

Because an S_N2 reaction takes place with inversion of configuration, only one substitution product is formed when an alkyl halide whose halogen atom is bonded to an asymmetric center undergoes an S_N2 reaction. The configuration of that product is inverted relative to the configuration of the alkyl halide. For example, the substitution product obtained from the reaction of hydroxide ion with (*R*)-2-bromopentane is (*S*)-2-pentanol. Thus, the mechanism proposed by Hughes and Ingold also accounts for the observed configuration of the product.

To draw the inverted product of an S_N2 reaction, draw the mirror image of the reactant and replace the halogen with the nucleophile.

the configuration of the product is inverted relative to the configuration of the reactant

$$CH_3CH_2C(CH_3)(H)Br + HO^- \longrightarrow HC(CH_3)(HO)CH_2CH_3 + Br^-$$

(*R*)-2-bromobutane → **(*S*)-2-butanol**

PROBLEM 3♦

Arrange the following alkyl bromides in order of decreasing reactivity in an S_N2 reaction: 1-bromo-2-methylbutane, 1-bromo-3-methylbutane, 2-bromo-2-methylbutane, and 1-bromopentane.

PROBLEM 4♦ SOLVED

Determine the product that would be formed from the S_N2 reaction of

a. 2-bromobutane and hydroxide ion.
b. (*R*)-2-bromobutane and hydroxide ion.
c. (*S*)-3-chlorohexane and hydroxide ion.
d. 3-iodopentane and hydroxide ion.

Solution to 4a The product is 2-butanol. Because the reaction is an S_N2 reaction, we know that the configuration of the product is inverted relative to the configuration of the reactant. The configuration of the reactant is not specified, however, so we cannot specify the configuration of the product.

the configuration is not specified

$$CH_3CH(Br)CH_2CH_3 + HO^- \longrightarrow CH_3CH(OH)CH_2CH_3 + Br^-$$

BIOGRAPHY

Paul Walden (1863–1957) *was born in Cesis, Latvia, the son of a farmer. His parents died when he was a child, and he supported himself at Riga University and St. Petersburg University by working as a tutor. Walden received a Ph.D. from the University of Leipzig and returned to Latvia to become a professor of chemistry at Riga University. Following the Russian Revolution, he went back to Germany to be a professor at the University of Rostock and, later, at the University of Tübingen.*

14.2 FACTORS THAT AFFECT S_N2 REACTIONS

We will now look at how the nature of the leaving group and the nucleophile affect the S_N2 reaction.

The Leaving Group in an S_N2 Reaction

If an alkyl iodide, an alkyl bromide, an alkyl chloride, and an alkyl fluoride all having the same alkyl group were allowed to react with the same nucleophile under the same conditions, we would find that the alkyl iodide is the most reactive and the alkyl fluoride is the least reactive.

	relative rates of reaction
$HO^- + RCH_2I \longrightarrow RCH_2OH + I^-$	30,000
$HO^- + RCH_2Br \longrightarrow RCH_2OH + Br^-$	10,000
$HO^- + RCH_2Cl \longrightarrow RCH_2OH + Cl^-$	200
$HO^- + RCH_2F \longrightarrow RCH_2OH + F^-$	1

The only difference between these four reactions is the nature of the leaving group. From the relative reaction rates, we can see that iodide ion is the best leaving group and fluoride ion is the worst. This brings us to an important rule in organic chemistry that you will encounter frequently: *the weaker the basicity of a group, the better is its leaving propensity*. The reason leaving propensity depends on basicity (even though the former is a kinetic concept and the latter a thermodynamic concept) is that *weak bases are stable bases*; they readily bear the electrons they formerly shared with a proton. Therefore, they do not share their electrons well. Thus a weak base is not bonded as strongly to the carbon as a strong base would be, and a weaker bond is more readily broken.

We have seen that iodide ion is the weakest base of the halide ions and fluoride ion is the strongest. Therefore, alkyl iodides are the most reactive of the alkyl halides and alkyl fluorides are the least reactive. In fact, the fluoride ion is such a strong base that alkyl fluorides essentially do not undergo S_N2 reactions.

relative reactivities of alkyl halides in an S_N2 reaction

most reactive → RI > RBr > RCl > RF ← too unreactive to undergo an S_N2 reaction

The weaker the base, the better it is as a leaving group.

Stable bases are weak bases.

At the beginning of this chapter, we saw that it is the polar carbon–halogen bond that causes alkyl halides to undergo substitution reactions. Carbon and iodine, however, have the same electronegativity. Why, then, does an alkyl iodide undergo a substitution reaction? We know that larger atoms are more polarizable than smaller atoms. (Recall that polarizability is a measure of how easily an atom's electron cloud can be distorted.) The high polarizability of the large iodine atom causes the C—I bond to react as if it were polar, even though, on the basis of the electronegativity of the carbon and iodine atoms, the bond is nonpolar.

The Nucleophile in an S_N2 Reaction

When we talk about atoms or molecules that have lone-pair electrons, sometimes we call them bases and sometimes we call them nucleophiles. What is the difference between a base and a nucleophile?

Basicity is a measure of how well a compound (a **base**) shares its lone pair with a proton. The stronger the base, the better it shares its electrons. Basicity is measured by an *equilibrium constant* (the acid dissociation constant, K_a) that indicates the tendency of the conjugate acid of the base to lose a proton.

Nucleophilicity is a measure of how readily a compound (a **nucleophile**) is able to attack an electron-deficient atom. Nucleophilicity is measured by a *rate constant* (k). In the case of an S_N2 reaction, nucleophilicity is a measure of how readily the nucleophile attacks an sp^3 carbon bonded to a leaving group. Because the nucleophile attacks the sp^3 carbon in the rate-determining step of the reaction, the rate of the reaction will depend on the strength of the nucleophile: the better the nucleophile, the faster will be the rate of the S_N2 reaction.

In general, *stronger bases are better nucleophiles*. For example, a species with a negative charge is a stronger base *and* a better nucleophile than a species that has the same attacking atom but that is neutral. Thus, HO^- is a stronger base and a better nucleophile than H_2O. Notice that bases are described as being strong or weak; nucleophiles are described as being good or poor.

stronger base, better nucleophile		weaker base, poorer nucleophile
HO^-	>	H_2O
CH_3O^-	>	CH_3OH
$^-NH_2$	>	NH_3
$CH_3CH_2NH^-$	>	$CH_3CH_2NH_2$

If hydrogens are attached to the second-row elements, the resulting compounds have the following relative acidities:

relative acid strengths

weakest acid — $NH_3 < H_2O < HF$

Because the weakest acid has the strongest conjugate base, the conjugate bases have the following relative base strengths *and* relative nucleophilicities:

relative base strengths and relative nucleophilicities

strongest base, best nucleophile — $^-NH_2 > HO^- > F^-$

Notice that the amide anion is the strongest base, as well as the best nucleophile.

If, however, the attacking atoms of the nucleophiles are *very different in size*, another factor comes into play: the polarizability of the atom. Because the electrons are farther away in the larger atom, they are not held as tightly and can, therefore, move more freely toward a positive charge. As a result, the electrons are able to overlap the orbital of carbon from farther away, as shown in Figure 14.5. This results in a greater degree of bonding in the transition state, which makes the transition state more stable.

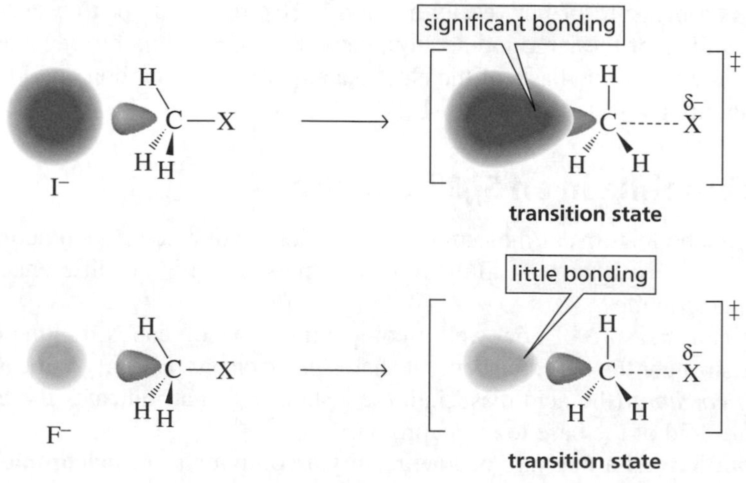

significant bonding

I^- → transition state

little bonding

F^- → transition state

▶ **Figure 14.5**
An iodide ion is larger and more polarizable than a fluoride ion. Therefore, when an iodide ion attacks a carbon, the relatively loosely held electrons of the ion can overlap the orbital of carbon from farther away. The tightly bound electrons of the fluoride ion cannot start to overlap the orbital of carbon until the reactants are closer together.

Now the question becomes, does the greater polarizability that helps the larger atoms to be better nucleophiles make up for the decreased basicity that causes them to be poorer nucleophiles? The answer depends on the solvent.

If the reaction is carried out in an **aprotic polar solvent**—meaning the solvent molecules *do not have* a hydrogen bonded to an oxygen or to a nitrogen—the direct relationship between basicity and nucleophilicity is maintained: the stronger bases are still the best nucleophiles. In other words, the greater polarizability of the larger atoms does not make up for their decreased basicity. *Therefore iodide ion is the poorest nucleophile of the* *halide ions in an aprotic polar solvent.* If, however, the reaction is carried out in a **protic solvent**—meaning the solvent molecules *have* a hydrogen bonded to an oxygen or to a nitrogen—the relationship between basicity and nucleophilicity becomes inverted. The largest atom is the best nucleophile even though it is the weakest base. *Therefore, iodide ion is the best nucleophile of the halide ions in a protic solvent.* (For a list of protic and aprotic solvents, see Table 14.5 on page 596.)

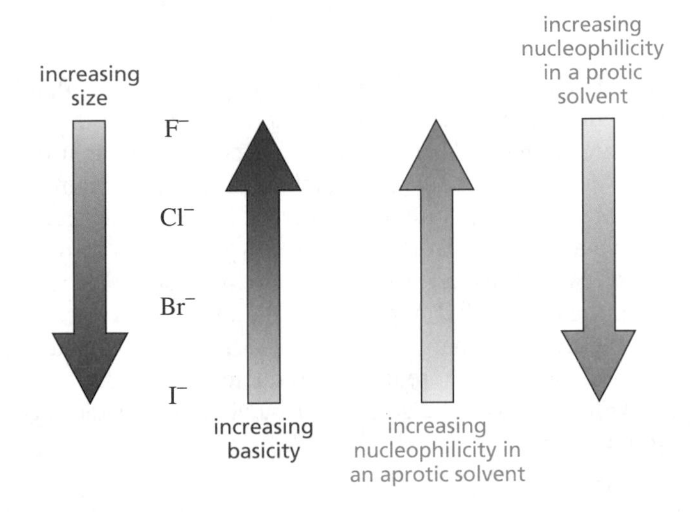

An aprotic solvent does not contain a hydrogen bonded to either an oxygen or a nitrogen.

A protic solvent contains a hydrogen bonded to an oxygen or a nitrogen.

PROBLEM 5 ♦

Indicate whether each of the following solvents is protic or aprotic:

a. chloroform ($CHCl_3$)
b. diethyl ether ($CH_3CH_2OCH_2CH_3$)
c. acetic acid (CH_3COOH)
d. hexane [$CH_3(CH_2)_4CH_3$]

Nucleophilicity Is Affected by the Solvent

Why, in a protic solvent, is the smallest atom the poorest nucleophile even though it is the strongest base? *How does a protic solvent make strong bases less nucleophilic?* When a negatively charged species is placed in a protic solvent, the ion becomes solvated. Protic solvents are hydrogen bond donors, so the solvent molecules arrange themselves with their partially positively charged hydrogens pointing toward the negatively charged species. The interaction between the ion and the dipole of the protic solvent is called an **ion–dipole interaction**.

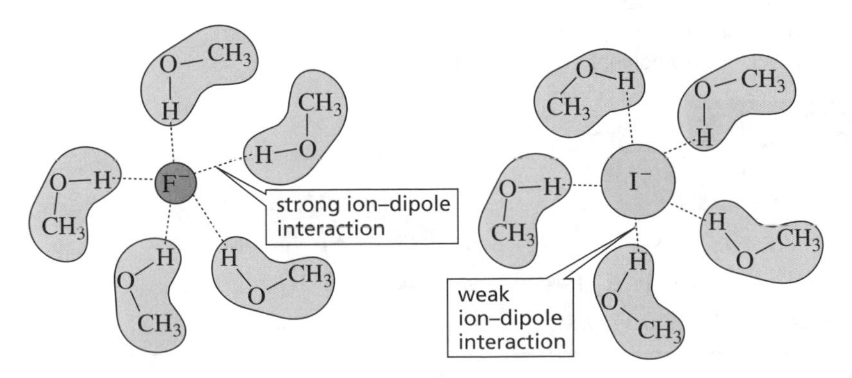

Because the solvent shields the nucleophile, at least one of the ion–dipole interactions must be broken before the nucleophile can participate in an S_N2 reaction. Weak bases interact weakly with protic solvents, whereas strong bases interact more strongly because they are better at sharing their electrons. It is easier, therefore, to break the ion–dipole interactions between an iodide ion (a weak base) and the solvent than between a fluoride ion (a stronger base) and the solvent. As a result, in a protic solvent, an iodide ion, even though it is a weaker base, is a better nucleophile than a fluoride ion (Table 14.2).

Table 14.2 Relative Nucleophilicity toward CH_3I in Methanol

$RS^- > I^- > {}^-C{\equiv}N > CH_3O^- > Br^- > NH_3 > Cl^- > F^- > CH_3OH$

← increasing nucleophilicity

Fluoride ion would be a better nucleophile in a *nonpolar solvent* than in a polar solvent because there would be no ion–dipole interactions between the ion and the nonpolar solvent; but ionic compounds are insoluble in most nonpolar solvents. They can, however, dissolve in aprotic polar solvents, such as dimethylformamide (DMF) or dimethyl sulfoxide (DMSO). An **aprotic polar solvent** is not a hydrogen bond donor because it does not have a hydrogen attached to an oxygen or to a nitrogen, so there are no positively charged hydrogens to form ion–dipole interactions. The molecules of an aprotic polar solvent have a partial negative charge on their surface that can solvate cations, but the partial positive charge is on the *inside* of the molecule, and therefore less accessible. Fluoride ion, therefore, is a good nucleophile in DMSO and a poor nucleophile in water. Fluoride ion is also a good nucleophile in the gas phase, where there are no solvent molecules.

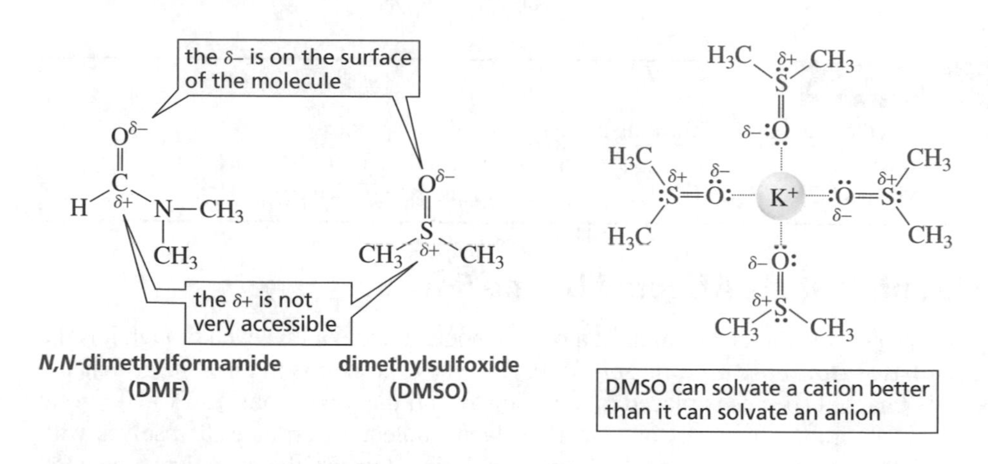
the δ– is on the surface of the molecule
the δ+ is not very accessible
N,N-dimethylformamide (DMF)
dimethylsulfoxide (DMSO)
DMSO can solvate a cation better than it can solvate an anion

PROBLEM 6 ♦

a. Which is a stronger base, RO^- or RS^-?
b. Which is a better nucleophile in an aqueous solution?
c. Which is a better nucleophile in DMSO?

PROBLEM 7 ♦

Which is a better nucleophile?

a. Br^- or Cl^- in H_2O
b. Br^- or Cl^- in DMSO
c. CH_3O^- or CH_3OH in H_2O
d. CH_3O^- or CH_3OH in DMSO
e. HO^- or ${}^-NH_2$ in H_2O
f. HO^- or ${}^-NH_2$ in DMSO
g. I^- or Br^- in H_2O
h. I^- or Br^- in DMSO

Nucleophilicity Is Affected by Steric Effects

Base strength is relatively unaffected by steric effects because a base removes a relatively unhindered proton. The strength of a base depends only on how well the base shares its electrons with a proton. Thus, *tert*-butoxide ion, in spite of its bulkier substituents, is a stronger base than ethoxide ion since *tert*-butanol ($pK_a = 18$) is a weaker acid than ethanol ($pK_a = 15.9$).

$CH_3CH_2O^-$	$CH_3C(CH_3)_2O^-$
ethoxide ion	***tert*-butoxide ion**
better nucleophile	**stronger base**

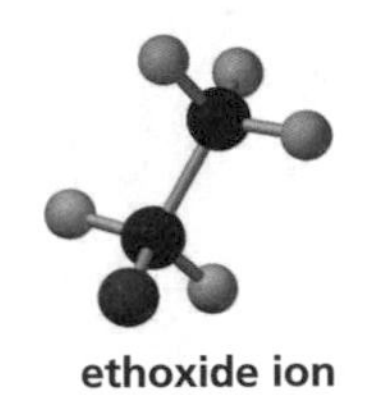

ethoxide ion

tert-butoxide ion

Steric effects, on the other hand, do affect nucleophilicity. A bulky nucleophile cannot approach the back side of a carbon as easily as a less sterically hindered nucleophile can. Thus, *tert*-butoxide ion, with its three methyl groups, is a poorer nucleophile than ethoxide ion, even though *tert*-butoxide ion is a stronger base.

PROBLEM 8 SOLVED

List the following species in order of *decreasing* nucleophilicity in an aqueous solution:

$$C_6H_5O^- \quad CH_3OH \quad HO^- \quad CH_3\overset{O}{\overset{\|}{C}}O^- \quad CH_3S^-$$

Solution Let's first divide the nucleophiles into groups. There is one nucleophile with a negatively charged sulfur, three with negatively charged oxygens, and one with a neutral oxygen. We know that in the polar aqueous solvent, the compound with the negatively charged sulfur is the most nucleophilic because sulfur is larger than oxygen. We also know that the poorest nucleophile is the one with the neutral oxygen atom. To complete the problem, we need to rank the three nucleophiles with negatively charged oxygens, which we can do by looking at the pK_a values of their conjugate acids. A carboxylic acid is a stronger acid than phenol, which is a stronger acid than water. Because water is the weakest acid, its conjugate base is the strongest base and the best nucleophile. Thus, the relative nucleophilicities are:

$$CH_3S^- > HO^- > C_6H_5O^- > CH_3\overset{O}{\overset{\|}{C}}O^- > CH_3OH$$

PROBLEM 9 ◆

For each of the following pairs of S_N2 reactions, indicate which occurs faster:

a. $CH_3CH_2Br + H_2O$ or $CH_3CH_2Br + HO^-$

b. $CH_3CH(CH_3)CH_2Br + HO^-$ or $CH_3CH_2CH(CH_3)Br + HO^-$

c. $CH_3CH_2Cl + CH_3O^-$ or $CH_3CH_2Cl + CH_3S^-$ **(in ethanol)**

d. $CH_3CH_2Cl + I^-$ or $CH_3CH_2Br + I^-$

14.3 THE REVERSIBILITY OF AN S_N2 REACTION DEPENDS ON THE BASICITIES OF THE LEAVING GROUPS IN THE FORWARD AND REVERSE DIRECTIONS

Many different kinds of nucleophiles can react with alkyl halides. Therefore, a wide range of organic compounds can be synthesized by means of S_N2 reactions. Notice that the second-to-last reaction on page 582 is the reaction of an alkyl halide with an acetylide ion. This is the reaction that is used to create longer carbon chains.

$$CH_3CH_2Cl + HO^- \longrightarrow CH_3CH_2OH + Cl^-$$
an alcohol

$$CH_3CH_2Br + HS^- \longrightarrow CH_3CH_2SH + Br^-$$
a thiol

$$CH_3CH_2I + RO^- \longrightarrow CH_3CH_2OR + I^-$$
an ether

$$CH_3CH_2Br + RS^- \longrightarrow CH_3CH_2SR + Br^-$$
a thioether

$$CH_3CH_2Cl + {}^-NH_2 \longrightarrow CH_3CH_2NH_2 + Cl^-$$
a primary amine

$$CH_3CH_2Br + {}^-C{\equiv}CR \longrightarrow CH_3CH_2C{\equiv}CR + Br^-$$
an alkyne

$$CH_3CH_2I + {}^-C{\equiv}N \longrightarrow CH_3CH_2C{\equiv}N + I^-$$
a nitrile

It may seem that the reverse of each of these reactions satisfies the requirements for a nucleophilic substitution reaction. For example, the reverse of the first reaction would be the reaction of chloride ion (a nucleophile) with ethanol (with an HO^- leaving group). But ethanol and chloride ion do *not* react.

Why does a nucleophilic substitution reaction take place in one direction, but not in the other? We can answer this question by comparing the leaving propensity of Cl^- in the forward direction and the leaving propensity of HO^- in the reverse direction. To compare leaving propensities means comparing basicities. Because HCl is a much stronger acid than H_2O (Table 14.3), Cl^- is a much weaker base than HO^-; and because it is a weaker base, Cl^- is a better leaving group. Consequently, HO^- can displace Cl^- in the forward reaction, but Cl^- cannot displace HO^- in the reverse reaction. This is shown graphically in Figure 14.6a: the free energy of activation in the forward direction is much smaller than the free energy of activation in the reverse direction. Thus, an S_N2 reaction proceeds in the direction that allows the stronger base to displace the weaker base (the better leaving group).

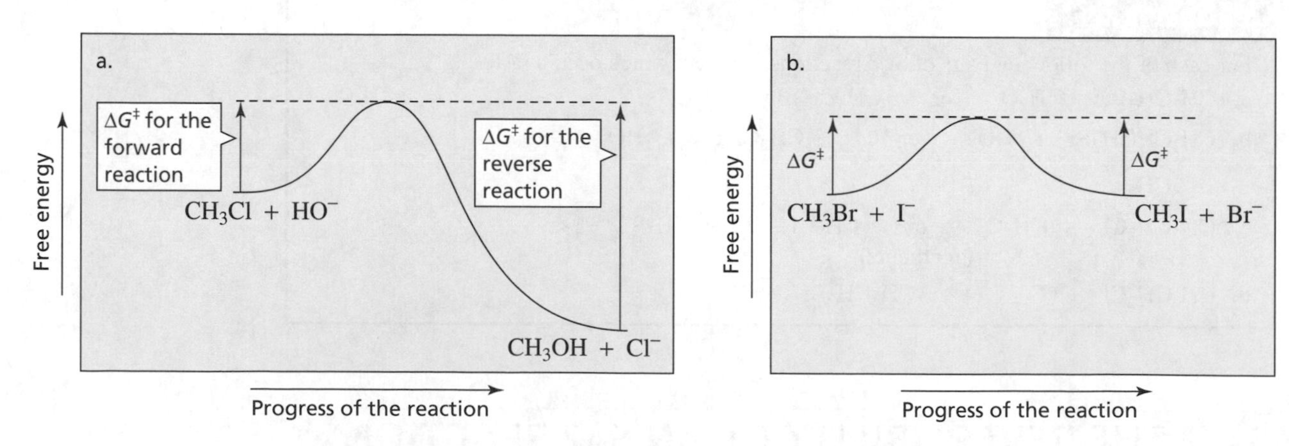

▲ Figure 14.6
(a) A reaction coordinate diagram for an irreversible S_N2 reaction.
(b) A reaction coordinate diagram for a reversible S_N2 reaction.

If the difference between the basicities of the nucleophile and the leaving group is not very large, the reaction will be reversible (Figure 14.6b). For example, in the reaction of bromoethane with iodide ion, Br^- is the leaving group in one direction and I^- is the leaving group in the other direction. The reaction is reversible because the pK_a values of the conjugate acids of the two leaving groups are similar (pK_a of HBr $= -9$; pK_a of HI $= -10$; see Table 14.3).

Table 14.3 The Acidities of the Conjugate Acids of Some Leaving Groups

Acid	pK_a	Conjugate base (leaving group)
HI	−10.0	I^-
HBr	−9.0	Br^-
HCl	−7.0	Cl^-
C_6H_5–SO_3H	−6.5	C_6H_5–SO_3^-
H_2SO_4	−5.0	HSO_4^-
$CH_3\overset{+}{O}H_2$	−2.5	CH_3OH
H_3O^+	−1.7	H_2O
HF	3.2	F^-
$CH_3\overset{O}{\overset{\Vert}{C}}OH$	4.8	$CH_3\overset{O}{\overset{\Vert}{C}}O^-$
H_2S	7.0	HS^-
$HC{\equiv}N$	9.1	$^-C{\equiv}N$
$\overset{+}{N}H_4$	9.4	NH_3
CH_3CH_2SH	10.5	$CH_3CH_2S^-$
$(CH_3)_3\overset{+}{N}H$	10.8	$(CH_3)_3N$
CH_3OH	15.5	CH_3O^-
H_2O	15.7	HO^-
$HC{\equiv}CH$	25	$HC{\equiv}C^-$
H_2	35	H^-
NH_3	36	$^-NH_2$

An S_N2 reaction proceeds in the direction that allows the stronger base to displace the weaker base.

$$CH_3CH_2Br + I^- \rightleftharpoons CH_3CH_2I + Br^-$$

an S_N2 reaction is reversible when the basicities of the leaving groups are similar

We have seen that a reversible reaction can be driven toward the desired products by removing one of the products as it is formed (Le Châtelier's principle). Thus, if the concentration of product C is decreased, A and B will react to form more C and D to maintain the value of the equilibrium constant.

$$A + B \rightleftharpoons C + D$$

$$K_{eq} = \frac{[C][D]}{[A][B]}$$

For example, the reaction of chloroethane with methanol is reversible because the difference between the basicities of the nucleophile and the leaving group is not very large. However, if the reaction is carried out in a neutral solution, the protonated product will lose a proton, disturbing the equilibrium and driving the reaction toward the products.

$$CH_3CH_2Cl + CH_3OH \rightleftharpoons CH_3CH_2\overset{+}{\underset{|}{O}}CH_3\ (H) + Cl^- \xrightarrow{\text{fast}} CH_3CH_2OCH_3 + H^+$$

If an equilibrium is disturbed, the system will adjust to offset the disturbance.

Eradicating Termites

Alkyl halides can be very toxic to biological organisms. For example, bromomethane is used to kill termites and other pests. Bromomethane works by methylating the NH_2 and SH groups of enzymes, thereby destroying the enzymes' ability to catalyze necessary biological reactions. Unfortunately, bromomethane has been found to deplete the ozone layer, so its production has recently been banned in developed countries, and developing countries will have until 2015 to phase out its use.

PROBLEM 10

Check to see whether the pK_a values listed in Table 14.3 predict correctly the direction of each of the reactions on page 582.

PROBLEM 11 ♦

What is the product of the reaction of bromoethane with each of the following nucleophiles?

a. $CH_3CH_2CH_2O^-$
b. $CH_3C{\equiv}C^-$
c. $(CH_3)_3N$
d. $CH_3CH_2S^-$

PROBLEM 12 SOLVED

The reaction of chloromethane with hydroxide ion at 30 °C has a $\Delta G°$ value of −21.7 kcal/mol. What is the equilibrium constant for the reaction?

Solution The equation needed to calculate K_{eq} from the change in free energy is given in Section 12.7.

$$\ln K_{eq} = \frac{-\Delta G°}{RT}$$

$$\ln K_{eq} = \frac{-(-21.7 \text{ kcal mol}^{-1})}{0.001986 \text{ kcal mol}^{-1}\text{ K}^{-1} \times 303 \text{ K}} = \frac{21.7}{0.60}$$

$$\ln K_{eq} = 36.1$$

$$K_{eq} = 4.8 \times 10^{15}$$

As expected, this highly exergonic reaction (Figure 14.6a) has a very large equilibrium constant.

PROBLEM 13 SOLVED

What product is obtained when ethylamine reacts with excess methyl iodide in a basic solution of potassium carbonate?

$$CH_3CH_2\ddot{N}H_2 + \underset{\text{excess}}{CH_3{-}I} \xrightarrow{K_2CO_3} ?$$

Solution Methyl iodide and ethylamine undergo an S_N2 reaction. The product of the reaction is a secondary amine that is predominantly in its basic (neutral) form since the reaction is carried out in a basic solution. The secondary amine can undergo an S_N2 reaction with another equivalent of methyl iodide, forming a tertiary amine. The tertiary amine can react with methyl iodide in yet another S_N2 reaction. The final product of the reaction is a quaternary ammonium iodide.

$$CH_3CH_2\ddot{N}H_2 + CH_3{-}I \longrightarrow CH_3CH_2\overset{+}{N}H_2CH_3\ I^- \overset{K_2CO_3}{\rightleftharpoons} CH_3CH_2\ddot{N}HCH_3$$

$$CH_3CH_2\ddot{N}HCH_3 \xrightarrow{CH_3{-}I} CH_3CH_2\overset{+}{N}H(CH_3)CH_3\ I^- \overset{K_2CO_3}{\rightleftharpoons} CH_3CH_2\ddot{N}(CH_3)CH_3$$

$$CH_3CH_2\ddot{N}(CH_3)CH_3 \xrightarrow{CH_3{-}I} CH_3CH_2\overset{+}{N}(CH_3)_2CH_3\ I^-$$

The reaction of an amine with sufficient methyl iodide to convert the amine into a quaternary ammonium iodide is called **exhaustive methylation**.

PROBLEM 14

a. Explain why the reaction of an alkyl halide with ammonia gives a low yield of primary amine.

b. Explain why a much better yield of primary amine is obtained from the reaction of an alkyl halide with azide ion ($^-N_3$), followed by catalytic hydrogenation. (*Hint*: An alkyl azide is not nucleophilic.)

$$CH_3CH_2CH_2Br \xrightarrow{^-N_3} \underset{\text{an alkyl azide}}{CH_3CH_2CH_2N{=}\overset{+}{N}{=}N^-} \xrightarrow[Pd/C]{H_2} CH_3CH_2CH_2NH_2 + N_2$$

Why Carbon Instead of Silicon?

There are two reasons living organisms are composed primarily of carbon, oxygen, hydrogen, and nitrogen: the *fitness* of these elements for specific roles in life processes and their *availability* in the environment. Of the two reasons, we can see that fitness was more important than availability because carbon rather than silicon became the fundamental building block of living organisms, even though silicon, which is just below carbon in the periodic table, is more than 140 times more abundant than carbon in the Earth's crust.

Abundance (atoms/100 atoms)

Element	In living organisms	In Earth's crust
H	49	0.22
C	25	0.19
O	25	47
N	0.3	0.1
Si	0.03	28

Why are hydrogen, carbon, oxygen, and nitrogen so well suited for the roles they play in living organisms? First and foremost, they are among the smallest atoms that form covalent bonds, and carbon, oxygen, and nitrogen can also form multiple bonds. Because the atoms are small and can form multiple bonds, they form strong bonds that give rise to stable molecules. The compounds that make up living organisms must be stable and, therefore, slow to react if the organisms are to survive.

Silicon has almost twice the diameter of carbon, so silicon forms longer and weaker bonds. Consequently, an S_N2 reaction at silicon would occur much more rapidly than an S_N2 reaction at carbon. Moreover, silicon has another problem. The end product of carbon metabolism is CO_2. The analogous product of silicon metabolism would be SiO_2. But unlike carbon that is doubly bonded to oxygen in CO_2, silicon is only singly bonded to oxygen in SiO_2. Therefore, silicon dioxide molecules polymerize to form quartz (sand). It is hard to imagine that life could exist, much less proliferate, if animals exhaled sand instead of CO_2!

14.4 THE MECHANISM FOR AN S_N1 REACTION

Given our understanding of S_N2 reactions, we would expect the rate of the reaction of 2-bromo-2-methylpropane with water to be very slow because water is a poor nucleophile and the alkyl halide is sterically hindered to attack by a nucleophile. It turns out, however, that the reaction is surprisingly fast. In fact, it is over 1 million times faster than the reaction of bromomethane (a compound with no steric hindrance) with water (Table 14.4). Clearly, the reaction must be taking place by a mechanism different from that of an S_N2 reaction.

$$\underset{\text{2-bromo-2-methylpropane}}{(CH_3)_3C{-}Br} + H_2O \longrightarrow \underset{\text{2-methyl-2-propanol}}{(CH_3)_3C{-}OH} + HBr$$

We have seen that in order to determine the mechanism of a reaction, we need to find out what factors affect the rate of the reaction, and we need to know the configuration of the products of the reaction. Finding that doubling the concentration of the alkyl halide doubles the rate of the reaction, but changing the concentration of the nucleophile has no effect on the rate of the reaction, allows us to write a rate law for the reaction:

$$\textbf{rate} = k[\textbf{alkyl halide}]$$

Table 14.4 Relative Rates of S_N1 Reactions for Several Alkyl Bromides (solvent is H_2O, nucleophile is H_2O)

Alkyl bromide	Class of alkyl bromide	Relative rate
$CH_3\overset{CH_3}{\underset{CH_3}{C}}-Br$	tertiary	1,200,000
$CH_3\underset{CH_3}{CH}-Br$	secondary	11.6
CH_3CH_2-Br	primary	1.00*
CH_3-Br	methyl	1.05*

*Although the rate of the S_N1 reaction of this compound with water is 0, a small rate is observed as a result of an S_N2 reaction.

The rate of the reaction depends linearly on the concentration of only one reactant. Thus, the reaction is a **first-order reaction.**

Because the rate law for the reaction of 2-bromo-2-methylpropane with water differs from the rate law for the reaction of bromomethane with hydroxide ion (Section 14.1), the two reactions must have different mechanisms. We have seen that the reaction between bromomethane and hydroxide ion is an S_N2 reaction. The reaction between 2-bromo-2-methylpropane and water is an **S_N1 reaction**, where "S" stands for substitution, "N" stands for nucleophilic, and "1" stands for unimolecular. **Unimolecular** means that only one molecule is involved in the transition state of the rate-determining step. The mechanism for an S_N1 reaction is based on the following experimental evidence:

1. The rate law shows that the rate of the reaction depends only on the concentration of the alkyl halide, which means that only the alkyl halide is involved in the transition state of the rate-determining step.
2. When the methyl groups of 2-bromo-2-methylpropane are successively replaced by hydrogens, the rate of the S_N1 reaction decreases progressively (Table 14.4). This is the opposite of the pattern of reactivity exhibited by alkyl halides in S_N2 reactions (Table 14.1).
3. The substitution reaction of an alkyl halide in which the halogen is bonded to an asymmetric center forms two stereoisomers: one with the same relative configuration as that of the reacting alkyl halide, and the other with the inverted configuration compared to that of the alkyl halide.

Unlike an S_N2 reaction, where the leaving group departs and the nucleophile approaches *at the same time*, the leaving group in an S_N1 reaction departs *before* the nucleophile approaches.

MECHANISM FOR THE S_N1 REACTION OF AN ALKYL HALIDE

$$CH_3\overset{CH_3}{\underset{CH_3}{C}}-Br \underset{}{\overset{\text{slow}}{\rightleftharpoons}} CH_3\overset{CH_3}{\underset{CH_3}{C}}{}^{+} + Br^- \quad + \; H_2\ddot{O}: \xrightarrow{\text{fast}} CH_3\overset{CH_3}{\underset{CH_3}{C}}-\overset{+}{\ddot{O}}H \;(\text{H} \;\; :\ddot{O}-H,\ H) \overset{\text{fast}}{\rightleftharpoons} CH_3\overset{CH_3}{\underset{CH_3}{C}}-\ddot{O}H + H_3O:^{+}$$

nucleophile adds to the carbocation

C—Br bond breaks

proton transfer

- In the first step of the mechanism, the carbon–halogen bond breaks and the previously shared pair of electrons stays with the halogen. As a result, a carbocation intermediate is formed.

- In the second step, the nucleophile reacts rapidly with the carbocation (an electrophile) to form a protonated alcohol.
- Whether the alcohol product will exist in its protonated (acidic) form or neutral (basic) form depends on the pH of the solution. At pH = 7, the alcohol will exist predominantly in its neutral form.

An S_N1 reaction is a two-step reaction.

Because the rate of an S_N1 reaction depends only on the concentration of the alkyl halide, the first step must be the slow (rate-determining) step. The nucleophile is not involved in the rate-determining step, so its concentration has no effect on the rate of the reaction. If you look at the reaction coordinate diagram in Figure 14.7, you will see why increasing the rate of the second step will not make an S_N1 reaction go any faster.

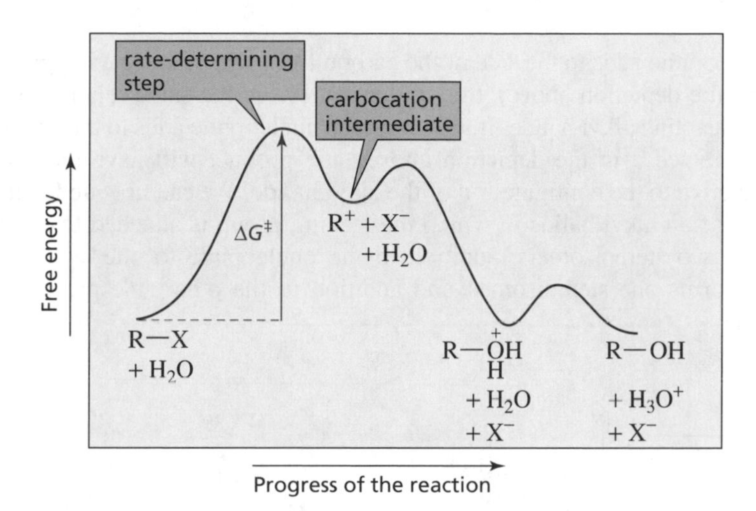

◀ **Figure 14.7**
A reaction coordinate diagram for an S_N1 reaction.

How does the mechanism for an S_N1 reaction account for the three pieces of experimental evidence? First, because the alkyl halide is the only species that participates in the rate-determining step, the mechanism agrees with the observation that the rate of the reaction depends only on the concentration of the alkyl halide; it does not depend on the concentration of the nucleophile.

Second, the mechanism shows that a carbocation is formed in the rate-determining step. We know that a tertiary carbocation is more stable and is therefore formed more easily than a secondary carbocation, which in turn is more stable and formed more easily than a primary carbocation. Tertiary alkyl halides, therefore, are more reactive than secondary alkyl halides, which are more reactive than primary alkyl halides. This relative order of reactivity agrees with the observation that the rate of an S_N1 reaction decreases as the methyl groups of 2-bromo-2-methylpropane are successively replaced by hydrogens (Table 14.4).

Carbocation stability: 3° > 2° > 1°

relative reactivities of alkyl halides in an S_N1 reaction

most reactive > 3° alkyl halide > 2° alkyl halide > 1° alkyl halide < too unreactive to undergo an S_N1 reaction

In reality, primary carbocations and methyl cations are so unstable that primary alkyl halides and methyl halides do not undergo S_N1 reactions. (The very slow reactions reported for bromoethane and bromomethane in Table 14.4 are S_N2 reactions.)

Primary alkyl halides and methyl halides cannot undergo S_N1 reactions.

Third, the positively charged carbon of the carbocation intermediate is sp^2 hybridized, which means the three bonds connected to it are in the same plane. In the second step of the S_N1 reaction, the nucleophile can approach the carbocation from either side of the plane.

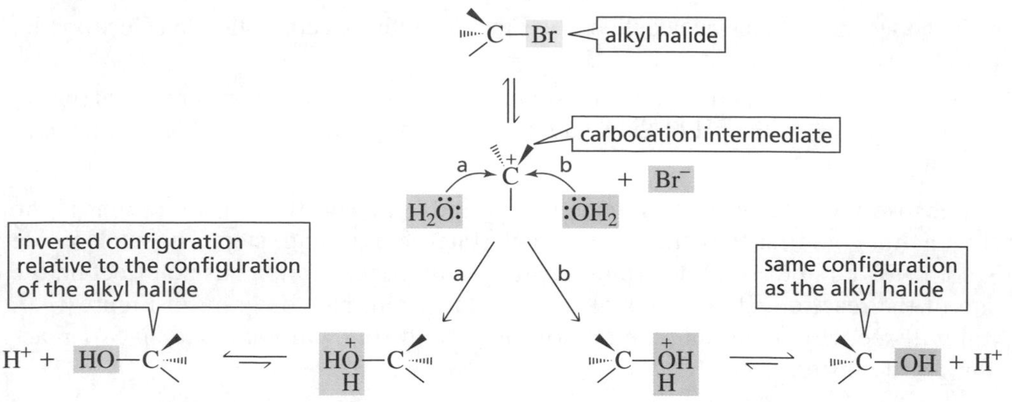

alkyl halide

carbocation intermediate

inverted configuration relative to the configuration of the alkyl halide

same configuration as the alkyl halide

If the nucleophile adds to the side of the carbon from which the leaving group departed (labeled b in the depiction above), the product will have the same relative configuration as that of the reacting alkyl halide. If, however, the nucleophile adds to the opposite side of the carbon (labeled a in the depiction above), the product will have the inverted configuration relative to the configuration of the alkyl halide. We can now understand why an S_N1 reaction of an alkyl halide in which the leaving group is attached to an asymmetric center forms two stereoisomers: addition of the nucleophile to one side of the planar carbocation forms one stereoisomer, and addition to the other side produces the other stereoisomer.

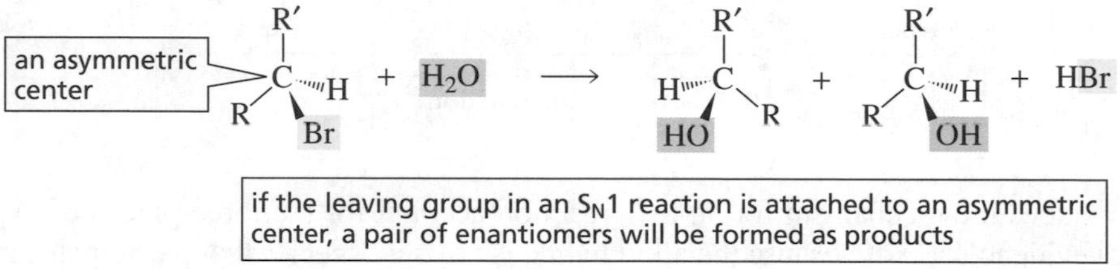

an asymmetric center

if the leaving group in an S_N1 reaction is attached to an asymmetric center, a pair of enantiomers will be formed as products

chem place Tutorial: S_N1

Tutorial: S_N1 racemization-inversion

Tutorial: S_N1 racemization-retention

PROBLEM 15 ♦

Arrange the following alkyl bromides in order of decreasing reactivity in an S_N1 reaction: 2-bromopropane, 1-bromopropane, 2-bromo-2-methylpropane, bromomethane.

PROBLEM 16

Explain why the rates given in Table 14.4 for the S_N2 reactions of bromoethane and bromomethane are so slow.

14.5 FACTORS THAT AFFECT S_N1 REACTIONS

We will now look at how the nature of the leaving group and the nucleophile affect S_N1 reactions, and we will see that these reactions can undergo carbocation rearrangements.

The Leaving Group in S_N1 Reactions

Because the rate-determining step of an S_N1 reaction is the dissociation of the alkyl halide to form a carbocation, two factors affect the rate of the reaction: (1) the ease with which the leaving group dissociates from the carbon, and (2) the stability of the carbocation that is formed. In the preceding section, we saw how carbocation stability affects the rate of the reaction. But how do we rank the relative reactivity of a series of alkyl halides with different leaving groups that dissociate to form the same carbocation?

As in the case of an S_N2 reaction, there is a direct relationship between basicity and leaving propensity in an S_N1 reaction: the weaker the base, the less tightly it is bonded to the carbon and the more easily the carbon–halogen bond can be broken. As a result, an alkyl iodide is the most reactive and an alkyl fluoride is the least reactive of the alkyl halides in both S_N1 and S_N2 reactions.

relative reactivities of alkyl halides in an S_N1 reaction

most reactive → RI > RBr > RCl > RF ← least reactive

The Nucleophile in S_N1 Reactions

We have seen that the rate-determining step of an S_N1 reaction is formation of the carbocation. Because the nucleophile does not participate until *after* the rate-determining step, the reactivity of the nucleophile has no effect on the rate of an S_N1 reaction (Figure 14.7).

In most S_N1 reactions, the solvent is the nucleophile. For example, the relative rates given in Table 14.4 are for the reactions of alkyl halides with water in water. Water serves as both the nucleophile and the solvent. Reaction with a solvent is called **solvolysis**. Thus, the relative rates in Table 14.4 are for the solvolysis of the indicated alkyl bromides in water.

Carbocation Rearrangements

We saw that a carbocation will rearrange if it becomes more stable in the process. If the carbocation formed in an S_N1 reaction rearranges, S_N1 and S_N2 reactions of the same alkyl halide can produce different constitutional isomers as products, since a carbocation is not formed in an S_N2 reaction and therefore the carbon skeleton cannot rearrange. For example, in the following reaction, the product obtained from an S_N1 reaction is different from the product obtained from an S_N2 reaction. When the reaction is carried out under conditions that favor an S_N1 reaction, the secondary carbocation formed initially undergoes a 1,2-hydride shift to form a more stable tertiary carbocation; this changes the carbon skeleton of the reactant. In Sections 14.8 and 14.9, you will see that we can exercise some control over whether an S_N1 or an S_N2 reaction takes place by selecting appropriate reaction conditions.

When a reaction forms a carbocation intermediate, always check for the possibility of a carbocation rearrangement.

2-bromo-3-methylbutane ($CH_3CH(Br)CH(CH_3)CH_3$)

S_N1: $CH_3\overset{+}{C}HCH(CH_3)CH_3 + Br^-$ (secondary carbocation) $\xrightarrow{\text{1,2-hydride shift}}$ $CH_3\overset{+}{C}(CH_3)CH_2CH_3$ (tertiary carbocation) $\xrightarrow{H_2O}$ $CH_3C(CH_3)(\overset{+}{O}H_2)CH_2CH_3$ $\underset{}{\overset{H_2O}{\rightleftharpoons}}$ $CH_3C(CH_3)(OH)CH_2CH_3 + H_3O^+$

2-methyl-2-butanol

S_N2 (HO^-): $CH_3CH(OH)CH(CH_3)CH_3 + Br^-$

3-methyl-2-butanol

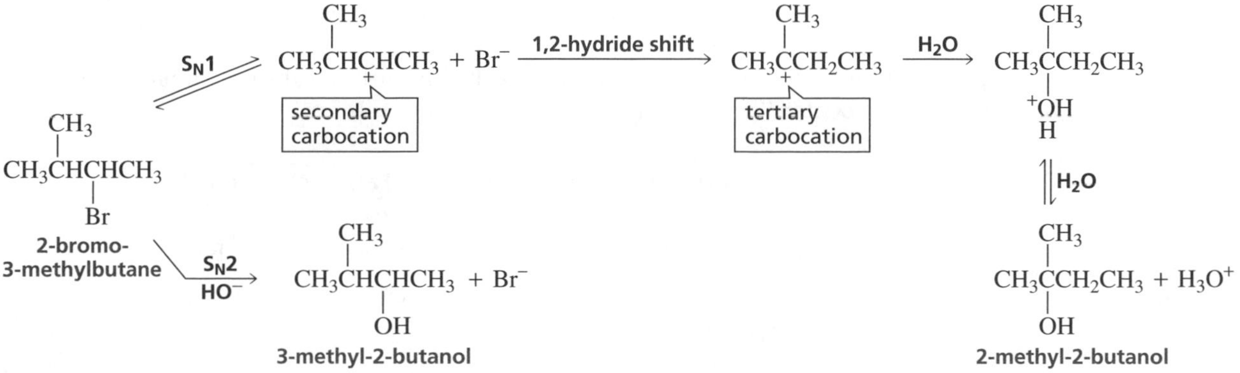

PROBLEM 17♦

Arrange the following alkyl halides in order of decreasing reactivity in an S_N1 reaction: 2-bromopentane, 2-chloropentane, 1-chloropentane, 3-bromo-3-methylpentane.

PROBLEM 18 ♦

Which of the following alkyl halides form a substitution product in an S_N1 reaction that is different from the substitution product formed in an S_N2 reaction?

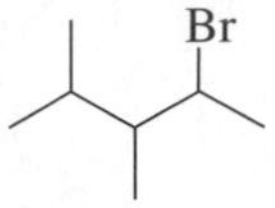

Br A Br C Cl E

CH_3 Cl B CH_3 Br D Br F

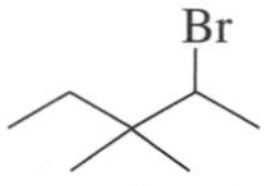

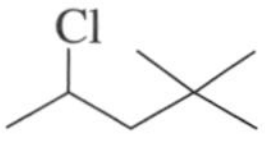

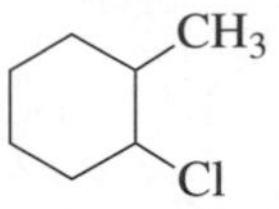

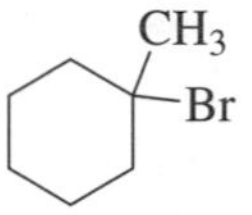

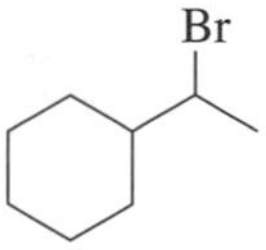

chem place Tutorial: Carbocation rearrangements

PROBLEM 19 ♦

Two substitution products result from the reaction of 3-chloro-3-methyl-1-butene with sodium acetate ($CH_3COO^-Na^+$) in acetic acid under conditions that favor an S_N1 reaction. Identify the products.

14.6 MORE ABOUT THE STEREOCHEMISTRY OF S_N2 AND S_N1 REACTIONS

We have seen that when an alkyl halide with a leaving group attached to an asymmetric center undergoes an S_N2 reaction, the product has an inverted configuration, but when it undergoes an S_N1 reaction, the product is a pair of enantiomers. Let's now look at some examples of the stereoisomers formed in S_N2 and S_N1 reactions.

The Stereochemistry of S_N2 Reactions

The reaction of 2-bromopropane with hydroxide ion forms a substitution product without any asymmetric centers. The product, therefore, has no stereoisomers.

$$\underset{\text{2-bromopropane}}{CH_3\underset{|}{C}HCH_3}\;(\text{Br}) + HO^- \longrightarrow \underset{\text{2-propanol}}{CH_3\underset{|}{C}HCH_3}\;(\text{OH}) + Br^-$$

The reaction of 2-bromobutane with hydroxide ion forms a substitution product with an asymmetric center. The product, therefore, has stereoisomers.

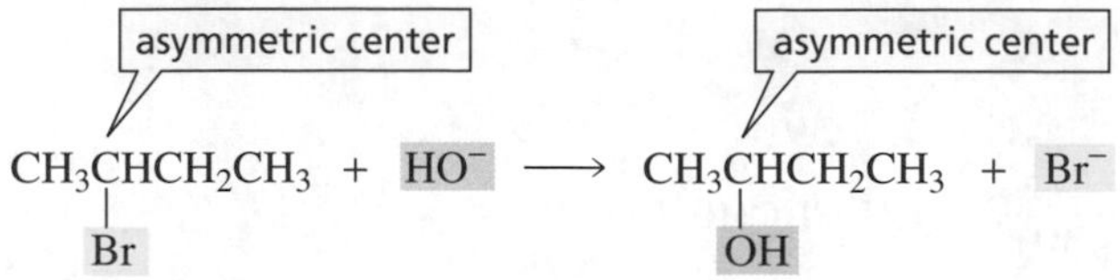

asymmetric center asymmetric center

$$\underset{\text{2-bromobutane}}{CH_3\underset{|}{C}HCH_2CH_3}\;(\text{Br}) + HO^- \longrightarrow \underset{\text{2-butanol}}{CH_3\underset{|}{C}HCH_2CH_3}\;(\text{OH}) + Br^-$$

However we cannot predict which stereoisomers of the product will be formed unless we know the configuration of the reactant *and* whether the reaction is an S_N2 or an S_N1 reaction.

For example, when (*S*)-2-bromobutane undergoes an S_N2 reaction, we know that the product will be (*R*)-2-butanol, because in an S_N2 reaction, the incoming nucleophile attacks the back side of the carbon that is attached to the halogen (Section 14.2). Therefore, the configuration of the product will be inverted relative to that of the reactant. (Recall that an S_N2 reaction takes place with *inversion of configuration*.)

An S_N2 reaction takes place with inversion of configuration.

the configuration is inverted relative to that of the reactant

CH_2CH_3 (S)-2-bromobutane $+ HO^-$ $\xrightarrow{S_N2 \text{ conditions}}$ CH_2CH_3 (R)-2-butanol $+ Br^-$

(S)-2-bromobutane → **(R)-2-butanol**

If the leaving group is attached to an asymmetric center, an S_N2 reaction forms the stereoisomer with the inverted configuration.

The Stereochemistry of S_N1 Reactions

In contrast to the S_N2 reaction, the S_N1 reaction of (*S*)-2-bromobutane forms two substitution products: one with the same relative configuration as the reactant and the other with the inverted configuration because, in an S_N1 reaction, the nucleophile can attack either side of the planar carbocation intermediate (Section 14.4).

product with the inverted configuration | product with the retained configuration

(S)-2-bromobutane $+ H_2O$ $\xrightarrow{S_N1 \text{ conditions}}$ **(R)-2-butanol** + **(S)-2-butanol** $+ HBr$

If the leaving group is attached to an asymmetric center, an S_N1 reaction forms a pair of enantiomers.

Although you might expect that equal amounts of both products should be formed in an S_N1 reaction, a greater amount of the product with the inverted configuration is obtained in most cases. Typically, 50 to 70% of the product of an S_N1 reaction is the inverted product. If the reaction leads to equal amounts of the two stereoisomers, the reaction is said to take place with **complete racemization**. When more of one of the products is formed, the reaction is said to take place with **partial racemization**.

An S_N1 reaction takes place with racemization.

Saul Winstein was the first to explain why a greater amount of inverted product is generally formed in an S_N1 reaction. He postulated that dissociation of the alkyl halide initially results in the formation of an **intimate ion pair**. In an intimate ion pair, the bond between the carbon and the leaving group has broken, but the cation and anion remain next to each other. When they move slightly father apart, they become a *solvent-separated ion pair*, meaning an ion pair with one or more solvent molecules between the cation and the anion. As the ions separate further, they become dissociated ions.

solvent

$R—X \longrightarrow R^+ X^- \longrightarrow R^+$ [solvent] $X^- \longrightarrow R^+$ [solvent] X^-

undissociated molecule | **intimate ion pair** | **solvent-separated ion pair** | **dissociated ions**

The nucleophile can attack any of these four species. If the nucleophile attacks only the completely dissociated carbocation, the product will be completely racemized. If the nucleophile attacks the carbocation of either the intimate ion pair or the solvent-separated ion pair, the leaving group will be in position to partially block the approach of the nucleophile to that side of the carbocation. As a result, more of the product with the inverted configuration will be formed.

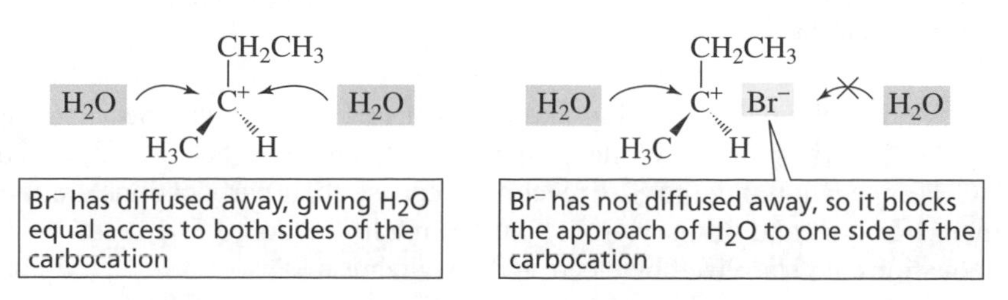
H2O
CH2CH3
C+
H3C
H
H2O
Br− has diffused away, giving H2O equal access to both sides of the carbocation
H2O
CH2CH3
C+
Br−
H3C
H
H2O
Br− has not diffused away, so it blocks the approach of H2O to one side of the carbocation

BIOGRAPHY

Saul Winstein (1912–1969) *was born in Montreal, Canada. He received a Ph.D. from the California Institute of Technology and was a professor of chemistry at the University of California, Los Angeles, from 1942 until his death.*

(Notice that if the nucleophile attacks the undissociated molecule, the reaction will be an S_N2 reaction and all of the product will have the inverted configuration.)

The difference between the products obtained from an S_N1 reaction and from an S_N2 reaction is a little easier to visualize in the case of cyclic compounds. For example, when *cis*-1-bromo-4-methylcyclohexane undergoes an S_N2 reaction, only the trans product is obtained because the carbon bonded to the leaving group is attacked by the nucleophile only on its back side.

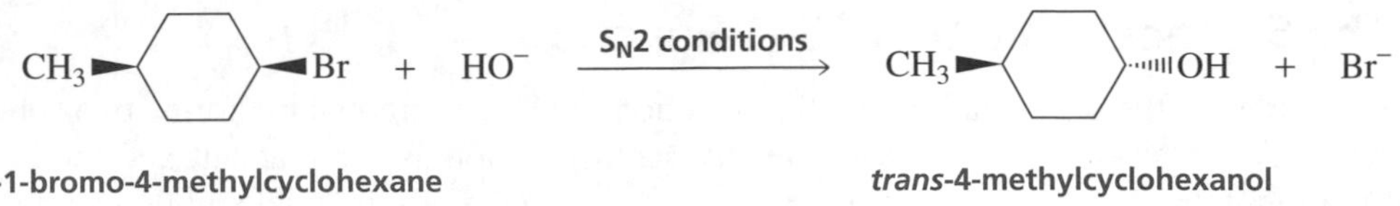

CH_3–C₆H₁₀–Br + HO^- $\xrightarrow{S_N2\text{ conditions}}$ CH_3–C₆H₁₀–OH + Br^-

cis-1-bromo-4-methylcyclohexane **trans-4-methylcyclohexanol**

However, when *cis*-1-bromo-4-methylcyclohexane undergoes an S_N1 reaction, both the cis and the trans products are formed because the nucleophile can approach the carbocation intermediate from either side.

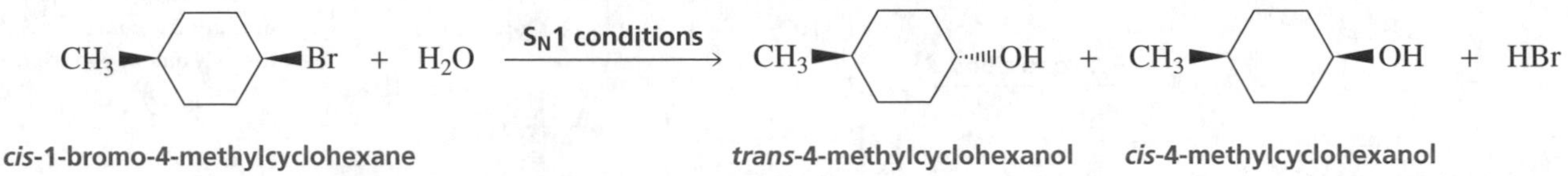

CH_3–C₆H₁₀–Br + H_2O $\xrightarrow{S_N1\text{ conditions}}$ CH_3–C₆H₁₀–OH + CH_3–C₆H₁₀–OH + HBr

cis-1-bromo-4-methylcyclohexane **trans-4-methylcyclohexanol** **cis-4-methylcyclohexanol**

PROBLEM 20

Give the substitution products that will be formed from the following reactions if:

a. the reaction is carried out under conditions that favor an S_N2 reaction.
b. the reaction is carried out under conditions that favor an S_N1 reaction.

1. *trans*-1-iodo-4-ethylcyclohexane + sodium methoxide/methanol
2. *cis*-1-chloro-3-methylcyclobutane + sodium hydroxide/water

14.7 BENZYLIC HALIDES, ALLYLIC HALIDES, VINYLIC HALIDES, AND ARYL HALIDES

Up to this point, our discussion of substitution reactions has been limited to methyl halides and primary, secondary, and tertiary alkyl halides. But what about benzylic, allylic, vinylic, and aryl halides?

Let's first consider benzylic and allylic halides. Unless they are tertiary, these halides readily undergo S_N2 reactions. Tertiary benzylic and tertiary allylic halides, like other tertiary halides, are unreactive in S_N2 reactions because of steric hindrance.

Benzylic and allylic halides undergo S_N1 and S_N2 reactions.

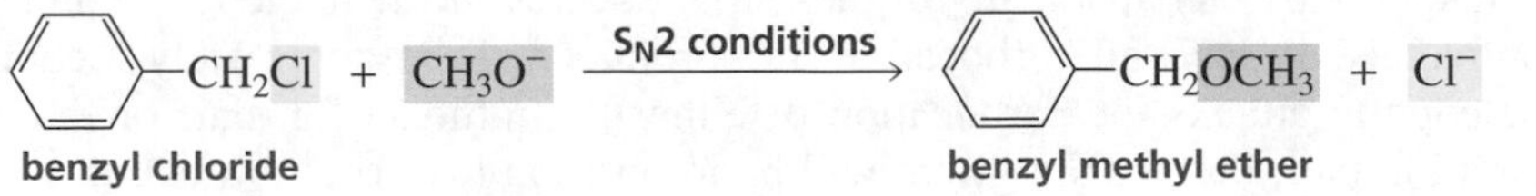

$C_6H_5CH_2Cl + CH_3O^- \xrightarrow{S_N2\text{ conditions}} C_6H_5CH_2OCH_3 + Cl^-$

benzyl chloride **benzyl methyl ether**

$CH_3CH{=}CHCH_2Br + HO^- \xrightarrow{S_N2\text{ conditions}} CH_3CH{=}CHCH_2OH + Br^-$

1-bromo-2-butene
an allylic halide
2-buten-1-ol

Benzylic and allylic halides readily undergo S_N1 reactions as well because they form relatively stable carbocations. While primary alkyl halides (such as CH_3CH_2Br and $CH_3CH_2CH_2Br$) cannot undergo S_N1 reactions because their carbocations are too unstable, primary benzylic and primary allylic halides readily undergo S_N1 reactions because their carbocations are stabilized by electron delocalization.

$$C_6H_5CH_2Cl \underset{}{\overset{S_N1}{\rightleftharpoons}} C_6H_5\overset{+}{C}H_2 + Cl^- \xrightarrow{CH_3OH} C_6H_5CH_2OCH_3 + H^+$$

$$CH_2{=}CHCH_2Br \overset{S_N1}{\rightleftharpoons} CH_2{=}CH\overset{+}{C}H_2 \longleftrightarrow \overset{+}{C}H_2CH{=}CH_2 + Br^- \xrightarrow{H_2O} CH_2{=}CHCH_2OH + H^+$$

If the two resonance contributors of the allylic carbocation intermediate are not symmetrical as they are in the above example, two substitution products will be formed. This is another example of how electron delocalization can affect the nature of the products formed in a reaction.

$$CH_3CH{=}CHCH_2Br \overset{S_N1}{\rightleftharpoons} CH_3CH{=}CH\overset{+}{C}H_2 \longleftrightarrow CH_3\overset{+}{C}HCH{=}CH_2 + Br^-$$

$$CH_3CH{=}CH\overset{+}{C}H_2 \xrightarrow{H_2O} CH_3CH{=}CHCH_2OH + H^+$$

$$CH_3\overset{+}{C}HCH{=}CH_2 \xrightarrow{H_2O} CH_3\underset{OH}{C}HCH{=}CH_2 + H^+$$

Vinylic halides and aryl halides (compounds in which the halogen is attached to an aromatic ring such as benzene) do not undergo S_N2 or S_N1 reactions. They do not undergo S_N2 reactions because, as the nucleophile approaches the back side of the sp^2 carbon, it is repelled by the π electron cloud of the double bond or the aromatic ring.

a nucleophile is repelled by the π electron cloud

$RCH{=}CHCl$ ✗ nucleophile — **a vinylic halide**

C_6H_5Br ✗ nucleophile — **an aryl halide**

There are two reasons vinylic halides and aryl halides do not undergo S_N1 reactions. First, vinylic and aryl cations are even more unstable than primary carbocations because the positive charge is on an *sp* carbon. Since *sp* carbons are more electronegative than the sp^2 carbons that carry the positive charge of alkyl carbocations, *sp* carbons are more resistant to becoming positively charged. Second, we have seen that sp^2 carbons form stronger σ bonds than do sp^3 carbons. As a result, when a halogen is bonded to an sp^2 carbon, it is harder to break the carbon–halogen bond.

$$\underset{sp^2\ \text{carbon}}{RCH{=}CH{-}Cl} \not\rightarrow \underset{sp\ \text{carbon}}{RCH{=}\overset{+}{C}H} + Cl^-$$

vinylic cation
too unstable to be formed

$$\underset{sp^2\ \text{carbon}}{C_6H_5{-}Br} \not\rightarrow \underset{sp\ \text{carbon}}{C_6H_5^+} + Br^-$$

aryl cation
too unstable to be formed

Vinylic and aryl halides do not undergo S_N1 or S_N2 reactions.

PROBLEM-SOLVING STRATEGY

Predicting Relative Reactivities

Which alkyl halide would you expect to be more reactive in an S_N1 solvolysis reaction?

Br or Br

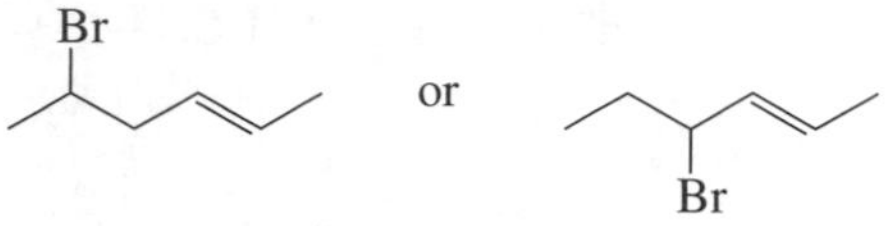

When asked to determine the relative reactivities of two compounds, we need to compare the $\Delta G^{\ddagger}$ values of their rate-determining steps. The faster-reacting compound will have the *smaller* $\Delta G^{\ddagger}$ value, that is, the smaller difference between its free energy and the free energy of its rate-determining transition state. Both alkyl halides have approximately the same stability, so the difference in their reaction rates will be due primarily to the difference in the stabilities of the transition states for their rate-determining steps. The rate-determining step is carbocation formation, and the transition state will resemble the carbocation more than it will resemble the reactant. Therefore, the compound that forms the more stable carbocation will be the one that has the faster rate of solvolysis. Unlike the carbocation formed by the compound on the left that does not have delocalized electrons, the carbocation formed by the compound on the right is stabilized by electron delocalization. Thus, the compound on the right will undergo solvolysis more rapidly.

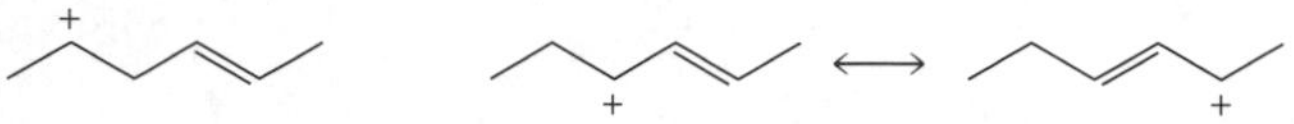

+   + $\longleftrightarrow$ +

Now continue on to Problems 21–22.

PROBLEM 21

Which alkyl halide would be expected to be more reactive in an S_N1 solvolysis reaction?

H, CH_2CH_3, C=C, CH_3CHCH_2 (Br), H   or   H, CH_3, C=C, CH_3CH_2CH (Br), H

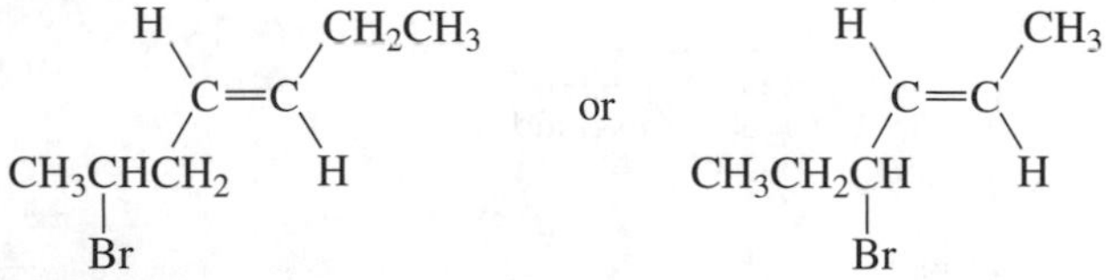

PROBLEM 22 ♦

Which alkyl halide would you expect to be more reactive in an S_N2 reaction with a given nucleophile? In each case, you can assume that both alkyl halides have the same stability.

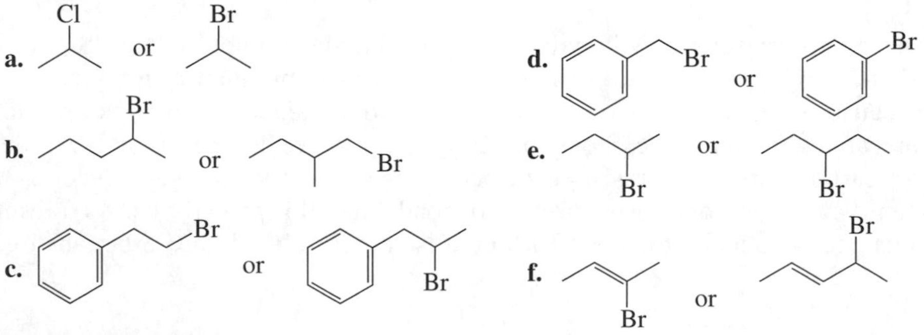

a. Cl or Br

b. Br or Br

c. Br or Br

d. Br or Br

e. Br or Br

f. Br or Br

PROBLEM 23 ♦

For pairs **a–f** in Problem 22, which compound would be more reactive in an S_N1 reaction?

PROBLEM 24

Give the products obtained from the following reaction and show their configurations:

a. under conditions that favor an S_N2 reaction.

b. under conditions that favor an S_N1 reaction.

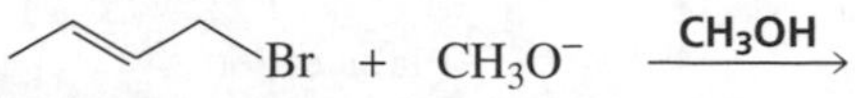

$$\text{Br} + CH_3O^- \xrightarrow{CH_3OH}$$

14.8 THE ROLE OF THE SOLVENT IN S_N2 AND S_N1 REACTIONS

The solvent in which a nucleophilic substitution reaction is carried out also influences whether an S_N2 or an S_N1 reaction will predominate. Before we can understand how a particular solvent favors one reaction over another, we must understand how solvents stabilize organic molecules.

The **dielectric constant** of a solvent is a measure of how well the solvent can insulate opposite charges from one another. Solvent molecules insulate a charge by clustering around it, so that the positive poles of solvent molecules surround negative charges while the negative poles of solvent molecules surround positive charges. Recall that the interaction between a solvent and an ion or a molecule dissolved in that solvent is called *solvation*. When an ion interacts with a polar solvent, the charge is no longer localized solely on the ion, but is spread out to the surrounding solvent molecules. Spreading out the charge stabilizes the charged species.

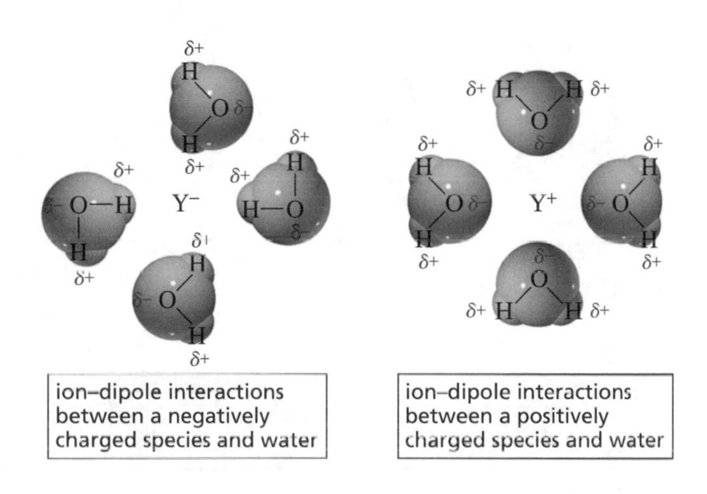

Polar solvents have high dielectric constants and thus are very good at insulating (solvating) charges. Nonpolar solvents have low dielectric constants and are poor insulators. The dielectric constants of some common solvents are listed in Table 14.5 where they are divided into two groups: protic solvents and aprotic solvents. Recall that **protic solvents** contain a hydrogen bonded to an oxygen or to a nitrogen. **Aprotic solvents** do not have a hydrogen bonded to an oxygen or to a nitrogen.

Stabilization of charges by solvent interaction plays an important role in organic reactions. For example, when an alkyl halide undergoes an S_N1 reaction, the first step is dissociation of the carbon–halogen bond to form a carbocation and a halide ion. Energy is required to break the bond, but with no bonds being formed, where does the energy come from? If the reaction is carried out in a polar solvent, the ions that are produced are solvated. The energy associated with a single ion–dipole interaction is small, but the additive effect of all the ion–dipole interactions that take place when a solvent stabilizes a charged species represents a great deal of energy. These ion–dipole interactions provide much of the energy necessary for dissociation of the carbon–halogen bond. So, in an S_N1 reaction, the alkyl halide does not fall apart spontaneously, but instead, polar solvent molecules pull it apart. An S_N1 reaction, therefore, cannot take place in a nonpolar solvent. It also cannot take place in the gas phase, where there are no solvent molecules and, consequently, no solvation effects.

Table 14.5 The Dielectric Constants of Some Common Solvents

Solvent	Structure	Abbreviation	Dielectric constant (ε, at 25 °C)	Boiling point (°C)
Protic solvents				
Water	H_2O	—	79	100
Formic acid	$HCOOH$	—	59	100.6
Methanol	CH_3OH	MeOH	33	64.7
Ethanol	CH_3CH_2OH	EtOH	25	78.3
tert-Butyl alcohol	$(CH_3)_3COH$	*tert*-BuOH	11	82.3
Acetic acid	CH_3COOH	HOAc	6	117.9
Aprotic solvents				
Dimethyl sulfoxide	$(CH_3)_2SO$	DMSO	47	189
Acetonitrile	CH_3CN	MeCN	38	81.6
Dimethylformamide	$(CH_3)_2NCHO$	DMF	37	153
Hexamethylphosphoric acid triamide	$[(CH_3)_2N]_3PO$	HMPA	30	233
Acetone	$(CH_3)_2CO$	Me_2CO	21	56.3
Dichloromethane	CH_2Cl_2	—	9.1	40
Tetrahydrofuran		THF	7.6	66
Ethyl acetate	$CH_3COOCH_2CH_3$	EtOAc	6	77.1
Diethyl ether	$CH_3CH_2OCH_2CH_3$	Et_2O	4.3	34.6
Toluene		—	2.4	110.6
Hexane	$CH_3(CH_2)_4CH_3$	—	1.9	68.7

Solvation Effects

The tremendous amount of energy provided by solvation can be appreciated by considering the energy required to break the crystal lattice of sodium chloride (table salt). In the absence of a solvent, sodium chloride must be heated to more than 800 °C to overcome the forces that hold the oppositely charged ions together. However, sodium chloride readily dissolves in water at room temperature because solvation of the Na^+ and Cl^- ions by water provides the energy necessary to separate the ions.

How a Solvent Affects Reaction Rates in General

One simple rule describes how a change in solvent will affect the rate of most chemical reactions: *increasing the polarity of the solvent will decrease the rate of the reaction if one or more reactants in the rate-determining step are charged and will increase the rate of the reaction if none of the reactants in the rate-determining step is charged.*

Now let's see why this rule is true. The rate of a reaction depends on the difference between the free energy of the reactants and the free energy of the transition state for the rate-determining step of the reaction. We can, therefore, predict how changing the polarity of the solvent will affect the rate of a reaction simply by looking at the charge on the reactants of the rate-determining step and the charge on the transition state of the rate-determining step, to see which of these species will be more stabilized by a polar solvent.

The greater or more concentrated the charge on a molecule, the stronger will be its interactions with a polar solvent and the more the charge will be stabilized. Therefore, if the size or concentration of the charge on the reactants is greater than that on the transition state, a polar solvent will stabilize the reactants more than it will stabilize the transition state, increasing the difference in energy ($\Delta G^{\ddagger}$) between them. Consequently, *increasing the polarity of the solvent will decrease the rate of the reaction*, as shown in Figure 14.8.

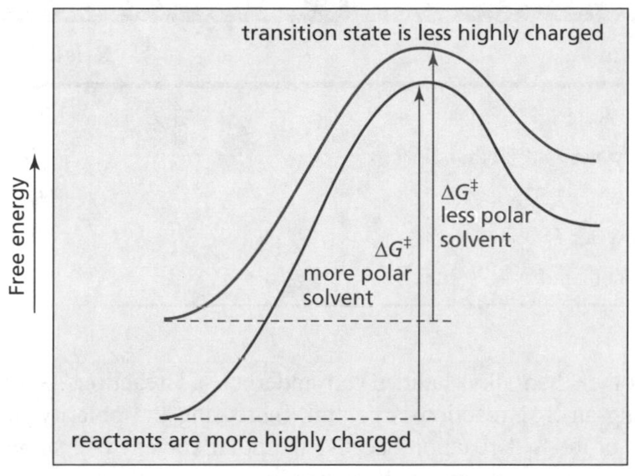

Increasing the polarity of the solvent will decrease the rate of the reaction if one or more reactants in the rate-determining step are charged.

◀ **Figure 14.8**
A reaction coordinate diagram for a reaction in which the charge on the reactants is greater than the charge on the transition state.

On the other hand, if the size or concentration of the charge on the transition state is greater than that on the reactants, a polar solvent will stabilize the transition state more than it will stabilize the reactants. Therefore, *increasing the polarity of the solvent* will decrease the difference in energy ($\Delta G^{\ddagger}$) between the transition state and the reactants, which *will increase the rate of the reaction*, as shown in Figure 14.9.

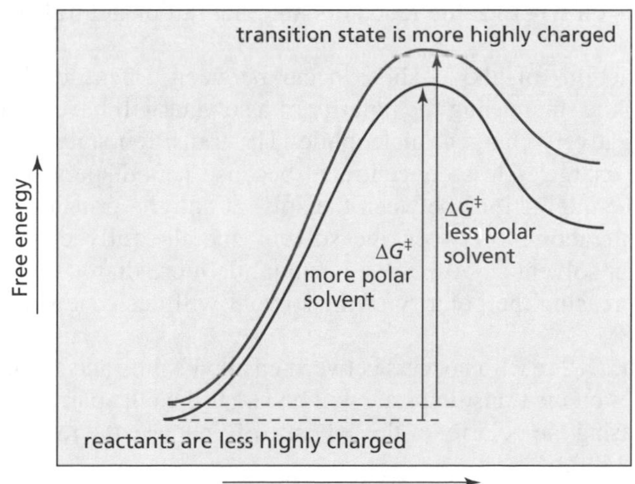

Increasing the polarity of the solvent will increase the rate of the reaction if none of the reactants in the rate-determining step is charged.

◀ **Figure 14.9**
A reaction coordinate diagram for a reaction in which the charge on the transition state is greater than the charge on the reactants.

How a Solvent Affects the Rate of an S_N1 Reaction

Now let's look at specific kinds of reactions, beginning with an S_N1 reaction of an alkyl halide. The alkyl halide, which is the only reactant in the rate-determining step of an S_N1 reaction, is a neutral molecule with a small dipole moment. The rate-determining transition state has greater partial charges because as the carbon–halogen bond breaks, the carbon becomes more positive and the halogen becomes more negative. Since the partial charges on the transition state are greater than the partial charges on the reactant, increasing the polarity of the solvent will stabilize the transition state more than the reactant and will increase the rate of the S_N1 reaction (Figure 14.9 and Table 14.6).

rate-determining step of an S_N1 reaction

$$\overset{\delta+}{C}-\overset{\delta-}{X} \longrightarrow \left[\overset{\delta+}{C}\text{-----}\overset{\delta-}{X} \right]^{\ddagger} \longrightarrow -C^{+} \quad X^{-}$$

reactant transition state products

Table 14.6 The Effect of the Polarity of the Solvent on the Rate of Reaction of 2-Bromo-2-methylpropane in an S_N1 Reaction

Solvent	Relative rate
100% water	1200
80% water / 20% ethanol	400
50% water / 50% ethanol	60
20% water / 80% ethanol	10
100% ethanol	1

Compounds other than alkyl halides can undergo S_N1 reactions. As long as the compound undergoing an S_N1 reaction is neutral, increasing the polarity of the solvent will *increase* the rate of the S_N1 reaction because the polar solvent will stabilize the dispersed charges on the transition state more than it will stabilize the relatively neutral reactant (Figure 14.9). If, however, the compound undergoing an S_N1 reaction is charged, increasing the polarity of the solvent will *decrease* the rate of the reaction because the more polar solvent will stabilize the full charge on the reactant to a greater extent than it will stabilize the dispersed charge on the transition state (Figure 14.8).

How a Solvent Affects the Rate of an S_N2 Reaction

The way in which a change in the polarity of the solvent affects the rate of an S_N2 reaction depends on whether the reactants are charged or neutral, just as in an S_N1 reaction.

Most S_N2 reactions of alkyl halides occur between a neutral alkyl halide and a charged nucleophile. Increasing the polarity of a solvent will have a strong stabilizing effect on the negatively charged nucleophile. The transition state also has a negative charge, but that charge is less concentrated because it is dispersed over two atoms. Consequently, the interactions between the solvent and the transition state are not as strong as the interactions between the solvent and the fully charged nucleophile. Therefore, a polar solvent stabilizes the nucleophile more than it stabilizes the transition state, so increasing the polarity of the solvent will decrease the rate of the reaction (Figure 14.8).

If, however, the S_N2 reaction occurs between an alkyl halide and a neutral nucleophile, the partial charges on the transition state will be larger than the partial charges on the reactants, so increasing the polarity of the solvent will increase the rate of the substitution reaction (Figure 14.9).

In summary, the way a change in solvent affects the rate of a substitution reaction does not depend on the mechanism of the reaction. It depends *only* on whether a reactant in the rate-determining step is charged. *If a reactant in the rate-determining step is charged, increasing the polarity of the solvent will decrease the rate of the reaction. If none of the reactants in the rate-determining step is charged, increasing the polarity of the solvent will increase the rate of the reaction.*

When we discussed the solvation of charged species by a polar solvent, the polar solvents we considered were hydrogen bond donors (protic polar solvents) such as water and alcohols. Some polar solvents—for example, *N,N*-dimethylformamide (DMF), dimethyl sulfoxide (DMSO), and hexamethylphosphoric acid triamide (HMPA)—are not hydrogen bond donors; they are aprotic polar solvents (Table 14.5).

Because a polar solvent decreases the rate of an S_N2 reaction when the nucleophile is negatively charged, we would like to carry out such a reaction in a nonpolar solvent. However, negatively charged nucleophiles generally will not dissolve in nonpolar solvents. Instead, an aprotic polar solvent is used. Because aprotic polar solvents are not hydrogen bond donors, they are less effective than polar protic solvents at solvating negative charges; indeed, we have seen that they solvate negative charges very poorly (Section 14.3). Thus, the rate of an S_N2 reaction with a negatively charged nucleophile will be greater in an aprotic polar solvent than in a protic polar solvent. Consequently, an aprotic polar solvent is the solvent of choice for an S_N2 reaction in which the nucleophile is negatively charged, whereas a protic polar solvent is used if the nucleophile is a neutral molecule.

We have now seen that when an alkyl halide can undergo both S_N2 *and* S_N1 *reactions, the* S_N2 *reaction will be favored by a high concentration of a good (negatively charged) nucleophile in an aprotic polar solvent, whereas the* S_N1 *reaction will be favored by a poor (neutral) nucleophile in a protic polar solvent.*

An S_N2 reaction of an alkyl halide is favored by a high concentration of a good nucleophile in an aprotic polar solvent.

An S_N1 reaction of an alkyl halide is favored by a poor nucleophile in a protic polar solvent.

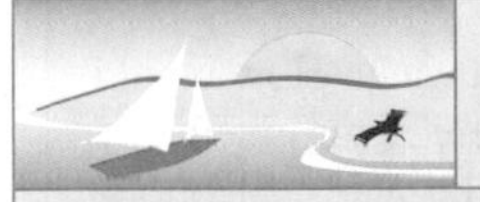

Environmental Adaptation

The microorganism *Xanthobacter* has learned to use alkyl halides that reach the ground as industrial pollutants as a source of carbon. The microorganism synthesizes an enzyme that uses the alkyl halide as a starting material to produce other carbon-containing compounds that it needs. This enzyme has several nonpolar groups at its active site (the pocket in the enzyme where the reaction it catalyzes takes place). The first step of the enzyme-catalyzed reaction is an S_N2 reaction with a charged nucleophile. The nonpolar groups on the surface of the enzyme provide the nonpolar environment needed to increase the rate of the reaction.

PROBLEM 25 ♦

Although amines are neutral molecules, they are good nucleophiles. How would the rate of an S_N2 reaction between an amine and an alkyl halide be faster in a protic polar solvent or in an aprotic polar solvent?

PROBLEM 26 ♦

How will the rate of each of the following S_N2 reactions change if it is carried out in a more polar solvent?

a. $CH_3CH_2CH_2CH_2Br + HO^- \longrightarrow CH_3CH_2CH_2CH_2OH + Br^-$

b. $CH_3\overset{+}{S}(CH_3)CH_3 + NH_3 \longrightarrow CH_3\overset{+}{N}H_3 + CH_3SCH_3$

c. $CH_3CH_2I + NH_3 \longrightarrow CH_3CH_2\overset{+}{N}H_3\,I^-$

PROBLEM 27 ♦

Which reaction in each of the following pairs will take place more rapidly?

a. $CH_3Br + HO^- \longrightarrow CH_3OH + Br^-$

$CH_3Br + H_2O \longrightarrow CH_3OH + HBr$

b. $CH_3I + HO^- \longrightarrow CH_3OH + I^-$

$CH_3Cl + HO^- \longrightarrow CH_3OH + Cl^-$

c. $CH_3Br + NH_3 \longrightarrow CH_3\overset{+}{N}H_3 + Br^-$

$CH_3Br + H_2O \longrightarrow CH_3OH + Br^-$

d. $CH_3Br + HO^- \xrightarrow{\text{DMSO}} CH_3OH + Br^-$

$CH_3Br + HO^- \xrightarrow{\text{EtOH}} CH_3OH + Br^-$

e. $CH_3Br + NH_3 \xrightarrow{\text{Et}_2\text{O}} CH_3\overset{+}{N}H_3 + Br^-$

$CH_3Br + NH_3 \xrightarrow{\text{EtOH}} CH_3\overset{+}{N}H_3 + Br^-$

PROBLEM 28 SOLVED

Most of the pK_a values given throughout this text are values determined in water. How would the pK_a values of the following classes of compounds change if they were determined in a solvent less polar than water such as 50% water/50% dioxane: carboxylic acids, alcohols, phenols, ammonium ions ($R\overset{+}{N}H_3$), and anilinium ions ($C_6H_5\overset{+}{N}H_3$)?

Solution A pK_a is the negative logarithm of an equilibrium constant, K_a. Because we are determining how changing the polarity of a solvent affects an equilibrium constant, we must look at how changing the polarity of the solvent affects the stability of the reactants and products (Section 12.7).

$$K_a = \frac{[B^-][H^+]}{[HB]} \qquad K_a = \frac{[B][H^+]}{[HB^+]}$$

a neutral acid — a positively charged acid

Carboxylic acids, alcohols, and phenols are neutral in their acidic forms (HB) and charged in their basic forms (B^-). A polar protic solvent will stabilize B^- and H^+ more than it will stabilize HB, thereby increasing K_a. Therefore, K_a will be larger in water than in a less polar solvent, so the pK_a values of carboxylic acids, alcohols, and phenols will be higher (they will be weaker acids) in a less polar solvent.

Ammonium ions and anilinium ions are charged in their acidic forms (HB^+) and neutral in their basic forms (B). A polar solvent will stabilize HB^+ and H^+ more than it will stabilize B. Because HB^+ is stabilized slightly more than H^+, K_a will be smaller in water than in a less polar solvent, so the pK_a values of ammonium ions and anilinium ions will be lower (they will be stronger acids) in a less polar solvent.

PROBLEM 29 ♦

Would you expect acetate ion ($CH_3CO_2^-$) to be a more reactive nucleophile in an S_N2 reaction with an alkyl halide carried out in methanol or in dimethyl sulfoxide?

PROBLEM 30 ♦

Under which of the following reaction conditions would (*R*)-2-chlorobutane form the most (*R*)-2-butanol: HO^- in 50% water and 50% ethanol or HO^- in 100% ethanol?

14.9 INTERMOLECULAR VERSUS INTRAMOLECULAR REACTIONS

A molecule with two functional groups is called a **bifunctional molecule**. If the two functional groups are able to react with each other, two kinds of reactions can occur. As an example, let's look at a molecule with two functional groups that can react in an S_N2 reaction: a strong nucleophile and an alkyl halide. The nucleophilic alkoxide ion of one molecule can displace the bromide ion of a second molecule. Such a reaction is called an intermolecular reaction. *Inter* is Latin for "between": an **intermolecular reaction** takes place between two molecules. If the product of this reaction subsequently reacts with a third bifunctional molecule (and then a fourth, and so on), a polymer will be formed. A polymer is a large molecule formed by linking together repeating units of small molecules.

an intermolecular reaction

$$BrCH_2(CH_2)_nCH_2O^- + Br{-}CH_2(CH_2)_nCH_2O^- \longrightarrow BrCH_2(CH_2)_nCH_2OCH_2(CH_2)_nCH_2O^- + Br^-$$

nucleophile; electrophile

Alternatively, the nucleophilic alkoxide ion of a molecule can displace the bromide ion of the same molecule, thereby forming a cyclic compound. Such a reaction is called an intramolecular reaction. *Intra* is Latin for "within": an **intramolecular reaction** takes place within a single molecule.

an intramolecular reaction

$$Br{-}CH_2(CH_2)_nCH_2O^- \longrightarrow \text{cyclic ether } (H_2C{-}(CH_2)_n{-}CH_2{-}O \text{ ring}) + Br^-$$

electrophile; nucleophile

Which reaction is more likely to occur, the intermolecular reaction or the intramolecular reaction? The answer depends on the *concentration* of the bifunctional molecule and the *size of the ring* that would be formed in the intramolecular reaction.

The intramolecular reaction has an advantage: the reacting groups are tethered together, so they do not have to diffuse through the solvent to find a group with which to react. Therefore, a low concentration of reactant favors an intramolecular reaction because the two functional groups have a better chance of finding each other if they are in the same molecule. A high concentration of reactant helps compensate for the advantage gained by tethering, increasing the likelihood of intermolecular reactions.

How much of an advantage an intramolecular reaction has over an intermolecular reaction depends on the size of the ring that is formed—that is, on the length of the tether. If the intramolecular reaction forms a five- or six-membered ring, it will be highly favored over the intermolecular reaction because five- and six-membered rings are stable and, therefore, easily formed.

$$^-O{-}CH_2CH_2CH_2CH_2CH_2{-}Cl \longrightarrow \text{tetrahydropyran} + Cl^-$$

$$(CH_3)_2N{-}CH_2CH_2CH_2CH_2{-}Br \longrightarrow \text{N,N-dimethylpyrrolidinium } (H_3C, CH_3 \text{ on } N^+) + Br^-$$

Three- and four-membered rings are strained, which makes them less stable than five- and six-membered rings and so less easily formed. The higher activation energy for three- and four-membered ring formation cancels some of the advantage gained by tethering.

Three-membered ring compounds are generally formed more easily than four-membered ring compounds. For a cyclic ether of any size to form, the nucleophilic oxygen atom must be oriented so that it can attack the back side of the carbon bonded to the halogen. Rotation about a C—C bond can produce conformations in which the groups point away from one another and are not able to react. The molecule that forms a three-membered ring ether has only one C—C bond that can rotate, whereas the molecule that forms a four-membered ring has two C—C bonds that can rotate. Therefore, the molecule that forms the three-membered rings is more apt to have its reacting groups in the conformation required for reaction.

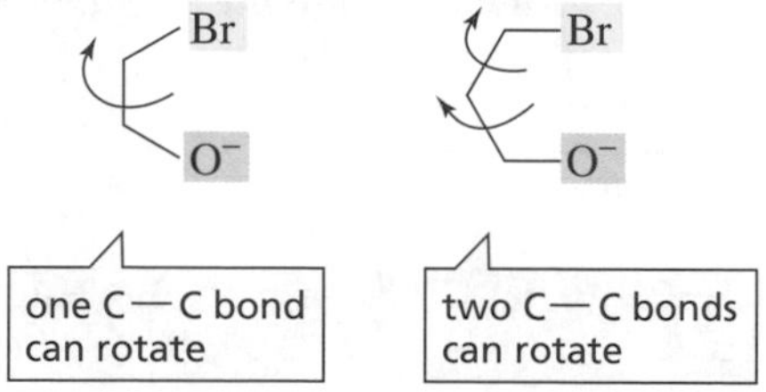

Br Br
O^- O^-
one C—C bond can rotate
two C—C bonds can rotate

The likelihood of the reacting groups finding each other decreases sharply when the groups are in compounds that would form seven-membered and larger rings. Therefore, the intramolecular reaction becomes less favored as the ring size increases beyond six members.

PROBLEM 31 ♦

Which compound in each pair, after removing a proton from the OH group, would form a cyclic ether more rapidly?

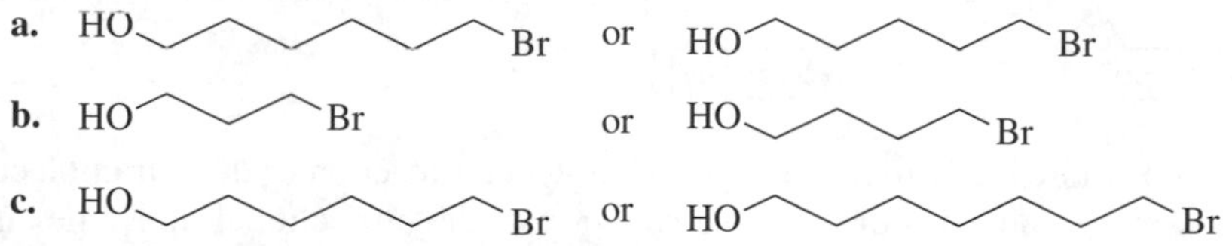

a. HO Br or HO Br

b. HO Br or HO Br

c. HO Br or HO Br

PROBLEM-SOLVING STRATEGY

Investigating How Stereochemistry Affects Reactivity

Which of the following compounds will form an epoxide as a result of reacting with sodium hydroxide?

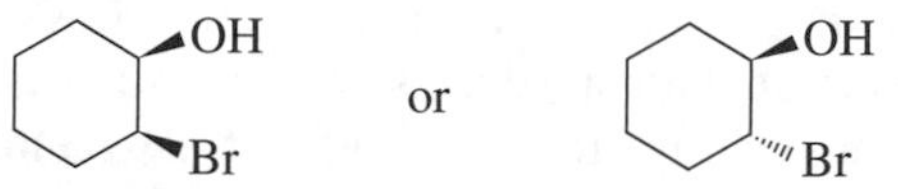

OH Br or OH Br

***cis*-2-bromocyclohexanol** ***trans*-2-bromocyclohexanol**

Hydroxide ion will remove a proton from the OH group, forming a strong nucleophile that can react with the alkyl halide in an S_N2 reaction to form an epoxide. An S_N2 reaction requires back-side attack. Only when the alkoxide ion and Br are on opposite sides of the cyclohexane ring will the alkoxide ion be able to attack the back side of the carbon that is attached to Br. Therefore, only *trans*-2-bromocyclohexanol will be able to form an epoxide.

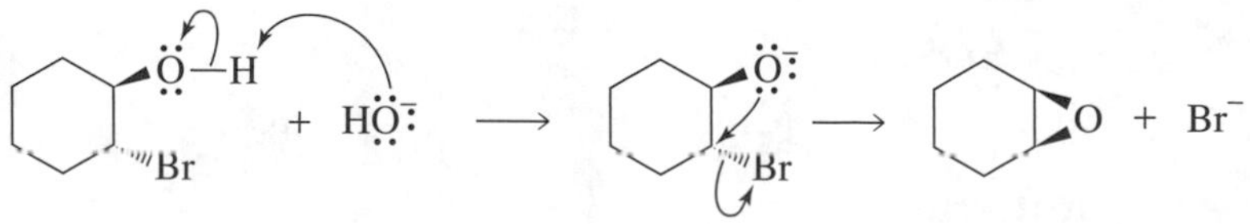

Ö—H Br + HÖ: ⟶ Ö: Br ⟶ O + Br^-

Now continue on to Problem 32.

PROBLEM 32♦

Give the products of the following reactions:

a. 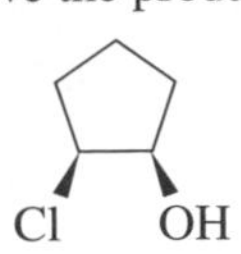 (cyclopentane with Cl and OH, cis) $\xrightarrow{\text{NaOH}}$

b. 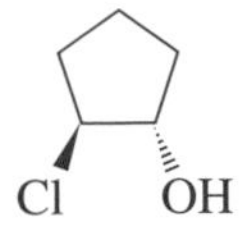 (cyclopentane with Cl and OH, trans) $\xrightarrow{\text{NaOH}}$

c. $BrCH_2CH_2CH_2CH_2CH_2OH \xrightarrow{\text{NaOH}}$

d. $CH_3CH_2C(CH_3)(OH)CH_2Cl \xrightarrow{\text{NaOH}}$

e. $CH_3CH_2CH_2CH{=}CH_2 \xrightarrow[\text{2. NaOH}]{\text{1. } Cl_2,\ H_2O}$

14.10 BIOLOGICAL METHYLATING REAGENTS HAVE GOOD LEAVING GROUPS

If an organic chemist wanted to put a methyl group on a nucleophile, methyl iodide would most likely be used as the methylating agent. Of the methyl halides, methyl iodide has the most easily displaced leaving group because I^- is the weakest base of the halide ions. In addition, methyl iodide is a liquid at room temperature, so it is easier to handle than methyl bromide or methyl chloride that are gases at room temperature. The reaction would be a simple S_N2 reaction.

$$\ddot{N}u + CH_3{-}I \longrightarrow CH_3{-}Nu + I^-$$

Methyl halides, however, are not available in a living cell. Because they are only slightly soluble in water, they are not found in the predominantly aqueous environments of biological systems. Instead, biological systems use *S*-adenosylmethionine (SAM; also called AdoMet), a water soluble compound, as a methylating agent. Although it looks much more complicated than methyl iodide, SAM performs the same function: it transfers a methyl group to a nucleophile. Notice that the methyl group of SAM is attached to a positively charged sulfur, which can readily accept the electrons left behind when the methyl group is transferred. In other words, the methyl group is attached to a very good leaving group, allowing biological methylation to take place at a reasonable rate.

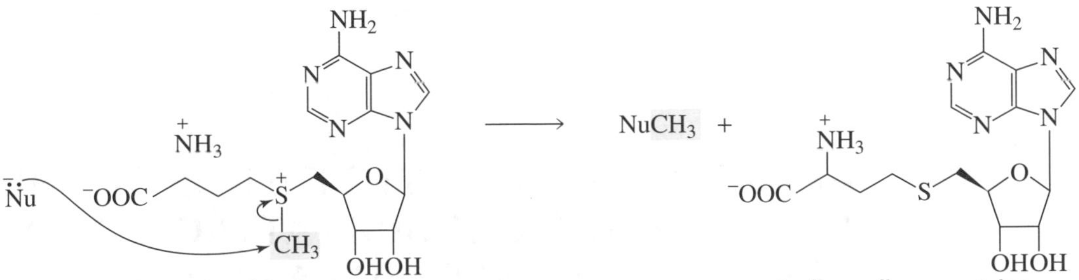

$\ddot{N}u$ + *S*-adenosylmethionine (SAM, AdoMet) ⟶ $NuCH_3$ + *S*-adenosylhomocysteine (SAH)

S-adenosylmethionine
SAM
AdoMet

S-adenosylhomocysteine
SAH

A specific example of a methylation reaction that takes place in biological systems is the conversion of noradrenaline (norepinephrine) to adrenaline (epinephrine). The reaction uses SAM to provide the methyl group. Noradrenaline and adrenaline are hormones that control glycogen metabolism; they are released into the bloodstream in response to stress. Adrenaline is more potent than noradrenaline.

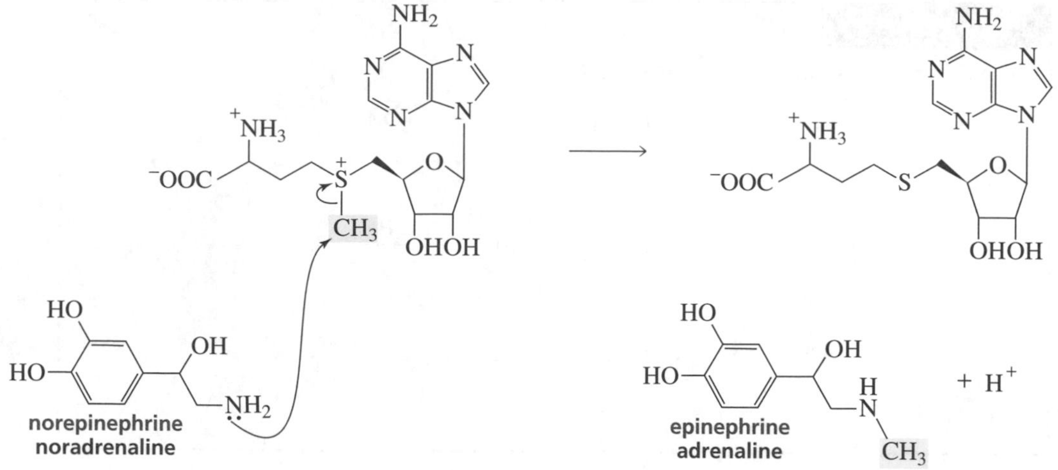

norepinephrine
noradrenaline

epinephrine
adrenaline

The conversion of phosphatidylethanolamine, a component of cell membranes, into phosphatidylcholine, another component of cell membranes, requires three methylations by three equivalents of SAM.

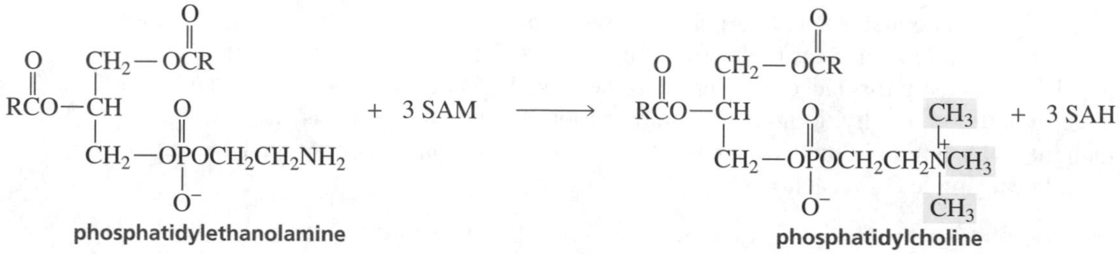

phosphatidylethanolamine + 3 SAM ⟶ phosphatidylcholine + 3 SAH

S-Adenosylmethionine: A Natural Antidepressant

Marketed under the name SAMe (pronounced Sammy), *S*-adenosylmethionine is sold in many health food and drug stores as a treatment for depression and arthritis. Although SAMe has been used clinically in Europe for more than two decades, it has not been rigorously evaluated in the United States and therefore has not been approved by the FDA. It can be sold, however, because the FDA does not prohibit the sale of most naturally occurring substances as long as the marketer does not make therapeutic claims. SAMe has also been found to be effective in the treatment of liver diseases, such as diseases caused by alcohol and the hepatitis C virus. The attenuation of liver injuries is accompanied by increased levels of glutathione in the liver. Glutathione is an important biological antioxidant. SAM is required for the biosynthesis of cysteine, an amino acid that, in turn, is required for the synthesis of glutathione.

14.11 CARBOCATION STABILITY DEPENDS ON THE NUMBER OF ALKYL GROUPS ATTACHED TO THE POSITIVELY CHARGED CARBON

Carbocations are classified according to the carbon atom that carries the positive charge: a **primary carbocation** has a positive charge on a primary carbon, a **secondary carbocation** has a positive charge on a secondary carbon, and a **tertiary carbocation** has a positive charge on a tertiary carbon. Thus, the stability of a carbocation increases as the number of alkyl substituents bonded to the positively charged carbon increases. In other words, tertiary carbocations are more stable than secondary carbocations, and secondary carbocations are more stable than primary carbocations. Keep in mind, however, that these stabilities are relative stabilities. Carbocations are rarely stable enough to isolate.

relative stabilities of carbocations

most stable → R_3C^+ (a tertiary carbocation) > R_2CH^+ (a secondary carbocation) > RCH_2^+ (a primary carbocation) > H_3C^+ (methyl cation) ← least stable

Alkyl groups stabilize carbocations: the greater the number of alkyl groups bonded to the positively charged carbon, the more stable the carbocation.

The reason for this pattern of decreasing stability is that alkyl groups bonded to the positively charged carbon decrease the concentration of positive charge on the carbon, and decreasing the concentration of positive charge makes the carbocation more stable. Notice that the blue (representing positive charge) in these electrostatic potential maps is most intense for the least stable methyl cation and is least intense for the most stable *tert*-butyl cation.

Carbocation stability: 3° > 2° > 1°

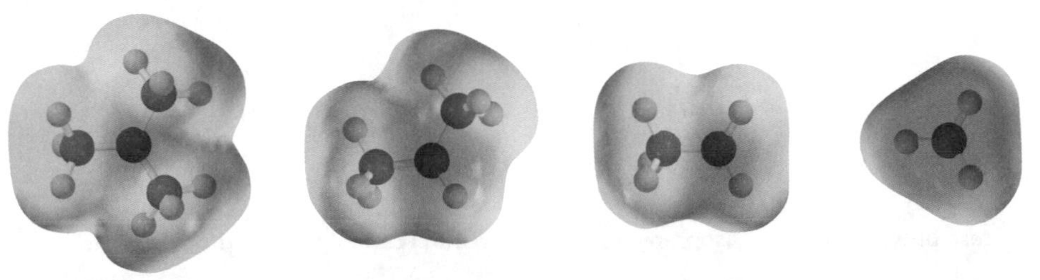

electrostatic potential map for the *tert*-butyl cation | electrostatic potential map for the isopropyl cation | electrostatic potential map for the ethyl cation | electrostatic potential map for the methyl cation

How do alkyl groups decrease the concentration of positive charge on the carbon? Recall that the positive charge on a carbon signifies an empty *p* orbital. Figure 14.10 shows that in the ethyl cation, the orbital of an adjacent C—H σ bond can overlap the empty *p* orbital. No such overlap is possible in the methyl cation. Movement of electrons from the σ bond orbital toward the vacant *p* orbital of the ethyl cation decreases the charge on the sp^2 carbon and causes a partial positive charge to develop on the atoms bonded by the σ bond. Therefore, the positive charge is no longer concentrated solely on one atom, but is delocalized—that is, spread out over a larger volume of space. This dispersion of positive charge stabilizes the carbocation because a charged species is more stable if its charge is spread out (delocalized) over more than one atom. Delocalization of electrons by the overlap of a σ bond orbital with an empty orbital on an adjacent carbon is called **hyperconjugation**. The simple molecular orbital diagram in Figure 14.11 is another way of depicting the stabilization achieved by the overlap of a filled C—H σ bond orbital with an empty *p* orbital.

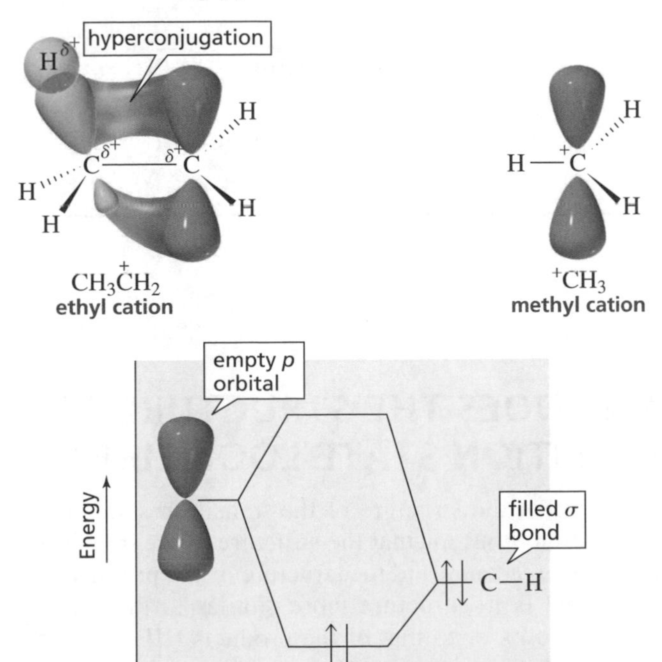

◀ Figure 14.10
Stabilization of a carbocation by hyperconjugation. The electrons of an adjacent C—H σ bond orbital of the ethyl cation spread into the empty *p* orbital. Note that hyperconjugation cannot occur in a methyl cation.

◀ Figure 14.11
A molecular orbital diagram showing the stabilization achieved by overlapping the electrons of a C—H bond with an empty *p* orbital.

Hyperconjugation occurs only if the σ bond orbital and the empty p orbital have the proper orientations. The proper orientations are easily achieved because there is free rotation about the carbon–carbon σ bond. Notice that the σ bonds capable of overlapping the empty p orbital are those *attached to an atom that is attached to the positively charged carbon.* In the *tert*-butyl cation, nine σ bond orbitals can potentially overlap the empty p orbital of the positively charged carbon. (The nine σ bonds are indicated below by red dots.) The isopropyl cation has six such orbitals, and the ethyl and propyl cations each have three. Therefore, there is greater stabilization through hyperconjugation in the tertiary *tert*-butyl cation than in the secondary isopropyl cation, and greater stabilization in the secondary isopropyl cation than in the primary ethyl or primary propyl cation. Notice that the ethyl and propyl cations each have about the same stability, because both C—H and C—C σ bond orbitals can overlap the empty p orbital.

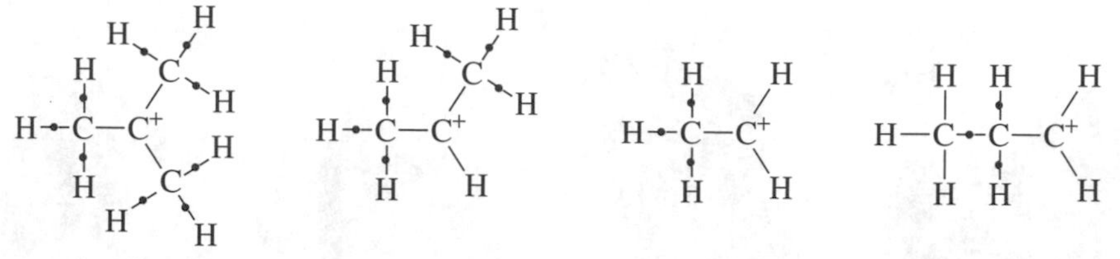

tert-butyl cation **isopropyl cation** **ethyl cation** **propyl cation**

PROBLEM 33 ♦

a. How many σ bond orbitals are available for overlap with the vacant p orbital in the methyl cation?

b. Which is more stable, a methyl cation or an ethyl cation?

PROBLEM 34 ♦

a. How many σ bond orbitals are available for overlap with the vacant p orbital in
1. the isobutyl cation **2.** the *n*-butyl cation **3.** the *sec*-butyl cation

b. Which of the carbocations in part **a** is most stable?

PROBLEM 35 ♦

List the following carbocations in order of decreasing stability:

a. $CH_3CH_2\overset{+}{C}(CH_3)CH_3$ $\quad CH_3CH_2\overset{+}{C}HCH_3$ $\quad CH_3CH_2CH_2\overset{+}{C}H_2$

b. $CH_3CH(Cl)CH_2\overset{+}{C}H_2$ $\quad CH_3CH(CH_3)CH_2\overset{+}{C}H_2$ $\quad CH_3CH(F)CH_2\overset{+}{C}H_2$

14.12 WHAT DOES THE STRUCTURE OF THE TRANSITION STATE LOOK LIKE?

Knowing something about the structure of the transition state can help you predict the products of a reaction. You saw that the structure of the transition state resembles both the structure of the reactants and the structure of the products. But which does it resemble more closely? Is its structure more similar to that of the reactants (I in the reaction scheme below), or to that of the products (III), or is its structure about equally similar to that of the reactants and that of the products (II)?

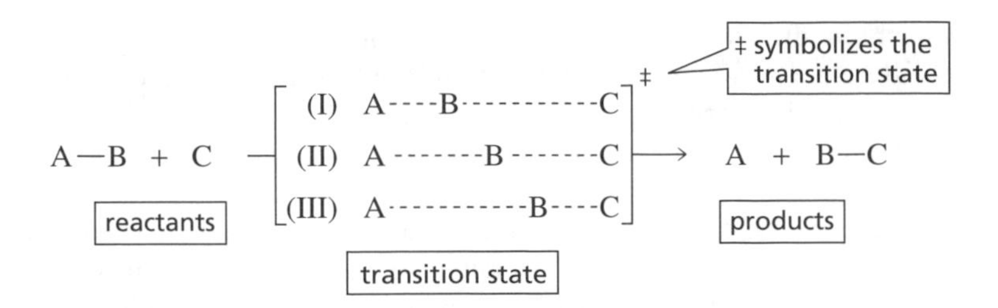

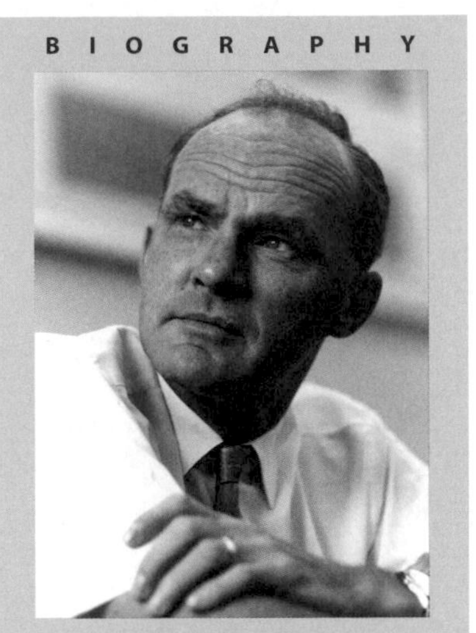

BIOGRAPHY

George Simms Hammond (1921–2005) *was born in Maine and received a B.S. from Bates College in 1943 and a Ph.D. from Harvard University in 1947. He was a professor of chemistry at Iowa State University and at the California Institute of Technology and was a scientist at Allied Chemical Co.*

This question is answered by the **Hammond postulate**, which says that *the transition state is more similar in structure to the species to which it is more similar in energy.* In an exergonic reaction, the energy of the transition state is more similar to the energy to the reactants than to the energy of the products (Figure 14.12, curve I), so its structure will more closely resemble that of the reactants. In an endergonic reaction (curve III), the energy of the transition state is more similar to the energy of the products, so its structure will more closely resemble that of the products. Only when the reactants and products have identical energies (curve II) would we expect the structure of the transition state to be exactly halfway between that of the reactants and that of the products.

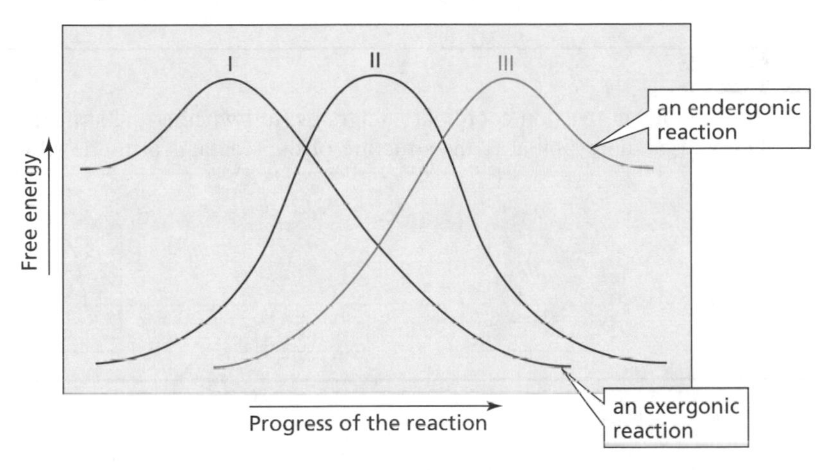

◀ **Figure 14.12**
Reaction coordinate diagrams for reactions with an early transition state (I), a midway transition state (II), and a late transition state (III).

Now we can understand why the *tert*-butyl cation is formed faster than the isobutyl cation when 2-methylpropene reacts with HCl. Because the formation of a carbocation is an endergonic reaction (Figure 14.13), the structure of the transition state resembles the structure of the carbocation product. This means that the transition state has a significant amount of positive charge on a carbon. The same factors that stabilize the positively charged carbocation stabilize the partially positively charged transition state. We know that the *tert*-butyl cation (a tertiary carbocation) is more stable than the isobutyl cation (a primary carbocation). Therefore, the transition state leading to the *tert*-butyl cation is more stable (lower in energy) than the transition state leading to the isobutyl cation. Note, however, that because the amount of positive charge in the transition state is not as great as the amount of positive charge in the carbocation product, the difference in the stabilities of the two transition states is not as great as the difference in the stabilities of the two carbocation products (Figure 14.13).

The transition state is more similar in structure to the species to which it is more similar in energy.

In an exergonic reaction, the transition state is more similar in energy to the reactants, so its structure resembles that of the reactants.

In an endergonic reaction, the transition state is more similar in energy to the products, so its structure resembles that of the products.

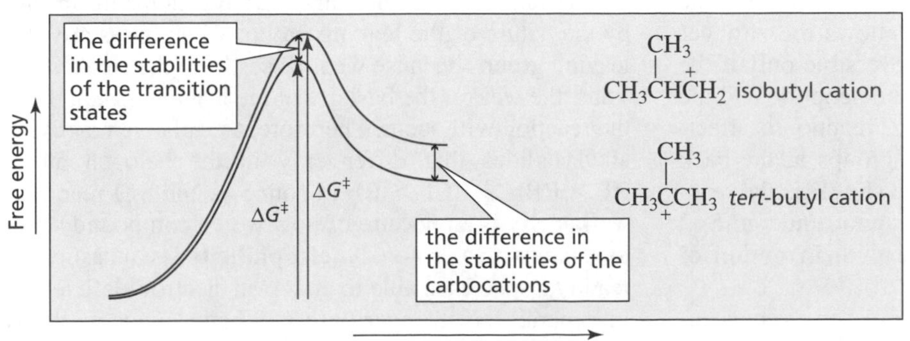

◀ **Figure 14.13**
Reaction coordinate diagram for the addition of H^+ to 2-methylpropene to form the primary isobutyl cation and the tertiary *tert*-butyl cation.

We have seen that the rate of a reaction is determined by the free energy of activation, which is the difference between the free energy of the transition state and the free energy of the reactant. Thus, the *tert*-butyl cation, with a smaller energy of activation, is formed faster than the isobutyl cation. *In an electrophilic addition reaction, the more stable carbocation is the one that is formed more rapidly.*

Formation of the carbocation is the rate-limiting step of the reaction. Therefore, the relative rates of formation of the two carbocations determine the relative amounts of the products that are formed. If the difference in the rates is small, both products will be formed, but the major product will be the one formed from reaction of the nucleophile with the more stable (faster formed) carbocation. If the difference in the rates is sufficiently large, the product formed from reaction of the nucleophile with the more stable carbocation will be the only product of the reaction. For example, when HCl adds to 2-methylpropene, the rates of formation of the two possible carbocation intermediates—one primary and the other tertiary—are sufficiently different to cause *tert*-butyl chloride to be the only product of the reaction.

$$CH_3\overset{CH_3}{\overset{|}{C}}{=}CH_2 + HCl \longrightarrow CH_3\underset{Cl}{\underset{|}{\overset{CH_3}{\overset{|}{C}}}}CH_3 \qquad CH_3\overset{CH_3}{\overset{|}{C}}HCH_2Cl$$

2-methylpropene

only product formed

not formed

PROBLEM 36♦

For each of the following reaction coordinate diagrams, tell whether the structure of the transition state will be more similar to the structure of the reactants or to the structure of the products:

a.

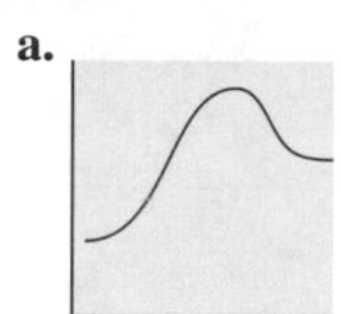

b.

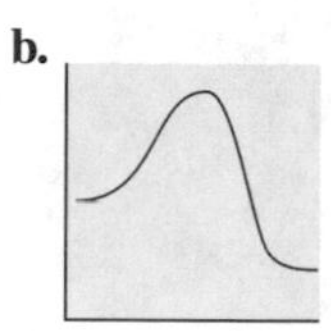

c.

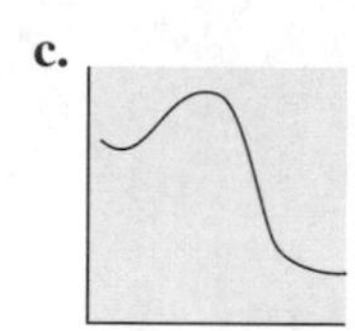

d.

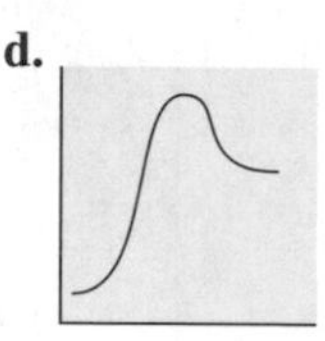

SUMMARY

Alkyl halides undergo two kinds of **nucleophilic substitution reactions**: S_N2 and S_N1. In both reactions, a nucleophile substitutes for a halogen. An S_N2 reaction is bimolecular: two molecules are involved in the transition state of the rate-limiting step. An S_N1 reaction is unimolecular; one molecule is involved in the transition state of the rate-limiting step.

The rate of an **S_N2 reaction** depends on the concentration of both the alkyl halide and the nucleophile. An S_N2 reaction has a one-step mechanism: the nucleophile attacks the back side of the carbon that is attached to the halogen. The reaction proceeds in the direction that allows the stronger base to displace the weaker base; it is reversible only if the difference between the basicities of the nucleophile and the leaving group is small. The rate of an S_N2 reaction is affected by steric hindrance: the bulkier the groups at the back side of the carbon undergoing attack, the slower is the reaction. Tertiary alkyl halides, therefore, cannot undergo S_N2 reactions. An S_N2 reaction takes place with **inversion of configuration**.

The rate of an **S_N1 reaction** depends only on the concentration of the alkyl halide. The halogen departs in the first step, forming a carbocation that is attacked by a nucleophile in the second step. Consequently, carbocation rearrangements can occur. The rate of an S_N1 reaction depends on the ease of carbocation formation. Tertiary alkyl halides, therefore, are more reactive than secondary alkyl halides because tertiary carbocations are more stable than secondary carbocations. Primary carbocations are so unstable that primary alkyl halides cannot undergo S_N1 reactions. An S_N1 reaction is accompanied by racemization. Most S_N1 reactions are **solvolysis** reactions: the solvent is the nucleophile.

The rates of both S_N2 and S_N1 reactions are influenced by the nature of the leaving group. Weak bases are the best leaving groups because weak bases form the weakest bonds. Thus, the weaker the basicity of the leaving group, the faster the reaction will occur. Therefore, the relative reactivities of alkyl halides that differ only in the halogen atom are $RI > RBr > RCl > RF$ in both S_N2 and S_N1 reactions.

Basicity is a measure of how well a compound shares its lone pair with a proton. **Nucleophilicity** is a measure of how readily a species is able to attack an electron-deficient atom. In general, the stronger base is a better nucleophile. However, if the attacking atoms are very different in size, the relationship between basicity and nucleophilicity depends on the solvent. Only in protic solvents are basicity and nucleophilicity reversed: the smaller stronger bases are poorer nucleophiles because of **ion–dipole interactions** between the ion and the solvent.

Methyl halides and primary alkyl halides undergo only S_N2 reactions; tertiary alkyl halides undergo only S_N1 reactions; vinylic and aryl halides undergo neither S_N2 nor S_N1 reactions; and secondary alkyl halides and benzylic and allylic halides (unless they are tertiary) undergo both S_N1 and S_N2 reactions. When the structure of the alkyl halide allows it to undergo both S_N2 and S_N1 reactions, the S_N2 reaction is favored by a high concentration of a good nucleophile in an aprotic polar solvent, whereas the S_N1 reaction is favored by a poor nucleophile in a protic polar solvent.

Protic solvents (H_2O, ROH) have a hydrogen attached to an O or an N; **aprotic solvents** (DMF, DMSO) do not have a hydrogen attached to an O or an N. The **dielectric constant** of a solvent tells how well the solvent insulates opposite charges from one another. Increasing the polarity of the solvent will decrease the rate of the reaction if one or more reactants in the rate-determining step are charged and will increase the rate of the reaction if none of the reactants in the rate-determining step is charged.

If the two functional groups of a **bifunctional molecule** can react with each other, both **intermolecular** and **intramolecular reactions** can occur. The reaction that is more likely to occur depends on the concentration of the bifunctional molecule and the size of the ring that would be formed in the intramolecular reaction.

SUMMARY OF REACTIONS

1. S_N2 reaction: a one-step mechanism

$$\ddot{Nu}^- + -\overset{|}{\underset{|}{C}}-X \longrightarrow -\overset{|}{\underset{|}{C}}-Nu + X^-$$

Relative reactivities of alkyl halides: $CH_3X > 1° > 2° > 3°$.
Only the inverted product is formed.

2. S_N1 reaction: a two-step mechanism with a carbocation intermediate

$$-\overset{|}{\underset{|}{C}}-X \longrightarrow -\overset{|}{\underset{|}{C^+}} + X^- \xrightarrow{\ddot{Nu}} -\overset{|}{\underset{|}{C}}-Nu$$

Relative reactivities of alkyl halides: $3° > 2° > 1° > CH_3X$
Both the inverted and noninverted products are formed.

KEY TERMS

aprotic polar solvent (p. 578/580)
aprotic solvent (p. 595)
back-side attack (p. 573)
base (p. 577)
basicity (p. 577)
bifunctional molecule (p. 601)
bimolecular (p. 572)
complete racemization (p. 591)
dielectric constant (p. 595)
elimination reaction (p. 570)
exhaustive methylation (p. 584)
first-order reaction (p. 586)
Hammond postulate (p. 607)
hyperconjugation (p. 605)
intermolecular reaction (p. 601)
intimate ion pair (p. 591)
intramolecular reaction (p. 601)
inversion of configuration (p. 576)
ion–dipole interaction (p. 579)
kinetics (p. 571)
leaving group (p. 570)
nucleophile (p. 577)
nucleophilicity (p. 577)
nucleophilic substitution reaction (p. 571)
partial racemization (p. 591)
primary carbocation (p. 604)
protic solvent (p. 579/595)
rate constant (p. 572)
rate law (p. 572)
second-order reaction (p. 572)
secondary carbocation (p. 604)
S_N1 reaction (p. 586)
S_N2 reaction (p. 572)
solvolysis (p. 589)
steric effects (p. 574)
steric hindrance (p. 574)
substitution reaction (p. 570)
tertiary carbocation (p. 604)
unimolecular (p. 586)

PROBLEMS

37. Give the product of the reaction of bromomethane with each of the following nucleophiles:
a. HO^- **b.** $^-NH_2$ **c.** CH_3SH **d.** HS^- **e.** CH_3O^- **f.** CH_3NH_2

38. Indicate how each of the factors listed below affects
a. an S_N1 reaction.
b. an S_N2 reaction.
1. the structure of the alkyl halide
2. the reactivity of the nucleophile
3. the concentration of the nucleophile
4. the solvent

39. Which is a better nucleophile in methanol?
a. H_2O or HO^- **b.** NH_3 or H_2O **c.** H_2O or H_2S **d.** HO^- or HS^- **e.** I^- or Br^- **f.** Cl^- or Br^-

40. Indicate which member of each pair in Problem 39 is a better leaving group.

41. What nucleophiles could be used to react with 1-iodobutane to prepare the following compounds?

a. 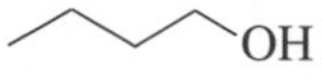 OH
b. 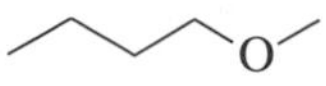 O
c. 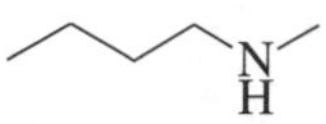 N H
d.  SH
e. 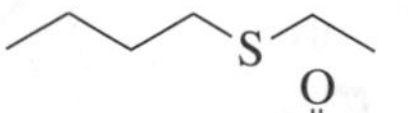 S
f. 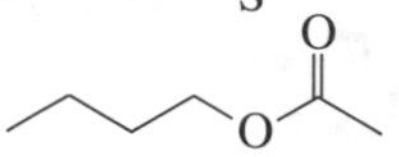 O O
g. 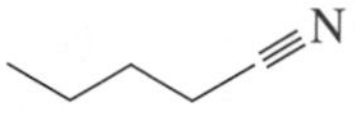 ≡N
h.

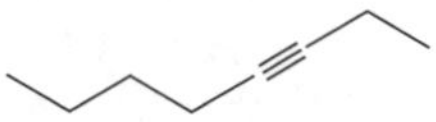

42. Starting with cyclohexene, how could the following compounds be prepared?
a. methoxycyclohexane **b.** dicyclohexyl ether **c.** cyclohexylmethylamine

43. Rank the following compounds in order of *decreasing* nucleophilicity:
a. $CH_3\overset{O}{\overset{\|}{C}}O^-$, $CH_3CH_2S^-$, $CH_3CH_2O^-$ in methanol
b. 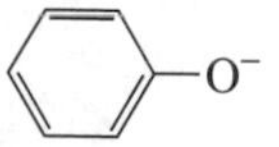 (benzene)–O^- and (cyclohexane)–O^- in DMSO
c. H_2O and NH_3 in methanol
d. Br^-, Cl^-, I^- in methanol

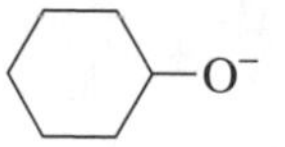

44. The pK_a of acetic acid in water is 4.76. What effect would a decrease in the polarity of the solvent have on the pK_a? Why?

45. **a.** Identify the substitution products that form when 2-bromo-2-methylpropane is dissolved in a mixture of 80% ethanol and 20% water.
b. Explain why the same products are obtained when 2-chloro-2-methylpropane is dissolved in a mixture of 80% ethanol and 20% water.

46. For each of the following reactions, give the substitution products; if the products can exist as stereoisomers, show what stereoisomers are obtained:
a. (*R*)-2-bromopentane + high concentration of CH_3O^-
b. (*R*)-2-bromopentane + CH_3OH
c. *trans*-1-chloro-2-methylcyclohexane + high concentration of CH_3O^-
d. *trans*-1-chloro-2-methylcyclohexane + CH_3OH
e. 3-bromo-2-methylpentane + CH_3OH
f. 3-bromo-3-methylpentane + CH_3OH

47. Give the products obtained from the solvolysis of each of the following compounds in ethanol:
a. 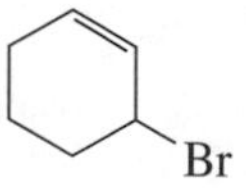 Br (3-bromocyclohexene) **b.** 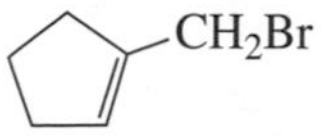 CH_2Br (cyclopentene) **c.** 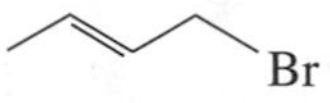 Br

48. Would you expect methoxide ion to be a better nucleophile if it were dissolved in CH_3OH or if it were dissolved in DMSO? Why?

49. Which reaction in each of the following pairs will take place more rapidly?
a. 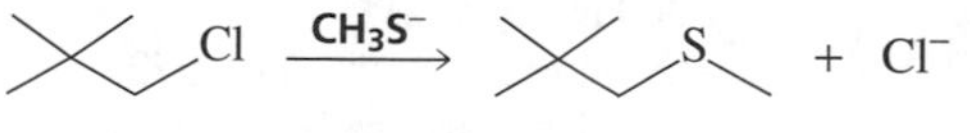 Cl $\xrightarrow{CH_3S^-}$ S + Cl^-
Cl $\xrightarrow{(CH_3)_2CHS^-}$ S + Cl^-
c. 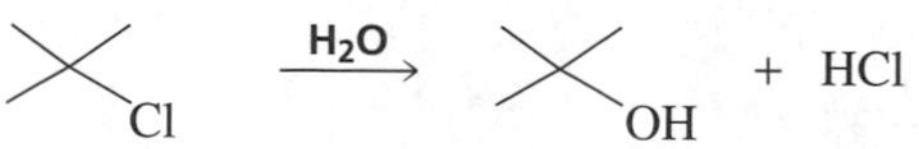 Cl $\xrightarrow{H_2O}$ OH + HCl
Cl $\xrightarrow{H_2O}$ OH + HCl

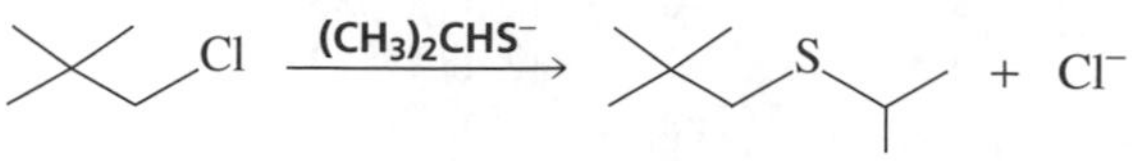

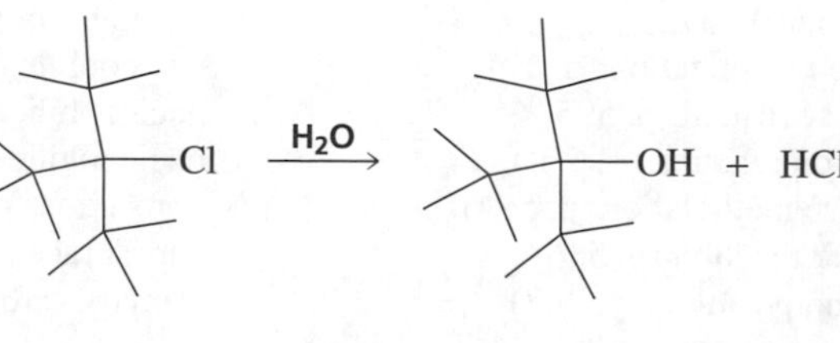

b. 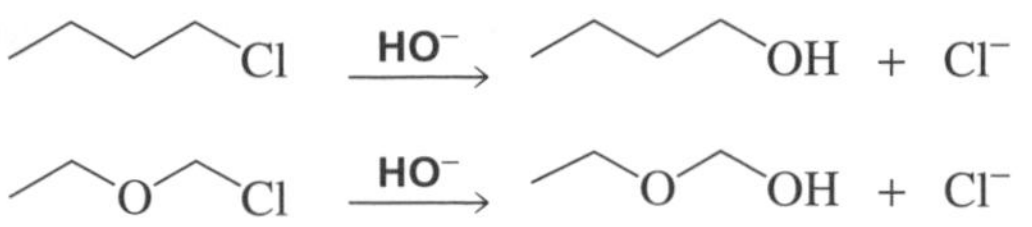 Cl-propyl $\xrightarrow{HO^-}$ propanol-OH + Cl^-

ethoxyethyl-Cl $\xrightarrow{HO^-}$ ethoxyethyl-OH + Cl^-

d. $(CH_3)_3CBr \xrightarrow{H_2O} (CH_3)_3COH + HBr$

$(CH_3)_3CBr \xrightarrow{CH_3CH_2OH} (CH_3)_3COCH_2CH_3 + HBr$

50. The reaction of an alkyl chloride with potassium iodide is generally carried out in acetone to maximize the amount of alkyl iodide that is formed. Why does the solvent increase the yield of alkyl iodide? (*Hint:* Potassium iodide is soluble in acetone, but potassium chloride is not.)

51. In Section 14.10, we saw that *S*-adenosylmethionine (SAM) methylates the nitrogen atom of noradrenaline to form adrenaline, a more potent hormone. If SAM methylates an OH group on the benzene ring instead, it completely destroys noradrenaline's activity. Give the mechanism for the methylation of the OH group by SAM.

noradrenaline + SAM ⟶ a biologically inactive compound + SAH

noradrenaline (HO, HO, OH, NH_2) — **a biologically inactive compound** (CH_3O, HO, OH, NH_2)

52. *tert*-Butyl chloride undergoes solvolysis in both acetic acid and formic acid.

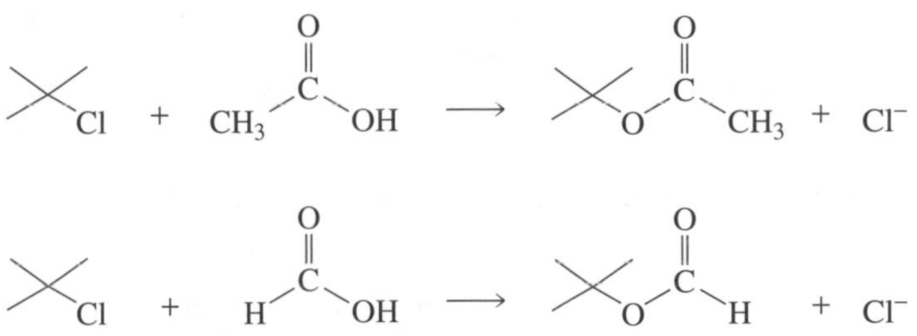

tert-butyl chloride + CH_3COOH ⟶ *tert*-butyl acetate + Cl^-

tert-butyl chloride + $HCOOH$ ⟶ *tert*-butyl formate + Cl^-

Solvolysis occurs 5000 times faster in one of the acids than in the other. In which solvent is solvolysis faster? Explain your answer. (*Hint*: See Table 14.3.)

53. For each of the following reactions, give the substitution products; if the products can exist as stereoisomers, show what stereoisomers are obtained:

a. (2*S*,3*S*)-2-chloro-3-methylpentane + high concentration of CH_3O^-
b. (2*S*,3*R*)-2-chloro-3-methylpentane + high concentration of CH_3O^-
c. (2*R*,3*S*)-2-chloro-3-methylpentane + high concentration of CH_3O^-
d. (2*R*,3*R*)-2-chloro-3-methylpentane + high concentration of CH_3O^-
e. 3-chloro-2,2-dimethylpentane + CH_3CH_2OH
f. benzyl bromide + CH_3CH_2OH

54. Give the substitution products obtained when each of the following compounds is added to a solution of sodium acetate in acetic acid.

a. 2-chloro-2-methyl-3-hexene **b.** 3-bromo-1-methylcyclohexene

55. Show how each of the following compounds can be synthesized from the given starting materials.

a. $CH_3CH_2CH_2Br \longrightarrow CH_3CH_2CH_2CH_2CH_3$
b. $CH_3CH_2CH_2Br \longrightarrow CH_3CH_2CH_2C(=O)CH_3$
c. $CH_3CH_2CH_2Br \longrightarrow CH_3CH_2CH_2CH_2CH(=O)$
d. $CH_3CH_2CH_2Br \longrightarrow CH_3CH_2CH{-}CH_2$ (epoxide, O bridging)

56. In which solvent would the equilibrium for the following S_N2 reaction lie farther to the right, ethanol or diethyl ether?

$$CH_3SCH_3 + CH_3Br \rightleftharpoons CH_3\overset{+}{S}(CH_3)CH_3 + Br^-$$

57. The rate of reaction of methyl iodide with quinuclidine was measured in nitrobenzene, and then the rate of reaction of methyl iodide with triethylamine was measured in the same solvent. The concentration of the reagents was the same in both experiments.

a. Which reaction had the larger rate constant?
b. The same experiment was done using isopropyl iodide instead of methyl iodide. Which reaction had the larger rate constant?
c. Which alkyl halide has the larger $k_{quinuclidine}/k_{triethylamine}$ ratio?

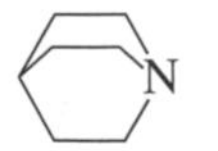

quinuclidine — **triethylamine** ($CH_3CH_2N(CH_2CH_3)CH_2CH_3$)

58. Only one bromoether (disregarding stereoisomers) is obtained from the reaction of the following alkyl dihalide with methanol. Give the structure of the ether.

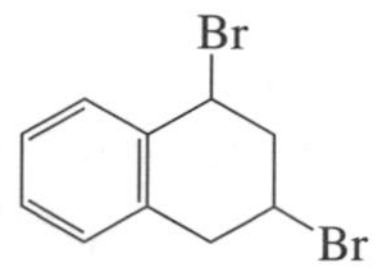

59. When equivalent amounts of methyl bromide and sodium iodide are dissolved in methanol, the concentration of iodide ion quickly decreases and then slowly returns to its original concentration. Account for this observation.

60. The rate constant of an intramolecular reaction depends on the size of the ring (n) that is formed. Explain the relative rates of formation of the cyclic secondary ammonium ions.

$$Br{-}(CH_2)_{n-1}{-}NH_2 \longrightarrow (CH_2)_{n-1}\ \overset{+}{N}H_2 + Br^-$$

n =	3	4	5	6	7	10
relative rate:	1×10^{-1}	2×10^{-3}	100	1.7	3×10^{-3}	1×10^{-8}

61. For each of the following reactions, give the substitution products, assuming that all the reactions are carried out under S_N2 conditions; if the products can exist as stereoisomers, show what stereoisomers are formed:

a. (3*S*,4*S*)-3-bromo-4-methylhexane + CH_3O^-
b. (3*S*,4*R*)-3-bromo-4-methylhexane + CH_3O^-
c. (3*R*,4*R*)-3-bromo-4-methylhexane + CH_3O^-
d. (3*R*,4*S*)-3-bromo-4-methylhexane + CH_3O^-

62. Explain why tetrahydrofuran can solvate a positively charged species better than diethyl ether can.

tetrahydrofuran

$CH_3CH_2OCH_2CH_3$
diethyl ether

63. Propose a mechanism for each of the following reactions:

a. (cyclobutyl)$CH(CH_3){-}Br \xrightarrow{H_2O}$ 1-methylcyclopentanol

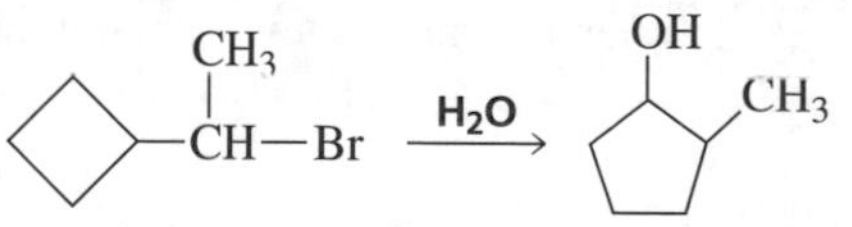

b. H_3C, $CHCH_3$ (Br) $\xrightarrow{H_2O}$ products with H, OH, CH_3, CH_3 + H, CH_3, OH, CH_3

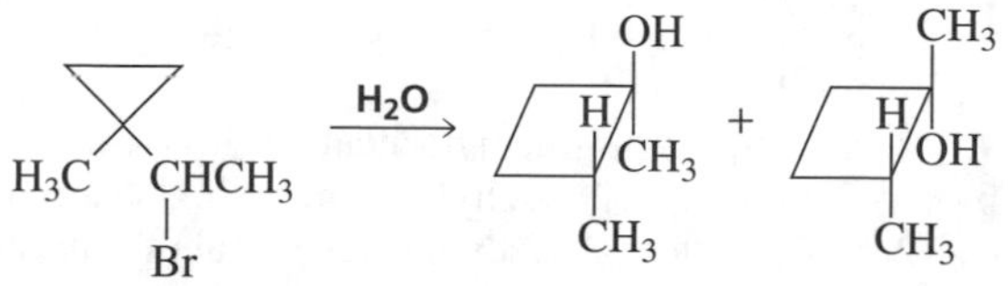

64. Which of the following will react faster in an S_N1 reaction, *cis*-1-bromo-4-*tert*-butylcyclohexane or *trans*-1-bromo-4-*tert*-butylcyclohexane?

65. Alkyl halides have been used as insecticides since the discovery of DDT in 1939. DDT was the first compound to be found that had a high toxicity to insects and a relatively low toxicity to mammals. In 1972, DDT was banned in the United States because it is a long-lasting compound and its widespread use was resulting in the accumulation of substantial concentrations in wildlife. Chlordane is an alkyl halide insecticide used to protect wooden buildings from termites. Chlordane can be synthesized from two reactants in a one-step reaction. One of the reactants is hexachlorocyclopentadiene. What is the other reactant?

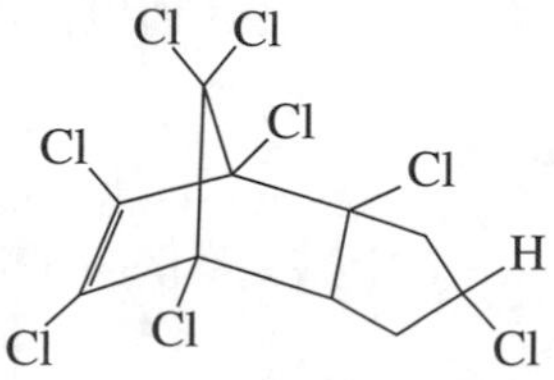

chlordane

66. Explain why the following alkyl halide does not undergo a substitution reaction, regardless of the conditions under which the reaction is run.

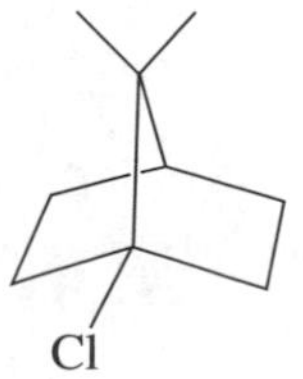

Data Tables

Appendix

TABLE A.1 Thermodynamic Properties of Substances at 298.15 K*. Substances are at 1 bar pressure. For aqueous solutions, solutes are at unit activity (roughly 1 M). Data for ions in aqueous solution are relative to values of *zero* for ΔH°_f, ΔG°_f, and S° for H^+

Inorganic Substances

	ΔH°_f, kJ mol^{-1}	ΔG°_f, kJ mol^{-1}	S°, J mol^{-1} K^{-1}	C_p, J mol^{-1} K^{-1}
Aluminum				
Al(s)	0	0	28.33	24.2
Al^{3+}(aq)	−531	−485	−321.7	—
$AlCl_3$(s)	−704.2	−628.8	110.7	91.1
Al_2Cl_6(g)	−1291	−1220.	490.	157.72
AlF_3(s)	−1504	−1425	66.44	75.1
Al_2O_3(a solid)	−1676	−1582	50.92	79.0
$Al(OH)_3$(s)	−1276	—	—	93.1
$Al_2(SO_4)_3$(s)	−3441	−3100.	239	259.4
Barium				
Ba(s)	0	0	62.8	28.1
Ba^{2+}(aq)	−537.6	−560.8	9.6	—
$BaCO_3$(s)	−1216	−1138	112.1	85.35
$BaCl_2$(s)	−858.6	−810.4	123.7	75.1
BaF_2(s)	−1207	−1157	96.36	71.2
BaO(s)	−553.5	−525.1	70.42	47.3
$Ba(OH)_2$(s)	−944.7	—	—	101.6
$Ba(OH)_2 \cdot 8\,H_2O$(s)	−3342	−2793	427	—
$BaSO_4$(s)	−1473	−1362	132.2	101.8
Beryllium				
Be(s)	0	0	9.50	16.4
$BeCl_2$(a solid)	−490.4	−445.6	82.68	62.4
BeF_2(a solid)	−1027	−979.4	53.35	51.8
BeO(s)	−609.6	−580.3	14.14	25.6
Bismuth				
Bi(s)	0	0	56.74	25.5
$BiCl_3$(s)	−379.1	−315.0	177.0	105.0
Bi_2O_3(s)	−573.9	−493.7	151.5	113.5
Boron				
B(s)	0	0	5.86	11.1
BCl_3(l)	−427.2	−387.4	206.3	106.7
BF_3(g)	−1137	−1120	254.1	50.45
B_2H_6(g)	35.6	86.7	232.1	56.7
B_2O_3(s)	−1273	−1194	53.97	62.8

*Data for inorganic substances and for organic compounds with up to two carbon atoms per molecule are adapted from D. D. Wagman, et al., "The NBS Tables of Chemical Thermodynamic Properties: Selected Values for Inorganic and C_1 and C_2 Organic Substances in SI Units" *Journal of Physical and Chemical Reference Data* 11 (1982) Supplement 2. Data for other organic compounds are from J. A. Dean, *Lange's Handbook of Chemistry*. 15th ed., McGraw-Hill, 1999, and other sources.

(continued)

Inorganic Substances	ΔH_f°, kJ mol^{-1}	ΔG_f°, kJ mol^{-1}	S°, J mol^{-1} K^{-1}	C_p, J mol^{-1} K^{-1}
Bromine				
$Br(g)$	111.9	82.40	175.0	20.8
$Br^-(aq)$	−121.6	−104.0	82.4	−141.8
$Br_2(g)$	30.91	3.11	245.5	36.0
$Br_2(l)$	0	0	152.2	75.7
$BrCl(g)$	14.64	−0.98	240.1	35.0
$BrF_3(g)$	−255.6	−229.4	292.5	66.6
$BrF_3(l)$	−300.8	−240.5	178.2	124.6
Cadmium				
$Cd(s)$	0	0	51.76	26.0
$Cd^{2+}(aq)$	−75.90	−77.61	−73.2	—
$CdCl_2(s)$	−391.5	−343.9	115.3	74.7
$CdO(s)$	−258.2	−228.4	54.8	43.4
Calcium				
$Ca(s)$	0	0	41.42	25.9
$Ca^{2+}(aq)$	−542.8	−553.6	−53.1	—
$CaCO_3(s)$	−1207	−1129	92.9	80.6
$CaCl_2(s)$	−795.8	−748.1	104.6	72.9
$CaF_2(s)$	−1220.	−1167	68.87	67.0
$CaH_2(s)$	−186.2	−147.2	42	41.0
$Ca(NO_3)_2(s)$	−938.4	−743.1	193.3	149.4
$CaO(s)$	−635.1	−604.0	39.75	42.0
$Ca(OH)_2(s)$	−986.1	−898.5	83.39	87.5
$Ca_3(PO_4)_2(s)$	−4121	−3885	236.0	227.8
$CaSO_4(s)$	−1434	−1322	106.7	99.7
Carbon (See also the table of organic substances.)				
$C(g)$	716.7	671.3	158.0	20.8
C(diamond)	1.90	2.90	2.38	6.1
C(graphite)	0	0	5.74	8.5
$CCl_4(g)$	−102.9	−60.59	309.9	83.3
$CCl_4(l)$	−135.4	−65.21	216.4	130.7
$C_2N_2(g)$	309.0	297.4	241.9	56.8
$CO(g)$	−110.5	−137.2	197.7	29.1
$CO_2(g)$	−393.5	−394.4	213.7	37.1
$CO_3^{2-}(aq)$	−677.1	−527.8	−56.9	—
$C_3O_2(g)$	−93.72	−109.8	276.5	67.0
$C_3O_2(l)$	−117.3	−105.0	181.1	—
$COCl_2(g)$	−218.8	−204.6	283.5	57.7
$COS(g)$	−142.1	−169.3	231.6	41.5
$CS_2(l)$	89.70	65.27	151.3	76.4
Chlorine				
$Cl(g)$	121.7	105.7	165.2	21.8
$Cl^-(aq)$	−167.2	−131.2	56.5	−136.4
$Cl_2(g)$	0	0	223.1	33.9
$ClF_3(g)$	−163.2	−123.0	281.6	63.9
$ClO_2(g)$	102.5	120.5	256.8	42.0
$Cl_2O(g)$	80.3	97.9	266.2	45.4
Chromium				
$Cr(s)$	0	0	23.77	23.4
$[Cr(H_2O)_6]^{3+}(aq)$	−1999	—	—	—
$Cr_2O_3(s)$	−1140.	−1058	81.2	118.7
$CrO_4^{2-}(aq)$	−881.2	−727.8	50.21	—
$Cr_2O_7^{2-}(aq)$	−1490.	−1301	261.9	—

Inorganic Substances	ΔH_f°, kJ mol^{-1}	ΔG_f°, kJ mol^{-1}	S°, J mol^{-1} K^{-1}	C_p, J mol^{-1} K^{-1}
Cobalt				
Co(s)	0	0	30.04	24.8
CoO(s)	−237.9	−214.2	52.97	55.2
$Co(OH)_2$(pink solid)	−539.7	−454.3	79	68.8
Copper				
Cu(s)	0	0	33.15	24.4
Cu^{2+}(aq)	64.77	65.49	−99.6	—
$CuCO_3 \cdot Cu(OH)_2$(s)	−1051	−893.6	186.2	—
CuO(s)	−157.3	−129.7	42.63	42.3
$Cu(OH)_2$(s)	−449.8	—	—	95.19
$CuSO_4 \cdot 5\,H_2O$(s)	−2280.	−1880.	300.4	—
Fluorine				
F(g)	78.99	61.91	158.8	22.7
F^-(aq)	−332.6	−278.8	−13.8	−106.7
F_2(g)	0	0	202.8	31.3
Helium				
He(g)	0	0	126.2	20.8
Hydrogen				
H(g)	218.0	203.2	114.7	20.8
H^+(aq)	0	0	0	0
H_2(g)	0	0	130.7	28.8
HBr(g)	−36.40	−53.45	198.7	29.1
HCl(g)	−92.31	−95.30	186.9	29.1
HCl(aq)	−167.2	−131.2	56.5	−136.4
$HClO_2$(aq)	−51.9	5.9	188.3	—
HCN(g)	135.1	124.7	201.8	35.9
HF(g)	−271.1	−273.2	173.8	—
HI(g)	26.48	1.70	206.6	29.2
HNO_3(l)	−174.1	−80.71	155.6	109.9
HNO_3(aq)	−207.4	−111.3	146.4	−86.6
H_2O(g)	−241.8	−228.6	188.8	33.6
H_2O(l)	−285.8	−237.1	69.91	75.3
H_2O_2(g)	−136.3	−105.6	232.7	43.1
H_2O_2(l)	−187.8	−120.4	109.6	89.1
H_2S(g)	−20.63	−33.56	205.8	34.2
H_2SO_4(l)	−814.0	−690.0	156.9	138.9
H_2SO_4(aq)	−909.3	−744.5	20.1	−293.0
Iodine				
I(g)	106.8	70.25	180.8	20.8
I^-(aq)	−55.19	−51.57	111.3	−142.3
I_2(g)	62.44	19.33	260.7	36.9
I_2(s)	0	0	116.1	54.4
IBr(g)	40.84	3.69	258.8	36.4
ICl(g)	17.78	−5.46	247.6	35.6
ICl(l)	−23.89	−13.58	135.1	135.1

(continued)

Inorganic Substances	ΔH_f°, kJ mol^{-1}	ΔG_f°, kJ mol^{-1}	S°, J mol^{-1} K^{-1}	C_p, J mol^{-1} K^{-1}
Iron				
Fe(s)	0	0	27.28	25.1
Fe^{2+}(aq)	−89.1	−78.90	−137.7	—
Fe^{3+}(aq)	−48.5	−4.7	−315.9	—
$FeCO_3$(s)	−740.6	−666.7	92.9	82.1
$FeCl_3$(s)	−399.5	−334.0	−142.3	96.7
FeO(s)	−272.0	—	—	49.91
Fe_2O_3(s)	−824.2	−742.2	87.40	103.9
Fe_3O_4(s)	−1118	−1015	146.4	143.4
$Fe(OH)_3$(s)	−823.0	−696.5	106.7	101.7
Lead				
Pb(s)	0	0	64.81	26.4
Pb^{2+}(aq)	−1.7	−24.43	10.5	—
PbI_2(s)	−175.5	−173.6	174.9	77.4
PbO_2(s)	−277.4	−217.3	68.6	64.6
$PbSO_4$(s)	−919.9	−813.1	148.6	103.2
Lithium				
Li(g)	159.4	126.7	138.8	20.8
Li(s)	0	0	29.12	24.8
Li^+(aq)	−278.5	−293.3	13.4	68.6
LiCl(s)	−408.6	−384.4	59.33	48.0
LiOH(s)	−484.9	−439.0	42.80	49.6
$LiNO_3$(s)	−483.1	−381.1	90.0	—
Magnesium				
Mg(s)	0	0	32.68	24.9
Mg^{2+}(aq)	−466.9	−454.8	−138.1	—
$MgCl_2$(s)	−641.3	−591.8	89.62	71.4
$MgCO_3$(s)	−1096	−1012	65.7	75.5
MgF_2(s)	−1123	−1070	57.24	61.6
MgO(s)	−601.7	−569.4	26.94	37.2
$Mg(OH)_2$(s)	−924.5	−833.5	63.18	77.0
MgS(s)	−346.0	−341.8	50.33	45.6
$MgSO_4$(s)	−1285	−1171	91.6	96.5
Manganese				
Mn(s)	0	0	32.01	26.3
Mn^{2+}(aq)	−220.8	−228.1	−73.6	50.0
MnO_2(s)	−520.0	−465.1	53.05	54.1
MnO_4^-(aq)	−541.4	−447.2	191.2	−82.0
Mercury				
Hg(g)	61.32	31.82	175.0	20.8
Hg(l)	0	0	76.02	28.0
HgO(s)	−90.83	−58.54	70.29	44.1
Nitrogen				
N(g)	472.7	455.6	153.3	20.8
N_2(g)	0	0	191.6	29.1
NF_3(g)	−124.7	−83.2	260.7	53.4
NH_3(g)	−46.11	−16.45	192.5	35.1
NH_3(aq)	−80.29	−26.50	111.3	—
NH_4^+(aq)	−132.5	−79.31	113.4	79.9
NH_4Br(s)	−270.8	−175.2	113	96.0
NH_4Cl(s)	−314.4	−202.9	94.6	84.1
NH_4F(s)	−464.0	−348.7	71.96	65.3
NH_4HCO_3(s)	−849.4	−665.9	120.9	—

Inorganic Substances	ΔH_f°, kJ mol^{-1}	ΔG_f°, kJ mol^{-1}	S°, J mol^{-1} K^{-1}	C_p, J mol^{-1} K^{-1}
$NH_4I(s)$	−201.4	−112.5	117	—
$NH_4NO_3(s)$	−365.6	−183.9	151.1	139.3
$NH_4NO_3(aq)$	−339.9	−190.6	259.8	−6.7
$(NH_4)_2SO_4(s)$	−1181	−901.7	220.1	187.5
$N_2H_4(g)$	95.40	159.4	238.5	48.4
$N_2H_4(l)$	50.63	149.3	121.2	98.9
$NO(g)$	90.25	86.55	210.8	29.9
$N_2O(g)$	82.05	104.2	219.9	38.6
$NO_2(g)$	33.18	51.31	240.1	37.2
$N_2O_4(g)$	9.16	97.89	304.3	79.2
$N_2O_4(l)$	−19.50	97.54	209.2	142.7
$N_2O_5(g)$	11.3	115.1	355.7	95.3
$NO_3^-(aq)$	−205.0	−108.7	146.4	−86.6
$NOBr(g)$	82.17	82.42	273.7	45.5
$NOCl(g)$	51.71	66.08	261.7	44.7
Oxygen				
$O(g)$	249.2	231.7	161.1	21.9
$O_2(g)$	0	0	205.1	29.4
$O_3(g)$	142.7	163.2	238.9	39.2
$OH^-(aq)$	−230.0	−157.2	−10.75	−148.5
$OF_2(g)$	24.7	41.9	247.4	43.3
Phosphorus				
P(α white)	0	0	41.09	23.8
P(red)	−17.6	−12.1	22.80	21.2
$P_4(g)$	58.91	24.44	280.0	67.2
$PCl_3(g)$	−287.0	−267.8	311.8	71.8
$PCl_5(g)$	−374.9	−305.0	364.6	112.8
$PH_3(g)$	5.4	13.4	210.2	37.1
$P_4O_{10}(s)$	−2984	−2698	228.9	211.71
$PO_4^{3-}(aq)$	−1277	−1019	−222	—
Potassium				
$K(g)$	89.24	60.59	160.3	20.8
$K(s)$	0	0	64.18	29.6
$K^+(aq)$	−252.4	−283.3	102.5	21.8
$KBr(s)$	−393.8	−380.7	95.90	52.4
$KCN(s)$	−113.0	−101.9	128.5	66.3
$KCl(s)$	−436.7	−409.1	82.59	51.3
$KClO_3(s)$	−397.7	−296.3	143.1	100.3
$KClO_4(s)$	−432.8	−303.1	151.0	112.4
$KF(s)$	−567.3	−537.8	66.57	49.0
$KI(s)$	−327.9	−324.9	106.3	52.9
$KNO_3(s)$	−494.6	−394.9	133.1	96.4
$KOH(s)$	−424.8	−379.1	78.9	68.9
$KOH(aq)$	−482.4	−440.5	91.6	−126.8
$K_2SO_4(s)$	−1438	−1321	175.6	131.5
Silicon				
$Si(s)$	0	0	18.83	20.0
$SiH_4(g)$	34.3	56.9	204.6	42.8
$Si_2H_6(g)$	80.3	127.3	272.7	80.8
SiO_2(quartz)	−910.9	−856.6	41.84	44.4

(continued)

Inorganic Substances				
	ΔH_f°, kJ mol^{-1}	ΔG_f°, kJ mol^{-1}	S°, J mol^{-1} K^{-1}	C_p, J mol^{-1} K^{-1}
Silver				
Ag(s)	0	0	42.55	25.4
Ag^{+}(aq)	105.6	77.11	72.68	21.8
AgBr(s)	−100.4	−96.90	107.1	52.4
AgCl(s)	−127.1	−109.8	96.2	50.8
AgI(s)	−61.84	−66.19	115.5	56.8
$AgNO_3$(s)	−124.4	−33.41	140.9	93.1
Ag_2O(s)	−31.05	−11.20	121.3	65.9
Ag_2SO_4(s)	−715.9	−618.4	200.4	131.4
Sodium				
Na(g)	107.3	76.76	153.7	20.8
Na(s)	0	0	51.21	28.2
Na^{+}(aq)	−240.1	−261.9	59.0	46.4
Na_2(g)	142.1	103.9	230.2	37.6
NaBr(s)	−361.1	−349.0	86.82	51.4
Na_2CO_3(s)	−1131	−1044	135.0	112.3
$NaHCO_3$(s)	−950.8	−851.0	101.7	87.6
NaCl(s)	−411.2	−384.1	72.13	50.5
NaCl(aq)	−407.3	−393.1	115.5	−90.0
$NaClO_3$(s)	−365.8	−262.3	123.4	—
$NaClO_4$(s)	−383.3	−254.9	142.3	111.3
NaF(s)	−573.6	−543.5	51.46	46.9
NaH(s)	−56.28	−33.46	40.02	36.4
NaI(s)	−287.8	−286.1	98.53	52.1
$NaNO_3$(s)	−467.9	−367.0	116.5	92.9
$NaNO_3$(aq)	−447.5	−373.2	205.4	−40.2
Na_2O_2(s)	−510.9	−447.7	95.0	89.2
NaOH(s)	−425.6	−379.5	64.46	59.5
NaOH(aq)	−470.1	−419.2	48.1	−102.1
NaH_2PO_4(s)	−1537	−1386	127.5	−116.86
Na_2HPO_4(s)	−1748	−1608	150.5	135.3
Na_3PO_4(s)	−1917	−1789	173.8	153.47
$NaHSO_4$(s)	−1126	−992.8	113.0	—
Na_2SO_4(s)	−1387	−1270	149.6	128.2
Na_2SO_4(aq)	−1390.	−1268	138.1	−201.0
$Na_2SO_4 \cdot 10\,H_2O$(s)	−4327	−3647	592.0	—
$Na_2S_2O_3$(s)	−1123	−1028	155	—
Sulfur				
S(g)	278.8	238.3	167.8	23.7
S(rhombic)	0	0	31.80	22.6
S_8(g)	102.3	49.63	431.0	156.06
S_2Cl_2(g)	−18.4	−31.8	331.5	124.3
SF_6(g)	−1209	−1105	291.8	97.0
SO_2(g)	−296.8	−300.2	248.2	39.9
SO_3(g)	−395.7	−371.1	256.8	50.7
SO_4^{2-}(aq)	−909.3	−744.5	20.1	−293.0
$S_2O_3^{2-}$(aq)	−648.5	−522.5	67	—
SO_2Cl_2(g)	−364.0	−320.0	311.9	77.0
SO_2Cl_2(l)	−394.1	—	—	−134.0
Tin				
Sn(white)	0	0	51.55	27.0
Sn(gray)	−2.09	0.13	44.14	25.8
$SnCl_4$(l)	−511.3	−440.1	258.6	165.3
SnO(s)	−285.8	−256.9	56.5	44.3
SnO_2(s)	−580.7	−519.6	52.3	52.6

Inorganic Substances	ΔH_f°, kJ mol^{-1}	ΔG_f°, kJ mol^{-1}	S°, J mol^{-1} K^{-1}	C_p, J mol^{-1} K^{-1}
Titanium				
Ti(s)	0	0	30.63	25.0
$TiCl_4$(g)	−763.2	−726.7	354.9	95.4
$TiCl_4$(l)	−804.2	−737.2	252.3	145.2
TiO_2(s)	−944.7	−889.5	50.33	55.0
Uranium				
U(s)	0	0	50.21	27.7
UF_6(g)	−2147	−2064	377.9	129.6
UF_6(s)	−2197	−2069	227.6	166.8
UO_2(s)	−1085	−1032	77.03	63.6
Zinc				
Zn(s)	0	0	41.63	25.4
Zn^{2+}(aq)	−153.9	−147.1	112.1	46.0
ZnO(s)	−138.3	−318.3	43.64	40.3

Organic Substances

	Name	ΔH_f°, kJ mol^{-1}	ΔG_f°, kJ mol^{-1}	S°, J mol^{-1} K^{-1}	C_p, J mol^{-1} K^{-1}
CH_4(g)	Methane(g)	−74.81	−50.72	186.3	35.7
C_2H_2(g)	Acetylene(g)	226.7	209.2	200.9	44.0
C_2H_4(g)	Ethylene(g)	52.26	68.15	219.6	42.9
C_2H_6(g)	Ethane(g)	−84.68	−32.82	229.6	52.5
C_3H_8(g)	Propane(g)	−103.8	−23.3	270.3	73.6
C_4H_{10}(g)	Butane(g)	−125.6	−17.1	310.2	97.5
C_6H_6(g)	Benzene(g)	82.6	129.8	269.3	82.4
C_6H_6(l)	Benzene(l)	49.0	124.5	173.4	136.0
C_6H_{12}(g)	Cyclohexane(g)	−123.4	32.0	298.4	106.3
C_6H_{12}(l)	Cyclohexane(l)	−156.4	26.9	204.4	154.9
$C_{10}H_8$(g)	Naphthalene(g)	150.6	224.2	333.2	131.9
$C_{10}H_8$(s)	Naphthalene(s)	77.9	201.7	167.5	165.7
CH_2O(g)	Formaldehyde(g)	−108.6	−102.5	218.8	35.4
CH_3CHO(g)	Acetaldehyde(g)	−166.2	−128.9	250.3	55.3
CH_3CHO(l)	Acetaldehyde(l)	−192.3	−128.1	160.2	89.0
CH_3OH(g)	Methanol(g)	−200.7	−162.0	239.8	44.1
CH_3OH(l)	Methanol(l)	−238.7	−166.3	126.8	81.1
CH_3CH_2OH(g)	Ethanol(g)	−235.1	−168.5	282.7	65.6
CH_3CH_2OH(l)	Ethanol(l)	−277.7	−174.8	160.7	112.3
C_6H_5OH(s)	Phenol(s)	−165.1	−50.4	144.0	127.4
$(CH_3)_2CO$(g)	Acetone(g)	−216.6	−153.0	295.0	74.5
$(CH_3)_2CO$(l)	Acetone(l)	−247.6	−155.6	200.5	126.3
CH_3COOH(g)	Acetic acid(g)	−432.3	−374.0	282.5	63.4
CH_3COOH(l)	Acetic acid(l)	−484.5	−389.9	159.8	123.3
CH_3COOH(aq)	Acetic acid(aq)	−485.8	−396.5	178.7	−6.3
C_6H_5COOH(s)	Benzoic acid(s)	−385.2	−245.3	167.6	146.8
CH_3NH_2(g)	Methylamine(g)	−22.97	32.16	243.4	50.1
$C_6H_5NH_2$(g)	Aniline(g)	86.86	166.8	319.3	107.9
$C_6H_5NH_2$(l)	Aniline(l)	31.6	149.2	191.3	191.9

TABLE A.2 Equilibrium Constants

A. Ionization Constants of Weak Acids at 25 °C

Name of acid	Formula	K_a	Name of acid	Formula	K_a
Acetic	$HC_2H_3O_2$	1.8×10^{-5}	Hyponitrous	HON=NOH	8.9×10^{-8}
Acrylic	$HC_3H_3O_2$	5.5×10^{-5}		$HON{=}NO^-$	4×10^{-12}
Arsenic	H_3AsO_4	6.0×10^{-3}	Iodic	HIO_3	1.6×10^{-1}
	$H_2AsO_4^-$	1.0×10^{-7}	Iodoacetic	$HC_2H_2IO_2$	6.7×10^{-4}
	$HAsO_4^{2-}$	3.2×10^{-12}	Malonic	$H_2C_3H_2O_4$	1.5×10^{-3}
Arsenous	H_3AsO_3	6.6×10^{-10}		$HC_3H_2O_4^-$	2.0×10^{-6}
Benzoic	$HC_7H_5O_2$	6.3×10^{-5}	Nitrous	HNO_2	7.2×10^{-4}
Bromoacetic	$HC_2H_2BrO_2$	1.3×10^{-3}	Oxalic	$H_2C_2O_4$	5.4×10^{-2}
Butyric	$HC_4H_7O_2$	1.5×10^{-5}		$HC_2O_4^-$	5.3×10^{-5}
Carbonic	H_2CO_3	4.4×10^{-7}	Phenol	HOC_6H_5	1.0×10^{-10}
	HCO_3^-	4.7×10^{-11}	Phenylacetic	$HC_8H_7O_2$	4.9×10^{-5}
Chloroacetic	$HC_2H_2ClO_2$	1.4×10^{-3}	Phosphoric	H_3PO_4	7.1×10^{-3}
Chlorous	$HClO_2$	1.1×10^{-2}		$H_2PO_4^-$	6.3×10^{-8}
Citric	$H_3C_6H_5O_7$	7.4×10^{-4}		HPO_4^{2-}	4.2×10^{-13}
	$H_2C_6H_5O_7^-$	1.7×10^{-5}	Phosphorous	H_3PO_3	3.7×10^{-2}
	$HC_6H_5O_7^{2-}$	4.0×10^{-7}		$H_2PO_3^-$	2.1×10^{-7}
Cyanic	HOCN	3.5×10^{-4}	Propionic	$HC_3H_5O_2$	1.3×10^{-5}
Dichloroacetic	$HC_2HCl_2O_2$	5.5×10^{-2}	Pyrophosphoric	$H_4P_2O_7$	3.0×10^{-2}
Fluoroacetic	$HC_2H_2FO_2$	2.6×10^{-3}		$H_3P_2O_7^-$	4.4×10^{-3}
Formic	$HCHO_2$	1.8×10^{-4}		$H_2P_2O_7^{2-}$	2.5×10^{-7}
Hydrazoic	HN_3	1.9×10^{-5}		$HP_2O_7^{3-}$	5.6×10^{-10}
Hydrocyanic	HCN	6.2×10^{-10}	Selenic	H_2SeO_4	strong acid
Hydrofluoric	HF	6.6×10^{-4}		$HSeO_4^-$	2.2×10^{-2}
Hydrogen peroxide	H_2O_2	2.2×10^{-12}	Selenous	H_2SeO_3	2.3×10^{-3}
Hydroselenic	H_2Se	1.3×10^{-4}		$HSeO_3^-$	5.4×10^{-9}
	HSe^-	1×10^{-11}	Succinic	$H_2C_4H_4O_4$	6.2×10^{-5}
Hydrosulfuric	H_2S	1.0×10^{-7}		$HC_4H_4O_4^-$	2.3×10^{-6}
	HS^-	1×10^{-19}	Sulfuric	H_2SO_4	strong acid
Hydrotelluric	H_2Te	2.3×10^{-3}		HSO_4^-	1.1×10^{-2}
	HTe^-	1.6×10^{-11}	Sulfurous	H_2SO_3	1.3×10^{-2}
Hypobromous	HOBr	2.5×10^{-9}		HSO_3^-	6.2×10^{-8}
Hypochlorous	HOCl	2.9×10^{-8}	Thiophenol	HSC_6H_5	3.2×10^{-7}
Hypoiodous	HOI	2.3×10^{-11}	Trichloroacetic	$HC_2Cl_3O_2$	3.0×10^{-1}

B. Ionization Constants of Weak Bases at 25 °C

Name of base	Formula	K_b	Name of base	Formula	K_b
Ammonia	NH_3	1.8×10^{-5}	Isoquinoline	C_9H_7N	2.5×10^{-9}
Aniline	$C_6H_5NH_2$	7.4×10^{-10}	Methylamine	CH_3NH_2	4.2×10^{-4}
Codeine	$C_{18}H_{21}O_3N$	8.9×10^{-7}	Morphine	$C_{17}H_{19}O_3N$	7.4×10^{-7}
Diethylamine	$(C_2H_5)_2NH$	6.9×10^{-4}	Piperdine	$C_5H_{11}N$	1.3×10^{-3}
Dimethylamine	$(CH_3)_2NH$	5.9×10^{-4}	Pyridine	C_5H_5N	1.5×10^{-9}
Ethylamine	$C_2H_5NH_2$	4.3×10^{-4}	Quinoline	C_9H_7N	6.3×10^{-10}
Hydrazine	NH_2NH_2	8.5×10^{-7}	Triethanolamine	$C_6H_{15}O_3N$	5.8×10^{-7}
	$NH_2NH_3^+$	8.9×10^{-16}	Triethylamine	$(C_2H_5)_3N$	5.2×10^{-4}
Hydroxylamine	NH_2OH	9.1×10^{-9}	Trimethylamine	$(CH_3)_3N$	6.3×10^{-5}

C. Solubility Product Constants[a]

Name of solute	Formula	K_{sp}
Aluminum hydroxide	$Al(OH)_3$	1.3×10^{-33}
Aluminum phosphate	$AlPO_4$	6.3×10^{-19}
Barium carbonate	$BaCO_3$	5.1×10^{-9}
Barium chromate	$BaCrO_4$	1.2×10^{-10}
Barium fluoride	BaF_2	1.0×10^{-6}
Barium hydroxide	$Ba(OH)_2$	5×10^{-3}
Barium sulfate	$BaSO_4$	1.1×10^{-10}
Barium sulfite	$BaSO_3$	8×10^{-7}
Barium thiosulfate	BaS_2O_3	1.6×10^{-5}
Bismuthyl chloride	$BiOCl$	1.8×10^{-31}
Bismuthyl hydroxide	$BiOOH$	4×10^{-10}
Cadmium carbonate	$CdCO_3$	5.2×10^{-12}
Cadmium hydroxide	$Cd(OH)_2$	2.5×10^{-14}
Cadmium sulfide[b]	CdS	8×10^{-28}
Calcium carbonate	$CaCO_3$	2.8×10^{-9}
Calcium chromate	$CaCrO_4$	7.1×10^{-4}
Calcium fluoride	CaF_2	5.3×10^{-9}
Calcium hydroxide	$Ca(OH)_2$	5.5×10^{-6}
Calcium hydrogen phosphate	$CaHPO_4$	1×10^{-7}
Calcium oxalate	CaC_2O_4	4×10^{-9}
Calcium phosphate	$Ca_3(PO_4)_2$	2.0×10^{-29}
Calcium sulfate	$CaSO_4$	9.1×10^{-6}
Calcium sulfite	$CaSO_3$	6.8×10^{-8}
Chromium(II) hydroxide	$Cr(OH)_2$	2×10^{-16}
Chromium(III) hydroxide	$Cr(OH)_3$	6.3×10^{-31}
Cobalt(II) carbonate	$CoCO_3$	1.4×10^{-13}
Cobalt(II) hydroxide	$Co(OH)_2$	1.6×10^{-15}
Cobalt(III) hydroxide	$Co(OH)_3$	1.6×10^{-44}
Copper(I) chloride	$CuCl$	1.2×10^{-6}
Copper(I) cyanide	$CuCN$	3.2×10^{-20}
Copper(I) iodide	CuI	1.1×10^{-12}
Copper(II) arsenate	$Cu_3(AsO_4)_2$	7.6×10^{-36}
Copper(II) carbonate	$CuCO_3$	1.4×10^{-10}
Copper(II) chromate	$CuCrO_4$	3.6×10^{-6}
Copper(II) ferrocyanide	$Cu_2[Fe(CN)_6]$	1.3×10^{-16}
Copper(II) hydroxide	$Cu(OH)_2$	2.2×10^{-20}
Copper(II) sulfide[b]	CuS	6×10^{-37}
Iron(II) carbonate	$FeCO_3$	3.2×10^{-11}
Iron(II) hydroxide	$Fe(OH)_2$	8.0×10^{-16}
Iron(II) sulfide[b]	FeS	6×10^{-19}
Iron(III) arsenate	$FeAsO_4$	5.7×10^{-21}
Iron(III) ferrocyanide	$Fe_4[Fe(CN)_6]_3$	3.3×10^{-41}
Iron(III) hydroxide	$Fe(OH)_3$	4×10^{-38}
Iron(III) phosphate	$FePO_4$	1.3×10^{-22}
Lead(II) arsenate	$Pb_3(AsO_4)_2$	4.0×10^{-36}
Lead(II) azide	$Pb(N_3)_2$	2.5×10^{-9}
Lead(II) bromide	$PbBr_2$	4.0×10^{-5}
Lead(II) carbonate	$PbCO_3$	7.4×10^{-14}
Lead(II) chloride	$PbCl_2$	1.6×10^{-5}
Lead(II) chromate	$PbCrO_4$	2.8×10^{-13}
Lead(II) fluoride	PbF_2	2.7×10^{-8}
Lead(II) hydroxide	$Pb(OH)_2$	1.2×10^{-15}
Lead(II) iodide	PbI_2	7.1×10^{-9}
Lead(II) sulfate	$PbSO_4$	1.6×10^{-8}
Lead(II) sulfide[b]	PbS	3×10^{-28}
Lithium carbonate	Li_2CO_3	2.5×10^{-2}
Lithium fluoride	LiF	3.8×10^{-3}
Lithium phosphate	Li_3PO_4	3.2×10^{-9}
Magnesium ammonium phosphate	$MgNH_4PO_4$	2.5×10^{-13}
Magnesium carbonate	$MgCO_3$	3.5×10^{-8}
Magnesium fluoride	MgF_2	3.7×10^{-8}
Magnesium hydroxide	$Mg(OH)_2$	1.8×10^{-11}
Magnesium phosphate	$Mg_3(PO_4)_2$	1×10^{-25}
Manganese(II) carbonate	$MnCO_3$	1.8×10^{-11}
Manganese(II) hydroxide	$Mn(OH)_2$	1.9×10^{-13}
Manganese(II) sulfide[b]	MnS	3×10^{-14}
Mercury(I) bromide	Hg_2Br_2	5.6×10^{-23}
Mercury(I) chloride	Hg_2Cl_2	1.3×10^{-18}
Mercury(I) iodide	Hg_2I_2	4.5×10^{-29}
Mercury(II) sulfide[b]	HgS	2×10^{-53}
Nickel(II) carbonate	$NiCO_3$	6.6×10^{-9}
Nickel(II) hydroxide	$Ni(OH)_2$	2.0×10^{-15}
Scandium fluoride	ScF_3	4.2×10^{-18}
Scandium hydroxide	$Sc(OH)_3$	8.0×10^{-31}
Silver arsenate	Ag_3AsO_4	1.0×10^{-22}
Silver azide	AgN_3	2.8×10^{-9}
Silver bromide	$AgBr$	5.0×10^{-13}
Silver carbonate	Ag_2CO_3	8.5×10^{-12}
Silver chloride	$AgCl$	1.8×10^{-10}
Silver chromate	Ag_2CrO_4	1.1×10^{-12}
Silver cyanide	$AgCN$	1.2×10^{-16}
Silver iodate	$AgIO_3$	3.0×10^{-8}
Silver iodide	AgI	8.5×10^{-17}
Silver nitrite	$AgNO_2$	6.0×10^{-4}
Silver sulfate	Ag_2SO_4	1.4×10^{-5}
Silver sulfide[b]	Ag_2S	6×10^{-51}
Silver sulfite	Ag_2SO_3	1.5×10^{-14}
Silver thiocyanate	$AgSCN$	1.0×10^{-12}
Strontium carbonate	$SrCO_3$	1.1×10^{-10}
Strontium chromate	$SrCrO_4$	2.2×10^{-5}
Strontium fluoride	SrF_2	2.5×10^{-9}
Strontium sulfate	$SrSO_4$	3.2×10^{-7}
Thallium(I) bromide	$TlBr$	3.4×10^{-6}
Thallium(I) chloride	$TlCl$	1.7×10^{-4}
Thallium(I) iodide	TlI	6.5×10^{-8}
Thallium(III) hydroxide	$Tl(OH)_3$	6.3×10^{-46}
Tin(II) hydroxide	$Sn(OH)_2$	1.4×10^{-28}
Tin(II) sulfide[b]	SnS	1×10^{-26}
Zinc carbonate	$ZnCO_3$	1.4×10^{-11}
Zinc hydroxide	$Zn(OH)_2$	1.2×10^{-17}
Zinc oxalate	ZnC_2O_4	2.7×10^{-8}
Zinc phosphate	$Zn_3(PO_4)_2$	9.0×10^{-33}
Zinc sulfide[b]	ZnS	2×10^{-25}

(continued)

D. Complex-Ion Formation Constants[c, d]

Formula	K_f	Formula	K_f	Formula	K_f
$[Ag(CN)_2]^-$	5.6×10^{18}	$[Co(ox)_3]^{3-}$	10^{20}	$[HgI_4]^{2-}$	6.8×10^{29}
$[Ag(EDTA)]^{3-}$	2.1×10^7	$[Cr(EDTA)]^-$	10^{23}	$[Hg(ox)_2]^{2-}$	9.5×10^6
$[Ag(en)_2]^+$	5.0×10^7	$[Cr(OH)_4]^-$	8×10^{29}	$[Ni(CN)_4]^{2-}$	2×10^{31}
$[Ag(NH_3)_2]^+$	1.6×10^7	$[CuCl_3]^{2-}$	5×10^5	$[Ni(EDTA)]^{2-}$	3.6×10^{18}
$[Ag(SCN)_4]^{3-}$	1.2×10^{10}	$[Cu(CN)_4]^{3-}$	2.0×10^{30}	$[Ni(en)_3]^{2+}$	2.1×10^{18}
$[Ag(S_2O_3)_2]^{3-}$	1.7×10^{13}	$[Cu(EDTA)]^{2-}$	5×10^{18}	$[Ni(NH_3)_6]^{2+}$	5.5×10^8
$[Al(EDTA)]^-$	1.3×10^{16}	$[Cu(en)_2]^{2+}$	1×10^{20}	$[Ni(ox)_3]^{4-}$	3×10^8
$[Al(OH)_4]^-$	1.1×10^{33}	$[Cu(NH_3)_4]^{2+}$	1.1×10^{13}	$[PbCl_3]^-$	2.4×10^1
$[Al(ox)_3]^{3-}$	2×10^{16}	$[Cu(ox)_2]^{2-}$	3×10^8	$[Pb(EDTA)]^{2-}$	2×10^{18}
$[CdCl_4]^{2-}$	6.3×10^2	$[Fe(CN)_6]^{4-}$	10^{37}	$[PbI_4]^{2-}$	3.0×10^4
$[Cd(CN)_4]^{2-}$	6.0×10^{18}	$[Fe(EDTA)]^{2-}$	2.1×10^{14}	$[Pb(OH)_3]^-$	3.8×10^{14}
$[Cd(en)_3]^{2+}$	1.2×10^{12}	$[Fe(en)_3]^{2+}$	5.0×10^9	$[Pb(ox)_2]^{2-}$	3.5×10^6
$[Cd(NH_3)_4]^{2+}$	1.3×10^7	$[Fe(ox)_3]^{4-}$	1.7×10^5	$[Pb(S_2O_3)_3]^{4-}$	2.2×10^6
$[Co(EDTA)]^{2-}$	2.0×10^{16}	$[Fe(CN)_6]^{3-}$	10^{42}	$[PtCl_4]^{2-}$	1×10^{16}
$[Co(en)_3]^{2+}$	8.7×10^{13}	$[Fe(EDTA)]^-$	1.7×10^{24}	$[Pt(NH_3)_6]^{2+}$	2×10^{35}
$[Co(NH_3)_6]^{2+}$	1.3×10^5	$[Fe(ox)_3]^{3-}$	2×10^{20}	$[Zn(CN)_4]^{2-}$	1×10^{18}
$[Co(ox)_3]^{4-}$	5×10^9	$[Fe(SCN)]^{2+}$	8.9×10^2	$[Zn(EDTA)]^{2-}$	3×10^{16}
$[Co(SCN)_4]^{2-}$	1.0×10^3	$[HgCl_4]^{2-}$	1.2×10^{15}	$[Zn(en)_3]^{2+}$	1.3×10^{14}
$[Co(EDTA)]^-$	10^{36}	$[Hg(CN)_4]^{2-}$	3×10^{41}	$[Zn(NH_3)_4]^{2+}$	4.1×10^8
$[Co(en)_3]^{3+}$	4.9×10^{48}	$[Hg(EDTA)]^{2-}$	6.3×10^{21}	$[Zn(OH)_4]^{2-}$	4.6×10^{17}
$[Co(NH_3)_6]^{3+}$	4.5×10^{33}	$[Hg(en)_2]^{2+}$	2×10^{23}	$[Zn(ox)_3]^{4-}$	1.4×10^8

[a]Data are at various temperatures around "room" temperature, from 18 to 25 °C.
[b]For a solubility equilibrium of the type $MS(s) + H_2O \rightleftharpoons M^{2+}(aq) + HS^-(aq) + OH^-(aq)$.
[c]The ligands referred to in this table are monodentate: Cl^-, CN^-, I^-, NH_3, OH^-, SCN^-, $S_2O_3^{2-}$; bidentate: ethylenediamine (en), oxalate ion (ox); tetradentate: ethylenediaminetetraacetato ion, $EDTA^{4-}$.
[d]The K_f values are cumulative or overall formation constants.

TABLE A.3 Standard Electrode (Reduction) Potentials at 25 °C

Reduction half-reaction	$E°$, V
$F_2(g) + 2\,e^- \longrightarrow 2\,F^-(aq)$	+2.866
$OF_2(g) + 2\,H^+(aq) + 4\,e^- \longrightarrow H_2O(l) + 2\,F^-(aq)$	+2.1
$O_3(g) + 2\,H^+(aq) + 2\,e^- \longrightarrow O_2(g) + H_2O(l)$	+2.075
$S_2O_8^{2-}(aq) + 2\,e^- \longrightarrow 2\,SO_4^{2-}(aq)$	+2.01
$Ag^{2+}(aq) + e^- \longrightarrow Ag^+(aq)$	+1.98
$H_2O_2(aq) + 2\,H^+(aq) + 2\,e^- \longrightarrow 2\,H_2O(l)$	+1.763
$MnO_4^-(aq) + 4\,H^+(aq) + 3\,e^- \longrightarrow MnO_2(s) + 2\,H_2O(l)$	+1.70
$PbO_2(s) + SO_4^{2-}(aq) + 4\,H^+(aq) + 2\,e^- \longrightarrow PbSO_4(s) + 2\,H_2O(l)$	+1.69
$Au^{3+}(aq) + 3\,e^- \longrightarrow Au(s)$	+1.52
$MnO_4^-(aq) + 8\,H^+(aq) + 5\,e^- \longrightarrow Mn^{2+}(aq) + 4\,H_2O(l)$	+1.51
$2\,BrO_3^-(aq) + 12\,H^+(aq) + 10\,e^- \longrightarrow Br_2(l) + 6\,H_2O(l)$	+1.478
$PbO_2(s) + 4\,H^+(aq) + 2\,e^- \longrightarrow Pb^{2+}(aq) + 2\,H_2O(l)$	+1.455
$ClO_3^-(aq) + 6\,H^+(aq) + 6\,e^- \longrightarrow Cl^-(aq) + 3\,H_2O(l)$	+1.450
$Au^{3+}(aq) + 2\,e^- \longrightarrow Au^+(aq)$	+1.36
$Cl_2(g) + 2\,e^- \longrightarrow 2\,Cl^-(aq)$	+1.358
$Cr_2O_7^{2-}(aq) + 14\,H^+(aq) + 6\,e^- \longrightarrow 2\,Cr^{3+}(aq) + 7\,H_2O(l)$	+1.33
$MnO_2(s) + 4\,H^+(aq) + 2\,e^- \longrightarrow Mn^{2+}(aq) + 2\,H_2O(l)$	+1.23
$O_2(g) + 4\,H^+(aq) + 4\,e^- \longrightarrow 2\,H_2O(l)$	+1.229

Reduction half-reaction	$E°$, V
$2\,IO_3^-(aq) + 12\,H^+(aq) + 10\,e^- \longrightarrow I_2(s) + 6\,H_2O(l)$	+1.20
$ClO_4^-(aq) + 2\,H^+(aq) + 2\,e^- \longrightarrow ClO_3^-(aq) + H_2O(l)$	+1.189
$ClO_3^-(aq) + 2\,H^+(aq) + e^- \longrightarrow ClO_2(g) + H_2O(l)$	+1.175
$NO_2(g) + H^+(aq) + e^- \longrightarrow HNO_2(aq)$	+1.07
$Br_2(l) + 2\,e^- \longrightarrow 2\,Br^-(aq)$	+1.065
$NO_2(g) + 2\,H^+(aq) + 2\,e^- \longrightarrow NO(g) + H_2O(l)$	+1.03
$[AuCl_4]^-(aq) + 3\,e^- \longrightarrow Au(s) + 4\,Cl^-(aq)$	+1.002
$VO_2^+(aq) + 2\,H^+(aq) + e^- \longrightarrow VO^{2+}(aq) + H_2O(l)$	+1.000
$NO_3^-(aq) + 4\,H^+(aq) + 3\,e^- \longrightarrow NO(g) + 2\,H_2O(l)$	+0.956
$Cu^{2+}(aq) + I^-(aq) + e^- \longrightarrow CuI(s)$	+0.86
$Hg^{2+}(aq) + 2\,e^- \longrightarrow Hg(l)$	+0.854
$Ag^+(aq) + e^- \longrightarrow Ag(s)$	+0.800
$Fe^{3+}(aq) + e^- \longrightarrow Fe^{2+}(aq)$	+0.771
$O_2(g) + 2\,H^+(aq) + 2\,e^- \longrightarrow H_2O_2(aq)$	+0.695
$2\,HgCl_2(aq) + 2\,e^- \longrightarrow Hg_2Cl_2(s) + 2\,Cl^-(aq)$	+0.63
$MnO_4^-(aq) + e^- \longrightarrow MnO_4^{2-}(aq)$	+0.56
$I_2(s) + 2\,e^- \longrightarrow 2\,I^-(aq)$	+0.535
$Cu^+(aq) + e^- \longrightarrow Cu(s)$	+0.520
$H_2SO_3(aq) + 4\,H^+(aq) + 4\,e^- \longrightarrow S(s) + 3\,H_2O(l)$	+0.449
$C_2N_2(g) + 2\,H^+(aq) + 2\,e^- \longrightarrow 2\,HCN(aq)$	+0.37
$[Fe(CN)_6]^{3-}(aq) + e^- \longrightarrow [Fe(CN)_6]^{4-}(aq)$	+0.361
$VO^{2+}(aq) + 2\,H^+(aq) + e^- \longrightarrow V^{3+}(aq) + H_2O(l)$	+0.337
$Cu^{2+}(aq) + 2\,e^- \longrightarrow Cu(s)$	+0.340
$PbO_2(s) + 2\,H^+(aq) + 2\,e^- \longrightarrow PbO(s) + H_2O(l)$	+0.28
$Hg_2Cl_2(s) + 2\,e^- \longrightarrow 2\,Hg(l) + 2\,Cl^-(aq)$	+0.2676
$HAsO_2(aq) + 3\,H^+(aq) + 3\,e^- \longrightarrow As(s) + 2\,H_2O(l)$	+0.240
$AgCl(s) + e^- \longrightarrow Ag(s) + Cl^-(aq)$	+0.2223
$SO_4^{2-}(aq) + 4\,H^+(aq) + 2\,e^- \longrightarrow 2\,H_2O(l) + SO_2(g)$	+0.17
$Cu^{2+}(aq) + e^- \longrightarrow Cu^+(aq)$	+0.159
$Sn^{4+}(aq) + 2\,e^- \longrightarrow Sn^{2+}(aq)$	+0.154
$S(s) + 2\,H^+(aq) + 2\,e^- \longrightarrow H_2S(g)$	+0.144
$AgBr(s) + e^- \longrightarrow Ag(s) + Br^-(aq)$	+0.071
$2\,H^+(aq) + 2\,e^- \longrightarrow H_2(g)$	0
$Pb^{2+}(aq) + 2\,e^- \longrightarrow Pb(s)$	−0.125
$Sn^{2+}(aq) + 2\,e^- \longrightarrow Sn(s)$	−0.137
$AgI(s) + e^- \longrightarrow Ag(s) + I^-(aq)$	−0.152
$V^{3+}(aq) + e^- \longrightarrow V^{2+}(aq)$	−0.255
$Ni^{2+}(aq) + 2\,e^- \longrightarrow Ni(s)$	−0.257
$H_3PO_4(aq) + 2\,H^+(aq) + 2\,e^- \longrightarrow H_3PO_3(aq) + H_2O(l)$	−0.276
$Co^{2+}(aq) + 2\,e^- \longrightarrow Co(s)$	−0.277
$In^{3+}(aq) + 3\,e^- \longrightarrow In(s)$	−0.338
$PbSO_4(s) + 2\,e^- \longrightarrow Pb(s) + SO_4^{2-}(aq)$	−0.356
$Cd^{2+}(aq) + 2\,e^- \longrightarrow Cd(s)$	−0.403
$Cr^{3+}(aq) + e^- \longrightarrow Cr^{2+}(aq)$	−0.424
$Fe^{2+}(aq) + 2\,e^- \longrightarrow Fe(s)$	−0.440
$2\,CO_2(g) + 2\,H^+(aq) + 2\,e^- \longrightarrow H_2C_2O_4(aq)$	−0.49
$Zn^{2+}(aq) + 2\,e^- \longrightarrow Zn(s)$	−0.763

(continued)

Reduction half-reaction	E°, V
$Cr^{2+}(aq) + 2\,e^- \longrightarrow Cr(s)$	−0.90
$Mn^{2+}(aq) + 2\,e^- \longrightarrow Mn(s)$	−1.18
$Ti^{2+}(aq) + 2\,e^- \longrightarrow Ti(s)$	−1.63
$U^{3+}(aq) + 3\,e^- \longrightarrow U(s)$	−1.66
$Al^{3+}(aq) + 3\,e^- \longrightarrow Al(s)$	−1.676
$Mg^{2+}(aq) + 2\,e^- \longrightarrow Mg(s)$	−2.356
$La^{3+}(aq) + 3\,e^- \longrightarrow La(s)$	−2.38
$Na^{+}(aq) + e^- \longrightarrow Na(s)$	−2.713
$Ca^{2+}(aq) + 2\,e^- \longrightarrow Ca(s)$	−2.84
$Sr^{2+}(aq) + 2\,e^- \longrightarrow Sr(s)$	−2.89
$Ba^{2+}(aq) + 2\,e^- \longrightarrow Ba(s)$	−2.92
$Cs^{+}(aq) + e^- \longrightarrow Cs(s)$	−2.923
$K^{+}(aq) + e^- \longrightarrow K(s)$	−2.924
$Rb^{+}(aq) + e^- \longrightarrow Rb(s)$	−2.924
$Li^{+}(aq) + e^- \longrightarrow Li(s)$	−3.040
Basic solution	
$O_3(g) + H_2O(l) + 2\,e^- \longrightarrow O_2(g) + 2\,OH^-(aq)$	+1.246
$ClO^-(aq) + H_2O(l) + 2\,e^- \longrightarrow Cl^-(aq) + 2\,OH^-(aq)$	+0.890
$H_2O_2(aq) + 2\,e^- \longrightarrow 2\,OH^-(aq)$	+0.88
$BrO^-(aq) + H_2O(l) + 2\,e^- \longrightarrow Br^-(aq) + 2\,OH^-(aq)$	+0.766
$ClO_3^-(aq) + 3\,H_2O(l) + 6\,e^- \longrightarrow Cl^-(aq) + 6\,OH^-(aq)$	+0.622
$2\,AgO(s) + H_2O(l) + 2\,e^- \longrightarrow Ag_2O(s) + 2\,OH^-(aq)$	+0.604
$MnO_4^-(aq) + 2\,H_2O(l) + 3\,e^- \longrightarrow MnO_2(s) + 4\,OH^-(aq)$	+0.60
$BrO_3^-(aq) + 3\,H_2O(l) + 6\,e^- \longrightarrow Br^-(aq) + 6\,OH^-(aq)$	+0.584
$2\,BrO^-(aq) + 2\,H_2O(l) + 2\,e^- \longrightarrow Br_2(l) + 4\,OH^-(aq)$	+0.455
$2\,IO^-(aq) + 2\,H_2O(l) + 2\,e^- \longrightarrow I_2(s) + 4\,OH^-(aq)$	+0.42
$O_2(g) + 2\,H_2O(l) + 4\,e^- \longrightarrow 4\,OH^-(aq)$	+0.401
$Ag_2O(s) + H_2O(l) + 2\,e^- \longrightarrow 2\,Ag(s) + 2\,OH^-(aq)$	+0.342
$Co(OH)_3(s) + e^- \longrightarrow Co(OH)_2(s) + OH^-(aq)$	+0.17
$2\,MnO_2(s) + H_2O(l) + 2\,e^- \longrightarrow Mn_2O_3(s) + 2\,OH^-(aq)$	+0.118
$NO_3^-(aq) + H_2O(l) + 2\,e^- \longrightarrow NO_2^-(aq) + 2\,OH^-(aq)$	+0.01
$CrO_4^{2-}(aq) + 4\,H_2O(l) + 3\,e^- \longrightarrow Cr(OH)_3(s) + 5\,OH^-(aq)$	−0.11
$S(s) + 2\,e^- \longrightarrow S^{2-}(aq)$	−0.48
$HPbO_2^-(aq) + H_2O(l) + 2\,e^- \longrightarrow Pb(s) + 3\,OH^-(aq)$	−0.54
$HCHO(aq) + 2\,H_2O(l) + 2\,e^- \longrightarrow CH_3OH(aq) + 2\,OH^-(aq)$	−0.59
$SO_3^{2-}(aq) + 3\,H_2O(l) + 4\,e^- \longrightarrow S(s) + 6\,OH^-(aq)$	−0.66
$AsO_4^{3-}(aq) + 2\,H_2O(l) + 2\,e^- \longrightarrow AsO_2^-(aq) + 4\,OH^-(aq)$	−0.67
$AsO_2^-(aq) + 2\,H_2O(l) + 3\,e^- \longrightarrow As(s) + 4\,OH^-(aq)$	−0.68
$Cd(OH)_2(s) + 2\,e^- \longrightarrow Cd(s) + 2\,OH^-(aq)$	−0.824
$2\,H_2O(l) + 2\,e^- \longrightarrow H_2(g) + 2\,OH^-(aq)$	−0.828
$OCN^-(aq) + H_2O(l) + 2\,e^- \longrightarrow CN^-(aq) + 2\,OH^-(aq)$	−0.97
$As(s) + 3\,H_2O(l) + 3\,e^- \longrightarrow AsH_3(g) + 3\,OH^-(aq)$	−1.21
$Zn(OH)_2(s) + 2\,e^- \longrightarrow Zn(s) + 2\,OH^-(aq)$	−1.246
$Sb(s) + 3\,H_2O(l) + 3\,e^- \longrightarrow SbH_3(g) + 3\,OH^-(aq)$	−1.338
$Al(OH)_4^-(aq) + 3\,e^- \longrightarrow Al(s) + 4\,OH^-(aq)$	−2.310
$Mg(OH)_2(s) + 2\,e^- \longrightarrow Mg(s) + 2\,OH^-(aq)$	−2.687

APPENDIX B

Physical Properties of Organic Compounds

Physical Properties of Alkenes

Name	mp (°C)	bp (°C)	Density (g/mL)
Ethene	−169	−104	
Propene	−185	−47	
1-Butene	−185	−6.3	
1-Pentene		30	0.641
1-Hexene	−138	64	0.673
1-Heptene	−119	94	0.697
1-Octene	−101	122	0.715
1-Nonene	−81	146	0.730
1-Decene	−66	171	0.741
cis-2-Butene	−180	37	0.650
trans-2-Butene	−140	37	0.649
Methylpropene	−140	−6.9	0.594
cis-2-Pentene	−180	37	0.650
trans-2-Pentene	−140	37	0.649
Cyclohexene	−104	83	0.811

Physical Properties of Alkynes

Name	mp (°C)	bp (°C)	Density (g/mL)
Ethyne	−82	−84.0	
Propyne	−101.5	−23.2	
1-Butyne	−122	8.1	
2-Butyne	−24	27	0.694
1-Pentyne	−98	39.3	0.695
2-Pentyne	−101	55.5	0.714
3-Methyl-1-butyne		29	0.665
1-Hexyne	−132	71	0.715
2-Hexyne	−92	84	0.731
3-Hexyne	−101	81	0.725
1-Heptyne	−81	100	0.733
1-Octyne	−80	127	0.747
1-Nonyne	−50	151	0.757
1-Decyne	−44	174	0.766

Physical Properties of Cyclic Saturated Alkanes

Name	mp (°C)	bp (°C)	Density (g/mL)
Cyclopropane	−128	−33	
Cyclobutane	−80	−12	
Cyclopentane	−94	50	0.751
Cyclohexane	6.5	81	0.779
Cycloheptane	−12	118	0.811
Cyclooctane	14	149	0.834
Methylcyclopentane	−142	72	0.749
Methylcyclohexane	−126	100	0.769
cis-1,2-Dimethylcyclopentane	−62	99	0.772
trans-1,2-Dimethylcyclopentane	−120	92	0.750

Physical Properties of Ethers

Name	mp (°C)	bp (°C)	Density (g/mL)
Dimethyl ether	−141	−24.8	
Diethyl ether	−116	34.6	0.706
Dipropyl ether	−123	88	0.736
Diisopropyl ether	−86	69	0.725
Dibutyl ether	−98	142	0.764
Divinyl ether		35	
Diallyl ether		94	0.830
Tetrahydrofuran	−108	66	0.889
Dioxane	12	101	1.034

Physical Properties of Alcohols

Name	mp (°C)	bp (°C)	Solubility (g/100 g H_2O at 25 °C)
Methanol	−97.8	64	∞
Ethanol	−114.7	78	∞
1-Propanol	−127	97.4	∞
1-Butanol	−90	118	7.9
1-Pentanol	−78	138	2.3
1-Hexanol	−52	157	0.6
1-Heptanol	−36	176	0.2
1-Octanol	−15	196	0.05
2-Propanol	−89.5	82	∞
2-Butanol	−115	99.5	12.5
2-Methyl-1-propanol	−108	108	10.0
2-Methyl-2-propanol	25.5	83	∞
3-Methyl-1-butanol	−117	130	2
2-Methyl-2-butanol	−12	102	12.5
2,2-Dimethyl-1-propanol	55	114	∞
Allyl alcohol	−129	97	∞
Cyclopentanol	−19	140	s. sol.
Cyclohexanol	24	161	s. sol.
Benzyl alcohol	−15	205	4

Physical Properties of Amines

Name	mp (°C)	bp (°C)	Solubility (g/100 g H_2O at 25 °C)
Primary Amines			
Methylamine	−93	−6.3	v. sol.
Ethylamine	−81	17	∞
Propylamine	−83	48	∞
Isopropylamine	−95	33	∞
Butylamine	−49	78	v. sol.
Isobutylamine	−85	68	∞
sec-Butylamine	−72	63	∞
tert-Butylamine	−67	46	∞
Cyclohexylamine	−18	134	s. sol.
Secondary Amines			
Dimethylamine	−93	7.4	v. sol.
Diethylamine	−50	55	10.0
Dipropylamine	−63	110	10.0
Dibutylamine	−62	159	s. sol.
Tertiary Amines			
Trimethylamine	−115	2.9	91
Triethylamine	−114	89	14
Tripropylamine	−93	157	s. sol.

Physical Properties of Alkyl Halides

	bp (°C)			
Name	*Fluoride*	*Chloride*	*Bromide*	*Iodide*
Methyl	−78.4	−24.2	3.6	42.4
Ethyl	−37.7	12.3	38.4	72.3
Propyl	−2.5	46.6	71.0	102.5
Isopropyl	−9.4	34.8	59.4	89.5
Butyl	32.5	78.4	100	130.5
Isobutyl		68.8	90	120
sec-Butyl		68.3	91.2	120.0
tert-Butyl		50.2	73.1	dec.
Pentyl	62.8	108	130	157.0
Hexyl	92	133	154	179

Physical Properties of Benzene and Substituted Benzenes

Name	mp (°C)	bp (°C)	Solubility (g/100 g H_2O at 25 °C)
Aniline	−6	184	3.7
Benzene	5.5	80.1	s. sol.
Benzaldehyde	−26	178	s. sol.
Benzamide	132	290	s. sol.
Benzoic acid	122	249	0.34
Bromobenzene	−30.8	156	insol.
Chlorobenzene	−45.6	132	insol.
Nitrobenzene	5.7	210.8	s. sol.
Phenol	43	182	s. sol.
Styrene	−30.6	145.2	insol.
Toluene	−95	110.6	insol.

Physical Properties of Carboxylic Acids

Name	mp (°C)	bp (°C)	Solubility (g/100 g H_2O at 25 °C)
Formic acid	8.4	101	∞
Acetic acid	16.6	118	∞
Propionic acid	−21	141	∞
Butanoic acid	−5	162	∞
Pentanoic acid	−34	186	4.97
Hexanoic acid	−4	202	0.97
Heptanoic acid	−8	223	0.24
Octanoic acid	17	237	0.068
Nonanoic acid	15	255	0.026
Decanoic acid	32	270	0.015

Physical Properties of Dicarboxylic Acids

Name	mp (°C)	Solubility (g/100 g H_2O at 25 °C)
Oxalic acid	189	S
Malonic acid	136	v. sol.
Succinic acid	185	s. sol.
Glutaric acid	98	v. sol.
Adipic acid	151	s. sol.
Pimelic acid	106	s. sol.
Phthalic acid	231	s. sol.
Maleic acid	130.5	v. sol.
Fumaric acid	302	s. sol.

Physical Properties of Acyl Chlorides and Acid Anhydrides

Name	mp (°C)	bp (°C)
Acetyl chloride	−112	51
Propionyl chloride	−94	80
Butyryl chloride	−89	102
Valeryl chloride	−110	128
Acetic anhydride	−73	140
Succinic anhydride		120

Physical Properties of Amides

Name	mp (°C)	bp (°C)
Formamide	3	200 d*
Acetamide	82	221
Propanamide	80	213
Butanamide	116	216
Pentanamide	106	232

* d means the substance decomposes.

Physical Properties of Esters

Name	mp (°C)	bp (°C)
Methyl formate	−100	32
Ethyl formate	−80	54
Methyl acetate	−98	57.5
Ethyl acetate	−84	77
Propyl acetate	−92	102
Methyl propionate	−87.5	80
Ethyl propionate	−74	99
Methyl butyrate	−84.8	102.3
Ethyl butyrate	−93	121

Physical Properties of Aldehydes

Name	mp (°C)	bp (°C)	Solubility (g/100 g H_2O at 25 °C)
Formaldehyde	−92	−21	v. sol.
Acetaldehyde	−121	21	∞
Propionaldehyde	−81	49	16
Butyraldehyde	−96	75	7
Pentanal	−92	103	s. sol.
Hexanal	−56	131	s. sol.
Heptanal	−43	153	0.1
Octanal		171	insol.
Nonanal		192	insol.
Decanal	−5	209	insol.
Benzaldehyde	−26	178	0.3

Physical Properties of Ketones

Name	mp (°C)	bp (°C)	Solubility (g/100 g H_2O at 25 °C)
Acetone	−95	56	∞
2-Butanone	−86	80	25.6
2-Pentanone	−78	102	5.5
2-Hexanone	−57	127	1.6
2-Heptanone	−36	151	0.4
2-Octanone	−16	173	insol.
2-Nonanone	−7	195	insol.
2-Decanone	14	210	insol.
3-Pentanone	−40	102	4.8
3-Hexanone		123	1.5
3-Heptanone	−39	149	0.3
Acetophenone	19	202	insol.
Propiophenone	18	218	insol.

APPENDIX C

pK_a Values

Compound	pK_a
$CH_3C{\equiv}\overset{+}{N}H$	−10.1
HI	−10
HBr	−9
$CH_3CH{=}\overset{+}{O}H$	−8
$CH_3C({=}\overset{+}{O}H)CH_3$	−7.3
HCl	−7
$C_6H_5SO_3H$	−6.5
$CH_3C({=}\overset{+}{O}H)OCH_3$	−6.5
$CH_3C({=}\overset{+}{O}H)OH$	−6.1
H_2SO_4	−5
protonated pyrrole ($\overset{+}{N}H$, CH_2)	−3.8
$CH_3CH_2\overset{+}{O}(H)CH_2CH_3$	−3.6
$CH_3CH_2\overset{+}{O}H_2$	−2.4
$CH_3\overset{+}{O}H_2$	−2.5
H_3O^+	−1.7
HNO_3	−1.3
CH_3SO_3H	−1.2
$CH_3C({=}\overset{+}{O}H)NH_2$	0.0
$F_3CC(=O)OH$	0.2
$Cl_3CC(=O)OH$	0.64
$C_5H_5\overset{+}{N}{-}OH$ (pyridine)	0.79
$O_2N{-}C_6H_4{-}\overset{+}{N}H_3$	1.0
pyrimidinium ($\overset{+}{N}H$)	1.0
$Cl_2CHC(=O)OH$	1.3
HSO_4^-	2.0
H_3PO_4	2.1
purinium ($H\overset{+}{N}$, N, N, NH)	2.5
$FCH_2C(=O)OH$	2.7
$ClCH_2C(=O)OH$	2.8
$BrCH_2C(=O)OH$	2.9
$ICH_2C(=O)OH$	3.2
HF	3.2
HNO_2	3.4
$O_2N{-}C_6H_4{-}C(=O)OH$	3.4
$HC(=O)OH$	3.8
$Br{-}C_6H_4{-}\overset{+}{N}H_3$	3.9
$Br{-}C_6H_4{-}C(=O)OH$	4.0
$C_6H_5C(=O)OH$	4.2
$CH_3{-}C_6H_4{-}C(=O)OH$	4.3
$CH_3O{-}C_6H_4{-}C(=O)OH$	4.5
$C_6H_5\overset{+}{N}H_3$	4.6
$CH_3C(=O)OH$	4.8
quinolinium ($\overset{+}{N}H$)	4.9
$CH_3{-}C_6H_4{-}\overset{+}{N}H_3$	5.1
pyridinium ($\overset{+}{N}H$)	5.2
$CH_3O{-}C_6H_4{-}\overset{+}{N}H_3$	5.3
$CH_3C(CH_3){=}\overset{+}{N}HCH_3$	5.5
$CH_3C(=O)CH_2C(=O)H$	5.9
$HO\overset{+}{N}H_3$	6.0
H_2CO_3	6.4
imidazolium (HN, $\overset{+}{N}H$)	6.8
H_2S	7.0
$O_2N{-}C_6H_4{-}OH$	7.1
$H_2PO_4^-$	7.2
C_6H_5SH	7.8

[a]pK_a values are for the red H in each structure

pK_a Values (continued)

Compound	pK_a	Compound	pK_a	Compound	pK_a
$(CH_2)_2\overset{+}{N}H_2$ (three-membered ring)	8.0	$CH_3\overset{O}{C}CH_2\overset{O}{C}OCH_2CH_3$	10.7	$(CH)_4NH$ (pyrrole ring)	~17
$H_2N\overset{+}{N}H_3$	8.1	$CH_3\overset{+}{N}H_3$	10.7	$CH_3\overset{O}{C}H$	17
$CH_3\overset{O}{C}OOH$	8.2	$C_6H_{11}\overset{+}{N}H_3$ (cyclohexyl)	10.7	$(CH_3)_3COH$	18
$C_6H_4(CO)_2NH$ (phthalimide)	8.3	$(CH_3)_2\overset{+}{N}H_2$	10.7	$CH_3\overset{O}{C}CH_3$	20
$CH_3CH_2NO_2$	8.6	$(CH_2)_5\overset{+}{N}H_2$ (six-membered ring)	11.1	$CH_3\overset{O}{C}OCH_2CH_3$	24.5
$CH_3\overset{O}{C}CH_2\overset{O}{C}CH_3$	8.9	$CH_3CH_2\overset{+}{N}H_3$	11.0	$HC{\equiv}CH$	25
$HC{\equiv}N$	9.1	$(CH_2)_4\overset{+}{N}H_2$ (five-membered ring)	11.3	$CH_3C{\equiv}N$	25
$O(CH_2CH_2)_2\overset{+}{N}H_2$ (six-membered ring)	9.3	$HOOH$	11.6	$CH_3\overset{O}{C}N(CH_3)_2$	30
$Cl{-}C_6H_4{-}OH$	9.4	HPO_4^{2-}	12.3	H_2	35
$\overset{+}{N}H_4$	9.4	CF_3CH_2OH	12.4	NH_3	36
$HOCH_2CH_2\overset{+}{N}H_3$	9.5	$CH_3CH_2O\overset{O}{C}CH_2\overset{O}{C}OCH_2CH_3$	13.3	$(CH_2)_4NH$ (five-membered ring)	36
$H_3\overset{+}{N}CH_2\overset{O}{C}O^-$	9.8	$HC{\equiv}CCH_2OH$	13.5	CH_3NH_2	40
$C_6H_5{-}OH$	10.0	$H_2N\overset{O}{C}NH_2$	13.7	$C_6H_5{-}CH_3$	41
$CH_3{-}C_6H_4{-}OH$	10.2	$(CH_3)_3\overset{+}{N}CH_2CH_2OH$	13.9	C_6H_6	43
HCO_3^-	10.2	imidazole ring (N, NH)	14.4	$CH_2{=}CHCH_3$	43
CH_3NO_2	10.2	CH_3OH	15.5	$CH_2{=}CH_2$	44
$H_2N{-}C_6H_4{-}OH$	10.3	H_2O	15.7	$(CH_2)_3$ (three-membered ring)	46
CH_3CH_2SH	10.5	CH_3CH_2OH	16.0	CH_4	60
$(CH_3)_3\overset{+}{N}H$	10.6	$CH_3\overset{O}{C}NH_2$	16	CH_3CH_3	> 60
		$C_6H_5{-}\overset{O}{C}CH_3$	16.0		

APPENDIX D

Derivations of Rate Laws

How to Determine Rate Constants

A **reaction mechanism** is a detailed analysis of how the chemical bonds (or the electrons) in the reactants rearrange to form the products. The mechanism for a given reaction must obey the observed rate law for the reaction. A **rate law** tells how the rate of a reaction depends on the concentration of the species involved in the reaction.

First-Order Reaction

The rate is proportional to the concentration of one reactant:

$$\mathrm{A} \xrightarrow{k_1} \text{products}$$

$$\text{Rate law:} \qquad \text{rate} = k_1[\mathrm{A}]$$

To determine the first-order rate constant (k_1):

Change in the concentration of A with respect to time:

$$\frac{-d[\mathrm{A}]}{dt} = k_1[\mathrm{A}]$$

Let a = the initial concentration of A;
let x = concentration of A that has reacted up to time t.
Therefore, the concentration of A left at time t is $(a - x)$
Substituting into the previous equation gives

$$\frac{-d(a-x)}{dt} = k_1(a-x)$$

$$\frac{-da}{dt} + \frac{dx}{dt} = k_1(a-x)$$

$$0 + \frac{dx}{dt} = k_1(a-x)$$

$$\frac{dx}{(a-x)} = k_1 dt$$

Integrating the previous equation yields

$$-\ln(a-x) = k_1 t + \text{constant}$$

At $t = 0$, $x = 0$; therefore,

$$\text{constant} = -\ln a$$

$$-\ln(a-x) = k_1 t - \ln a$$

$$\ln\frac{a}{a-x} = k_1 t$$

$$\ln\frac{a-x}{a} = -k_1 t$$

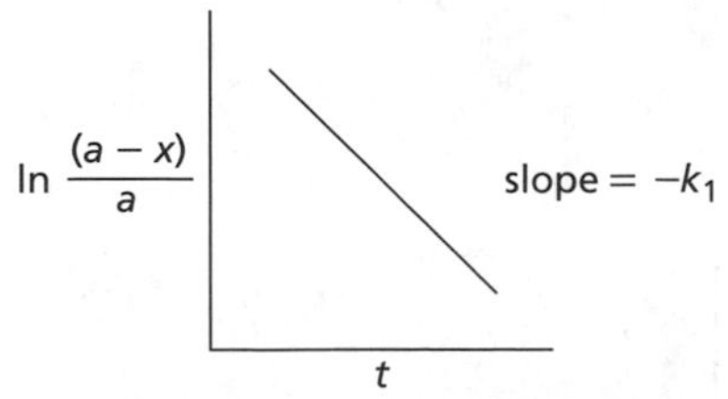

Half-Life of a First-Order Reaction

The **half-life** ($t_{1/2}$) of a reaction is the time it takes for half the reactant to react (or for half the product to form). To derive the half-life of a reactant in a first-order reaction, we begin with the equation

$$\ln \frac{a}{(a - x)} = k_1 t$$

At $t_{1/2}$, $x = \frac{a}{2}$; therefore,

$$\ln \frac{a}{\left(a - \frac{a}{2}\right)} = k_1 t_{1/2}$$

$$\ln \frac{a}{\frac{a}{2}} = k_1 t_{1/2}$$

$$\ln 2 = k_1 t_{1/2}$$

$$0.693 = k_1 t_{t/2}$$

$$t_{1/2} = \frac{0.693}{k_1}$$

Notice that the half-life of a first-order reaction is independent of the concentration of the reactant.

Second-Order Reaction

The rate is proportional to the concentration of two reactants:

$$\mathrm{A} + \mathrm{B} \xrightarrow{k_2} \text{products}$$

Rate law: rate $= k_2[A][B]$

To determine the second-order rate constant (k_2):

Change in the concentration of A with respect to time:

$$\frac{-d[\mathrm{A}]}{dt} = k_2[\mathrm{A}][\mathrm{B}]$$

Let $a =$ the initial concentration of A;
let $b =$ the initial concentration of B;
let $x =$ the concentration of A that has reacted at time t.

Therefore, the concentration of A left at time $t = (a - x)$, and the concentration of B left at time $t = (b - x)$.

Substitution gives

$$\frac{dx}{dt} = k_2(a - x)(b - x)$$

For the case where $a = b$ (this condition can be arranged experimentally),

$$\frac{dx}{dt} = k_2(a - x)^2$$

$$\frac{dx}{(a - x)^2} = k_2\, dt$$

Integrating the equation gives

$$\frac{1}{(a - x)} = k_2 t + \text{constant}$$

At $t = 0$, $x = 0$; therefore,

$$\text{constant} = \frac{1}{a}$$

$$\frac{1}{(a - x)} - \frac{1}{a} = k_2 t$$

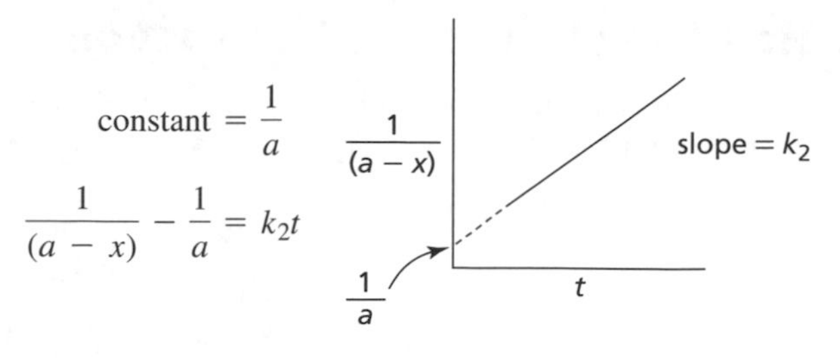

Half-Life of a Second-Order Reaction

$$\frac{1}{(a - x)} - \frac{1}{a} = k_2 t$$

At $t_{1/2}$, $x = \frac{a}{2}$; therefore,

$$\frac{1}{a} = k_2 t_{1/2}$$

$$t_{1/2} = \frac{1}{k_2 a}$$

Pseudo-First-Order Reaction

It is easier to determine a first-order rate constant than a second-order rate constant because the kinetic behavior of a first-order reaction is independent of the initial concentration of the reactant. Therefore, a first-order rate constant can be determined without knowing the initial concentration of the reactant. The determination of a second-order rate constant requires not only that the initial concentration of the reactants be known but also that the initial concentrations of the two reactants be identical in order to simplify the kinetic equation.

However, if the concentration of one of the reactants in a second-order reaction is much greater than the concentration of the other, the reaction can be treated as a first-order reaction. Such a reaction is known as a **pseudo-first-order reaction** and is given by

$$\frac{-d[\text{A}]}{dt} = k_2[\text{A}][\text{B}]$$

If $[\text{B}] \gg [\text{A}]$, then

$$\frac{-d[\text{A}]}{dt} = k_2'[\text{A}]$$

The rate constant obtained for a pseudo-first-order reaction (k_2') includes the concentration of B, but k_2 can be determined by carrying out the reaction at several different concentrations of B and determining the slope of a plot of the observed rate versus [B].

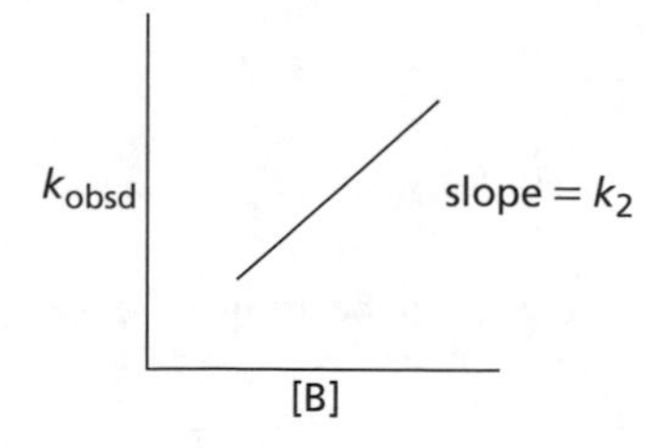

APPENDIX E

Summary of Methods Used to Synthesize a Particular Functional Group

SYNTHESIS OF ALKYL HALIDES

1. Addition of hydrogen halide (HX) to an alkene (4.1).
2. Addition of HBr + peroxide to an alkene (12.7).
3. Addition of halogen to an alkene (4.8).
4. Addition of hydrogen halide or a halogen to an alkyne (6.6).
5. Radical halogenation of an alkane, an alkene, or an alkyl benzene (12.2, 12.9).
6. Reaction of an alcohol with hydrogen halide, $SOCl_2$,PCl_3, or PBr_3 (10.1, 10.2).
7. Reaction of a sulfonate ester with halide ion (10.3).
8. Cleavage of an ether with HI or HBr (10.7).
9. Halogenation of an a-carbon of an aldehyde, a ketone, or a carboxylic acid (19.5, 19.6).

SYNTHESIS OF ALKYNES

1. Elimination of hydrogen halide from a vinyl halide (9.9).
2. Two successive eliminations of hydrogen halide from a vicinal dihalide or a geminal dihalide (9.9).
3. Reaction of an acetylide ion (formed by removing a proton from a terminal alkyne) with an alkyl halide (6.11).
4. Alkyne metathesis (11.6).

SYNTHESIS OF AMIDES

1. Reaction of an acyl chloride, an acid anhydride, or an ester with ammonia or with an amine (17.8, 17.9, 17.10).
2. Reaction of a carboxylic acid and an amine with dicyclohexylcarbodiimide (23.10).
3. Reaction of a nitrile with a secondary or tertiary alcohol (p. 768).

SYNTHESIS OF AMINES

1. Reaction of an alkyl halide with NH_3,RNH_2, or R_2NH (8.3).
2. Reaction of an alkyl halide with azide ion, followed by reduction of the alkyl azide (8.3).
3. Reduction of an imine, a nitrile, or an amide (17.19, 18.6, 20.2).
4. Reductive amination of an aldehyde or a ketone (18.8).
5. Gabriel synthesis of primary amines: reaction of a primary alkyl halide with potassium phthalimide (17.18).
6. Reduction of a nitro compound (16.1).
7. Condensation of a secondary amine and formaldehyde with a carbon acid (p. 882).

SYNTHESIS OF AMINO ACIDS

1. Hell–Volhard–Zelinski reaction: halogenation of a carboxylic acid, followed by treatment with excess NH_3 (19.6).
2. Reductive amination of an a-keto acid (23.6).
3. The *N*-phthalimidomalonic ester synthesis (Section 23.6).
4. The acetamidomalonic ester synthesis (Section 23.6).
5. The Strecker synthesis: reaction of an aldehyde with ammonia, followed by addition of cyanide ion and hydrolysis (Section 23.6).

SYNTHESIS OF CARBOXYLIC ACIDS

1. Oxidation of a primary alcohol (10.5, 20.4).
2. Oxidation of an aldehyde (10.5, 20.4).
3. Ozonolysis of a monosubstituted alkene or a 1,2-disubstituted alkene, followed by workup under oxidizing conditions (20.9).
4. Oxidation of an alkyl benzene (16.1).
5. Hydrolysis of an acyl halide, an acid anhydride, an ester, an amide, or a nitrile (17.8, 17.9, 17.10, 17.16, 17.19).
6. Haloform reaction: reaction of a methyl ketone with excess Br_2 (or Cl_2 or I_2) $+ HO^-$ (19.5).
7. Reaction of a Grignard reagent with CO_2 (18.4).
8. Malonic ester synthesis (19.20).
9. Favorskii reaction: reaction of an a-haloketone with hydroxide ion (p. 880).

SYNTHESIS OF CYANOHYDRINS

1. Reaction of an aldehyde or a ketone with sodium cyanide and HCl (18.7).

SYNTHESIS OF 1,2-DIOLS

1. Reaction of an epoxide with water (10.7).
2. Reaction of an alkene with osmium tetroxide or potassium permanganate (20.7).

SYNTHESIS OF DISULFIDES
1. Mild oxidation of a thiol (23.8).

SYNTHESIS OF ENAMINES
1. Reaction of an aldehyde or a ketone with a secondary amine (18.8).

SYNTHESIS OF EPOXIDES
1. Reaction of an alkene with a peroxyacid (4.10).
2. Reaction of a halohydrin with hydroxide ion (p. 448).
3. Reaction of an aldehyde or a ketone with a sulfonium ylide (p. 827).

SYNTHESIS OF ESTERS
1. Reaction of an acyl halide or an acid anhydride with an alcohol (17.8, 17.9).
2. Acid-catalyzed reaction of an ester or a carboxylic acid with an alcohol (17.10, 17.15).
3. Reaction of an alkyl halide with a carboxylate ion (9.8).
4. Reaction of a sulfonate ester with a carboxylate ion (10.3).
5. Oxidation of a ketone (20.5).
6. Preparation of a methyl ester by the reaction of a carboxylate ion with diazomethane (16.12).

SYNTHESIS OF ETHERS
1. Acid-catalyzed addition of an alcohol to an alkene (4.6).
2. Alkoxymercuration–demercuration of an alkene (4.9).
3. Williamson ether synthesis: reaction of an alkoxide ion with an alkyl halide (9.9).
4. Formation of symmetrical ethers by heating an acidic solution of a primary alcohol (10.4).

SYNTHESIS OF HALOHYDRINS
1. Reaction of an alkene with Br_2 (or Cl_2) and H_2O (4.8).
2. Reaction of an epoxide with a hydrogen halide (10.6).

SYNTHESIS OF IMINES
1. Reaction of an aldehyde or a ketone with a primary amine (18.8).

SYNTHESIS OF KETALS
1. Acid-catalyzed reaction of a ketone with two equivalents of an alcohol (18.10).

SYNTHESIS OF KETONES
1. Addition of water to an alkyne (6.7).
2. Hydroboration–oxidation of an alkyne (6.8).
3. Oxidation of a secondary alcohol (10.5, 20.4).
4. Cleavage of a 1,2-diol with periodic acid (20.8).
5. Ozonolysis of an alkene (20.9).
6. Friedel–Crafts acylation of an aromatic ring (15.15).
7. Preparation of a methyl ketone by the acetoacetic ester synthesis (19.21).
8. Preparation of a cyclic ketone by the reaction of the next-size-smaller cyclic ketone with diazomethane (p. 829).

SYNTHESIS OF α, β-UNSATURATED KETONES
1. Elimination from an a-haloketone (19.7).
2. Selenenylation of a ketone, followed by oxidative elimination (p. 883).

SYNTHESIS OF NITRILES
1. Reaction of an alkyl halide with cyanide ion (8.3).

SYNTHESIS OF SUBSTITUTED BENZENES
1. Halogenation with Br_2 or Cl_2 and a Lewis acid (15.11).
2. Nitration with $HNO_3 + H_2SO_4$ (15.12).
3. Sulfonation: reaction with H_2SO_4 (15.13).
4. Friedel–Crafts acylation (15.14).
5. Friedel–Crafts alkylation (15.15, 15.16).
6. Sandmeyer reaction: reaction of an arenediazonium salt with CuBr, CuCl, or CuCN (16.10).
7. Formation of a phenol by reaction of an arenediazonium salt with water (16.13).
8. Formation of an aniline by reaction of a benzyne intermediate with $^{-}NH_2$ (16.13).
9. Reaction of a Gilman reagent with an aryl halide (11.4).
10. Heck reaction: couples a benzyl halide or an aryl halide or a triflate with an alkene in a basic solution in the presence of PdL_2 (11.5).
11. Suzuki reaction: couples a benzyl or aryl halide with an organoborane in the presence of PdL_2 (11.5).

SYNTHESIS OF SULFIDES
1. Reaction of a thiol with an alkyl halide (10.11).
2. Reaction of a thiol with a sulfonate ester (10.3).

SYNTHESIS OF THIOLS
1. Reaction of an alkyl halide with hydrogen sulfide (8.3).
2. Catalytic hydrogenation of a disulfide (23.8).

Appendix

Answers to Concept Assessment Questions

Note: Your answers may differ slightly from those given here, depending on the number of steps used to solve a problem and whether any intermediate results were rounded off.

CHAPTER 1

Concept Assessment 1-1 (1). (e) 0.025 M $RbNO_3$, the only strong electrolyte of the group. **(2). (a)** a strong electrolyte with a total ion concentration of 0.024 M. **1-2.** Predicted as soluble based on guidelines in Table 1.1: **(a), (c), (g)**. Predicted as insoluble based on Table 1.1: **(b), (e), (h), (i)**. Inconclusive based on Table 1.1: **(d)** Li_2CO_3 might be soluble (Li^+ is a group 1 cation), but also might be one of the exceptions referred to in Table 1.1. **(f)** No data are available in Table 1.1 concerning permanagnates, so the solubility of $Mg(MnO_4)_2$ is uncertain. **1-3.** $H_2O(l)$ is suitable for $K_2CO_3(s)$ and $ZnSO_4(s)$, and HCl(aq) is suitable for CaO(s) and $BaCO_3(s)$. $H_2SO_4(aq)$ would not be suitable for CaO(s) and $BaCO_3(s)$ because $CaSO_4(s)$ and $BaSO_4(s)$ might precipitate. **1-4.** No reaction would occur in **(a)**. Two reduction half-reactions and no oxidation half-reaction. Reaction could occur under appropriate conditions in **(b)** because $Cl_2(g)$ undergoes both oxidation and reduction. **1-5.** This can occur as seen, for example, in the reverse of the disproportionation reaction directly above on this page. **1-6.** An inaccurate statement. An oxidizing agent is necessary to oxidize $Cl^-(aq)$ to $Cl_2(g)$, but neither HCl(aq) or NaOH(aq) is an oxidizing agent. **1-7.** An exactly neutral NaCl(aq) formed when 3.11×10^{-3} mol each of H^+ and OH^- ions neutralize one another.

CHAPTER 2

Concept Assessment 2-1. A water siphon passes over a "hump" from a pool of water at a higher level to a receiver at a lower level. After the siphon is initially filled with water, the pressure of the atmosphere pushes water over the hump, beyond which the water flows freely. In a suction pump, air pressure pushes water up a partially evacuated pipe. **2-2. (b) 2-3. (a) 2-4.** The direct proportionality of V and T must be based on an absolute temperature scale. While a change from 100 K to 200 K produces a doubling of V, a change from 100 °C to 200 °C produces only a 27% increase: $[(200 + 273)/(100 + 273)] = 1.27$. **2-5.** Consider these facts. **(1)** V is directly proportional to the number of moles of $O_2(g)$, and this must be 60.0 g O_2/32.00 g O_2 mol^{-1}. Only responses **(c)** and **(d)** meet this requirement. **(2)** The effect of changing P and T on the STP-volume must be expressed through the product $[(760 \text{ mmHg}/825 \text{ mmHg}) \times (303 \text{ K}/273 \text{ K})]$. The only correct response is **(d)**. **2-6. (a)** 0.667 L $SO_2(g)$/1.00 L $O_2(g)$, because the actual P and T are immaterial as long as the two gases are compared at the same t and P. **(b)** The 0.667 L $SO_2(g)$ has to be adjusted for the an increase in T (by the factor 298 K/273 K) and a decrease in P (by the factor 760 mmHg/745 mmHg), leading to $V = 0.743$ L $SO_2(g)$. **2-7.** The correct responses—**(b)** and **(e)**—follow from basic ideas. Dalton's law of partial pressures dictates that P_{He} is not affected by any other gases present, and addition of 0.50 mol H_2 (1.0 g) will increase the total mass of gas by 1.0 g, independent of anything else that may happen. By simple estimates the other three statements can be shown to be false. **2-8.** He(g) at 1000 K has twice the u_{rms} as at 250 K (change T to $4T$ in equation 6.20). At 250 K, u_{rms} of $H_2(g)$ exceeds that of He(g) by the factor $\sqrt{2}$ (change M to $\frac{1}{2}M$ in equation 2.20). The two-fold increase in the first case exceeds the $\sqrt{2}$-fold increase in the second. He(g) at 1000 K has a greater u_{rms} than $H_2(g)$ at 250 K. **2-9.** The correct responses are **(a)** and **(c)**. The average kinetic energy of gas molecules depends only on T, and to two significant figures the mass of 0.50 mol He is the same as that of 1.0 mol H_2. **2-10.** Rearrange equation (2.14) to the form $R = MP/dT$. Substitute molar masses, $P = 1$ atm (exactly), $T = 293.2$ K, and the density data. Solve for three values of R and see how closely they conform to the ideal gas constant $R = 0.08206$ L atm mol^{-1} K^{-1}. Increasing adherence to ideal gas behavior: $OF_2(R = 0.0724) < NO(R = 0.08194) < O_2(R = 0.08200)$.

CHAPTER 3

Concept Assessment 3-1. The intermolecular interactions are both London dispersion forces and hydrogen bonds. In substances with small molecules, hydrogen bonding usually dominates. **3-2.** Because the ball drops faster through it, the 10W oil is less viscous than the 40W oil. Viscosity is inversely proportional to T, and the lower weight oil (10W) is preferred for low-temperature use (where higher weight oils might solidify). In hot desert regions higher weight oils (40W) are preferred because light-weight oils might become so mobile as to lose their lubricating properties. The strengths of intermolecular forces are directly related to viscosity, and hence the higher viscosity 40W oil has the stronger intermolecular forces. **3-3.** Because of the different elevation (and barometric pressure) between landlocked, mountainous Switzerland and sea-level Manhattan Island, the lower boiling temperature results in a longer cooking time. **3-4.** Hydrogen bonding occurs in NH_3 but not in N_2, resulting in stronger intermolecular attractions and consequently lower vapor pressures, a higher boiling point, and a higher critical temperature in NH_3 than in N_2. **3-5.** The greater number of electrons (much larger molar mass) in CCl_4 causes the intermolecular attractions (London dispersion forces) to outweigh the effect of the polar bonds in CH_3Cl. **3-6.** Dew forms in the condensation of $H_2O(g)$ to $H_2O(l)$ and frost from the deposition of $H_2O(g)$ as $H_2O(s)$. Both processes are exothermic and give off heat to the surroundings—more heat in frost formation, because $\Delta H(\text{deposition}) = \Delta H(\text{condensation}) + \Delta H(\text{freezing})$. **3-7.** Wet books are placed in a cold, evacuated chamber. Moisture in the books freezes and the ice that is formed sublimes to $H_2O(g)$. This process avoids heating and involves a minimum of handling of the damaged books. **3-8.** According to the Bragg equation, $n\lambda = 2d \sin\theta$, if the extra distance traveled by the diffracted wave ($2d \sin\theta$) is to remain the same when n is doubled, the wavelength of the wave must be halved, so that $2n(\lambda/2) = n\lambda$. The required multiple is $\frac{1}{2}$. **3-9.** The fcc unit cell contains four C_{60} molecules. The unit cell has four octahedral and eight tetrahedral holes occupied by 12 K atoms. The formula based on the unit cell is $K_{12}(C_{60})_4$, and the molecular formula is $K_3(C_{60})$.

CHAPTER 4

Concept Assessment 4-1. Dynamite exploding in an underground cavern is a close approximation to an isolated system. Titration of an acid with a base is an open system. A steam-filled cylinder in a steam engine with all valves closed constitutes a closed system. **4-2.** Basic principle: law of conservation of energy. Assumptions: no heat loss to surroundings, d and *sp. ht.* of $H_2O(l)$ independent of T. Because the mass of hot water is twice that of the colder water, the initial temperature difference of 60.00 °C is divided into a 40.00 °C warming of the cold water and a 20.00 °C cooling of the hot water; final $T = 50.00$ °C. **4-3.** The ΔT of a fixed mass of substance is inversely proportional to its specific heat; thus the object with the smaller ΔT has the greater specific heat. The second question requires us to recognize the difference in enthalpy of transition for the solid and liquid form of water. The enthalpy of fusion for ice is less than the enthalpy of vaporization for the liquid, meaning that the amount of heat required to vaporize water is greater than that for ice. **4-4.** This is accomplished by adding a measured amount of a substance in which the heat of reaction is known. **4-5.** This is a closed system. Since the pressure dropped while the volume remained constant then the temperature must have decreased. The internal energy of the system decreased. Therefore the energy transferred across the boundary was in the form of heat. The direction of energy transfer was from the system to the surroundings. **4-6.** The balloon feels warm because the dissolution of $NH_3(g)$ in $H_2O(l)$ is exothermic, $q < 0$. The balloon shrinks because the atmosphere (surroundings) does work on the system, $w > 0$. **4-7.** In the bottom row T is uniform throughout the object while in the top row the object is hotter at the edges than in its interior. Heating in the top row is irreversible; the process is far from equilibrium. The bottom row represents reversible heating; removal of just a tiny amount of heat can change heating to cooling. **4-8.** Enthalpy is a function of state. When a process returns a system to its initial state H returns to its initial value, meaning that $\Delta H = 0$. **4-9.** The enthalpy change in forming 1 mol $C_2H_2(g)$ from its elements is represented by the top line; that for forming 1 mol $C_2H_4(g)$ is the next line down. Both of these lines are above the broken line representing $\Delta H = 0$. The formation of 1 mol C_2H_6 has $\Delta H < 0$ and is the first line below the broken line. $\Delta H°$ for the reaction of interest is represented by the distance between the first and third lines. **4-10.** Yes, this can be done. The additional data needed are heat capacities as a function of T. The procedure is outlined in Figure 4-16.

CHAPTER 5

Concept Assessment 5-1. No, spontaneous and nonspontaneous refer to the thermodynamics of a process, not the kinetics. A nonspontaneous process will not occur without external intervention, and a spontaneous reaction is not necessarily fast; it can occur very slowly. **5-2.** Doubling the volume available to the gas in Figure 5-1. is equivalent to doubling the length of the box from L to $2L$ in Figure 5-3a. The expansion of the gas in Figure 5-1 seems driven by a tendency to fill all the available volume. The gas expansion can also be explained, however, as the tendency of the system energy to be distributed among the greater number of available energy levels in the $2L$ box compared to the L box. **5-3.** ΔH as a function of T is a straight line with only a slight slope (positive or negative), in the negative energy region. The $T\Delta S$ line, in the same energy region, has a steep negative slope and intersects the ΔH line. The distance between the two lines ($\Delta H - T\,\Delta S$) represents ΔG. At the point of intersection, $\Delta G = 0$, at T below the intersection $\Delta G < 0$, and at T above the intersection $\Delta G > 0$. **5-4.** $G° = 326.4$ kJ mol^{-1} means that the Gibbs energy change for the system is 326.4 kJ when 3 mol O_2 is converted into 2 mol O_3. If 1.75 mol O_2 reacts, then the Gibbs energy change for the system is (326.4 kJ/3 mol O_2) × (1.75 mol O_2) = 190.4 kJ. **5-5.** $H_2O(l, 1\ atm) \rightleftharpoons H_2O(g, 1\ atm)$, is a process in which $\Delta H > 0$ and $\Delta S > 0$, as represented by Figure 5-9. Below 100 °C, condensation of $H_2O(g, 1\ atm)$ is favored and at 100 °C (the normal boiling point) condensation and vaporization are at equilibrium and $\Delta G = 0$. At 120 °C, vaporization predominates, $\Delta G < 0$, and $T\,\Delta S > \Delta H$.

CHAPTER 6

Concept Assessment 6-1. (a) represents solubility-phase equilibrium; **(b)** phase equilibrium; **(c)** chemical equilibrium.

6-2. $Q = \dfrac{a_{Cu^+(aq)}a_{H_2(g)}}{a_{Cu(s)}a^2_{H^+(aq)}} = \dfrac{[Cu^{2+}]P_{H_2}}{[H^+]^2}$.

6-3. Into the expression $K = [B]/[A]$, substitute $[B] = 54 - [A]$ and the given value of K; solve for [A] and [B]. If $K = 0.02$, [A] (open circles) = 53 and [B] (filled circles) = 1. If $K = 0.5$, [A] = 36 and [B] = 18. If $K = 1$, [A] = [B] = 27. **6.4.** If $K > 1$ for the 2nd reaction, K for the 1st reaction will be the larger of the two, but if $K < 1$ for the 2nd reaction, K for the 1st reaction will be the smaller of the two. **6-5.** Reverse given equation (invert its K value). To that equation add $CH_4(g) + H_2O(g) \rightleftharpoons CO(g) + 3\,H_2(g)$; $CO(g)$ cancels and the overall equation is the one we seek; its K is the ratio of the other two K values. **6-6.** The balanced equation is sufficient to determine the outcome of a reaction that goes to completion. If the reaction is reversible and reaches a state of equilibrium, the value of K is required as well. **6-7. (a)** incorrect: would require that $CO(g)$ and $H_2O(g)$ be completely consumed—impossible with $K_p = 10.0$. **(b)** incorrect: would be violation of the law of conservation of mass. **(c)** incorrect; would require the consumption of some $CO_2(g)$, but the direction of net change must be in the forward reaction. **(d)** correct: an outcome that would result from a net change in the forward direction. **(e)** incorrect: sufficient data are given to calculate the composition of the equilibrium mixture. **6-8.** Even though the pressure increases because of the addition of an inert gas, the reaction will shift to the right since the volume of the reaction vessel decreased. **6-9. (a)** True—more $H_2(g)$ will form at the expense of the $H_2S(g)$ and $CH_4(g)$. **(b)** False—an inert gas has no effect on a constant-volume equilibrium condition. **(c)** True—K changes with T and so does the composition of the equilibrium mixture. **(d)** Uncertain—the partial pressures of $H_2S(g)$ and $CH_4(g)$ will rise because a net reaction occurs to the left, but the increase in partial pressures of $CS_2(g)$ and $H_2(g)$ caused by forcing these two gases into a smaller volume will be at least partly offset by the equilibrium shift to the left. **6-10.** Equilibrium shifts in the forward direction, the endothermic reaction. Student B, by holding the beaker, stimulates heat flow into the reaction mixture, probably achieving a higher yield of product.

CHAPTER 7

Concept Assessment 7-1. At the anode, Zn(s) is oxidized to $Zn^{2+}(aq)$ and, to preserve charge balance, $NO_3^-(aq)$ migrates in from the salt bridge. At the cathode, $Cu^{2+}(aq)$ is reduced to Cu(s) and, to preserve charge balance, $K^+(aq)$ migrates in from the salt bridge. **7-2.** No changes in mass at the inert Pt(s) electrodes; a gain in mass at the Cu(s) electrode through the half reaction $Cu^{2+}(aq) + 2\,e^- \longrightarrow Cu(s)$; and a loss in mass at the Zn(s) electrode through the half reaction $Zn(s) \longrightarrow Zn^{2+}(aq) + 2\,e^-$. **7-3.** Standard-state conditions for $ClO_4^-(aq)$ and $H^+(aq)$ are $a \approx 1$ M; for $Cl_2(g)$, $a = 1$ bar ≈ 1 atm; for $H_2O(l)$, $a = 1$. **7-4.** The cell with $E° > 0$ proceeds toward the formation of more products. A net reaction also occurs in the case where $E° < 0$, but in the reverse direction; the concentrations on the left side of the equation increase and those on the right decrease, until equilibrium is reached. **7-5.** $E_{cell} = E°_{cell}$ if all reactants and products are in their standard states, but also for any set of concentrations where $Q = 1$ in equation (20.18). **7-6.** The precipitate is $PbSO_4(s)$, thereby reducing $[Pb^{2+}]$ in the anode compartment and increasing the value of E_{cell}, so that $E_{cell} > E°_{cell}$. **7-7.** The cell diagram $Pt(s)|Cl_2(g, 1\ atm)|Cl^-(0.50\ M)||Cl^-(0.10\ M)|Cl_2(g, 1\ atm)|Pt(s)$ has the net cell reaction: $0.50\ M\ Cl^-(aq) \longrightarrow 0.10\ M\ Cl^-(aq)$ and $E_{cell} = -0.0592\ V \times \log(0.10/0.50) = 0.041$ V. **7-8.** In a calomel electrode, reduction potential depends on the chloride potential. Therefore, the standard reduction potential for a calomel electrode has a different chloride concentration from the saturated calomel electrode. **7-9.** Dry cells and lead-acid cells "run down" as the concentrations of reactants and products eventually reach their equilibrium values, where ΔG and E_{cell} both become 0. This does not happen in a fuel cell because fuel is continuously added. **7-10.** Both Al and Zn can be used because they are more active than Fe; Ni and Cu are less active and cannot be used.

CHAPTER 8

Concept Assessment 8-1. (a) is a conjugate acid/base pair; HCO_3^- can transfer a proton to a base (e.g., OH^-) yielding CO_3^{2-}, and CO_3^{2-} can react with an acid (e.g., H_3O^+) to reform HCO_3^-. **(b)** is not a conjugate acid/base pair; SO_4^{2-} can be produced from HSO_3^- only through an oxidation process not in an acid–base reaction. **(c)** is not a conjugate acid/base pair; it is a pair of unrelated acids. **(d)** yes;

(e) no. **8-2.** With pH = log$[H_3O^+]$, the vast majority of solutions would have negative pH values. It is more convenient to incorporate the negative sign in the definition than to carry it in individual pH values. With pH = $-\ln[H_3O^+]$ the close relationship between pH and the powers of ten used in scientific notation would be completely lost. (The desire to establish this relationship was why the pH concept was devised in the first case.) **8-3.** A concentrated solution of a weak acid may often have a lower pH than a dilute solution of a strong one. For example, the pH of 0.10 M $HC_2H_3O_2$—calculated as pH = 2.89 in Example 16-6—is lower than the pH of 0.0010 M HCl. **8-4.** The bottle labeled $K_a = 7.2 \times 10^{-4}$ contains the more acidic solution. The bottle labeled $K_a = 1.9 \times 10^{-5}$ has the acid with the larger pK_a. The relevant equations are $^+NH_3CH_2CH_2NH_3^+(aq) + H_2O(l) \rightleftharpoons H_3O^+(aq) + NH_2CH_2CH_2NH_3^+(aq)$ $pK_1 = 6.85$ and $NH_2CH_2CH_2NH_3^+(aq) + H_2O(l)$ $H_2O(l) \rightleftharpoons H_3O^+(aq) + NH_2CH_2CH_2NH_2(aq)$ $pK_2 = 9.92$. From equation (8.18), the values of the base ionization constants are $pK_{b_1} = 14.00–9.92 = 4.08$ and $pK_{b_2} = 14.00–6.85 = 7.15$.

The base ionization reactions are $NH_2CH_2CH_2NH_2(aq) + H_2O(l) \rightleftharpoons NH_2CH_2CH_2NH_3^+(aq) + OH^-(aq)$ $pK_{b_1} = 4.08$ and $NH_2CH_2CH_2NH_3^+(aq) + H_2O(l) \rightleftharpoons {}^+NH_3CH_2CH_2NH_3^+(aq) + OH^-(aq)$ $pK_{b_2} = 7.15$ $^+NH_3CH(CH_3)COOH + H_2O \rightleftharpoons NH_3CH(CH_3)COO^- + H_3O^+$ $pK_a = 2.34$ $^+NH_3CH(CH_3)COO^- + H_2O \rightleftharpoons NH_2CH(CH_3)COO^- + H_3O^+$ $pK_a = 9.87$

$pK_{b_1} = 14.00–2.63 = 11.37$

$pK_{b_2} = 14.00–9.87 = 4.13$

$NH_2CH(CH_3)COO^- + H_2O \rightleftharpoons {}^+NH_2CH(CH_3)COO^- + OH^-$ $pK_{b_1} = 4.13$ $^+NH_3CH(CH_3)COO^- + H_2O \rightleftharpoons {}^+NH_3CH(CH_3)COOH + OH^-$ $pK_{b_1} = 11.37$. **8-6.** Consider HPO_4^{2-}, which can act as an acid: $HPO_4^{2-}(aq) + H_2O(l) \rightleftharpoons H_3O^+(aq) + PO_4^{3-}(aq)$, $K_a = 4.2 \times 10^{-13}$ or as a base: $HPO_4^{2-}(aq) + H_2O(l) \rightleftharpoons H_2PO_4^-(aq) + OH^-(aq)$ $K_b = K_w/K_a = 1.00 \times 10^{-14}/4.2 \times 10^{-13} = 2.4 \times 10^{-2}$. Because K_b is much greater than K_a, $HPO_4^{2-}(aq)$ is basic. In a similar way, $H_2PO_4^-(aq)$ is seen to be acidic. Thus, depending on *K* values, ions in aqueous solutions may have pH values ranging from acidic to neutral to basic. **8-7.** We should expect pK_a for *ortho*-chlorophenol to be smaller than for phenol because of the electron-withdrawing effect of the Cl atom. (Its pK_a is 8.55 compared with 10.00 for phenol.) **8-8.** Picture three Br atoms joined by single bonds to a Fe(III) atom on which there is also a lone pair of electrons: Br_3Fe: Now imagine that a Br_2 molecule dissociates into Br^+ and Br^- ions. The electron-deficient Br^+, a Lewis acid, attaches to the lone-pair electrons of Fe(III), a Lewis base, forming $[FeBr_4]^+$. The final product is $[FeBr_4]^+Br^-$.

CHAPTER 9

Concept Assessment 9-1. (a) no; NH_4Cl lowers the pH through the common-ion effect **(b)** yes, but only slightly. Diethylamine is a somewhat stronger base than NH_3, but only a rather small amount is being added. **(c)** no; HCl is a strong acid that will neutralize some of the NH_3, producing an aqueous solution of NH_3 and NH_4Cl. **(d)** no; since the added $NH_3(aq)$ is more dilute than the 0.10 M $NH_3(aq)$ the overall solution will be 0.075 M $NH_3(aq)$. **(e)** yes; $Ca(OH)_2(s)$ is a strong base. **9-2.** benzoic acid/benzoate with a 1:2 ratio. **9-3. (a)** yellow; a low pH **(b)** yellow; a CH_3COOH/CH_3COO^- buffer solution is formed but its pH is about 5 **(c)** yellow; the buffer completely neutralizes the small amount of added OH^- **(d)** red; the buffer capacity is exceeded and the solution becomes basic. **9-4.** Choice **(c)** is the correct one; 0.60 mol $NaCH_3COO$, converts all the HCl to CH_3COOH, producing a $CH_3COOH/NaCH_3COO$ buffer solution of pH ≈ 4. Choices **(a)** and **(b)** have essentially no effect on the pH, and while choice **(d)** would neutralize 80% of the acid, the amount of strong acid remaining would still produce a pH ≈ 1. **9-5.** This is the titration of a weak base that ionizes in two stages. The titration curve would begin at a moderately high pH; the pH would drop during the titration, and there would be two equivalence points. In general, the curve would resemble that in Figure 9-13, but flipped from bottom to top. The two buffer regions and pH − pK_b values would be in segments of the curve between the two equivalence points. **9-6. (a)** six species: K^+, H_3O^+, I^-, CH_3COO^-, OH^-, CH_3COOH **(b)** most abundant, K^+ (the spectator ion in highest concentration); 2nd most abundant, CH_3COO^- (produced in the neutralization of 3/4 of the CH_3COOH) **(c)** least abundant, OH^- (the final solution is acidic, so $[OH^-] < 10^{-7}$ M); 2nd least abundant, H_3O^+ (final solution a buffer with pH ≈ 5)

CHAPTER 10

10-1. 8 + 8, 8 + 9, 8 + 10 **10-2. a.** 3 **b.** 5 **c.** 6 **d.** 7 **10-3. a.** Cl $1s^22s^22p^63s^23p^5$; Br $1s^22s^22p^63s^23p^64s^23d^{10}4p^5$; I $1s^22s^22p^63s^23p^64s^23d^{10}4p^65s^24d^{10}5p^5$ **b.** 7 **10-5. a.** 1 **b.** 4*s* **10-6. a.** Cl—CH_3 **b.** H—OH **c.** H—F **d.** Cl—CH_3 **10-7. a.** KCl **b.** Cl_2 **10-10. a.** $\overset{\delta-}{HO}$—$\overset{\delta+}{H}$ **b.** $\overset{\delta-}{F}$—$\overset{\delta+}{Br}$ **c.** $\overset{\delta+}{H_3C}$—$\overset{\delta-}{NH_2}$ **d.** $\overset{\delta+}{H_3C}$—$\overset{\delta-}{Cl}$ **e.** $\overset{\delta-}{HO}$—$\overset{\delta+}{Br}$ **f.** $\overset{\delta-}{H_3C}$—$\overset{\delta+}{MgBr}$ **10-11. a.** LiH and HF **b.** Its hydrogen has the greatest electron density. **c.** HF **10-12. a.** oxygen **b.** oxygen **c.** oxygen **d.** hydrogen **10-15. a.** CH_3CH_2OH CH_3OCH_3 **b.** $CH_3CH_2CH_2OH$ $CH_3CH(OH)CH_3$ $CH_3CH_2OCH_3$

10-16. a. $CH_3CH_2\ddot{N}H_2$ **c.** $CH_3CH_2\ddot{O}H$ **e.** $CH_3CH_2\ddot{Cl}$: **b.** $CH_3\ddot{N}HCH_3$ **d.** $CH_3\ddot{O}CH_3$ **f.** $H\ddot{O}\ddot{N}H_2$

10-17. a. $CH_3CH_2CH_2Cl$ **c.** $CH_3CH_2C(=O)N(CH_3)CH_2CH_3$ **b.** $CH_3C(=O)OCH_2CH_3$ **d.** $CH_3CH_2C{\equiv}N$

10-18. a. Cl **b.** O **c.** N **d.** C and H **10-20.** yes

10-21. a. π^* **b.** σ^* **c.** π **d.** σ **10-22.** The C—C bonds are formed by sp^3–sp^3 overlap; the C—H bonds are formed by sp^3–*s* overlap. **10-24.** > 104.5° < 109.5° **10-25.** 107.3° **10-26.** the nitrogen **10-27.** most = water; least = methane **10-28. a.** relative lengths: $Br_2 > Cl_2$; relative strengths: $Cl_2 > Br_2$ **b.** relative lengths; $CH_3Br > CH_3Cl > CH_3F$; relative strengths: $CH_3F > CH_3Cl > CH_3Br$ **10-29. a. 1.** C-I **2.** C-Cl **3.** H-Cl **b. 1.** C-Cl **2.** C-C **3.** H-H **10-30.** σ **10-31.** sp^2–sp^2 is stronger because the more *s* character, the stronger the bond **10-33. a.** 109.5° **b.** 107.3° **c.** 109.5° **d.** 109.5° **10-35.** hydrogen **10-37.** a, e, g, h **10-38. a. 1.** $^+NH_4$ **2.** HCl **3.** H_2O **4.** H_3O^+ **b. 1.** $^-NH_2$ **2.** Br^- **3.** NO_3^- **4.** HO^- **10-39. a.** 5.2 **b.** 3.4×10^{-3} **10-40.** 8.16×10^{-8} **10-41.** $K_a = 1.51 \times 10^{-5}$; weaker **10-43. a.** basic **b.** acidic **c.** basic

10-44. a. $CH_3CH_2\overset{+}{O}H_2$ **b.** CH_3CH_2OH **c.** $CH_3CH_2\overset{+}{N}H_3$ **d.** 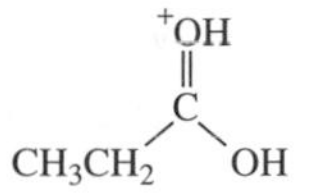 $CH_3CH_2C(={}^+OH)OH$

10-45. a. CH_3COO^- **b.** $^-NH_2$ **c.** H_2O

10-46. $CH_3NH^- > CH_3O^- > CH_3NH_2 > CH_3C(=O)O^- > CH_3OH$ **10-50. a.** 2.0×10^5 **b.** 3.2×10^{-7} **c.** 1.0×10^{-5} **d.** 4.0×10^{-13} **10-51. a.** oxygen **b.** H_2S **c.** CH_3SH **10-52. a.** HBr **b.** $CH_3CH_2CH_2\overset{+}{O}H_2$ **c.** the one on the right **d.** 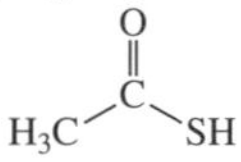 $H_3C–C(=O)–SH$ **10-53. a.** F^- **b.** I^-

10-54. a. HO **b.** NH_3 **c.** CH_3O^- **d.** CH_3O^- **10-55. a.** $CH_3OCH_2CH_2OH$ **b.** $CH_3CH_2CH_2\overset{+}{O}H_2$ **c.** $CH_3CH_2OCH_2CH_2OH$ **d.** $CH_3CH_2C(=O)OH$ **10-56.** $CH_3CH(F)CH_2OH > CH_3CH(Cl)CH_2OH > CH_2(Cl)CH_2CH_2OH > CH_3CH_2CH_2OH$

10-57. a. $CH_3CH(Br)C(=O)O^-$ **b.** $CH_3CH(Cl)CH_2C(=O)O^-$ **c.** $CH_3CH_2C(=O)O^-$ **d.** $CH_3C(=O)CH_2CH_2O^-$

10-59. $CH_3S(=O)_2–OH$

10-60. a. $O=C(O^-)O^- \longleftrightarrow {}^-O–C(=O)–O^- \longleftrightarrow {}^-O–C(O^-)=O$ **b.** 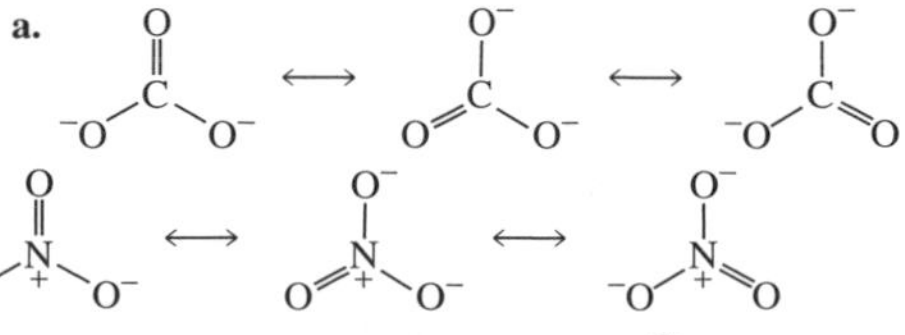 $O=\overset{+}{N}(O^-)O^- \longleftrightarrow O=\overset{+}{N}(O^-)–O^- \longleftrightarrow {}^-O–\overset{+}{N}(O^-)=O$

10-61. a. $CH_3C{\equiv}\overset{+}{N}H$ **b.** CH_3CH_3 **c.** $F_3CC(=O)OH$ **d.** sp^2 **e.** $HC{\equiv}CH > CH_2{=}CH_2 > CH_3CH_3$ **f.** HNO_3 **10-62. a.** CH_3COO^- **b.** $CH_3CH_2\overset{+}{N}H_3$ **c.** H_2O **d.** Br^- **e.** $^+NH_4$ **f.** $HC{\equiv}N$ **g.** NO_2^- **h.** NO_3^- **10-63. b. 1.** charged **2.** charged **3.** charged **4.** charged **5.** neutral **6.** neutral **c. 1.** neutral **2.** neutral **3.** neutral **4.** neutral **5.** neutral **6.** neutral

10-64. **a.** 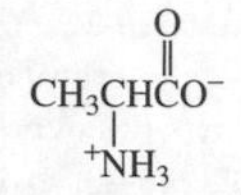 **b.** no **c.** 6.02
10-65. **a.** 10.4 **b.** 2.7 **c.** 6.4 **d.** 7.3 **e.** 5.6
10-66. **a.** **1.** 4.9 **2.** 10.7 **b.** **1.** > 6.9 **2.** < 8.7
10-67. 10.4
10-68. **a.** $CH_3COO^- + H^+ \rightleftharpoons CH_3COOH$
b. $CH_3COOH + HO^- \rightleftharpoons CH_3COO^- + H_2O$

CHAPTER 11

11-1. **a.** *n*-propyl alcohol or propyl alcohol **b.** dimethyl ether **c.** *n*-propylamine or propylamine
11-2. **a.** 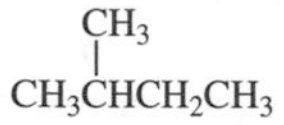
2-methylbutane
b. 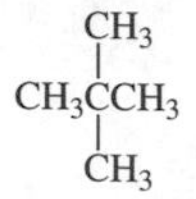
2,2-dimethylpropane
11-3. **1.** $CH_3CH_2CH_2CH_2Br$ 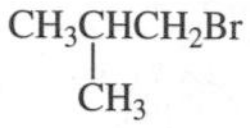
butyl bromide or *n*-butyl bromide; isobutyl bromide
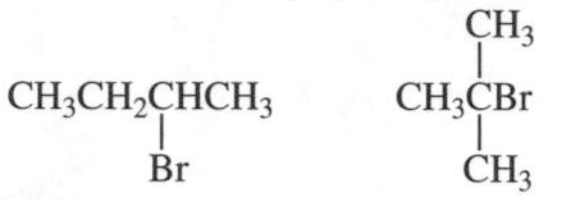
sec-butyl bromide; *tert*-butyl bromide
11-4. c **11-5.** **a.** 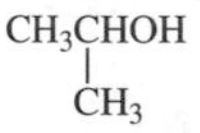 **b.** 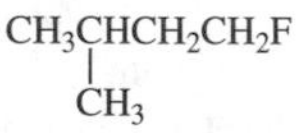
c. 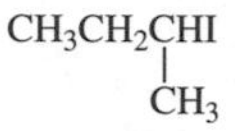 **d.** 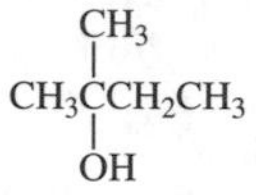
e. 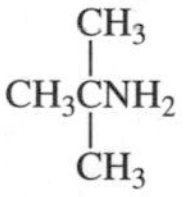
f. $CH_3CH_2CH_2CH_2CH_2CH_2CH_2CH_2Br$
11-6. **a.** ethyl methyl ether **b.** methyl propyl ether **c.** *sec*-butylamine **d.** *n*-butyl alcohol **e.** isobutyl bromide **f.** *sec*-butyl chloride
11-7. **a.** 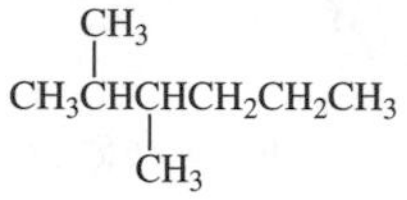
b. 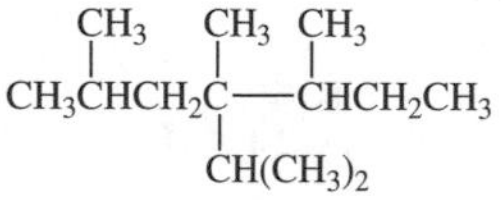
c. 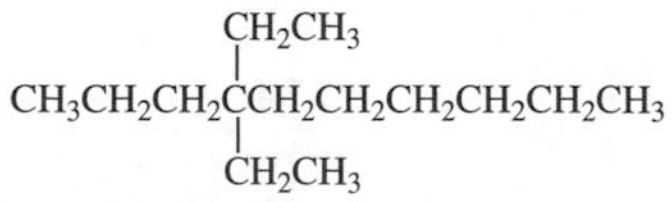
d. 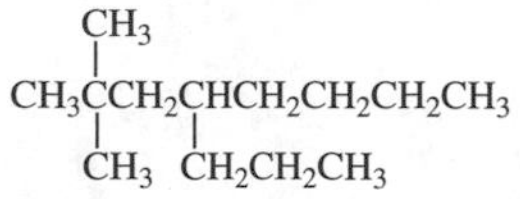
e. 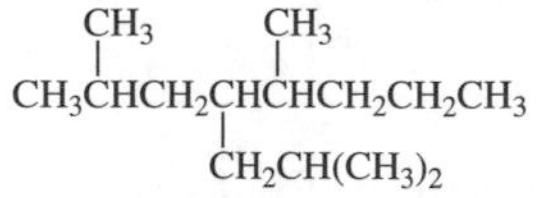
f. 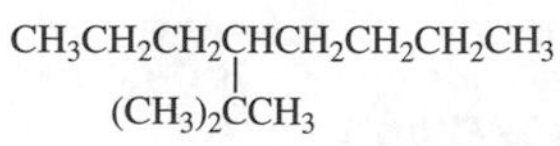
11-9. **a.** 2,2,4-trimethylhexane **b.** 2,2-dimethylbutane **c.** 3-methyl-4-propylheptane **d.** 2,2,5-trimethylhexane **e.** 3,3-diethyl-4-methyl-5-propyloctane **f.** 5-ethyl-4,4-dimethyloctane **g.** 3,3-diethylhexane **h.** 4-isopropyloctane **i.** 2,5-dimethylheptane
11-10. **a.** $CH_3CH_2CH_2CH_2CH_3$ **b.** 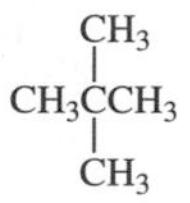
pentane; 2,2-dimethylpropane
c. 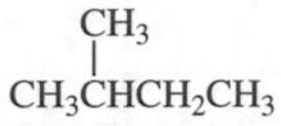 **d.** 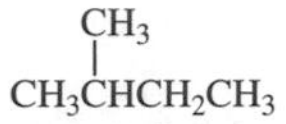
2-methylbutane; 2-methylbutane
11-12. **a.** 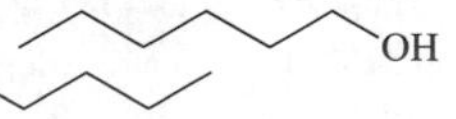
b. 
c. 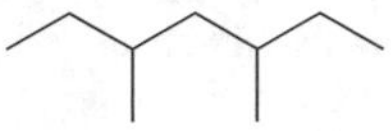
d. 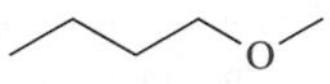
e. 
f. 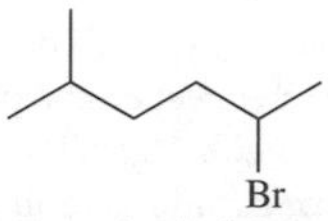
11-15. **a.** 1-ethyl-2-methylcyclopentane **b.** ethylcyclobutane **c.** 4-ethyl-1, 2-dimethylcyclohexane **d.** 3,6-dimethyldecane **e.** 2-cyclopropylpentane **f.** 1-ethyl-3-isobutylcyclohexane **g.** 5-isopropylnonane **h.** 1-*sec*-butyl-4-isopropylcyclohexane
11-16. **a.** *sec*-butyl chloride, 2-chlorobutane, **secondary** **b.** cyclohexyl bromide, bromocyclohexane, **secondary** **c.** isohexyl chloride, 1-chloro-4-methylpentane, **primary** **d.** isopropyl fluoride, 2-fluoropropane, **secondary** **11-18.** **a.** **1.** methoxyethane **2.** ethoxyethane **3.** 4-methoxyoctane **4.** 1-isopropoxy-3-methylbutane **5.** 1-propoxybutane **6.** 2-isopropoxypentane **b.** no **c.** **1.** ethyl methyl ether **2.** diethyl ether **4.** isopentyl isopropyl ether **5.** butyl propyl ether **11-20.** **a.** 1-pentanol, **primary** **b.** 5-chloro-2-methyl-2-pentanol, **tertiary** **c.** 5-methyl-3-hexanol, **secondary** **d.** 2,6-dimethyl-4-octanol, **secondary**
11-21. 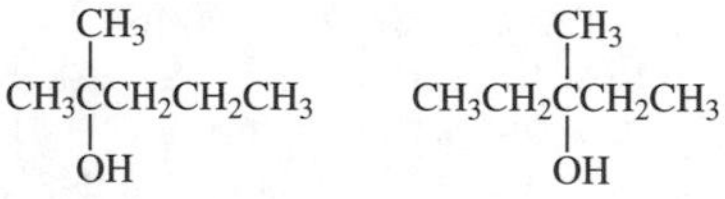
2-methyl-2-pentanol; 3-methyl-3-pentanol
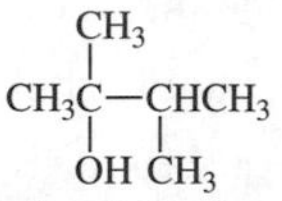
2,3-dimethyl-2-butanol
11-22. **a.** 4-chloro-3-ethylcyclohexanol, **secondary** **b.** 7, 8-dimethyl-3-nonanol, **secondary** **c.** 1-bromo-5,5-diemthyl-3-heptanol, **secondary** **d.** 4-methylcyclohexanol, **secondary** **11-23.** **a.** tertiary **b.** tertiary **c.** primary **11-24.** **a.** hexylamine, 1-hexanamine, **primary** **b.** *sec*-butylisobutylamine, *N*-isobutyl-2-butanamine, **secondary** **c.** diethylmethylamine, *N*-ethyl-*N*-methylethanamine, **tertiary** **d.** butylpropylamine, *N*-propyl-1-butanamine, **secondary** **e.** diethylpropylamine, *N,N*-diethyl-1-propanamine, **tertiary** **f.** no common name, *N*-ethyl-3-methylcyclopentanamine, **secondary**
11-25. **a.** 
b. $CH_3CH_2NHCH_2CH_3$
c. 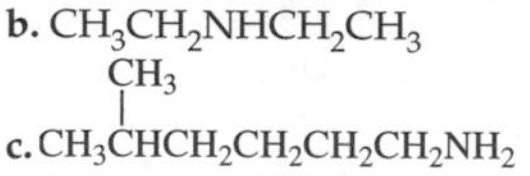
d. 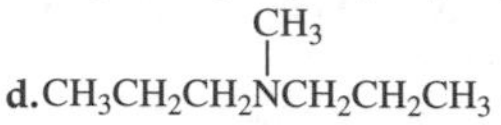 **e.** 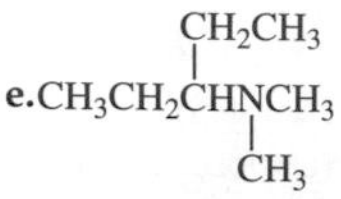
f. 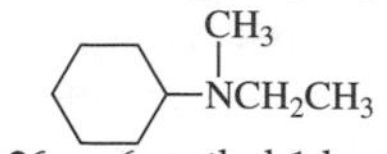
11-26. **a.** 6-methyl-1-heptanamine, isooctylamine, **primary** **b.** cyclohexanamine, cyclohexylamine, **primary** **c.** 3-methyl-*N*-propyl-1-butanamine, isopentylpropylamine, **secondary** **d.** 2,5-dimethylcyclohexanamine, no common name, **primary** **11-27.** **a.** 104.5° **b.** 107.3° **c.** 104.5° **d.** 109.5° **11-28.** pentane **11-29.** **a.** 1, 4, 5 **b.** 1, 2, 4, 5, 6
11-31. 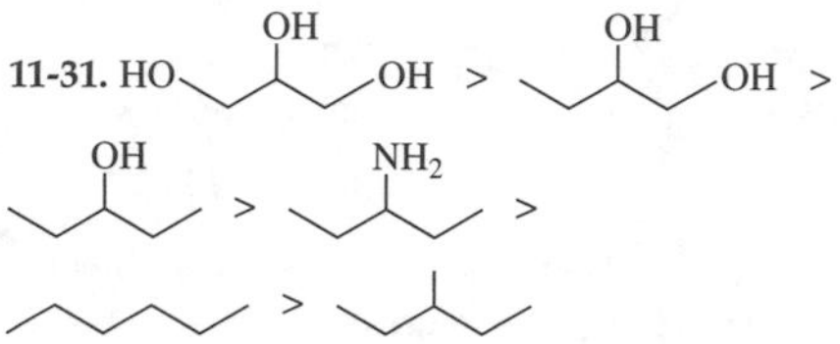
11-33. **a.** 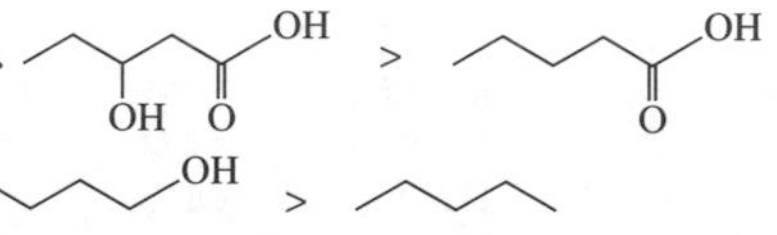
b. $HOCH_2CH_2CH_2OH > CH_3CH_2CH_2OH > CH_3CH_2CH_2CH_2OH > CH_3CH_2CH_2CH_2Cl$
11-34. ethanol **11-36.** **a.** 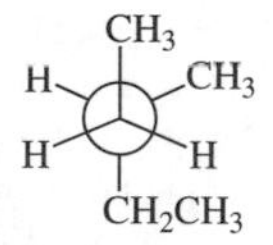
b. 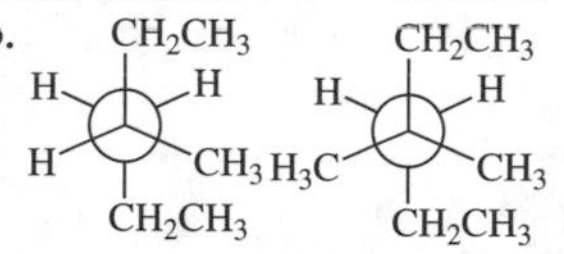
11-37. **a.** 135° **b.** 140° **11-38.** hexethal **11-40.** 6.2 kcal/mol **11-41.** 0.13 kcal/mol **11-42.** 84% **11-43.** **a.** cis **b.** cis **c.** cis **d.** trans **e.** trans **f.** trans **11-44.** *cis*-1-*tert*-butyl-3-methylcyclohexane **11-46.** **a.** one equatorial and one axial **b.** both equatorial and both axial **c.** both equatorial and both axial **d.** one equatorial and one axial **e.** one equatorial and one axial **f.** both equatorial and both axial **11-47.** **a.** 3.6 kcal/mol **b.** 0

CHAPTER 12

12-1. **a.** C_5H_8 **b.** C_4H_6 **c.** $C_{10}H_{16}$ **d.** C_8H_{10}
12-2. **a.** 3 **b.** 4 **c.** 1 **d.** 3 **e.** 13
12-4. **a.** 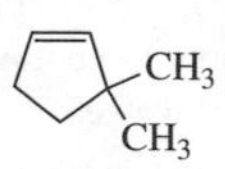 **b.** 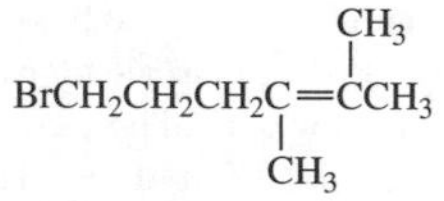
c. $CH_3CH_2OCH{=}CH_2$ **d.** $CH_2{=}CHCH_2OH$
3-5. **a.** 4-methyl-2-pentene **b.** 2-chloro-3, 4-dimethyl-3-hexene **c.** 1-bromocyclopentene **d.** 1-bromo-4-methyl-3-hexene **e.** 1,5-dimethyl-cyclohexene **f.** 1-butoxy-1-propene **g.** 8,8-dimethyl-1-nonene
12-6. **a.** 5 **b.** 4 **c.** 4 **d.** 6 **12-7.** **a.** 1 and 3
12-9. $CH_3CH_2CH_2CH{=}CH_2$ 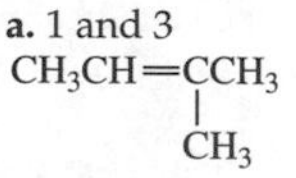 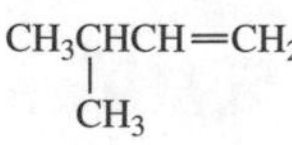
12-10. C **12-11.** **a.** $-I > -Br > -OH > -CH_3$ **b.** $-OH > -CH_2Cl > -CH{=}CH_2 > -CH_2CH_2OH$

$-CH_2CH_2OH$ **12-14. a.** (*E*)-2-heptene **b.** (*Z*)-3,4-dimethyl-2-pentene **c.** (*Z*)-1-chloro-3-ethyl-4-methyl-3-hexene **12-18.** electrophiles: $CH_3\overset{+}{C}HCH_3$ nucleophiles: H^- CH_3O^- $CH_3C{\equiv}CH$ NH_3

CHAPTER 13

13-1. a. $CH_3CH_2CH_2OH$ $CH_3CH(CH_3)OH$ $CH_3CH_2OCH_3$ **b.** 7 **13-3. a.**, **b.**, **c.**, **f.**, **h. 13-4. a.** P, F, J, L, G, R, Q, N, Z **b.** T, M, O, A, U, V, H, I, X, Y **13-5.** a, c, and f **13-7.** a, c, and f **13-10.** A, B, and C

13-11. a. $-CH_2OH$ (1) $-CH_3$ (3) $-H$ (4) $-CH_2CH_2OH$ (2)
b. $-CH{=}O$ (2) $-OH$ (1) $-CH_3$ (4) $-CH_2OH$ (3)
c. $-CH(CH_3)_2$ (2) $-CH_2CH_2Br$ (3) $-Cl$ (1) $-CH_2CH_2CH_2Br$ (4)
d. $-CH{=}CH_2$ (2) $-CH_2CH_3$ (3) phenyl (1) $-CH_3$ (4)

13-12. a. *R* **b.** *R* **c.** *R* **d.** *R* **13-13. a.** *S* **b.** *R* **c.** *S* **d.** *S* **13-14. a.** identical **b.** enantiomers **c.** enantiomers **d.** enantiomers **13-16. a.** levorotatory **b.** dextrorotatory **13-17.** +168 **13-18. a.** −24 **b.** 0 **13-19. a.** +79 **b.** 0 **c.** −79 **13-20. a.** do not know **b.** 98.5% dextrorotatory; 1.5% levorotatory **13-23.** no **13-24. a.** enantiomers **b.** identical **c.** diastereomers **13-25. a.** 8 **b.** $2^8 = 256$ **13-29.** 1-chloro-1-methylcyclooctane, *cis*-1-chloro-5-methylcyclooctane, *trans*-1-chloro-5-methylcyclooctane **13-31.** A = identical, B = enantiomer, C = diastereomer, D = identical **13-32.** b, d, and f **13-36.** asymmetric carbon on left = *R*; asymmetric carbon on right = *R* **13-38.** the second one **13-39. a.** (2*R*,3*R*)-2,3-dichloropentane **b.** (2*S*,3*S*)-2-bromo-3-chloropentane **c.** (1*R*,3*S*)-1,3-cyclopentanediol **d.** (3*R*,4*S*)-3-chloro-4-methylhexane **13-42.** *S*

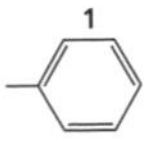

CHAPTER 14

14-1. It will be 0.50 of the original rate. **14-2.** decrease

14-3. $CH_3CH_2CH_2CH_2CH_2Br > CH_3CH(CH_3)CH_2CH_2Br > CH_3CH_2CH(CH_3)CH_2Br > CH_3CH_2C(CH_3)_2Br$

14-4. a. (*S*)-2-butanol **b.** (*R*)-2-hexanol **c.** 3-pentanol **14-5. a.** aprotic **b.** aprotic **c.** protic **d.** aprotic **14-6. a.** RO^- **b.** RS^- **c.** RO^- **14-7. a.** Br^- **b.** Cl^- **c.** CH_3O^- **d.** CH_3O^- **e.** $^-NH_2$ **f.** $^-NH_2$ **g.** I^- **h.** Br^- **14-9. a.** $CH_3CH_2Br + HO^-$ **b.** $CH_3CH(CH_3)CH_2Br + HO^-$ **c.** $CH_3CH_2Cl + CH_3S^-$ **d.** $CH_3CH_2Br + I^-$ **14-11. a.** $CH_3CH_2OCH_2CH_2CH_3$ **b.** $CH_3CH_2C{\equiv}CCH_3$ **c.** $CH_3CH_2\overset{+}{N}(CH_3)_3Br^-$ **d.** $CH_3CH_2SCH_2CH_3$

14-15. $CH_3C(CH_3)_2Br > CH_3CH(CH_3)Br > CH_3CH_2CH_2Br > CH_3Br$

14-17. $CH_3CH_2C(CH_3)(Br)CH_2CH_3 > CH_3CH(Br)CH_2CH_2CH_3 > CH_3CH(Cl)CH_2CH_2CH_3 > ClCH_2CH_2CH_2CH_2CH_3$

14-18. A, B, C, E **14-19.** 3-aceto-3-methyl-1-butene and 1-aceto-3-methyl-2-butene

14-22. a. 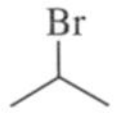 [2-bromopropane structure] **b.** 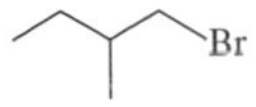 [bromoalkane structure] **c.** 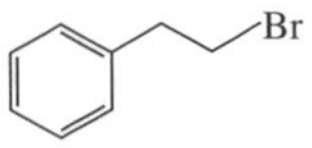 [structure] **d.** 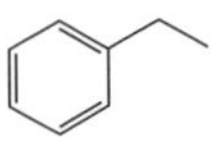 [structure] **e.** 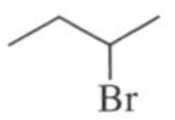 [structure] **f.** 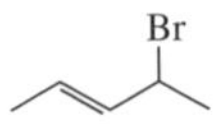 [structure]

14-23. a. 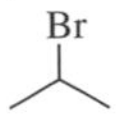 [structure] **b.** 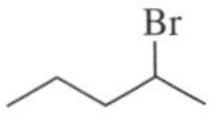 [structure] **c.** 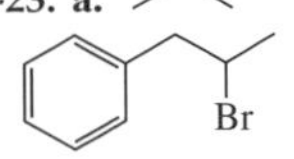 [structure] **d.** 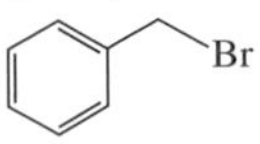 [structure] **e.** equally reactive **f.** 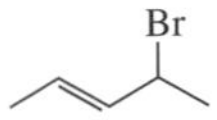 [structure]

14-25. protic **14-26. a.** decrease **b.** decrease **c.** increase

14-27. a. $CH_3Br + HO^- \longrightarrow CH_3OH + Br^-$
b. $CH_3I + HO^- \longrightarrow CH_3OH + I^-$
c. $CH_3Br + NH_3 \longrightarrow CH_3\overset{+}{N}H_3 + Br^-$
d. $CH_3Br + HO^- \xrightarrow{DMSO} CH_3OH + Br^-$
e. $CH_3Br + NH_3 \xrightarrow{EtOH} CH_3\overset{+}{N}H_3 + Br^-$

14-29. dimethyl sulfoxide **14-30.** HO^- in 50% water/50% ethanol

14-31. a.  HO~~~Br **b.** HO~~~Br **c.** 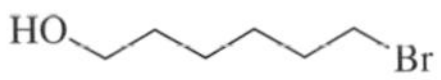 HO~~~Br

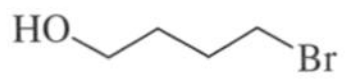

14-33. a. 0 **b.** ethyl cation **14-34. a. 1.** 3 **2.** 3 **3.** 6 **b.** *sec*-butyl cation

14-35. a. $CH_3CH_2\overset{+}{C}(CH_3)CH_3 > CH_3CH_2\overset{+}{C}HCH_3 > CH_3CH_2CH_2\overset{+}{C}H_2$
b. $CH_3CH(CH_3)CH_2\overset{+}{C}H_2 > CH_3CH(Cl)CH_2\overset{+}{C}H_2 > CH_3CH(F)CH_2\overset{+}{C}H_2$

14-36. a. products **b.** reactants **c.** reactants **d.** products

Glossary

Appendix

absolute configuration the three-dimensional structure of a chiral compound. The configuration is designated by *R* or *S*.

achiral (optically inactive) an achiral molecule has a conformation identical to (superimposable upon) its mirror image.

acid (Brønsted) a substance that donates a proton.

An **acid** is (1) a hydrogen-containing compound that can produce hydrogen ions, H^+ (Arrhenius theory); (2) a proton donor (Brønsted–Lowry theory); (3) an atom, ion, or molecule that can accept a pair of electrons to form a covalent bond (Lewis theory).

An **acid–base indicator** is a substance used to measure the pH of a solution or to signal the equivalence point in an acid–base titration. The nonionized weak acid form has one color and the anionic form, a different color.

acid–base reaction a reaction in which an acid donates a proton to a base or accepts a share in a base's electrons.

acid dissociation constant a measure of the degree to which an acid dissociates in solution.

An **acid ionization constant, K_a**, is the equilibrium constant for the ionization reaction of a weak acid.

Activity is the effective concentration of a species. It is obtained as the product of an activity coefficient and the ratio of the stoichiometic concentration or pressure to that of a reference state.

acyclic noncyclic.

addition reaction a reaction in which atoms or groups are added to the reactant.

An **adduct** is a compound formed by joining together two simpler molecules through a coordinate covalent bond, such as the adduct of $AlCl_3$ and $(C_2H_5)_2O$ pictured on page 948.

Adhesive forces are intermolecular forces between unlike molecules, such as molecules of a liquid and of a surface with which it is in contact.

alcohol a compound with an OH group in place of one of the hydrogens of an alkane; (ROH).

Alcohols contain the functional group —OH and have the general formula ROH.

alkane a hydrocarbon that contains only single bonds.

Alkane hydrocarbon molecules have only single covalent bonds between carbon atoms. In their chain structures alkanes have the general formula C_nH_{2n+2}.

alkene a hydrocarbon that contains a double bond.

Alkene hydrocarbons have one or more carbon-to-carbon double bonds in their molecules. The simple alkenes have the general formula C_nH_{2n}.

Alkyl groups are alkane hydrocarbon molecules from which one hydrogen atom has been extracted. For example, the group $—CH_3$ is the **methyl** group; $—CH_2CH_3$ is the **ethyl** group.

alkyl halide a compound with a halogen in place of one of the hydrogens of an alkane.

alkyl substituent (alkyl group) formed by removing a hydrogen from an alkane.

allyl group $CH_2{=}CHCH_2—$

allylic carbon an sp^3 carbon adjacent to a vinylic carbon.

amine a compound with a nitrogen in place of one of the hydrogens of an alkane; (RNH_2, R_2NH, R_3N)

An **amine** is an organic base having the formula RNH_2 (primary), R_2NH (secondary), or R_3N (tertiary), depending on the number of hydrogen atoms of an NH_3 molecule that are replaced by R groups.

amine inversion the configuration of an sp^3 hybridized nitrogen with a nonbonding pair of electrons rapidly turns inside out.

Amphiprotic substances can act either as an acid or as a base.

angle strain the strain introduced into a molecule as a result of its bond angles being distorted from their ideal values.

An **anion** is a negatively charged ion. An anion migrates toward the anode in an electrochemical cell.

The **anode** is the electrode in an electrochemical cell at which an oxidation half-reaction occurs.

In the **anti** conformation, the methyl groups are diagonally opposite each other.

anti addition an addition reaction in which two substituents are added at opposite sides of the molecule.

antibonding molecular orbital a molecular orbital that results when two atomic orbitals with opposite signs interact. Electrons in an antibonding orbital decrease bond strength.

anti conformer the most stable of the staggered conformers.

aprotic solvent a solvent that does not have a hydrogen bonded to an oxygen or to a nitrogen.

asymmetric center an atom bonded to four different atoms or groups.

atomic number the number of protons (or electrons) that the neutral atom has.

atomic orbital an orbital associated with an atom.

atomic weight the average mass of the atoms in the naturally occurring element.

aufbau principle states that an electron will always go into that orbital with the lowest available energy.

Avogadro's law (hypothesis) states that at a fixed temperature and pressure, the volume of a gas is directly proportional to the amount of gas and that equal volumes of different gases, compared under identical conditions of temperature and pressure, contain equal numbers of molecules.

axial bond a bond of the chair conformation of cyclohexane that is perpendicular to the plane in which the chair is drawn (an up–down bond).

back-side attack nucleophilic attack on the side of the carbon opposite the side bonded to the leaving group.

banana bond the σ bonds in small rings that are weaker as a result of overlapping at an angle rather than overlapping head-on.

One **bar** is equal to 100 kilopascals (1 bar = 100 kPa).

A **barometer** is a device used to measure the pressure of the atmosphere.

Barometric pressure is the prevailing pressure of the atmosphere as indicated by a barometer.

base[1] a substance that accepts a proton.

A **base** is (1) a compound that produces hydroxide ions, OH^-, in water solution (Arrhenius theory); (2) a proton acceptor (Brønsted–Lowry theory); (3) an atom, ion, or molecule that can donate a pair of electrons to form a covalent bond (Lewis theory).

basicity the tendency of a compound to share its electrons with a proton.

A **battery** is a voltaic cell [or a group of voltaic cells connected in series (+ to −)] used to produce electricity from chemical change.

bifunctional molecule a molecule with two functional groups.

biochemistry (biological chemistry) the chemistry of biological systems.

boat conformation the conformation of cyclohexane that roughly resembles a boat.

Boiling is a process in which vaporization occurs throughout a liquid. It occurs when the vapor pressure of a liquid is equal to barometric pressure.

boiling point the temperature at which the vapor pressure from a liquid equals the atmospheric pressure.

A **bomb calorimeter** is a device used to measure the heat of a combustion reaction. The quantity measured is the heat of reaction at constant volume, $q_V = \Delta U$.

bonding molecular orbital a molecular orbital that results when two in-phase atomic orbitals interact. Electrons in a bonding orbital increase bond strength.

bond length the internuclear distance between two atoms at minimum energy (maximum stability).

bond strength the energy required to break a bond homolytically.

Buffer capacity refers to the amount of acid and/or base that a buffer solution can neutralize while maintaining an essentially constant pH.

Buffer range is the range of pH values over which a buffer solution can maintain a fairly constant pH.

A **buffer solution** resists a change in its pH. It contains components capable of neutralizing small added amounts of acids and base.

The **calorie (cal)** is the quantity of heat required to change the temperature of one gram of water by one degree Celsius.

A **calorimeter** is a device (of which there are numerous types) used to measure a quantity of heat.

carbanion a compound containing a negatively charged carbon.

The **cathode** is the electrode of an electrochemical cell where a reduction half-reaction occurs.

Cathodic protection is a method of corrosion control in which the metal to be protected is joined to a more active metal that corrodes instead. The protected metal acts as the cathode of a voltaic cell.

A **cation** is a positively charged ion. A cation migrates toward the cathode in an electrochemical cell.

A **cell diagram** is a symbolic representation of an electrochemical cell that indicates the substances entering into the cell reaction, electrode materials, solution concentrations, etc.

The **cell voltage (potential), E_{cell}**, is the potential difference (voltage) between the two electrodes of an electrochemical cell.

chair conformation the conformation of cyclohexane that roughly resembles a chair. It is the most stable conformation of cyclohexane.

Charles's law states that the volume of a fixed amount of gas at a constant pressure is directly proportional to the Kelvin (absolute) temperature.

Chemical energy is the energy associated with chemical bonds and intermolecular forces.

chiral (optically active) a chiral molecule has a nonsuperimposable mirror image.

chromatography a separation technique in which the mixture to be separated is dissolved in a solvent and the solvent is passed through a column packed with an absorbent stationary phase.

A **closed system** is one that can exchange energy but not matter with its surroundings.

cis fused two cyclohexane rings fused together such that if the second ring were considered to be two substituents of the first ring, one substituent would be in an axial position and the other would be in an equatorial position.

cis isomer the isomer with the hydrogens on the same side of the double bond or cyclic structure.

cis–trans isomers geometric isomers.

Cohesive forces are intermolecular forces between like molecules, such as within a drop of liquid.

The **common-ion effect** describes the effect on an equilibrium by a substance that furnishes ions that can participate in the equilibrium.

common name nonsystematic nomenclature.

complete racemization the formation of a pair of enantiomers in equal amounts.

In a **concentration cell** identical electrodes are immersed in solutions of different concentrations. The voltage (emf) of the cell is a function simply of the concentrations of the two solutions.

Condensation is the passage of molecules from the gaseous state to the liquid state.

configurational isomers stereoisomers that cannot interconvert unless a covalent bond is broken. Cis–trans isomers and optical isomers are configurational isomers.

conformation the three-dimensional shape of a molecule at a given instant that can change as a result of rotations about σ bonds.

Conformations refer to the different spatial arrangements possible in a molecule. Examples are the "boat" and "chair" forms of cyclohexane.

conformational analysis the investigation of the various conformations of a compound and their relative stabilities.

conformers different conformations of a molecule.

conjugate acid a species accepts a proton to form its conjugate acid.

A **conjugate acid** is formed when a Brønsted–Lowry base gains a proton. Every base has a conjugate acid.

conjugate base a species loses a proton to form its conjugate base.

A **conjugate base** remains after a Brønsted–Lowry acid has lost a proton. Every acid has a conjugate base.

constitutional isomers (structural isomers) molecules that have the same molecular formula but differ in the way their atoms are connected.

Constitutional isomers have different bond connectivities, and thus different skeletal structures.

Coupled reactions are sets of chemical reactions that occur together. One (or more) of the reactions taken alone is (are) *nonspontaneous* and other(s), *spontaneous*. The overall reaction is *spontaneous*.

covalent bond a bond created as a result of sharing electrons.

The **critical point** refers to the temperature and pressure at which a liquid and its vapor become identical. It is the highest temperature point on the vapor pressure curve.

cycloalkane an alkane with its carbon chain arranged in a closed ring.

Dalton's law of partial pressures states that in a mixture of gases, the total pressure is the sum of the partial pressures of the gases present. (See also **partial pressure**.)

degenerate orbitals orbitals that have the same energy.

delocalization energy (resonance energy) the extra stability a compound achieves as a result of having delocalized electrons.

Deposition is the passage of molecules from the gaseous to the solid state.

dextrorotatory the enantiomer that rotates polarized light in a clockwise direction.

diastereomer a configurational stereoisomer that is not an enantiomer.

1,3-diaxial interaction the interaction between an axial substituent and the other two axial substituents on the same side of the cyclohexane ring.

dielectric constant a measure of how well a solvent can insulate opposite charges from one another.

dipole–dipole interaction an interaction between the dipole of one molecule and the dipole of another.

dipole moment (μ) a measure of the separation of charge in a bond or in a molecule.

Dispersion (London) forces are intermolecular forces associated with instantaneous and induced dipoles.

In a **disproportionation reaction,** the same substance is both oxidized and reduced.

double bond a σ bond and a π bond between two atoms.

eclipsed conformation a conformation in which the bonds on adjacent carbons are aligned as viewed looking down the carbon–carbon bond.

***E* isomer** the isomer with the high-priority groups on opposite sides of the double bond.

An **electrochemical cell** is a device in which the electrons transferred in an oxidation–reduction reaction are made to pass through an electrical circuit. (See also **electrolytic cell** and **voltaic cell**.)

An **electrode** is a metal surface on which an oxidation–reduction equilibrium is established between the metal and substances in solution.

Electrolysis is the decomposition of a substance, either in the molten state or in an electrolyte solution, by means of electric current.

An **electrolyte** is a substance that provides ions when dissolved in water.

An **electrolytic cell** is an electrochemical cell in which a nonspontaneous reaction is carried out by electrolysis.

Electromotive force (emf) is the potential difference between two electrodes in a voltaic cell, expressed in volts.

electronegative element an element that readily acquires an electron.

electronegativity tendency of an atom to pull electrons toward itself.

electrophile an electron-deficient atom or molecule.

electrophilic addition reaction an addition reaction in which the first species that adds to the reactant is an electrophile.

electropositive element an element that readily loses an electron.

electrostatic attraction attractive force between opposite charges.

elimination reaction a reaction that involves the elimination of atoms (or molecules) from the reactant.

enantiomerically pure containing only one enantiomer.

enantiomeric excess (optical purity) how much excess of one enantiomer is present in a mixture of a pair of enantiomers.

enantiomers nonsuperimposable mirror-image molecules.

An **endothermic reaction** results in a lowering of the temperature of an isolated system or the absorption of heat by a system that interacts with its surroundings.

The **end point** is the point in a titration where the indicator used changes color. A properly chosen indicator has its end point coming as closely as possible to the equivalence point of the titration.

Energy is the capacity to do work. (See also **work**.)

An **enthalpy diagram** is a diagrammatic representation of the enthalpy changes in a process.

Enthalpy (heat) of formation (See **standard enthalpy of formation**.)

Entropy, *S*, is a thermodynamic property related to the number of energy levels among which the energy of a system is spread. The greater the number of energy levels for a given total energy, the greater the entropy.

Entropy change, ΔS, is the difference in entropy between two states of a system.

enzyme a protein that is a catalyst.

An **equation of state** is a mathematical expression relating the amount, volume, temperature, and pressure of a substance (usually applied to gases).

equatorial bond a bond of the chair conformer of cyclohexane that juts out from the ring in approximately the same plane that contains the chair.

Equilibrium refers to a condition where forward and reverse processes proceed at equal rates and no further net change occurs. For example, amounts of reactants and products in a reversible reaction remain constant over time.

equilibrium constant the ratio of products to reactants at equilibrium or the ratio of the rate constants for the forward and reverse reactions.

An **equilibrium constant expression** describes the relationship among the concentrations (or partial pressures) of the substances present in a system at equilibrium.

The **equivalence point** of a titration is the condition in which the reactants are in stoichiometric proportions. They consume each other, and neither reactant is in excess.

erythro enantiomers the pair of enantiomers with similar groups on the same side as drawn in a Fischer projection.

ether a compound containing an oxygen bonded to two carbons (ROR).

An **ether** has the general formula R—O—R′.

Evaporation is the physical process of a liquid changing to a vapor. (See also **vaporization**.)

excited-state electronic configuration the electronic configuration that results when an electron in the ground-state electronic configuration has been moved to a higher energy orbital.

exhaustive methylation reaction of an amine with excess methyl iodide to form a quaternary ammonium iodide.

An **exothermic reaction** produces an increase in temperature in an isolated system or, for a system that interacts with its surroundings, the evolution of heat.

The **Faraday constant, F,** is the charge associated with one mole of electrons, 96,485 C/mol e^-.

The **first law of thermodynamics,** expressed as $\Delta U = q + w$, is an alternative statement of the law of conservation of energy. (See also **law of conservation of energy**.)

first-order reaction (unimolecular reaction) a reaction whose rate depends on the concentration of one reactant.

Fischer projection a method of representing the spatial arrangement of groups bonded to an asymmetric center. The asymmetric center is the point of intersection of two perpendicular lines; the horizontal lines represent bonds that project out of the plane of the paper toward the viewer, and the vertical lines represent bonds that point back from the plane of the paper away from the viewer.

Fission (See **nuclear fission**.)

flagpole hydrogens (transannular hydrogens) the two hydrogens in the boat conformation of cyclohexane that are closest to each other.

A **flow battery** is a battery in which materials (reactants, products, electrolytes) pass continuously through the battery. The battery is simply a converter of chemical to electrical energy.

Freezing is the conversion of a liquid to a solid that occurs at a fixed temperature known as the **freezing point**.

A **fuel cell** is a voltaic cell in which the cell reaction is the equivalent of the combustion of a fuel. Chemical energy of the fuel is converted to electricity.

A **function of state (state function)** is a property that assumes a unique value when the state or present condition of a system is defined. This value is *independent* of how the state is attained.

functional group the center of reactivity in a molecule.

A **functional group** is an atom or grouping of atoms attached to a hydrocarbon residue, R. The functional group often confers specific properties to an organic molecule.

Galvanic cell (See **voltaic cell**.)

Gamma (γ) rays are a form of electromagnetic radiation of high penetrating power emitted by certain radioactive nuclei.

In a **gas,** atoms or molecules are generally much more widely separated than in liquids and solids. A gas assumes the shape of its container and expands to fill the container, thus having neither definite shape nor volume.

The **gas constant, *R*,** is the numerical constant appearing in the ideal gas equation ($PV = nRT$) and in several other equations as well.

gauche conformer a staggered conformer in which the largest substituents are gauche to each other.

gauche interaction the interaction between two atoms or groups that are gauche to each other.

The **general gas equation** is an expression based on the ideal gas equation and written in the form $P_1V_1/n_1T_1 = P_2V_2/n_2T_2$.

geometric isomers cis–trans (or E,Z) isomers.

Gibbs energy, *G*, is a thermodynamic function designed to produce a criterion for spontaneous change. It is defined through the equation $G = H - TS$.

Gibbs energy change, ΔG, is the change in Gibbs energy that accompanies a process and can be used to indicate the direction of spontaneous change. For a spontaneous process at constant temperature and pressure, $\Delta G < 0$. (See also **standard Gibbs energy change**.)

Global warming refers to the warming of Earth that results from an accumulation in the atmosphere of gases such as CO_2 that absorb infrared radiation radiated from Earth's surface.

ground-state electronic configuration a description of which orbitals the electrons of an atom or molecule occupy when all of the electrons of atoms are in their lowest-energy orbitals.

A **half-cell** is a combination of an electrode and a solution. An oxidation–reduction equilibrium is established on the electrode. An electrochemical cell is a combination of two half-cells.

half-chair conformation the least stable conformation of cyclohexane.

A **half-reaction** describes one portion of an overall oxidation–reduction reaction, either the oxidation or the reduction.

Heat is a transfer of thermal energy as a result of a temperature difference.

Heat capacity is the quantity of heat required to change the temperature of an object or substance by one degree, usually expressed as J $°C^{-1}$ or cal $°C^{-1}$. **Specific heat capacity** is the heat capacity per gram of substance, i.e., J $°C^{-1}$ g^{-1}, and **molar heat capacity** is the heat capacity per mole, i.e., J $°C^{-1}$ mol^{-1}.

heat of formation the heat given off when a compound is formed from its elements under standard conditions.

A **heat of reaction** is energy converted from chemical to thermal (or vice versa) in a reaction. In an isolated system, this energy conversion causes a temperature change, and in a system that interacts with its surroundings, heat (q) is either evolved to or absorbed from the surroundings.

Heisenberg uncertainty principle states that both the precise location and the momentum of an atomic particle cannot be simultaneously determined.

The **Henderson–Hasselbalch equation** has the form, pH = pK_a + log [conjugate base]/[acid], in which stoichiometric concentrations of the weak acid and its conjugate base are used in place of the equilibrium concentrations. There are limitations on its validity.

Hess's law states that the enthalpy change for an overall or net process is the sum of enthalpy changes for individual steps in the process.

homolog a member of a homologous series.

homologous series a family of compounds in which each member differs from the next by one methylene group.

hormone an organic compound synthesized in a gland and delivered by the bloodstream to its target tissue.

Hund's rule states that when there are degenerate orbitals, an electron will occupy an empty orbital before it will pair up with another electron.

hybrid orbital an orbital formed by mixing (hybridizing) orbitals.

hydride ion a negatively charged hydrogen.

hydrocarbon a compound that contains only carbon and hydrogen.

hydrogen bond an unusually strong dipole–dipole attraction (5 kcal/mol) between a hydrogen bonded to O, N, or F and the nonbonding electrons of an O, N, or F of another molecule.

A **hydrogen bond** is an intermolecular force of attraction in which an H atom covalently bonded to one atom is attracted simultaneously to another highly nonmetallic atom of the same or a nearby molecule.

hydrogen ion (proton) a positively charged hydrogen.

Hydrolysis is a special name given to acid–base reactions in which ions act as acids or bases. As a result of hydrolysis, many salt solutions are not pH neutral, that is, pH $\neq$ 7.

Hydronium ion, H_3O^+, is the form in which protons are found in aqueous solution. The terms "hydrogen ion" and "hydronium ion" are often used synonymously.

hyperconjugation delocalization of electrons by overlap of carbon–hydrogen or carbon–carbon σ bonds with an empty *p* orbital.

An **ICE table** is a format for organizing the data in an equilibrium calculation. It is based on the **initial** concentrations of reactants and products, changes in concentrations to attain equilibrium, and equilibrium concentrations.

An **ideal (perfect) gas** is one whose behavior can be predicted by the ideal gas equation.

Ideal gas constant (See **gas constant**.)

The **ideal gas equation** relates the pressure, volume, temperature, and number of moles of ideal gas (n) through the expression $PV = nRT$.

An **indicator** is an added substance that changes color at the equivalence point in a titration.

induced-dipole–induced-dipole interaction an interaction between a temporary dipole in one molecule and the dipole the temporary dipole induces in another molecule.

inductive electron withdrawal withdrawal of electrons through a σ bond.

intermolecular reaction a reaction that takes place between two molecules.

The **internal energy, *U*,** of a system is the total energy attributed to the particles of matter and their interactions within a system.

intimate ion pair pair such that the covalent bond that joined the cation and the anion has broken, but the cation and anion are still next to each other.

intramolecular catalysis (anchimeric assistance) catalysis in which the catalyst that facilitates the reaction is part of the molecule undergoing reaction.

inversion of configuration turning the configuration of a carbon inside out like an umbrella in a windstorm, so that the resulting product has a configuration opposite that of the reactant.

The **ion product of water, K_w,** is the product of $[H_3O^+]$ and $[OH^-]$ in pure water or in an aqueous solution. This product has a unique value that depends only on temperature. At 25 °C, $K_w = 1.0 \times 10^{-14}$.

ion–dipole interaction the interaction between an ion and the dipole of a molecule.

ionic bond a bond formed through the attraction of two ions of opposite charges.

An **irreversible** process takes place in one or several finite steps such that the system is not in equilibrium with its surroundings.

An **isolated system** is one that exchanges neither energy nor matter with its surroundings.

isomers nonidentical compounds with the same molecular formula.

isotopes atoms with the same number of protons, but different numbers of neutrons.

IUPAC nomenclature systematic nomenclature of chemical compounds.

Kekulé structure a model that represents the bonds between atoms as lines.

The **Kelvin** temperature is an **absolute** temperature. That is, the lowest attainable temperature is 0 K = −273.15 °C (the temperature at which molecular motion ceases). Kelvin and Celsius temperatures are related through the expression $T\ (\text{K}) = t(°\text{C}) + 273.15$.

A **kilopascal (kPa)** is a unit of pressure equal to 1000 pascals (Pa) or 1000 N/m^{-2}. The standard atmosphere of pressure is 101.325 kPa.

Kinetic energy is energy of motion. The kinetic energy of an object with mass *m* and velocity *u* is K.E. $= \frac{1}{2}mu^2$.

kinetics the field of chemistry that deals with the rates of chemical reactions.

Gay-Lussac's law of combining volumes states that, when compared at the same temperature and pressure, the volumes of *gases* involved in a reaction are in the ratio of small whole numbers.

The **law of conservation of energy** states that energy can neither be created nor destroyed in ordinary processes.

Le Châtelier's principle states that an action that tends to change the temperature, pressure, or concentrations of reactants in a system at equilibrium stimulates a response that partially offsets the change while a new equilibrium condition is established.

leaving group the group that is displaced in a nucleophilic substitution reaction.

Lewis acid a substance that accepts an electron pair.
Lewis acid (See **acid**.)

Lewis base a substance that donates an electron pair.

Lewis base (See **base**.)

Lewis structure a model that represents the bonds between atoms as lines or dots and the valence electrons as dots.

lone-pair electrons (nonbonding electrons) valence electrons not used in bonding.

London forces (See **dispersion forces**.)

mass number the number of protons plus the number of neutrons in an atom.

A **manometer** is a device used to measure the pressure of a gas, usually by comparing the gas pressure with barometric pressure.

mechanism of a reaction a description of the step-by-step process by which reactants are changed into products.

melting point the temperature at which a solid becomes a liquid.

meso compound a compound that contains asymmetric centers and a plane of symmetry.

methylene group a CH_2 group.

A **millimeter of mercury (mmHg)** is a unit of pressure, usually applied to gases. For example, standard atmospheric pressure is equal to the pressure exerted by a 760-mm column of mercury.

A **millimole (mmol)** is one-thousandth of a mole (0.001 mol). It is especially useful in titration calculations.

Mole fraction describes a mixture in terms of the fraction of all the molecules that are of a particular type. It is the amount of one component, in moles, divided by the total amount of all the substances in the mixture.

molecular orbital an orbital associated with a molecule.

molecular orbital theory describes a model in which the electrons occupy orbitals as they do in atoms, but with the orbitals extending over the entire molecule.

The **Nernst equation** is used to relate E_{cell}, E°_{cell} and the activites of the reactants and products in a cell reaction.

A **net ionic equation** represents a reaction between ions in solution in such a way that all nonparticipant (spectator) ions are eliminated from the equation. The equation must be balanced both atomically and for net electric charge.

In a **neutralization reaction**, an acid and a base react in stoichiometric proportions, so that there is no excess of either acid or base in the final solution. The products are water and a salt.

node that part of an orbital in which there is zero probability of finding an electron.

nonbonding electrons (lone-pair electrons) valence electrons not used in bonding.

A **nonelectrolyte** is a substance that is essentially non-ionized, both in the pure state and in solution.

nonpolar covalent bond a bond formed between two atoms that share the bonding electrons equally.

A **nonspontaneous process** is one that will not occur naturally. A nonspontaneous process can be brought about only by intervention from outside the system, as in the use of electricity to decompose a chemical compound (electrolysis).

The **normal boiling point** is the temperature at which the vapor pressure of a liquid is 1 atm. It is the temperature at which the liquid boils in a container open to the atmosphere at a pressure of 1 atm.

nucleophile an electron-rich atom or molecule.

nucleophilic acyl substitution reaction a reaction in which a group bonded to an acyl or aryl group is substituted by another group.

observed rotation the amount of rotation observed in a polarimeter.

octet rule states that an atom will give up, accept, or share electrons in order to achieve a filled shell. Because a filled second shell contains eight electrons, this is known as the octet rule.

An **open system** is one that can exchange both matter and energy with its surroundings.

optically active rotates the plane of polarized light.

optically inactive does not rotate the plane of polarized light.

organic compound a compound that contains carbon.

An **overpotential** is the voltage in excess of the theoretical value required to produce a particular electrode reaction in electrolysis.

Oxidation is a process in which electrons are "lost" and the oxidation state of some atom increases. (Oxidation can occur only in combination with reduction.)

In an **oxidation–reduction (redox)** reaction certain atoms undergo changes in oxidation state. The substance containing atoms whose oxidation states *increase* is **oxidized**. The substance containing atoms whose oxidation states *decrease* is **reduced**.

An **oxidizing agent (oxidant)** makes possible an oxidation process by itself being *reduced*.

packing the fitting of individual molecules into a frozen crystal lattice.

parent hydrocarbon the longest continuous carbon chain in a molecule.

A **partial pressure** is the pressure exerted by an individual gas in a mixture, independently of other gases. Each gas in the mixture expands to fill the container and exerts its own partial pressure.

partial racemization formation of a pair of enantiomers in unequal amounts.

A **pascal (pa)** is a pressure of one N/m^2.

Pauli exclusion principle states that no more than two electrons can occupy an orbital and that the two electrons must have opposite spin.

The **percent ionization** of a weak acid or a weak base is the percent of its molecules that ionize in an aqueous solution.

A **perfect gas** is one whose behavior can be predicted by the ideal gas equation. It is also used to describe a gas whose molecules are "point masses" that do not interact with one another. (See also **ideal gas**.)

perspective formula a method of representing the spatial arrangement of groups bonded to an asymmetric center. Two bonds are drawn in the plane of the paper; a solid wedge is used to depict a bond that projects out of the plane of the paper toward the viewer, and a hatched wedge is used to represent a bond that projects back from the plane of the paper away from the viewer.

pH the pH scale is used to describe the acidity of a solution ($pH = -\log[H^+]$).

pH is a shorthand designation for $[H_3O^+]$ in a solution. It is defined as $pH = -\log[H_3O^+]$.

A **phase diagram** is a graphical representation of the conditions of temperature and pressure at which solids, liquids, and gases (vapors) exist, either as single phases or states of matter or as two or more phases in equilibrium.

pi (π) bond a bond formed as a result of side-to-side overlap of *p* orbitals.

pK_a describes the tendency of a compound to lose a proton ($pK_a = -\log K_a$, where K_a is the acid dissociation constant).

plane of symmetry an imaginary plane that bisects a molecule into mirror images.

pOH is a shorthand designation for $[OH^-]$ in a solution: $pOH = -\log[OH^-]$.

polar covalent bond a covalent bond between atoms of different electronegativites.

polarimeter an instrument that measures the rotation of polarized light.

Polarizability describes the ease with which the electron cloud in an atom or molecule can be distorted in an electric field, that is, the ease with which a dipole can be induced.

Polymorphism refers to the existence of a solid substance in more than one crystalline form.

A **polyprotic acid** is capable of losing more than a single proton per molecule in acid–base reactions. Protons are lost in a stepwise fashion, with the first proton being the most readily lost.

Potential energy is energy due to position or arrangement. It is the energy associated with forces of attraction and repulsion between objects.

A **precipitate** is an insoluble solid that deposits from a solution as a result of a chemical reaction.

Pressure is a force per unit area. Applied to gases, pressure is most easily understood in terms of the height of a liquid column that can be maintained by the gas.

Pressure–volume work is work associated with the expansion or compression of gases.

A **primary carbon** is attached to one other carbon atom.

primary alcohol an alcohol in which the OH group is bonded to a primary carbon.

primary alkyl halide an alkyl halide in which the halogen is bonded to a primary carbon.

primary amine an amine with one alkyl group bonded to the nitrogen.

primary carbon a carbon bonded to only one other carbon.

primary hydrogen a hydrogen bonded to a primary carbon.

protic solvent a solvent that has a hydrogen bonded to an oxygen or a nitrogen.

proton a positively charged hydrogen (H^+); a positively charged particle in an atomic nucleus.

A **proton acceptor** is a base in the Brønsted–Lowry acid–base theory.

A **proton donor** is an acid in the Brønsted–Lowry acid–base theory.

proton transfer reaction a reaction in which a proton is transferred from an acid to a base.

quaternary ammonium salt a quaternary ammonium ion and an anion ($R_4N^+X^-$).

racemic mixture (racemate, racemic modification) a mixture of equal amounts of a pair of enantiomers.

radical an atom or a molecule with an unpaired electron.

rate constant a measure of how easy or difficult it is to reach the transition state of a reaction (to get over the energy barrier to the reaction).

***R* configuration** after assigning relative priorities to the four groups bonded to an asymmetric center, if the lowest priority group is on a vertical axis in a Fischer projection (or pointing away from the viewer in a perspective formula), an arrow drawn from the highest priority group to the next-highest-priority group goes in a clockwise direction.

A **reducing agent (reductant)** makes possible a reduction process by itself becoming *oxidized*.

A **reduction** process is one in which electrons are "gained" and the oxidation state of some atom decreases. (Reduction can only occur in combination with oxidation.) (See also **extractive metallurgy**.)

regioselective reaction a reaction that leads to the preferential formation of one constitutional isomer over another.

relative configuration the configuration of a compound relative to the configuration of another compound.

resolution of a racemic mixture separation of a racemic mixture into the individual enantiomers.

resonance contributor (resonance structure, contributing resonance structure) a structure with localized electrons that approximates the true structure of a compound with delocalized electrons.

resonance hybrid the actual structure of a compound with delocalized electrons; it is represented by two or more structures with localized electrons.

A **reversible process** is one that can be made to reverse direction by just an infinitesimal change in a system property.

ring-flip (chair–chair interconversion) the conversion of the chair conformer of cyclohexane into the other chair conformer. Bonds that are axial in one chair conformer are equatorial in the other.

A **salt bridge** is a device (a U-tube filled with a salt solution) used to join two half-cells in an electrochemical cell. The salt bridge permits the flow of ions between the two half-cells.

Salts are ionic compounds in which hydrogen atoms of acids are replaced by metal ions. Salts are produced by the neutralization of acids with bases.

S configuration after assigning relative priorities to the four groups bonded to an asymmetric center, if the lowest priority group is on a vertical axis in a Fischer projection (or pointing away from the viewer in a perspective formula), an arrow drawn from the highest priority group to the next-highest priority group goes in a counterclockwise direction.

secondary alcohol an alcohol in which the OH group is bonded to a secondary carbon.

secondary alkyl halide an alkyl halide in which the halogen is bonded to a secondary carbon.

secondary amine an amine with two alkyl groups bonded to the nitrogen.

secondary carbon a carbon bonded to two other carbons.

A **secondary carbon** is attached to two other carbon atoms.

secondary hydrogen a hydrogen bonded to a secondary carbon.

second-order reaction (bimolecular reaction) a reaction whose rate depends on the concentration of two reactants.

Self-ionization is an acid–base reaction in which one molecule acts as an acid and donates a proton to another molecule of the same kind acting as a base.

sigma (σ) bond a bond with a cylindrically symmetrical distribution of electrons.

single bond a σ bond.

skeletal structure shows the carbon–carbon bonds as lines and does not show the carbon–hydrogen bonds.

A **skeletal structure** is an arrangement of atoms in a Lewis structure to correspond to the actual arrangement found by experiment.

SN_1 reaction a unimolecular nucleophilic substitution reaction.

SN_2 reaction a bimolecular nucleophilic substitution reaction.

The **solubility** of a substance is the concentration of its saturated solution.

solvation the interaction between a solvent and another molecule (or ion).

solvolysis reaction with the solvent.

The **specific heat** of a substance is the quantity of heat required to change the temperature of one gram of the substance by one degree Celsius.

specific rotation the amount of rotation that will be caused by a compound with a concentration of 1.0 g/mL in a sample tube 1.0 dm long.

A **spontaneous (natural) process** is one that is able to take place in a system left to itself. No external action is required to make the process go, although in some cases the process may take a very long time.

staggered conformation a conformation in which the bonds on one carbon bisect the bond angle on the adjacent carbon when viewed looking down the carbon–carbon bond.

A **standard cell potential, $E°$,** is the voltage of an electrochemical cell in which all species are in their standard states. (See also **cell potential**.)

Standard conditions of temperature and pressure (STP) refers to a gas maintained at a temperature of exactly 0 °C (273.15 K) and 760 mmHg (1 atm).

A **standard electrode potential, $E°$,** is the electric potential that develops on an electrode when the oxidized and reduced forms of some substance are in their *standard* states. Tabulated data are expressed in terms of the reduction process, that is, standard electrode potentials are standard reduction potentials.

The **standard enthalpy of formation, ΔH_f°,** of a substance is the enthalpy change that occurs in the formation of 1 mol of the substance in its standard state from the reference forms of its elements in their standard states. The reference forms of the elements are their most stable forms at the given temperature and 1 bar pressure.

The **standard enthalpy of reaction, $\Delta H°$,** is the enthalpy change of a reaction in which all reactants and products are in their standard states.

Standard Gibbs energy change, $\Delta G°$, is the Gibbs energy change of a process when the reactants and products are all in their standard states. The equation relating standard free energy change to the equilibrium constant is $\Delta G° = -RT \ln K$.

The **standard Gibbs energy of formation, ΔG_f°,** is the standard free energy change associated with the formation of 1 mol of compound from its elements in their most stable forms at 1 bar pressure.

The **standard hydrogen electrode (SHE)** is an electrode at which equilibrium is established between H_3O^+ (a = 1) and H_2 (g, 1 bar) on an inert (Pt) surface. The standard hydrogen electrode is *arbitrarily* assigned an electrode potential of exactly 0 V.

The **standard molar entropy ($S°$)** is the absolute entropy evaluated when one mole of a substance is in its standard state at a particular temperature.

The **standard state** of a substance refers to that substance when it is maintained at 1 bar pressure and at the temperature of interest. For a gas it is the (hypothetical) pure gas behaving as an ideal gas at 1 bar pressure and the temperature of interest.

Standardization of a solution refers to establishing the exact concentration of the solution, usually through a titration.

stereochemistry the field of chemistry that deals with the structures of molecules in three dimensions.

stereogenic center (stereocenter) an atom at which the interchange of two substituents produces a stereoisomer.

stereoisomers isomers that differ in the way their atoms are arranged in space.

stereoselective reaction a reaction that leads to the preferential formation of one stereoisomer over another.

stereospecific reaction a reaction in which the reactant can exist as stereoisomers and each stereoisomeric reactant leads to a different stereoisomeric product or set of products.

steric effects effects due to the fact that groups occupy a certain volume of space.

steric hindrance refers to bulky groups at the site of a reaction that make it difficult for the reactants to approach each other.

steric strain (van der Waals strain, van der Waals repulsion) the repulsion between the electron cloud of an atom or a group of atoms and the electron cloud of another atom or group of atoms.

steroid a class of compounds that contains a steroid ring system.

straight-chain alkane (normal alkane) an alkane in which the carbons form a continuous chain with no branches.

A **strong acid** is an acid that is completely ionized in aqueous solution.

A **strong base** is a base that is completely ionized in aqueous solution.

A **strong electrolyte** is a substance that is completely ionized in solution.

Sublimation is the passage of molecules from the solid to the gaseous state.

Surface tension is the energy or work required to extend the surface of a liquid.

The **surroundings** represent that portion of the universe with which a system interacts.

symmetrical ether an ether with two identical substituents bonded to the oxygen.

syn addition an addition reaction in which two substituents are added to the same side of the molecule.

A **system** is the portion of the universe selected for a thermodynamic study. (See also **open, closed**, and **isolated** systems.)

systematic nomenclature nomenclature based on structure.

tertiary alcohol an alcohol in which the OH group is bonded to a tertiary carbon.

tertiary alkyl halide an alkyl halide in which the halogen is bonded to a tertiary carbon.

tertiary amine an amine with three alkyl groups bonded to the nitrogen.

tertiary carbon a carbon bonded to three other carbons.

tertiary hydrogen a hydrogen bonded to a tertiary carbon.

tetrahedral bond angle the bond angle (109.5°) formed by adjacent bonds of an sp^3 hybridized carbon.

tetrahedral carbon an sp^3 hybridized carbon; a carbon that forms covalent bonds by using four sp^3 hybridized orbitals.

Thermal energy is energy associated with random molecular motion.

The **thermodynamic equilibrium constant, K**, is an equilibrium constant expression based on activities. In dilute solutions activities can be replaced by molarities and in ideal gases, by partial pressures in atm. The activities of pure solids and liquids are 1.

The **third law of thermodynamics** states that the entropy of a pure perfect crystal is zero at the absolute zero of temperature, 0 K.

threo enantiomers the pair of enantiomers with similar groups on opposite sides when drawn in a Fischer projection.

The **titrant** is the solution that is added in a controlled fashion through a buret in a titration reaction. (See also **titration**.)

Titration is a procedure for carrying out a chemical reaction between two solutions by the controlled addition (from a buret) of one solution to the other. In a titration a means must be found, as by the use of an indicator, to locate the equivalence point.

A **titration curve** is a graph of solution pH versus volume of titrant. It outlines how pH changes during an acid–base titration, and it can be used to establish such features as the equivalence point of the titration.

A **torr** is a unit of pressure equal to the unit millimeter of mercury.

trans fused two cyclohexane rings fused together such that if the second ring were considered to be two substituents of the first ring, both substituents would be in equatorial positions.

trans isomer the isomer with the hydrogens on opposite sides of the double bond or cyclic structure. the isomer with identical substituents on opposite sides of the double bond.

trigonal planar carbon an sp^2 hybridized carbon.

triple bond a σ bond plus two π bonds.

A **triple point** is a condition of temperature and pressure at which three phases of a substance (usually solid, liquid, and vapor) coexist at equilibrium.

Trouton's rule states that at their normal boiling points the entropies of vaporization of many liquids have about the same value: 87 J mol^{-1} K^{-1}.

twist-boat conformation (skew-boat conformation) a conformation of cyclohexane.

unimolecular reaction (first-order reaction) a reaction whose rate depends on the concentration of one reactant.

unsaturated hydrocarbon a hydrocarbon that contains one or more double or triple bonds.

unsymmetrical ether an ether with two different substituents bonded to the oxygen.

valence electron an electron in an unfilled shell.

valence shell electron-pair repulsion (VSEPR) model combines the concept of atomic orbitals with the concept of shared electron pairs and the minimization of electron pair repulsion.

van der Waals forces (London forces) induced-dipole–induced-dipole interactions.

The term **van der Waals forces** is used to describe, collectively, intermolecular forces of the London type and interactions between permanent dipoles.

Vaporization is the passage of molecules from the liquid to the gaseous state.

Vapor pressure is the pressure exerted by a vapor when it is in dynamic equilibrium with its liquid at a fixed temperature.

A **vapor-pressure curve** is a graph of vapor pressure as a function of temperature.

vinyl group $CH_2{=}CH{-}$

vinylic carbon a carbon in a carbon–carbon double bond.

Viscosity refers to a liquid's resistance to flow. Its magnitude depends on intermolecular forces of attraction and in some cases, on molecular sizes and shapes.

A **volt (V)** is the SI unit for cell voltage. It is defined as 1 joule per coulomb.

A **voltaic (galvanic) cell** is an electrochemical cell in which a *spontaneous* chemical reaction produces electricity.

wave equation an equation that describes the behavior of each electron in an atom or a molecule.

wave functions a series of solutions of a wave equation.

A **weak acid** is an acid that is only partially ionized in aqueous solution in a reversible reaction.

A **weak base** is a base that it only partially ionized in aqueous solution in a reversible reaction.

A **weak electrolyte** is a substance that is only partially ionized in solution in a reversible reaction.

Work is a form of energy transfer between a system and its surroundings that can be expressed as a force acting through a distance.

Photo Credits

CHAPTER 1 p. 1, Richard Megna/Fundamental Photographs, NYC; **p. 2, 1-1a,** Tom Pantages; **1-1b,** C Squared Studios/ Photodisc/Getty Images; **p. 4, 1-4a/b/c,** Richard Megna/Fundamental Photographs, NYC; **p. 7, 1-6,** Richard Megna/ Fundamental Photographs, NYC; **1-7a/b/c,** Richard Megna/Fundamental Photographs, NYC; **p. 8, 1-8,** Carey B. Van Loon; **p. 11, 1-9,** Carey B. Van Loon; **p. 14, 1-10,** Nicola Keegan/ iStockphoto.com; **p. 16, 1-11,** Tom Pantages; **p. 17, 1-12a/b/c,** Joel Gordon; **p. 19, 1-13,** Carey B. Van Loon; **p. 24, 1-14,** Phil Degginger/ Color-Pic, Inc.; **p. 26, 1-16,** Kristen Brochmann/ Fundamental Photographs, NYC; **p. 28, 1-17a/b/c,** Carey B. Van Loon; **p. 30, 1-18a/b/c,** Carey B. Van Loon; **p. 32,** Carey B. Van Loon; **p. 37 (a&b),** William H. Breazeale/Francis Marion University; **(c),** Tom Pantages

CHAPTER 2 p. 42, Carlos Caetano/Shutterstock; **p. 43, 2-1,** Carey B. Van Loon; **2-2,** Kristen Brochmann/Fundamental Photographs, NYC; **p. 44, 2-3,** Richard Megna/Fundamental Photographs, NYC; **p. 51,** Science Source/Photo Researchers, Inc.; **p. 52,** Stamp from the private collection of Professor C. M. Lang. Photography by Gary J. Shulfer, University of Wisconsin, Stevens Point. "1956, Italy (Scott #714)"; Scott Standard Postage Stamp Catalogue, Scott Pub. Co., Sidney, Ohio; **p. 53, 2-9,** Carey B. Van Loon; **p. 60, 2-11,** Carey B. Van Loon; **p. 68 (both)** Richard Megna/Fundamental Photographs, NYC

CHAPTER 3 p. 78, Brytta/iStockphoto.com; **p. 79, 3-1,** Tom Pantages; **p. 80, 3-3a/b,** Carey B. Van Loon; **p. 84, 3-8,** Richard Megna/ Fundamental Photographs, NYC; **p. 85,** Uros Medved/Dreamstime.com; **p. 88, 3-10,** Carey B. Van Loon; **p. 89, 3-12,** Carey B. Van Loon; **3-13,** Ed Degginger/Color-Pic, Inc.; **3-14;** Carey B. Van Loon; **p. 90, 3-15,** Tom Pantages; **p. 97, 3-21 (both),** Carey B. Van Loon; **p. 98,** Richard Megna/ Fundamental Photographs, NYC; **3-22 (all),** Images of critical point of benzene taken from Chemistry Comes Alive! By Jerrold J. Jacobsen, John W. Moore, et al., published by Journal of Chemical Education Software; **p. 101, 3-25,** Carey B. Van Loon; **p. 103,** Richard Megna/Fundamental Photographs, NYC;

CHAPTER 4 p. 113, Richard Megna/ Fundamental Photographs, NYC; **p. 114, 4-1,** Kristen Brochmann/Fundamental Photographs, NYC; **p. 115, 4-2,** Richard Megna/ Fundamental Photographs, NYC; **p. 116,** Science Photo Library; **p. 121 (a&b),** Carey B. Van Loon; **p. 140,** Tom Pantages; **p. 141,** Carey B. Van Loon; **p. 150,** Simon Fraser/Science Photo Library

CHAPTER 5 p. 167, Mason Dixon Historical Society, Inc.; **p. 168 (top),** Stockbyte/Getty Images; **(bottom),** Michael Dalton/Fundamental Photographs, NYC; **p. 170,** Central Library for Physics, Vienna, Austria; **p. 182,** Bettmann/Corbis

CHAPTER 6 p. 211, BigEye Photography/ iStockphoto.com; **p. 212, 6-1,** Carey B. Van Loon; **p. 219,** Alexandra Winkler/Reuters/Corbis; **p. 234,** N.P. Alexander/Visuals Unlimited, Inc.; **p. 236, 6-8a/b,** Richard Megna/Fundamental Photographs, NYC

CHAPTER 7 p. 253, Thomas Kienzle/AP Images; **p. 254, 7-1,** Carey B. Van Loon; **p. 264,** Thomas Phillips/Bettmann/Corbis; **p. 267, 7-7,** Diane Hirsch/Fundamental Photographs, NYC; **p. 270,** Stamp from the private collection of Professor C. M. Lang. Photography by Gary J. Shulfer, University of Wisconsin, Stevens Point. "1980, Sweden (Scott #1344)"; Scott Standard Postage Stamp Catalogue, Scott Pub. Co., Sidney, Ohio; **p. 279 (top),** Carey B. Van Loon; **7-15,** Marek Pawluczuk/Shutterstock; **p. 280,** David Wood/Dreamstime.com; **p. 283,** Courtesy of Toyota Motor Sales, U.S.A., Inc.; **p. 284, 7-20,** Carey B. Van Loon; **p. 285 (top),** Gary Woodard/GW Photographics/iStockphoto.com; **(bottom),** Missouri Dry Dock and Repair Company, Inc.; **p. 288,** B. Runk/S. Schoenberger/ Grant Heilman Photography/ Alamy; **p. 291,** Charles E. Rotkin/Corbis; **p. 292,** Sam Ogden/Science Photo Library

CHAPTER 8 p. 307, Monia33/Dreamstime.com; **p. 308,** Carey B. Van Loon; **p. 319, 8-7,** Tom Pantages; **p. 327,** Carey B. Van Loon; **p. 330,** Carey B. Van Loon; **p. 334, 8-9,** Carey B. Van Loon; **p. 344, 8-13,** Tom Pantages

CHAPTER 9 p. 355, Richard Megna/ Fundamental Photographs, NYC; **p. 356, 9-1,** Carey B. Van Loon; **p. 358, 9-2,** Carey B. Van Loon; **p. 359, 9-3,** Carey B. Van Loon; **p. 360, 9-4 (all),** Carey B. Van Loon; **p. 369,** Tom Pantages; **p. 371,** ElenaRooraid/PhotoEdit, Inc.

CHAPTER 10 p. 394 Edgar Fahs Smith Memorial Collection **p. 395** (top) Science & Society Picture Library\The Image Works **p. 395** (bot.) Stephane Alix\USDA/APHIS Animal And Plant Health Inspection Service **p. 396** National Academy of Sciences, © 1978 Robert Berks **p. 397** UPI\CORBIS **p. 398** (top) AP Photo **p. 398** (bot.) American Institute of Physics/Emilio Segre Visual Archives **p. 399** (top) CERN, courtesy AIP Emilio Segre Visuals Archives **p. 399** (bot.) Foto-blankhorn, Gottingen, courtesy AIP Emilio Segre Visual Archives **p. 400** Courtesy of the Bancroft Library, University of California, Berkeley. **p. 401** Shutterstock **p. 404** Edgar Fahs Smith Memorial Collection **p. 418** Joe McNally/Getty Images **p. 433** Edgar Fahs Smith Memorial Collection **p. 436** NYC Parks Photo Archive—Fundamental Photo **p. 436** Kristen Brochmann\Fundamental Photographs **p. 451** Richard Megna\Fundamental Photographs, NYC

CHAPTER 11 p. 482 Photo by Gen. Stab. Lit. Anst., courtesy AIP Emilio Segre Visual Archives, W.F. Meggers Gallery of Nobel Laureates and Weber Collections **p. 488** Simon Fraser/Science Photo Library\Photo Researchers **p. 490** Dr. John D. Roberts

CHAPTER 12 p. 512 iStockphoto

CHAPTER 13 p. 545 (top) Photos.com **p. 545** (bot.) The Nobel Foundation **p. 546** Diane Schiumo\Fundamental Photographs, NYC

CHAPTER 14 p. 571 age photostock/Photolibrary **p. 572** (top) University College London Special Collections **p. 572** (bot.) SPL\Photo Researchers **p. 574** From F. J. Moore, 'A History of Chemistry', McGraw-Hill, 1918 **p. 576** Edgar Fahs Smith Collection/University of Pennsylvania Library **p. 591** AP Photo **p. 607** Leigh Wiener/CalTech Archives

Index

D

Q

T